An International Survey of the World's Warbird Population

The Third Edition of the Warbirds Directory

John Chapman & Geoff Goodall

Edited by Paul Coggan

Published by Warbirds Media Company Ltd

under licence from

Warbirds Worldwide Ltd., P.O. Box 99,
Mansfield, Notts NG19 9GU England

ISBN 1 870601 46 7

1st Edition published December 1989

2nd Edition published December 1992

● Designed by Paul Coggan on Apple Macintosh Computers using licenced Quark Xpress and fonts

● Reprographics by Studiograph, Unit 1, Gauntley Court, Ward Street, Nottingham NG7 5HD
Telephone: 0115 9423812

● Printed by Clearpoint Colourprint, Salops Street, Daybrook, Nottingham
Telephone 0115 9671234

● ***Worldwide Trade Distribution by***

Midland Counties Publications
Unit 3 Maizefield, Hinckley,
LEICS LE10 1YF

U.K. Tel : 01455 233747 Fax 01455 233737

● ***North American Trade Distribution by***

Motorbooks International, Box 2, 729 Prospect Avenue,
Osceola,
WI 54020
USA

Tel: (715) 294 3345 Fax: (715) 294 4448

Printed in Great Britain

● *Cover photograph shows Charles Osborne's P-47 flown by Connie Bowlin (who's husband Ed will surely forgive us for pointing out Connie must be the most glamourous Thunderbolt pilot in the world) in formation with the same owners P-51D Mustang and Corsair* (Tom Smith photograph). *Inset: Swiss Air Force Hawker Hunter just prior to being surplussed by that air arm high over the Swiss Alps* (Erich Gandet).

● *Conceived, designed, originated and printed in Sherwood Forest, Nottinghamshire - the true home of Robin Hood.*

Foreward

I have a claim to fame. I am most certainly the first person to read the entire contents of this third edition of the *Warbirds Directory* from cover to cover. Since the second edition I have learned many things. The most important is that you can insult a man's wife, pour scorn on his standard of living, his home, laugh at his car and criticise his driving skill without harm - but omit his warbird from this volume and you are dead meat. I am now going into hiding.

In all seriousness this third edition is the results of thousands more hours work from the two authors and myself. I totally underestimated the length of time it would take to edit this third edition - but here we are at last. A truly international survey presented in good faith, and we feel representative of the warbird movement worldwide. There are many new types included in this edition. Perhaps not surprisingly the 'traditional' warbird type files have also grown, largely due to the influx of aircraft from the former Soviet Union, and with aircraft like the Hawker Hunter being declared surplus to requirements by the Swiss Air Force the jet files have also grown. The axis types have expanded as collectors and hunters continue to scour the world for the raw material required to rebuild a flying warbird. I know the activity is set to continue, and most certainly the next edition - which is already at the planning stage - will require a radical review of types to be included. Though we have added some types others have been omitted. Frankly, there is little room to manoeuvre before we will have to give out a complimentary fork lift truck with every edition of this book. Some have suggested we leave out the Harvard, which to my mind would be completely wrong - for it is a true warbird and set to increase in numbers as the South African Air Force sell theirs into the civilian market. Others have suggested two volumes which I will resist. There is little point in splitting our marketing effort. There is still healthy debate about Stearmans, T-34s and even some of the transport aeroplanes like the Constellation, which has seen an increase in flyable numbers since the last edition.

Many of you have sent in lists of types. Whilst we are grateful for every snippet of information and do not wish to sound arrogant in any way, lists are fine but generally contain the same errors, and though I would not pretend we are right with every single entry, I think we have a pretty good grip on the big picture. Sightings of aircraft are much more useful. A *sighting* is worth a thousand lists!

When the last edition was published there were a number of people who took great pleasure from pointing out we had missed a Hurricane from that type's file. Little or no mention of the other thousands of aeroplanes listed! I have always said we appreciate constructive criticism, and we do, and will continue to accept it in the spirit in which it is presented - but do not forget that though computers play a powerful part in the production we are human and will make mistakes. I am constantly amazed when people dash up the *Warbirds Worldwide* stand at airshows and bombard me with "....did you know you'd missed a Lartigi Punt from page 326?" with a grin of glee wrapped twice around their face. "... Ah...which column dear boy?" I suppose should be the retort. Seriously, do send in your reports and sightings, though we regret we cannot enter into lengthy correspondence about sources of information etc. And please do not expect the Editor know every aircraft history intimately!

Several readers, and some owners, continue to bring up the subject of replicas. When is an aircraft a replica, a restoration, a rebuild ? The answer is, on a personal level, twofold. Firstly there are several owners and collectors who in private voice their opinions and concerns but will not go into print. Until they go on record the argument, or more constructively the basis for an agreement to which we can all work to, will never be formulated. There is no danger in an aircraft being a replica - indeed there is some magnificent work being done in this field by reputable engineers who openly admit to replica building. The real danger is when a few years down the road that replica suddenly develops an provenance which makes it worth, in some peoples eyes more money. Miraculously it is suddenly George Preddy's Mustang. Often Editor's of magazines and Journals (including myself) are expected to contradict themselves a few issues later when a Lartigi Punt replica become's Alice in Wonderland's personal transport. To put this into context though this is a minor activity and as long as the buyer is *aware*, little can go wrong.

One last plea. With this publication there should be a questionnaire on the back of a post paid card. Please fill it in. It is your chance to shape the next edition. Meantime, go on, be the first, send in a sighting report. Whilst I regain my sanity you will hopefully spend some happy hunting time.

WW Paul Coggan, Editor, Warbirds Directory, June 1996.

This book is dedicated to the unsung heroes of the warbird industry:
the engineers and mechanics worldwide who spent several thousand hours per year keeping the warbirds airworthy.

Contents

JETS SECTION

Introduction

This third edition of the Warbirds Directory presents listings of 200 different types of " warbirds" : retired military combat and training aircraft subsequently flown under civil registration markings by civil owners.

The World War Two era aircraft types listed also include all known survivors of the type: those which may not have received civil markings but which still exist on static display in museums, held in storage, or even derelict on some remote airfield. Experience has shown that even the most battered and stripped airframe 'hulk' or wreck can be rebuilt into a pristine airworthy showpiece by skilled restorers. A perusal of the aircraft histories in this book will reveal examples of flying warbird restorations based on hulks salvaged from the bottom of lakes, displayed in parks for over thirty years, and even buried under landfill on a remote farm on the Canadian prairie.

The individual aircraft histories do not pretend to be the whole story- they give known owners, accident details and other significant events in the aircraft's career. The authors and Editor are well aware, from many years of aircraft research, that the full story of any aircraft is unlikely to be found in official records. This is particularly true of warbirds, given the often original clandestine sourcing of the airframes by the various military air arms.

Even warbirds with less colourful backgrounds often come from such hardworking previous careers as aerial tankers for fire bombing or agricultural work, prone to major accidents and rebuilding, sometimes losing their true identities along the way. Researching original military disposal records, official civil authorities' records and even the aircraft's own logbooks may fail to reveal the whole story. Restorations using major components from other aircraft and emerging with a new identity, swapping or even creating manufacturers data plates; warbirds seemingly destroyed in severe accidents only to reappear a short time later as pristine restorations- such is the warbird fraternity's mystique and fascination.

The aircraft histories in the Warbirds Directory are compiled from official information as extracted from the public- domain records of civil and military authorities. This is supplemented by information gleaned from aviation publications, correspondence with aircraft owners, and the authors' and Editor's personal research and observations. Where there is doubt over the identity, or there is conflicting information published, a notation is made. Over the years there has been an increasing duplication of the odd military serial here and there. Where there is more than one airframe with a particular military identity attached the Warbirds Directory should *not* be taken as an authority or the last word on the matter. Information is presented here in good faith, following considerable research and note making. However your interpretation of the records may be different, and we do not pretend to be an authority on right of title. Should you the owners wish to put the record straight with more information Paul Coggan would be delighted to hear from you. **John Chapman & Geoff Goodall** April 1996

The Photographs

When Paul Coggan asked me to edit the pictures for the Warbirds Directory, I was pleased to be able to try to improve a useful facet of the publication. I believe that a picture (as the cliche has it) really is worth a thousand words, and the pictures chosen have been carefully selected to add something extra to this volume.

It is worth explaining the parameters we have set: The keynote is diversity; of types, colours, usage, location and era. We have tried to cover as many of the types listed as possible (at last pictures of a Culver PQ-14 and a Tachikawa Ki-36 'Ida') while acknowledging the pre-eminence of types such as the Mustang, Spitfire and Fortress. I hope that some of the pictures will provoke the interested reader to delve a little further; for instance, reference to earlier editions will reveal pictures of Hawker Fury N85SF No88, shown in the first edition and updated here; while the second edition also covers Messerschmitt Bf109G G-USTV and Lancaster PA474 with, again, a different view being offered in this edition.

As we go to press the Spitfire's 60th anniversary has just recently been celebrated, and as Paul Coggan has pointed out, Warbird history is always being made. We hope the pictures (which go back to just post-W.W.II) serve to show the changes sometimes familiar aircraft have undergone in this important fifty year period. Finally, I would like to sincerely thank all those who supplied photographs and details, often at short notice, and from all quarters of the globe. If you have any comments or additions to make we would be interested in hearing from you; preliminary work on the fourth edition has already started. We are always interested in previously unpublished photographs here at Warbirds Worldwide, so please continue to send them in. **James Kightly** May 96.

Acknowledgements

The authors have referred to a wide range of aviation specialist publications for much of the detail used to compile this third edition of the Warbirds Directory. *Air Britain News, Aviation Letter* and *American Civil Air Registers Quarterly Review (AMCAR)* continue to provide base data, supplemented by information from various magazines and of course the Quarterly *Warbirds Worldwide* Journal

Many new aviation books have been published over the last three years, with the following being highly recommended to readers:

Aircraft Collections & Museums of the World - various publications by Bob Ogden
Central American & Caribbean Air Forces - Dan Hagedorn
Foreign Invaders - Dan Hagedorn & Leif Hellstrom
Final Cut: The Postwar B-17 Flying Fortress - Scott Thompson
B-17 In Blue: The Flying Fortress in USN service - Scott Thompson
P-Screamers: Surviving P-38 Lightnings - A. Kevin Grantham
Harvard File - Air Britain
Harvard! - David C. Fletcher & Doug Macphail
War Prizes Phil Butler by Midland Publishing

The authors wish to thank fellow Australian researchers David Prossor, Gordon Reid, Tony Arbon, Noel Oxlade, John Hopton, and Melvyn Davies for their continuing support. Correspondents Jerry Vernon and Robert Stitt (Canada), Larry Webster, Gary Killion, and Bill Larkins (USA), Peter Arnold and Bob Ogden (UK), Leif Hellstrom (Sweden), and Ken Smy (South Africa) have all generously provided valuable information. Finally, special thanks to Peter Anderson (Australia) for access to his extensive warbird library and records and hospitality well beyond the call of duty!

The Spitfire list has been updated by Spitfire historian Peter R. Arnold who has personally inspected and verified each and every extant Spitfire and rebuild project, with the exception of PR422 in Burma where access was refused by the authorities.

Included are all known Spitfire rebuild projects, some of which may be little more than a firewall bulkhead with authenticated identity and a collection of parts. It is the intention of their owners that they will eventually flourish into full static or flying restorations, but some will fall by the wayside or be absorbed into other rebuild projects. Not included are the remains of high impact buried wartime crashes recovered by museums in the U.K, best described as aviation archaeology, fascinating though they are.

A word on the complex topic of Spitfire construction numbers: the main construction number of a Spitfire is to be found on a small plate on the right hand side of the cockpit. A manufacturer's plate with a different number is to be found on the frame firewall bulkhead, referring to this sub-assembly. These numbers are not guaranteed sequential due to the broad spread of Spitfire construction locations during World War II but they give a general guide to the probable military serial number range based on previously identified examples. There are no known records that tie construction numbers to military serials. In the following listing, the cockpit c/n is quoted in preference to the firewall c/n if both are known.

Previous editions of this Directory have used B-25 construction numbers as published in several reference sources. However some late production c/n blocks conflicted with identities quoted by the civil authorities and NAA plates on surviving airframes. A revised range of North American Aviation c/n blocks for B-25 production has subsequently been verified and these c/n's are incorporated into the following listing. We'd like to thank Bob Ogden for his guidance on this.

Finally a note from the Editor. I'd very much like to thank each and every one of you that has written in with snippets of information and in some cases extensive listings and comments on previous editions of the *Warbirds Directory*. I'd personally like to say thanks to Alan Allen for his input on British Jets,and Mark Sheppard for his input on axis and Hawker Hurricanes - and to all those that continue to write in with information on aircraft noted at various venues around the world. Our advertisers also deserve a Thank you - though I sincerely believe they get excellent value for money it does cost to advertise and we are pleased they have faith in the power of this publication to reach high numbers of owners and enthusiasts. If we've missed anyone it is not intentional, and please continue to write in and send information on sightings.

How to use this Directory

The *Warbirds Directory* covers the history of each aircraft following it's disposal by the military. From Left to Right the following details are given: Manufacturer's Construction Number - in bold type where extant (when this is also immediately followed by a dot, the aircraft is believed to be still extant) ; the aircraft's abbreviated type designation or model; the original military serial number again in bold type; the civil registration; owners and details; and in the extreme right column relevant dates. With regard to the dot system, don't assume that an aircraft is no longer extant if there is not a dot; airframes ' disappear' - there are aircraft to be discovered out there!

Dates are presented in English format: Date/Month/Year. Ownership is usually based on perusal of civil aircraft registers for the year or period quoted. "63/75" signifies that ownership "by" 1963 and until 1975 at the least, whereas ".63/75" indicates that the aircraft was acquired by that owner "during" 1963 and still with the same owner by 1975. "5.63" means the change of ownership or event occurred during May 1963.

When looking for a particular aircraft, changes of ownership and registration are listed in chronological date order so the most recent or current registration and owner will be at the bottom of each aircraft's history, and in this edition is in bold type. Because many warbirds, while painted in authentic military colour schemes, do not carry the correct serial for that airframe, where space permits this is covered by a note in each entry. However, paint schemes often change when the owners changes so be prepared to investigate further!

When a (1 or (2 appears after a civil registration, it refers to more than one allocation of the same registration to that particular aircraft type only.

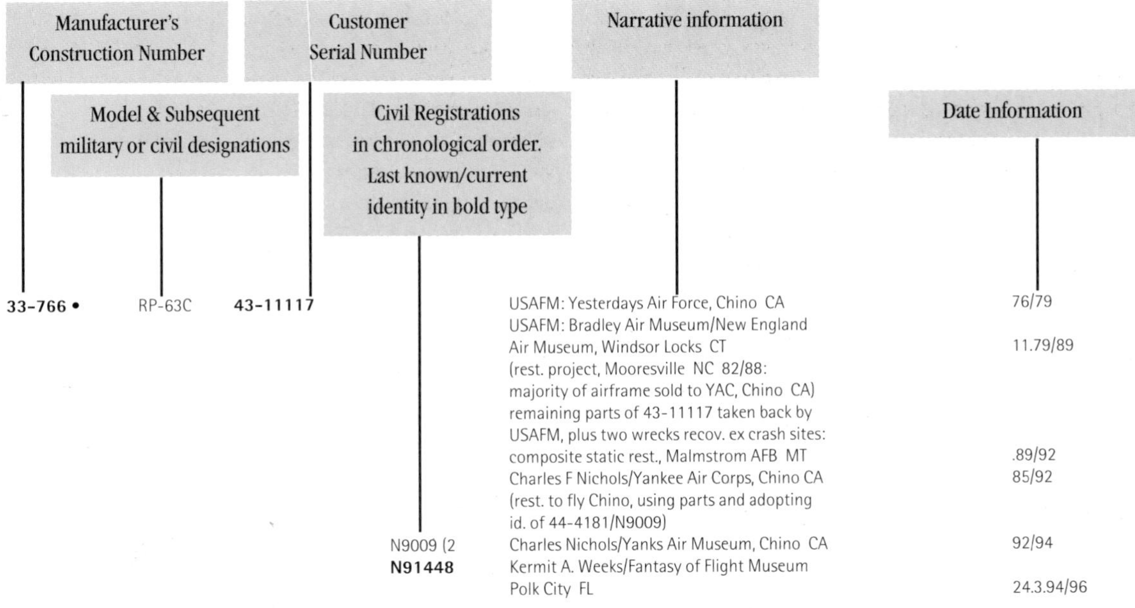

Page/Type headings in this edition are self explanatory. Major type headings are black with white letters and left hand page headings are usually continuation bars.Please note that we have a 'rare and unique section in this edition (page 635) which lists those more obscure types.

What's in this Directory

● Selected WW2 era combat and trainer military aircraft types: those allocated civil registrations, existing since 1970 plus known survivors since 1970 and

● Selected post-WW2 military aircraft types: those allocated civil registrations since 1970

Due to space considerations, aircraft which ceased to exist prior to 1970 have been excluded, this date having been chosen as a benchmark for the serious worldwide warbird movement. Applying the inclusion criteria , the hundreds of jet fighters on poles and guarding the entrances to military bases around the world will not be found in this book, nor early post-war civil conversions such as Mustangs and Lightning flown in the Cleveland Air Races 1946-49, except of course for those which survived beyond 1970.

Abbreviations

Relating to Canada:

BC	British Colombia
ALTA	Alberta
SASK	Saskatchewan
MAN	Manitobe
ONT	Ontario
NB	New Brunswick

Australia:

WA	Western Australia
SA	South Australia
VIC	Victoria
NSW	New South Wales
QLD	Queensland
NT	Northern Territory
TAS	Tasmania

General:

NZ	New Zealand
PNG	Papua New Guinea
HKG	Hong Kong
PI	Philippine Islands
PR	Puerto Rico
USVI	US Virgin Islands
RCAF	Royal Canadian Air Force
RCN	Royal Canadian Navy
RAAF	Royal Australian Air Force
RAN	Royal Australian Navy
IDFAF	Israeli Defence Force Air Force
ROKAF	Republic of Korea Air Force
TNI-AU	Indonesian Air Force
AURI	Indonesian Air Force
SAAF	South African Air Force
USAF	U.S. Air Force
USAAF	U.S. Army Air Force
USN	U.S. Navy
USMC	U.S. Marine Corps
USANG	U.S. Air National Guard
RAF	Royal Air Force
RNFAA	Royal Navy Fleet Air Arm
NASM	National Air and Space Museum
USNAM	U.S. Navy Air Museum, renamed National Museum of Naval Aviation
USVI	U.S. Virgin Islands
WAA	War Assets Administration (USA 1945-48)

arr.	Arrived
c/n number	construction number/manufacturer's serial
Conv.	Converted
cr.	crashed
del.	delivered
dep.	departed
dest.	destroyed
dism	dismantled
displ	displayed
ff	first flight
fuse	fuselage
id	identity
inst. airframe	instructional airframe
k	killed
lsd	leased

mod.	modified
mus	museum
ntu	registration not taken up
op	operated by
orig.	original
pres.	presumed
recov.	recovered
reg.	registration
rep	reported
rereg	re-registered
res.	reserved
rest.	restored
ret	returned
tfd	transferred
u/c	undercarriage
wfu	withdrawn from use

Civil Registration Prefixes/Country Codes

AP-	Pakistan
B-	Taiwan, Republic of China
C- & CF-	Canada
CC-	Chile
CP-	Bolivia
CS-	Portugal
CU-	Cuba
CX-	Uruguay
D-	Germany
EC-	Spain
EI-	Eire
EP-	Iran
F-O	French Overseas Protectorates
F-	France
G-	Great Britain
HB-	Switzerland
HC-	Ecuador
HH-	Haiti
HI-	Dominican Republic
HK-	Colombia
HP-	Panama
HR-	Honduras
HS-	Thailand
I-	Italy
JA-	Japan
LN-	Norway
LV-	Argentina
N & NC	United States*
OB-	Peru
OE-	Austria
OO-	Belgium
OY-	Denmark
PH-	Netherlands
PK-	Indonesia
PP & PT	Brazil
RP- & PI-	Philippines
SE-	Sweden
TG-	Guatemala
TI-	Costa Rica
TR-	Gabon
VH-	Australia
VR-B	Bermuda
VR-H	Hong Kong
VT-	India
XA-XB-,XC-	Mexico
YS-	El Salvador
YV-	Venezuela
ZK-	New Zealand
ZP-	Paraguay
XS- ZS-ZU-	South Africa
4X-	Israel

* Many U.S. registered warbird aircraft fly in the Experimental category with an X suffix to the N and in the Limited category with an L suffix to the N and before the number sequence in each case. The Federal Aviation Administration civil listings do not differentiate and so this Directory uses the N number only. an NC or NX registration is quoted when it refers to the earlier registration series up to 1949.

United States Two letter State abbreviations

As the U.S. postal zip code system is in widespread use around the world and the majority of people are more than familiar with it we will not insult your intelligence by running a list in this edition!

Arado Ar96

Nr4210 •	Ar 96B-1			"PD+EJ" crashed Lake Biscarosse, France	.42
				(recov. ex lake c81)	
				Musee de l'Air, Paris-Le Bourget	84/88
				Museum fur Historische Wehrtechnik,	
				Nurnburg, Germany	92
Nr4246 •	Ar 96B-1			"PI+OT" (1/JG5 "Yellow 13")	
				fcd. landing on ice, sank, Lake Storavatnat 13.3.43	
				recov. from Lake Storavatnat , Norway 7.11.92	
				Aircraft Historical Museum, Sola, Norway	92/96

Arado Ar196

Nr623167 •	Ar 196A-3			T3+BH: captured on board German cruiser	
				Prinz Eugen sailed from Germany to USA	1.46
				(test catapult shots, Philadelphia PA .46)	
				NAS Norfolk VA: displ. as "GA+DX" 55/60	
				NASM, Silver Hill MD	11.60/96
Nr623183 •	Ar 196A-3			T3+HK: captured on board German cruiser	
				Prinz Eugen: sailed from Germany to USA	1.46
				Philapelphia Navy yard: stored	46/49
				NAS Willow Grove PA: displ. as "T3+HK"	.49/70
- •	Ar 196A-3			Morski Muzei, Varna, Bulgaria	74/84

Avro Lancaster

- •	B Mk. I	**R5868**		RAF Wroughton: arr. for storage	1.9.47/58
				RAF Scampton: gate guard	.58/70
				RAF Bicester: rest. for RAF Museum	24.8.70/72
				RAF Museum, Hendon: arr.	20.3.72/96
				(displ. as "R5868/PO-S")	
- •	B Mk. 1	**W4783**		(to RAAF as A66-2: ex 460 Sqdn AR-G)	10.44
				Australian War Memorial, Canberra ACT	60/95
				(displ. as "W4783/AR-G")	
- •	B Mk. X 10 (MR)	**FM104**		(to RCAF as FM104): BOC 13.8.45: SOC	10.9.64
				Canadian Nat. Exhibition Grounds, Toronto ONT	65/91
				(displ. on pole as "GA-R")	
- •	B Mk. X	**FM118**		(to RCAF as FM118): BOC 7.9.45: SOC 22.3.48	
				BCATP Museum, Brandon BC	86
				(derelict hulk recov. from RCAF gunnery range)	
				Nanton Lancaster Society, Nanton ALTA	90/91
				(derelict remains only)	
- •	B Mk. X 10 (MR)	**FM136**		(to RCAF as FM136): BOC 7.9.45: SOC	10.4.61
			CF-NJQ	ntu	
				Centennial Planetarium, Calgary ALTA	.61/90
				(displ. on pole as "VN-N", later "NA-P")	
				Aero Space Museum, Airport, Calgary ALTA	90/96
				(removed from pole 23.4.92: poss. rest. to fly)	
- •	B Mk. X 10 (MR)	**FM159**		(to RCAF as FM159): BOC 7.9.45: SOC	4.10.60
				G. White, H. Armstrong, F. Garratt/	
				Nanton Lancaster Society, Nanton ALTA	4.8.60/94
				(arr. Nanton by road ex Vulcan AB 28.9.60,	
				displ. in open as "RX-159", later "RJ-N")	
				moved to new hangar Nanton, for static rest.	22.5.91/96

No.		Type	Serial	Reg.	History	Date
					(displ. as "F2-T")	
–	•	B Mk. X	**FM212**		(to RCAF as FM212): BOC 26.9.46: SOC	9.10.64
		10 (P)			Jackson Park Sunken Gardens, Windsor ONT	.65/93
					(displ. on plinth as "CF-S")	
–	•	B Mk. X	**FM213**		(to RCAF FM213): BOC 21.8.46: SOC	30.6.64
		10 (MR)			displ. on pole as "VR-A", Godrich ONT	14.6.64/79
					Canadian Warplane Heritage, Hamilton ONT	.77/88
					(airlifted by chopper to Hamilton 5.11.79)	
				C-GVRA	Canadian Warplane Heritage, Hamilton ONT	1.9.88/96
					(rest. Hamilton, ff 11.9.88 as "KB726/VR-A")	
					minor dam. hangar fire, Hamilton (repaired)	15.2.93
–	•	B Mk. X	**KB839**		(to RCAF as KB839): BOC	6.7.45
					CFB Greenwood NS	65/96
					(displ. as "KB976/107" later "FM107/AF-K")	
–	•	B Mk. X	**KB882**		(to RCAF as KB882): BOC 6.7.45: SOC	26.5.64
		10(AR)			St Jacques Airport, Edmunston NB: displ.	7.64/96
–	•	B Mk. X	**KB889**		(to RCAF as KB889): BOC 6.7.45: SOC	21.5.65
					Age of Flight Museum, Niagara Falls ONT	65/70
					Ken Short/The Lancaster Club, Oshawa ONT:	
					barged ex Niagara Falls .71, open storage	.70/84
					Warbirds of GB Ltd, Blackbushe	.84
					(shipped Oshawa ONT to UK .84,	
					stored dism. Blackbushe, later Bitteswell)	
				G-LANC	Warbirds of GB Ltd, Bitteswell	31.1.85/86
					Imperial War Museum, Duxford : arr. dism.	14.5.86/96
					(static rest. Duxford 86/94, unveiled 1.11.94	
					displ. as "RAF KB889/NA-I")	
–		B Mk. X	**KB941**		(to RCAF as KB941): BOC 28.6.45: SOC	22.1.47
					Victor Leonhardt, Drumheller ALTA	.47
					(disposal ex Claresholm AB ALTA, towed to	
					his farm on road .47: broken up for parts)	
					Mr. Spinks, Lethbridge ALTA	86
					Charles Church Ltd, Manchester UK	90
					(centre section only)	
–	•	B Mk. X	**KB944**		(to RCAF as KB944): BOC	28.6.45
		10(S)			Canadian National Aeronautical Collection,	
					Rockcliffe AB ONT	.64/82
					National Aviation Museum, Rockcliffe, ONT	9.82/93
					(displ. as KB944/NA-P/*Winnie*)	
277	•	B Mk X	**KB976**		(to RCAF as KB976): BOC 28.6.45: SOC	26.5.64
		10(AR)			Dr. E. Johnson, Calgary ALTA : del.	.64/69
				CF-AMD	Air Museum of Canada, Calgary ALTA	65
				CF-TQC	Northwestern Air Lease, St Albert ALTA	.69/73
					(conv. to fire tanker not completed)	
				G-BCOH	Sir W. J. D. Roberts/Strathallan Collection	24.9.74/87
					(del. to Strathallan ex Edmonton: arr. 11.6.75)	
					Charles Church Ltd, Manchester	.87/90
					trucked to BAe Woodford for rest. to fly: arr	9.4.87
					badly dam. by falling hangar roof, Woodford	12.8.87
					(rebuild abandoned, arr. dism. Bedford 11.88 with	
					sections KB994 & RF342 for planned rest. by	
					Cranfield Institute of Technology: stored 88/90)	
					Warbirds of GB Ltd, Biggin Hill	
					later Bournemouth	8.90/92
					(planned rebuild, using KB994 and Lincoln RF342:	
					KB976 & KB994 trucked dism. from Biggin Hill to	
					Bournemouth 8.10.92)	

Continued on page 18

One of the two Arado Ar196A-3 which became War Prizes aboard the Battleship *Prinz Eugen*, pictured at Pensicola many years ago bearing a rather bizzare scheme. In the background is the Kawanishi N1K 'George' 62387. **APN.**

When first made airworthy at Waddington by 44 Squadron, Lancaster PA474 did not have a nose or mid-upper turret, both of which were eventually found. PA474 is in its first commemorative scheme, the matt colours of Wg.Cdr Nettleton, a previous 44 Squadron Commanding Officer. **APN.**

Now at East Kirby, Lancaster B.Mk.X NX611 (G-ASXX) served with the Aeronavale in the far east in an overall white scheme (a variation of which it wore for its return from Australia to England) and previously in dark blue, as in this picture. **APN.**

Boulton Paul Defiant N1671, seen at R.A.F. St Athan, was painted in a rather mixed day scheme in the 1960s, before being repainted in night fighter colours for the 1968 Abingdon R.A.F.review. **Mark Ansell Collection.**

Europe was a haven for B17's in the sixties and seventies thanks to the I.G.N. G-FORT was only one of many of these aircraft snapped up by collectors on retirement. **APN.**

The Confederate Air Force have been flying *Fifi*, their Boeing B-29 for 25 years now; a most impressive achievement. **W.W. Collection.**

				Kermit A. Weeks/Weeks Air Museum FL	.92
				struck off reg: sold to USA	23.2.93
- •	B Mk. X	KB994		(to RCAF as KB994): BOC 28.6.45: SOC	22.1.47
				Victor Leonhardt, Drumheller ALTA	.47
				(disposal ex Claresholm AB ALTA, towed to	
				his farm on road .47: broken up for parts)	
				fuse. moved to farm, Pidgeon Lake ALTA	.63/84
				Neil Menzies, Edmonton ALTA: fuse only	
				408th Tactical Helicopter Squadron Museum	
				CFB Edmonton ALTA (under rest.)	.84/88
				(fuse. only, code "EQ-K": recov. by chopper from	
				Pidgeon Lake to Edmonton 25/26.7.84)	
				Charles Church Ltd, Manchester : arr. UK	8.88/90
				Warbirds of GB Ltd, Biggin Hill	
				later Bournemouth	8.90/92
				(stored dism. Bedford, Biggin Hill; fuselage	
				to be used in rebuild of G-BCOH; trucked	
				Biggin Hill to Bournemouth 8.10.92)	
			G-BVBP	Aces High Ltd, North Weald	4.8.93/94
				(fuse. stored North Weald 94)	
- •	B Mk. X 10(MR)	KB999		(to RCAF as KB999): BOC 28.6.45: SOC	22.10.53
				derelict in Manitoba	86/90
- •	B Mk. VII MR. Mk.7	NX611		(to Aeronavale as WU-15, New Caledonia)	6.52/64
				del. Noumea-Sydney,Australia for HAPS	8.64
			G-ASXX	Malcolm D. N. Fisher/Historic Aircraft	
				Preservation Society, Biggin Hill	10.64/67
				(del. Biggin Hill ex Sydney: arr. 13.5.65)	
				Reflectaire Museum, Lavenham/Squires Gate	19.5.67/72
				last flight: del. Lavenham to Squires Gate	26.6.70
				Lord Lilford of Nateby	4.72/83
				RAF Scampton: loan, arr. dism.	8.73/88
				(rest. as gate guard "YF-C", dedicated 4.74)	
				Fred & Harold Panton/Lincolnshire Aviation	
				Heritage Centre, East Kirby	.83/96
				(trucked to East Kirby 4.88 ex Scampton,	
				rest. to taxy condition 95: *Just Jane*)	
- •	B Mk. VII MR. Mk.7	NX622		(to Aeronavale as WU-16, New Caledonia)	6.52/62
				RAAF Assoc., displ. Perth Airport WA: del.	12.62/75
				Air Force Association Aviation Museum,	
				Bullcreek, Perth WA: displ. as "NX622"	.75/96
- •	B Mk. VII MR. Mk.7	NX664		(to Aeronavale as WU-21, New Caledonia)	8.52/63
				dam. landing, Mata Uti, Wallis Island,	
				South West Pacific : stripped & abandoned	21.1.63/84
				Ailes Anciennes Ile de France, Paris	.84/96
				(hulk recov. ex Wallis Island .84;	
				shipped to France: long-term static rest. at	
				Paris-Le Bourget 85/95 for Musee de l'Air)	
- •	B Mk. VII MR. Mk.7	NX665		(to Aeronavale as WU-13, New Caledonia)	5.52/64
				Museum of Transport & Technology,	
				Auckland NZ: del.	15.4.64/96
				(displ. as "ND752/AA-O & PB457/SR-V")	
- •	B Mk. I	PA474		Royal Aircraft Establishment/College of	
				Aeronautics, Cranfield: aerofoil flight trials	3.54/62
				RAF Museum, RAF Henlow: del. for storage	25.9.64/73
				(del. RAF Waddington 18.8.65 for rest: ff 7.11.67)	
				RAF Battle of Britain Memorial Flight	11.73/96
				(Major service/respar)	95/96

Avro Lincoln

C/n	Mark	Serial	Reg	History	Dates
1414 •	B Mk. 2	**RE408**		(to FA Argentina as B-010)	
				Museo Nacional de Aeronautica, Aeroparque,	
				Buenos Aires, Argentina	.68/95
- •	B Mk. 2	**RF342**	G-APRJ	D. Napier & Sons Ltd, Luton: icing research	12.58/62
				College of Aeronautics, Cranfield: del.	11.62/67
				Historic Aircraft Museum, Southend: del.	9.5.67/83
				Doug Arnold/Warbirds of GB Ltd, Blackbushe	10.5.83/86
				Aces High Ltd, North Weald: arr. dism.	10.9.86/94
				Charles Church Ltd, Manchester: arr. dism.	6.12.88/90
				Warbirds of GB Ltd, Biggin Hill	8.90/92
				(stored dism. North Weald 92/94, planned to be	
				used in rebuild of Lancaster G-BCOH)	
- •	B Mk. 2	**RF398**		RAF Watton	63
				RAF Museum, RAF Henlow : del.	30.4.63
				RAF Museum, RAF Cosford	75/95
- •	B Mk. 2	-		(to FA Argentina as B-017)	
				rep. displ. Villa Reynolds AB, Argentina	90

Avro Shackleton

C/n	Mark	Serial	Reg	History	Dates
- •	MR. 2 AEW. 2	**WL747**		Savvas Constantinides, Cyprus: del. Paphos	15.7.91/93
- •	MR. 2 AEW. 2	**WL756**		RAF St.Mawgan : del.	7.91/92
				(spares source for MR.2 WL795)	
- •	MR. 2 AEW. 2	**WL757**		Savvas Constantinides, Cyprus: del. Paphos	19.7.91/93
- •	MR. 2 AEW. 2	**WL790**		Shackleton Preservation Trust: del. Coventry	9.7.91/94
				Air Atlantique, Coventry	.94/95
			N790WL	Atlantic Gulf Aviation, Macon GA	4.8.94
				(dep. Coventry 7.9.94, del. via Reykjavik to	
				Macon GA for US certification:	
				planned to return to UK for airshow flying)	
- •	MR. 2 AEW. 2	**WR963**		Shackleton Preservation Trust: del. Coventry	9.7.91/94
				Air Atlantique, Coventry	.94
				(for rest. to fly, prob. sale to USA)	
- •	MR. 3/3	**WR974**		Peter Vallance/Vallance ByWays Collection,	
				Charlwood	93/96
- •	MR. 3/3	**WR982**		Peter Vallance/Vallance ByWays Collection,	
				Charlwood	93/94
				(maintained in engine-running condition)	
-	MR. 3	**SAAF1716**		wfu Swartkop: open storage (Code "J")	11.84/93
				SAAF Museum, Swartkop AB	4.12.84/93
				(stored, ground run condition, Swartkop AB 88;	
				rest. to airworthy condition 94)	
				crashed, forced landing in desert, Mauritania	13.7.94
				(en route to UK for airshows)	
- •	MR. 3	**SAAF1717**		wfu by SAAF (Code "O")	12.84
				Midmar Dam Nature Reserve, Natal: displ.	10.87/96
				(shipped Capetown AB to Durban, by road to	
				Midmar Dam 10.87)	

- •	MR. 3	**SAAF1719**	wfu by SAAF (Code "L") Stellenbosch Flying Club, Stellenbosch (del. ex Ysterplaat AB .87: used as club house) SAAF Museum Table Bay Harbour, Cape Town: displ.	12.84 .87/94 .94 94/96
- •	MR. 3	**SAAF1720**	wfu by SAAF (Code "M") Ysterplaat AB: gate guard as "SAAF 1719/L"	12.84 .84/95
- •	MR. 3	**SAAF1721**	wfu Swartkop: open storage (Code "N") SAAF Museum, Swartkop AB (stored, ground run condition 88/95)	11.84 4.12.84/95
- •	MR. 3	**SAAF1722**	wfu by SAAF (Code "P") SAAF Museum, Ysterplaat AB: del. (stored, ground run condition, Capetown AB 88, rest. 94/95, ff 18.2.95 as "1722/P")	12.84 6.12.91/95
- •	MR. 3	**SAAF1723**	wfu by SAAF (Code "Q") Vic's Viking Garage, Pretoria (displ. on roof)	12.84 87/95

BELL P-39 AIRACOBRA

15-141 •	P-39D	**41-6802**	shot down by Japanese, PNG William G. Chapman/Air Museum of PNG Kokoda Track War Museum, PNG N. M. Armstrong, Auckland NZ: loaned to Museum of Transport & Technology, Auckland N. Monty Armstrong, Melbourne VIC	12.5.42 70/72 .72 75/79 88
15-290 •	P-39D	**41-6951**	forced landing nr Weipa QLD : abandoned recov. by Cairns Aircraft Recovery Group Sid Beck/Townsville Aero Museum QLD Sid Beck, Mareeba QLD: static rest.	1.5.42/72 9.72 .72/87 .87/96
15-309	P-39D	**41-6970**	William G. Chapman/Air Museum of PNG (recov. ex Gaire PNG, stored Port Moresby) broken up and buried as junk, Port Moresby	.69 c72
15-554 •	P-39F	**41-7215**	forced landing nr Weipa QLD : abandoned recov. by Cairns Aircraft Recovery Group Nick Watling/CARG, Cairns QLD stored Cairns, Mount Isa, later Mossman QLD (static rest., to be displ. Townsville QLD)	1.5.42/72 9.72 72/92 72/92
- •	P-39K	**42-4312**	dam. during ground engine run, Narewa Field, Woodlark Island PNG Bob Jarrett/South Australian Aviation Museum, Port Adelaide SA (hulk recov. ex Woodlark Island by Jarrett .82, static rest. Adelaide, using wing of 42-4368) The Fighter Collection, Duxford UK Weeks Air Museum, Tamiami FL: stored dam. by Hurricane Andrew, Tamiami FL	 18.3.43 .82/91 .91 .91/92 24.8.92
- •	P-39N	**42-4949**	David C. Tallichet/Yesterdays Air Force, Chino CA (recov. from crash site, Fort Nelson BC 11.71)	 11.71/93
- •	P-39N	**42-8740**	David C. Tallichet/Yesterdays Air Force, Chino CA	 .74/89

				N81575	(hulk recov. from Tadji PNG .74 for YAF by Charles Darby & Monty Armstrong NZ) (rest. commenced at Tulsa OK) Charles F Nichols/Yankee Air Corps, Chino CA Charles Nichols/Yanks Air Museum, Chino CA (rest. to fly, Chino CA 90/95: id. also erroneously rep. as 42-8881)	 3.89 12.90/95
-	•	P-39N	**42-18403**		David C. Tallichet/Yesterdays Air Force, Chino CA (hulk recov. ex Tsili Tsili PNG .74 for YAF by Charles Darby & Monty Armstrong NZ)	 .74/93
-	•	P-39N	**42-18408**		David C. Tallichet/Yesterdays Air Force, Chino CA (hulk recov. ex Tsili Tsili PNG .74 for YAF by Charles Darby & Monty Armstrong NZ)	 .74/93
-	•	P-39N	**42-18811**		David C. Tallichet/Yesterdays Air Force, Chino CA (hulk recov. ex Tsili Tsili PNG .74 for YAF by Charles Darby & Monty Armstrong NZ)	 .74/93
-	•	P-39N	**42-18814**		David C. Tallichet/Yesterdays Air Force, Chino CA (hulk recov. ex Tadji PNG .74 for YAF by Charles Darby & Monty Armstrong NZ) noted stored Tallichet compound Chino CA	 .74/93 88
-	•	P-39N	**42-19027**		David C. Tallichet/Yesterdays Air Force, Chino CA (*Small Fry* recov. ex Tadji PNG .74 for YAF by Charles Darby & Monty Armstrong NZ) Frederick A. Johnsen/Museum Aeronautica, Tacoma WA (trucked Tacoma ex Chino .87, rest. to fly)	 .74/87 .87/91
-	•	P-39N	**42-19034**		David C. Tallichet/Yesterdays Air Force, Chino CA (hulk recov. ex Tadji PNG .74 for YAF by Charles Darby & Monty Armstrong NZ) noted stored Tallichet compound Chino CA	 .74/93 88
-	•	P-39N	**42-19039**		Air Force Association, Goroka PNG (hulk recov. ex Tadji, West Sepik PNG .67) J. K. McCarthy Museum, Goroka PNG (displ. on pole as "USAAC 039")	.67 72/93
-	•	P-39Q	**42-19597**	 N6968	fcd. ldg., Hobbs NM: abandoned by USAAF Capitan High School, Lincoln NM: displ. Chet Kochan: recov. derelict ex Lincoln NM Joe Brown, Hobbs NM: stored derelict Don Hull, Sugarland TX (rest. .68/74, ff 21.10.74 in Soviet AF sc., dam. belly landing on first flight; repaired .74) Confederate Air Force, Harlingen/Midland TX	20.7.45 4.56 62 .68/74 3.12.74/96
-	•	P-39Q	**42-19991**		David C. Tallichet/Yesterdays Air Force, Chino CA (hulk recov. ex Tadji PNG .74 for YAF by Charles Darby & Monty Armstrong NZ)	 .74/93
-	•	P-39Q	**42-19993**		d'E. C. Darby & N. M. Armstong, Auckland NZ (hulk recov. from Tadji, West Sepik PNG .74) stored Auckland NZ	.74 .74/76

				N. M. Armstrong/Australian Aerospace Museum,	
				Essendon Airport, Melbourne VIC	82/88
				(static rest., displ. as "Brooklyn Bum 2nd")	
				displ. Drage Air World, Wangaratta VIC	89
				Don Whittington, Fort Lauderdale FL	.89/91
			N139DP	David G. Price/Museum of Flying,	
				Santa Monica CA	.91/94
				(arr. Santa Monica from FL .92, static rest.)	
				(displ. as "USAAC 219993/Brooklyn Bum 2nd")	
				The Fighter Collection, Duxford UK	.94/95
- •	P-39Q	**42-19995**		(8th FG/36th FS: Maj. William A. Shomo :	
				"Snooks 2nd")	
				David C. Tallichet/Yesterdays Air Force,	
				Chino CA	.74/92
				(hulk recov. ex Tadji PNG .74 for YAF	
				by Charles Darby & Monty Armstrong NZ)	
				lsd. Air Heritage Inc, Beaver Falls PA	91/92
				(rest. to fly, Beaver Falls PA)	
- •	P-39Q	**42-20007**		David C. Tallichet/Yesterdays Air Force,	
				Chino CA	.74/93
				(hulk recov. ex Tadji PNG .74 for YAF	
				by Charles Darby & Monty Armstrong NZ)	
				noted stored Tallichet compound Chino CA	88
				Virginia Air & Space Centre, Hampton VA	93/95
				(VASC quotes 42-20027: prob. this airframe)	
- •	P-39Q	**42-20339**		David C. Tallichet/Yesterdays Air Force,	
				Chino CA	.74/93
				(hulk recov. ex Tadji PNG .74 for YAF	
				by Charles Darby & Monty Armstrong NZ)	
26E-433 •	P-39Q	**44-2433**	NX57591	Ortman & Mighton Aviation Co, Tulsa OK	.46
				(race #12 *Juba*, pilot Charles W. Bing)	
			N57591	Elizabeth (Betty) Hass, Scarsdale NY	10.46/50
				(race #12 *Galloping Gertie*)	
				Smithsonian Institute/NASM: stored dism.	.50/69
				(stored Park Ridge IL, later Silver Hill MD)	
				NASM: loan EAA Museum, Hales Corner WI	.69/84
				(static rest. as 42433/*Galloping Gertie*)	
				NASM, Silver Hill MD & Washington DC	.84/95
				(displ. as USAAC 42433/*Galloping Gertie*)	
- •	P-39Q	**44-2438**		David C. Tallichet/Yesterdays Air Force,	
				Chino CA	.74/93
				(hulk recov. ex Tadji PNG .74 for YAF	
				by Charles Darby & Monty Armstrong NZ)	
				noted stored Tallichet compound Chino CA	88
- •	P-39Q	**44-2485**		(to Soviet AF as ....)	
				forced landing on frozen lake during del. flight,	
				Carpenter Lake BC	6.12.43
				Garry R. Larkins, Auburn CA	7.90/91
				(recov. from lake by Garry Larkins 7.90;	
				rebuild to fly, Auburn CA : to go to BC museum)	
- •	P-39Q	**44-2664**		(to Soviet AF as 26)	
				forced landing, Aunus, Finland: captured	6.44
				Finnish Air Force: stored	45/81
				Aviation Museum of Central Finland,	
				Luonetjarvi AB, Tikkakoski	.81/92
				(complete fuselage: to be rest. with wings from	
				44-3255, forced landing Inkeroinen 17.6.44)	

	Type	Serial	Reg.	History	Date
- •	P-39Q	**44-3291**	**N56HA**	US Historic Aircraft Preservation Museum,	
				Anchorage AK : reg. res.	3.85
- •	P-39Q	**44-3887**		Jack B. Hardwick/Hardwick Aircraft Co,	
	RP-39Q			El Monte CA	.47/66
	TP-39Q			(trucked from airfield IL to El Monte: stored,	
				became derelict in Hardwick's yard)	
				USAFM, Wright-Patterson AFB, Dayton OH	7.66/90
				(rest. El Monte .66 as a single-seat P-39Q, flown	
				by Hardwick to Wright Patterson AFB 7.66)	
				(displ. as "43887/31"; later "17073")	
- •	RP-39Q	**44-3908**	NX4829N	W. H. Ostenberg, Scotts Bluff NE	4.46/50
	TP-39Q			(ex War Assets Admin., Altus AFB OK)	
				(race #15)	
			N4829N	Paul Addy, Fostoria OH	.50
				Archie Baldocchi, San Salvador, El Salvador	54
			N40A	E. D. Weiner, Hayward CA	57/63
				(stored, not flown, Orange County CA 59/71)	
				Robert M. Lindquist, Santa Ana CA	63
				Donald D. Randall, Santa Ana CA	.63/69
				Mira Slovak, Van Nuys	.71/75
				(stored dism. Orange County CA; rest. Van Nuys	
				as race #21 *Mr Mennen;* later #39)	
				Rebco Inc/Confederate AF,San Antonio TX:del.	29.7.75/81
				Preston Parish/Kalamazoo Aviation History	
				Museum, Kalamazoo MI	10.81/96
				(flies in USAAC P-400 camouflage sc.)	
- •	P-39Q	44-71500	**N57697**	US Historical Aircraft Museum, Anchorage AK	10.84/86
				wartime crash : purchased in situ ex USAF	10.10.84
				American Vets Memorial Museum, Denver CO	6.88/96
- •	P-400	AP335		(USAAF) forced belly landing, LG Bulldog,	
				Lakekamu River PNG : abandoned	2.8.43/84
				recov. by RAAF Chinook for Jack Taft	30.11.84
				Jack N. Taft/US Military Aircraft Museum,	
				Jackson MI	.85/90
- •	P-400	AP347		(USAAC) forced landing, LG Bulldog,	
				Lakekamu River PNG : abandoned	20.8.43/84
				recov. by RAAF Chinook for Jack Taft	29.11.84
				Jack N. Taft/US Military Aircraft Museum,	
				Jackson MI (in deal with PNG Govt.)	.84
				National Museum, Port Moresby PNG	.85/90
				stored, unrest. Pt.Moresby-Jacksons Airport	90/94
- •	P-400	BW157		(USAAC 67th PS, New Caledonia)	
				fuselage recov. Henderson Field, Guadalcanal	.74
				War Museum, Guadalcanal	.74/79
- •	P-39D	-		(to Soviet AF)	
				Central Armed Forces Museum, Moscow	50s
				Zhukovsky Memorial Museum, Moscow	85
- •	P-39Q	-		(to Soviet AF)	
				Pouryshkin Museum, Novosibirsk	88
- •	P-39N	-		David C. Tallichet/Yesterdays Air Force,	
				Chino CA	.74/88
				(hulk recov. ex Tsili Tsili PNG .74 for YAF	
				by Charles Darby & Monty Armstrong NZ)	
				(id. not found when recov.: P-39N-5 model)	
				(poss. aircraft rep. as 42-20000 at March AFB)	

- •	P-39N	-		David C. Tallichet/Yesterdays Air Force,	
				Chino CA	74
				Ed Maloney/The Air Museum, Chino CA	77/95
				(static rest. as "42-19027 *Little Sir Echo*",	
				later *Small Fry*)	
				(id. rep. as 42-18547: was one of the Tallichet	
				aircraft listed above)	
- •	P-39Q	-		David C. Tallichet/MARC, Chino CA	.74/80
				(recov. by d'E. C. Darby & N. M. Armstrong	
				for YAF from Tadji, West Sepik PNG .74)	
				(stored dism., unrest., Chino CA 75/80)	
				Naval & Servicemens Park, Buffalo NY	.80/92
				(arr. dism. Buffalo 29.12.80 for static rest.,	
				unveiled 28.3.81 as 219995/*Snooks 2nd*:	
				(one of the Tallichet aircraft listed above)	

Bell P-63 Kingcobra

- •	P-63A	**42-68864**		Elliott White Springs Park,	
	RP-63A			Lancaster SC: memorial displ.	50/60
				Don Whittington, Ft Lauderdale FL: hulk	
				Confederate Air Force, Harlingen TX	84/88
				(hulk stored dism., Mesa AZ & Harlingen TX)	
				Robert J. Pond/Planes of Fame East,	
				Minneapolis-Flying Cloud MN	.88/92
				(rest. Chino CA 89/92, ff 2.10.92	
				as 268864/*Pretty Polly*)	
			N163BP	Robert J. Pond, Eden Prairie MN	5.92/95
				(USCR quotes id. "091263RP")	
- •	P-63A	**42-68895**		Walter Soplata Collection, Newbury OH	85
				(incomplete fuselage, recov. ex Buffalo NY)	
33-11 •	P-63A	**42-68941**	NX75488	Steven H. Christenson, Houston TX	47/64
			N75488	(open storage, Dallas-Love Field TX 49/65)	
			N191H	Olin C. Crabtree/CAF, Mercedes TX	.66/72
				(rest., flew as "CAF/*Tumbleweed*")	
				M. D. Johnson, Rolling Fork/Grenda MS	73/91
				Confederate Air Force, Midland TX	9.91/95
- •	P-63A	**42-69021**	NX90805	stored in open, Van Nuys CA	.46/67
			N90805	Ronald Hasz, Scott City KS	70/72
				(stored dism. in hangar, Van Nuys CA 73,	
				being rest. Van Nuys 87/92)	
				Warbirds of GB Ltd, Bournemouth UK	.92
- •	P-63A	**42-69080**	NX32750	Cal Aero Technical Institute, Glendale CA	
			N32750	Ed Maloney/The Air Museum, Claremont CA	.53/69
				Ed Maloney/The Air Museum, Ontario CA	69
			N94501	Ed Maloney/Planes of Fame, Chino CA	76/79
				Charles F Nichols/Yankee Air Corps, Chino CA	9.77/95
				(rest. Palomar CA .79 "269080/*Fatal Fang*)	
				Charles Nichols/Yanks Air Museum, Chino CA	92/96
33-397 •	P-63A	**42-69097**	NX52113	Flamingo Aircraft Inc	28.4.47
	RP-63A			Alfred T. Whiteside (race #87 "Kismet")	6.47/52
			N52113	Jack Becker, Switzerland (stored in USA)	54
				David B. Robinson, Miami FL	63/64
				(last FAA annual inspection 11.51)	
				Johan M. Larsen, Minneapolis MN	66/72
				David C. Tallichet/MARC, Chino CA	73/88
				Warbirds of GB Ltd, Biggin Hill	5.88/90

				(shipped to UK 5.88, stored dism.)	
				Old Flying Machine Co, Duxford	5.90/91
			G-BTWR	The Fighter Collection, Duxford	7.10.91/95
				(rest. Duxford, ff 12.8.94 "269097/Trust Me")	
				(USCR quotes id. as 33-37: 42-68897)	
- •	RP-63A	**42-70255**		NASM, Silver Hill MD	65/87
33-766 •	RP-63C	**43-11117**		USAFM: Yesterdays Air Force, Chino CA	76/79
				USAFM: Bradley Air Museum/New England Air Museum, Windsor Locks CT	11.79/89
				(rest. project, Mooresville NC 82/88: majority of airframe sold to YAC, Chino CA) remaining parts of 43-11117 taken back by USAFM, plus two wrecks recov. ex crash sites:	
				composite static rest., Malmstrom AFB MT	.89/92
				Charles F Nichols/Yankee Air Corps, Chino CA	85/92
				(rest. to fly Chino, using parts and adopting id. of 44-4181/N9009)	
			N9009 (2	Charles Nichols/Yanks Air Museum, Chino CA	92/94
			N91448	Kermit A. Weeks/Fantasy of Flight Museum Polk City FL	24.3.94/95
296E-11 •	P-63F	**43-11719**	NX1719	H. L. Pemberton (race #21)	.46/47
			N1719	Trans American Aviation Service, Chicago IL	54
			N443	Trans American Aviation Service, Chicago IL	54/64
				A. T. George, Atlanta GA	66/69
			N447AG	A. T. George, Atlanta GA	69/70
				Dr. Smith, Sarasota FL	70
			N6763	Jack W. Flaherty/Flaherty Factors Inc, Monterey CA (race #28; #4; later #6)	74/77
				Whittington Brothers, Fort Lauderdale FL	77/81
				Confederate Air Force, Harlingen/Midland TX	10.8.81/95
				(flies as "411719")	
- •	P-63E	**43-11727**		(to FA Hondurena as FAH 400) del.	15.10.48
			N9003R	Bob Bean Aircraft, Hawthorne CA	2.2.60/70
				(open storage Phoenix-Sky Harbour 60/68, then Moseley Field, Phoenix AZ 69/70)	
				USAFM, Pima County Air Museum, Tucson AZ	73/93
				(displ. as "Soviet AF 8/311727")	
- •	P-63E	**43-11728**	NX41964	Bell Aircraft Corp (second cockpit mod.)	
				(to FA Hondurena as 401): del.	10.48
				dam. landing del. flight, Tegucigalpa Honduras	15.10.48
				(FAH spares source, Tegucigalpa AB 50s)	
				Bell Aircraft Corp, Buffalo NY	57
				USAFM, Wright-Patterson AFB, Dayton OH	1.58/90
- •	P-63E	**43-11729**		(to FA Hondurena as 402): del.	13.12.48
				crash landing FAH service	
				(FAH spares souce, Tegucigalpa AB 50s)	
			N9001R	ntu: Bob Bean Aircraft, Hawthorne CA	2.2.60
				Tegucigalpa AB: displ. on pole as "FAH402"	83/92
- •	P-63E	**43-11730**		(to FA Hondurena as 403): del.	9.7.49
				dam. in FAH service	
			N9002R	ntu: Bob Bean Aircraft, Hawthorne CA	2.2.60
				rep. with Dan Chvatal, Jordan MN	83
				also rep. displ. on pole in Honduras	
33-766	P-63C	**44-4181**	NX73744	Frank Singer (race #53)	47/49
				dam. landing, Ravenswood airstrip, Chicago IL	c49
			N73744	Harry R. Snoke, Fort Wayne IN	54
				Bruce M. Madison, Phoenix AZ	63/66

				rep. crashed, Chicago IL	6.68
				Darryl G. Greenamyer, Las Vegas NV	69/70
			N9009 (1	Larry H. Havens/Pylon Air, Long Beach CA	71/72
				(rebuilt Long Beach as highly modified racer,	
				using several airframes: race #90)	
				crashed in Pacific Ocean on test flight from	
				Long Beach CA: pilot baled out	7.9.72
				Don Anklin, Mooresville NC: salvaged wreck	84
				Yankee Air Corps, Chino CA	85/92
				(wreck: parts used in rest. of 43-11117,	
				which adopted id. N9009: que se)	
33-978	P-63C	44-4393	NX62822	Bird Airways, Long Beach CA (race #17)	.46/48
	RP-63C		N62822	Galen F. Bartmus, Kingman AZ	54
				Bruce M. Madison, Phoenix AZ	63/66
				(last FAA annual inspection 1.51)	
				John R. Sandberg, Minneapolis MN	69/75
				(hulk rest. as racer #28 "Tipsy Miss")	
				Mike Smith, Johnson KS	12.75/79
				(race #28 "270134/What Price Speed")	
				Bob Reiser/Southport Aviation Inc, Reno NV	11.81/90
				(flew in red scheme as "44393/Cobra")	
				The Fighter Collection, Duxford	.87/90
				(lease: shipped ex Chino, arr. Duxford 6.1.88)	
				ff Duxford 12.5.88, flew in Soviet AF scheme)	
				crashed, dest., near La Ferte-Alais, France (John Larcombe k)	4.6.90
_ •	RP-63G	**45-57295**		USAFM, Lackland AFB TX	65/95
	QF-63G			(displ. as "557295")	
- •	RP-63C	-		displ. on pole, Fresno Air Terminal CA	50/68
				Charles F Nichols/Yankee Air Corps, Chino CA	85/89
				(rest. to fly, Chino CA)	

Boeing B-17 Flying Fortress

2125 •	B-17D	**40-3097**		(19th BG, Philippines: *The Swoose*): BOC	25.4.41
	RB-17D			(personal aircraft, General George H. Brett,	
				Australia & South America 42/44)	
				City of Los Angeles CA : displ. LA Airport	6.4.46/49
				Smithsonian Institution, Washington DC	3.49/61
				(stored Park Ridge IL, Pyote TX, Andrews AFB)	
				NASM, stored dism., Silver Hill MD	4.61/96
2257 •	B-17E	**41-2446**		forced landing, Agaiambo Swamp PNG	23.2.42
				in situ in swamp, complete, only minor dam.	70/94
				Travis Historical Society, Travis AFB CA	85/94
				(*Swamp Ghost* planned recov. project)	
2406 •	B-17E	**41-2595**		(conv. to XC-108A, to Africa/India .44)	
	XC-108A			sold as scrap, Dow Field, Bangor ME	c12.45
				stored, cut-up in sections, on local farm	45/85
				Steve Alex, Bangor ME	.85
				Michael W. Kellner, Crystal Lake IL: recov.	.85
				stored Galt Airport IL, long-term rest.	.85/90
2504 •	B-17E	**41-9032**		ditched on ice cap, Greenland	.41
				(on del. to Britain, *My Gal Sal*)	
				recov. Gary Larkins/Institute of Aeronautical	
				Archaeological Research, Auburn CA	8.95
				(planned rest. to fly .98)	

2562 •	B-17E	**41-9090**		ditched in fjord, Narsassuaq, Greenland	.41
				(on del. to Britain, *The Sooner*)	
			N3142U	Gary Larkins/Institute of Aeronautical	
				Archaeological Research, Auburn CA	10.3.95
				(planned recov. and rest. to fly)	
2677	B-17E	**41-9205**		recov. from Bennett Lake, Canada	c72
				no further details	
2682 •	B-17E	**41-9210**		University of Minnesota - memorial displ.	8.11.45/52
			N5842N	Lysdale Flying Service, St. Paul MN	29.8.52
				Leeward Aeronautical Service, Ft. Wayne IN	3.12.52/55
			CF-ICB	Kenting Aviation, Toronto ONT	4.3.55/64
			N9720F	Four Star Aviation Inc, Miami FL	22.6.64
			CP-753	Compania Boliviana de Aviacion, La Paz	23.7.64
				Frigorificos Reyes, La Paz, Bolivia	74/90
				port u/c collapsed taxying La Paz	3.1.74
				crashed, landing San Borja, Bolivia	8.76
				(noted being rebuilt, La Paz 80/90)	
			N8WJ	World Jet Inc, Fort Lauderdale FL: del.	3.90/91
				Scott D. Smith, Colorado Springs CO	11.91/96
3170 •	B-17F	**41-24485**		(324th BS/*Memphis Belle*)	
	TB-17F			City of Memphis TN : displ. Memphis	3.46/60
				open displ., Memphis Airport TN	65/84
				(complete static rest., Memphis ANGB 84/87)	
				Mud Island Museum, Memphis TN	5.87/95
				(displ. as 124485/DF-A/*Memphis Belle*)	
7944 •	B-17F	**42-3008**		ditched into lake, Poeskallavik, Sweden	8.5.44
(-DL)				located intact, planned salvage from lake	.93
8310 •	B-17F	**42-3374**		MGM Studios, Culver City CA: stored dism.	.45/70
(-DL)	RB-17F			Planes of Fame, Chino CA: stored dism.	.70/81
				USAFM, Beale AFB CA: rest. and displ.	.81/89
				USAFM, Offutt AFB NE: arr. dism.	5.89/95
				(static rest., displ. as "230230/L")	
6403	B-17F	**42-6107**		Dept of Public Institutions, Clarkston WA	.46
(-VE)	TB-17F			(instructional airframe - became derelict)	
			N1340N	Columbia Airmotive, Troutdale OR	18.11.53
				Aero Enterprises, Troutdale OR (tanker #35) 54/63	
				King Baker/Aero Enterprises Inc, Willows CA	
				& Fresno CA (tanker #E34)	13.9.64
				Aero Flite Inc, Cody WY (tanker #A34)	19.1.68/70
				(re-engined with 4 x RR Dart turboprops .69)	
				cr. dest. fire bombing, Dubois WY	18.8.70
4896 •	B-17F	**42-29782**		City of Stuttgart AR: war memorial	9.46/53
	RB-17F			Gerald C. Francis, Stuttgart AR	.53
	TB-17F		N6015V	Max & John Biegert, Lincoln NE	4.53
			N17W	Max L. Biegert, Lincoln NE : sprayer	3.54/61
				Central Aircraft Corp, Yakima WA : lease	54/55
				Abe Sellard, Stafford AZ : lease	60/61
				(conv. to fire tanker 5.60, tanker #E84)	
				Abe's Aerial Service, Stafford AZ	10.61/63
				Aircraft Specialties Inc, Mesa AZ	17.4.63/81
				(tanker #C84, #C44, #44, #04)	
				(flew in movie *1000 Plane Raid* .68,	
				del. Hawaii for film *Tora Tora Tora* 1.69)	
				Globe Air Inc, Mesa AZ (tanker #04)	18.2.81/85
				Bob Richardson/Portage Bay Inc, Seattle WA	11.6.85/90
				(del. Mesa to Seattle-Boeing Field 20.6.85)	
				(del. Duxford UK for film *Memphis Belle* 27.6.89)	
				Museum of Flight, Seattle-Boeing Field WA	9.90/96

				(rest. by Boeing at Renton WA: del. 2.91/94)	
5291	B-17F	**42-30177**		(to l'Armee de l'Air as 230177)	
				(*Charlene/Bir Hakiem*), Wahn, W. Germany	54
			F-BGSG	Institut Geographique National, Creil	55
				unconv., spares use only, scrapped Wahn	8.73
7190 •	B-17G	**42-32076**		91st BG/401st BS/ *Shoo Shoo Shoo Baby*	
				interned, Bulltofta, Malmo, Sweden	29.5.44
			SE-BAP	SAAB, reg. for flight test	2.11.45
			OY-DFA	DDL-Danish Airlines *Stig Viking*	5.11.45
				belly landing Blackbushe, UK	27.11.45
				(repaired, del. DDL Copenhagen 25.2.46) wfu	25.6.47
				(to R. Danish Army Air Corps as 67-672:	
				Store Bjoern)	31.3.48
				(to R. Danish Navy as 67-672)	1.12.49
				(to R. Danish AF as 67-672)	24.10.52
				retired, stored	1.10.53
				Babb Co Inc, New York NY	2.2.55
			F-BGSH	Institut Geographique National, Creil: del.	6.4.55/72
				last flight: retired Creil, became derelict	15.7.61/72
				USAFM : hulk donated by French Government	23.1.72/92
				airfreighted dism. to Wright Patterson AFB	4.2.72/78
				(rest. Dover AFB DE 80/88)	
				USAFM, Wright Patterson AFB, Dayton OH	10.88/95
				(del. Dover AFB-Wright Patterson AFB 13.10.88,	
				displ. as 232076/91st BG/*Shoo Shoo Baby*)	
8946	B-17G	**42-38160**		Martin Shaffner, Lake Zug, Switzerland	.52/65
				(recov. complete from Lake Zug 8.52, displ.	
				various locations Switzerland .52/53)	
				displ. St Gallen, Switzerland	68
				displ. St Moritz, Switzerland	.70/72
				(displ. as "238160/*Lonesome Polecat*/G")	
				scrapped Suhr, Switzerland	.72
7743	B-17G	**42-97270**	N5069P	reg. res.	1.88/92
				(FAA records show file created in error following	
				enquiry regarding possible existance of a B-17	
				flown by a relative during World War II)	
8217	B-17G	**42-102715**		Boy Scouts, Polo IL (memorial *Polo Queen*)	9.46/52
	TB-17G		N66573	California Atlantic Airways, St Petersburg FL	12.4.52
				Fairchild Aerial Surveys ("*Batmobile* #33")	8.9.53
				Ewing Aviation, Los Angeles CA (#E85)	20.11.61
				Black Hills Aviation, Spearfish SD, later	
				Alamogordo NM (tanker #A10,#B10, #10)	15.7.64/79
				crashed, fire bombing, Cayuse Saddle MT	7.79
				(FAA quote id. 32226)	
9300	B-17G	**43-38322**		Oklahoma Mil. Academy, Rogers County OK	46
				Frank J. Abel	5.1.48
				Alvin B. Graff, Dallas TX	11.5.49
			N66568	California Atlantic Airways, St Petersburg FL	18.1.51
			CB-80	Lloyd Aero Boliviano - LAB, La Paz	5.8.51
			CP-580	Lloyd Aero Boliviano - LAB, La Paz	1.10.54
				crashed La Paz, Bolivia (rebuilt)	7.2.65
			CP-936	Frigorificos Reyes, La Paz	.71
				crashed, San Ignacio de Moxos, Bolivia	11.2.72
9613 •	B-17G	**43-38635**	**N3702G**	National Metals Company, Phoenix AZ	31.7.59
	TB-17G			Louis A. Kordish, Long Beach CA	14.11.59
	EB-17G			Chas J. Fischer, Los Angeles CA	22.4.60
	ETB-17G			Edgar A. Neely/Fast-Way Air Service,	

	TB-17G			Long Beach CA	21.7.60/67
				(conv. to fire tanker .60, tanker #E61)	
				TBM Inc, Tulare CA (tanker #E61, #61)	25.4.67/79
				Aero Union Corp, Chico CA	1.11.79
				USAFM, Castle AFB CA	11.79/96
				(del. Castle ex Chico 26.11.79,	
				displ. as 38635/A-N/*Virgin's Delight*)	
22616 •	B-17G	**44-6393**		Government of Bolivia: ex Davis Monthan AFB	6.56
(-DL)	CB-17G			(civil conv. by Hamilton Aircraft, Tucson AZ)	
	VB-17G		CP-627	Lloyd Aero Boliviano - LAB, La Paz	1.57
	CB-17G			crashed, La Paz-El Alto	27.8.68
	VB-17G			(rebuilt, using parts of CP-580/43-38322)	
			CP-891	Frigorifico Reyes, La Paz	9.69/80
				USAFM, March AFB CA: del. ex La Paz	10.1.81/96
				(displ. 230092/*2nd Patches*, later "46393")	
7943 •	B-17G	**44-8543**		Federal Telecommunications Corporation,	
(-VE)	TB-17G			Teterboro NJ : leased ex USAF	.52/59
	ETB-17G			wfu, del. Teterboro-Davis Monthan AFB AZ	3.59
	JTB-17G		**N3701G** (2	American Compressed Steel, Cincinatti OH	18.8.59/60
				Aero American Corp, Tucson AZ	9.5.60/61
				Albany Building Corp, Fort Lauderdale FL	6.2.61
				(op. Leroy Brown:freight ops. Bahamas 61)	
				John B. Gregory, Fort Lauderdale FL	15.5.62
				Dothan Aviation Corp, Dothan AL : sprayer	7.3.63/79
				Dr. William D. Hospers/B.C. Vintage Flying	
				Museum, Fort Worth-Meacham Field TX	4.10.79/96
				(rest., flies as 48543/*Chuckie*)	
8246 •	B-17G	**44-8846**		(351st BG Polebrook, 305th BG Chelveston)	
(-VE)	RB-17G		F-BGSP	Institut Geographique National, Creil	9.12.54/85
			ZS-DXM	ntu: South African survey operations	.65
			F-BGSP	Institut Geographique National, Creil	65/85
			F-AZDX	IGN/Association GMF/Amicale J-B Salis/	
				Association Forteresse Toujours Volant en France,	
				La Ferte-Alais: based Paris-Orly	7.85/96
				(flew as 48846/W/*Lucky Lady*)	
				(based UK 6.89 for movie *Memphis Belle*,	
				flew as 25703/DF-S/*Mother & Country*)	
				(flies as 22955/ZQ-X/Mother & Country (port)	
				122960/G-MF/*The Pink Lady* (starboard)	
8289 •	B-17G	**44-8889**	F-BGSO	Institut Geographique National, Creil	12.8.54/76
(-VE)				Musee de l'Air, Paris-Le Bourget	8.9.76/93
31957	B-17G	**44-83316**		retired to Davis Monthan AFB AZ	12.56/59
(-DL)	VB-17G			Norton AFB CA : del. for planned museum	4.59/64
				20th Century Fox Studios CA: dism.	.64/66
				(fuselage used as film prop. for TV series	
				"*12 O'Clock High*" as "11868", Chino CA)	
				badly dam. by movie "special effects", Chino	.66
				Black Hills Aviation, Spearfish SD	c67
				(forward fuse. used to rebuild B-17 N6694C)	
				Weeks Air Museum, Tamiami FL: fuse. hulk	c83/96
				(fuse. sections stored Ocotillo Wells CA 88/94)	
32103 •	B-17G	**44-83462**		(to FA Brasileira as B17-5408)	.54
(-DL)	SB-17G			Natal AB, Brazil: displ.	
				Museu Aeroespacial, Campo Afonsos, Rio	81/96
				(44-83718 also quoted)	
32153 •	B-17G	**44-83512**		USAFM, Lackland AFB, San Antonio TX	.56/96
(-DL)	TB-17G			(displ. as "483512/Heavens Above/H-T")	

32155 • (-DL)	B-17G RB-17G DB-17G DB-17P	**44-83514**		retired to Davis-Monthan AFB AZ	27.1.59
			N9323Z	Acme Aircraft Parts, Compton CA	31.7.59/60
				Western Air Industries, Anderson CA	11.60/62
				(conv. Anderson CA .60 to fire tanker #E17)	
				Aero Union Corp, Chico CA (#C17, #17)	6.6.62/78
				(rest. to USAAF "483514/Class of 44" .77)	
				Confederate Air Force, Mesa AZ	17.1.78/95
				dam. landing Burbank CA (repaired)	11.11.88
				(flies as "483514/*Sentimental Journey*")	
32166 • (-DL)	B-17G DB-17G	**44-83525**		retired to Davis-Monthan AFB, Tucson AZ	4.59
				last B-17 held at Davis Monthan AFB: displ.	64/67
			N83525	Tallmantz Aviation, Orange County CA: del.	12.1.68
				(flew in movie "1000 Plane Raid", Santa Maria CA 1.68 as "25053/KY-L/Balls of Fire")	
			N4250	ntu: Tallmantz Aviation	
			N83525	Tallmantz/International Flight & Space Museum, Orange County CA	68/72
				I. N. Burchinall Jnr, Paris TX	10.72/83
				(flew for film MacArthur as KY-L/*Suzy Q*)	
				(displ. in museums Kissimmee FL & Eloy AZ)	
				Kermit Weeks/Weeks Air Mus., Tamiami FL	11.4.83/96
				(del. Tamiami FL 6.6.87, ex storage Paris TX, static displ. as "KY-L/Suzy Q")	
				dam. Tamiami FL, Hurricane Andrew	24.8.92
				(rest. to fly, Kissimmee FL 93/94)	
32183 (-DL)	B-17G DB-17G DB-17P	**44-83542**	**N9324Z**	Acme Aircraft Parts, Compton CA	10.9.59
				Western Air Industries, Anderson CA	11.60/62
				(conv. to fire tanker 10.61, tanker #E16)	
				Aero Union Corp, Anderson, later Chico CA	6.6.62/71
				(tanker #C18, #E18)	
				crashed firebombing, near Benson AZ	12.7.71
				Desert Air Parts, Tucson AZ : wreck	75/82
				New England Air Museum CT : not collected	
				Kermit Weeks/Weeks Air Mus., Tamiami FL	87/96
				(dam. fuse. stored Ocotillo Wells CA 88/94; rest. Kissimmee FL .94 for walk-through displ.)	
				Kermit Weeks/Fantasy of Flight, Polk City FL	94/96
32187 • (-DL)	B-17G CB-17G VB-17G	**44-83546**		stored Davis-Monthan AFB AZ	10.54/59
			N3703G	National Metals Company, Phoenix AZ	31.7.59
				Edgar A. Neely/Fast-Way Air Service, Long Beach CA	11.9.59/67
				(conv. to fire tanker 7.60, #E75, later #E78)	
				TBM Inc, Tulare CA	25.4.67/82
				(tanker #E78, later #E68, #68)	
				David C. Tallichet/MARC, Chino CA	9.82/95
				(flew as "230604/LN-T")	
				USAFM, March AFB CA: loan	83/91
				(rest. Chino 88/89 as 124485/*Memphis Belle* del. Duxford UK for movie *Memphis Belle* 20.6.89)	
32200 • (-DL)	B-17G DB-17G DB-17P	**44-83559**		USAFM, Offutt AFB NE : del.	5.59/94
				(displ. as 23474/EP-B/*King Bee*)	
32204 • (-DL)	B-17G CB-17G VB-17G	**44-83563**		American Compressed Steel, Cincinatti OH	18.8.59
			N9563Z	Aero American Corp, Tucson AZ	9.5.60/63
				Columbia Pictures Inc, New York NY: lease	11.10.61
				(del. Gatwick 8.10.61 for movie *The War Lover* dep. Gatwick 16.5.62 on del. back to USA: stored Tucson-Ryan Field AZ 62/63)	
				Aircraft Specialties Inc, Mesa AZ	2.2.63/81

				(tanker #E24, #C24, #24, #89)	
				(flew to Hawaii for film Tora Tora Tora 1.69)	
				Globe Air Inc, Mesa AZ (tanker #89)	18.2.81/85
				National Warplane Museum, Geneseo NY	10.85/96
				(flies as 297400/*Fuddy Duddy*/K-E)	
32216 •	B-17G	**44-83575**		used for atomic tests, Yucca Flats NV	.52
(-DL)	B-17H			(abandoned at desert test site 52/65)	
	TB-17H			Valley Scrap Metal, Phoenix AZ	4.65
	SB-17G		**N93012**	Abe Sellards/Aircraft Specialities, Mesa AZ 5.5.65/81	
				(rebuilt test site NV, ferried to Mesa 14.5.65;	
				stored unconv., Mesa: spares source 68/77;	
				conv. to tanker, Mesa .77, #99 *Lady Yucca*)	
				Globe Air Inc, Mesa AZ (tanker #99)	4.81/85
				Collings Foundation, Stowe MA	10.85/96
				(del. Mesa-Kissimmee FL for rest. 28.1.87,	
				ff 7.87 as "231909/Nine-O-Nine/A-R")	
				accident, landing Beaver County PA	23.8.87
				(repaired, del. Kissimmee 1.91 for full rest.,	
				flies as 231909/OR-R/*Nine-O-Nine*)	
32265 •	B-17G	**44-83624**		USAFM, Wright-Patterson AFB OH : del.	17.6.57/89
(-DL)	MB-17G			(displ. as "483624/VE")	
	TB-17P			USAFM, Dover AFB DE : arr. dism. for rest.	16.6.89/91
	DB-17P				
32304 •	B-17G	**44-83663**		(to FA Brasileira as B17-5400)	5.51
(-DL)	TB-17G			USAFM, Wright-Patterson AFB OH : stored	10.68/73
				(arr. Wright-Patterson on del. ex Brazil 5.10.68)	
			N47780	USAFM: loan David C. Tallichet/	
				Yesterdays Air Force, Chino CA	15.6.73/86
				displ. Combat Air Museum, Topeka KS : del.	.77/80
				displ. Yesterdays AF, St. Petersburg FL: del.	13.7.80/86
				USAFM, Hill AFB UT: arr. dism.	11.86/93
				(rest., displ. as 483663/*Short Bier*)	
32325 •	B-17G	**44-83684**		last operational USAF B-17, retired to	
	DB-17G			Davis Monthan AFB AZ	8.59
	DB-17P		**N3713G**	Ed Maloney/The Air Museum, Claremont CA	24.9.59/70
				The Air Museum, Ontario, later Chino CA	.63/71
				(used in TV series *12 O'Clock High*, Chino CA	
				64/66 as "23921/Piccadilly Lily/HP-V")	
				Planes of Fame Museum, Chino CA	71/96
				(static displ. Chino as "483684/Picadilly Lilly")	
32331 •	B-17G	**44-83690**		USAFM, Grissom AFB IN	.61/96
(-DL)	DB-17G			(displ. as "48385/*Tarnished Angel*/WF-Y,	
	DB-17P			later "231255/*Miss Liberty Belle*/XK-D")	
32359 •	B-17G	**44-83718**		(to FA Brasileira as B17-5408)	.55
(-DL)	TB-17H			Natal AB, Brazil: displ.	70
	SB-17G			Museu do FAB, Rio de Janeiro: displ.	80/96
32363 •	B-17G	**44-83722**		used for atomic tests, Yucca Flats NV	.52
(-DL)	B-17H			(abandoned at desert test site 52/65)	
	TB-17H			Valley Scrap Metal, Phoenix AZ: hulk	4.65
	SB-17G			Aircraft Specialities Inc, Mesa AZ	.65/81
				(trucked NV-Mesa 5.65, stripped for spares)	
				Globe Air, Mesa AZ: stored hulk	2.81/85
				Kermit Weeks/Weeks Air Mus., Tamiami FL	.85/96
				(dism. hulk stored, Ocotillo Wells CA 88/96)	
32370	B-17G	44-83729		Institut Geographique National, Creil	10.12.47
(-DL)			F-BEED	Institut Geographique National, Creil "Denise"	11.6.48
				wfu and broken-up for spares, Creil	.62

				hulk rep. still at Creil	70/73
32376 •	B-17G	**44-83735**	NL68269	Transocean Air Lines Inc, Oakland CA	17.2.47
(-DL)				(conv. to executive configuration Oakland CA)	
				Col. Andres Soriano/San Miguel Brewery,	
				Manila: "San Miguel"	.47/49
			N68629	Assembly of God Inc, Springfield MO	4.10.49/51
				Leeward Aeronautical, Fort Wayne IN	7.11.51
			F-BDRS	Institut Geographique National, Creil	23.8.52/75
				(wfu Creil: noted as stripped hulk, Creil by 72)	
				Euroworld Ltd, Duxford UK	24.5.75/78
				Imperial War Museum, Duxford	.78/96
				(rest., displ. as 231983/*Mary Alice*/IY-G)	
32398	B-17G	44-83757	N5198N	SECA, Le Bourget	
(-DL)				Institut Geographique National, Creil	25.7.50
			F-BDRR	Institut Geographique National, Creil	16.9.50/72
				retired, Creil	.62
				noted as derelict hulk, Creil	72
32426 •	B-17G	**44-83785**	N809Z	Atlantic General Enterprises, Washington DC	1.9.60/62
(-DL)	CB-17G			Intermountain Aviation Inc, Marana AZ	4.10.62/75
	VB-17G			(CIA operations,"Skyhook" in nose; conv. to	
				fire tanker, Marana 7.69, #22, #C71, #B71)	
				Evergreen Helicopters, Marana AZ (#71)	1.3.75/78
			N207EV	Evergreen Helicopters, Marana AZ (#22)	6.3.79/92
				Evergreen Heritage Collection, Marana AZ	19.7.85/96
				(rest. to military config., Marana AZ .89/90,	
				flies as 483785/K/*Shady Lady*)	
32431 •	B-17G	**44-83790**		forced landed, Newfoundland	24.12.47
(-DL)				located almost intact (5429N/6612W)	.70
32455 •	B-17G	**44-83814**		North Dakota Public School District, Hazen ND	.47/51
(-DL)			N66571	California Atlantic Airways, St Petersburg FL	20.6.51/53
			CF-HBP	Kenting Aviation Ltd, Toronto ONT: del.	12.5.53/71
				Photographic Survey Corp, Toronto ONT	15.5.57/60
				Hunting Survey Corp, Toronto ONT	11.2.60/62
				Kenting Aviation Ltd, Toronto ONT	9.4.62/71
			N66571	Arnold Kolb/Black Hills Aviation,	
				Spearfish SD, later Alamogordo NM	1.4.71/82
				(conv. to tanker #A18,#18,#C13,#09)	
				NASM, Washington DC	19.1.82/96
				Pima Air Museum AZ: displ. as "483814"	82/84
				del. to Washington-Dulles for NASM: stored	25.4.84/92
32504 •	B-17G	**44-83863**		(to USN as Bu77231): BOC 16.7.45 SOC	10.7.56
(-DL)	PB-1W		N6464D	ntu: American Compressed Steel Corp	12.57
			N5233V	American Compressed Steel Corp, Dallas TX	2.12.57/60
				(unconv., USN "TE-", Dallas-Love 58/60)	
				Marson Equipment & Salvage Co, Tucson AZ	26.2.60/61
				Aero Union Corp, Anderson CA	27.9.61/62
				Rogue Flying Services, Medford OR	3.1.62/63
				(conv. to fire tanker Medford 7.62, #F71)	
				Aero Ag Inc, Medford OR (tanker #F71)	1.4.63/69
				Idaho Aircraft Corp, Boise ID	71
				Aero Union Corp, Chico CA (tanker #D1,#18)	6.6.71/75
				USAFM, Eglin AFB FL: del.	19.6.75/96
				(displ. as "4-83863", later "46106/X")	
32505	B-17G	44-83864		(to USN as Bu77232): BOC 14.7.45 SOC 10.7.56	
(-DL)	PB-1W		N6465D	ntu: American Compressed Steel Corp	12.57
			N5234V	American Compressed Steel Corp, Dallas TX	2.12.57/58
			XB-BOE	CIA Mexicana Aero Foto, Mexico City	3.1.58/63

			N5234V	Mark Hurd Aerial Surveys, Goleta CA	2.3.64
				Cal Nat Airways, Grass Valley CA	6.3.64/66
			N73648	Cal Nat Airways, Grass Valley CA	66
				(rebuilt Grass Valley, conv. to tanker #B11)	
				Black Hills Aviation, Spearfish SD (#E56)	2.4.68/72
				crashed, Silver City NM	12.7.72
32509 •	B-17G	**44-83868**		(to USN as Bu77233): BOC 14.7.45 SOC	10.7.56
(-DL)	PB-1W		N6466D	ntu: American Compressed Steel Corp	12.57
			N5237V	American Compressed Steel Corp, Dallas TX	12.57/60
				(unconv., USN "XD-2", Dallas-Love .58/60)	
				Ashland Corp, Tucson AZ	26.2.60
				Marson Equipment & Salvage Co, Tucson AZ	7.7.60/61
				Aero Union Corp, Anderson CA	27.9.61
				Calvin J. Butler/Butler Farm Air/	
				Butler Aircraft Co, Redmond OR	12.61/70
				(conv. for fire bombing 5.62; spraying 8.62)	
				(tanker #E15, later #F15; #65)	
				TBM Inc, Sequoia CA (tanker #65)	79/83
				RAF Museum, Hendon: arr.	9.12.83/96
				(rest. to military config. as "483868" at	
				Sequoia CA, del. to RAF Museum 3-13.10.83)	
32513 •	B-17G	**44-83872**		(to USN as Bu77235): BOC 16.7.45 SOC	10.7.56
(-DL)	PB-1W			arr. NAS Litchfield Park AZ for storage	15.1.55/58
			N7227C	Aero Service Corp, Philadelphia PA	1.10.57/67
				op. on survey work, by Aeroflex: wfu	10.63
				Confederate Air Force, Mercedes TX, later	
				Harlingen, Midland TX	13.4.67/96
				(flew as 124592/*Texas Raiders*,	
				later 483872/*Texas Raiders*/VP-X)	
32525 •	B-17G	**44-83884**		(to USN as Bu77244): BOC 23.7.45 SOC	10.7.56
(-DL)	PB-1W		N6471D	ntu: American Compressed Steel Corp	12.57
			N5230V	American Compressed Steel Corp, Dallas TX	2.12.57/60
				(stored unconv."XD-10", Dallas-Love 58/61)	
				Marson Equipment & Salvage Co, Tucson AZ	10.60/61
				Aero Union Corp, Anderson/Chico CA	27.9.61/79
				(tanker #C19, #E19, #19)	
				USAFM, Barksdale AFB LA: del.	.80/96
				(displ. as 338289/*Yankee Doodle II*, later	
				483884/*Yankee Doodle II*, "333284")	
8492 •	B-17G	**44-85583**		(to FA Brazil as B17-5402)	6.53
(-VE)	TB-17H			Recife AB, Brazil : displ.	3.73/89
	SB-17G				
8503	B-17G	44-85594		Institut Geographique National, Creil	28.9.54
(-VE)			F-BGSQ	Institut Geographique National, Creil - broken up	7.10.54/72
8508 •	B-17G	**44-85599**		USAF, retired to Davis Monthan AFB AZ	8.59
(-VE)	EDB-17G			96th BG Memorial Association, Abilene TX	
	DB-17G			Municiple Airport, Abilene TX : del.	10.60/74
	DB-17P			(displ. as 0-5599/X/*Black Hawk*)	
				USAFM, Dyess AFB, Abilene TX	.74/96
				(rest., displ. as "485599/A", later "238133")	
8552	B-17G	44-85643		Institut Geographique National, Creil	12.12.47
(-VE)			F-BEEA	Institut Geographique National, Creil	22.6.48/89
				Chateau de Verneuil	
				(based UK for film "Memphis Belle" 6.89)	
				crashed and dest. by fire, RAF Binbrook UK	25.7.89
8627 •	B-17G	**44-85718**		Institut Geographique National, Creil	10.12.47
(-VE)			F-BEEC	Institut Geographique National, Creil	3.8.48

			ZS-EEC	I.G.N., "*Charlotte*"	8.65/66
			F-BEEC	Institut Geographique National, Creil	8.66/84
				wfu Creil	.78/84
			G-FORT	Warbirds of GB, Blackbushe: del.	8.6.84/86
				Patina Ltd, Duxford	.86/87
			N900RW	Air SRV Inc, Anderson TX	9.6.87
				(del. ex Duxford, arr. Houston TX 16.7.87)	
				Lone Star Flight Museum, Houston	
				later Galveston TX	11.87/95
				(flies as 238050/BN-U/*Thunderbird*)	
8637	B-17G	44-85728	NX4600	Trans World Airlines, Kansas City MO	26.6.46
(-VE)	Model			executive conversion, by Boeing at Seattle	.46
	299AB		NL1B	TWA (Fleet #242)	2.12.46/47
			EP-HIM	Shah of Persia, Tehran	4.47
			F-BGOE	SECA, Le Bourget, Paris	
				Institut Geographique National, Creil	12.7.52/70
				last flight 22.8.67 : broken-up, Creil	.70
8643 •	B-17G	**44-85734**		Esperado Mining Co, Altus OK : for scrap	25.6.47
(-VE)	Model		N5111N	Pratt & Whitney Engines, Hartford CT	11.47/67
	299Z			(civil conv. by Boeing, Seattle .48, 5th engine in	
				nose, tested P&W T34 & T64 turboprops)	
				Bradley Air Museum, Windsor Locks CT: del.	16.6.67/81
				badly damaged at museum, by tornado	3.10.79
				New England Air Museum CT : wreck stored	81/87
				Tom Reilly Vintage Aircraft, Kissimmee FL	.87/96
				(wreck stored Windsor Locks CT 79/92;	
				trucked dism. to Kissimmee .93 for rebuild,	
				using parts of N6694C)	
8647 •	B-17G	**44-85738**		AMVETS Chapter 56, Tulare CA: del.	4.8.58/93
(-VE)	DB-17G			displ. Perry's Coffee House, Tulare CA	.71/81
	EDB-17G			displ. AMVETS compound, Tulare CA	.81/94
	DB-17G			dam. by truck running off highway (repaired)	8.82
				(displ. as "0-85738/K/Preston's Pride")	
8649 •	B-17G	**44-85740**		Metal Products Inc, Amarillo TX : scrap	17.6.47
(-VE)			NL5017N	Universal Aviation Inc, Tulsa OK	10.7.47
				Charles T. Winters, Miami FL	2.8.47
				Vero Beach Export & Imp. Co, Vero Beach FL	16.8.47/49
			N5017N	Aero Service Corp, Philadelphia PA	27.6.49/62
				Chris D. Stoltzfus & Assoc., Coatesville PA	10.8.62/66
				Dothan Aviation Corp, Dothan AL : sprayer	12.66/78
				William E. Harrison, Tulsa OK	20.2.78/79
				EAA Aviation Foundation, Oshkosh WI	21.5.79/95
				(flies as "85740/*Aluminium Overcast*/FU-D",	
				later "2102516/30-H")	
8683	B-17G	44-85774		Government of Bolivia: ex Davis Monthan AFB	22.6.56
(-VE)	VB-17G			(civil conv. by Hamilton Aircraft, Tucson AZ)	
	CP-621			Lloyd Aero Boliviano, La Paz	12.56/68
			N621L	Aircraft Specialties Inc, Mesa AZ	12.68/75
				(flew to Hawaii for film *Tora Tora Tora* 1.69)	
				(tanker #C64, #64)	
				crashed, dest.	7.75
8687 •	B-17G	**44-85778**	**N3509G**	Ace Smelting Inc, Phoenix AZ	14.8.59
(-VE)	TB-17G			Sonora Flying Service, Columbia CA	20.9.60/61
	VB-17G			Leo J. Demers, Madras OR (tanker #97)	25.5.61/66
				Aero Union Corp, Chico CA (tanker #E16)	29.4.66/72
				William A. Dempsay/Central Air Service,	
				Rantoul KS (tanker #F42,#42,#102)	2.6.72/78
				Western Air Contractors, American Fork UT	6.7.78/81

				Westernair of Albuquerque, Albuquerque NM	15.6.81/82
				Richard Vartanian/Aircraft Component Equipment Supplies Inc, Klamath Falls OR	28.3.82/90
				(stored Stockton CA 84/91)	
				Arthur W. McDonnell, Mojave CA	7.90
				Don Whittington/Florida Aircraft Leasing Corp, Fort Lauderdale FL	2.91
				Robert L. Waltrip/Lone Star Flight Museum, Galveston TX & Don Whittington/World Jet International, Fort Lauderdale FL	4.91/92
				(flew as 4485778/*Miss Museum of Flying*)	
				Warbirds of GB ntu.	.92
				Robert J. Pond/Planes of Fame East, Minneapolis-Flying Cloud MN	5.93/95
				(flies as 4485778/*Miss Angela*)	
8693 •	B-17G	44-85784		General Electric Flight Test Center,	
(-VE)	EB-17G			Schenectady NY : leased ex USAF	9.50/54
	ETB-17G		F-BGSR	Institut Geographique National, Creil	10.54/75
			N17TE	Ted White & Duane Egli/Euroworld Inc, Biggin Hill/Duxford UK: del. ex Creil	16.3.75
			G-BEDF	M. H. Campbell, Duxford	5.8.76/79
				B-17 Preservation Trust Ltd, Duxford	.79/96
				(flies as "124485/DF-A/*Sally B*)	
8699 •	B-17G	**44-85790**		Art Lacey, Milwaukie, Portland OR	5.3.47/95
(-VE)				(del. flight ex Altus AFB OK 8-10.3.47)	
				displ. Lacey's gas station, Oregon City OR	.47/96
				(called Lacey's Bomber Restaurant by 95)	
8721	B-17G	44-85812		(to USCG as Bu77246): BOC 12.8.46 SOC	14.2.58
(-VE)	PB-1G		N4710C	Delta Leasing Corp, Charlotte NC	16.5.58/59
				Leroy Brown, Miami FL	23.1.59
				(civil conv. 7.59: plywood cargo floor)	
				M. E. Brown Inc, Bowling Green FL	12.1.60/61
				Challenger Leasing Corp, Fort Lauderdale FL	4.4.61/63
				Dothan Aviation Corp, Dothan AL : sprayer	16.4.63/76
				crashed dest., in-flight fire, Blakeley GA	5.8.76
8722 •	B-17G	**44-85813**		Curtiss-Wright Corp, Caldwell NJ : leased	10.45/57
(-VE)	EB-17G			(conv. Boeing,Wichita KS .46: 5th engine position	
	JB-17G			in nose: tested engines & propellers 9.47/66)	
	Model		N6694C	Curtiss-Wright Corp, Woodbridge CT	30.8.57/66
	299Z			Ewing Aviation Co, San Ramon CA	1.12.66/69
				Ewing-Kolb Aircraft, Spearfish SD	15.8.69/70
				Arnold Kolb/Black Hills Aviation, Spearfish SD, later Alamogordo NM	30.7.70/80
				(rebuilt Spearfish .69/70, fitted standard forward fuse. ex 44-83316: tanker #C12,#12)	
				crashed, firebombing, Bear Pen NC	16.4.80
				Tom Reilly Vintage Aircraft, Kissimmee FL	85/96
				(major components recov. from crash site, stored Kissimmee to be used in rebuild of N5111N)	
8737 •	B-17G	44-85828		(to USCG as Bu 77254): BOC	14.8.45
(-VE)	PB-1G			disposal ex NAS Elizabeth City NC: del.	14.10.59
			N9323R	Joe E. Marrs, Opa Locka FL	8.3.60
				Serv-Air Inc, Westchester NY	9.4.60/62
				Tropical Export Trading Co, Ft. Lauderdale FL	23.5.62
				Hugh Wheelless/Dothan Aviation, Dothan AL	17.7.62
				(conv. for aerial spraying 7.62)	
				Black Hills Aviation, Spearfish SD	4.10.62/69
				(conv. from sprayer to tanker: tanker #B30)	
				Aeroflite Inc, Cody WY (tanker #B30,#37)	71/75
				Bruce Kinney/Kinney Air Tankers, Richey MT	12.75/78

				Aircraft Specialties Inc, Mesa AZ (#37)	18.5.78/80
				USAFM, Pima County Air Museum, Tucson AZ	7.12.80/96
				(del. Mesa-Davis Monthan AFB 11.80, rest. Pima	
				as "485828", later 231892/*I'll Be Around*)	
8738 •	B-17G	**44-85829**		(to USCG as Bu 77255): BOC	6.12.46
(-VE)	PB-1G			offered for disposal ex NAS Elizabeth City NC	8.58
			N3193G	Ace Smelting Inc, Phoenix AZ	11.5.59
				Fairchild Aerial Surveys, Los Angeles CA	11.59/65
				(mod. for photographic/magnetometer survey)	
				Aero Service Corp, Philadelphia PA	2.8.65
				Biegert Bros, Shickley NE: sprayer	1.10.65/66
				Aircraft Specialties Inc, Mesa AZ	19.3.66/81
				(conv. 1.68 to fire tanker: #43, #C34, #34)	
				(del. to Hawaii for movie "Tora Tora Tora" 1.69)	
				Globe Air Inc, Mesa AZ (tanker #34)	18.2.81/86
				Yankee Air Force Inc, Willow Run MI: del.	2.7.86/95
				(rest. Willow Run .86/95, ff 13.7.95 as	
				485829/*Yankee Lady*)	
8749	B-17G	44-85840		Government of Bolivia: ex Davis Monthan AFB	22.6.56
(-VE)	TB-17G			(civil conv. Tucson AZ by Hamilton Aircraft)	
	VB-17G		CP-620	Lloyd Aero Boliviano, La Paz	11.56/68
			N620L	Aircraft Specialties Inc, Mesa AZ	12.68/73
				(del. Hawaii for movie "Tora Tora Tora" 1.69)	
				dam. landing during filming, Honolulu HI	c3.69
				(tanker #C54, #54)	
				crashed firebombing, near Elko NV	12.7.73

BOEING B-29 SUPERFORTRESS

4452 •	B-29	**42-24791**		NAS China Lake CA: target use, open storage	.56/80
				USAFM, Beale AFB CA: *Big Time Operator*	86/96
				(nose only, grafted to museum building)	
7287	B-29	42-93880		NAS China Lake CA: target use, open storage	56/75
7374 •	B-29A	**42-93967**		American Legion Post, Cordele GA	73/85
	F-13A			Georgia Veterans Memorial State Park,	
	FB-29A			Cordele GA	94
	RB-29A				
1056 •	B-29	**44-69729**		NAS China Lake CA: target use, open storage	56/85
	KB-29			USAFM, Lowry AFB CO: rest., displ.	.86/93
				Museum of Flight, Seattle-Boeing Field WA	93/94
				(displ. as "469729/T Square 54")	
10789	B-29	44-69957		NAS China Lake CA: target use, open storage	56/75
				removed, destination unknown, by	85
10804 •	B-29	**44-69972**	N6735C	USNAM, NAS Pensacola FL	4.2.94/96
10815 •	B-29	**44-69983**		NAS China Lake CA: target use, open storage	56/68
				Sandia Atomic Museum, Kirtland AFB NM	74/76
				derelict, dismantled (museum failed) by	76
				USAFM, Saipan, Marianas (unconf.)	85
				USAFM, Travis AFB CA (forward fuse only)	86/92
10816	B-29	44-69984		NAS China Lake CA: target use, open storage	56/75
10848 •	B-29	**44-70016**		displ. MASDC, Davis-Monthan AFB AZ	65/69
	TB-29			USAFM, Pima County Air Museum, Tucson AZ	.69/93
				(displ. as 470016/*City of Quaker City*)	

10881 •	B-29	**44-70049**		NAS China Lake CA: target use, open storage USAFM, Travis AFB CA : (listed) Weeks Air Museum, Tamiami FL (stored dism., Ocotillo Wells CA 88/94)	56/85 87 87/94
10896	B-29	**44-70064**		NAS China Lake CA: target use, open storage USAFM, Castle AFB CA (used in composite rebuild with 44-61535: displ. as 461535/*Raz'n Hell*	57/80 .80
10934	B-29	44-70102		NAS China Lake CA: target use, open storage removed by	56/75 85
10945 •	B-29 TB-29	**44-70113**		Aberdeen Proving Grounds MD: target use Florence Air & Missile Museum, Florence SC (stored dism. Florence as "Z-58" 90/94)	60/73 .73/94
11012 •	B-29A	**44-61535**		NAS China Lake CA: open storage: del. USAFM, Castle AFB CA (composite rebuild with 44-70064: displ. as 461535/*Raz'n Hell*)	2.57/80 .80/93
11032	B-29	44-61555		NAS China Lake CA: target use, open storage	56/75
11146 •	B-29A SB-29A	**44-61669**	N3299F	NAS China Lake CA: target use, open storage USAFM: loaned David C. Tallichet/ Yesterdays Air Force: stored Barstow CA USAFM, March AFB CA: del. (displ. as "461669/Mission Inn")	56/74 74/81 5.8.81/95
11148 •	B-29A SB-29A	**44-61671**		Aberdeen Proving Grounds MD: target: del. USAFM, Pease AFB NH (displ. as 89/*The Great Artiste*) USAFM, Whiteman AFB MO: trucked dism.	.57/74 79/92 .92/94
11216 •	B-29A TB-29A	**44-61739**		Aberdeen Proving Grounds MD: target use USAFM, Robins AFB GA: nose only	60/85 94
11225 •	B-29A TB-29A	**44-61748**	G-BHDK	NAS China Lake CA: open storage: del. Imperial War Museum, Duxford (del. China Lake-Tucson AZ 11.79; del. UK ex Tucson 17.2.80 arr. Duxford displ. as 461748/*Hawg Wild*)	11.56/79 27.9.79/96 12.3.80:
11434	B-29A	44-61957		NAS China Lake CA: target use, open storage	56/75
11452 •	B-29A TB-29A	**44-61975**		Aberdeen Proving Grounds MD: target use Bradley Air Museum, Windsor Locks CT: arr. badly damaged by tornado at museum New England Air Museum, Windsor Locks CT (displ. as "461975")	60/73 21.6.73/85 3.10.79 84/92
11469	B-29A	44-61992		NAS China Lake CA: target use, open storage	56/75
11499 •	B-29A	**44-62022**		NAS China Lake CA: target use, open storage Fred E. Weisbrod Aircraft Museum, Pueblo CO (displ. as 62022/18/*Peachy*)	56/75 78/96
11532	B-29A	44-62055		NAS China Lake CA: target use, open storage	56/75
11547 •	B-29A	44-62070	N4249	NAS China Lake CA: target use, open storage Confederate Air Force, Harlingen TX (rest. China Lake, del. to Harlingen 3.8.71, flies as *Fifi*)	56/71 23.3.71/81

			N529B	Confederate Air Force, Harlingen/Midland TX	8.81/96
11565	B-29A	44-62088		NAS China Lake CA: target use, open storage	56/75
11589 •	B-29A	**44-62112**		Pima County Air Museum, Tucson AZ	83/92
				(forward fuselage only; rear to Disney studios)	
11616 •	B-29A	**44-62139**		USAFM, Wright-Patterson AFB, Dayton OH	90/92
				(fuselage only: displ. as *Command Decision*)	
11637	B-29A	44-62160		NAS China Lake CA: target use, open storage	56/75
11680 •	B-29A	**44-62203**		stored Aberdeen Proving Grounds MD	60/85
11691 •	B-29A	**44-62214**		USAF: last flight	16.9.54
				partly submerged in lake, Eielson AFB AK	60/92
11697 •	B-29A	**44-62220**		Aberdeen Proving Grounds MD: target use	60/85
				USAFM, Kelly AFB TX	88/94
11699 •	B-29A	**44-62222**		NAS China Lake CA: target use, open storage	56/75
				Pima County Air Museum, Tucson AZ	83/92
				(forward fuselage only; rear to Disney studios)	
12430 •	B-29	**44-87627**		Aberdeen Proving Grounds MD: target use	60/85
	TB-29			USAFM, Barksdale AFB LA	94
12582 •	B-29	**44-87779**		USAF, retired to Davis-Monthan AFB AZ	7.56
	TB-29			NAS China Lake CA: target use: del.	.56/85
	B-29M			USAFM, Ellsworth AFB SD: arr. dism	6.12.85/96
	KB-29B			(rest., displ. as *Legal Eagle*)	
13633 •	B-29	**45-21739**		NAS China Lake CA: target use, open storage	56/68
				Korean War Museum, Seoul, South Korea	72/92
				(displ. as "521739/W-48")	
13643 •	B-29A	**45-21749**		USAFM, Chanute AFB IL	65/92
				USAFM, Kirtland AFB NM	94/96
13662	B-29	45-21768		(*Kee Bird*): forced landing shallow water,	
	F-13A			180m north of Thule AFB, Greenland	21.2.47
	FB-29A			abandoned complete, minor dam., in situ	2.47/93
				Darryl G. Greenamyer & Associates CA	.93
			N70887	Gary Larkins/Institute of Aeronautical	
				Archeological Research, Auburn CA	10.8.93/94
				Darryl G. Greenamyer, Ocala FL	21.3.94
				Kee Bird Limited Liability Co, Ocala FL	8.8.94/95
				(recov. expedition and planned ferry to USA .95)	
				dest. by fire just prior to ff.	21.5.95
13681 •	B-29	**45-21787**		(to USN as P2B-1S Bu84029)	
	P2B-1S			(to NACA as NACA137 *Fertile Myrtle*)	
				NAS Litchfield Park AZ: del. for storage	10.59/69
			N91329	Ralph W. & Stephen Johnson/	
				American Air Museum, Oakland CA	.69/84
				(rest. Tucson AZ, del. to Oakland CA 11.69;	
				retired Oakland 10.74, rest. ff 27.4.78,	
				open storage Oakland 79/89)	
				Kermit A. Weeks, Tamiami FL	7.84
				(aborted del. flight Oakland-Stockton CA .84)	
			N29KW	Weeks Air Museum,Tamiami FL	8.85/96
				(trucked Oakland-Tamiami .89, stored dism.)	
- •	B-29	**42-65281**		NAS China Lake CA: target use	.56/85

	WB-29 TB-29		USAFM, Travis AFB CA (stripped hulk airfreighted dism. to Travis by C-5A: rest. completed .94, displ. as *Miss America* 62)	.85/95
- •	B-29	**44-27297**	(509th CG/ 393rd CS: *Bock's Car*) Davis-Monthan AFB AZ: open storage USAFM, Wright-Patterson AFB OH: del.	 48/61 26.9.61/96
- •	B-29 WB-29	**44-27343**	Aberdeen Proving Grounds MD: target use USAFM, Tinker AFB OK	60/85 .85/96
- •	B-29B TB-29B	**44-84053**	Aberdeen Proving Grounds MD: target use USAFM, Robins AFB GA	60/83 .83/94
- •	B-29B TB-29B	**44-84076**	USAFM, Offutt AFB NE (displ. as "0-484076/*Man-O-War*")	65/96
- •	B-29B SB-29B	**44-84084**	NAS China Lake CA: target use, open storage USAFM, Travis AFB CA: (listed) Weeks Air Museum, Tamiami FL (stored dism., Ocotillo Wells CA 90/94)	56/85 87 87/96
- •	B-29	**44-86292**	(509th CG/393rd CS: *Enola Gay*) NASM, Andrews AFB MD: open storage NASM, Silver Hill MD: stored dism. (nose section rest. for displ. NASM 94/95)	 59 65/96
-	B-29	44-86402	Aircraft Industries Museum, Louisville KY	72
- •	B-29	**44-86408**	USAFM, Hill AFB UT (displ. as 4486408/*Hagarty's Hag*)	88/96
- •	B-29	-	USAF: forced landing, wheels-up, in snow Elizabeth Islands, near North Pole : abandoned recov. project, planned to fly out	 .47/90 90
- •	B-29	-	USAFM, Barksdale AFB LA (under rest. for static displ.)	92
225008 •	Tu-4		(to Chinese AF as 4134): turboprop conv. People's Liberation Army Air Force Museum, Changping, China	 90/94
2806501•	Tu-4		(to Chinese AF as 4114): turboprop AEW conv. People's Liberation Army Air Force Museum, Changping, China	 90/94
2805103•	Tu-4	-	(Soviet AF ......) Soviet AF Museum, Monino AB, Moscow (displ. as "01")	 90/92

BOULTON PAUL DEFIANT

- •	Mk. I	**N1671**	RAF St.Athan : displ. as "N1617" RAF Finningley: stored RAF Museum, Hendon (displ. as "N1671/EW-D")	61/67 69 74/96
- •	Mk. I	**N3378**	crashed Near Bleaklow Stones Boulton Paul Association (incomplete wreck recov: static rest. project combined with parts from spare RAFM airframe)	29.8.41 91/96

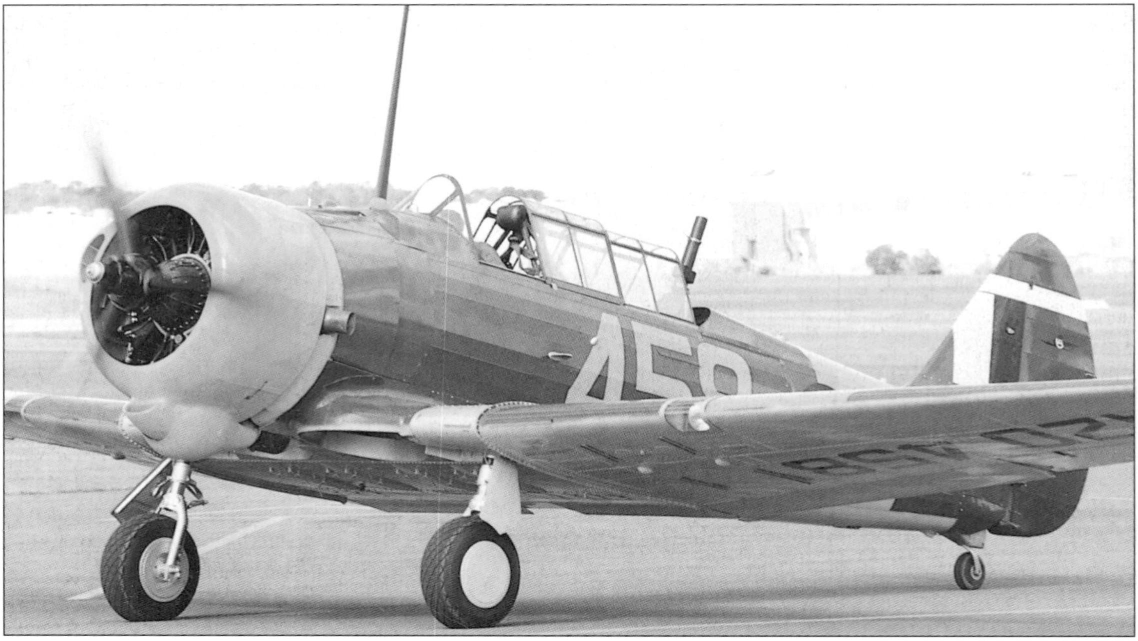

Above: Classic Aviation restored C.A.C. CA9 Wirraway A20-458, seen here at Bankstown. It is one of a growing number of Commonwealth Aircraft Corporation machines taking to the air since the last edition of the directory. **Alan Scoot.** **Below:** One of these C.A.C.types entering civilian hands in increasing numbers is the Winjeel, here represented by Richard Hourigan's example, A85-450 VH-HOY at Point Cook. **Roger Wallsgrove.**

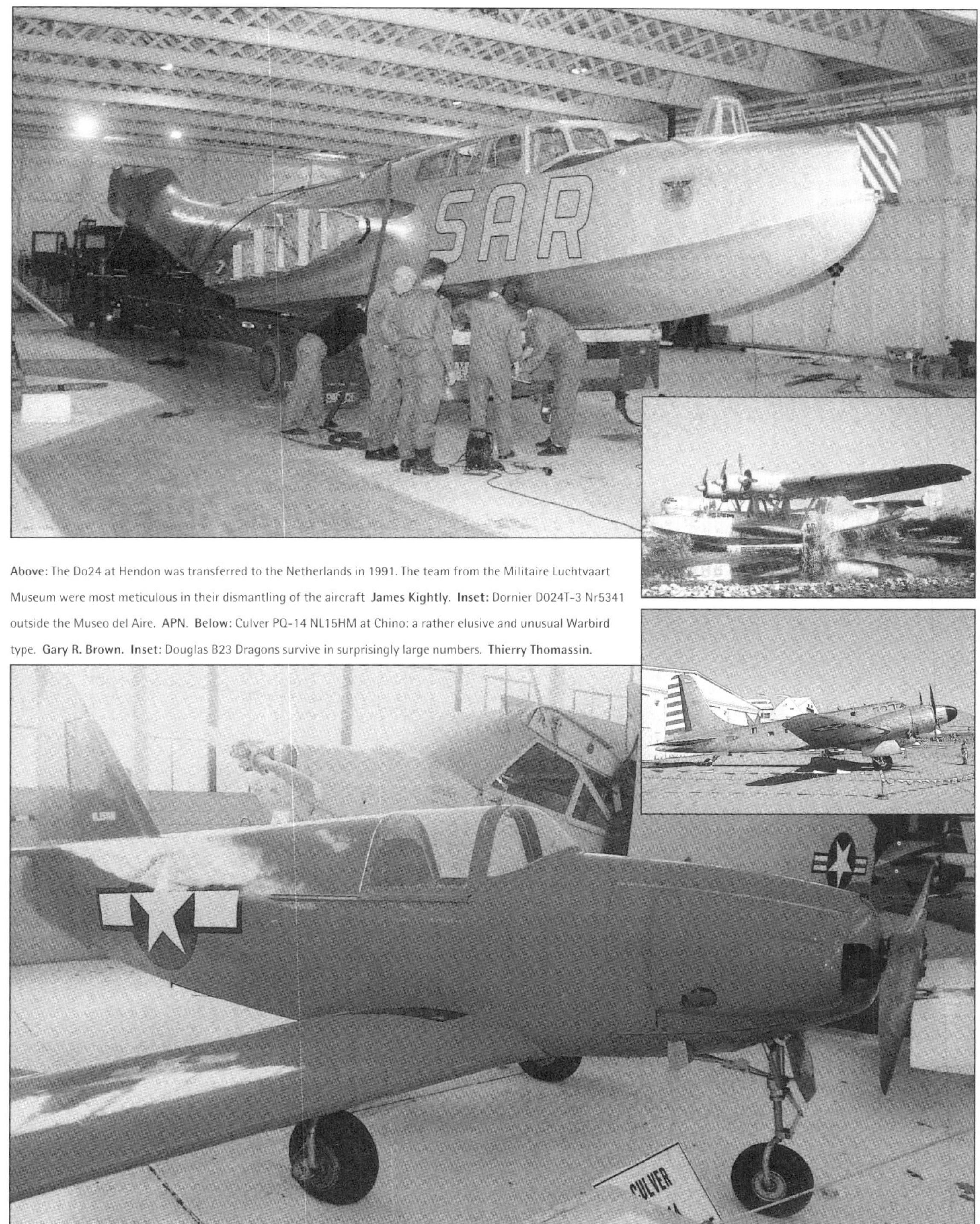

Above: The Do24 at Hendon was transferred to the Netherlands in 1991. The team from the Militaire Luchtvaart Museum were most meticulous in their dismantling of the aircraft **James Kightly. Inset:** Dornier DO24T-3 Nr5341 outside the Museo del Aire. **APN. Below:** Culver PQ-14 NL15HM at Chino: a rather elusive and unusual Warbird type. **Gary R. Brown. Inset:** Douglas B23 Dragons survive in surprisingly large numbers. **Thierry Thomassin.**

Brewster A-34/SB2A Bermuda

		Type	Serial	Reg.	History	Date
-	•	A-34	**FF860**		(not del. RAF, div. to USAAC as ....)	
		Mk. I			abandoned on airfield dump, Tullahoma TN	45/73
					David C. Tallichet/MARC, Chino CA	.73/88
-	•	A-34	-		(not del. RAF, div. to USAAC as ....)	
		Mk. I			abandoned on airfield dump, Tullahoma TN	45/73
					David C. Tallichet/MARC, Chino CA	.73/88
-	•	A-34	-		(not del. RAF, div. to USAAC as ....)	
		Mk. I			abandoned on airfield dump, Tullahoma TN	45/73
					David C. Tallichet/MARC, Chino CA	.73/80
					Brewster Restoration Project/Naval Air Development Center, Warminster PA	.80/96
					(under rest.)	
-	•	A-34	-		(not del. RAF, div. to USAAC as ....)	
		Mk. I			abandoned on airfield dump, Tullahoma TN	c53/73
					hulk displ., Tullahoma TN	84/88

Bristol Beaufighter

		Type	Serial	Reg.	History	Date
-	•	Mk.1c	**T5049**		(to RAAF as A19-43): BOC 6.42: SOC	9.10.47
					to inst. airframe, RAAF Nhill VIC	20.10.44
					Keith Oldfield, Nhill VIC : moved to farm	.47/71
					Moorabbin Aircraft Museum, Melbourne VIC	1.71/86
					(hulk recov. from farm nr Nhill VIC 10.1.71)	
					Roger Cloy, Canada	.86
					USAFM, Wright-Patterson AFB, Dayton OH	.88/96
					(static rest., Lowry AFB CO by 90; cockpit area airfreighted by C-141 to Sydney 4.93 for rest. by Historical Aircraft Restoration Society)	
-	•	Mk. 1f	**X7688**		RAF Halton : engine test rig	53/70
					(front half of airframe, attached to hut)	
					RAF Museum: stored dism. Halton	70/87
					Tim E. Moore/Skysport Engineering, Bedford	12.87/91
				G-DINT	Tim E. Moore, Hatch	17.6.91/96
					(rebuild to fly Hatch)	
-	•	Mk. XIc	**JL946**		(to RAAF as A19-148): BOC	11.7.43
					crashed landing, RAAF Drysdale WA	22.1.44
					(hulk recov. from Drysdale Strip, Kalumburu WA by Robert Greinert & Assoc., Sydney NSW .80)	
					Robert Greinert & Martin Mednis/Historic Aircraft Restoration Society, Sydney NSW	80/94
					(composite rest. to fly, Sydney: with A19-144)	
-	•	Mk. XI	**JM135**		(to RAAF as A19-144): BOC	2.7.43
					crashed landing, RAAF Drysdale WA	3.1.44
					(hulk recov. from Drysdale Strip, Kalumburu WA by Robert Greiner & assoc., Sydney NSW .80)	
					Robert Greinert & Martin Mednis/Historic Aircraft Restoration Society, Sydney NSW	80/96
					(composite rest. to fly, Sydney: with A19-148)	
-	•	TF Mk. X	**RD253**		(to FA Portuguesa as BF-13): del.	17.3.45
					Lisbon Technical Institute, Lisbon, Portugal	50/65
					RAF Museum	.65/72
					RAF Bicester & RAF St.Athan: rest.	65/72
					(parts used in rest. of RD867 at RAF Bicester, then complete static rest. RAF St. Athan)	

			RAF Museum, Hendon	.72/96
- •	TF Mk. X TT Mk.10	**RD867**	RAF Museum Store, RAF Henlow (recov. derelict ex RAF Takali, Malta .64; composite rebuild with RD253 at RAF Bicester, remains to RAF St.Athan .67 for static rest.)	.64/69
			RAF Abingdon: displ. as "BQ-I"	.68
			Canadian National Aeronautical Collection, Rockcliffe AB ONT	.69/82
			National Aviation Museum, Rockcliffe ONT	9.82/95
- •	TF Mk. X TT Mk.10		(to FA Portuguesa as BF-10)	
			Lisbon Technical Institute, Lisbon Portugal	50/65
			Museo do Ar, Alverca AB, Portugal: unrest.	66/83
			SAAF Museum, Swartkop AB: stored	27.5.83/92
- •	Mk. 21	**A8-186**	RAAF Wagga NSW: inst. airframe No.8	20.1.47/50
			G. Strong, Boree Creek NSW: moved to farm	.50/65
			Harold Thomas/Camden Museum of Aviation, Camden, later Narellan NSW: recov. (recov. from farm Boree Creek NSW .65, rest. displ. as A8-186/DU-I/*Beau-Gunsville*)	.65/96
- •	Mk. 21	**A8-324**	Robert Greinert & Martin Mednis/Historic Aircraft Restoration Society, Sydney NSW (fuselage only, recov. ex backyard storeshed, Balwyn, Melbourne VIC)	85/91
			The Fighter Collection, Duxford UK: shipped (long-term rest. to fly, Duxford)	.91/96
- • TT	Mk. 21	**A8-328**	Lord Mayors Childrens Camp, Portsea VIC	11.56/62
			Moorabbin Air Museum, Melbourne VIC (recov. derelict ex camp playground, rest. as "A8-328", later "A8-39": engines run up)	4.62/95
- •	Mk. 21	**A8-371**	Moorabbin Aircraft Museum, Melbourne VIC (fuselage only, recov. ex backyard storeshed, Frankston, Melbourne VIC 17.5.87)	.87
			Roger Cloy USA	.87
			USAFM, Wright-Patterson AFB, Dayton OH (nose section airfreighted to Sydney NSW .93, for rest. at Sydney-Bankstown by HARS	.88/96

BRISTOL BEAUFORT

- •	Mk.V	**T9552**	(to RAAF as A9-13): BOC	1.42
			d'E. C. Darby & N. M. Armstong, Auckland NZ (hulk recov. ex Tadji PNG .74 "A9-13/FX-B", shipped to Auckland NZ .74, stored .74/75)	.74/75
			N. M. Armstrong/Australian Aerospace Museum, Melbourne VIC : static rest.	77/89
			Jack McDonald, Melbourne VIC	89/91
			loan: Museum of Army Flying, Oakey QLD	.90/92
- •	Mk.VII	**A9-141**	dam. RAAF Tocumwal NSW: written off	1.44
			Pearce Dunn/Warbirds Aviation Museum, Mildura VIC : displ. unrest.	70/85
			Ralph Cusack, Brisbane QLD (rest. to fly, Eagle Farm, Brisbane: using rear fuselage ex A9-485 recov. from Gorrie Strip NT)	12.85/96
- •	Mk.VIII	**A9-210**	David C. Tallichet/Yesterdays Air Force/ MARC, Chino CA ("QH-D" recov. ex Tadji PNG for YAF .74	.74/91

			by Charles Darby & Monty Armstrong NZ)	
- •	Mk.VIII	**A9-414**	David C. Tallichet/Yesterdays Air Force/	
			MARC, Chino CA	.74/91
			("UV-Q" recov. ex Tadji PNG for YAF .74	
			by Charles Darby & Monty Armstrong NZ)	
- •	Mk.VIII	**A9-501**	dam. landing RAAF Gove NT : abandoned	3.45/80
			displ. in compound, Gove NT	80/92
- •	Mk.VIII	**A9-535**	David C. Tallichet/Yesterdays Air Force/	
			MARC, Chino CA	.74/91
			(hulk recov. ex Tadji PNG for YAF .74	
			by Charles Darby & Monty Armstrong NZ)	
- •	Mk.VIII	**A9-557**	crashed landing Tadji PNG (100 Sqdn/QH-L)	20.1.45
			recov. from Tadji, West Sepik PNG	.74
			Ian Whitney, Melbourne VIC	.74/90
			(rest. commenced at RAAF Point Cook VIC,	
			fitted with rear fuselage A9-639)	
			Robert Greinert & Martin Mednis/Historic	
			Aircraft Restoration Society, Sydney NSW	.90/91
			Australian War Memorial, Canberra ACT	.91/95
			(arr. dism. Canberra 15.2.91, stored unrest.)	
- •	Mk.VIII	**A9-559**	David C. Tallichet/Yesterdays Air Force/	
			MARC, Chino CA	.74/91
			("QH-F" recov. ex Tadji PNG for YAF .74	
			by Charles Darby & Monty Armstrong NZ)	
- •	Mk.VIII	**A9-637**	David C. Tallichet/Yesterdays Air Force/	
			MARC, Chino CA	.74/89
			("KT-B" recov. ex Tadji PNG for YAF .74	
			by Charles Darby & Monty Armstrong NZ)	
- •	Mk.VIII	-	David C. Tallichet/MARC, Chino CA	.74/91
			RAF Museum Store, Cardington : arr.	.91
			(static rest. Hawkins TX, completed Cardington)	
			RAF Museum, Hendon	12.91/95
			(arr. 10.12.91, displ. as RAF "DD931/L")	
			(composite: using MARC RAAF airframes above)	

BRISTOL BLENHEIM/FAIRCHILD BOLINGBROKE

- •	Mk. IV	-	(to Finnish AF as BL-200)	
			Luonetjarvi AB, Finland: displ. as "BL-200"	68
			Jyvaskla AB, Finland: displ. as memorial	69
			Aviation Mus. of Central Finland, Jyvaskyla	68/80
			Tampereen Teknillinen Museo, Tampere	79/88
			stored Tikkakoski, Finland	91/94
- •	Mk. IV	**RCAF9041**	RCAF BOC 3.10.41: SOC	1.10.46
			disposal RCAF Calgary: to farmer for parts	.46
			John Hutchinson, Cochrane ALTA: to farm	.47/88
			Jonathan Spinks, Lethbridge ALTA	.88/94
			(hulk recov. ex farm .88: rest. cockpit area	
			displ. Nanton Lancaster Memorial, Nanton ALTA;	
			planned full static rest. using new rear fuselage.)	
- •	Mk. IV	**RCAF9048**	RCAF BOC 8.10.41: SOC	21.8.46
			Wes Agnew, Hartney MAN	
			David C. Tallichet/ MARC, Chino CA	.72/76
			(railed to Ontario CA .72, stored Chino CA)	

				Yankee Air Corps Museum, Chino CA (static rest. almost complete, YACM Chino by 84)	81/84
- •	Mk. IV	**RCAF9059**		RCAF BOC 5.12.41: SOC Wes Agnew, Hartney MAN Commonwealth Air Training Plan Museum, Brandon MAN	21.8.46 75 88/91
11-880-203 •	Mk. IVD	**RCAF9073**	 **N4260C**	RCAF BOC 12.1.42: SOC Wes Agnew, Hartney MAN Weeks Air Museum, Tamiami FL Kermit A. Weeks, Tamiami FL	15.5.46 88/91 6.91/95
11-880-107 •	Mk. IV	**RCAF9104**		RCAF BOC 8.1.42: SOC George Maude, Saltspring Island BC (disposal ex Patricia Bay $35, barged in 12.46) M. Lacy, Saltspring Island BC (stripped for farm parts, derelict fuse. hulk Fulford Harbour, Salt Spring Island BC by 76) David Maude/North American Interplanetary Society, Sidney BC (recov. by chopper to Patricia Bay 7.11.81) David Maude/Canadian Military Aviation Museum BC B. C. Aviation Museum, Sidney BC (static rest., Victoria Airport BC using parts from RCAF 9093 & 10163, displ. as "RCAF BK-L")	6.9.46 10.46 1.47/80 11.80/82 10.82/83 84/95
- •	Mk. IVT	**RCAF9869**		RCAF BOC 5.5.42: SOC Western Canada Aviation Museum, Winnipeg MAN	15.5.46 79/91
- •	Mk. IVT	**RCAF9883**		RCAF BOC 23.5.42: SOC Commonwealth Air Training Plan Museum, Brandon MAN (static rest. commenced 11.94 ex open storage)	9.7.46 88/95
- •	Mk. IVT	**RCAF9887**		RCAF BOC 1.6.42: SOC disposal RCAF MacDonald: to farmer for parts George Morris, MacDonald MAN : on farm	15.5.46 .46 .46/92
- •	Mk. IVTD	**RCAF9889**		RCAF BOC 3.6.42: SOC Bart Bourne, Winnipeg MAN Canadian Warplane Heritage, Hamilton ONT	15.5.46 76/79 88/96
- •	Mk. IVT	**RCAF9892**		RCAF BOC George Maude, Saltspring Island BC (disposal ex Patricia Bay $50, barged in 12.46) RCAF Collection: recov. for static rest. Canadian National Aeronautical Collection, Rockcliffe AB ONT National Aviation Museum, Rockcliffe ONT (displ. as "9892/YO-X")	9.6.42 48/63 5.63/64 6.6.64/82 9.82/96
- •	Mk. IVT	**RCAF9893**		RCAF BOC 6.6.42: SOC Wes Agnew, Hartney MAN Ormond Haydon-Baillie, Vancouver BC Ormond Haydon-Baillie, Duxford UK: shipped British Aerial Museum, Duxford: stored dism. Duxford Imperial War Museum, Duxford	15.5.46 .72 .74/78 .79/86 88/96
- •	Mk. IVT	**RCAF9895**		RCAF BOC 9.6.42: SOC Wes Agnew, Hartney MAN Musee Royal de L'Armee Koninklijk	15.5.46 69/71

				Legermuseum, Brussels	.71/96
				(static rest. of 9895/10038 commenced .88)	
- •	Mk. IVT	**RCAF9896**		RCAF BOC 10.6.42: SOC	22.5.46
				R. Yancié, Legend ALTA: to farm	c46/81
				Canadian Museum of Flight & Transportation,	
				Vancouver BC : arr. dism.	10.81/95
				(complete aircraft, stored dism.)	
- •	Mk. IVT	**RCAF9897**		RCAF BOC 11.6.42: SOC	21.7.47
				disposal ex RCAF Vulcan ALTA: to farmer	c46
				G.Thomson, Nanton ALTA	c46/80
				Jonathan Spinks, Lethbridge ALTA : hulk	88/92
- •	Mk. IVT	**RCAF9904**		RCAF BOC 20.6.42: SOC	15.5.46
				Wes Agnew, Hartney MAN	
				Stan Reynolds/Reynolds Aviation Museum,	
				Wetaskiwin ALTA	88/92
				Byron Reynolds, Wetaskiwin ALTA	96
- •	Mk. IVT	**RCAF9911**		RCAF BOC 13.7.42: SOC	1.10.46
				Wes Agnew, Hartney MAN	
				Harry Whereatt/Whereatt's Warbirds,	
				Assiniboia SASK	88/93
- •	Mk. IVT	**RCAF9937**		RCAF BOC 5.8.42: SOC	15.5.46
				Bart Bourne, Winnipeg MAN	76/79
				Canadian Warplane Heritage, Hamilton ONT	88/91
- •	Mk. IVT	**RCAF9940**		RCAF BOC 8.8.42: SOC	21.8.46
				Wes Agnew, Hartney MAN	72
				Sir W. J. D. Roberts/Strathallan Aircraft	
				Collection, Auchterader, Scotland	12.72/81
				Museum of Flight, East Fortune, Scotland	14.7.81/96
11-880-264	Mk. IVT	**RCAF9947**		RCAF BOC 17.8.42: SOC	15.5.46
				owner, Carman MAN	73/82
			OO-BLH	ntu: Eric Vormezeele, Brasschaat, Belgium	.82/85
				(under rest. Brasschaat 83)	
				Musee de l'Air, Paris-Le Bourget	21.8.85/90
				dest. in museum hangar fire, Le Bourget	17.5.90
- •	Mk. IVT			RCAF BOC 19.8.42: SOC	15.5.46
				Bart Bourne, Winnipeg MAN	76/79
				Canadian Warplane Heritage, Hamilton ONT	88/91
- •	Mk. IV	**RCAF9978**		RCAF BOC 25.9.42: SOC	14.5.47
				Nanton Lancaster Society, Nanton ALTA	94
				(displ. unrest. at Lancaster memorial)	
- •	Mk. IVT	**RCAF9981**		RCAF BOC 29.9.42: SOC	15.5.46
				Western Canada Aviation Museum,	
				Winnipeg MAN	79
				Jonathan Spinks, Lethbridge ALTA	.83/90
				Canadian Warplane Heritage, Hamilton ONT	91
11-880-202 •	Mk. IVTT	**RCAF9983**		RCAF BOC 1.10.42: SOC	21.8.46
				Wes Agnew, Hartney MAN	
				Commonwealth Air Training Plan Museum,	
				Brandon MAN	88
				Weeks Air Museum,Tamiami FL	88/91
			N4311Z	Kermit A. Weeks, Tamiami FL	6.91/95
- •	Mk. IVTT	**RCAF9987**		RCAF BOC 10.11.42: SOC	21.8.46

				Wes Agnew, Hartney MAN	
				Harry Whereatt/Whereatt's Warbirds,	
				Assiniboia SASK	88/93
- •	Mk. IVT	**RCAF9989**		RCAF BOC 8.10.42: SOC	15.5.46
				Wes Agnew, Hartney MAN	76
				Canadian Warplane Heritage, Hamilton ONT	91
- •	Mk. IVT	**RCAF9990**		RCAF BOC 9.10.42: SOC	21.8.46
				Stan Reynolds/Reynolds Aviation Museum,	
				Wetaskiwin ALTA	91/92
- •	Mk. IVTT	**RCAF9991**		RCAF BOC 30.10.42: SOC	15.5.46
				John Coussens, Springfield MO	91
- •	Mk. IVT	**RCAF10001**		RCAF BOC 20.10.42: SOC	15.5.46
				Canadian National Aeronautical Collection,	
				Rockcliffe ONT	
				RAF Museum store, RAF Henlow	.69
				(static rest. RAF Boscombe Down 72/78)	
				RAF Museum, Hendon	.78/95
				(displ. as Blenheim "L8756/XD-E")	
-	Mk. IVT	RCAF10038		RCAF BOC 6.12.42: SOC	15.5.46
				derelict on farm, Winnipeg MAN	
				recov. by Wes Agnew, Hartney MAN	.69
				(some parts to Brussels with 9895 .71)	
				Ormond Haydon-Baillie, Vancouver BC	.72/79
				(shipped to UK, stored Duxford .74/78)	
			G-BLHM	ntu: British Aerial Museum, Duxford	.79
			G-MKIV	British Aerial Museum, Duxford	26.3.82/87
				(rest. Duxford, ff. 22.5.87 as "V6028/GB-D")	
				crashed Denham	21.6.87
				(wreck stored Duxford: parts to 10201 rebuild)	
- •	Mk. IVT	**RCAF10040**		RCAF BOC 10.12.42: SOC	15.5.46
				Western Canada Aviation Museum,	
				Winnipeg MAN	76/79
				Canadian Warplane Heritage, Hamilton ONT	.83/91
- •	Mk. IVT	**RCAF10070**		RCAF BOC 20.1.43: SOC	15.5.46
				Wes Agnew, Hartney MAN	75
				John Coussens, Springfield MO	76/91
- •	Mk. IVT	**RCAF10073**		RCAF BOC 21.1.43: SOC	21.8.46
				David C. Tallichet/MARC, Chino CA	72/93
				(railed to Ontario CA .72, stored Chino 87/91)	
- •	Mk. IVT	**RCAF10074**		RCAF BOC 22.1.43: SOC	1.10.46
				RCAF disposal: A. Beauman, to farm	c46/70
				Jonathan Spinks, Lethbridge ALTA : hulk	91/93
- •	Mk. IVTT	**RCAF10076**		RCAF BOC 25.1.43: SOC	21.8.46
				David C. Tallichet/MARC, Chino CA	72/93
				(stored MARC compound, Chino 87)	
- •	Mk. IVT	**RCAF10078**		RCAF BOC 11.2.43: SOC	15.5.46
				Wes Agnew, Hartney MAN	75
				Vince O'Connor, Uxbridge ONT	88/91
- •	Mk. IVT	**RCAF10107**		RCAF BOC 27.2.43: SOC	21.8.46
				Commonwealth Air Training Plan Museum,	
				Brandon MAN	88/91
- •	Mk. IVT	**RCAF10117**		RCAF BOC 4.3.43: SOC	15.5.46

				Bart Bourne, Winnipeg MAN	76/79
				Canadian Warplane Heritage, Hamilton ONT (rest. project)	88/91
- •	Mk. IVT	RCAF10120		RCAF BOC 8.3.43: SOC	21.7.47
				Stan Reynolds/Reynolds Aviation Museum, Wetaskiwin ALTA	88/92
- •	Mk. IVT	RCAF10121		RCAF BOC 8.3.43: SOC	21.8.46
				Tony Kucher, Dauphin MAN : derelict on farm	70/82
				Canadian Museum of Flight & Transportation, Vancouver BC (static rest., displ. as "RCAF 9120")	7.82/95
				Fondation Aerovision Quebec, St Hubert QUE (trucked ex CMFT 10.95)	10.95
- •	Mk. IVT	RCAF10122		RCAF BOC 9.3.43: SOC	1.10.46
				Gerry Schook, Assiniboia SASK: to farm	.46/92
				Frank Thompson, Readlyn SASK (recov. ex farm Assiniboia, for static rest.)	.92
- •	Mk. IVT	RCAF10184		RCAF BOC 1.5.43: SOC	15.5.46
				Western Canada Aviation Museum, Winnipeg MAN	76/79
				Canadian Warplane Heritage, Hamilton ONT	.83/91
- •	Mk. IVT	RCAF10201		RCAF BOC 18.5.43: SOC	15.5.46
				Wes Agnew, Hartney MAN	
				Sir W. J. D. Roberts/Strathallan Aircraft Collection, Scotland : rest. project, arr.	.84/88
				British Aerial Museum, Duxford arr. by road for rest.	27.1.88
			G-BPIV	The Aircraft Restoration Co, Duxford (rest. Duxford, ff 18.5.93 as "Z5722/WM-Z")	15.2.89/96
- •	Mk. IVT	RCAF10223		RCAF BOC 2.6.43: SOC	15.5.46
				disposal ex RCAF MacDonald ALTA: to farmer	c46
				J. Weibe ALTA	c46/70
				J Coussens, Springfield MO	91
- •	Mk. IVT	RCAF		Stan Reynolds/Reynolds Aviation Museum, Wetaskiwin ALTA	91/92

COMMONWEALTH AIRCRAFT CORPORATION BOOMERANG

826	CA-12	A46-3		South Australian Air Museum, Adelaide SA (cockpit area only, recov. ex scrap dump, Tocumwal NSW)	91
848 •	CA-12	A46-25		Les Arthur/Toowoomba Aero Museum QLD (hulk recov. from farm, Oakey QLD)	72/89
				CAC, Fishermans Bend, Melbourne VIC (fuselage only, static rest. project)	.89/91
853 •	CA-12	A46-30		(flew in movie "Smithy", as Lockheed Altair "VH-USB/Lady Southern Cross" .46)	
				Australian Air League, Blacktown NSW	8.46/64
				RAAF Williamtown NSW: gate guard "SH-B" (rest. by CAC Fishermans Bend VIC .77/80, rolled out 19.11.80)	.64/77
				Australian War Memorial, Canberra ACT	.81/95
				RAAF Museum, RAAF Point Cook VIC: loan (displ. as "A46-30/SH-B")	90/96

877 •	CA-12	**A46-54**		Les Arthur/Toowoomba Aero Museum QLD (hulk recov. from farm, Oakey QLD)	70/77
			VH-MHB	Greg Batts, Brisbane QLD (rest. Hendra, Brisbane: new wings built 95; to fly as "A46-54/MH-B")	c77/96
878 •	CA-12	**A46-55**		Richard E. Hourigan, Melbourne VIC (hulk recov. from farm, Nhill VIC 3.3.69)	3.69/75
				Ron Lee, Melbourne VIC (composite rest. project)	75/91
890 •	CA-12	**A46-57**		Harold Thomas/Camden Museum of Aviation Camden, later Narellan NSW: cockpit section	
				Greg Batts, Brisbane QLD	90/96
900 •	CA-12	**A46-77**		Col Pay, Scone NSW	
				Greg Batts, Brisbane QLD (fuselage only: stored)	91/96
910 •	CA-12	**A46-87**		Nick Wattling/Cairns Aircraft Recovery Group, Cairns QLD (wings & parts recov. from crash hulk "LB-V" on beach Pt Stewart, Princess Charlotte Bay QLD)	74
				Richard E. Hourigan, Melbourne VIC	75/96
924 •	CA-12	**A46-101**		fuselage frame recov. ex Tocumwal NSW Robert Greinert/Historical Aircraft Restoration Society, Sydney NSW	
				Dennis Baxter/HARS, Sydney NSW (rest. project, Bankstown NSW 94/95)	90/96
945 •	CA-13	**A46-122**		hulk recov. from farm, Oakey QLD John Hill, Springbrook QLD	
			VH-MHR	Matthew Denning, Brisbane QLD (rest. Hendra, Brisbane, new wings built 95; to fly as "A46-122/MH-R")	8.75/95
946 •	CA-13	**A46-124**		Peter Sledge, Sydney NSW (under rest. Nowra NAS NSW .87)	86/87
				Darwin Aviation Museum, Darwin NT (cockpit section only: static rest. project)	90/93
952 •	CA-13	**A46-129**		recov. ex farm, Oakey QLD	c64
				Camden Museum of Aviation, Camden NSW later Narellan NSW: fuselage only	65/92
962 •	CA-13	**A46-139**		Les Arthur/Toowoomba Aero Museum QLD (hulk recov. from farm, Oakey QLD) Guido Zuccoli, Toowoomba QLD	
				Dennis R. Sanders & Dale Clarke, Chino CA	.84/91
			N32CS	Dennis R. Sanders & Dale Clarke, Chino CA (Boomerang replica, using T-6 and parts from A46-139, ff Chino 20.7.91; flies as RAAF A46-139/*Phooey*)	8.91/96
965 •	CA-13	**A46-142**		Les Arthur/Toowoomba Aero Museum QLD (hulk recov. from farm, Toowoomba QLD)	72/79
				Jeff Trappett, RAAF Point Cook VIC	.89
				Don Brown, Konowak, Leongatha VIC (fuselage only, rest. project)	.91/92
970 •	CA-13	**A46-147**		Harold Thomas/Camden Museum of Aviation, Camden, later Narellan NSW: fuselage only	
				Greg Batts, Brisbane QLD: stored	90/96

988 •	CA-13	**A46-165**		Ralph Cusack, Brisbane QLD	
				Robert Greinert, Sydney NSW	78/87
				(fuse. under rest. Nowra NAS NSW .86)	
				Kermit A. Weeks/Weeks Air Museum,	
				Tamiami FL	.87/96
				rep. dam. Tamiami, Hurricane Andrew	24.8.92
				(fuselage rest., to be fitted with new wings	
				constructed Brisbane QLD 95)	
997 •	CA-13	**A46-174**		crashed Cape Gloucester PNG: "QE-Y"	18.5.44
				barged to Nadzab for rebuild, abandoned	.44
				d'E. C. Darby & N. M.Armstrong, Auckland NZ	.74/83
				(hulk recov. ex Nadzab .74, stored Auckland NZ)	
				Kermit A. Weeks/Weeks Air Museum,	
				Tamiami FL	88/96
				(fuselage frame & wing centre-section only)	
				rep. dam. Tamiami, Hurricane Andrew	24.8.92
1029 •	CA-19	**A46-206**		John Woods, Toowoomba QLD: hulk	
				(hulk, parts collected from farms,Toowoomba)	
				Bill Martin, Toowoomba QLD	80
				Guido Zuccoli, Toowoomba QLD	87/92
				(partially rest. fuselage at Oakey AB QLD 5.88)	
			N4234K	Guido Zuccoli/Sanders Aircraft, Chino CA	5.91/92
				(shipped to Chino CA: A46-206 fuselage frame	
				rebuilt with modified T-6 mainplane and tail;	
				parts of A46-10,122,127,145,146,147,165)	
			VH-BOM	Guido Zuccoli/Aerotech Pty Ltd, Darwin NT	1.10.92/96
				(ff Chino 12.6.92; shipped to Darwin, ff 3.10.92	
				as A46-206/MH-Y/*Milingimbi Ghost*;	
				ff 29.12.93 with wings rebuilt in Australia)	
1073 •	CA-19	**A46-249**		Richard E. Hourigan, Melbourne VIC	10.61/94
				(fuse. recov ex farm, Colac VIC 22.10.61)	
				(static rest. project : using parts recov. from	
				A46-21, 55, 81, 147, 219 and wings ex A46-87)	
- •	CA-	**A46-**		Arthur Griffiths, Sydney NSW	94
				(rest. to fly, Sydney-Bankstown NSW 94)	

COMMONWEALTH AIRCRAFT CORPORATION WINJEEL

1526 •	CA-22	**A85-618**		first prototype, ff Fishermans Bend VIC	3.2.51
				RAAF Wagga NSW : inst. airframe	.57/77
				RAAF Museum, RAAF Point Cook VIC	.77/92
1527 •	CA-22	**A85-364**		2nd prototype: ff	7.51
				RAAF Wagga NSW : inst. airframe	.57/77
				RAAF Museum, RAAF Point Cook VIC	.77/92
25-1 •	CA-25	**A85-401**		first production aircraft, ff	23.2.55
				RAAF Museum, RAAF Point Cook VIC	83/88
			VH-NTY	RAAF Museum, RAAF Point Cook VIC	18.1.88/96
				(rest. Point Cook, ff 1.88 as "A85-401";	
				retired to static displ. RAAF Museum .94)	
25-2 •	CA-25	**A85-402**		disposal ex RAAF Point Cook (TT7207 hrs)	2.5.79
				Malcolm J. Long, Melbourne VIC	.79/82
			VH-BFX	Malcolm J. Long, Melbourne VIC	8.4.82/96
25-3 •	CA-25	**A85-403**		RAAF Wagga NSW: inst. airframe	80/86

Continued on page 59

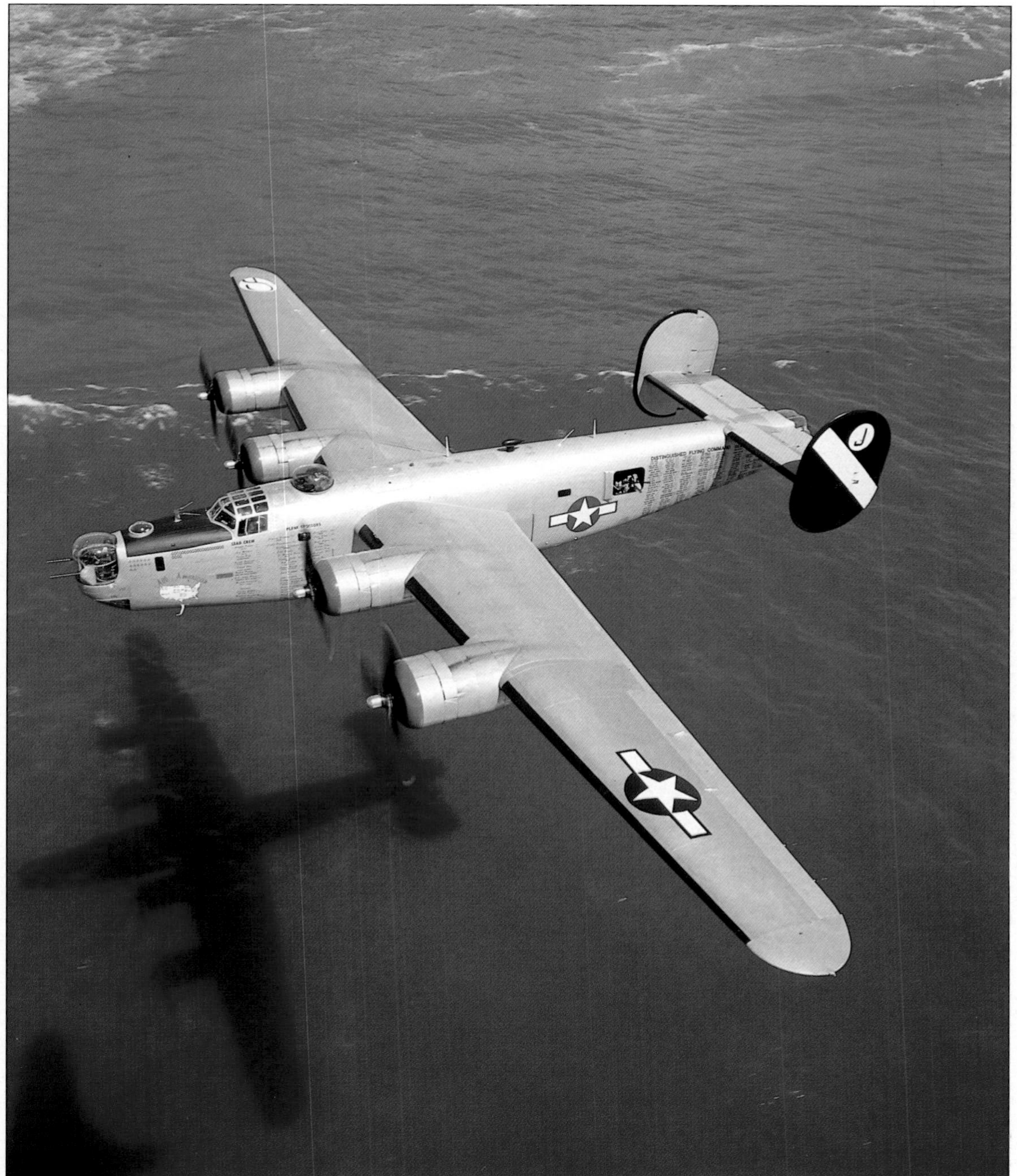

Too few Consolidated Libarators have been kept airworthy over the years, and Collings Foundation B24J N224J, the *All American*, seen here over the San Francisco bay, has been carrying the flag for the type since 1989 and touring the U.S.A. with the aim of showing that the B17 was not the only U.S. four-engined bomber. **Patrick Bunce.**

Now displayed as GA-R, Lancaster B.Mk.X FM104 makes an imposing sight up a pole in Toronto 1989, the fate of quite a few of these survivors, particularly in Canada during the ninteen-sixties. Most are now being properly restored, and moved inside; while Canada has the only other airworthy Lancaster in the world as well. **Theirry Thomassin**.

Two deHavilland D.H.98 Mosquitoes in the air together is a very rare sight these days, and was last seen when BAe's T3 RR299 and Kermit Weeks' B35 RS712 formated over the home counties, just before RS712 departed for the U.S. With restorations underway in New Zealand, Canada, Australia and Britain, this should be a sight we get to see again before too long. **Darryl Cott/BAe.**

The Beaufighter will enjoy something of a revival over the next few years, so the sacrifice of the engine runs once carried out by Moorabbin's A8-328 while it was kept outside, for a better preservation conditions by its moving inside is all to the good. The imaginative way this exibit is displayed adds to the Museum's appeal. **James Kightly**.

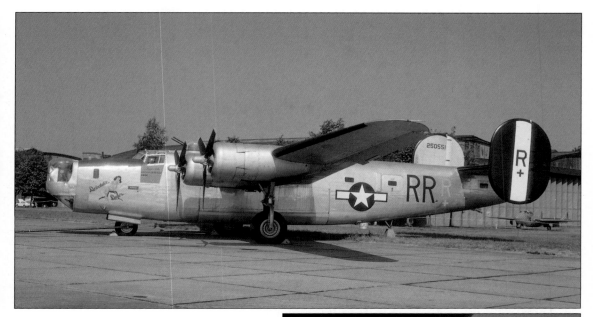

Above: Consolidated B24 numbers were boosted in the seventies by the demobilisation of a batch of Indian Air Force machines. Yersterday's Air Force example N94459 spent two years at Duxford (seen here) before going on to the U.S. in 1975. **James Kightly Collection**. **Right:** *Diamond Lil* arrived in the U.K. about 50 years late, but was to partner long term European resident *Sally B* for a season: The stars? B24 N24927 and B17G G-BEDF. **James Kightly. Below**: For a brief period, I.W.M. Duxford was home to two Curtiss P-40s in R.A.F. colours. The Fighter Collection's P-40M 43-5802, N1009N hides John Paul's P-40E AK933 N94466; Both machines have since departed to other climes; T.F.C.'s to France and a Flying Tiger scheme, and John Paul's back to the U.S. **James Kightly.**

Unfortunately, a large number of PBY Catalinas have been crashed and destroyed in the service of protecting Canada's vast forests, due to heavy usage as a firefighter. N9505C is seen here in 1988 in fire-bomber configuration. **Philip Wallick.**

One of the world's most historic marine cities was graced by several historic aircraft splashing in during 1995, part of the *Cielo e Acqua* (Sky & Water) seaplane meeting. Catalina N9521C is seen here facing St Mark's Square, Venice. **Maurizio Torcoli.**

The Curtiss P40 is only rarely seen as an air racer, but it does happen; 2106396, Race 17 *Spud Lug*, is seen at Reno in 1989. **Jim Winchester**.

Above: Gloster Gladiator G-AMRK has been a real stalwart on the display circuit; seen here in its first civil scheme **(APN)** and its current Battle of Britain colours. **James Kightly**. **Below:** Bob Pond has decided to restore this SBD-5 Dauntless (seen here at Chino in 1995) to static condition. **Thierry Thomassin. (Inset)** Chino is home to the Yankee Air Corps SBD Dauntless as well. **Theirry Thomassin.**

Above: Fiat G59 Ciao Bella has had a varied life and is now a single seater in pseudo WWII colours in Australia. It is seen here back in 1988 while being flown by Dennis Sanders in the U.S. **Philip Wallick.** **Below:** A very affordable warbird, the Fiat G46 has been quietly popular. I-AEXT is still based in Italy. **W.W. Collection.**

Contrarary to many reports, two Grumman Ducks were used to make the incredible flying seqences in the film *Murphy's War*, not one, as well as a replica which was 'shot up' by the submarine. One of the fliers is seen on the River Orinoco during filming. **BFI Stills.**

Despite having the taller tail of the later FM2 Wildcat, The Fighter Collection's machine looks very at home in the Fleet Air Arm colours of the earlier Martlet. **Richard Paver.**

Solid Gold Power: *Rare Bear*, a most impressive warbird, and fastest piston aircraft in the world. The recent racing history of this Bearcat has almose eclipsed the not inconsiderable achievments of Darryl Greenamayer's N1111L *Conquest 1*. The *Bear* is seen in August 1994, at Reno; where else! **Theirry Thomassin.**

Hurricane MkIIc ZK-TPL seen here with Hawker Restorations at Milden, Suffolk, U.K., is now in New Zealand with Air New Zealand having systems installed prior to being delivered to Sir Tim Wallis' Alpine Fighter Collection. **Barry McKee.**

In better days, LF363 shows off some rather gaudy colours at Staverton on March 31st, 1968. Like many other aspects of the warbird scene, the accuracy of colour schemes have vastly improved since the 1960's **Adrian Balch.**

As we write, the Shuttleworth Collection's hook and catapult spool equipped Hawker Sea Hurricane has just been presented to its supporters, as seen here outside Duxford's control tower and will be launched onto the 1996 U.K. airshow round, a rare machine indeed. **Richard Paver.**

				RAAF Wagga NSW: gate guard	87/94
25-4 •	CA-25	**A85-404**		disposal ex RAAF Point Cook VIC (TT4234)	2.5.79
				Noel R. Vinson/Aviation Salvage Pty Ltd, Bankstown NSW	6.79
			VH-WHZ	John Weymouth/Heli-Muster Pty Ltd, Sydney NSW & "Victoria River Downs" NT	20.3.81/96
25-5 •	CA-25	**A85-405**		RAAF East Sale VIC: gate guard	90/92
25-7 •	CA-25	**A85-407**		RAAF Wagga NSW: inst. airframe	80/89
			VH-NTJ	Brian Chadwick/Winrye Aviation, Bankstown NSW	.89/95
				(rest. Bankstown, ff 20.9.91 as "A85-443")	
25-11 •	CA-25	**A85-411**		disposal RAAF Williamtown NSW: airworthy	28.10.95
25-15 •	CA-25	**A85-415**		disposal RAAF Williamtown NSW: airworthy	28.10.95
			VH-BUM	Rodney J. Hall, Port Macquarie NSW	9.11.95
25-17 •	CA-25	**A85-417**		disposal ex RAAF Point Cook VIC	26.5.70
				Peninsula Air Services, Moorabbin VIC	.70/72
				(open storage, dism., Moorabbin)	
				Robert L. Eastgate, Melbourne VIC : stored	74/79
				Don Brown, Korumburra VIC (rest. to fly)	91/92
25-18 •	CA-25	**A85-418**		disposal ex RAAF Pt. Cook VIC (TT 5623)	2.5.79
				Mike Wansey/Confederate Air Force, Newcastle NSW	6.79
				Moorabbin Air Museum, Moorabbin VIC	6.79/94
25-21 •	CA-25	**A85-421**		disposal ex RAAF Point Cook VIC	26.5.70
				Peninsula Air Services, Moorabbin VIC	.70/72
				(open storage, dism., Moorabbin)	
				Robert L. Eastgate, Melbourne VIC : stored	74/92
				(arr. Sydney-Bankstown 9.95 for rest. to fly)	
25-22 •	CA-25	**A85-422**		disposal ex RAAF Point Cook VIC (TT4635)	2.5.79
				Robert Eastgate & Ed Field, Melbourne VIC	6.79
			VH-SOB	Robert L. Eastgate, Melbourne VIC	12.81/95
				Ed Field Syndicate, Caboolture QLD	10.95
25-26 •	CA-25	**A85-426**		disposal RAAF Williamtown NSW: airworthy	28.10.95
25-29 •	CA-25	A85-429		disposal ex RAAF Point Cook VIC	26.5.70
				Nelson R. Wilson, Coldstream VIC	78/82
				Matthew Onslow, Walcha NSW	90/92
				(rest. to fly, Bankstown NSW)	
25-30 •	CA-25	**A85-430**		disposal ex RAAF Point Cook VIC	26.5.70
				Noel R. Vinson/Aviation Salvage Pty Ltd, Bankstown NSW: open storage Bankstown	70/72
				Casula Auto Wreckers, Casula NSW	
				"Adventureland" Playground, Liverpool NSW	73/78
				Camden Museum of Aviation, Narellan NSW	84/88
				South Australian Historical Aviation Museum, Port Adelaide SA	89/96
25-32 •	CA-25	**A85-432**		Museum of Army Flying, Oakey AB QLD	5.78/94
				(flies as "A85-432")	
25-34 •	CA-25	**A85-434**		disposal ex RAAF Point Cook VIC	26.5.70
				Jeff Trappett, Morwell VIC	.70/83
				(stored Essendon VIC 74, rest. Morwell VIC)	

			VH-AGP	Peter Furlong, Morwell VIC	25.8.83/89
				Roger Richards, Melbourne VIC	5.4.89/92
			VH-EDA	J. Courtney, Rosanna VIC	27.7.93/96
25-36 •	CA-25	**A85-436**		disposal ex RAAF Point Cook VIC (TT4429)	2.5.79
				Noel R. Vinson/Aviation Salvage Pty Ltd, Bankstown NSW	6.79
			VH-WIJ	Noel R. Vinson, Bankstown NSW	6.11.80/84
				Roger Richards, Melbourne VIC	19.9.84/96
25-38 •	CA-25	**A85-438**		disposal ex RAAF Point Cook VIC (TT4489)	2.5.79
			VH-IOX	William J. McMonagle, Brisbane QLD	19.3.81/96
25-39 •	CA-25	**A85-439**		RAAF Wagga NSW: inst. airframe	80/94
				RAAF Museum, RAAF Point Cook VIC	.94
			VH-FTS	RAAF Museum, RAAF Point Cook VIC	11.94/96
				(arr. dism. Sydney-Bankstown NSW 6.4.94	
25-40 •	CA-25	**A85-440**		RAAF Air Training Corps, Cambridge TAS	.76/85
			VH-HFM	Alf Medley, Horsham, later Donald VIC : del.	25.4.85/96
25-41	CA-25	**A85-441**		crashed RAAF Point Cook VIC, after midair collision with A85-408	5.6.64
				wreck to Aeronautical Research Laboratory, Fishermans Bend, Melbourne	10.64
				Australian War Memorial, Canberra ACT	90/92
				(rear fuse & parts in storage Duntroon .90)	
25-43 •	CA-25	**A85-443**		disposal RAAF Williamtown NSW: airworthy	28.10.95
25-44 •	CA-25	**A85-444**		disposal ex RAAF Point Cook VIC	26.5.70
				Noel Vinson/Aviation Salvage Pty Ltd, Bankstown NSW	.70
				Casula Auto Wreckers, Casula NSW: displ.	72/73
				Nick Challinor, Murwillumbah NSW	.73/77
				Chewing Gum Field Air Museum, Tallebudgera QLD: stripped, derelict	8.77/89
				Jeff Trappett, Morwell VIC	31.3.89/96
				(rest. RAAF Pt Cook VIC, Morwell VIC 90, Toowoomba QLD 93/95: ff Toowoomba 7.4.95)	
			VH-AGR	Jeff Trappett, Kingaroy QLD	7.4.95
25-45 •	CA-25	**A85-445**		disposal ex RAAF Point Cook VIC (TT 4137)	2.5.79
				Noel R. Vinson/Aviation Salvage Pty Ltd, Bankstown NSW	6.79/83
			VH-JJG	Murray Griffiths, Deniliquin NSW	9.83/88
				(rebuilt Tocumwal NSW, ff 6.4.84)	
				Doug Hamilton, Wangaratta VIC	12.88/94
				John Mathewson NZ: shipped ex Sydney	3.94
			ZK-JJG	John Mathewson/MB Aero Trust, Ranfurly	17.5.94/95
				(flies in camouflage as "RAAF A85-445")	
25-47 •	CA-25	**A85-447**		disposal ex RAAF Point Cook VIC	26.5.70
				Pensinsula Air Services, Moorabbin VIC	.70
				(open storage, dism., Moorabbin)	
				playground, Bacchus Marsh Lion Park VIC	74/82
				David Spring-Brown, Monegeeta VIC: derelict	.83
				Rod Swallow, Gisborne VIC: rest. project	90/91
25-48 •	CA-25	**A85-448**		disposal ex RAAF Pt.Cook VIC	26.5.70
				open storage, dism., Moorabbin VIC	71/73
				playground, Bacchus Marsh Lion Park VIC	74/82
				David Spring-Brown, Monegeeta VIC: derelict	.83
				Rod Swallow, Gisborne VIC: rest. project	90/91

25-49 •	CA-25	**A85-449**		Port Moresby Technical College PNG: del.	6.78
				National Museum, Port Moresby PNG	90/94
				(stored dism., Jacksons Airport, Pt. Moresby)	
25-50 •	CA-25	**A85-450**		disposal ex RAAF Point Cook VIC	26.5.70
				Noel R. Vinson/Aviation Salvage Pty Ltd, Bankstown NSW	.70
				open storage, dism., Moorabbin VIC	71
				Robert L. Eastgate, Melbourne VIC: stored	74
				Jack McDonald, Melbourne VIC	
				Pearce Dunn/Warbirds Aviation Museum, Mildura VIC	80/82
				Richard E. Hourigan, Melbourne VIC	15.5.82
				(trucked Mildura-Melbourne 6.82 for rest.)	
			VH-HOY	Richard E. Hourigan, Harkaway VIC	22.9.86/95
				(ff Moorabbin 20.9.86, flies as "A85-450")	
25-57 •	CA-25	**A85-457**		disposal ex RAAF Point Cook VIC (TT6026)	2.5.79
				Nelson R. Wilson, Wandin North VIC	3.80/86
			VH-HFE	Nelson R. Wilson, Lilydale VIC	10.86/95
				(rest., ff Lilydale VIC 19.10.86)	
25-60 •	CA-25	**A85-460**		Dept. of Aviation, Essendon VIC: inst. airfr.	8.79/86
			VH-HWI	John Dorward, Melbourne VIC	14.3.89/95
25-61 •	CA-25	**A85-461**		disposal ex RAAF Point Cook VIC (TT 3674)	2.5.79
				Blayney Airfarmers, Blayney NSW: arr dism	7.79/80
			VH-WIU	John Weymouth/Helimuster Pty Ltd, Sydney NSW & "Victoria River Downs", NT	9.7.82/85
				Don Williamson/Banneret Pty Ltd, Perth WA	29.8.85/95
				(flies in FAC camouflage as "A85-461")	
25-62 •	CA-25	**A85-462**		last production aircraft: ff.	21.11.57
				RAAF Point Cook VIC: displ. Cadets Mess	75/92

COMMONWEALTH AIRCRAFT CORPORATION WIRRAWAY

7 •	CA-1 Mk. 1	**A20-9**		fuse. frame recov. ex farm, Tocumwal NSW	c78
				Ashley Briggs, Melbourne VIC	87/92
				(rest. project, using parts ex A20-722,731 id. unknown, will use plate ex A20-9)	
8 •	CA-1 Mk. 1	**A20-10**		Commonwealth Aircraft Corp, Melbourne VIC	31.5.60/63
				Moorabbin Air Museum, Melbourne VIC	1.11.63/95
				(displ. as "A20-10")	
11 •	CA-1 Mk. 1	**A20-13**		Commonwealth Aircraft Corp, Melbourne VIC	5.60/63
				W. Gordon Scrap Metals, Werribee VIC	11.63
				Tom King, Melbourne VIC	11.63/66
				National Museum, Port Moresby PNG	68/90
79 •	CA-3 Mk. II	**A20-81**		Pearce Dunn/Warbirds Aviation Museum, Mildura VIC	75/80
				Michael Muelders, Adelaide SA	85
				Peter Sledge, Sydney NSW	.85/91
				(rest. to fly, Essendon VIC 87/89)	
				Ed Field, Melbourne VIC & Hong Kong	.91/92
				Ed Field & Darryl K. Hill/Wirraway 81 Pty Ltd Hong Kong	5.92/95
			VH-WWY	Wirraway 81 Pty Ltd, Caboolture QLD	1.3.95
				(rest. Caboolture 92/95, ff 24.3.95 as A20-176)	
97 •	CA-3 Mk. II	**A20-99**		Ralph Moyle, Kenmare VIC : dism. on farm	60/74
				RAAF Air Training Corps, Ballarat VIC: loan	70/74

c/n	Type	Serial	Reg	Owner / History	Dates
			VH-JML	Eric Lundberg, RAAF Richmond NSW	.74/95
				(rest. to fly, RAAF Richmond & Bankstown NSW)	
103 •	CA-5 Mk. II	**A20-103**		Australian War Memorial, Canberra ACT	.59/95
				(shot down a Zero, Rabaul PNG 12.42)	
136 •	CA-7 Mk. II	**A20-136**		noted stripped, RAAF Tocumwal NSW	4.62
				Pearce Dunn/Warbirds Aviation Museum, Mildura VIC	70/82
				Jack McDonald, Melbourne VIC: stored	.82
			VH-CAC	ntu: Peter N. Anderson, Sydney NSW	84/93
				(rest. project, Bankstown NSW)	
				Jack McDonald, Caboolture QLD: project	.93/96
223 •	CA-7 Mk. II	**A20-223**		Commonwealth Aircraft Corp, Melbourne VIC	6.60/63
				W. Gordon Scrap Metals, Werribee VIC	11.63
				Mark Pilkington, Lara VIC	85/92
				(rest. project, using parts A20-601, -605)	
224 •	CA-7 Mk. II	**A20-224**		Commonwealth Aircraft Corp, Melbourne VIC	3.60/63
				W. Gordon Scrap Metals, Werribee VIC	11.63
				Bob Hogg, Noble Park, Melbourne VIC	
				(fuse. in backyard garage: childs plaything)	
				Robert Greinert & John White/Historical Aircraft Restoration Society, Sydney NSW	85/92
				Dennis Baxter & Bob Mather/HARS, Sydney	94/96
				(rest. to fly 94/95)	
703 •	CA-9 Mk. II	**A20-502**		Richard E. Hourigan & Ron Lee, Melbourne VIC	70/95
				Warbirds Aviation Museum, Mildura VIC: loan	71/76
				Ballarat Aviation Museum, Ballarat VIC: loan	85/96
				(displ. as "A20-502/BF-O")	
807	CA-9 Mk. II	**A20-606**		Commonwealth Aircraft Corp, Melbourne VIC	4.60/63
				Airfarm Associates, Tamworth NSW	11.63/67
				Les Arthur/Toowoomba Aero Museum QLD	70/80
				Murray Griffiths, Deniliquin NSW: stripped	
1101 •	CA-16 Mk. III	**A20-649**		Commonwealth Aircraft Corp, Melbourne VIC	12.58/71
				(Ceres engine testrig, Fishermans Bend factory)	
				Moorabbin Air Museum, Melbourne VIC	.71/88
			VH-WIR	ntu: Moorabbin Air Museum	8.74/88
				(planned rest. to fly, engine runs RAAF Point Cook VIC 8.74: not testflown, stored Point Cook)	
				Alan Searle, Melbourne VIC	2.88
				Kermit A. Weeks/Weeks Air Museum, Tamiami FL: stored pending rest. to fly	.88/96
1103 •	CA-16 Mk. III	**A20-651**		Commonwealth Aircraft Corp, Melbourne VIC	5.60/64
				(rest. by CAC, stored Fishermans Bend 64)	
				Institute of Applied Science, Melbourne VIC	64/68
				Science Museum of Victoria, Melbourne VIC	70/93
				Hawker deHavilland, Pt. Melbourne VIC: loan	86/88
				Scienceworks, Spotswood VIC: displ.	9.93
1104 •	CA-16 Mk. III	**A20-652**		Commonwealth Aircraft Corp, Melbourne VIC	4.60/63
				J. A. Frierson, Fleetwings Service Station, Laverton VIC: displ.	11.63
				displ. garage, Pascoe Vale, Melbourne VIC	65/69
				displ. garage, Reservoir, Melbourne	72/83
				Dusty Lane, Geoff Milne, Vin Thomas & assoc.	.83/86
			VH-WIR	Geoff Milne & Vin Thomas, Albury NSW	26.8.86/96
				(rest. Essendon VIC, ff 19.9.86 as "A20-652")	

1108 •	CA-16 Mk. III	A20-656		Commonwealth Aircraft Corp, Melbourne VIC	6.60/63
				Airland Improvements, Cootamundra NSW	11.63/70
				Richard Hourigan & Ron Lee, Melbourne VIC	.70/91
				(stored dism. Moorabbin 70/91)	
				Rob Black, Brian Jones & Graham Waddington, Melbourne VIC	.91/92
				(moved to Tyabb VIC .91, rest. project)	
1122 •	CA-16 Mk. III	A20-670		Commonwealth Aircraft Corp, Melbourne VIC	3.60/63
				W. Gordon Scrap Metals, Werribee VIC	11.63
				Ken Baird, Geelong VIC	75/88
				RAAF Museum, RAAF Point Cook VIC: loan	87/88
				(displ. as rest. fuselage only)	
1137 •	CA-16 Mk. III	A20-685		disposal : RAAF Tocumwal NSW	9.59
				Marshall Spreading Service, Albury NSW	3.60/67
				(rest. to taxying condition, Albury .64)	
				Camden Museum of Aviation, Camden NSW later Narellan NSW: displ. as "A20-685"	.67/96
1139 •	CA-16 Mk. III	A20-687		disposal : RAAF Tocumwal NSW	9.59
				Marshalls Spreading Service, Albury NSW	.60/67
				Ken Baird, Geelong VIC	.67/68
				Richard Hourigan, Pat Capron & Ron Lee, Melbourne VIC : arr. Moorabbin dism.	18.8.68/92
				(rest. Moorabbin VIC .67 as "A20-561/QE-B")	
				RAAF Museum, RAAF Point Cook VIC: loan	.77/95
1140 •	CA-16 Mk. III	A20-688		Midland Technical College, Perth Airport WA	5.59/71
				(inst. airframe: del. ex RAAF Pearce 27.5.59)	
				RAAF Assoc. Aviation Museum, Bullcreek WA	.71/95
				(airlifted by chopper to Bullcreek 20.7.73, rest., displ. as "A20-688/BF-R")	
1147 •	CA-16 Mk. III	A20-695		Commonwealth Aircraft Corp, Melbourne VIC	3.60/63
				W. Gordon Scrap Metals, Werribee VIC	11.63
				Pearce Dunn/Warbirds Aviation Museum, Mildura VIC	70/82
				Jack McDonald, Melbourne VIC: stored	.82
				Ed Field & David Jones, Melbourne VIC	86/91
				(rest. to fly, RAAF Point Cook VIC)	
				Ed Field/Mustang Fighter Trust	94
				(rest. to fly, Caboolture QLD 94)	
1156 •	CA-16 Mk. III	A20-704		owner, Bankstown NSW: del. ex RAAF Mallala	21.2.60/62
				Airfarm Associates, Tamworth NSW	67
				Les Arthur/Toowoomba Aero Museum QLD	74/85
				Murray Griffiths, Deniliquin NSW	9.85/95
				(rest. to fly Deniliquin, later Moorabbin VIC)	
1171 •	CA-16 Mk. III	A20-719		Commonwealth Aircraft Corp, Melbourne VIC	3.60/63
				W. Gordon Scrap Metals, Werribee VIC	11.63
				Pearce Dunn/Warbirds Aviation Museum, Mildura VIC	67/82
				Jack McDonald, Melbourne VIC	.82/88
				(rest. to fly, RAAF Point Cook VIC)	
				Robert Greinert/Historical Aircraft Restoration Society, Sydney NSW	91/94
			VH-WRX	Robert Greinert & Associates, Sydney NSW	17.8.94/95
				(rest. Romsey VIC, completed Bankstown NSW, ff 18.8.94 Bankstown as "RAAF A20-458")	
1174 •	CA-16 Mk. III	A20-722		Nelson Wilson, Wandin VIC	
				(recov. ex farm near Horsham VIC)	
				Borg Sorensen, Melbourne VIC	85/94

				(rebuild to fly, Moorabbin VIC, using parts from A20-512 ex farm Horsham VIC, & A20-731)	
			VH-CAC	Borg Sorensen, Melbourne VIC	22.9.94
28-14 •	CA-28 Ceres			Channel Seven Vintage Museum, Perth WA	72/87
				(conv. back to Wirraway from CA-28 Ceres VH-DAT, displ. as "A20-47/GA-B")	
				WA Museum of Aviation, Perth WA	87/90
				(stored dism., Jandakot Airport WA)	
				moved to Sydney for Wirraway rest. project	.91/92
- •	CA-16 Mk. III	-	**VH-BFF**	Geoff Schutt & Ron Lee, Melbourne VIC	5.12.75/80
				(composite rebuild Moorabbin VIC, adopted id. c/n 1105/A20-653, ff Moorabbin 4.12.75)	
				Malcolm Long & Ron Lee, Coolangatta QLD	10.6.80/94
				displ. Chewing Gum Field Air Museum QLD	83/88
				displ. Drage Air World, Wangaratta VIC	.88/94
				(flies as "A20-653/BF-F")	
- •	-	-		Pearce Dunn/Warbirds Aviation Museum, Mildura VIC	70/81
				Flygvapnets Flygmuseum, Malmslatt Sweden	.81
				(complete composite aircraft, for rest. by FM to represent a R.Swedish AF SAAB Sk.14A)	
				(note: wings & centre-section later traded to Peter Sledge, Sydney NSW for A20-81 project)	
- •	-	-		W. Gordon Scrap Metals, Werribee VIC	
				Ian A. Whitney, Romsey VIC	80/94
				(rest. to fly, RAAF Point Cook, Essendon & Romsey VIC : to be flown as "A20-395")	
- •	-	-		Jack McDonald, Caboolture QLD	92
				(stored pending rebuild, id. rep. as A20-148)	
- •	-	-		Ed Field, Melbourne VIC & Hong Kong	92
				(stored pending rebuild, id. rep. as A20-233)	
- •	CA-7	-		Paul L. Wheeler, Melbourne VIC	96
				(under rest. 95)	

CONSOLIDATED PBY CATALINA/CANSO

110 •	PBY-5A	**Bu05021**	N33301	(also rep. as NC18444?)	
			VP-BAR	Caribbean International Airways Ltd, Nassau	8.50
			VP-JAU	Caribbean International Airways Ltd, Kingston	26.2.51
			CF-HFL	Eastern Provincial Airways, Halifax NS	11.53/57
				fcd. ldg. & abandoned, near Goose Bay LAB	1.10.57
				Atlantic Canada Aviation Museum, Halifax NS	.86
				recov. complete, by helicopter	27.10.86
				Western Canada Aviation Mus., Winnipeg MAN	88
117 •	PBY-5A	**Bu05028**		(rep. to RAF as PBY-5B FP216: not del.)	
				NAS Pensacola, Land Survival Training Centre	.45/96
				(fuse. built into wall of building)	
300 •	PBY-5A	**Bu2459**		disposal USCG Elizabeth City NC: SOC	31.10.45
			NC18446	Rio Ten Airways	26.9.46/47
				California Maritime Airways	12.47/49
			N18446	Aero Corp	8.6.49/50
				R. Paul Weesner & George Lewis	25.9.50/52
				Paramount Aquarium, Miami FL	26.3.51/52
				Indamer Corp	20.10.52

					W. Clayton Lemon	10.52
				CF-HHR	Transair Ltd, Winnipeg MAN	3.10.53/69
					Field Aviation Co Ltd, Calgary ALTA	12.69/72
					Avalon Aviation Ltd, Red Deer ALTA	25.9.72/79
					(fire tanker ops. in Chile 8.75)	
				C-FHHR	Avalon Aviation Ltd, Parry Sound ONT	.79/95
					(tanker #3; #793)	
					(wfu, stored Parry Sound ONT 10.86/95)	
					Cat Air Foundation, Overveen, Netherlands	28.2.95
					(rest. Parry Sound ff 1.4.95; conv. for 16 pax, dep. Toronto ONT 9.5.95 on del. as "MLD Y-74", via North Weald to Rotterdam 14.5.95)	
				PH-PBY	Cat Air Foundation, Overveen: reg. res	11.94/95
					(id. prev. quoted as PBV-1A c/n CV-300)	
382	•	PBY-5 Mk. IIa	**RCAF9734**		(to RAF as VA734)	
					(to RAAF as A24-19): BOC 3.42 : SOC	1.46
					Kingsford Smith Aviation Service, Sydney-Bankstown NSW	10.46
					(broken-up for parts, RAAF Lake Boga VIC, airframe sections to local farm)	
					rebuild for static displ., Wallan VIC	86/90
					(c/n also quoted as 317)	
407	•	PBY-5A Mk. Ia Landseaire	**RCAF9742**	N68740	Southern California Aircraft Corp, Ontario CA	51/52
					(conv. to "Landseaire" air yacht completed 5.51)	
					Crocket & Gamboy Inc, Fresno CA	54
					Flying Bonefish Inc, Carson City NV	63/64
					Geraldine Cromack, New York NY	66
					Freeport Indonesia Inc, New York NY	67/70
					(op. Darwin NT-West Irian: mining courier run)	
					Lee Otterson & Bill Farinon, Colusa CA	.72/78
					(arr. Singapore 9.77 ex SFO on world cruise)	
					University of Hawaii, Honolulu HI	81/88
					(stored by Aero Nostalgia, Stockton CA 83/89)	
					Gary R. Larkins, Auburn CA	90
					(stored USNAM, NAS Pensacola FL 90)	
					Lone Star Flight Museum, Galveston TX	.91/94
				N6208H	H. Wells: reg. candidate	29.12.92
417	•	PBY-5A Mk. Ia Landseaire	**RCAF 9746**	N68741	Charles H. Babb Inc, Burbank CA	.46
					Southern California Aircraft Corp, Ontario CA	54
				N59D	reg.	10.56
				N5907	rereg.	11.58
					Bird Corp, Palm Springs CA	.62/69
					"The Wandering Albatross"	
					dam. wheels-up landing, Memphis TN	6.12.63
			Bird Innovator		(conv. to prototype Bird Innovator .67: additional 2 Lycoming GSO-480 engines)	
				N81RD	Bird Corp, Palm Springs/Richmond CA	4.69/76
				N5907	Madden Aircraft Sales Inc,	7.76
					Atlas Aircraft Corp, Long Beach CA	78
					Pyramid Aviation, Cotati CA	10.78/81
					Research Data Inc, Miami FL	9.81/90
					Dick Durand/Westernair Inc, Albuquerque NM	.90/91
				N5PY	Westernair Inc, Albuquerque NM	7.91/96
427	•	PBY-5A Mk. Ia	**RCAF9750**	CF-DIL	reg.	3.46
					Wheeler Airlines, St Jovite Station QUE	60/66
					Wheeler Northland Airways, St Jean QUE	68/70
				C-FDIL	Ilford Riverton Airways, Winnipeg MAN	72/73
					Can Air, Vancouver BC "Fisherman's Special"	.74/83
					The Flying Fireman Ltd, Victoria BC	83/92
					(tanker #5; #775)	
					op: Awood Air Ltd, Thunder Bay ONT	.88/92

				sold to Spain, struck-off reg.	3.93
			EC-313	Servicios Aereos Espanoles SA-SAESA,	
				Cuatro Vientos	.92/93
			EC-FRG	SAESA, Cuatro Vientos (tanker #73)	.93/96
920	PBY-5A	Bu08101	N5588V	Thomas W. Kendall/Catalina Ltd, La Verne CA	64
				Troy G. Hawkins, Wichita Falls TX	66
				Bird Aircraft, Palm Springs CA	
				Antilles Air Boats, St Thomas USVI	68/74
				Victor W. Newman	10.1.75
				crashed, forced landing, near Wikieup AZ	2.75
928 •	PBY-5A	**Bu08109**		(to RDAF as 82-857, later L-857)	
				RDAF Museum Collection, Vaerlose AB: stored	79/89
				Flyhistorisk Museum, Sola, Norway: arr.	17.11.89/96
1166 •	PBY-5	**Bu08272**		(to RAAF as A24-46): BOC	3.43
				C. K. Campbell/Asian Airlines, Sydney NSW	11.47
				(no civil conv., broken-up RAAF Lake Boga VIC,	
				hulk moved to farm near Lake Boga)	
				Pearce Dunn/Warbirds Aviation Museum,	
				Mildura VIC: stored dism.	68/89
				John Bell/Whaleworld Museum, Albany WA	.89/96
				(static rest. using parts recov. from farms	
				in Lake Boga VIC area: displ. in USN sc.)	
1211 •	PBY-5	**Bu08317**		NAS Norfolk VA: stored	65
				NASM, Silver Hill MD	73/94
				USNAM, NAS Pensacola FL: loan	73/96
- •	PBY-5A	**Bu21232**	N5609V	Paul Mantz Aviation	.47/49
	Steward-			International Aviation Corp, Glendale CA	.49/51
	Davis		CF-GHU	Queen Charlotte Airlines, Vancouver BC	.51/57
	Super Cat.			*Kitmat Queen*	
				Pacific Western Airlines, Vancouver BC	.57
			N2763A	Alaska Coastal-Ellis Airlines, Juneau AK	.57/64
				Alaska Coastal Airlines, Juneau AK	66
				Alaska Airlines, Seattle WA	69/70
				Antilles Air Boats, St Thomas USVI	70/73
				Marine Associates, Worcester MA	78
				wfu stripped: Watsonville CA	78/80
				Gerald W. Todd, Santa Cruz CA	8.4.81
				Robert P. Schlaefli/SLAFCO, Moses Lake WA	7.82/96
1520 •	PBY-5A	**Bu33966**	**N3936A**	used by DEW-line contractor, Philadelphia PA	c52
				wfu, Bradley Field, Windsor Locks CT	c55
				J. B. Terrill, Tulsa OK	58
				(remained derelict, Bradley Field 55/88)	
				Americada Corp, New York NY	60/64
				Bradley Air Museum, Windsor Locks CT	29.5.64/81
				New England Air Museum, Windsor Locks CT	81/89
				Kermit A. Weeks/Weeks Air Museum,	
				Tamiami FL (rest. project)	11.89/96
1522 •	PBY-5A	**Bu33968**	N5582V	Thomas W. Kendall/Catalina Ltd, La Verne CA	64
				Troy G. Hawkins, Wichita Falls TX	66/70
			C-GVTF	ntu	
			N84857	Diversified Drilling Muds, Cheyenne WY	10.10.80
				IDFAF Museum, Hazerim AB, Israel	5.85
				fell down steep slope, taxiing Lewistown MT	
				prior del. flight to Israel: badly dam.	9.5.85
				Ben Kalka, Oakland CA: USCR	10.89/96
				Ray Cox, Renton WA	90/92
				(rebuild to fly, Lewistown MT)	

1547 •	PBY-5A	**Bu33993**		(to USAAF as 43-43847)	
	OA-10A		N4760C	Alaska Coastal Airlines, Juneau AK	54/66
	Steward-			Alaska Airlines, Seattle WA	69/70
	Davis			Stan Burnstein, Tulsa OK	72
	Super Cat			Lee Maples/Maples Aviation Co/Geoterrex,	
				Vichy MO	74/84
				op: Terra Surveys/Geoterrex, Ottawa ONT	82/83
				forced landing, crashed, Lynn WI	22.3.83
				David C. Tallichet/MARC, Chino CA: dam.	87
				USAFM, McChord AFB WA: arr. dism.	12.87/93
				(rest., displ. as OA-10A "434033")	
1566 •	PBY-5A	**Bu34012**	N1947M		
			CF-IEE	Transair Ltd, Winnipeg MAN	53/67
				Austin Airways, Toronto ONT	.67/70
				sunk during storm, Sugluk QUE	.70
				(to FA Colombiana as FAC 612)	
				(rebuilt with PBY-6 tailplane)	
			HK-2115X	Ana Zazzu de Borde	82
				(to FA Colombiana as FAC 612)	
				Barroblanco AB, Madrid, Colombia: stored	92
			HK-2115	Transportes Aereos Latinamericanos-TALA	.94
				(noted Madrid-Barroblanca, airworthy 9.94)	
1570 •	PBY-5A	Bu34016	N5583V	H & F Flying Club, Carlsbad-Palomar CA	64/70
				reg. pending: (noted Haywood CA 6.73)	72
				sank, Infernillo Reservoir, Mexico	19.3.74
				(rep scuttled in course of drug interception)	
				wreckage located, rep. may be recov.	91
1581 •	PBY-5A	**Bu34027**	**N9505C**	Alcan Airways, Kingman AZ (tanker #9)	64/66
	Super			Intercapital Inc, Las Vegas NV	69
	Cat			Robert P. Schlaefli/SLAFCO, Moses Lake WA	70/96
				(tanker #53)	
1584	PBY-5A	Bu34030	N5804N	Remmert Werner Inc, St Louis MO	54
	Super			Monsanto Chemical Co, St. Louis MO	55
	Cat			(*The Pelican*, lifeboats hung under wings)	
			N19Q	re-reg.	57
				Edgar M. Queeny, St. Louis MO	63/64
				Alfran Corp, Milwaukee WI	66/70
				Lone Star Industries	.70
				James Stewart/Stewart Enterprises,	
				Minneapolis MN	72
				crashed into Mediterranean, nr Monte Carlo	15.8.72
1637	PBY-5A	Bu48275	N1556M	Air Corp of Miami, Miami FL	54
			CF-NTJ		
			CF-HTN	Transair Ltd, St James MAN	56/66
				Field Aviation Co Ltd, Toronto ONT	68/71
				cr. firebombing, 500m north Edmonton ALTA	3.9.71
1643	PBY-5A	Bu48281	N1540M	Charlotte Aircraft Corp, Charlotte NC	54
			CF-IHJ	Dorval Air Transport, Montreal QUE	56
			N68623	Steward-Davis Inc, Long Beach CA	
				(stripped hulk, Long Beach CA 67/68)	
				broken up, Long Beach CA	70
1649 •	PBY-5A	**Bu48287**	N10017		
	Steward-		CF-JMS	Questor Surveys Ltd, Toronto ONT	59
	Davis		VH-UMS	Selco Exploration/Australian Selection P/L	24.4.64
	Super Cat.		CF-JMS	Barringer Surveys Ltd, Toronto ONT	11.64/66
				Questor Surveys Ltd, Toronto ONT	70
			N16647	Questor Surveys	73/74

			C-GGDW	Austin Airways, Timmins ONT	8.75/77
				Geoterrex Ltd/Terra Surveys Ltd, Ottawa	80/85
			N16647	Jack Leavis, Davie FL	8.85/90
				(wfu, open storage, Opa Locka FL 87/90)	
				Jim Dent/Air Adventures, Ft. Lauderdale FL	2.90
				Super Three Inc, Fort Lauderdale FL	7.90/91
			N287	Super Three Inc, Fort Lauderdale FL	7.91/95
				(rest., flies in USN sc as *Black Cat*)	
1656 •	PBY-5A	**Bu48294**	**N9521C**	O. W. Noble, North Little Rock AR	64/66
				V. & N. Enterprises Inc, North Little Rock AR	69/72
				Two Jacks Inc, Olive Branch MS	78
				Buddy Woods, Palmer AK	.78
				Catalina Flying Inc, Anchorage AK	8.83/87
				Galen S. (Gus) Vincent, Zephyr Cove NV	88/94
				(based Santa Rosa CA, flies as "USN 48294")	
				Riverdale Limited Liability Co, Cheyenne WY	22.7.94
				Joseph Tosolin & Guido Bonfiglio, Switzerland	.94/95
				(del. USA to Switzerland, via Reykjavik 19.5.95)	
				op:Simpson Wallace Enterprises,Vergiate Italy	96
1658	PBY-5A	Bu48296	N68746	Southern California Aircraft Corp, Ontario CA	54
				Multiple Management Corp, Long Beach CA	64
				James N. Routh, Long Beach CA	63
			CF-AAD	Austin Airways Ltd, Toronto ONT	.66/73
				crashed, Great Whale QUE	24.9.72
1679 •	PBY-5A	**Bu48317**	N1495V		
				(to MLD/Dutch Navy as 16-212)	.47
				Bosbad Amusement Park, Hoeven, Holland	2.8.57/83
				Militaire Luchtvaart Museum, Soesterberg AB	84/96
				(also rep. as c/n 1885 or 28109)	
1735	PBY-5A	Bu48373	N10018		
			N95R	Remmert Werner Inc, St Louis MO	58/59
			VH-BRI	Ansett Flying Boat Services, Rose Bay NSW	10.59/62
				"*Golden Islander*"	
				(del. St Louis MO to Sydney 10-19.10.59)	
				sank at moorings, Hayman Island QLD	8.7.62
				Vic O'Hara, Proserpine QLD: salvaged and	
				hull conv. to houseboat *Henrietta Hoh*	
				in use as houseboat, Shute Harbour QLD	85/96
1736 •	PBY-5A	**Bu48374**	N9507C	George B. Alder, Chatanooga TN	63/64
				Carolina Aircraft Corp, Miami FL	
				Orinoco Mining Co, Pittsburgh PA	.65
			YV-P-DPZ	Orinoco Mining Co, Puerto Ordaz, Venezuela	.65
			YV-O-CFO	Corporacion Ferrominera de Orinoco CA,	.75
				Puerto Ordaz (full reg. YV-O-CFO-2)	
			YV-63CP	ntu:	
			YV-584CP	Camaronera del Sur CA: ops. for Orinoco	3.83/87
				Italo Compagna/SERVES, Caracas	89/93
				(wfu .79, open storage Puerto Ordaz 79/93)	
1737 •	PBY-5A	**Bu48375**	N4937V	Fleetway Inc, Burbank CA: USCR	64/70
				(rep. to Argentine Navy as .....)	
				rep. flew Juan Peron's escape to Paraguay	9.55
				(to FA Paraguaya as T-29, later 2002)	11.57/93
				(open storage, Asuncion 77/88)	
				rest. to flying condition, Nu Guazau AB	.88
				Frank Porter, Fort Worth TX	.93
			N96FP	Frank's Aircraft Sales, Fort Worth TX	6.93
				(noted Asuncion 4.94 as N96FP awaiting del. flight)	
				Caribbean Air Transport Inc, Carolina IN	22.6.94/96

1750	PBY-5A	Bu48388	N1521V		
			HK-1020	Lineas Aereas Interiores de Catalina - LAICA	73
				crashed, Villavicencio, Colombia	11.6.73
1759 •	PBY-5A	Bu48397	**N5593V**	Thomas W. Kendall/Catalina Ltd, La Verne CA	58/64
				ran up beach reef, Ash Shaykh Humayd, Aqaba, Saudi Arabia, while under machine-gun fire from bedouins, 300 bullet holes : abandoned	22.3.60
				still on beach Aqaba, complete but derelict	84/92
1768 •	PBY-5A	**Bu48406**	N5590V	Thomas W. Kendall/Catalina Ltd, La Verne CA	.56/78
				lsd: Catalina Enterprise "Tiare Tahiti"	60
				(open storage, Van Nuys CA 78/86)	
				International Centre for Environmental Research, Wilmington DE	84
				Thomas W. Kendall, Laguna Beach CA	86
				San Diego Aerospace Museum, San Diego CA	1.86/93
				(rest. Van Nuys, del. to San Diego 12.86, displ. on pole as USN "48406")	
1774 •	PBY-5A	**Bu48412**	N10024	Trade Ayer, Linden NJ: USN surplus	4.9.56
				Cole Brock Inc PA	7.5.57/59
			N96R	Remert Werner Inc, St Louis MO	.59
			YV-P-EPX	Orinoco Mining Co, Puerto Ordaz, Venezuela	10.59/61
			YV-P-EPZ	Orinoco Mining Co, Puerto Ordaz	7.61/75
			YV-O-CFO	Corporacion Ferrominera de Orinoco CA, Puerto Ordaz (full reg. YV-O-CFO-4)	.75/83
				struck sand bank, sunk, San Felix (repaired)	27.1.76
			YV-56CP	ntu:	
			YV-585CP	Camaronera del Sur CA: ops for Orinoco	3.83/87
			YV-485C	Italo Compagna/SERVES, Caracas-Maiquetia	89/93
1781	PBY-5A	**Bu48419**	PP-ABC	(to FA Brasileira as FAB C-10A 65....)	
			PP-PDR	Panair do Brasil, Sao Paulo: lsd. *Bandeirante Pedro Vaz de Barros*	65/71
				(to FA Brasileira as FAB C-10A-65...)	12.71
				Museu Aeroespacial, Rio de Janeiro	82/85
1785 •	PBY-5A	Bu48423	N4002A		
			CF-JJG	Survair Ltd, Ottawa ONT	65/66
				Canadian Aero Service Ltd, Hull QUE	68/70
				(magnetometer equiped) "Explorer"	60/69
				Spartan Air Services, Ottawa ONT	73/74
			C-FJJG	Kenting Earth Sciences, Ottawa ONT	76/86
			N423RS	Red Stevenson, Jenks OK	6.86
				Bruce Redding, Reno NV: del.	7.86
				APEXX Company Inc, Canby OR	8.86/87
				Reginald Slade/Northern Air Inc, Dallas TX	11.87/96
1788 •	PBY-5A Steward-Davis Super Cat	Bu48426	**N31235**	US Navy/Transocean Airlines, Guam	4.52/55
				op: Trust Territory Air Service: "Taloa Saipan"	
				Thorne Engineering Co, Los Angeles CA	.55
				fcd. landing at sea 275m W San Francisco CA	30.9.55
				(recov. by ship, dam. during salvage 10.55)	
				Long Beach Aeromotive Inc CA: rebuilt	56
				C. S. Bearson	.56
				R. Lyle Golding, Long Beach CA	.56/58
				Pacific Airlines, San Francisco CA	.58/61
				Alaska Coastal-Ellis Airlines, Juneau AK	.61/64
				Alaska Coastal Airlines, Juneau AK	66
				Alaska Airlines, Seattle WA	69/70
				Robert P. Schlaefli/SLAFCO, Moses Lake WA (tanker #80, #98)	72/96

1791 •	PBY-5A	Bu48429	N1565M	Charlotte Aircraft Corp, Charlotte NC	54
			CF-IGJ	Province of Newfoundland, St Johns NFLD	65/74
			C-FIGJ	Prov. of Newfoundland & Labrador, St Johns (tanker #2)	79/80
				crashed forced landing, Sherbrooke QUE	19.12.80
				struck-off 8.81: wreckage noted, St Jean QUE	9.82/92
1808	PBY-5A	Bu48446	N5591V	Ellwood L. Schultz, Los Angeles CA	63/70
				Transamerica Trade, Mableton GA	78
			YV-209CP	Peter Bottome, Caracas	.78/85
			N285NJ	Thaddeus B. Bruno Jr, Fort Lauderdale FL	8.85/89
				Enrico Recchi, Turin, Italy	.87
				(del. to Italy, via Reykjavik 1.9.87)	
				crashed dest., Turin, Italy	21.5.89
1817	PBY-5A	Bu46453	N1518V		
				(to FA Colombiana as ....)	
			HK-2116X	Ana Zazzu de Borde	82
1820 •	PBY-5A	**Bu46456**		(to FA Brasileira as FAB C-10A 6509)	
			N4582T	David C. Tallichet/Project Catalina Inc/ MARC, Chino CA	12.83/90
				MCAM, MCAS Cherry Point NC	88/95
1821 •	PBY-5A	**Bu46457**		(to FA Brasileira as FAB C-10A 6510)	
			N4582U	David C. Tallichet/Project Catalina Inc/ MARC, Chino CA	12.83/90
				USAFM, Kirtland AFB NM	.84/95
				(displ. as "USAF OA-10A 34077")	
1846	PBY-5A	Bu46482	N5584V	Thomas W. Kendall/Catalina Ltd, La Verne CA	.56/64
	Steward-			Alaska Coastal-Ellis Airlines, Juneau AK	66
	Davis			Alaska Airlines, Seattle WA	69
	Super Cat			Antilles Air Boats, St Thomas USVI	70/71
				wfu St Croix USVI	7.71
1868 •	PBY-5A	Bu46504	N1513V		
			OB-LBA-251		
			OB-M-251		
			OB-T-251	Loretana de Aviacion - LORASA, Iquitos, Peru	
				ops. ceased: wfu stored Iquitos, Peru	8.76/77
				derelict, Lima-Jorge Chavez	83/87
				rep. stored Lima-Iquitos	92
1886 •	PBY-5A	**Bu46522**	N5585V	Summer Institute of Linguistics, Glendale CA	63/66
				Jungle Aviation & Radio Service, Waxhaw NC	69/70
			CF-FFA	Richard L. Rude/Flying Fireman, Sidney BC	.72
			C-FFFA	The Flying Fireman Ltd, Sidney BC (tanker #7; #777)	.77/88
				Awood Air Ltd, Victoria BC	.88/90
			N2172N	Erickson Air Crane Co, Medford OR	1.90/95
				(flew as "USN 46522")	
				badly dam. near Lincoln City OR: struck boat house during water takeoff	8.7.94
1891	PBY-5A	Bu46527	N6473C	noted derelict, unconv., Fort Worth TX	68
				reg. res: USCR (no evidence this exists)	83/92
1903 •	PBY-5A	**Bu46539**	N1563M	Charlotte Aircraft Corp, Charlotte NC	54/70
				(unconv., derelict, Elizabeth City NC.47/85)	
				Gary R. Larkins, Auburn CA	.85/90
				(complete static rest. Auburn CA)	
				Darryl Greenamyer, Van Nuys CA	.90
				Indonesian AF Museum, Yogyakarta	.90/96

				(displ. as "AURI PB-505")	
1946 •	PBY-5A	**Bu46582**		(to FA Brasileira as FAB C-10A 6520)	
			N4583A	David C. Tallichet/Project Catalina Inc/	
				MARC, Chino CA	12.83
				USNAM, NAS Jacksonville FL	86/96
				(displ. as "4934", later "6582/J1-P-17")	
				(FAA quotes incorrect id. "46852")	
1954 •	PBY-5A Landseaire	**Bu46590**	N68756	Southern California Aircraft Corp, Ontario CA	.50/52
				(conv. to Landseaire completed 25.2.52)	
				Fullerton Oil Co, Pasadena CA	.52/60
				Herbert A. Schriner, Larchmont NY	.60/69
				Endicot P. Davison, New Canaan CT	.69/77
				Quebec Labrador Mission Found., Ipswitch MA	9.77/79
				Michael Wansey/Australian Wing CAF	18.9.79/83
				Confederate Air Force, Harlingen/Midland TX	83/96
				(flew as "RAAF A24-387/Sea Bitch/NB-N"; wfu Harlingen TX, open storage stripped .86/94)	
				rep. removed for static rest.	.94
1959 •	PBY-5A	**Bu46595**	N9501C		
			PT-AXM	Panair do Brasil: op for Petrobras	63
				(to FA Brasileira as FAB C-10A 6551)	
			N4583B	David C. Tallichet/Project Catalina Inc/	
				MARC, Chino CA	12.83/84
				USAFM, Wright-Patterson AFB OH : del.	7.84/96
				(nose gear collapsed on landing W-P 7.84; displ. as "OA-10A 433879/*Snafu Snatchers*")	
1960 •	PBY-5A Super Canso	**Bu46596**	N6070C		
			N45998		
			CF-FFW	The Flying Fireman Ltd, Sidney BC	.67/76
				(tanker #4)	
			C-FFFW	The Flying Fireman Ltd, Sidney BC	81/92
				(tanker #774)	
				sank Silver Lake ONT (salvaged, repaired)	5.84
				op: Awood Air Ltd, Thunder Bay ONT	.88/92
				sold to Spain, struck-off reg.	3.93
			EC-314	Servicios Aereos Espanoles SA-SAESA,	
				Cuatro Vientos (tanker #74)	.92/93
			EC-693	SAESA, Cuatro Vientos	93/96
1966 •	PBY-5A	**Bu46602**	N6071C		
			CF-FFZ	The Flying Fireman Ltd, Sidney BC	68/76
			C-FFFZ	The Flying Fireman Ltd, Sidney BC	81/86
				(tanker #3; #773)	
			N4NC (1	ntu: Wilson C. Edwards, Big Spring TX	3.86
			N607CC	AP Inc, Auburn CA	6.86/90
				USNAM, NAS Pensacola FL: displ.	90/96
				(displ. as "46602/45-P-3")	
1988 •	PBY-5A	**Bu46624**	**N9502C**	Southland Flying Service, Tchula MS	64/69
				David C. Tallichet/MARC, Chino CA	79
				sale rep., Long Beach CA	84/92
				(prob. the Catalina displ. at 94th Aero Squadron Restaurant, Clearwater FL 81)	
1997 •	PBY-5A Super Canso	**Bu46633**		USN, retired to NAS Litchfield Park AZ	11.52
			N10023	Trade Ayer Inc, Linden NJ	.56
			CF-MIR	Miron & Freres Ltd, Cartierville QUE	7.57/64
				(conv. to Super Canso 1000 by Noorduyn Aircraft, Montreal QUE, completed 9.12.60)	
				Laurentian Air Services Ltd, Ottawa ONT	9.64/65
				Survair Ltd, Ottawa ONT	9.65/66

			N608FF	Equitable Leasing Co Corp, Burbank CA	7.67/69
				lsd: Firefly Inc, Portland OR	7.67
				lsd: Aeroservice Corp, Philadelphia PA	
				lsd: Barringer Research	
			C-FMIR	Geoterrex Ltd/Terra Surveys, Ottawa ONT	.70/84
				(survey ops. in Europe, Ireland & South Africa)	
			G-BLSC	Plane Sailing Air Displays Ltd, Duxford	12.84/94
				(del. Johannesburg to UK 14-20.2.85,	
				flew as "RAF JV928/Y", later "RCAF 9754")	
			VR-BPS	Plane Sailing (Bermuda) Ltd, Duxford UK	11.2.94/95
				(rereg. for passenger charters to USA)	
2007 •	PBY-6A	**Bu46643**	N9556C	Aircraft Instrument Corp, Miami FL: USCR	66/70
				(to FA Brasileira as FAB CA-10 6552)	
			PT-BBQ		
			PP-PEB	Panair do Brazil, Sao Paulo: lsd. from FAB	65
				Cruzeiro do Sul, Rio de Janeiro: lsd. from FAB	1.7.65/71
				(ret. to FAB as CA-10-6552): struck-off reg.	17.12.71
				displ. Belem, Brazil	90/93
2008 •	PBY-6A	**Bu46644**	N6458C	Farmers Air Service, Klamath Falls OR	63/64
				Liston Aircraft, Klamath Falls OR	66
				(tanker #F46)	
				Hemet Valley Flying Service, Hemet CA	69/78
				(tanker #E83)	
			C-GFFH	The Flying Fireman Ltd, Sidney BC	5.79/89
				(tanker #8; #778)	
				op: Atwood Air Ltd, Victoria BC	.88/89
			EC-359	Servicios Aereos Espanoles SA-SAESA,	
				Cuatro Vientos	.89/90
			EC-EVK	SAESA, Cuatro Vientos	5.7.90/96
2009 •	PBY-6A	**Bu46645**	N10013	reg.	5.56
			CF-IZO	Montreal Air Service, Montreal QUE	30.6.56/64
				Sakatchewan Govt., Sakatoon SASK	29.5.64
				North Canada Air Ltd, Prince Albert SASK	3.9.65/73
				(tanker #12)	
			C-FIZO	Norcanair Ltd, Prince Albert SASK	75/81
				Avalon Aviation, Parry Sound ONT	4.8.81/89
				(tanker #8; #798) : fitted PBY-5 tailplane	
				(wfu, open storage Parry Sound ONT 88/89)	
				B. Johnson/Tacair Systems, Toronto ONT	.89
				Militaire Luchtvaart Museum, Soesterberg	.89
				(del. Eindhoven 28.9.89 ex Oshawa ONT)	
				op: Flight Support Europe, Eindhoven	.89/91
				Norwegian AF Museum/Forsvarsmuseet	.91/94
				(rest. Gardermoen AB as "FP535/X")	
				Norwegian Aviation Museum, Bodo: del.	.94
2017	PBY-6A	Bu46653	N6459C	Farmers Air Service, Klamath Falls OR	63/64
				Liston Aircraft, Klamath Falls OR	66
				(tanker #F11)	
				Hemet Valley Flying Service, Hemet CA	69/70
				(tanker #77)	
				crashed Columbia CA	18.7.70
2019 •	PBY-6A	**Bu46655**	N10014		
			CF-IZU	World Wide Airways	56
				Montreal Air Services, Montreal QUE	65
				Province of Newfoundland, St Johns NFLD	66/74
			C-FIZU	Province of Newfoundland & Labrador,	
				St Johns NFLD (tanker #4, #704)	79/96
2026 •	PBY-6A	**Bu46662**	N9588C		

	CF-VIG		N788C	Carl H. Ingwer, Tucson AZ	63/64
				Mural Rearment Inc, New York NY	66
			CF-VIG	Great Lakes Paper Co, Fort Williams ONT	.67/73
				Avalon Aviation Ltd, Red Deer ALTA	75
			N1022G		3.79
			N999AR	Anchor & Cattle Corp, Grundy VA	6.80
				Red Stevenson, Leonard OK: "The Searcher"	84
				Wilson C. Edwards, Big Spring TX	8.84/86
			N4NC (2	Wilson C. Edwards, Big Spring TX	3.86/96
2029 •	PBY-6A	**Bu46665**	N9555C		
			CC-CNG	TRANSA, Santiago, Chile (stored)	.57/59
			CC-CNP	Roberto Parrague/Aeroservicio Parrague Ltda/ ASPAR, Santiago "Manutara II"	.59/93
				(ferried to Canada .70 for firebomber conv., tanker #65, later #35)	
				ICONA/Spanish Ministry of Land & Forest Management: lease, del. to Spain ex Chile	7.88/92
				Fumigacion Aerea Andaluza SA/FAASA, Palma del Rio, Spain: leased (tanker #35)	92/96
2043 •	PBY-6A	**Bu46679**	N9562C	Aircraft Instrument Corp, Miami FL: USCR	64/70
			CC-CNF	TRANSA, Santiago, Chile	.57/59
				Roberto Parrague/Aeroservicio Parrague Ltda, Santiago: stored Santiago	.59/80
			CC-CCS	Aeroservicio Parrague Ltda/ASPAR, Santiago	4.80/94
				(conv. to fire tanker #34)	
				sank, landing, Lago Gotierrez, Argentina	27.1.86
				salvaged, returned to service	.88/94
				ICONA/Spanish Ministry of Land & Forest Management: leased, del. to Spain ex Chile	7.6.91
				Fumigacion Aerea Andaluza SA/FAASA, Palma del Rio, Spain: leased (tanker #34)	92/96
2063 •	PBY-6A	**Bu63993**		(to RDAF as 82-866, later L-866)	
				RAF Museum, RAF Colerne: del.	30.5.74/75
				RAF Museum, RAF Cosford	10.75/96
2066	PBY-6A	Bu63996	N6456C	Sonora Flying Service, Columbia CA (tanker #E38)	62/66
				Jack R. Urich, Chiloquin OR	69
				Hemet Valley Flying Service, Hemet CA (tanker #E84; #84)	72/78
				dam. by fire on ground, Stockton CA	.77
			C-GFFJ	Flying Fireman Ltd, Sidney BC (tanker #9)	6.80
				cr. & dest., water pick-up, Sioux Lookout ONT	12.7.81
2068	PBY-6A	Bu63998		(to RDAF as 82-863, later L-863): del.	8.57
			N16KL	Larkin Aircraft Corp, Monterey CA: del.	13.7.72
				American Air Mus. Society, San Francisco CA	72
				Confederate Air Force, Harlingen TX	10.82/84
				cr. & dest., Gulf of Mexico, nr. Harlingen TX	13.10.84
2070	PBY-6A	Bu64000		(to RDAF as 82-868, later L-868)	
			N15KL	Larkin Aircraft Corp, Monterey CA: del.	9.6.72
				John Church, Monterey CA	.72
				Confederate Air Force, Harlingen TX	12.72/75
				cr. & dest. near Harlingen TX	18.8.75
2072	PBY-6A	Bu64002	N9548C	Joe G. Marrs FL	62/64
			N331RS	Rolled Steel Corp, Skokie IL	69
				Victory Air Museum, Mundelein IL	72/76
2087 •	PBY-6A	**Bu64017**	N2846D	Jaydon Enterprises, Riverside CA (tanker #E87)	62/63

				Air Tankers Inc, Seattle WA (tanker #E87)	.63
				Richard Gross, Yreka CA	64
			F-ZBAV	Protection Civile, Marseille	.64/73
				(*Green Pelican*)	
			CF-HNH	Avalon Aviation Ltd, Red Deer ALTA	74/79
			C-FHNH	Avalon Aviation Ltd, Parry Sound ONT	.79/88
				(tanker #6; #796)	
				Haydn Air, Norway: lsd. for firebombing	.78/85
				(del. East Midlands UK 2.9.85 ex Norway,	
				open storage East Midlands/Exeter 86/88	)
			G-BPFY	Aces High Ltd, North Weald	25.10.88
			N212DM	Consolidated Aviation Ent., Burlington VT	25.10.88
			G-BPFY	Aces High Ltd, North Weald	23.12.88
			N212DM	Universal Aviation Corp, Dover DE	6.6.89
			G-BPFY	Aces High Ltd, North Weald	5.3.90
				Warbirds of GB del Biggin Hill.	15.3.90/92
2104	PBY-6A	Bu64034	N2886D	Burson Associates Inc, Columbia CA	63/66
				Sis-Q Flying Service Inc, Santa Rosa CA	69/72
				(tanker #E49)	
				Robert P. Schlaefli/SLAFCO, Pt. Orchard WA	78/95
				(tanker #E49, #49)	
				sank in lake, Northport WA	29.7.85
2105 •	PBY-6A	**Bu64035**		(to RDAF as 82-861, later L-861)	
				Vaerlose AB, Denmark: wfu, stored	70/85
				RDAF Museum Collection, Engagergard AB	79/88
				Flyvevabnets Historiske Museum,Vaerlose AB	91/94
				(rest. Vaerlose 94, due to displ. at Elsinore)	
2111 •	PBY-6A	**Bu64041**	N6453C	Leo J. Demers, Salem OR	
				Rosenbalm Aviation, Medford OR	59
				Sonora Flying Service, Columbia CA	
				B. B. Burson Associates Inc, Columbia CA	63/66
				(tanker #E54)	
				Hemet Valley Flying Service, Hemet CA	68/78
				(tanker #E54, #54)	
			C-GFFI	Flying Fireman Ltd, Victoria BC (tanker #9)	5.79
			N85U	Bud Rude/Flying Fireman Inc, Spanaway WA	
				(tanker #85)	3.86/95
				op: Awood Air Ltd, Spanaway WA	.88/89
2133	PBY-6A	Bu64063	PT-BBP	Servicios Aerotaxie Abast do Vale, Belem	83
2134 •	PBY-6A	**Bu64064**	CF-IZZ	World Wide Airways	56
				Montreal Air Services, Montreal QUE	65/66
				Kenting Aviation Ltd, Toronto ONT	66
				Field Aviation Co, Toronto ONT	68/70
				lsd: Protection Civile, Marseille, France	5.66/73
				(del. via Dublin 20.5.66; "Black Pelican")	
			F-ZBAZ	lsd: Protection Civile, Marseille	
			CF-IZZ	Field Aviation Co Ltd, Toronto ONT: del.	6.73
			C-FIZZ	Avalon Aviation Ltd, Montreal QUE	75/79
				Avalon Aviation Ltd, Parry Sound ONT	.79/91
				(tanker #5; #795: rebuilt with PBY-5A tailplane,	
				wfu Parry Sound ONT 88/90)	
				Servicios Aereos Espanoles SA-SAESA,	
				Cuatro Vientos, Spain: del. ex Canada	4.7.91/92
			EC-940	SAESA, Cuatro Vientos	.92
			EC-FMC	SAESA, Cuatro Vientos (tanker #795, #72)	.92/96
2141 •	PBY-6A	**Bu64071**	NC48129		45
			N6457C	Sonora Flying Service, Columbia CA	62/63
				(tanker #E49)	

				Calypso Air Charters Inc, Miami FL	.63/69
			N48129	Interport Inc	.68
				(del. Arizona to Dominican Rep. 2.68)	
				Carl H. Jurgens, Dominican Republic	69/70
				(open storage, Fort Lauderdale FL 71/74)	
			N101CS	Jacques Cousteau/American Equipment Funding, Wilmington DE	74/75
				Cousteau Society Inc, Los Angeles CA	.76/78
				crashed and sank, River Tagus, Portugal	28.6.79
				Museo do Ar, Alverca AB, Lisbon: wreck	92
42 •	PBY-6A	**Bu64072**	**N7057C**	George J. Priester, Wheeling IL	63/64
				John W. Dorr, Malibu CA	66/70
				Aeroborne Enterprises, Davie FL	78
				P & P Charters Inc, Fort Lauderdale FL	84
				Hill Air Company Inc, Fort Lauderdale FL	6.85/87
				National Warplane Museum Inc, Geneseo NY	10.87/96
				(flies as "USN/70-P")	
62 •	PBY-6A	**Bu64092**	N6881C	Carstedt Sales Corp, Long Beach CA	63
			CF-PIU	Northward Air Service, Calgary ALTA	65
				Northward Aviation, Edmontonton ALTA	66
				Northland Airlines, Winnipeg MAN	68
				Midwest Airlines, Winnipeg MAN	69/70
				Ilford Riverton Airways, Winnipeg MAN	73
				St Felicien Air Service, Robervale QUE	.73/76
			C-FPIU	Avalon Aviation Ltd, Parry Sound ONT	.79/95
				(tanker #7; #797)	
				wfu, open storage Parry Sound ONT	88/96
67 •	PBY-6A	**Bu64097**		USN BOC 20.9.45: wfu NAS Litchfield Park	12.56
			N7082C	Babb Co, Phoenix-Sky Harbour AZ	3.57
				James Routh/Routh Aircraft, Long Beach CA	1.59/63
				(tanker #E94)	
				Multiple Management Corp, Long Beach CA	.63/64
			F-ZBAW	Protection Civile, Marseille "Yellow Pelican"	4.64/73
			C-FHNF	Avalon Aviation Ltd, Montreal QUE	75/79
				Avalon Aviation Ltd, Parry Sound ONT	.79/91
				(tanker #4, #794)	
				Haydn Air, Norway: lsd. for fire bombing	76/77
				(wfu Parry Sound ONT 28.2.88/90)	
			N7179Y	Peter Ettinger & Tom Boy/ Aircraft Marketing Inc, Albuquerque NM	5.3.91/94
				(stored Ft Lauderdale FL, USN sc., 91/94)	
				Confederate Air Force, Midland TX: del.	12.2.94/96
				(DoT & FAA quote id. as "225")	
68	PBY-6A	Bu64098	N2887D	B. B. Burson & Associates, Columbia CA	63
				(tanker #E93)	
				James N. Routh/Routh Aircraft, Tucson AZ	63/70
76	PBY-6A	Bu64106	N6454C	Sonora Flying Service, Columbia CA	63/64
				William J. Deangelis, Las Vegas NV	66
				(noted open storage, Long Beach CA 9.67)	
				Fred J. Wynne/Wynnes Inc, Jacksonville FL	69/70
77 •	PBY-6A	**Bu64107**		NASM, Washington DC : listed as stored	65
			N9825Z	Florida Forestry Board, Tallahassee FL	64/72
				Robert P. Schlaefli/SLAFCO, Moses Lake WA 78/95	
				(tanker #158)	
				(note: FAA quote id. "235")	
981 •	PBY-5A Canso A	**RCAF9752**		BOC 3.12.43: SOC	4.10.46
				(to FA Brasileira as FAB C10A-6527)	
				Museu Aerospacial do FAB, Rio de Janeiro	82/96

21986 •	PBY-5A	**RCAF9757**		BOC 21.1.43: SOC	18.11.46
	Canso A		CF-SAT	Saskatchewan Government Airways SASK	54
				Central Northern Airlines	.54/55
				Transair Ltd, St James MAN	56/66
				Northland Airlines, Winnipeg MAN	68
				William P. Bernard, Edmonton ALTA	69/73
				Can-Air Services Ltd, Edmonton ALTA	76/86
				(op. scheduled service ex Truk, Pacific 12.84/85)	
				crashed and sank, landing, Maui HI	14.4.86
				Ray Cox, Renton WA: wreck recov.	.86
				Alaska Aviation Heritage Museum, Anchorage	92/96
				(major parts stored Anchorage-Lake Hood,	
				to be used in static rest. of CV.465)	
21996 •	PBY-5A	RCAF9767		BOC 4.3.43: SOC	1.4.46
	Canso A			(162 Sqn, Reykjavik: sank U-342 17.4.44)	
			CF-CRR	Canadian Pacific Airlines, Montreal QUE	1.4.46/60
				dam. landing on water, Prince Rupert BC	23.4.59
				Northland Airlines, Winnipeg MAN	.60/68
				dam. by storm God's Lake MAN	5.10.60
				Midwest Airlines, Winnipeg MAN	.69/70
				Ilford Riverton Airways, Winnipeg MAN	73
				Avalon Aviation Ltd, Red Deer ALTA	77/79
				(tanker #1; #791)	
				dam. sank, taking off Complex Lake SASK	27.5.78
			C-FCRR	Avalon Aviation Ltd, Parry Sound ONT	.79/95
				sank, water pick-up, Complex Lake SASK	30.5.81
				(salvaged, returned to service)	
				(wfu, stored Parry Sound ONT 88/95)	
				Legend Air, Dinard, France: del.	4.95
				(noted Toulouse 10.95, *Okavago* titles)	
22018 •	PBY-5A	**RCAF9789**		BOC 28.4.43: SOC	2.10.43
	Canso A			crashed, Bella Bella BC	30.7.43
				complete airframe still in situ at crash site	92
22022	PBY-5A	RCAF9793		BOC 10.5.43: SOC	8.4.46
	Canso A		YV-P-APE	Texas Petroleum Co/TEXACO Ltda	55
			OB-LDM-349	2.55	
			HK-996X		60
			HP-289	Southern Air Transport, Miami FL	60/61
				op. for C.I.A. as communications post during	
				'Bay of Pigs' attempted Cuban invasion.	4.61
				Turismo Aero: struck-off reg.	13.8.63
			VP-KUD	stored Fort Lauderdale FL	64
			5Y-KUD	Atlantic General Enterprises	65
			HR-236	Caribbean Seafood Production Corp	66
			N6108	Steward-Davis Inc, Long Beach CA	7.68/70
				(flew in film "Tora Tora Tora", Hawaii .69)	
				Aviation Contractors of Boca Chica,	
				Wenatchee WA	72
				Bombers Inc	
				JK Flying Service	
				Paloma Air Oklahoma, Tulsa OK	78
				(based Costa Rica 77/78)	
			TG-BIV	Troya SA, Guatemala	11.80/86
				Meldy Fernandez, La Aurora, Guatamala	86/88
			N5404J	Alan Preston, Houston TX	10.88
				Tailwinds Aviation, Houston TX	1.89
				Aircraft Marketing Inc, Albuquerque NM	1.90
				Henry L. Hancock/Tropical Sea Air,	
				Harrisburg IL	8.90/92
				(stored, St Louis MO 91, USN scheme)	

				Neptune Aero Marine Inc, Cheyenne WY	11.93
			ZK-PBY (1	ntu: New Zealand Warbirds, Auckland-Ardmore	
				Spirit of the Coral Route	.93/94
				ditched near Christmas Island en route Hawaii-	
				Tahiti on del. flight, sank: 7 crew rescued	16.1.94
1154 •	PB2B-2	**Bu44248**		(to RAF as JX630)	
	Mk.VI			(to RAAF as A24-385): BOC 3.9.45: SOC	22.8.50
			VH-AGB	ntu: Captain P. G. Taylor, Sydney NSW	1.51
			VH-ASA	P. G. Taylor, Sydney NSW: "Frigate Bird II"	12.3.51/61
				(exploratory flights to South America)	
				wfu, stored RAAF Rathmines NSW 6.54/59,	
				barged to storage Rose Bay NSW 7.7.59/69)	
				Museum of Arts & Applied Sciences, Sydney	.61/87
				(moved to Museum storage Ultimo 12.69/74)	
				Camden Museum of Aviation NSW: loan, arr.	30.3.74/83
				Power House Museum, Sydney NSW: displ.	87/96
V-240	PBV-1A	RCAF9806		RCAF BOC 5.4.43: SOC	18.11.46
	Canso A			(to FA Brasileira as FAB CA-10 65...)	
			PP-PCX	Panair do Brasil, Sao Paulo	57/65
				Bandeirante Antonio Pedroso de Alvarenga	
				dam. Rio Branco, Brazil (repaired)	27.1.57
				(ret. to FA Brasileira as .....): struck-off reg.	17.12.71
V-244 •	PBV-1A	**RCAF9810**		RCAF BOC 30.3.44: SOC	20.2.47
	Canso A			(to R Swedish AF as Fv47001): BOC	28.6.49/66
				BOC: to R Swedish AF Historical Collection	1.8.66/84
				Flygvapenmuseum Malmen, Linkoping, Sweden	.84/96
				(displ. as "RSwAF 47001/79")	
V-249 •	PBV-1A	**RCAF9815**		RCAF BOC 2.6.43: SOC	25.5.61
	Canso A		CF-NJB	Kenting Aviation Ltd, Toronto ONT	20.6.63/66
			F-ZBAR	lsd: Protection Civile, Marseille: del.	6.5.66
			CF-NJB	Kenting Aviation: returned	11.66
			F-ZBBC	lsd: Protection Civile, Marseille: del.	5.68
			CF-NJB	Kenting Aviation: del. via Dublin	18.9.68/74
			C-FNJB	Norcanair Ltd, Prince Albert SASK	26.4.74/79
				Province of Saskatchewan, La Ronge SASK	23.6.80/96
				(tanker #9)	
V-264 •	PBV-1A	RCAF9830		RCAF BOC 31.7.43: SOC	26.9.61
	Canso A		CF-PQK	Department of Transport, Quebec QUE	65/73
			C-FPQK	Government of Quebec, Quebec City QUE	79/94
				(tanker #712)	
				Fondation Aerovision Quebec, St Hubert QUE	1.6.94/96
V-271 •	PBV-1A	**RCAF9837**		RCAF BOC 7.9.43: SOC	29.11.45
	Canso A		CF-CRP	Canadian Pacific Airlines, Vancouver BC	11.45/57
				Trans Labrador Airlines	9.5.57/58
				Eastern Provincial Airways, Gander NFLD	65/70
				Province of Newfoundland & Labrador	73/79
			C-FCRP	Province of Newfoundland & Labrador,	
				St Johns NFLD (tanker #6)	79/90
				struck-off reg.	6.90
				North Atlantic Aviation Museum, Gander NFLD	.90/92
V-272 •	PBV-1A	**RCAF9838**		RCAF BOC 20.9.43: SOC	31.10.46
	Canso A			(to FA Brasileira as FAB C-10A 6525)	
			N4934H	Airplane Sales International, Beverly Hills CA	5.85
				(del. as N4934H Belem-Albuquerque NM 7.84)	
				USNAM, NAS Corpus Christi TX	88/94
				(displ. as "USN 6525")	
				USS Lexington Museum, Corpus Christi: listed	94

CV-281	PBV-1A	RCAF11003		RCAF BOC 16.11.43: SOC	6.1.61
	Canso A		CF-UKR	Kenting Aircraft Ltd, Toronto ONT	66
				Field Aviation Co Ltd, Toronto ONT	68/70
			F-ZBAX	lsd: Protection Civile, Marseille: del.	20.5.66/68
				(to French Aeronavale as No.81/F-YEIC)	.68
				(del. to Tahiti, via Bahrein 12.4.68)	
				retired Papeete, Tahiti	.71/73
			CC-CDS	Roberto Parrague/Aeroservicio Parrague Ltda,	
				Santiago-Los Cerillos (tanker #31)	8.73/79
				crashed fire bombing, nr Chiguayante, Chile	8.4.79
CV-283 •	PBV-1A	**RCAF11005**		RCAF BOC 27.10.43: SOC	25.5.61
	Canso A		CF-NJF	Kenting Aviation Ltd, Toronto ONT	.63/74
			F-ZBAY	lsd: Protection Civile, Marseille: del.	6.5.66
			CF-NJF	Kenting Aviation Ltd : returned	11.66
			F-ZBBD	lsd: Protection Civile, Marseille: del.	6.5.68
			CF-NJF	Kenting Aviation Ltd : returned via Dublin	21.9.68/74
			C-FNJF	Norcanair Ltd, Prince Albert SASK	26.4.74/79
				Province of Saskatchewan, La Ronge SASK	23.6.80/96
				(tanker #7)	
CV-285 •	PBV-1A	**RCAF11007**		RCAF BOC 30.10.43: SOC	13.4.45
	Canso A			fcd. ldg. Tofino, Vancouver Island: abandoned	8.2.45
				Commonwealth Military Aviation Museum,	
				Sidney BC: planned recov. by helicopter	92
CV-302 •	PBV-1A	**RCAF11024**		RCAF BOC 7.12.43: SOC	20.10.61
	Canso A		CF-NTK	ntu	
			CF-UAW	Kenting Aircraft Ltd, Toronto ONT	22.4.66/71
			C-FUAW	Norcanair Ltd, Prince Albert SASK	12.5.71/80
				Province of Saskatchewan, La Ronge SASK	.80/96
				(tanker #8)	
				(note: DoT quote id. "CV201")	
CV-311	PBV-1A	RCAF11029		RCAF BOC 30.12.43: SOC	2.2.47
	Canso A		CF-IDS	Northland Airlines, Winnipeg MAN	65/66
				North Canada Air Ltd, Prince Albert SASK	68/70
				Norcanair Ltd, Prince Albert SASK	73
CV-332 •	PBV-1A	Bu67844		(to USAAF as 44-33880)	
	OA-10A		TF-RVR	Icelandair/Flugfelag Islands, Keflavik	
			CF-FKV	Maritime Central Airlines, Charlottetown PEI	54
				Wheeler Airlines, St Jovite Station QUE	65
			F-BMKS	Unions de Transports Aeriens - UTA, Tahiti	24.2.66
				(to French Aeronavale as No. 32/F-YCHB)	
				retired Papeete, Tahiti	.71/73
			CC-CDT	Roberto Parrague/Aeroservicios Parrague Ltda/	
				ASPAR, Santiago-Los Cerillos (tanker #32)	8.73/93
				ICONA/Spanish Ministry of Land & Forest	
				Management: leased, del. Spain ex Chile	7.88/92
				Fumigacion Aerea Andaluza SA/FAASA,	
				Palma del Rio, Spain: leased (tanker #32)	92/96
CV-333 •	PBV-1A	**RCAF11042**		RCAF BOC 12.2.44: SOC	15.12.60
	Canso A		CF-PQF	Department of Transportation, Quebec QUE	65/73
			C-FPQF	Government of Quebec, Quebec City QUE	79/94
				(tanker #711)	
				Pro Air Aviation, Bonsecours PQ	6.94
				sold to Cyprus: struck-off reg.	8.94
			5B-PBY	Athenian Airlift Services Ltd, Nicosia/Athens	8.94
				Villa Franca: del. Quebec-Athens, arr.	10.9.94/95
				(based Athens, flying between Greek islands)	
CV-343 •	PBV-1A	**RCAF11047**		RCAF BOC 24.2.44: SOC	26.4.62

	Canso A		CF-OFI	Province of Newfoundland, St Johns NFLD	65/73
			C-FOFI	Government of Newfoundland & Labrador, St Johns NFLD (tanker #703)	79/96
-353	PBV-1A Canso A	RCAF11052		RCAF BOC 11.3.44: SOC	27.6.47
			CF-FVE	Maritime Central Airlines, Charlottetown PEI	54
				Wheeler Airlines, St Jovite Station QUE	65
				Wheeler Northland Airways, St Jean QUE	66/73
				struck-off reg.	6.73
-357 •	PBV-1A Canso A	RCAF11054		RCAF BOC 20.3.44: SOC	27.6.47
				Lee Crutchell, San Jose, Costa Rica	.54/55
				(civil conv. by SALA, San Jose, Costa Rica .55)	
			CF-JCV	Eastern Canada Stevedoring Co, Montreal QUE	7.56/60
				Notre Dame Air Transport: lease	3.57
				Austin Airways, Timmins ONT	5.60/76
			C-FJCV	Aero Trades Western Ltd, Winnepeg MAN	9.76/82
				(open storage Reno-Stead NV 80/82)	
				Air Caledonia, Vancouver BC	3.82/86
				Pierre Jaunet/The Catalina Safari Co	.87/90
				(based Cairo for Eastern African tours: del. US - Victoria Falls 9.88)	
			Z-CAT	The Catalina Safari Co, Harare, Zimbabwe	7.90/94
				Catalina Syndicate/NZ Warbirds: reg. res.	.94/95
				(del. Harare to NZ, via Darwin NT 22.10.94, arr. New Plymouth NZ 26.10.94)	
			ZK-PBY (2	The Catalina Co NZ Ltd, Auckland	23.3.95
-369 •	PBV-1A Canso A Super Catalina	**RCAF11060**		RCAF BOC 5.4.44: SOC	25.5.61
			N609FF	Firefly Inc, Portland OR	66/72
				lsd. Cal-Nat Airways, Grass Valley CA (tanker #E40)	66
				Terra Surveys Ltd, Ottawa ONT: leased	68/72
			VH-EXG	Terra Surveys Ltd, Ottawa ONT	6.72/89
				op: Executive Air Services, Essendon VIC	6.72/89
				(del. Essendon 27.6.72 ex survey ops. Africa)	
				RAAF Museum, RAAF Point Cook VIC	.89/95
				(wfu Essendon VIC 88/93, trucked 6.93 to RAAF Laverton VIC for static rest., trucked to RAAF Amberley QLD .95)	
-383	PBV-1A Canso A	RCAF11067		RCAF BOC 14.4.44: SOC	20.10.61
			CF-NTL	National Air Tankers Ltd, Calgary ALTA	65
				Leaseway Ltd, Toronto ONT	66/70
				The Flying Fireman Ltd, Sidney BC	71/78
				crashed fire bombing, Snow Lake MAN	21.5.78
-397 •	PBV-1A Canso A	**RCAF11074**		RCAF BOC 5.5.44: SOC	7.11.61
			CF-OWE	Ontario Central Airlines, Kenora ONT	65/70
			C-FOWE	Ilford Riverton Airways, Winnipeg MAN	77/83
				Northland Outdoors of Canada	83
			N691RF	Robert J. Franks, Los Angeles CA	6.84
			C-FOWE	Jonathon Seagull Holdings, Vancouver BC	9.85
				damaged landing, Plymouth Harbour UK	30.5.86
				repaired : dep. on ret. flight to Canada	8.10.86
			N69RF	Robert J. Franks, Los Angeles CA	3.89
				Flying Catalina Corp, Los Angeles CA	6.90/96
-399	PBV-1A Canso A	RCAF11075		RCAF BOC 5.5.44: SOC	7.6.62
			CF-OMO		
			N610FF	Firefly Inc, Portland OR	64/70
				Barringer Research Co, Toronto ONT: lsd	65/70
				crashed on survey flt, Rhinelander WI	15.10.70
-407	PBV-1A	RCAF11079		RCAF BOC 23.5.44: SOC	29.11.62

	Canso A		CF-PQP	Department of Transportation, Quebec QUE	.64/74
			C-FPQP	Government of Quebec, Quebec City QUE	86/87
				crashed landing, La Cache QUE	18.7.87
CV-417 •	PBV-1A	**RCAF11084**		RCAF BOC 24.5.44: SOC	26.9.61
	Canso A		CF-PQL	Department of Transportation, Quebec QUE	.63/73
			C-FPQL	Government of Quebec, Quebec City QUE	79/94
				(tanker #713)	
				Conifair/Royal Aviation, Mont-Joli QUE	14.6.94/96
				(tanker #13)	
CV-420	PBV-1A	Bu67888		(to USAAF as 44-33924)	
	OA-10A		CF-NCJ	Government of Newfoundland & Lab., St Johns	73
CV-421 •	PBV-1A	**RCAF11086**		RCAF BOC 29.5.44: SOC	5.6.45
	Canso A			dam., 25m E. Ucluelet, Vancouver Island BC	2.12.44
				airframe still in situ, Ucluelet BC	92
CV-423 •	PBV-1A	**RCAF11087**		RCAF BOC	5.6.44
	Canso A			Canadian National Aeronautical Collection,	
				Rockcliffe AB ONT	.64/82
				National Aviation Museum, Rockcliffe ONT	9.82/96
CV-425 •	PBV-1A	RCAF11088		RCAF BOC 5.6.44: SOC	12.12.60
	Canso A		CF-GMS		
			CF-PQM	Department of Transportation, Quebec QUE	65/73
			C-FPQM	Government of Quebec, Quebec City QUE	79/94
				(tanker #714)	
				Conifair/Royal Aviation, Mont-Joli QUE	14.6.94/96
				(tanker #14)	
CV-427 •	PBV-1A	RCAF11089		RCAF BOC 3.6.44: SOC	29.11.62
	Canso A		CF-PQO	Department of Transportation, Quebec QUE	.63/73
			C-FPQO	Government of Quebec, Quebec City QUE	79/92
				(tanker #15)	
				Pro Air Aviation International, Bromont QUE	94/96
CV-430 •	PBV-1A	Bu67893		(to USAAF as 44-33929)	
	OA-10A		CF-NJC	Eastern Provincial Airways, Gander NFLD	65
				Province of Newfoundland, St Johns NFLD	68/74
			C-FNJC	Province of Newfoundland & Labrador,	
				St Johns NFLD (tanker #5, #701)	85/96
CV-435 •	PBV-1A	**RCAF11093**		RCAF BOC 16.6.44: SOC	10.4.61
	Canso A		CF-NJL	David T. Dorosh, Edmonton ALTA	.62/95
				(stored in hangar, Gananoque ONT 62/95)	
CV-437 •	PBV-1A	**RCAF11094**		RCAF BOC 22.6.44: SOC	25.5.61
	Canso A		CF-NJE	Chiupka Airways Ltd, Lynn Lake MAN	65/66
				Northland Airlines, Winnipeg MAN	68
				Midwest Airlines, Winnipeg MAN	69/71
				Nordair Airways, Winnipeg MAN	2.9.71/72
				Ilford Riverton Airways, Winnipeg, Manitoba	73
				St Felicien Air Service, Roberval QUE	.73/76
				op: Survair Ltd	77
			C-FNJE	Province of Newfoundland & Labrador,	
				St Johns NFLD (tanker #7,#702)	5.78/96
CV-441	PBV-1A	RCAF11096		RCAF BOC 23.6.44: SOC	4.10.46
	Canso A		CF-IHN	Northern Wings Ltd, Seven Islands QUE	65/69
				The Flying Fireman Ltd, Sidney BC	70/74
			C-GFFD	The Flying Fireman Ltd, Sidney BC	5.75/84
				crashed, dest., Thunder Bay ONT	14.5.84

CV-449	PBV-1A	RCAF11100		RCAF BOC 3.7.44: SOC	10.4.61
	Canso A		CF-NJP		
			F-ZBAR	Securite Civile, Marseille-Merignane	
				(broken-up: nose section stored Merignane 77)	
				Ailes Anciennes Marseille-Escadrille Pegase,	
				Aix-Les Milles: nose section only	89
				Musee des Traditions de l'Aeronautique Navale,	
				Rochefort-Soubise AB: loan, nose only	91
CV-465 •	PBV-1A	**Bu67918**		(to USAAF as 44-33954)	
	OA-10A			forced landing, abandoned, Dago Lake AK	30.9.47
				R. S. Richards, Anchorage AK (salv. rights)	10.48/78
				Alaska Historical Aircraft Society, Anchorage	.78
			N44BY	Alaska Historical Aircraft Society, Anchorage	5.84
				(airlifted from Dago Lake by helicopter 30.9.84)	
			N57875	U.S. Historical Aircraft Preservation Museum,	
				Anchorage AK	5.85
				Alaska Aviation Heritage Museum, Lake Hood	
				Anchorage Airport AK: displ. unrest.	.84/94
CV-483 •	PBV-1A	**Bu67936**		(to USAAF as 44-33972)	
	OA-10A		CF-IIW	reg.	.55
				Austin Airways, Timmins ONT: leased	63
				Northern Wings Ltd, Seven Islands QUE	65/68
			N3202	Universal Air Leasing Co, Grand Blanc MI	.69
				Richard L. Rude/Flying Fireman, Victoria BC	70
			C-GFFC	The Flying Fireman, Victoria BC (tanker #6)	6.75/88
				Awood Air Ltd, Victoria BC	8.88/89
				op: SLAFCO Inc, Moses Lake WA	91/92
CV-520 •	PBV-1A	**Bu67973**		(to USAAF as 44-34009)	
	OA-10A		N62043		
			CF-IHC	Wheeler Airlines, St Jovite Station QUE	.55/56
				Leasair Ltd, Ottawa ONT	65
			F-WMKR	Union de Transports Aerien, Tahiti	.66
			F-BMKR	Union de Transports Aerien, Tahiti	9.2.66
				(to French Aeronavale as No. 20/F-YCHA)	
				wfu, stored Tahiti	.71/73
			CC-CDU	Roberto Parrague/Aeroservicio Parrague Ltda/	
				ASPAR, Santiago	5.73
			CC-CGY	Aeroservicio Parrague Ltda, Santiago	80/93
				(allocated tanker #33)	
				open storage, stripped, Santiago-Los Cerillos	80/93
				(unconv., in faded Aeronavale scheme)	
CV-560 •	PBV-1A	**Bu68013**		(to USAAF as 44-34049)	
	OA-10A		CF-GLX	Queen Charlotte Airlines, Vancouver BC	.51
				Pacific Western Airlines, Vancouver BC	60
				Northland Airlines, Winnipeg MAN	65/68
				Midwest Airlines, Winnipeg MAN	69/70
				Transair Ltd, St.James MAN	72
				Ilford Riverton Airways, Winnipeg, MAN	74
			C-FGLX	Avalon Aviation Ltd, Red Deer ALTA	77/79
				Avalon Aviation Ltd, Parry Sound ONT	.79/95
				(tanker #2; #792)	
				(wfu, stored Parry Sound ONT 88/95)	
CV-592 •	PBV-1A	**Bu68045**		(to USAAF as 44-34081)	
	OA-10A		VR-HDH	Cathay Pacific Airways Ltd, Hong Kong	11.46
				Macau Air Transport, Macau	
				Trans Australian Airlines - TAA	6.7.62
			VH-SBV	Trans Australian Airlines, Pt. Moresby PNG	.63/66
				wfu Port Moresby PNG: last flight	5.1.66
				(retired to fire practice area, Port Moresby-	
				Jacksons Airport: partially burnt c68)	

				Museum of Transport & Technology, Auckland NZ: stored dism.	75/86
				(shipped dism. Pt. Moresby-Auckland 9.75)	
				RNZAF Museum, Wigram AB	87/96
				(long term static rest. Whenuapai AB 87/88 & Wigram AB 94/95: to be displ. in RNZAF sc.)	
CV-605 •	PBV-1A	**Bu68058**		(to USAAF as 44-34094)	
	OA-10A		NC65715		
			TF-RVG	Icelandair/Flugflelag Islands, Keflavik	.49/52
			CF-DFB	Aero Magnetic Surveys Ltd, Toronto ONT	.52/56
				Kenting Aviation Ltd, Toronto ONT	56/59
				Hunting Survey Corp, Toronto ONT	.60
				Kenting Aviation Ltd, Toronto ONT	4.62
				Wheeler Airlines, St Jovite Station QUE	65
				Wheeler Northland Airways, St Jean QUE	66/71
				Austin Airways, Timmins ONT	2.6.71/76
				Wheeler Northland Airways Ltd, St Jean QUE	1.3.76/78
			C-FDFB	Province of Newfoundland & Labrador, St. Johns NFLD (tanker #1)	10.78/8.90
				struck-off reg.	8.90
				displ. Botwood NFLD	91/92
-	PBY-5	-		Hemet Valley Flying Service, Hemet CA	
				fus. noted unconv. USN "204", Hemet CA	10.78
-	PBY-5	-	ZP-CBA	Lineas Aereas de Transportes Nacionales Corp: L.A.T.N. "Mixta"	
				wfu, open storage Asuncion, Paraguay	69/72
- •	PBY-5A	-		(to RAAF as A24-.....)	
				war memorial displ., Lake Boga VIC	88/96
				(static composite rest. from several aircraft recov. from farms; displ. as "A24-30")	
- •	PBY-5A	-		(to FA Colombiana as FAC 619)	
				Madrid-Barroblanco AB, Colombia: derelict	92/96
- •	PBY-5A	-		(to FA Ecuatoriana as 53602)	
				\Museo Aero de FAE, Mariscal Sucre AB, Quito	77/93

CONSOLIDATED/CONVAIR P4Y-2 PRIVATEER

- •	PB4Y-2	Bu59701	N3432G		
	P4Y-2 Super Privateer		**N6884C(2**	International Air Applicators, Los Angeles CA	.59/64
				Rosenbalm Aviation, Medford OR (tanker #84)	66/70
				Hawkins & Powers Aviation, Greybull WY (tanker #127)	9.70/96
-	PB4Y-2	Bu59754	N3191G	Rosenbalm Aviation, Medford OR (tanker #F85)	62/64
	P4Y-2			Flick Aviation, La Grande OR	66
				Rosenbalm Aviation, Medford OR (tanker #85)	69/70
				ditched and sank, Diamond Lake OR	27.7.70
- •	PB4Y-2	Bu59763		(to FA Hondurena as FAH792): del.	.56/62
	P4Y-2B		**N7237C**	Wesley Lewis, Pampa TX	63/66
				George H. Stell, Phoenix AZ (tanker #3..., later #C50)	.67/72
				SS & T Aerial Contractors, Phoenix AZ	72/74
				crashed Safford AZ (rep. as dest.)	.74

				Ronald R. Sathre, Union City CA: added USCR	9.5.94/96
- •	PB4Y-2 P4Y-2	Bu59819	**N3739G**	Flight Enterprises Inc, Prescott AZ SS & T Aerial Contractors, Phoenix AZ (tanker #C30) Air Tankers Inc, Buckeye AZ (tanker #C30) Sergio A. Tomassoni/T & G Aviation Inc, Buckeye/Chandler AZ (tanker #30) Lone Star Flight Museum, Galveston TX: del. (rest. Galveston to mil. config, due to fly .97)	.60/64 66/73 77/90 17.1.91/96
- •	PB4Y-2 P4Y-2 P4Y-2G Super Privateer	Bu59876	 **N6813D**	(to USCG as 59876) Lysdale Flying Service, St. Paul MN (del. ex Litchfield Park NAS AZ as "N6319D") Cisco Aircraft Inc, Lancaster CA (sprayer) Sun Valley Insurance Agency, Burbank CA National City Aircraft Leasing, Chicago IL Turbo-Mod Inc FL Michael T. Loening/Loening Air, Boise ID (del. Mojave CA to Boise ID 29.3.65) Cal-Nat Airways, Grass Valley CA Hawkins & Powers Aviation, Greybull WY (tanker #A25, #B25,#125) dam. landing, Port Hardy BC: ran into sea Canadian Museum of Flight & Transportation, Richmond BC museum sydicate, Detroit MI: arr. dism. (stored dism., planned rest. as B-24 abandoned) Yankee Air Force, Willow Run MI: arr. dism. (static rest. as tanker #125)	 12.57/59 3.12.59/61 11.61/62 7.62/65 29.1.65 9.2.65/67 10.4.67/69 11.69/72 9.8.75 .76/81 .81/86 10.86/93
- •	PB4Y-2 P4Y-2 P4Y-2G Super Privateer	**Bu59882**	 **N7962C**	(to US Coast Guard as 59882) Avery Aviation, Greybull WY Christler & Avery Aviation Co, Greybull WY Hawkins & Powers Aviation, Greybull WY (tanker #B26; #126)	 .59 64/71 7.71/95
-	PB4Y-2 P4Y-2	Bu59905	N6816D	reg. Wenairco Inc, Wenatchee WA (tanker #42) burnt out on runway, Wenatchee WA Sergio Tomassoni, Buckeye AZ (remains) struck-off USCR rear fuselage and parts noted, Buckeye AZ	.58 63/72 9.72 12.77 1.79
- •	PB4Y-2 PB4Y-2M P4Y-2	**Bu59932**	 **N9829C**	NAS Litchfield Park AZ: del. for storage Walter Metals, Compton CA Air International Inc, Miami FL George T. Baker Aviation School, Miami Airport FL: inst. airframe Buster Droznenk, Miami FL dism., fuselage trucked to Big Cyprus FL Yesterdays Air Force, St. Petersburg FL Jay Wisler, Kissimmee FL (fuse. recov. as shanty house Everglades FL .90) Tom Reilly Vintage Aircraft, Kissimmee FL (planned rebuild, using B-24D wreck ex Canada)	10.54/57 1.10.57 .57 60/71 .71 .71 .90/94
-	PB4Y-2 P4Y-2	Bu60001	PT-BEG	AZAS Importadoras e Exportadora Ltda, Rio "Alexandrina"; noted derelict, Belem	63/69 75
- •	PB4Y-2 P4Y-2 P4Y-2G Super Privateer	**Bu66260**	**N7620C**	(to US Coast Guard as 66260) Big Piney Aviation, Big Piney WY Avery Aviation, Greybull WY (tanker #B23) Hawkins & Powers Aviation, Greybull WY (tanker #123)	 63/64 66/69 6.69/96

- •	PB4Y-2	**Bu66261**	N7682C	Avery Aviation, Greybull WY	.59
	P4Y-2			unconv. stripped for spares, Greybull WY	59/81
				(rebuilt .81 Greybull to USN sc., with parts of	
				N2870G/66304: adopted id. 66304;	
				del. Greybull-Pensacola FL 16/17.1.83)	
				USNAM, NAS Pensacola FL	1.83/94
				(displ. as USN "66304/F202/Oakland")	
- •	PB4Y-2	**Bu66300**		(to US Coast Guard as 66300)	
	P4Y-2G			offered for disposal ex NAS Elizabeth City NC	8.58
			N2872G	Ace Smelting Inc, Phoenix AZ	.59
	Super			Avery Aviation, Greybull WY (tanker #B24)	.59/70
	Privateer			Hawkins & Powers Aviation, Greybull WY	3.70/96
				(tanker #124)	
- •	PB4Y-2	**Bu66302**		(to US Coast Guard as 66302)	
	P4Y-2G			offered for disposal ex NAS Elizabeth City NC	8.58
			N2871G	Ace Smelting Inc, Phoenix AZ	.59
	Super			Avery Aviation, Greybull WY	.59/69
	Privateer			(tanker #A20; #B21; #A23)	
				Hawkins & Powers Aviation, Greybull WY	7.69/96
				(tanker #121)	
- •	P4Y-2	**Bu66304**		(to US Coast Guard as 66304)	
	P4Y-2G			offered for disposal ex NAS Elizabeth City NC	8.58
			N2870G	Ace Smelting Inc, Phoenix AZ	.59
	Super			Avery Aviation, Greybull WY (tanker #B22)	.59/69
	Privateer			Hawkins & Powers Aviation, Greybull WY	.69/80
				(tanker #B22; #122)	
				crashed on take-off, Ramona CA	27.8.80
				(used to rebuild N7682C/66261 Greybull .81)	
				major sections on dump, Greybull WY	87/92

CONSOLIDATED/CONVAIR B-24 LIBERATOR

18 •	LB-30A	**AM927**		dam. in Canada: not del. to RAF	.41
	RLB-30			op: Consolidated Vultee Corp, San Diego CA	.41/47
			NL24927	Consolidated Vultee Corp, San Diego CA	1.4.47
			N1503	Continental Can Co, Morristown NJ	11.48/59
				Petroleos Mexicanos - PEMEX	11.4.59
			XC-CAY	Petroleos Mexicanos - PEMEX	11.59
			N12905	Confederate Air Force, Harlingen TX	.67/90
				(del. ex Mexico 5.68; flew as "*Diamond Lil*")	
			N24927	Confederate Air Force, Harlingen/Midland TX	10.90/96
				(flies as "402366/Diamond Lil",	
				visited UK for airshows, del. via Prestwick	
				10.6.92, ret. to USA via Prestwick 16.7.92)	
55 •	LB-30	**AL557**	G-AGZI	Scottish Aviation Ltd, Prestwick	21.9.46/48
			SX-DAA	Hellenic Airlines, Athens "Maid of Athens"	2.48/51
			N9981F	Morrison Knudson Construction Co	.51
			N68735	Morrison Knudson Construction Co	12.51/53
			N92MK	Morrison Knudson Construction Co	
				crashed landing, nr Anchorage AK: abandoned	.58
				Alaska Aviation Heritage Museum,	
				Anchorage AK (planned recov. for rest.)	10.86/96
25 •	B-24D	**40-2367**		forced landing, Bechevin Bay, Atka AK	9.12.42
			N58246	US Historical Aircraft Preservation Museum,	
				Anchorage AK	7.84/88
				American Vets Memorial Museum, Denver CO	6.88/95
				(awaiting recov., Atka AK)	

- •	B-24D	**41-24301**		(514th BS/376th BG "*Lady Be Good*")	
				forced landing, 700km south of Tobruk, Libya	5.4.43
				discov. nr intact, Ron MacLean & S. V. Sykes	9.11.58
				recov. dismantl., Dr Fadel Ali Mohamed,	
				Antiquities Department, Cyrene, Libya	10.8.94
				stored, Army Barracks, Tobruk	.94/96
				(for eventual displ., Military Museum, Tobruk)	
1538	B-24D	42-40461		(to RAF as BZ734)	
	B Mk. III			(to RCAF as 599): BOC 29.5.43: SOC	31.5.45
				David C. Tallichet/Yesterdays Air Force,	
				Chino CA: recov. ex farm ALTA Canada	.72
				(arr. dism. by train, badly dam. in transit 2.72)	
				broken-up, only nose retained Chino	76/92
				(nose "T1" displ. USAFM, March AFB CA 85)	
1634 •	B-24D	42-40557		(to RAF as BZ755)	
	B Mk. III			(to RCAF as 600): BOC 4.6.43: SOC	14.8.46
				David C. Tallichet/Yesterdays Air Force,	
				Chino CA: recov. ex farm ALTA Canada	.72
				arr. dism. by train, badly damaged in transit	2.72
				broken-up, only nose retained Chino	76/92
2413 •	B-24D	**42-72843**		(512nd BS/376th BG, "Strawberry Bitch")	
				USAFM: stored Davis-Monthan AFB AZ	46/59
				USAFM, Wright-Patterson AFB, OH: del.	18.5.59/92
				(displ. as "Strawberry Bitch")	
5852 •	B-24M	**44-41916**		(to USN as Bu90165)	
	PB4Y-1		N5141N		
			N4K	Salem Engineering Co, Salem NY	c50
			N4907L		
			CB-76	Compania Boliviana de Aviacion, La Paz	22.3.51
			CP-576	Bolivian Overseas Airways, La Paz, Bolivia	
				(wfu stripped for spares, La Paz, Bolivia 73/75)	
				Frigorifico Reyes, La Paz (stored u/s)	80
				La Mercantil de Seguros, La Paz, Bolivia	82
				USAFM, Castle AFB CA	5.82/93
				(arr. dism. 29.5.82, static rest. Castle 82/89;	
				displ. as 441916/RE-H/*Shady Lady*)	
				(note: id. also quoted as 44-41906/Bu90155)	
- •	B-24M	**44-41956**		(to RAAF as A72-176): BOC 7.1.45 SOC	3.48
				George Toye, Moe VIC : as scrap	.48/95
				(fuselage trucked ex RAAF East Sale VIC .48;	
				complete fuse. stored in yard, Moe VIC .48/95)	
				B-24 Memorial Fund, Melbourne VIC	7.6.95
				(planned static rest. using wings from B-24D	
				42-41091 hulk, Faita PNG: wings recov. .92)	
-	B-24M	44-42067		(to USN as Bu90232)	69
	PB4Y-1		PT-AZX	Frigopar, Rio de Janeiro	69
				noted abandoned, derelict Belem	75
1347 •	B-24J	**44-44052**		(to RAF as KH191: Indian AF 'T-18')	
	B. Mk. VII			Indian AF Technical College, Jalahalli, India	72
	GR. Mk. VI			Warbirds of GB Ltd, Blackbushe	82/86
				(airfreighted to Blackbushe by Belfast 6.5.82;	
				stored dism. Blackbushe, trucked to docks 10.9.85)	
				Collings Foundation, Stowe MA	.85/89
				(shipped USA .85; rebuild Kissimee FL: ff 8.8.89)	
			N224J	Collings Foundation, Stowe MA	31.5.89/96
				(flies as *All American*)	

1470 •	B-24J	**44-44175**		(to RAF as KH304: Indian AF as HE877)	
	B. Mk. VII			retired IAF, stored Poona AB	31.12.68
			N7866	Pima County Air Museum, Tucson AZ	.69/96
				(dep. Poona AB on del. to Tucson 28.3.69:	
				displ. as "444175/HE877/"Paisano" &	
				Shoot You're Covered")	
1508 •	B-24J	**44-44213**		(to RAF as KH...... : Indian AF as HE924/L)	
	B. Mk. VII			Indian AF Museum, Palam AB, New Delhi	68/91
1567 •	B-24J	**44-44272**		(to RAF as KH401: Indian AF as HE771)	
	B. Mk. VII			retired IAF, stored Poona AB	31.12.68
			N94459	David C. Tallichet/Yesterdays Air Force,	
				Chino CA : del. to Duxford UK ex Poona	28.10.73
				(del. ex Duxford to USA, via Prestwick 27.8.75,	
				(nosewheel collapse Prestwick, dep. 11.9.75)	
				David C. Tallichet/MARC, Chino CA	9.6.80/94
				USAFM, March AFB CA: loan	84/85
				Liberal Air Museum, Liberal KS: loan	.87/88
				Fantasy of Flight Museum,	
				Polk City FL	7.9.94/96
				(flies as 250551/RR/*Delectable Doris/Joe*)	
1603	B-24J	44-44308		(to RCAF as KK237): BOC 22.11.44: SOC	8.10.46
	B. Mk. VII			recov. from farm, adv. for sale, Chase BC	.71
3636 •	B-24J	**44-48781**		Spartan School of Aeronautics, Tulsa OK	.46/60
				(instr. airframe: later stripped and derelict)	
				open storage, derelict, Tulsa Airport OK	66/74
				USAFM, Barksdale AFB LA	12.78/94
				(airlifted by CH-54: rest. as "*Laden Maiden*")	
-	B-24J	**44-49001**		Ed Maloney/The Air Museum, Ontario CA	67/73
				(fuselage only)	
-	B-24L	44-49112		(to RCAF as 11120): BOC 26.3.45: SOC	7.10.46
	B. Mk. VII			recov. from farm, adv. for sale, Chase BC	.71
5009 •	B-24L	**44-50154**		(to RAF as KN820)	
	B. Mk. VII			(to Indian AF as HE773)	
				Canadian National Aeronautical Collection,	
				Rockcliffe AB ONT	.68/82
				(del. Poona AB, India to Rockcliffe 5-17.6.68)	
				National Aviation Museum, Rockcliffe ONT	9.82/92
				(displ. as "RCAF 11130")	
6707L •	B-24L	**44-50206**		(to RAF as KN751)	
	B Mk. VII			(to Indian AF as HE807)	
				wfu IAF, stored Poona AB	31.12.68
				(del. Poona to RAF Cosford: arr. 11.7.74)	
				RAF Museum, RAF Colerne	.74/76
				RAF Museum, RAF Cosford	1.76/95
-	B-24M	**44-50801**	N299A		
	C-87		CP-611	Boliviana de Aviacion, La Paz	4.56
				damaged, Trinidad, Bolivia	27.3.64
			CP-787	Compania Boliviana de Aviacion, La Paz	
				wfu and broken-up, La Paz, Bolivia	.75
6083 •	B-24M	**44-51228**		USAF Aero Icing Research Laboratory	
	EZB-24M			wfu, stored Lackland AFB TX	.53/56
				USAFM, Lackland AFB TX	.56/94
				(displ. as *The Blasted Event*/RE)	

- •	B-24D	-		Lee Shrum	94
			N8224P	A. J. Brinkerhoff, Granbury TX	2.2.94/96
				(id. quoted as "42-14835": not a B-24 serial)	
- •	B-24	-		(to Chinese AF as ......)	
				personal aircraft for Chinese Premier	
				rep. retired, Air Base, Northern China	88/90
				attempted purchase by Western collectors	.90
- •	B-24D	-		(to RCAF as ....)	
				recov. ex crash site Labrador	c90
				Tom Reilly Vintage Aircraft, Kissimmee FL	.90/94
				(planned use in rebuild of P4Y-2 to fly:	
				dispatch ex Canada foundered by 94)	

CULVER PQ-14

N-256 •	PQ-14A	-	**N4744N**	James E. Bass, College Park GA	63
				George R. McSween, Flanklin NC	.63/64
				Spencer B. Miller, Winnsboro TX	3.64/92
				sale rep., St Simons Island GA	96
N-427 •	PQ-14A	-	**N75380**	Ransom J. Heath, Deridder LA	63
				D. J. Wilkins, Gooding ID	.63/70
				sale rep.	84/92
				Harry E. Pick, Chenoa IL	12.92/96
N-763 •	PQ-14A	**44-21819**	**N1063M**	Michael Leach, Jessup PA	63/64
				Albert W. Mosley, Pennsauken NJ	66
				William Smela, Washington Crossing PA	69
				Robert B. Metcalfe, Mesa AZ	70
				Pima County Air Museum, Tucson AZ	72/96
				(displ. as "421819")	
N-839 •	PQ-14A			(to USN as Bu79573)	
	TD2C-1		N89573	Howard C. Martin, Hayward CA	69
				(noted Oakland CA, flying in USAAF sc. 75)	
			N15HM	The Air Museum, Chino CA	6.79/96
N-917 •	PQ-14B		N5526A	Dial Wilson, Sarasota FL	63
				Ronald A. Billib, Sarasota FL	.63/66
				Robert V. Campbell, Oskaloosa IA	69/72
				Airpower Museum, Blakesburg IA	12.74/96
- •	PQ-14A	**44-68334**	N10146	USAFM, Wright-Patterson AFB, Dayton OH	63/64
	PQ-14B			EAA Air Museum, Hales Corner WI	67/76
			N999ML	Morton W. Lester, Martinsville VA	12.86/88
				EAA Air Museum, Oshkosh WI	.88/96
N-1059 •	PQ-14B	**44-68462**	N5389N	Kenneth L. Farris, Bedias TX	63/70
				Robert E. Parcell, Fort Worth TX	76/84
				USAFM, Wright-Patterson AFB, Dayton OH	87/88
N-2402 •	PQ-14A	-	**N5092V**	D. C. Lawton, San Antonio TX	63/70
				sale rep., San Antonio TX	72/95
N-2432 •	PQ-14A	-	**N4648V**	Serge T. Winkler, Tucson AZ	63
				D. J. Wilkins, Gooding ID	.63/66
				George B. Harris, Hickory NC	1.68/94
N-2804 •	PQ-14A	-	N1676M	Glen D. Martin, Pacoima CA	63/84
- •	PQ-14A	**43-44439**	N5281N	Robert Hoskins, Oklahoma City OK	63/84
- •	PQ-14B	**45-58816**		(to USN as Bu120035)	

		TD2C-1			NASM, Silver Hill MD	65/88
]						
-	•	PQ-14B	**45-58863**		(to USN as Bu120082)	
		TD2C-1			NAS Norfolk VA (stored)	65
					USNAM, NAS Pensacola FL	65/96
-	•	PQ-14B	**45-59043**		(to USN as Bu120262)	
		TD2C-1		N2775	Ed Maloney/The Air Museum, Claremont CA	.58
					Leon Brodie, Los Angeles CA	63/66
					(noted airworthy at Torrance CA 68)	
					Mack S. Johnson, Kalispell MT	69/70
					David L. Cronk, Glendora CA	2.71/96

CURTISS SB2C HELLDIVER/A-25 SHRIKE

-	•	SB2C-3	**Bu19075**		Ed Maloney/The Air Museum, Ontario CA	67/78
					David C. Tallichet/Yesterdays Air Force, Chino CA	79/81
				N4250Y	David C. Tallichet/MARC, Chino CA	7.81/87
					Charles F Nichols/Yankee Air Corps, Chino CA	.87/95
					(stored unconv., Chino CA 95)	
-	•	SB2C-1	**Bu75552**		(A-25A diverted to USMC)	
					ditched, Lake Washington, Seattle WA	
					recov. by Mike Rawson, Minneapolis MN	90
-	•	SB2C-1	**Bu76805**		(A-25A 42-80449 ntu: diverted to USMC)	
					ditched, Lake Washington, Seattle WA	
					recov. by Mike Rawson, Minneapolis MN	90
-	•	SB2C-5	**Bu83321**		(to R Hellenic AF as 83321)	
					Helenic War Museum, Athens	67/96
					(displ. as "83321", to be moved to Tatoi .95)	
					Hellenic Air Force Museum, Tatoi AB	95
366	•	SB2C-5	**Bu83410**		(to R Thai AF as 3-4/97)	
					RTAF Museum, Don Muang AB, Bangkok	67/96
-	•	SB2C-5	**Bu83479**		NASM, stored Silver Hill MD	65/94
					USNAM, NAS Pensacola FL: loan	.76/96
					(displ. as "H-212")	
83725	•	SB2C-5	**Bu83589**		Trade School MT, ferried to Ontario CA	.62
					("NAS Glenview/VA-103")	
					Ed Maloney/The Air Museum, Ontario CA	c62/70
				N92879	Confederate Air Force, Harlingen/Midland TX	.70/96
					(rest. CA, del. Harlingen 11.71 as USN "5")	
					accident Harlingen TX	8.85
					(rebuilt Breckenridge TX: ff 27.9.88 "83589/32")	
-		SB2C-5	Bu89255		(to Aeronavale as 89255)	
					Lann-Bihone AB, Lorient, France: displ.	65/c70
-	•	SB2C-1	-		ditched, Lake Washington, Seattle WA	
					recov. by Mike Rawson, Minneapolis MN	90
-	•	SB2C-1	-		Ted Darcy, Kailua HI : recov. from dump	c87
-	•	SB2C-1	-		Ted Darcy, Kailua HI : recov. from dump	c87
-	•	SB2C-3	-		Sea-Air-Space Museum, New York NY	91
					(displ. as USN "44" on board *USS Intrepid*)	

Curtiss O-52 Owl

14279 •	0-52	**40-2746**		Confederate Air Force, Harlingen TX	74/84
				Charles F Nichols/Yankee Air Corps, Chino CA	.84/87
				(arr. unconv. from TX, Chino CA .86)	
				David C. Tallichet/ MARC, Chino CA	.87/93
				(awaiting rest. in Tallichet yard, Chino 88)	
14296 •	0-52	**40-2763**		USAFM, Wright-Patterson AFB, Dayton OH	65/89
				(displ. as "119")	
14302 •	0-52	**40-2769**	**N61241**	B & F Aircraft Inc, Oaklawn IL	64/70
				(last FAA annual inspection 10.54)	
				M. Foose & G. Courtwright, Oaklawn IL	
				EAA Air Museum, Hales Corners WI: displ.	67/76
				Charles F Nichols/Yankee Air Corps, Chino CA	81/96
				(rest., ff Chino CA 6.82: flies as "02769")	
14337 •	0-52	**40-2804**	**N50143**	Walter Soplata Collection, Newbury OH	76/85

Curtiss P-40 Warhawk/Kittyhawk

13162 •	P-40B	**39-285**		crashed Hawaii	.41
				Curtiss Wright Historical Association,	
				Torrance, CA: wreck recov. ex Hawaii	c89/96
				(stored pending planned rest. to fly:	
				parts used in rest. of 41-123297)	
13164 •	P-40B	**39-287**		crashed Hawaii	10.41
				Curtiss Wright Historical Association,	
				Torrance, CA: wreck recov. ex Hawaii	c89/96
				(stored pending planned rest. to fly:	
				parts used in rest. of 41-123297)	
- •	P-40B	-		(to RAF as ......, retained by USAAC)	
				(to Soviet AF as ...., Code "53")	.42
				recov. ex crash site Russia	c90
				The Fighter Collection, Duxford UK: arr.	.92/96
				(wings shipped to Chino CA: rest. to fly .93/96)	
				(id. quoted as "2380")	
16073 •	P-40B	**41-13297**		lost on patrol Hawaii	1.42
				Curtiss Wright Historical Association,	
				Torrance, CA: wreck recov. ex Hawaii	c89/96
				(rest. to fly Torrance CA, using parts ex	
				P-40Bs 39-285 & 287 recov. ex Hawaii)	
14737 •	P-40C Tomahawk Mk. IIb	**AK255**		(to Soviet AF as ....)	.42
				recov. ex crash site Russia	c90
				Tom Wilson/Brooks Aviation, Douglas GA	92/96
14777 •	P-40C Tomahawk Mk. IIb	**AK295**		(to Soviet AF as ....)	.42
				recov. ex crash site Russia	c90
				Tom Wilson/Brooks Aviation, Douglas GA	92/96
15452 •	P-40C Tomahawk Mk. IIb	**AK498**		USAAC Air Volunteer Group, Burma	.41
				wreck recov. from crash site, Thailand	.90
				Royal Thai Air Force Museum, Chiang Mai AB	.90/96
				(substantial remains, displ. as wreck)	
15133 •	P-40E Kittyhawk Mk. 1	**AK752**		(to RCAF as 1028): BOC 9.10.41: SOC	16.8.46
				surplus, Vulcan AB ALTA ; to local farm	.47
				stripped by farmer, later buried on farm	.53

Continued on page 92

This Wildcat is unique in being the only warbird recovered from underwater and flown. F4F-3 N12260 was fished from Lake Michigan and painstakingly restored. **Dick Phillips.**

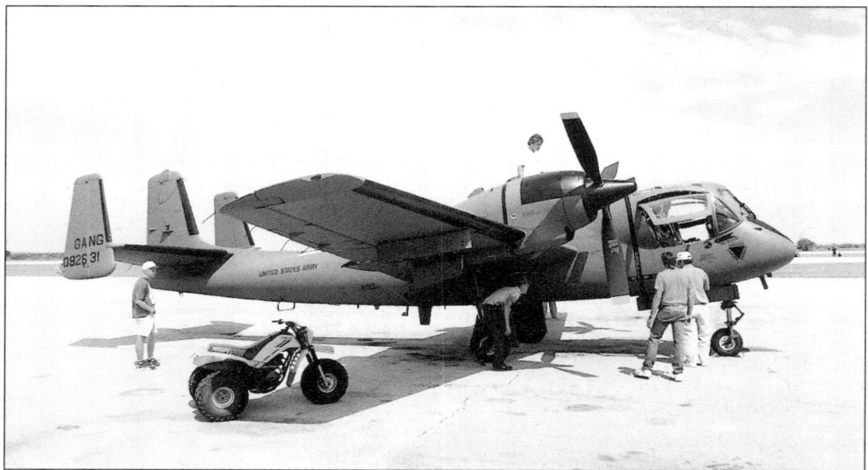

Recent addition to the warbird panthion is the Grumman OV-1 Mohawk. Sanders Lead Co.'s 59-2631 N4376U was present at Breckenridge in 1994. **Gary Robert Brown.**

One Halifax from a Norwegian lake bed was a rare find, but the recovery of this Halifax in 1995 confounded many expectations. It's encouraging to think that the Handley Page Halifax, although not likely to become an airworthy type is now safe from extinction with three groups working towards static display examples via Mark Shepperd.

Rare in that it is a single seater, Hawker Sea Fury target tug WG599/D-CACY at Uetersen being prepared for its airlift to the U.K. in 1995. This aircraft has Korean war history and is currently with the Old Flying Machine Company in the U.K. **Mike Kröger.**

We are still awaiting the first airworthy Hawker Tempest restoration. One contender is Tempest Mk.II MW376 photographed at Audley End after moving from Spanhoe, after its owner mysteriously disapeared, . **Paul Coggan.**

We make no appology for re-running this picture, of possibly the most impressive wind machine ever, first seen in W.W.5. Dept of Construction, N.S.W. **Via Peter Anderson.**

				excavated, recov. by John Paul	.75
			N96045	John R. Paul, Alamo CA	.75
				Steve Seghetti, Vacaville CA	76/85
				Col Pay, Scone NSW (rest. project)	.85
			VH-KTH	Col Pay, Scone NSW	12.89/94
				(rest. Scone, ff 15.12.89 as "AK752/ZR-J")	
				dam. landing Coolangatta QLD (repaired)	2.91
				crashed, forced landing, Wee Waa NSW	5.9.92
				(rebuilt Scone NSW, ff 10.6.94)	
			N440PE	James E. Smith, Fortine MT	8.94/96
15184 •	P-40E Mk. 1	**AK803**		(to RCAF as 1034): BOC 16.10.41: SOC	23.8.46
				George Maude, Fulford Harbour BC	8.46/74
				(disposal ex Patricia Bay AB, Vancouver Island, by barge to Maude's home Saltspring Island .46)	
				stored in open, Saltspring Island BC	46/74
			C-GHTM	George Maude, Victoria BC	.74/89
				(to Victoria BC for rest. to fly 8.74, fitted with new mainplane ex RCAF 1057)	
				Commonwealth Military Aviation Museum, Sidney BC	89/93
15208 •	P-40E Mk. 1	**AK827**		(to RCAF as 1038): BOC 22.10.41: SOC	23.8.46
			N1223N	Fred Dyson, Boeing Field, Seattle WA	13.9.47/49
				(disposal ex Patricia Bay AB, Vancouver Island, barged to Boeing Field, Seattle WA .47)	
				Bob Sturges, Troutdale OR	.49
				Leo J. Demers, Salem OR	
				Rogue River Water Association, Medford OR	54
				Weather Modification Co, Redlands CA	.54/57
				Bill Ruch, Pompano Beach FL	.59
				David B. Robinson, Miami Fl	.59/69
				(advertising display at drive-in theatre, then parked derelict Pompano Beach Airport 60/64)	
				William Ross, Chicago IL (dism.)	.69
				Robert L. Goodman, Litte Rock AR (dism.)	.70
				Charles F. Nichols, Covina CA (dism.)	76/86
			N40245	Yankee Air Corps Museum	
				Yanks Air Museum, Chino CA	4.83/96
				(rest. Chino CA, flies as "136483")	
15244 •	P-40E Mk. 1	**AK863**		(to RCAF as 1044): BOC 3.11.41: SOC	16.8.46
				John Stansall, Hartney MAN : on farm	.47
				John R. Paul, Alamo CA later Boise ID	.76/92
				(recov. ex farm near Tabor ALTA .76 by John Paul; rest. project, Caldwell ID)	
15346 •	P-40E Mk. 1	**AK875**		(to RCAF as 1047): BOC 3.11.41: SOC	23.8.46
			NX1048N	Fred Dyson, Boeing Field, Seattle WA	23.10.47
				(disposal ex Patricia Bay AB, Vancouver Island, barged to Boeing Field, Seattle WA .47)	
			N1048N	Ellis R. Meaker, Albany NY	2.4.48/49
				Ken Van Buren, Newfield NJ	8.2.49/51
				Munsey E. Crost, Ashbury Park NJ	6.3.51/52
				James W. Boy, West Durham NC	20.4.52
				Choctaw Area Boy Scouts, Meridian MS	6.8.52/64
				NASM, Silver Hill MD : del. dism. by C-119	.64/74
				(static rest. Andrews AFB .74/76)	
				NASM, Washington DC, displ. as "194"	2.76/96
15370 •	P-40E Mk. 1	**AK899**		(to RCAF as 1051): BOC 6.11.41: SOC	23.8.46
				Fred Dyson, Boeing Field, Seattle WA	23.10.47
				(disposal ex Patricia Bay AB, Vancouver Island, barged to Boeing Field, Seattle WA .47)	

				Tony Dire, Everett WA	48/68
				(displ. Dire's gas station roof, Everett 48/68	)
				Bruce Goessling/Unlimited Aircraft Inc,	
				Chino CA: removed from gas station	12.2.68/70
				M. E. Batchelor, Reseda CA	70
				David C. Tallichet/Yesterdays Air Force,	
				Chino CA: arr. dism. Chino	.73
			N9837A	David C. Tallichet/ MARG, Chino CA	79/85
				(rest. Chino CA, flew as two-seater)	
				John D. Pearl/Rudulphs Flying Circus,	
				Chino CA	15.1.85
				Brian O'Farrell/Johnson Aviation, Miami FL	.87
				Richard W. Hansen, Batavia IL	5.87/96
				(trucked to Janesville WI .87 ex storage dism. FL;	
				rest. Janesville & Rock County Airport IL,	
				ff 1.2.92 as USAAC 11456/*Old Exterminator*)	
				(USCR quotes id. 15280)	
15376 •	P-40E Mk. 1	**AK905**		(to RCAF as 1052): BOC 6.11.41: SOC	16.8.46
				Bob Warden, Vulcan ALTA: stored on his farm	
			CF-OGZ	Robert J. Warden, Edmonton ALTA	.63/68
			N11122	William D. Ross, Chicago IL	.68/72
				Don J. Plumb,Windsor ONT	.72/76
				(rest., flew as "474850/40")	
				Max R. Hoffman, Fort Collins CO	.76
			N40PE	Rudolf A. Frasca/Antiques & Classics Inc/	
				Frasca Air Museum, Champaign IL	12.76/96
				(USCR orig. quoted id. 15286, later AK905)	
15404 •	P-40E Mk. 1	**AK933**		(to RCAF as 1057): BOC 2.2.42: SOC	16.8.46
				disposal ex Vulcan ALTA to farm Champion ALTA	
				Bob Warden, Calgary ALTA: recov. ex farm	
				Neil Rose, Vancouver WA	
				(mainplane to George Maude, BC for RCAF 1034)	
				George Perez, Pacifica CA	
				(rest. project, using P-40F wings recov. by	
				George Maude ex Cutbank MT .59)	
				hulk stored, Half Moon Bay CA	66
			N94466	John R. Paul, Alamo CA	12.66/95
				(rest. Livermore CA, ff .69)	
				op. Ray Hanna/Old Flying Machine Co,	
				Duxford UK: arr. on del.	17.6.84/89
				John R. Paul/Warhawk Air Museum, Boise ID	4.89/96
				(dep. Duxford crated 28.4.89, shipped to US)	
				(USCR quotes id. AK899: see RCAF1051 above)	
15411 •	P-40E Mk. 1	**AK940**		(to RCAF as 1058): BOC 6.11.41: SOC	16.8.46
				"Vancouver VIII; Popeye X"	
				disposal RCAF Vulcan ALTA: to local farmer	.46
				displ. on roof, gas station, Red Deer ALTA	50/66
				Bob Warden Calgary ALTA	68
				David Harrington, Edmonton ALTA	
				Carman MAN	11.69/70
				William Anderson, Geneseo NY	.70
				(stored dism. unrest., by road Carman-NY .70)	
			N940AK	Stewart Schwartz & Bill Pryor, Pontiac MI	76/77
				(rest. to fly, Ft Collins CO 76)	
				Norton Aero Ltd, Athol ID	84
				William Anderson/Rangoon Airways Inc,	
				Las Vegas NV & Geneseo NY	9.84/96
				accident forced landing, Phelps NY	11.5.95
				(USCR quotes id. 15321; flew as "115321")	
18723 •	P-40E Mk. 1	**AK979**		(to RCAF as 1064): BOC 23.4.42: SOC	23.8.46
				Fred Dyson, Boeing Field, Seattle WA	13.9.47

c/n	Type	Serial	Reg	History	Date
				(disposal ex Patricia Bay AB, Vancouver Island, barged to Boeing Field, Seattle WA .47)	
				Duane W. Myler, Fostoria OH	.47
			N5672N	Joseph L. Ulman, Fostoria OH	2.48
				Van's Air Service, St Cloud MN	49/50
				B. H. Roberts/Continental Steel Buildings, Burbank CA	11.50/56
				(rebuilt as mod. cockpit 2 seater, ff. 7.51)	
				Shelby H. Curlee, St Louis MO	.56/63
				Bruce Goessling, Monterey CA	63
				forced landing, Hollister CA	.63
				Gilbert N. Macy, Monterey CA	.63/70
				(to Hawaii on carrier "Yorktown" for film "Tora Tora Tora", dam. during filming .69)	
				EAA Museum, Hales Corner WI: loan	69/73
			N151U	Gilbert N. Macy, Monterey CA	72
				Thomas L. Camp, Livermore CA	11.72/78
				(trucked Hales Corner to Livermore .73, rest., ff 13.12.73, flew as "USAAC 11496/7")	
			N9DA	rereg.	9.79
			N151U	ntu: Aircraft Sales Inc, Mooresville NC	4.80
			N41JR	Rourke Aircraft Sales, Bartlesville NC	5.80
				Tiger International Inc, Los Angeles CA	.80
			N41JA	Tiger International Inc, Los Angeles CA	9.80
			N40FT	Flying Tiger Line/Tiger International Inc, Los Angeles CA (flew in camouflage "67")	12.83/89
				loan: San Diego Aerospace Museum CA	87/93
				Federal Express Corp, Memphis TN	10.89/95
18731 •	P-40E Mk. 1	**AK987**		(to RCAF as 1068): BOC 28.1.42: SOC	23.8.46
			N1237N	Fred Dyson, Boeing Field, Seattle WA	13.9.47
				(disposal ex Patricia Bay AB, Vancouver Island, barged to Boeing Field, Seattle WA .47)	
			N5673N	Duane W. Myler, Fostoria OH	48
				Robert L. Holderman, Fostoria OH	8.6.48
				Harrison E. Rogers, Quincy MI	8.9.49
				Charles Finkenbine, Coldwater MI	11.52/57
				Frank G. Tallman, Glenview IL	9.9.57
				Walter H. Erikson Jr, Minneapolis MN	.58
				Charles P. Doyle, Rosemount MN	11.58/65
				crashed on del. flight, nr. Fostoria OH	1.12.58
				USAFM, Wright-Patterson AFB OH	c65/90
				(static rest., displ. as "104")	
18757	P-40E Mk. 1	AL113		(to RCAF as 1073): BOC 28.1.42: SOC	23.8.46
			N1251N (1	Fred Dyson, Boeing Field, Seattle WA	13.9.47/48
				(disposal ex Patricia Bay AB, Vancouver Island, barged to Boeing Field, Seattle WA .47)	
				Edwin F. Hill, Portland OR	29.7.48
				Eugene H. Akers, Oxnard CA	2.8.48/51
				Bob Downey, Whittier CA	3.3.51
				George E. Mokski, Montebello CA	24.4.52
				Howard Gidovlenko/Avia Union,Montebello CA	28.7.52
				crashed Montebello and later scrapped	c53
				(id. tfd. to 44-7619: que se)	
18779 •	P-40E Mk. 1	**AL135**		(to RCAF as 1076): BOC	23.3.42
				(stored Vulcan, Chater, MacDonald ABs 47/60)	
				Canadian National Aeronautical Collection, Rockcliffe AB ONT	.64/82
				National Aviation Museum, Rockcliffe ONT	9.82/95
18781	P-40E Mk. 1	AL137		(to RCAF as 1078): BOC 2.2.42: SOC	23.8.46
				Fred Dyson, Boeing Field, Seattle WA	23.10.47

c/n	Type	Mil. ser.	Registration	History	Date
				(disposal ex Patricia Bay AB, Vancouver Island, barged to Boeing Field, Seattle WA .47)	
				H. William Porter, Herscher IL	10.1.48
				Jimmie Fulcher, Las Vegas NV: not del.	.48
				aircraft stolen from Seattle-Boeing Field WA	c49
			N88917	H. William Porter, Kilgore TX/Herscher IL	.73/96
18796 •	P-40E Mk. 1	**AL152**		(to RCAF as 1082): BOC 3.12.41: SOC	23.8.46
			N1207V	Fred Dyson, Boeing Field, Seattle WA	13.9.47/48
				(disposal ex Patricia Bay AB, Vancouver Island, barged to Boeing Field, Seattle WA .47)	
				Charles Wenzel, Flushing NY	6.2.48/50
				Bradley J. Hurd/ Washington County Crop Protective Association, Akron CO	14.6.50
				Burt Mushkin, Moosic CT	
				Gordon C. Clouser, Norman OK	53
				K. C. Benbow/American Aviation Service, Greenville NC	25.3.53
				(stored Wilkes-Barre PA c50/54)	
				Walter H. Erickson, Minneapolis MN	13.9.54/58
				(trucked to Minneapolis, rebuilt, ff .57)	
				Frank G. Tallman, Glenview IL	31.1.58
				Tallmantz Aviation/Movieland of the Air Riverside CA, then Orange County CA	.59/66
				Rosen-Novak Auto Co, Omaha NE	18.2.66
				(displ. Tallmantz, until auctioned 29.5.68)	
				A. Richard Woodson, San Mateo CA	29.5.68/78
				(used in filming "Tora Tora Tora" Hawaii .68)	
				(rest. Livermore CA, ff 15.12.73)	
				Eric Mingledorff, Monroe LA	12.77/85
				(trucked CA to LA 2.78, rest. to fly)	
			N95JB	John MacGuire, El Paso TX	6.86/90
				John MacGuire/War Eagles Air Museum, Santa Teresa NM	90/96
				(flies as "41-36402/38")	
18815 •	P-40E Mk. 1	**AL171**		(to RCAF1084): BOC 2.2.42: SOC	16.8.46
				disposal at Vulcan AB ALTA: "Vancouver IV"	.46
				Walter Harris Motors, Champion ALTA	
				fuselage hulk recov. by Bob Warden, Calgary	
				Neil M. Rose, Vancouver WA: fuselage only	
				Ed Maloney/The Air Museum, Ontario CA	65/73
				John R. Paul, Alamo CA : rest. project	.73
			N62435	John R. Paul, Livermore CA	76/79
				(rest. to fly, Livermore CA)	
				Kermit A. Weeks/Weeks Air Museum, Tamiami FL (flew as "428370/42")	2.82/96
				dam. landing Tamiami FL (repaired)	3.90
				dam. Tamiami FL, Hurricane Andrew	24.8.92
				(rebuild Salinas CA 94)	
				(USCR quotes c/n 28370: ie. 42-104608)	
- •	P-40E Mk. 1a	**41-5336**		(to RAAF as A29-28): BOC 3.42: SOC	9.47
				Pearce Dunn/Warbirds Aviation Museum, Mildura VIC	68/85
				(forward fuse. only: recov. ex farm Mildura)	
				Jack McDonald, Essendon VIC/Caboolture QLD	.85/96
				(rest. to fly, Melbourne-Essendon later Oakey AB QLD & Caboolture QLD 87/95)	
- •	P-40E Mk. 1a	**41-5709**		(to Soviet AF as .....)	
				(recov. ex crash site Russia)	
				Tom Wilson/Brooks Aviation, Douglas GA	92/96
6738 •	P-40E	**41-13522**		(to RAAF as A29-53): BOC 3.42: SOC	2.49

	Mk. 1a			disposal ex storage RAAF Werribee VIC	2.49
				B. Lang, Beeac via Colac VIC	.49/66
				Moorabbin Air Museum, Melbourne VIC	12.66/95
				(fus. recov. ex farm, Colac VIC 10.12.66:	
				rest., displ. as "A29-53" using Mustang mainplane)	
19128 •	P-40E	**41-25109**		(to RAF as ET433)	
	Mk. 1a			retained by USAAC: 68th Pursuit Sqn, Tonga	42
				(to RNZAF as NZ3094)	10.42
				Asplin's Supplies, Rukahia NZ: scrapyard	59/71
				John Chambers, Auckland NZ	.71/90
				("FE-L1": recov. from scrapyard .71, stored	
				dism. owner's house Howick, Auckland .71/87)	
				Mike Subritzky, Auckland-Dairy Flat	91/94
				(stored, rest. project, Dairy Flat 88/94)	
				Col Pay, Scone NSW: shipped ex NZ	6.94/96
				(rest. to fly)	
19177 •	P-40E	**41-25158**		(to RAF as ET482)	
	Mk. 1a			(to RNZAF as NZ3009)	4.42
				Asplin's Supplies, Rukahia NZ: scrapyard	59
				d'E. C. Darby & R. H. McGarry, Auckland NZ	.59/94
				("FE-F": recov. ex scrapyard Rukahia)	
				Museum of Transport & Technology,	
				Auckland NZ: loan, displ. as "NZ3009"	64/94
				(rest. using wings of NZ3202)	
				Old Flying Machine Co, Duxford UK	.94/96
				(rest. to fly Auckland-East Tamaki NZ .94/95)	
18448 •	P-40E	**41-35927**		(to RAF as ET573)	
	Mk. 1a			(to Soviet AF as .....)	
				(recov. ex crash site Russia)	
				Tom Wilson/Brooks Aviation, Douglas GA	92/96
18539 •	P-40E	**41-36018**		(to RAF as ET664)	
	Mk. 1a			(to Soviet AF as 25)	
				(recov. ex crash site Murmansk, Russia)	
				Pacific Aircraft Ltd, Auckland NZ	.94/96
				(stored Auckland pending rest. to fly)	
18605 •	P-40E	**41-36084**		(to RAF as ET730)	
	Mk. 1a			(to RAAF as A29-133): BOC 6.42 SOC	8.2.49
				Nelson R. Wilson, Wandin VIC	.60/92
				(recov. derelict ex orchard, Melbourne VIC)	
			VH-NRW	Nelson R. Wilson, Wandin VIC: reg. res.	87/92
				(long-term rest. to fly, almost complete)	
				Australian War Memorial, Canberra ACT	.92/96
				(displ. as "A29-133/S/Polly")	
18931 •	P-40E	**41-36410**		(to RAF as EV156)	
	Mk. 1a			(to RNZAF as NZ3043)	4.42
				Asplin's Supplies, Rukahia NZ: scrapyard	55/65
				John R. Smith, Mapua, Nelson NZ: stored	67/96
				("FE-B": recov. ex scrapyard Rukahia)	
19364 •	P-40E	**41-36843**		(to RAF as EV589)	
	Mk. 1a			(to Soviet AF as .....)	
				(recov. ex crash site Russia)	
				Tom Wilson/Brooks Aviation, Douglas GA	92/96
- •	P-40F	**41-14112**		fcd. ldg. Errumango Island, Vanuatu	20.12.42
				(hulk recov. by Robert Grienert & Martin Mednis,	
				Sydney NSW 11.89 : shipped to Australia)	
				Judy E. Pay, Tyabb VIC	.90/96

c/n	Type	Serial	Reg.	History	Date
				(rest. to fly, Tyabb VIC)	
- •	P-40F	**41-14205**		fcd. ldg. Errumango Island, Vanuatu	20.12.42
				(hulk recov. by Robert Grienert & Martin Mednis, Sydney NSW 11.89 : shipped to Australia)	
				Ian A. Whitney, Romsey VIC	.89/91
				Graham Hosking, Tyabb VIC	.91/96
				(rest. to fly, Tyabb VIC)	
21117 •	P-40K	**42-9733**		abandoned Amchitka Island, Aleutians	
				Bob Sturges, Troutdale OR: recov.	.69
			N4363	Joseph A. Morasky, Guildford CT	72/74
				George Enhorning/ Wolcott Air Services, Wolcott CT	78/84
				Bob Byrne, Bloomfield Hills MI: stored	86/88
			ZK-FRE	ntu: Alpine Fighter Collection, Wanaka	.88/92
				(rest. Wanaka NZ 88/92, ff 18.4.92)	
			ZK-PXL	Tim Wallis/Alpine Fighter Collection, Wanaka	3.4.92/96
				(flies as "RNZAF NZ3108/18")	
21133 •	P-40K	**42-9749**		forced landing nr. Port Hyden, Aleutians AK	.44
				Al Reddick & Steve Myers, Reno NV	.75
				(recov. ex fresh water swamp Pt. Hyden .75)	
				David M. Boyd, Tulsa OK: stored	
			N67253	Airpower Inc, Chelan WA	76/84
			N293FR	Bob Byrne, Bloomfield Hills MI	5.86/87
				(rest., ff. Ft Lauderdale FL 5.86 "USAAC 47071")	
				Bob Byrne & Roy Stafford, Jacksonville FL/ Repatria Inc: flew as "FR293"	88/90
				William Clark, State College PA	.87
				Evergreen Heritage Collection, Marana AZ	5.90/96
				(flies as 21-05006/53/*Burma Rascal*)	
				(USCR quotes id. "FR293" for N293FR; 23-4275" for N67253)	
21650 •	P-40K	**42-10266**		recov. ex Fairbanks crash site by Red Berry	
			N40K	Bill Stebbins, Louisville KY (rest. project)	76/89
15921 •	P-40K Mk. III	**42-46111**		(to Soviet AF as .....)	
				(recov. ex crash site Russia)	
				Tom Wilson/Brooks Avation, Douglas GA	92/96
27466 •	P-40M Mk.III	**43-5778**		(to RCAF as 832): BOC 26.1.43: SOC	23.8.46
			N1228N	Fred Dyson, Boeing Field, Seattle WA	13.9.47
				(disposal ex Patricia Bay AB, Vancouver Island, barged to Boeing Field, Seattle WA .47)	
				Bill March, Phoenix AZ	51
				Lloyd P. Nolen, Mercedes TX	.51
				James M. Cook, Jacksboro TX: weather ops.	.53
				Leo J. Demers, Salem OR	55
				W. Keith Larkin/Weather Modification Company, Redlands CA	.55/60
				(del. by Larkin to museum, Ocala FL .60/61)	
				Joe E. Jones/Confederate AF, Rio Hondo TX	10.6.61
				(del. Ocala FL to TX, by Lefty Gardner 10.6.61)	
				Lloyd P. Nolen/Confederate AF, Mercedes TX	63/65
				crashed. Rebel Field, Mercedes TX	13.3.65
				Texas Air Museum, Rio Hondo TX	92/96
				(under rest. to fly, Rio Hondo 94)	
27483 •	P-40M Mk. III	**43-5795**		(to RCAF as 845): BOC 5.2.43: SOC	23.8.46
			N1232N	Vance B. Roberts, Seattle WA	27.9.47/50
				(disposal ex Patricia Bay AB, Vancouver Island, barged to Boeing Field, Seattle WA .47)	
				Art J. Bell/Bell Air Services,Boeing Field WA	21.7.50/51

				Jerry L. McMullin, Marysville CA	13.1.51
				John W. Davis/Davis Dusters, Colusa CA	18.9.51/56
				Clyde R. Mallory, Clatskanie OR	9.3.56/57
				W. Keith Larkin/Weather Modification Company, San Jose CA	12.6.57/61
				M. N. Farr & Larry.W. Hamilton, Sonoma CA	10.6.61/64
				Morrill Farr, Sonoma CA	27.3.64
				Harrah's Club Automobile & Aircraft Collection, Reno NV: static displ. as "AK845"	8.12.64/82
				Bill Destefani, Bakersfield CA	6.82/91
				(rest. Shafter CA, ff .83 as "AK845/GM-D")	
				Lone Star Flight Museum, Galveston TX	.91/96
27490 •	P-40M Mk. III	**43-5802**		(to RCAF as 840): BOC 29.1.43: SOC	20.11.44
			N1233N	Vance B. Roberts, Seattle WA	27.9.47/50
				(disposal ex Patricia Bay AB, Vancouver Island, barged to Boeing Field, Seattle WA .47)	
				Art J. Bell/Bell Air Services,Boeing Field WA	21.7.50
				Oregon State University : inst. airframe	.51/54
				Bob Sturges/Columbia Airmotive, Troutdale OR	.54/66
				(advertising displ., Troutdale Airport 54/61)	
			N1009N (2	Columbia Airmotive, Troutdale OR	2.67/79
				(stored dism. Troutdale, adopted id. of scrapped P-40N N1009N (1 (43-23494/RCAF 877)	
				Thomas L. Camp, Livermore CA/Las Vegas NV	.79/92
				(ex stock military: rest. Livermore CA, ff .82)	
				The Fighter Collection, Duxford	2.85/94
				arr. dism. Duxford 14.2.85, ff 27.2.85; flew as "FR870/GA-S")	
			F-AZPJ	Yak Warbird Ltd, Dijon	11.7.94/96
				(flies as "P-8196/34")	
27501 •	P-40M Mk. III	**43-5813**		(to RNZAF as NZ3119)	5.43
				Asplin's Supplies, Rukahia NZ: scrapyard	55/69
				John Chambers, Auckland NZ	.69/94
				("FE-C1": recov. ex scrapyard .69, stored dism. at owner's house Howick, Auckland .69/87)	
				John Chambers & Mike Subritzky, Auckland	90/96
				(rest. to fly, Auckland-Dairy Flat 89/95)	
28492 •	P-40N Mk. IV	**42-104730**		(to RAAF as A29-448): BOC	8.43/46
				crashed landing, Tadji Strip PNG	5.44
				(fuse. used in field rebuild of P-40N A29-1050)	
				dam. abandoned Tadji PNG "GA-C": SOC	11.46
				d'E. C. Darby & N. M. Armstrong, Auckland	.74
				(hulk recov. from Tadji, West Sepik PNG .74)	
				d'E. Charles Darby, Auckland NZ: stored	.74/96
28580 •	P-40N Mk. IV	**42-104818**		(to RAAF as A29-405): BOC	7.43/46
				dam. in collision at Tadji Strip PNG: "HU-S"	4.44
				(fuse. used in field rebuild of P-40N A29-1068)	
				dam., abandoned Tadji PNG "HU-S: SOC	11.46
				David C. Tallichet/Yesterdays Air Force, Chino CA	.74/93
				(hulk recov. ex Tadji PNG .74 for YAF by Charles Darby & Monty Armstrong NZ)	
28721 •	P-40N	**42-104959**		David C. Tallichet/Yesterdays Air Force, Chino CA	.74/93
				(hulk recov. ex Finschaffen PNG .74 for YAF by Charles Darby & Monty Armstrong NZ) wing/cockpit section: shipped to YAF with fuselage of 42-105861 from Dumpu & tail	

				surfaces of 42-105526 from Finschhafen)	
28723 •	P-40N	**42-104961**		David C. Tallichet/Yesterdays Air Force,	
				Chino CA	.74/93
				(hulk recov. ex Tsili Tsili PNG 9.73 for YAF	
				by Charles Darby & Monty Armstrong NZ)	
28813 •	P-40N	**42-105051**		(to RAAF as A29-462): BOC	8.43
	Mk.IV			forced landed, Rattlesnake Island QLD	7.45
				Keith W. Hopper, Townsville QLD	86/96
				(recov. from Rattlesnake Island, rest. to fly)	
28954 •	P-40N	**42-105192**		(to RCAF as 858): BOC 22.6.43: SOC	23.8.46
	Mk.IV		N1197N	Fred Dyson, Boeing Field, Seattle WA	23.10.47
				(disposal ex Patricia Bay AB, Vancouver Island,	
				barged to Boeing Field, Seattle WA .47)	
				Royale Silver Co, Los Angeles CA	
				Bajorling Aircraft Co, Detroit MI	
				W. P. Bridges Real Estate, Jackson MS	.52/54
				Louis Rice, Marysville CA	.54
				Richard B. Rowlette, Riverside CA	.54
				Walter Brockin, Riverside-Flabob CA	55
				W. Keith Larkin/Weather Modification Co,	
				San Jose CA	.55/59
				dam., wheels-up landing near Denver CO	.58
				Ed Maloney/The Air Museum, Ontario CA	.60/70
				(wreck trucked ex Denver, rest. for static displ.)	
			N85104	Planes of Fame Museum, Chino CA	10.80/96
				(rest. Chino 77/80, ff 10.80: flies as "USAAC 47")	
- •	P-40N	**42-105306**		Pacific Aircraft Ltd, Auckland NZ	94/96
				(stored dism. awaiting rest. to fly)	
29269 •	P-40N	**42-105513**		Ian A. Whitney/Australian Aerospace Museum,	
				Melbourne VIC	87/95
				(recov. from Finschhafen PNG by Whitney)	
				(rest. project, Essendon & Romsey VIC)	
29282 •	P-40N	**42-105526**		Ian A. Whitney, Romsey VIC	.74/89
				(fuselage recov. from Finschhafen PNG .74	
				by Charles Darby & Monty Armstrong NZ:	
				fuse. used in 42-105513 rest. project)	
				Mike Nicholls, Blenheim NZ	94/96
				(major components: planned rest. to fly)	
29464 •	P-40N	**42-105702**		USAFM, England AFB LA: displ.	80/90
				USAFM, Pope AFB NC: displ.	93/94
				(prev. rep. as fibreglass replica)	
29472 •	P-40N	**42-105710**		(to RAAF as A29-528): BOC	9.43
	Mk. IV			ditched Bergen Bay PNG	3.44
				(fuse. used in field rebuild of P-40N A29-1134)	
				crashed Keningau Strip PNG: "HU-V"	6.45
				David C. Tallichet/Yesterdays Air Force,	
				Chino CA	.74/93
				(hulk recov. ex Tadji PNG .74 for YAF	
				by Charles Darby & Monty Armstrong NZ)	
29606 •	P-40N	**42-105844**		(to RCAF as 864): BOC 17.9.43: SOC	23.8.46
	Mk. IV			Canadian Museum of Flight & Transportation,	
				Vancouver BC	88/95
				(wing & parts: recov. ex farm, Courtenay BC)	
				Charles Darby/Pacific Aircraft, Auckland NZ	.96
				(incomplete hulk: planned rest. to fly)	

29629 •	P-40N	**42-105867**		(to RCAF as 867): BOC 17.9.43: SOC	23.8.46
	Mk. IV			Robert H. Farrington, Seattle WA	12.8.47
				(disposal ex Patricia Bay AB, Vancouver Island,	
				barged to Boeing Field, Seattle WA .47)	
			N1226N	Jim P. Swann/Universal Aircraft, Seattle WA	29.9.47/51
				Robert B. Harmon, Nabnasset MA	24.2.51
				Gordon Clouser, Norman OK: weather mods	1.6.51/57
				Isaac Newton Burchinall Jnr, Paris TX	27.7.57/58
				dam. landing, Paris TX	.58
				Glen Parker, Nederland TX: dism.	11.11.58
				Michael J. Dillon, Mesa AZ	63/65
				Confederate Air Force, Mercedes TX later	
				Harlingen, Midland TX	5.65/96
				(flies as "29629/48")	
29675 •	P-40N	**42-105913**		N. Monty Armstrong, Melbourne VIC	90/96
				(stored QLD: composite rest. project)	
29677 •	P-40N	**42-105915**		(to Chinese AF: not del., retained by USAAF)	
				d'E. Charles Darby, Auckland NZ	.74
				(recov. by d'E. C. Darby & N. M. Armstrong	
				from Tadji, West Sepik PNG .74)	
				Malcolm J. Long, Melbourne VIC	.74/91
				RAAF Museum, RAAF Point Cook VIC: loan	77
				Chewing Gum Field Museum,	
				Tallebudgera QLD: loan	
				(displ. visible faded Chinese/USAAC marks)	
				Drage Air World, Wangaratta VIC: loan	
				Jack McDonald & John Rayner, Melbourne VIC	
				(rest. to fly, Caboolture QLD 92/95)	
29689 •	P-40N	**42-105927**		NAS Willow Grove PA	
	TP-40N			NASM, Silver Hill MD	
				USAFM, Gunter AFB GA	
				USAFM, Peterson AFB CO	
				(displ. on pedestal as "25927")	
				USAFM, Robins AFB GA: stored	
29713 •	P-40N	**42-105951**		David C. Tallichet/Yesterdays Air Force,	
				Chino CA	
				(hulk recov. ex Tadji PNG .74 for YAF	
				by Charles Darby & Monty Armstrong NZ)	
				(wings held by d' E.C. Darby, Auckland NZ:	
				fuselage rep. stored, Barstow CA)	
29858 •	P-40N	**42-106096**		rep. recov. from PNG (id. poss. 42-106196)	
				Dan Chvatal, Spring Valley MN: project	81
				rep. sold in Miami FL	c83
29863 •	P-40N	**42-106101**		(to RAAF as A29-556/A29-1134): BOC	10.43
	Mk. IV			(fuse. used in field rebuild of P-40N A29-1134)	
				hit by landing aircraft, Tadji Strip	5.44
				David C. Tallichet/Yesterdays Air Force,	
				Chino CA (rep. stored, Barstow CA)	.74/93
				(hulk recov. ex Tadji PNG .74 for YAF	
				by Charles Darby & Monty Armstrong NZ)	
30158 •	P-40N	**42-106396**		(to RCAF as 880): BOC 11.9.44: SOC	23.8.46
	Mk. IV		NL1195N	Fred Dyson, Boeing Field, Seattle WA	23.10.47
				(disposal ex Patricia Bay AB, Vancouver Island,	
				barged to Boeing Field, Seattle WA .47)	
			N1195N	Jack B. Hardwick/Hardwick Aircraft,	
				Rosemead CA	53/54
				dam. wheels-up landing	

				(stored Hardwick's yard, El Monte CA 55/76)	
				John R. Paul, Alamo CA (stored dism.)	.76/78
				John R. Paul, Hamilton MT later Boise ID	84/93
				Warhawk Air Museum, Boise-Caldwell ID	90/96
				(rest., flew as"130158", later "2106396";	
				race #77, #17 *Spud Lag*)	
30901 •	P-40N Mk. IV	**43-22962**		(to RNZAF as NZ3220)	.43
				Asplin's Supplies, Rukahia NZ: scrapyard	59/65
				John R. Smith, Mapua, Nelson NZ: stored	67/96
				("FE-T/*Gloria Lyons* recov. ex scrapyard)	
31423	P-40N Mk. IV	43-23484		(to RCAF as 877): BOC 27.1.44: SOC	23.8.46
			NL1009N	Jim P. Swann/Universal Aircraft, Seattle WA	12.8.47/51
				(disposal ex Patricia Bay AB, Vancouver Island,	
				barged to Boeing Field, Seattle WA .47)	
			N1009N (1	Edward L. Gerry, Dracut MA	24.2.51
				Gordon Clouser, Norman OK : weather mods	1.6.51/53
				dam., forced landing, Effingham IL	c53
				Earl & Ray Reinert, Arlington Heights IL	8.4.53/58
				(purchased dam., further damaged by fire while	
				stored Wheeling IL, for Victory Air Museum c57)	
				USAFM, Wright Patterson AFB OH : dam.	.58
				used for spares, scrapped by USAFM	c65
				(rep. id. /paperwork to RCAF 840)	
32824 •	TP-40N	**44-7084**		NASM, Washington DC	
				USAFM, Wright-Patterson AFB, Dayton OH	61/65
				Charles P. Doyle, Rosemount MN	.65/78
			N999CD	Charles P. Doyle, Rosemount MN	.78
				Robert J. Pond/Planes of Fame East,	
				Minneapolis-Flying Cloud MN	80/96
				(flies as "Miss Josephine")	
32932 •	P-40N	**44-7192**		Paul Mantz, Glendale CA	19.2.46/60
				(USAAF disposal ex Stillwater AFB OK 19.2.46)	
				displ. Griffith Park, Los Angeles CA	
				Tallmantz Collection, Orange County CA	60/67
			N4161K	San Diego Aerospace Museum, San Diego CA	67/72
				(displ. as "14192")	
			N10626	Doug Champlin/Windward Aviation, Enid OK	.72/81
				Champlin Fighter Museum, Mesa AZ	.81/96
				(USCR quotes id. "4192"; also quoted as	
				33097/44-7357)	
32943	P-40N	44-7203		Paul Mantz, Glendale CA	19.2.46/60
				(USAAF disposal ex Stillwater AFB OK 19.2.46)	
				rep. displ. Chino CA	c72
33032 •	P-40N Mk. IV	**44-7292**		(to RAAF as A29-915): BOC	7.44
				crashed on flight ex Rockhampton QLD	9.45
				Bill Martin, Toowoomba QLD	88/96
				(hulk recov. ex crash site Charters Towers QLD,	
				long-term rest. project)	
33109 •	P-40N	**44-7369**		Cal Aero Technical Institute, Glendale CA	
				Ed Maloney/The Air Museum, Claremont CA	
				later Ontario CA: static displ.	c57/70
			N94500	Lou Kauffman (rest. Van Nuys CA .71)	.71/72
			C-GTGR	Don Plumb/Spitfire Ltd,Windsor ONT	1.74/76
				Max R. Hoffman, Fort Collins CO	.76
			N40PN	John Williams, Tampa FL	76/77
				Joseph G. Mabee, Midland TX	12.77/95
				(flies as "USAAC 447369/40")	

c/n		Type	Mil. ID	Reg.	Owner / History	Date
33359	•	P-40N	**44-7619**	N5038V	Chowchilla Union High School, Chowchilla CA	.46/50
					Carroll Collier, Chowchilla CA: caryard displ.	.50/52
					George Mokski/Avia-Union, Montebello CA	.52
				N1251N (2	Avia-Union, Montebello CA	.54
					(adopted id. crashed Avia-Union P-40E N1251N: c/n 18757, AL113/RCAF 1073)	
					(wfu, open storage Fullerton CA 54/59: mod. racer with F-80 canopy, not flown)	
					Ed Maloney/The Air Museum, Ontario CA	11.59/69
					(stored dism. Addison TX 71)	
					Frank Sanders, Long Beach CA	.72
					(rest. Long Beach CA 73/76 using parts of 44-6519: ff .76 as "USAAC 47619")	
				N222SU	Suzanne Parish/Kalamazoo Aviation History Museum, Kalamazoo MI	.73/96
32440	•	P-40N	**44-7700**		(to FA Brasileira as 4064)	
					Museu Aeroespacial, Campo dos Afoncos, Rio	79/96
33723	•	P-40N	**44-7983**		Paul Mantz, Glendale CA	19.2.46/60
					(USAAF disposal ex Stillwater AFB OK 19.2.46)	
					Frank G. Tallman/Movieland of the Air, Orange County CA	60/70
					(stored Tallmantz Collection, USAAF sc. 60/70)	
				N9950	David C. Tallichet/Yesterdays Air Force, Chino CA : arr. dism.	7.70/89
					(derelict hulk, rest. Chino, ff .75)	
					Warbirds of Great Britain Ltd, Biggin Hill/ Bournemouth UK	.89/92
					(rest. Chino CA 89/91, shipped to UK 7.91)	
					Ice Strike Corp, Dover DE	8.6.94/96
33915	•	TP-40N	44-47923	**N923**	H. L. Pemberton, Niles MI	
					Paul Mantz, Los Angeles CA	.59
					Frank G. Tallman/Tallamantz Aviation/ Movieland of the Air, Orange County CA	63/84
					Kermit A. Weeks/Weeks Air Museum, Tamiami FL	3.85/96
					(stored 85/93, under rest. to fly Tamiami FL 94)	
-	•	P-40K	-	N67254	Airpower Inc, Chelan WA	76/84
					rep. awaiting recov. from Aleutians	
					(USCR quoted id. "23-4279")	
-	•	P-40	-	**N6969**	USNAM, NAS Pensacola FL: USCR	5.93/96
					(USCR quotes id. "60")	
-	•	P-40N Mk. IV	-		(to SAAF as 5067)	
					crashed in swamp near Umkomaas, Natal	30.3.44
					recov. planned	89
-	•	P-40C	-		(to Soviet AF as .....)	
					Armed Forces Central Museum, Moscow	50s
					Zhukovsky Institute, Moscow	85
-	•	P-40E Mk. 1a	-		(to RCAF as ....)	
					Granger Taylor, Duncan BC	77
					(rep. static rest. of several scrapyard hulks)	
					Owner in Carman MAN	82/87
-	•	P-40E	-		(to RNZAF as .....)	
					Pacific Aircraft, Auckland-East Tamaki NZ	94
					(composite static rest. as "NZ3039")	
					Museum of Transport & Technology, Auckland	.94/96

- •	P-40E	-	(to Soviet AF as .....)	
			(recov. ex crash site Russia)	
			The Fighter Collection, Duxford UK	92/95
			(rep. rest. to fly, Russia)	
- •	P-40E	-	(to Soviet AF as .....)	
			(recov. ex crash site Russia)	
			owner, Australia	.95/96
- •	P-40K	-	Roy M. Stafford, Jacksonville FL	c88
			rep. recov. ex Aleutians, stored unrestored at Aero Trader, Chino CA	88/91
- •	P-40	-	David C. Tallichet/Yesterdays Air Force, Chino CA: one of the PNG aircraft above	.74/89
			RAF Museum: composite static rebuild	.90
			RAF Museum, Hendon	.92/96
			(displ. as RAF Kittyhawk IV "FX760/GA-?")	
- •	P-40N	-	Ian A. Whitney, Romsey VIC	76
			(hulk recov. ex Iron Range QLD .76)	
			Ron Lee, Melbourne VIC	90/91
			Graham Hosking, Tyabb VIC	.91/92
			(stored Tyabb, pending rest.)	
- •	P-40N	-	forced landing in swamp, Everglades FL	.43
			Hal Thompson, Arcadia FL	.86/92
			(recov. ex swamp .86: static rest. project)	
- •	P-40	-	Tom Reilly/Warbirds Museum, Kissimmee FL	90/94
			(recov. from burial site)	

DE HAVILLAND MOSQUITO

98001 •	Mk. I	**W4050**	(prototype E-0234): first flight	25.11.40
			De Havilland Technical School, Salisbury Hall	.46
			W. J. S. Baird, Hatfield	.46/59
			(stored Hatfield, Panshanger, Hatfield, Chester, Hatfield: moved to Salisbury Hall 10.58)	
			Mosquito Aircraft Museum, Salisbury Hall, London Colney: unveiled	15.5.59/96
- •	NF Mk. II	**HJ711**	RAF Air Training Corps, Chingford: fwd fuse.	63
			Reflectaire auction, Blackpool	.71/72
			Tony Agar/Night Fighter Preservation Team/ Yorkshire Air Museum, Elvington	29.4.72/96
			(static rest. project, using fuse. RS715 and components of PF498 & VA878: "VI-C")	
- •	FB Mk. VI	**HR339**	(to RNZAF as NZ2382)	
			disposal Woodbourne AB (75 Sqn "YC-C")	.55
			Ferrymead Aeronautical Soc., Christchurch	79/96
			(proposed composite static rest. with TE758/NZ2328: stored dism. 95)	
- •	FB Mk. VI	**HR621**	M. Powell, Tomingley NSW: on farm	50/68
			Camden Museum of Aviation, Camden NSW later Narellan NSW	5.68/96
			(hulk recov. ex farm Tomingley .68: static rest. project, using parts from other farm hulks)	
- •	FB Mk. 26	**KA114**	(to RCAF as KA114): BOC 22.2.45: SOC	13.4.48
			to farm Milo ALTA, disposal ex Vulcan ALTA	.48/78
			Canadian Museum of Flight & Transportation,	

				Vancouver BC	79/91
				(recov. as derelict hulk, long-term rest. project)	
- •	B Mk. XX	**KB336**		(to RCAF as KB336): BOC	12.6.44
				Canadian National Aircraft Collection	.51/64
				(stored Chater, McDonald & Calgary)	
				Canadian National Aviation Museum,	
				Rockcliffe ONT (displ. as "KB336/U")	6.2.64/96
- •	PR Mk. IX	**LR480**		(to SAAF as LR480)	12.44
				South African National Museum of Military	
				History, Saxonwold, Johannesburg	.46/92
				(displ. as LR480/*Lovely Lady*)	
- •	PR Mk. XVI	**NS631**		(to RAAF as A52-600): del.	13.12.44
				RAAF Ballarat VIC: inst. airframe	21.7.47
				RAAF Air Training Corps, Ballarat VIC	50/54
				E. Vollaire, Mildura VIC : stored on farm	11.54/66
				Pearce Dunn/Warbirds Aviation Museum,	
				Mildura VIC: stored dism. "SU-A"	12.66/83
			VH-JUX	Vincent Thomas, Alan Lane, Geoff Milne,	
				Albury NSW: ntu, stored dism.	9.83/87
				RAAF Museum, RAAF Point Cook VIC	.87/96
				(long-term rest. to fly, RAAF Laverton VIC 88,	
				later RAAF Richmond NSW 92/96)	
PAC. LF	FB Mk.VI	**PF670**		Jack Amman Photogrammetric Engineering Inc, -30	
				San Antonio TX: purchased ex RAF	11.5.56/60
			N9868F	Jack Amman/IREX Survey Co.,Tripoli, Libya	18.5.56/60
				(del. Hatfield-Libya for survey ops. 10.56/57,	
				del. Libya to USA via Prestwick 5.11.57)	
				(wfu, open storage San Antonio TX .59/64,	
				derelict by 64)	
				J. B. Terrell, Tulsa OK	2.2.60/61
				L. N. Childress, Amarillo TX	12.61
				Confederate Air Force, Harlingen TX: parts	c66/88
				(derelict San Antonio TX, broke up during dism.	
				for transporting to Harlingen: parts only held)	
- •	FB Mk. VI	**PZ474**		(to RNZAF as NZ2384): del. 3.48 BOC	15.4.47
				Bob Bean & Arthur Kaplan/Aircraft Sales Inc,	
				Los Angeles CA: disposal ex Woodbourne AB	9.53
			ZK-BCV	Aircraft Supplies (NZ) Ltd, Palmerston North	7.53
				(on behalf of Aircraft Sales Inc): del. to USA	2.55
			N9909F	Insurance Finance Corp, Studio City CA	c55/66
				(rep. used in South America by CIA)	
				Marvin E. Whiteman, Whiteman Air Park CA	70
				Ed Maloney/The Air Museum, Ontario CA	65/67
				(derelict, Whiteman Air Park CA 59/70)	
				parts held John Caler, Sun Valley CA	75
				Jim Merizan, Placentia/Yorba Linda CA	.70/95
				(under rest. Chino CA for static displ.)	
				Flygvapenmuseum, Malmen, Sweden: listed	92/95
- •	FB Mk. VI	**RF597**		(to RNZAF as NZ2383)	
				Bob Bean & Arthur Kaplan/Aircraft Sales Inc	11.52
			ZK-BCU	Aircraft Supplies (NZ) Ltd, Palmerston North	7.53
				(on behalf of Aircraft Sales Inc CA)	
				export to USA stopped by NZ Government	
				broken-up unconv., Dunedin NZ	.57
				RNZAF Museum, Wigram AB: hulk remains	95
				(composite rest. project with NZ2355/TE863)	
983157	PR Mk. 34	RG300		Jack Amman Photogrammetric Engineering Inc,	

				San Antonio TX: purchased ex RAF	11.5.56
			N9871F	Jack Amman/IREX Survey Co, Tripoli, Libya	18.5.56/59
				(del. UK to USA, via Prestwick 7.12.56)	
				op: Trans World Aero Surveys	12.56
				(wfu, open storage San Antonio TX .59/64, noted there derelict 64)	
				J. B. Terrell, Tulsa OK	2.2.60/61
				L. N. Childress, Amarillo TX	12.61/69
				Confederate Air Force, Harlingen TX	
				(broke up during dism. for transporting to Harlingen TX: parts only retained)	
984597 •		NF Mk. 30	**RK952**	(to Belgian AF as MB24): del.	23.10.53
				Musee Royal de l'Armee, Brussels, Belgium	17.3.57/95
				(displ. as "MB24/ND-N")	
-	•	T Mk. 3	**RR299**	Hawker Siddeley Aviation Ltd, Hawarden	3.63
			G-ASKH	Hawker Siddeley Aviation Ltd, Hawarden	7.63/84
				(flew in film *Mosquito Squadron* 6.68)	
				British Aerospace, Hatfield/Hawarden	84/95
				dam. landing, Hawarden	7.7.88
				(repaired, flies as "RR299/HT-E")	
-	•	B Mk. 35 PR. Mk. 35	**RS700**	CF-HMS Spartan Air Services Ltd, Ottawa ONT	9.12.54/70
				(del. to Burnaston for civil conv. 12.54)	
				(del. to Canada, via Prestwick 28.6.56)	
				C of A expired	13.5.61
				Centennial Planetarium, Calgary ALTA	70/88
				(stored dism., good condition)	
				Calgary Air & Space Museum, Calgary ALTA	90/96
				(rest. to fly, CFB Cold Lake ALTA 91, displ. at CASM, Calgary Airport 94)	
-	•	B Mk. 35 TT Mk. 35	**RS709**	G-ASKA Mirisch Films Ltd, Bovington	11.7.63/64
				(flew in film *633 Squadron*, Bovington 7.63)	
				T. G. Mahaddie	8.64
				Peter F. M. Thomas/Skyfame Museum, Staverton: del.	10.64/69
				(flew in movie *Mosquito Squadron* .68)	
				Ed A. Jurist/Vintage Aircraft International, Nyack NY	8.69/71
			N9797	Confederate Air Force, Harlingen TX	12.71/75
				(del. Luton to Harlingen TX 11.12.71-2.1.72)	
				David C. Tallichet/Yesterdays Air Force, Chino CA	4.75/79
				Combat Air Museum, Topeka KS : loan	.76/79
				Warbirds of GB, Blackbushe	28.11.79
				(del. Topeka-Blackbushe, arr. 28.11.79)	
			G-MOSI	Warbirds of GB, Blackbushe	10.11.81
				(rebuild at Blackbushe : ff 9.83)	.81/83
				David Zeuschel, Van Nuys CA	.84
				USAFM, Wright-Patterson AFB, Dayton OH	7.84/96
				(del. to USAFM via Prestwick 14.10.84, displ. as USAAF Mk.PR.XVI "NS519/P")	
-	•	B Mk. 35 TT Mk. 35	**RS712**	G-ASKB Mirisch Films Ltd, Bovington	11.7.63
				(flew in movie *633 Squadron*, Bovington 7.63)	
				T. G. Mahaddie, Bovingdon & Henlow	8.64/72
				(flew in movie *Mosquito Squadron*, Bovington 6.68; stored West Malling 70/72)	
				Sir W. J. D. Roberts, Shoreham	2.72/75
				Sir William Roberts/Strathallan Collection, Auchterader Scotland : del.	8.11.75/81
				Kermit A. Weeks, Tamiami FL	14.6.81
			N35MK	Weeks Air Museum Tamiami FL	17.6.83

		Mark	Serial	Reg	History	Date
				G-ASKB	rest. Auchterader, flown to Booker	21.12.84
					(rest. Booker, dep. UK on del. USA 29.9.87)	
				N35MK	Kermit Weeks/Weeks Air Museum,Tamiami FL	.87/95
					loan: EAA Museum, Oshkosh WI	91/96
					(flies as "RS712/EG-F")	
-		B Mk. 35	**RS715**		RAF Exeter: noted wfu	8.62
		TT Mk. 35			Mirisch Films Ltd, Bovingdon: arr. dism	3.7.63
					(used in ground scenes movie "633 Squadron")	
					transported to MGM Studios, Borehamwood	.63/73
					fuselage hulk to Tony Agar, York	.73
					(used in static rest. of HJ711)	
-	•	FB Mk. VI	**TA122**		RAF Celle, West Germany: stored	6.50/51
					Delft Technical University, Delft, Holland	6.51
					R Netherlands AF Museum: fus. only "UP"	70/78
					(stored Woensdrecht AB, later Gilze-Rijen AB)	
					Mosquito Aircraft Museum, London Colney	26.2.78/96
					(static rest. with mainplane of TW233 recov. ex	
					Kibbutz Beit Alfa, Israel: airfreight to UK 26.7.80:	
					rest. completed, displ. as "TA122/UP-G")	
-	•	B Mk. 35	**TA634**		City of Liverpool Corporation, Speke	6.11.63/70
		TT Mk. 35			(planned display, but stored in hangar)	
				G-AWJV	City of Liverpool Corporation	21.5.68/70
					(ff Liverpool 17.6.68, for use in movie	
					Mosquito Squadron, Bovington 6.68)	
					Mosquito Aircraft Museum, London Colney	7.10.70/96
					(displ. as "HX922/EF-G", static rest. .80/90,	
					rolled-out 14.10.90 as "TA634/8K-K")	
-	•	B Mk. 35	**TA639**		Mirisch Films, Bovingdon: loan ex RAF: del.	15.7.63
		TT Mk. 35			(flew in movie "633 Squadron" 7.63)	
					RAF Museum Store, Henlow	5.7.67
					RAF Museum, RAF Cosford	70/96
					(displ. camouflaged as "TA639/AZ-E")	
-		B Mk. 35	TA717	N9911F	Fotogrametric Engineers Inc, Los Angeles CA	5.56
					(del. to USA, via Prestwick 5.56)	
				XB-TOX	McIntyre & Quiros, Mexico City	14.6.56
				N6867C	McIntyre & Quiros, Los Angeles CA	5.57
				XB-TOX	McIntyre & Quiros, Mexico City	7.57
					open storage, derelict, Mexico City Airport	66/79
					Mike Meeker, Mission City BC	.79/88
					(hulk recov. ex Mexico City, parts used in	
					rebuild of VR796/CF-HML)	
					Jim Merizan, Yorba Linda CA	.88/90
					(parts only, for rebuild of PZ474/N9909F)	
-	•	B Mk. 35	**TA719**	G-ASKC	P. F. M. Thomas/Skyfame Museum, Staverton	7.63/78
		TT Mk.35			Film Aviation Services, Elstree : loan	7.63
					(flew in movie *633 Squadron*, Bovington 7.63)	
					badly dam., crash landing Staverton	27.7.64
					(ground crash scene, film *Mosquito Squadron*	
					at MGM Borehamwood Studios 6.68)	
					Imperial War Museum, Duxford: rest., displ.	.78/95
-	•	FB Mk. VI	**TE758**		(to RNZAF as NZ2328): BOC	3.4.47
					disposal Woodbourne AB (75 Sqn "YC-F")	.55
					Jas W. Clarke Syndicate, Totara, nr. Oamaru	.55/72
					(fuselage & major components stored on farm)	
					Ferrymead Aeronautical Soc., Christchurch	9.72/95
					(composite static rest. with HR339/NZ2382)	

-	•	FB Mk. VI	**TE863**		(to RNZAF as NZ2355): BOC	7.47
					disposal Woodbourne AB	.55
					Cliff Horrel, Ashburton NZ	.55
					Ted Packer, Christchurch NZ: rest. project	
					RNZAF Museum, RNZAF Wigram: stored	88/95
					(composite static rest. project with RF597/ZK-BCV, plus parts of NZ2324, NZ2334, NZ2381, NZ2395: all stripped hulks recov.ex farms)	
-	•	FB Mk. VI	**TE910**		(to RNZAF as NZ2336): BOC	24.4.47
					disposal Woodbourne AB (75 Sqn "YC-B")	.56
					John R. Smith, Gardeners Valley, Mapua NZ	7.56/96
					(trucked dism. to owner's farm Mapua, reassembled static rest: stored under cover "NZ2336/YC-B")	
-	•	B Mk. 35 TT Mk. 35	**TH998**		NASM, Washington DC: donated by RAF	31.8.62
					(airfreighted by C-124C Duxford - USA)	
					NASM, Silver Hill MD: stored	63/96
-	•	B Mk. 35 TT Mk. 35	**TJ138**		RAF Bicester: travelling displ. as "VO-L"	7.59
					RAF Museum, RAF Colerne	67/75
					RAF Museum Store, RAF Finningley	.75
					RAF Museum Store, RAF Swinderby	84/86
					RAF Museum, RAF St Athan	11.86/92
					RAF Museum, Hendon	2.92/96
					(displ. as "TJ138/VO-L")	
-	•	T Mk. 3	**TV959**		Mirisch Films Ltd, Bovingdon: loan	7.63
					(ground scenes in film *633 Squadron* 7.63)	
					Imperial War Museum, Lambeth, London	8.63/88
					(displ. as "TV959/AF-V")	
					Imperial War Museum, Duxford : stored	89/92
					The Fighter Collection, Duxford	.92/96
					(stored Duxford pending rest.)	
-	•	T Mk. 3	**TW117**		RAF Museum Store, RAF Henlow	30.5.63/67
					Mirisch Films Ltd, Bovingdon: loan	7.63
					(flew in film *633 Squadron*, Bovington 7.63)	
					RAF Museum, Hendon	.72/91
					Tacair Systems, Toronto ONT	11.91/92
					loan: Royal Norwegian Air Force Museum, Gardermoen AB: shipped ex UK , arr.	3.2.92/93
-	•	B Mk. 35	**VP189**	CF-HMQ	Spartan Air Services Ltd, Ottawa ONT	9.12.54/57
					(civil conv. Burnaston UK 54/55)	
					(del. to Canada, arr. Ottawa 2.6.55)	
				VP-KOM	ntu: Spartan Air Services (Eastern) Ltd	11.57
					(del. Ottawa - Nairobi, Kenya 11.57)	
				CF-HMQ	Spartan Air Services Ltd, Ottawa ONT	.57/67
					(returned to Canada, via Prestwick 4.5.58)	
					last flight, Grand Prairie - Uplands ONT	7.10.63
					J. K. Campbell, Edmonton ALTA	14.9.67
					CFB Edmonton: displ. as "TH-F"	68/75
					City of Edmonton, Artifacts Centre: stored	.75/91
					Edmonton Aviation Heritage Centre	93
					(static rest., arr. ex storage 6.4.93)	
-	•	B Mk. 35	**VR796**	CF-HML	Spartan Air Services Ltd, Ottawa ONT	11.54/66
					(del. Burnaston - Ottawa 2:5.55)	
					last flight, retired at Uplands, Ottawa ONT	10.6.63
					Don Campbell, Kapuskasing ONT	12.66/86
					(rebuild commenced CFB Kapuskasing .67/79, moved to Matsqui BC .79 for continued rest. by Mike Meeker, using parts ex TA717)	
					Ed & Rose Zalesky, Surrey BC	.86/96

c/n	Type	Serial	Reg	History	Date
				(rest. to fly, Surrey BC)	
- •	FB Mk. 40	A52-1053		(A52-19 ntu: to RAAF as A52-1053): BOC	8.46
	T Mk. 43			(to RNZAF as NZ2305): del.	18.12.46
				M. Galpin, Marton NZ: trucked to his farm	.55
				Museum of Transport & Technology, Auckland	.64/96
				(long-term static rest. project)	
- •	FB Mk. 40	A52-1054		(A52-20 ntu: to RAAF as A52-1054): BOC	8.46/47
	T Mk. 43			(to RNZAF as NZ2308): del.	6.47
				John Morgan, Nelson NZ	.56/60
				(trucked to his farm Riwaka 8.56, became derelict)	
				Glyn Powell & associates, Auckland NZ	90/96
				(planned rest. project to fly: fuse. used as	
				pattern for new build fuse. Auckland 96)	
DH.3236 •	FB Mk. 40	A52-319		(A52-210 ntu: to RAAF as A52-319): BOC	18.2.48/53
	PR Mk. 41			Cpt. James Woods/Woods Airways, Perth WA	20.3.53
				(del. to Perth 10.9.53, for London to	
				Christchurch Air Race: entry withdrawn)	
			VH-WAD	James Woods, Perth WA "The Quokka"	23.9.53/69
				C of A suspended and struck-off reg.	12.10.53
				stored in hangar, Perth Airport WA	.53/63
				Air Force Association, Perth Airport : displ.	1.63/67
				became derelict, moved to airport dump	7.67/69
				James A. Harwood, Perth WA	1.69
				fuselage badly dam. during dismantling	8.1.69
				stored dism. in warehouse, Perth WA	1.69/72
				Vintage Aircraft International, Nyack NJ	.69
				David M. Kubista, Tucson AZ	6.71
				crated aboard SS Manora, ex Fremantle	23.5.72
				stored Port Melbourne, pending transit USA	72/79
				auctioned to recover shipping costs	22.1.79
				Australian War Memorial, Canberra ACT	22.1.79/96
				(static rest., Bankstown NSW 79/95)	
- •	FB Mk. 26	-	-	People's Liberation Army Air Force Museum,	
	repl.			Da Tang Shan, Beijing, China	90/94
				(replica based on Tu-2, some genuine wing parts)	

DORNIER DO-24

c/n	Type	Serial	Reg	History	Date
Nr467 •	Do 24T-3			(to Spanish AF as HD.5-... later HR.5-...)	
			N99240	Dolph D. Overton, Kenley NC	77
				sale rep., Apple Valley CA	90/95
Nr1101 •	Do 24T-3			(Luftwaffe "W4+DH")	
				recovered from Lake Biscarosse, France	2.80
				Association de Protection des Epaves du	
				Lac du Biscarosse, Biscarosse, France	80/89
				(recov. from Lake Biscarrosse 2.80)	
Nr1107 •	Do 24T-3			(Luftwaffe "W4+BH")	
				Association de Protection des Epaves du	
				Lac du Biscarosse, Biscarosse, France	80/89
				(recov. from Lake Biscarrosse 9.81)	
Nr5341 •	Do 24T-3			(to Spanish AF as 65-2)	12.44
				later reserialled HR.5-2, HD.5-2)	
				Museo del Aire, Cuatro Vientos AB, Madrid	.71/93
				(displ. on artificial lake as "HD.5-2/SAR/58-2")	
Nr5342 •	Do 24T-3		EC-DAF	(to Spanish AF as 65-6, HR.5-1, HD.5-1)	12.44

			N99225	Dolph D. Overton, Kenley NC not collected, stored Pollensa, Majorca RAF Museum, Hendon UK: arr. dism. Militaire Luchvaartmuseum, Kamp van Ziest, Netherlands: displ. as "X-24"	2.77 78 30.6.82/91 11.91/96
Nr5344 •	Do 24T-3		 N99222	(to Spanish AF as 65-3, HR.5-3, HD.5-3) Dolph D. Overton, Kenley NC: not del. Dornier Research Centre, Immenstaad WG (del. ex Spain, landed Lake Constance 28.8.71 Dornier Werke Museum, Oberpfaffenhofen (fitted with wings from Nr5345/HD.5-4, displ. in Spanish AF sc. "SAR")	12.44 70 .71/74 84/93
Nr5345 •	Do 24T-3		 **D-CATD**	(to Spanish AF as 65-4, HR.5-4, HD.5-4) Dornier Research Centre, Immenstaad WG (del. ex Spain, landed Lake Constance WG .71) Dornierwerke GmbH, Oberpfaffenhofen (prototype experimental Do ATT, three PT-6A turboprops: ff 25.4.83) Dornier Werke Museum, Oberpfaffenhofen Flugwerft Schleissheim Deutsches Museum, Oberschleissheim, Munich: loan	12.44 .71/83 Do ATT 4.83 86/93 92/93
- •	Do 24T			Technikmuseum, Speyer, Germany (Luftwaffe, complete fuselage and stub wing displ. as recov. from Lake Muritz, Germany)	95/96

DOUGLAS A-20 BOSTON/HAVOC

3839 •	DB-7B (DB-73) Boston III	**AL907**		(to Armee de l'Air as ....): not del. (to RAF as AL907): not del. (to Kon Marine 240) : diverted to Australia (to RAAF as A28-8) : "DU-J/*Jessica*" crashed landing, Goodenough Island PNG RAAF Museum, RAAF Point Cook VIC (recov. ex Vivigani strip, Goodenough Island 2.87; static rest. RAAF Wagga NSW 88/92, continuing at RAAF Amberley QLD 92/96)	 1.42 29.3.42/43 12.9.43 2.87/96
-	A-20G	**42-86615**		(417th BG/675th BS): crashed Saidor PNG RAAF Museum: hulk recov. ex Yamai, Saidor (components used in static rest. projects, RAAF Wagga 88/92, RAAF Amberley 92/96)	16.4.44 21.11.84
-	A-20G	**42-86772**		crashed Annamberg PNG RAAF Museum: hulk recov. by chopper (components used in static rest. projects, RAAF Wagga 88/92, RAAF Amberley 92/96)	.44 11.84
- •	A-20G	**42-86786**		(388th BS): *Hell'n Pelican II* forced landing Gogol River, Amamion PNG RAAF Museum: hulk recov. by chopper (static rest. RAAF Wagga NSW .88/92, continuing at RAAF Amberley 92/96) PNG National Museum, Port Moresby: when rest.	 16.4.44 11.84/96
-	A-20G	**43-9401**		(417th BG/675th BS): fcd. ldg., Saidor PNG RAAF Museum: hulk recov. ex Yamai, Saidor (components used in static rest. projects, RAAF Wagga 88/92, RAAF Amberley 92/96)	16.4.44 22.11.84
- •	A-20G	**43-9436**		USAAC "Big Nig" : forced landing in swamp, Bumbura, Annamberg, Ramu Valley PNG RAAF Museum: recov. ex swamp	 3.5.44 10.94/96

c/n	Type	Serial	Reg.	Owner/History	Date
				(airlifted complete by Mil-26 helicopter 10.94,	
				airfreighted to RAAF Amberley QLD 23.11.94	
				for Boston rest. projects, RAAF Amberley)	
-	A-20G	**43-9686**		(417th BG) forced landing, Wabusarik PNG	.44
				RAAF Museum: recov. ex Wabusarik	26.11.84
				(components used in static rest. projects,	
				RAAF Wagga 88/92, RAAF Amberley 92/95)	
				(id. also quoted as 43-9628)	
21274 •	A-20G	**43-21627**		(312th BG/387th BS)	
				recov. by d'E. C. Darby & N. M. Armstrong	
				for YAF, from Tadji, West Sepik PNG	.74
				David C. Tallichet/Yesterdays Air Force,	
				Chino CA	.74/93
21305 •	A-20G	**43-21658**	N5069N	Delta Drilling Co/Texas Engineering &	
				Manufacturing Co, Dallas TX	25.6.47
				Texas Aircraft Trading Co, Tyler TX	20.8.47
				Universal Aviation Company, Tulsa OK	1.6.48
				Leonard Burns, San Francisco CA	22.7.48
				US Marshal, Miami FL: seized	.48/49
				American Airmotive Corporation, Miami FL	4.4.49/52
				Chas T. Frew/Keystone Mapping Company Inc,	
				York PA	23.6.52/55
				Spartan Aircraft Company, Tulsa OK	5.7.55
				Trade-Ayer Co, Linden NJ	31.8.55
				Roberts Aircraft Co, Boise ID (sprayer)	18.4.56/70
				(USCR quotes id. as 44-337: ie. A-20K c/n 23560)	
21356 •	A-20G	**43-21709**		Paul Mantz, Burbank CA (ex Altus AFB OK)	19.2.46
			NC67932	Paul Mantz Air Service, Burbank CA	10.5.48/51
			N67932	Potter Aircraft Service Inc, Burbank CA	11.4.51
			N22M	Glen L. McCarthy, Houston TX	11.51/54
				Valley Hail Suppression, Scottsbluff NE	15.2.54/55
				James M. Cook Co., Jacksboro TX	15.3.55
				C. T. McLaughlin, Snyder TX	31.8.55/59
				Vest Aircraft & Finance Co, Denver CO	23.11.59
				Jack Adams Aircraft Sales, Memphis TN	12.59/60
				George Treadwell, Shelby TN	62
				Billy Hicks, McGehee AR	21.2.62/67
				Jupiter Inc, Houston TX	9.1.67/68
				I. N. Burchinall Jr, Paris TX	12.68/70
				William F. Farah, El Paso TX	6.8.70/74
			N3WF	William F. Farah, El Paso TX	.74/89
				NASM, Washington DC (donated)	25.9.89/91
				ret. by Court Order, to Farah estate	24.3.91
				Lone Star Flight Museum, Galveston TX	16.9.91/96
				(arr. Galveston on del. 11.91)	
21844 •	A-20G	**43-22197**	NX34920	Hughes Tool Co, Culver City CA	.46/47
				(flown for instrument development for XF-11)	
			N34920	Hughes Aircraft Co, Culver City CA	49/72
				(wfu, open storage Culver City 63/70)	
				Antelope Valley Aero Museum, Lancaster CA	c73/86
				Milestones of Flight Museum, Lancaster CA	.86/91
				(stored dism., Lancaster-Fox Field CA 73/91)	
				Weeks Air Mus., Tamiami FL	.91/96
				(stored dism. Ocotillo Wells CA 93/94)	
21847 •	A-20G	**43-22200**	NL63004	H. L. Gogerty, Los Angeles CA	22.1.46
				J. G. Hurst, Miami FL	10,47/49
				(rep. to FA Nicaragua as G.N.60)	7.49
				William M. Ambrose, Miami FL	13.9.49/50

			N63004	W. R. Robinson, Miami FL	16.1.50/51
				Grant Foster, Falcon, Venezuela	20.9.51/53
				(adv. for sale by Potter Aircraft Service, Burbank CA 6.52: 6 seat executive conv.)	
				L. B. Smith Aircraft Corp, Miami FL	17.2.53/55
				Florida Aircraft Corp, Miami FL	22.8.55/60
				American Airmotive Corp, Miami FL	19.9.60
				Bankers Life & Casualty Co, Chicago IL	20.9.60
				USAFM, Wright-Patterson AFB, Dayton OH	30.9.61/92
				(displ. as "0-22200; later "322200")	
21857	A-20G	43-22210		Hearst Magazines Inc, San Francisco CA	3.6.46/48
			NL67921	Hearst Magazines Inc, San Francisco CA	12.2.48/50
			N67921	W. G. Spillman, Burbank CA	30.1.50/52
				Thorne Engineering Corp, Las Vegas NV	9.1.52/56
				Roberts Aircraft Co, Reno NV	27.4.56/58
				W. Lynn Roberts/Roberts Aircraft Co, Boise ID (sprayer)	12.5.58/59
				Ray C. Wilcox, Boise ID	8.7.59/65
				Donald C. Magnuson & Ralph E. Knight Aircraft Service and Repair Co, Boise ID	14.4.65
				(wfu open storage, Boise c59/66)	
				Confederate Air Force, Harlingen TX	5.10.65/88
				(ferried Boise-Harlingen TX 12.9.66, rest. 71/76: ff .76 as "322210/T")	
				crashed dest., near Harlingen TX	8.10.88
23243 •	A-20H	**44-20**	N5066N	Delta Drilling Co/Texas Engineering & Manufacturing Co, Dallas TX	25.6.47
				Texas Aircraft Trading Co, Tyler TX	20.8.47
				Universal Aviation Company, Tulsa OK	1.6.48
				Leonard Burns, San Francisco CA	22.7.48
				American Airmotive Corporation, Miami FL	4.4.49/56
				(noted as executive conv., Miami FL 55)	
				(to FA Nicaragua as G.N.50)	
				(displ. in park, Carretera del Sur, Managua, Nicaragua 75/77)	
			N99385	David C. Tallichet/MARC, Chino CA	14.3.77/96
				(open storage Chino as "FAN 50" 80/91)	
				lease: Air Heritage Inc, Beaver Falls PA	.91/93
				(trucked from Chino to Beaver Falls PA 7.91, stored dism. Beaver Falls, planned rest. to fly)	
23762 •	A-20K	**44-539**		(to FA Brasileira as FAB 5159)	
				Museu Aeroespacial, Campo dos Afoncos, Rio	79/88
- •	A-20	-		(to FA Brasileira as FAB 6085)	
				Quaratingueta AB, Sao Paulo: displ.	68/88
- •	A-20	-		Soviet AF Museum, Monino, Russia	92/96
				(rep. as replica, displ. as "Soviet AF 310052")	

DOUGLAS A-26 INVADER

6874 •	A-26B	**41-39161**	N317V	Humphrey's Gold Corp, FL	.56
	B-26B			Humphrey's Engineering Co, Denver CO	63/66
	On Mark		N317W	Metropolitan State College, Denver CO	69
				Air Mayo Inc, Lakewood CO	70/72
				Slaco Inc, Fort Lauderdale FL	77
			N26RP	Robert P. Lammerts, Oklahoma City OK	9.81/84
				ADA Aircraft Museum, Oklahoma City OK	86/90
				dam. landing, Fort Worth-Meacham TX	18.10.87
				Colonel Aircraft Sales, Oklahoma City OK	5.91/96
				(flies as "436874/L")	

6875	A-26B B-26C B-26Z	41-39162	 N72Y	Alex Oser: ex USAF, for scrap Texas Railway & Equipment Co, Houston TX Eastern Aircraft Sales, New York NY (to l'Armee de l'Air as Z007, 41-39162):BOC (conv. to B-26Z target tug): wfu 12.65, SOC gate guard, Blois-Le Breuil ("CAEM/Z") Musee de l'Air: stored Blois-Le Breuil Musee de l'Air: stored Paris-Le Bourget dest. hangar fire, Paris-Le Bourget	.50 19.2.52/54 20.1.54 15.5.54/67 29.12.67 71 9.78 90 17.5.90
6903 •	A-26B B-26B	41-39190	**N9404Z**	Idaho Air Tankers Inc, Boise ID Moseley Aviation, Tolleson AZ Donaire Sales Inc, Phoenix AZ Conair Ltd, Abbotsford BC : for parts only sale rep., USCR	64 66/72 73 78/96
6928 •	A-26B B-26B On Mark	**41-39215**	N5292V N4000M N200M N142ER	Recta Air Enterprises On Mark Engineering Co, Van Nuys CA L. B. Maytag Jr, Miami FL Embry Riddle Institute, Daytona Beach FL Milt Stollak, Burbank CA Gold Coast Classic Cars, Fort Lauderdale FL Courtesy Aircraft Inc, Rockford IL ADA Aircraft Museum, Oklahoma City OK crashed during del. flight, Lawton OK Aero Nostalgia Inc, Stockton CA (static rest.) USNAM, NAS Pensacola FL (displ. as "JD-1 USN/Bu77141/446928")	 63/64 66 69/74 77 5.82 2.84 2.85 17.3.85 86/89 90/96
6934 •	A-26B B-26B Marksman	**41-39221**	N9636C N3035S (1 N256H (2 N26GT	Farrah Manufacturing Co Inc Southern Natural Gas Co, Birmingham AL Mapco Inc, Tulsa OK Bancroft Manufacturing Co, McComb MS Park Meadow Inc/ Ligon Air Inc, Ligonier IN Garrett AiResearch Corp, Phoenix AZ (mod. for testing turbine engine in nose) Garrett Corp, Phoenix-Sky Harbour AZ Allied Signal Inc, Phoenix AZ struck-off USCR Phoenix-Sky Harbour to local school: by road	 63/66 69 70/72 77 c79 4.83/88 12.88/90 10.1.92 93
6936 •	A-26B B-26B B-26Z	**41-39223**	 N74Y	Alex Oser: ex USAF, for scrap Texas Railway & Equipment Co, Houston TX Eastern Aircraft Sales, New York NY (to l'Armee de l'Air as Z009, 41-39223):BOC (conv. to B-26Z target tug): wfu 9.65, SOC Mont de Marsan: stored Saintes-Thernac: gate guard Musee de l'Air, Paris-Le Bourget (rest. to fly, Tremons 94)	.50 19.2.52 .54 11.54/65 20.10.65 72 78 93/96
6943 •	A-26B B-26B	**41-39230**	**N9682C**	H. R. Wells Flight Inc, Dallas TX D & D Aero Spraying Inc, Rantoul KS (tanker #105) Harley Wilke/CAF, Harlingen TX Confederate Air Force, Harlingen/Midland TX (flew as "139230/P/Panhandle's Pride") (rest North Las Vegas NV, due to fly .96 as 139230/N/*Vegas Vixen*)	 63/66 69/80 .80/82 21.8.82/96
6990 •	A-26B B-26B	**41-39277**	**N74834**	Madden & Smith Aircraft Corp, Miami FL sale rep., USCR (probably bu 1960s)	64/69 78/96

7001 •	A-26B B-26B B-26C B-26B	**41-39288**		(to FA Brasileira as B-26C 5159) (rebuilt Tucson AZ .68 by Hamilton Aircraft as B-26B, redel. as FAB B-26B 5159) Museu Aeroespacial, Campo dos Afoncos, Rio	.56 .68 81/94
7016 •	A-26B B-26C	**41-39303**	**N5589A**	W. C. Powell, Tereboro NJ Charles Woods Homes Inc, Dothan AL Institute of Aviation Technology, Ozark AL Paramount Inc, Atlanta GA John M. Sliker, Wadley GA John J. Stokes/Central Texas Aviation, San Marcos TX (dism.) Lynch Air Tankers, Billings MT (dism.) Pacific Coast Air Museum, Santa Rosa CA (trucked Billings-Santa Rosa: rest project)	58 64/66 69 70 70/72 77 .78/92 25.9.92/96
7035	A-26B B-26B	41-39322	XB-BUI	Aerografica y Constructora SA, Mexico City noted derelict, Mexico City	63/64 5.70
7057 •	A-26B B-26B	**41-39344**	**N4185A**	Arrow Sales Inc, Los Angeles CA sale rep., USCR (probably by 1960s)	64/70 72/95
7072 •	A-26B B-26C	**41-39359**	N91281 CF-BMR C-FBMR **N26BP**	Aero Union Corp, Chico CA Conair Aviation Ltd, Abbotsford BC (tanker #321) Conair Aviation Ltd, Abbotsford BC Jerry C. Janes, Rockford IL Robert J. Pond/Planes of Fame East, Minneapolis-Flying Cloud MN (flies as "39359/21")	66/69 3.70 79/86 .87 11.87/95
7091 •	A-26B TB-26B B-26K A-26A	**41-39378** 64-17653		(rebuilt as B-26K by On Mark) Davis Monthan AFB AZ: del. for storage Pima County Air Museum, Tucson AZ	10.64 11.1.70/74 4.1.74/96
7111	A-26B B-26C	41-39398	N91317 CF-DFC	Greg Board/Aero Associates Inc, Tucson AZ (planned sale to FA Portuguesa: not completed) Allied Aircraft Sales, Phoenix AZ Flight Enterprises Inc, Prescott AZ Conair Aviation Ltd, Abbotsford BC (tanker #324) crashed, landing Prince George BC crashed, dest., Stoyoma Mountain BC	65 66 69/70 5.71 10.8.71 11.8.74
7114 •	A-26B B-26C	**41-39401**	N3457G **N39401**	John R. Moore, Los Angeles CA (wfu Van Nuys CA "Whistler's Mother" 59/82) Challenge Publications Inc, Canoga Park CA Challenge Publications Inc, Van Nuys CA (rebuilt Van Nuys CA: ff 18.8.83) American Aeronautical Foundation, Van Nuys Weeks Air Museum, Tamiami FL (flew as 139401/*Whistler's Mother*) dam. Tamiami FL, Hurricane Andrew	.59/70 11.82 5.83 1.85/87 7.87/96 24.8.92
7140 •	A-26B B-26B	**41-39427**	N75Y **N240P**	Texas Railway Equipment Co, Houston TX Brown & Root Inc Barnwell Drilling Co, Shreveport LA William V. Wright, Long Beach CA Aircraft Holdings, Miami FL Earl Parks, Amarillo TX Confederate Air Force, Harlingen/Midland TX (wfu Amarillo TX 76/80, del. Waco TX 2.8.80, rest. Waco 80/82 as "437140/R/Spirit of Waco")	54 59 63/66 69/72 76 .76 10.5.77/96

7181	A-26B	41-39468	N91354	Greg Board/Aero Associates Inc, Tucson AZ	65
	B-26B			(planned sale to FA Portuguesa: not completed)	
				Allied Aircraft Sales, Phoenix AZ	66/69
				Thompson Flying Service, Salt Lake City UT	70
				Reeder Flying Service, Twin Falls ID	72/84
				(tanker #28)	
				ground collision, dest. by fire, Boise ID	
				struck-off USCR	5.84
7185 •	A-26B	**41-39472**	N86482	John P. Wilds, Escalon CA	63/64
	B-26B			Kimberley Leasing Corp, St Paul MN	66/69
				(to FA Salvadorena as 601): BOC	8.69/74
			N26VC	John V. Crocker, San Mateo CA	4.74/80
				(del. El Salvador-San Diego CA 16-18.4.74)	
				USAFM, Castle AFB CA	10.80/93
				(arr. on del. 26.10.80, displ. as "24-6093",	
				later 435648/*Lil' Sal*)	
7199 •	A-26B	**41-39486**	N9432Z	Transport Aircraft Inc, Sacramento CA	
	B-26B			John A. Thompson, Santa Clara CA	c63
			N90711	John A. Thompson, Santa Clara CA	3.71/96
				(wfu Fresno CA, derelict as N9432Z 68/77)	
				trucked ex Fresno by Thompson	.77
7210 •	A-26B	**41-39497**		Alex Oser: ex USAF, for scrap	.50
	B-26B		N71Y	Texas Railroad Equipment Co, Houston TX	.52
				Eastern Aircraft Sales, New York NY	53
				(planned sale to l'Armee de l'Air)	
				Standard Oil Co, Chicago IL	54/64
				Ralph D. Tait, Greensburg PA	66
				Aviation Inc, Charleston WV	69/72
				Robert Kelley, Inglewood CA	77
			HK-..59	reg.	
			N71Y	Jeremiah S. Boehmer, Grants Pass OR	2.85/96
				(impounded Bogota-El Dorado, Colombia 75/95)	
7228	A-26B	41-39515	N67805	Stanolind Oil & Gas Co, Tulsa OK	54
	B-26B			Pan American Petroleum Corp, Tulsa OK	61/64
				noted in scrapyard, Tulsa OK	4.73
7229 •	A-26B	41-39516	**N237Y**	Standard Oil Co, Chicago IL	54/63
	B-26B			Alsam Inc, Youngstown OH	64/69
	On Mark			PBF Enterprises, Akron OH	70/72
				Calspan Corp, Buffalo NY/Edwards AFB CA	77/92
				National Warplane Museum, Geneseo NY	.92/96
7230	A-26B	41-39517	N91349	Greg Board/Aero Associates Inc, Tucson AZ	65
	B-26B			(to FA Portuguesa as 7106): del.	8.65/75
				(rebuilt Tucson AZ .65 by Hamilton Aircraft for FAP)	
				(conv. from B-26B to B-26C in FAP service)	
				wfu, abandoned Luanda, Angola	75
7309 •	A-26B	**41-39596**		(rebuilt as B-26K by On Mark)	23.3.65
	B-26B	64-17676		Davis Monthan AFB AZ: del. for storage	10.69/71
	B-26K		N268G	State of Georgia Forestry Comm., Macon GA	.71/77
	A-26A			(open storage unconv., Macon GA 72/77)	
			C-GXTF	Air Spray Ltd, Edmonton ALTA	.77
				(del. Macon-Billings MT, open storage Billings	
				due certification dispute with Canadian DoT 77/78)	
				Arnie Carnegie, Edmonton ALTA	78
			N29939	Arthur W. McDonnell, Mojave CA	7.78/80
				(noted camoufl. 'C-GXTF', Mojave CA 10.78,	
				raced Mojave 6.79 "The Mojave Kid")	

				USAFM, Wright-Patterson AFB, Dayton OH	11.80/96
18428 •	A-26B	**43-22281**	**N61B**	Parker Pen Co, Janesville WI	61/64
	B-26B			Kwiki Systems Inc, Leawood KS	66
				On Mark Engineering Corp, Van Nuys CA	69
				North American Rockwell Corp, El Segundo CA	70/77
				sale rep., Miami FL (probably bu 1960s)	84/96
18506 •	A-26B	**43-22357**	N91348	Greg Board/Aero Associates Inc, Tucson AZ	65
	B-26B			(planned sale to FA Portuguesa: not completed)	
				Hamilton Aircraft Co Inc, Tucson AZ	66/69
			CF-BMS	Conair Aviation Ltd, Abbotsford BC	4.70
				(tanker #322)	
			C-FBMS	Conair Aviation Ltd, Abbotsford BC	86/89
				B. C. Aviation Museum, Sidney BC: del.	29.8.89/96
				(c/n per Douglas records: 18504 prev. quoted)	
18532 •	A-26B	43-22374	**N6843D**	Rock Island Oil & Refining Co, Wichita KS	64/66
	B-26B			Consolidated Aero Export, Los Angeles CA	69/72
				David C. Tallichet/MARC, Chino CA	11.73/93
				(ferried to Chino .74, ex storage Hutchinson KS;	
				open storage MARC compound, Chino 86/93)	
				Baron Thomas AZ	94
				Michael Hay: rest. to fly, Chino CA	94/96
				(c/n per Douglas records: 18521 prev. quoted)	
18561	A-26B	43-22392	N7719C	Aero Atlas Inc, Red Bluff CA	63/64
	B-26B			Rosenbalm Aviation, Medford OR	66/70
				rep. dest. in hangar fire, Medford OR	
				(c/n per Douglas records: 18539 prev. quoted)	
18574 •	A-26C	**43-22494**		displ. gate, Davis Monthan AFB, Tucson AZ	.60/65
	JDB-26C			Pima County Air Museum, Tucson AZ	.69/93
				(displ. as "0-3494/BC-494")	
				(c/n per Douglas records: 18641 prev. quoted)	
18584 •	A-26C	**43-22499**	**N86481**	John P. Wilds, Escalon CA	63/64
	B-26C			Consolidated Aircraft Sales Inc, Fairfield NJ	66/70
				Bradley Air Museum, Windsor Locks CT	9.71/84
				New England Air Museum, Windsor Locks CT	84/96
				(c/n per Douglas records: 18646 prev. quoted)	
18608	A-26C	43-22511	N86469	Aeroflight Inc, Troutdale OR	63/69
	B-26C			Aero Union Corp, Chico CA	70
				(c/n per Douglas records: 18658 prev. quoted)	
18629	A-26B	43-22427	N91350	Acme Aircraft Parts, Compton CA: ex USAF	.59
	B-26B			Transit Equipment Co, New York NY	.59
				Hamilton Aircraft Co, Tucson AZ	12.7.65
				Greg Board/Aero Associates Inc, Tucson AZ	65
				(to FA Portuguesa as 7105): del.	6.8.65/75
				(rebuilt Tucson AZ .65 by Hamilton Aircraft for FAP)	
				wfu, abandoned Luanda, Angola	11.75
				(c/n per Douglas records: 18574 prev. quoted)	
18632 •	A-26C	**43-22523**	N4050A	Korda Leasing Corp, New York NY	63/64
	B-26C			DEC Aviation Corp, Madison WI	66
				May Air Inc, Boulder CO	69/70
				I. N. Burchinall Jr, Paris TX	76
				Ronald L. Bryant, Springfield MO	.77
				derelict at Fort Lauderdale FL by	10.79/81
				Hill Air Company Inc, Fort Lauderdale FL	10.84/87
				Jim Ricketts/Aero Nostalgia, Stockton CA	.87/90
				(trucked FLL to Stockton, static rest. for USAFM	
				using parts from 44-34156: que se)	

				USAFM, Vance AFB OK	.90/96
				(displ. as "434156/BC-156")	
				(c/n per Douglas records: 18670 prev. quoted)	
18651	A-26C	43-22533	N6845D	Rock Island Oil & Refining Co, Wichita KS	64/66
	B-26C			Consolidated Aero Export, Los Angeles CA	69/72
				(c/n per Douglas records: 18680 prev. quoted)	
18690	A-26C	43-22559	N91359	Greg Board/Aero Associates Inc, Tucson AZ	65
	B-26C			(planned sale to FA Portuguesa: not completed)	
				Flight Enterprises Inc, Prescott AZ	66/69
				derelict, unconv., Tucson AZ	69/75
				(c/n per Douglas records: 18706 prev. quoted)	
18694 •	A-26B	**43-22452**	**N74832**	Madden & Smith Aircraft Corp, Miami FL	64/69
	B-26B			sale rep., USCR (probably bu 1960s)	78/95
				(c/n per Douglas records: 18599 prev. quoted)	
18705	A-26C	43-22569	N3478G	L. B. Smith Aircraft Corp, Miami FL	64/70
	B-26C			(c/n per Douglas records: 18716 prev. quoted)	
18718	A-26B	43-22460	N100Y	On Mark Engineering Co, Van Nuys CA	
	B-26B			Purolator Products Inc, New York NY	61
	Marksman			Transelco Inc, Rahway NJ	63/64
			N190Y	Occidental Leasing Corp, Los Angeles CA	66
				Occidental of Libya Inc, Los Angeles CA	69
				(c/n per Douglas records: 18607 prev. quoted)	
18749 •	A-26C	**43-22602**	N9990Z	Taywin Investment Co, Lakewood CO	64
	B-26C			Kimberley Leasing Corp, St Paul MN	66/69
	On Mark			Harold W. Buker, New London NH	70
				Cutless Aviation	
				Carlton B. Baker, Simsbury CT	72/74
				(open storage, Springfield VT 68/74)	
				David C. Tallichet/MARC, Chino CA	74/95
				gear collapsed Orlando FL, on del. to MARG	.75
				displ. Wings & Wheels Museum, Orlando FL	75/81
				museum closed	.81
				(noted West Palm Beach FL "3-2260" 84/91)	
18753	A-26C	43-22606		USAF: donated City of Boise ID	1.2.61
	GB-26C			displ. Boise ID	.61/72
18759	A-26C	43-22612	N3710G	Reading Aviation Service, Reading PA	61/64
	B-26C			Photo File Surveys Inc, Philadelphia PA	66
				Aero Service Corp, Washington DC	69/72
				Duane A. Egli, Fabens TX	77/80
				John Dozzo/Euroworld, Biggin Hill UK : del.	12.5.78/80
				op. by Cavalier Air Force, Biggin Hill	
				crashed dest. during airshow, Biggin Hill	21.9.80
18768	A-26C	43-22621	N9161Z	Blue Mountain Air Service, La Grande OR	
	B-26C			Hillcrest Aircraft Co, La Grande OR	63/64
				Butler Aircraft Co, Redmond OR (tanker #23)	66/70
				rep. dest. in hangar fire, Medford OR	
18796 •	A-26C	**43-22649**		(rebuilt as B-26K by On Mark)	11.11.64
	B-26C	64-17657		Davis Monthan AFB AZ: del. for storage	10.69/74
	B-26K		N62104	Arthur W. McDonnell, Mojave CA	25.7.74
	A-26A		N99218	Arthur W. McDonnell, Mojave CA	5.12.74/78
				crashed Chino CA	2.78
				(wreck noted Air Museum yard, Chino 10.78)	
				Rod & Rex Cadman, Canterbury UK	.86
				nose section shipped to Southend: spares use	7.86

				Booker Aircraft Museum:cockpit section displ.	4.88/94
18799 •	A-26C	**43-22652**	N8018E	L. B. Smith Aircraft Aircraft Corp, Miami FL	
	B-26C			Aerojet General Corp, Azusa CA	61/72
				Arthur W. McDonnell, Mojave CA	7.9.73/74
			C-GHCE	Conair Aviation Ltd, Abbotsford BC	6.74/88
				(tanker #3)	
				USAFM, Travis AFB CA: del.	18.7.88/94
				(displ. as "B-26K USAF/43-652/TA652")	
18800 •	A-26C	**43-22653**	N9402Z	Idaho Air Tankers Inc, Boise ID	63/64
	B-26C			Reeder Flying Service, Twin Falls ID	66/72
				(tanker #26)	
			C-GPTW	Air Spray Ltd, Red Deer ALTA (tanker #26)	5.81/96
18807 •	A-26C	**43-22660**	N3711G	D & O Equipment Co, Charlotte NC	63/64
	B-26C			John M. Sliker, Wadley GA	66
				Kem Air Inc, Worland WY	69/70
			CF-EZX	Air Spray Ltd, Edmonton ALTA (tanker #3)	.72/86
			C-FEZX	Air Spray Ltd, Red Deer ALTA (tanker #3)	89/96
18815 •	A-26C	**43-22668**	N3691G	R. K. Sanabria, Chicago IL	63
	B-26C			Will Martin/MACO Corp, Chicago IL	63
				(to FA Nicaragua as 602): del.	11.63/77
			N99422	David C. Tallichet/MARC, Chino CA	28.3.77/96
				(not del. to USA: abandoned Managua-Mercedes,	
				open storage as N99422 77/79)	
				(FAN 602/N99422 prev. incorrectly quoted as	
				41-39423: USCR quotes id. "423")	
18820	A-26C	43-22673	N9159Z	Blue Mountain Air Service, La Grande OR	
	B-26C			Hillcrest Aircraft Co, La Grande OR	63/64
				Butler Aircraft Co, Redmond OR	66/72
				(tanker #18)	
			C-GHLM	Conair Aviation Ltd, Abbotsford BC	4.75
				(tanker #324)	
				crashed fire bombing, Gates Lake BC	2.7.75
18826 •	A-26C		**43-22679**	(to R Saudi AF as 302): del.	18.2.54
	B-26B			(noted derelict, scrapyard, Riyadh 75/80)	
				King Faisal Air Academy, Riyadh: gate guard	90/96
18875	A-26C	43-22728		(to FA Chile as 842): BOC	9.3.58
	B-26C			Confederate Air Force, Harlingen TX: not del.	3.80
	B-26D			noted derelict, camoufl. FAC sc., Santiago	4.80
18876	A-26C	43-22729	N9424Z	Richard H. Steves, Miami FL	63/64
	B-26C			F. A. Conner, Miami FL	66/70
				stored Conner scrap compound, Miami FL	78
18877	A-26C	43-22730	N8027E	Madden & Smith Aircraft Corp, Miami FL	64
	B-26C			Consolidated Air Parts Co, Los Angeles CA	66/72
				derelict, unconv., Tucson AZ	69/72
27381	A-26B	44-34102	N4060A	noted USAF black sc., Teterboro NJ	8.59
	B-26C			John M. Sliker, Wadley GA	66
				Kem Air Inc, Worland WY	69/70
				Lynch Air Tankers, Billings MT (tanker #01)	72/83
				crashed fire bombing, Hubbards Fork KY	5.3.83
27382	A-26B	44-34103		(to R Saudi AF as 303): del.	16.4.55
	B-26B			open storage derelict, Jeddah Airport	76/80
27383 •	A-26B	44-34104	N9484Z	Will Martin/MACO Corp, Chicago IL	63
	B-26B			(to FA Nicaragua as 420, later 604): BOC	7.9.63/77

c/n	Type	Mil. serial	Civil reg.	Owner / history	Date
			N99420	David C. Tallichet/MARC, Chino CA	3.77/95
				Combat Air Museum, Topeka KS: loan	85/93
				(flew as "USAAF 434104/O-D")	
				(N99420 prev. incorrectly rep. as 41-39507:	
				USCR quotes id. "507", changed to 44-34104)	
27393	A-26B	44-34114		(to R Saudi AF as 305): del.	16.4.55
	B-26B			open storage derelict, Jeddah Airport	75/80
27398 •	A-26B	44-34119		(rebuilt as B-26K by On Mark)	19.9.64
	TB-26B	64-17651		Davis Monthan AFB AZ: del. for storage	17.1.70/71
	B-26K			Korean War Museum, Seoul, South Korea	73/96
	A-26A			(displ. as "USAF 65-17651/TA-651")	
27400 •	A-26B	**44-34121**	**N4805E**	Rock Island Oil & Refining Co, Wichita KS	64/69
	B-26B			Koch Industries Inc, Hutchison KS	72
	Monarch			Reeder Flying Service, Twin Falls ID	
				(conv. to tanker at Twin Falls; not op. by Reeder)	
				Lynch Air Tankers, Billings MT (tanker #58)	75/92
				Jerry Slater, Seattle WA	25.9.92
				Tony N. Grout, Spanaway WA	8.93/96
27413 •	A-26B	**44-34134**	N4974N		
	B-26B		N115RG	R. G. LeTourneau Inc, Longview TX	.54/66
	C-26B			Sam Sexton, Fort Smith AR: USCR	69/70
				impounded smuggling, Brasilia, Brazil	21.6.66
				(to FA Brasileira as FAB C-26B 5176)	21.6.66/75
				Museu de Armas e Veiculos Motorizados Antigos,	
				Bebedouro, Sao Paulo, Brazil	1.75/85
27415 •	A-26B	**44-34136**	N8017E	Madden & Smith Aircraft Corp, Miami FL	64
	B-26B			Donaire Inc, Phoenix AZ	66/69
				Thomas W. Hammon, Phoenix AZ	70
			CF-KBM	Kenting Aircraft Ltd, Toronto ONT	8.72
				Conair Aviation Ltd, Abbotsford BC	8.73
				(tanker #320)	
			C-FKBM	Air Spray Ltd, Red Deer ALTA (tanker #20)	.85/96
27423	A-26B	44-34144		(to R Saudi AF as 308): del.	16.4.55
	B-26B			open storage derelict, Jeddah Airport	76
27425	A-26B	44-34146	N5426E	Rock Island Oil & Refining Co, Wichita KS	
	B-26B			Aeronautical Services Corp, Cheyenne WY	64
				Don A. Goodman, Missoula MT	69/72
				crashed, Idaho Falls ID	10.7.73
				crashed and dest., Grand Valley CO	16.7.76
27427	A-26B	44-34148	N6842D	Rock Island Oil & Refining Co, Wichita KS	64/69
	B-26B			Consolidated Aero Export Corp, Los Angeles	70/72
				(probably bu 1960s)	
27432	A-26B	44-34153	N8022E	Madden & Smith Aircraft Corp, Miami FL	64
	B-26B			Consolidated Air Parts Co, Los Angeles CA	66/69
				derelict, unconv., Tucson AZ	69/72
27435	A-26B	44-34156	XB-COM	Altos Hornos de Mexico	
	TB-26B		XC-CAZ	Petroleos Mexicanos - PEMEX	60/67
			N190M	JRT Aero Service Co, Wichita Falls TX	69
				John E. Morgan, Las Vegas NV	70
				Antonio Ortiz, Santee CA	76
				Joseph Morgan, Leucadia CA	77
				Toni Widham	81
				I. N. Burchinall Jr, Paris TX	84
				Jim Ricketts/Aero Nostalgia Inc, Stockton CA	8.85/88

				crashed on del., Pattonville TX (parts used in static rest. of 43-22523 at Stockton 86/88 as "434156/BC-156")	17.8.85
27444 •	A-26B TB-26B	**44-34165**	N9146H	Cornell Aero Laboratory Inc, Buffalo NY Calspan Corp, Buffalo NY/Edwards AFB CA USAFM, Edwards AFB CA: stored	.63/72 .72/86 86/96
27451 •	A-26B B-26C	**44-34172**	N4806E	Rock Island Oil & Refining Co, Wichita KS Consolidated Aero Export Corp, Los Angeles Dennis W. Childers, Claremore OK Courtesy Aircraft Inc, Rockford IL (stored unconv. 60/85, no civil conversion) Rod & Rex Cadman, Canterbury, Kent UK shipped to UK for rebuild: arr. Southend A-26 Europe Inc, Rockford IL: USCR (rest. to fly, Southend UK)	64/66 69/72 4.83/84 85 .86/91 17.7.86 6.88/96
27473	A-26B B-26B	44-34194		(to R Saudi AF as 309) open storage derelict, Jeddah Airport	6.55 76/80
27477 •	A-26B B-26B B-26K A-26A	**44-34198** 64-17679	 N269G C-GXTG **N4988N**	(rebuilt as B-26K by On Mark) Davis Monthan AFB AZ: del. for storage State of Georgia Forestry Comm., Macon GA (open storage unconv., Macon GA 72/77) Air Spray Ltd, Edmonton ALTA: not del. dam. on landing during test flight, Macon GA Arnie Carnegie, Edmonton ALTA: dam. Denny Lynch/Lynch Air Service, Billings MT (rebuilt Macon .78, flies as "USAF IF-679")	15.4.65 10.69/71 .71/77 .77 .77 78 9.78/96
27490	A-26B B-26C	44-34211	N8024E	Madden & Smith Aircraft Corp, Miami FL Consolidated Air Parts Co, Los Angeles CA derelict, unconv., (LA.ANG) Tucson AZ	64 66/69 69/71
27592 •	A-26B B-26B	**44-34313**	N5457V **C-GHLK**	Aero Atlas Inc, Red Bluff CA Wilson Aviation Industries, Lewiston ID Butler Aircraft, Redmond OR (tanker #A20; #16) Conair Aviation Ltd, Abbotsford BC (tanker #323) Reynolds Aviation Museum, Wetaskiwin ALTA Don Crowe, Victoria BC Canadian Warplane Heritage, Hamilton ONT (flies as "French AF 434313/K/BC-313")	 63/64 66/70 4.75/87 5.87/88 89/90 .90/96
27607	A-26B B-26B B-26C	44-34328	N9422Z	Atlas Investment, Los Angeles CA: ex USAF Belcher Aircraft Corp, Mojave CA Acme Aircraft Parts Inc, Compton CA Allied Aircraft Sales, Litchfield Park AZ Oliver D. Terry, Tucson AZ Aeronautic Services Corp, Cheyenne WY Ralph S. Johnson/RALCO, Cheyenne WY Greg Board/Aero Associates Inc, Tucson AZ (to FA Portuguesa as 7102): del. (rebuilt Tucson AZ .65 by Hamilton Aircraft for FAP) (conv. from B-26B to B-26C in FAP service) wfu, abandoned Luanda, Angola	15.3.60 18.8.60/61 7.2.61 14.3.61/62 14.3.62/63 14.8.63/64 15.5.64/65 25.3.65 6.65/75 11.75
27623	A-26B B-26B	44-34344	N91356	Greg Board/Aero Associates Inc, Tucson AZ (planned sale to FA Portuguesa: not completed) Ames Applicator Corp, Ames IA: sprayer Aero Union Corp, Chico CA dam., nose wheel collapse, Ames IA broken up, Ames IA	65 66/70 72 .72 c74

c/n	Type	Serial	Reg.	Owner / Notes	Date
27669	A-26B	44-34390		(to l'Armee de l'Air as 44-34390): BOC	16.2.54
	B-26C			based Indochina: ret. to USAF	10.11.55
				(open storage Clark AFB, Philippines 55/58)	
			N6836D	Rock Island Oil & Refining Co, Wichita KS	64/69
				Wells Aircraft Inc, Hutchinson KS	.70/72
				Edron Co, Las Vegas NV	77
				sale rep. (probably bu 1960s)	78
27694	A-26B	44-34415	HP-322	CIA: "Operation Pluto", Cuba	10.60/61
	B-26B		N5002X (2	CIA/Gulf Air Inc, Miami FL	12.7.62/63
				CIA/Intermountain Aviation Inc, Marana AZ	30.1.63
				On Mark Aviation, Van Nuys CA	7.63/64
	Marksman			(rebuilt by On Mark to approx Marksman config:	
				test aircraft for On Mark covert modifications)	
			N900V	CIA/Intermountain Aviation Inc, Marana AZ	15.2.64
				CIA/Atlantic General Enterprises,	
				Washington DC	4.8.64/65
				CIA/Intermountain Aviation Inc, Marana AZ	29.3.65/67
				CIA/Pan Aero Investment Corp, Reno NV	3.2.67
			N46598	CIA/Air America: Laos ops: "Blue Goose"	5.4.67/68
				CIA/Overseas Aeromarine Inc, Seattle WA	30.3.68
				rep. dest., struck-off USCR	18.9.68
				(note: N5002X id. changed from 44-35242 to	
				44-34415 6.62)	
27702	A-26B	44-34423	N9594Z	Stahmann Farms Inc, Las Cruces NM	63/72
	B-26B			Victor W. Newman	73
	On Mark		C-GHLI	Conair Aviation Ltd, Abbotsford BC	1.75
				(tanker #329) : struck-off reg.	6.86
27787 •	A-26B	44-34508	**N74874**	Kreitzberg Aviation, Salem OR	63/66
	B-26B			Rosenbalm Aviation, Medford OR	69/72
				William Dempsay, East Wenatchee WA	77
				(tanker #107)	
				Bruce Kinney, Richey MT (tanker #107)	6.81/96
27799 •	A-26B	44-34520	N9420Z	A. S. Wilstrom Inc, New York NY	63/72
	B-26B		C-GHCF	Conair Aviation Ltd, Abbotsford BC	4.74/88
				(tanker #328)	
				USAFM: for trade	.88
			N94207	Hawkins & Powers Aviation, Greybull WY	21.11.88
			N126HP	Hawkins & Powers Aviation, Greybull WY	7.89/96
				(tanker #28)	
27802 •	A-26B	44-34523	N9174Z	On Mark Engineering Co, Van Nuys CA	63
	B-26B			Garrett Corp, Los Angeles CA & Phoenix AZ	64/77
				(turboprop flight-testing in nose position)	
			C-GTOX	Air Spray Ltd, Red Deer ALTA (tanker #14)	1.82/96
27805 •	A-26B	44-34526	N827W	A. M. Wheaton Glass Corp	
	B-26B		N551EH	E.T.S. Hokin & Galvin Corp, San Francisco CA	64/66
	Marksman		N400V	CWC Air Inc, Flushing MI	69
			N7977	Certified Check & Title Corp, Wilkesboro NY	70
				Twin Cities Aviation, Edina MN	72
			N26AB	Dennis M. Sherman, West Palm Beach FL	76/78
				Oklahoma Aircraft Sales, Yukon OK	4.81/86
				Continental Jet Inc, Clarksville TN	3.87
				Charles Bella, El Paso TX/ Chaparral NM	3.88/96
				(wfu Santa Rosa NM 90/95 *Intimate Invader*)	
27814 •	A-26B	**44-34535**	N8020E	L. B. Smith Aircraft Corp, Miami FL: ex USAF	12.6.59
	B-26B			Smith LAtin Americana Inc, Wilmington DE	29.12.61
				Madden & Smith Aircraft Corp, Miami FL	25.1.62/63

				Hamilton Aircraft Co, Tucson AZ	5.11.63
				Aero Union Corp, Anderson CA	11.63/65
				Greg Board/Aero Associates Inc, Tucson AZ	26.3.65
				(to FA Portuguesa as 7101): del.	6.65/75
				wfu, abandoned Luanda, Angola	11.75
				recov. to Cuba by Cuban forces in Angola	
				Museum of the Revolution, Playa Giron, Cuba	90/96
				(displ. as "FAR 933")	
27817 •	A-26B	**44-34538**		(to l'Armee de l'Air as 44-34538): BOC	3.1.51/55
	B-26B			based Indochina: ret. to USAF	22.10.55
				(open storage Clark AFB, Philippines 55/58)	
			N6839D	Rock Island Oil & Refining Co, Wichita KS	64
				Hughes Aircraft Co, Culver City CA	66/87
				Gower Lebel Inc, Seattle WA	88
				William Tinner/A & T Productions Inc CA	5.90
			N34538	A & T Productions Inc, Pacific Palisades CA	9.90/96
				(flies in black USAF sc. as	
		"		434538/BC-538/T/*Feeding Frenzy*)	
27829	A-26B	44-34550	N7769C	On Mark Engineering Co, Van Nuys CA	
	B-26B		CF-CCR	Canadian Comstock Co, Toronto ONT	.62/66
	On Mark		N355Q	Orange County Airways Inc, Montgomery NY	69/70
			HK-1247W	J. R. Acosta & L. C. H. Lizcano	
			HK-1247P	J. R. Acosta & L. C. H. Lizcano	
				crashed on take-off, Bogota-El Dorado	21.9.88
27834 •	A-26B	**44-34555**		(to l'Armee de l'Air as 44-34555): BOC	3.1.51/55
	B-26B			based Indochina: ret. to USAF	10.11.55
				(open storage Clark AFB, Philippines 55/58)	
	On Mark		N84W	E. G. Rodman/Rodman Supply Co, Odessa TX	63/70
			N841W	Carl W. Swan, Oklahoma City OK	.71/72
			N5BP	rereg.	.73
			N550	Rojo Inc, Hilton Head Island SC	77
				Bank of Beaufort, Hilton Head Island SC	.78
				Larry S. Jeter, Lubbock TX	84/89
				Southwest Aviation Inc, Fairacres NM	8.89
			N26HK	Hal Kaden/Southwest Aviation, Fairacres NM	9.90/96
				(open storage, Opa Locka FL 84/91: noted	
				dism., Las Cruces NM 10.95)	
27838 •	A-26B	**44-34559**		USAFM, Jackson ANGB, Jackson MS	73/94
	B-26B			(displ. on pole as "USAF 0-34559")	
27846 •	A-26B	**44-34567**	N9412Z	On Mark Engineering Co, Van Nuys CA	
	B-26B		ZS-CVD	South African Iron & Steel Industrial Corp,	
	Marksman			Wonderboom, South Africa	2.62/71
				damaged, belly landing, Omaruru	13.1.71
				SAAF Museum, Ysterplaat AB	.77/82
				SAAF Museum, Sanke Valley AB: stored	2.82/96
27847 •	A-26B	**44-34568**		(to l'Armee de l'Air as 44-34568): BOC	3.1.51/55
	B-26B			based Indochina: ret. to USAF	16.11.55
				(open storage Clark AFB, Philippines 55/58)	
			N202PP	Purolator Products, New York NY	59/64
				J. P. O'Connor, Fort Lauderdale FL: USCR	66/70
				op: Daniel H. Walcott/Trans Atlantic Airlines,	
				Frankfurt WG: rep. gun-running in Pakistan	.65
			AP-AVV	M. Anwar Khan, Karachi	.70
				wfu, open storage Karachi	81/92
27860	A-26B	44-34581	N8038E	Madden & Smith Aircraft Corp, Miami FL	64
	B-26C			Consolidated Air Parts Co, Los Angeles CA	66/72
				derelict, unconv., Tucson AZ	69/72

27865	A-26B XB-26F	44-34586	N66368	Lindsay Hopkins Vocational School, Miami FL (probably bu 1960s)	64/72
27869	A-26B B-26B	44-34590	HP-323 N5000X (2 N19777	CIA: "Operation Pluto" Cuba CIA/Gulf Air Inc, Miami FL CIA/Continental Air Co, Miami FL rep. dism., struck-off USCR (note: N5000X changed id. from 44-34376 to 44-34590 6.62)	10.60 4.6.62/63 1.11.63/65 22.6.65
27871	A-26B TB-26B	44-34592	N8631E CF-FJG C-FFJG	Rock Island Oil & Refining Co, Wichita KS Consolidated Air Parts Co, Los Angeles CA Da Pro Rubber Inc, Van Nuys CA Mercury Flights, Edmonton ALTA Conair Aviation Ltd, Abbotsford BC (tanker #329) crashed, dest., Mercury ALTA	64/66 69 70/72 4.73 6.74 29.9.74
27881 •	A-26B B-26B Monarch	**44-34602**	N8392H **N167B**	Stahmann Farms Inc, Las Cruces NM RLS 51 Ltd, San Francisco CA (del. Oslo 5.88 "434602": 8 gun nose) RLS 51 Ltd, San Francisco CA op: Scandinavian Historical Flight, Oslo (flies as "434602/BC-602/*Sugarland Express*)	64/87 .87/88 2.89/95 .88/96
27886	A-26B TB-26B	44-34607	N8395H CF-FBV	Stahmann Farms Inc, Las Cruces NM (noted Tucson AZ, unconv. USAF sc. 4.68) Conair Aviation Ltd, Abbotsford BC (tanker #323) crashed , dest.	64/70 5.71 3.12.74
27888 •	A-26B B-26B	44-34609	**N4819E**	Rock Island Oil & Refining Co, Wichita KS John Hamacher, San Francisco CA Thomas W. Hammon, Phoenix AZ Don Underwood/Donaire Inc, Phoenix AZ Global Air Museum: stored Litchfield Park AZ (open storage, ex tanker, Buckeye AZ 78/95)	 63/69 70 2.81/96 72
27889 •	A-26B VB-26B	**44-34610**		(ANG Bureau: last flying USAF B-26): SOC handed over to NASM at Andrews AFB MD NASM, Silver GHills Store MD	12.10.72 17.9.72 .72/88
27894	A-26B B-26C	44-34615	N4817E	Rock Island Oil & Refining Co, Wichita KS Consolidated Air Parts Co, Los Angeles CA Hamilton Aircraft Co, Tucson AZ (to FA Brasileira as B-26C 5173): BOC (rebuilt Tucson AZ .69 by Hamilton for FAB)	64/66 69 68/69 6.69/75
27895	A-26B VB-26B L.A.S. Super 26	44-34616	N300V	Commonwealth Plan Inc, Boston MA Daniel G. Van Clief, Esmont VA Omni Investment Corp, Washington DC sale rep., USCR	 64/66 69/70 .78/96
27899	A-26B B-26B	44-34620	HP-318-P N5001X (1	Los Hermanos Sebastian y Gomez SA, Panama (ex CIA covert ops. Indonesia .58) CIA/Gulf Air Inc, Miami FL (to USAF "Project Farm Gate" Vietnam .63) (note: N5001X id. changed from 44-34620 to 44-35698 6.62)	61 .62
27903	A-26B B-26B	44-34624	N6101C	Farah Manufacturing Co, El Paso TX Rogers Brothers, Beaumont TX Texas State Optical Corp Confederate Air Force, Harlingen TX	63/64 66/69 69 1.70/77

				(flew as "RG-A")	
27921	A-26B	44-34642	N8626E	Rock Island Oil & Refing Co, Wichita KS	64/66
	TB-26B			Allied Aircraft Sales Corp, Tucson AZ	69
				derelict, unconv., Tucson AZ	69/72
27932	A-26B	44-34653	N9417H	Cornell Aeronautical Laboratories, Buffalo NY	63/72
	B-26B			Calspan Corp, Buffalo NY	77
				wing failed, crashed near Edwards AFB CA	3.3.81
27938 •	A-26B	**44-34659**	N9163Z	National Flight Services Inc, Toledo OH	63/64
	B-26B			David Voltz, Phoenix AZ	66
				Aircraft Specialties Inc, Mesa AZ	69/72
				Kenting Aviation, Toronto ONT	74
				struck-off USCR	30.5.74
				Mackie's Moving & Storage Co, Oshawa ONT	75/94
				(displ. on warehouse roof Oshawa 75/94)	
27944 •	A-26B	**44-34665**		ANG Bureau, Washington DC: wfu	19.11.69
	TB-26B			USAFM, Offutt AFB NE	74/94
	VB-26B				
27950	A-26B	44-34671		(to R Saudi AF as 301)	5.55
	TB-26B			open storage derelict, Jeddah Airport	76/80
27961	A-26B	44-34682	HP-319	Los Hermanos Sebastian y Gomez SA, Panama	61
	B-26B			(ex CIA ops Indonesia .58, to USAF	
				Operation Farm Gate Vietnam .63)	
				crashed	22.9.66
				(also quoted as 44-34672; -34682 bel. correct)	
27976 •	A-26B	**44-34697**	N4807E	Rock Island Oil & Refining Co, Wichita KS	64/66
	B-26B			Consolidated Aero Export, Los Angeles CA	69/72
				David C. Tallichet/MARC, Chino CA	12.73/92
27987	A-26B	44-34708	N4808E	Rock Island Oil & Refining Co, Wichita KS	64/66
	B-26B			Consolidated Aero Export, Los Angeles CA	69/72
				(probably bu 1960s)	
27992 •	A-26B	**44-34713**		(to l'Armee de l'Air as 44-34713): BOC	26.1.54/55
	B-26B			based Indochina: ret. to USAF	10.11.55
	B-26C			(open storage Clark AFB, Philippines 55/58)	
			N706ME	Star Flite Inc	61
	Marketeer			On Mark Engineering Co, Van Nuys CA	63/64
			N36BB (2	W. R. Bailard, Ventura CA	66/72
			N26MR	Micky Rupp, Mansfield OH	74
				Sherman Aircraft Sales, West Palm Beach FL	1.75
			N26WB	Don Whittington, Fort Lauderdale FL	.75
				A. S. Barber Inc, Kirksville MO	77
				sale rep., Danville IL	84/86
				Mid South Aircraft Sales Inc, Memphis TN	3.87
				Wayne County Sheriff Dept, Detroit MI	7.88
				National Warplane Museum, Geneseo NY	88/92
			N706ME	Nostalgia Inc, Denton TX	11.92/96
28001 •	A-26B	**44-34722**	N3222T	Wilson C. Edwards/CAF, San Angelo TX	63/69
	TB-26B			(to FA Salvadorena as 600): del.	8.69/74
			N62289	John J. Stokes, San Marcos TX	.74/81
			N3222T	John J. Stokes, San Marcos TX	4.81/92
				(flew as "4434722/Frantic Fraye")	
				Courtesy Aircraft Inc, Rockford IL	4.92
				Northaire Inc, Wilmington DE	10.92/94
				Wally Fisk/Amjet Aircraft Corp, St. Paul MN	2.94
				Jack A. Erickson, Medford OR	4.96
				(N62289 quoted as id. "1125": SOR 7.84)	

c/n	Model	Serial	Reg	Owner / History	Date
28003	A-26B	44-34724	N7662C	The Robert Dollar Company	61
	B-26B			Pacific Flight Services Inc, Angwin CA	63/66
				Kem Air Inc, Worland WY	69/70
			CF-BVH	Dontuss Industries, Edmonton ALTA	8.70/74
				Air Spray Ltd, Edmonton ALTA	76/80
				(tanker #6)	
			C-FBVH	Air Spray Ltd, Red Deer ALTA	80
				crashed while firebombing, Slave Lake ALTA	24.4.80
28004	A-26B	44-34725	N4824E	Rock Island Oil & Refining Co, Wichita KS	64
	B-26B			Manuel S. Jovenich, New York NY	66/70
				stripped, derelict hulk, Homer AK	73
28005 •	A-26B	**44-34726**	N3152G	Aeronautic Services Corp, Cheyenne WY	64
	B-26B			RALCO, Cheyenne WY: USCR	66/70
				Greg Board/Aero Associates Inc, Tucson AZ	65
				(to FA Portuguesa as 7104): del.	7.65/76
				(rebuilt Tucson by Hamilton Aircraft for FAP)	
				Museo do Ar, Alverca AB, Portugal	.76/96
				(stored: incomplete, major components)	
28015	A-26B	44-34736	N4821E	Rock Island Oil & Refining Co, Wichita KS	64/66
	B-26C			Allied Aircraft Sales Corp, Tucson AZ	69/72
				derelict unconv. ("MATS/Cont.") Tucson AZ	69/72
28017 •	A-26B	**44-34738**	N600D	Dean Milk Co, Franklin Park IL	64/72
	B-26B		N808D		
	On Mark		**C-GWLU**	Air Spray Ltd, Red Deer ALTA	5.75/96
				(tanker #8 *Old Yeller*)	
28020 •	A-26C	**44-34741**		(to FA Chile as FAC 848): BOC	2.60
	TB-26B			displ. Municipal Park, Mejillones, Chile	82
	TB-26D			El Bosque AB, Santiago: displ. as "FAC 846"	92/96
				(see also 44-35937)	
28025	A-26B	44-34746		displ. VFW Post 382, El Reno OK	73
	B-26B				
28028 •	A-26B	**44-34749**	N4823E	Rock Island Oil & Refining Co, Wichita KS	64/66
	B-26B			Hamilton Aircraft Co, Tucson AZ	68/69
	B-26C			(to FA Brasileira as B-26C 5174): BOC	6.69/75
				(rebuilt Tucson AZ .69 by Hamilton for FAB)	
				wfu, SOC FAB	12.75
				ESPAer, Sao Paulo: instructional airframe	
			N4959K	Don Davis/Tired Racing Team, Casper WY	9.84
				(ferried Brazil-US .84, rest. as *Puss in Boots*)	
				Guarantee Federal Bank, Casper WY	.87
				Airplane Sales Intnl., Beverly Hills CA	8.87/88
				Gary Abrams/Abrams Airborne Manufacturing,	
				Tucson AZ (flies as 85/*Puss in Boots*)	10.89/96
28034	A-26B	44-34755		not del. USAF: to Reconstruction Finance Corp	.45/46
			N67839	Superior Oil Co, Lafayette LA	54
				Ken McGee Oil Industries Inc	
			N256H (1	Flint Steel Corp, Tulsa OK	63/64
				Mid America Pipeline Co, Tulsa OK	66
			N3035S (2	John Rourke, Bartlesville OK	69
				Intercontinental Mining, New York NY	70/72
				Rebel Aviation Inc, Atlanta GA	77
				struck-off USCR	.78
28035	A-26B	44-34756		not del. USAF: to Reconstruction Finance Corp	.45/46
			NL67157	Charles H. Babb Co, Glendale CA	6.2.46
				(surplus sale, Kingman Field AZ 2.46)	

				Fairchild Aerial Surveys, Los Angeles CA	12.46/47
			YV-C-CTV	Fairchild Aerial Surveys, Venezuala	1.47
			N67157	B. B. Ranch, Ventura CA: USCR	30.8.47/51
	B-26C			(to l'Armee de l'Air as 157, 44-34756): BOC	.51/68
	B-26TMR			op. by CEV for weapons tests: wfu, scrapped	.68
28037	A-26B	44-34758		not del. USAF: to Reconstruction Finance Corp	.45/46
			NL67908	Charles H. Babb Co, Glendale CA	6.2.46/48
				(surplus sale, Kingman Field AZ 2.46)	
			N67908	Ford Motor Co, Detroit MI	6.2.48/52
				(to l'Armee de l'Air as 908, 44-34758): BOC	4.2.52
				wfu, stored Chateaudun AB, France	8.67/72
28038 •	A-26B	**44-34759**		not del. USAF: to Reconstruction Finance Corp	.45/46
			NX67834	Milton Reynolds ("Reynolds Bombshell")	.47/48
				(Around-World record flight 7-10.8.47)	
			N67834	Phillips Drilling Corp, San Antonio TX	.49/54
				(exec. conv. completed at Dallas TX 10.49)	
				Earl F. Slick/Piedmont Airlines	
				Jack Davis NC: adv. for sale	12.55
			N28W	rereg.	
			N956	Colorado Interstate Gas, Colorado Springs CO	59/64
			N956R	Colorado Oil & Gas Corp, Denver CO	66
				Northrop Corp, Newbury Park CA	69/72
				Jerry Cornell, Tehran, Iran	77
				Bell Helicopter International Inc, Tehran	78
				wfu, abandoned Tehran, Iran	76/86
28040 •	A-26B	**44-34761**		not del. USAF: to Reconstruction Finance Corp	.45/46
	Marksman		N67158	Superior Oil Co, Lafayette LA	54
			N400E	Colorado Interstate Gas, Colorado Springs CO	61/64
				Occidental Leasing Corp, Los Angeles CA	66/69
			N60XY	Occidental Chemical Corp, Los Angeles CA	70/72
			N60XX	sale rep., Fort Lauderdale FL: USCR	76/95
28041 •	A-26B	**44-34762**		not del. USAF: to Reconstruction Finance Corp	.45/46
			N4000	Swiflite Aircraft Corp, New York NY	54
			N4000K	Slick Airways, San Antonio TX	
				Aero Service Corp, Philadelphia PA	63/66
				Aero Service Corp, Manila, Philippines	69/72
				abandoned, Dili, Portuguese Timor	75/86
28044 •	A-26B	**44-34765**		not del. USAF: to Reconstruction Finance Corp	.45/46
			N67160	Sperry Gyroscope Co, Great Neck NY	54/64
				R. C. Johnson, Las Vegas NV	66
				International Commercial Aviation Service Ltd,	
				Kennedy International Airport NY	69/70
				(del. to Europe via Shannon 10.7.69)	
			D-CAFY	Walter Rall, Munich: reg. res.	12.68
			N67160	lsd: Antwerspe Kreesten Central, Antwerp	68/69
				(impounded Antwerp, Belgium .69,	
				open storage Antwerp Airport 69/74)	
				Musee Royal de l'Armee, Brussels: displ.	76/95
28045 •	A-26B	**44-34766**		not del. USAF: to Reconstruction Finance Corp	.45/46
			N67807	Dianna Cyrus (race #91)	.47/49
				Stanolind Oil & Gas Co, Tulsa OK	54
			N1243	Pan American Petroleum Corp, Tulsa OK	61/64
				Standard Oil Co (Indiana), Chicago IL	31.5.65
			N910G	Nine Ten Corp, Chicago IL	4.8.65/66
			N9150	Paramount Trading Co, Vero Beach CA	68/69
				Miami Aircraft Ventures Inc, Miami FL	70/72
				Vicky Miller, Burbank CA	77
				USAFM, Castle AFB CA	83
				(displ. Castle as "USN JD-1 34766" port side;	

c/n	Type	Serial	Reg	Owner / History	Date
				and "USAF 34766/*Mary Jo*" starboad side)	
				(noted at Stockton CA, camouflaged 7.84)	
				V. Mark Johnson, Lakewood CO	12.84/87
				Donald Douglas Museum, Santa Monica CA	.87/90
				(displ. as 434766/*Pretty Patti/J*)	
				Larry Leaf, Williston FL	90/91
				David Brady, Cartersville GA	91/92
				dam. in midair collision with Brady's T-37,	
				landed safely Cartersville GA	7.6.91
				Reva J. Brady, Cartersville GA	2.92
				Museum of Flying, Santa Monica CA	93
				(rest. Mojave CA .93/95 to exec. config.)	
			N26BK	Howard B. Keck/Thermco Aviation,	25.5.94/96
				Coachella CA	
28048 •	A-26B	**44-34769**		not del. USAF: to Reconstruction Finance Corp	.45/46
	On Mark		N67162	Superior Oil Co Inc, Lafayette LA	50/54
			N500M	Fletcher Oil & Gas	
				H. B. Zachry Co, San Antonio TX	64/66
				George J. Rivera, Milton CA	69
				Priority Air Transport System, Redwood CA	70
				Lloyd A. Hamilton, Santa Rosa CA (race #16)	71/72
			N29711	John J. Mark, Hales Corner WI	77
				George J. Rivera, San Jose CA	12.81
			N500MR	George J. Rivera, San Jose CA	3.82/89
				William M. Farrell, Cincinatti OH	5.90/92
				Sea Link Aviation Inc, Wilmington DE	6.95
				(flies as 434769/K/*Gator Invader*,	
				del. via Keflavik 9.9.95 en route to Greece)	
28052 •	A-26B	**44-34773**		not del. USAF: to Reconstruction Finance Corp	.45/46
				Charles H. Babb Co, Los Angeles CA	2.46
				(sold as surplus, Kingman Field AZ 2.46)	
			N67944	Stevens & Co, New Orleans LA	51
	B-26C			(to l'Armee de l'Air as 052, 44-34773): BOC	5.10.51/70
	B-26TMR			Musee de l'Air et de l'Espace, Paris	.70/93
				(stored Paris Le Bourget-Dugny AB 93)	
28053 •	A-26B	**44-34774**		not del. USAF: to Reconstruction Finance Corp	.45/46
			N67163	Standard Oil Co, Chicago IL	49/54
			N163Y	Standard Oil Co of Indiana, Chicago IL	61/64
				Pan American Petroleum Corp, Tulsa OK	65
				Standard Oil Co of Indiana, Chicago IL	31.5.65
			N910Y	Nine Ten Corp, Chicago IL	4.8.65
			N917Y	Greenacres Farm Inc, Lexington KY	66/72
				Joel McNeal, San Diego CA	77/84
				Courtesy Aircraft Inc, Rockford IL	.85
				Collings Foundation, Stowe MA	3.85/90
				Warbird & Vehicles Inc, Seattle WA	11.90/96
28056 •	A-26B	**44-34777**		not del. USAF: to Reconstruction Finance Corp	.45/46
			N66661	Stanolind Oil & Gas Co, Tulsa OK	54
	Marksman		N1242	Pan American Petroleum Corp, Tulsa OK	61/64
				Standard Oil Co (Indiana), Chicago IL	31.5.65
			N910F	Nine Ten Corp, Chicago IL	4.8.65/66
			N919P	Republic National Bank of Tulsa, Tulsa OK	69/70
				ditched in Lake Michigan (later salvaged)	c.71
				Walter Soplata Collection, Newbury OH	83/85
28057 •	A-26B	**44-34778**		not del. USAF: to Reconstruction Finance Corp	.45/46
			N67943	Raytheon Manufacturing Co, Bedford MA	54/75
			C-GWLT	Air Spray Ltd, Red Deer ALTA	5.75/96
				(tanker #7, #98)	

28480	A-26C B-26C	44-35201	N8025E N137WG N437W	L. B. Smith Aircraft Corp, Miami FL Woodward Governor Co, Rockford IL Supreme Machine Products, Rockford IL Stan Burnstein, Tulsa OK Lester Risley, Anchorage AK	 63/66 69/70 72 77
28483 •	A-26C B-26C	**44-35204**		USAFM, Chanute AFB IL USAFM, Laughlin AFB TX (displ. Chanute & Laughlin as "434314")	65/91 96
28496	A-26C B-26C	44-35217	N4820E CF-FIM C-FFIM	Rock Island Oil & Refining Co, Wichita KS Flight Enterprises Inc, Prescott AZ (tanker #C29) Air Spray Ltd, Edmonton ALTA Air Spray Ltd, Red Deer ALTA tanker #5" crashed near Calgary ALTA	 63/72 5.73 84 13.7.84
28503 •	A-26C B-26C	**44-35224**	N9421Z **N6240D**	Belcher Aircraft Corporation Fred M. Strozer, Beverley Hills CA John Moore, Toluca Lake CA I. N. Burchinall Jr, Brookston & Paris TX Milt Stollak, Burbank CA USAFM, March AFB CA: del. (displ. as "44-35224/*Sweet Miss Lillian*)	 63/64 66 69/77 4.78 4.78/96
28511	A-26C B-26B TB-26B GB-26B	44-35232		USAF/Inter-American Air Forces Academy, Howard AFB, Panama Canal Zone (ground inst. airframe, marked "G-5")	 74
28517	A-26C B-26C	44-35238	N3477G	L. B. Smith Aircraft Corp, Miami FL derelict, unconv. Miami FL	64/70 68/72
28519	A-26C B-26C	44-35240	N122Y N1221	Ayer Associates Automobile Inc Trathan Drilling, Shreveport LA W. L. Bostwick, Palm Beach FL Wilco Aviation, Jacksonville FL John P. Coate, Miami FL	 63/66 69 70 72
28546	A-26C B-26B	44-35267	 N8034E	(to l'Armee de l'Air as 44-35267): BOC based Indochina: ret. to USAF Madden & Smith Aircraft Corp, Miami FL Consolidated Air Parts Co, Los Angeles CA derelict, unconv., Tucson AZ	7.4.54 4.9.54 64 66/72 69/72
28550	A-26C RB-26C	44-35271	N4809E	Rock Island Oil & Refining Co, Wichita KS Consolidated Aero Export Corp, Los Angeles (probably bu 1960s)	64/66 69/72
28602 •	A-26C RB-26C	**44-35323**	N8026E CF-CDD N8026E	L. B. Smith Aircraft Corp, Miami FL Kreitzberg Aviation, Salem OR Aeroflight Inc, Troutdale OR Aero Union Corp, Chico CA Conair Aviation Ltd, Abbotsford BC Aero Union Corp, Chico CA (tanker #C55) William Dempsay, East Wenatchee WA (tanker #55) Don A. Goodman, Missoula MT (tanker) Lester Risley, Anchorage AK (sand tanker) Don Rogers, Anchorage AK The Air Museum, Chino CA: del. (flies as "435323/*Ginny Sue*")	 64/66 69 .69 5.70 9.70/72 77 .77 78 79/80 7.80/96
28605 •	A-26C B-26C	**44-35326**	**N401Y**	Boothe Leasing Corp, San Francisco CA Business Aircraft Lessors, Elyria OH	63/66 69/70

				Active Air Inc, Wakeman OH	77
				George J. Rivera, San Jose CA	.81/84
				Endless Turn Inc, Leoti KS	87/88
				Stallion Aircraft, Bensenville IL	5.90/96
28624	A-26C	44-35345	N8031E	(to l'Armee de l'Air as 44-35345): BOC	7.4.54
	B-26B			based Indochina: ret. to USAF	27.8.54
				(open storage Clark AFB, Philippines 55/57)	
				Madden & Smith Aircraft Co, Miami FL	64
				Consolidated Air Parts Co, Los Angeles CA	66/69
				derelict, unconv., Tucson AZ	69/71
28637	A-26C	44-35358	N7774C	D. P. Carlo, Tehachapi CA	63/66
	RB-26C			Da Pro Rubber, Van Nuys CA	69
				Barry W. Morse, Los Angeles CA	70
				(noted Mojave CA "Precision Components" 11.69)	
28642	A-26C	44-35363	N91347	Hamilton Aircraft Co, Tucson AZ	64
	RB-26C			Greg Board/Aero Associates Inc, Tucson AZ	65
				(to FA Portuguesa as 7107): del.	8.65/75
				(rebuilt Tucson by Hamilton Aircraft for FAP)	
	B-26B			(conv. to B-26B in FAP service)	
				wfu, abandoned Luanda, Angola	75
28644	A-26C	44-35365	N91353	Greg Board/Aero Associates Inc, Tucson AZ	65
	B-26C			(planned sale to FA Portuguesa: not completed)	
				Flight Enterprises Inc, Prescott AZ	66/69
				derelict, unconv. ("MT ANG") Tucson AZ	69/72
28650 •	A-26C	**44-35371**	**N4818E**	Rock Island Oil & Refining Co, Wichita, KS	64/66
	TB-26C			Consolidated Air Parts Co, Los Angeles CA	67
				Denny Lynch/Lynch Air Tankers, Billings MT	.67/96
				(tanker #A28, later #59)	
28651 •	A-26C	**44-35372**		(to l'Armee de l'Air as 44-35345): BOC	7.4.54
	B-26B			based Indochina: ret. to USAF	27.8.54
			N8028E	Madden & Smith Aircraft Corp, Miami FL	64
				Consolidated Air Parts Co, Los Angeles CA	66/95
				(open storage derelict unconv., Tucson AZ 69/72)	
				Pima County Air Museum, Tucson AZ	76/96
				(stored dism. unconv., Pima)	
28664	A-26C	44-35385	N91352	Greg Board/Aero Associates Inc, Tucson AZ	65
	RB-26C			(planned sale to FA Portuguesa: not completed)	
	TB-26C			Flight Enterprises Inc, Prescott AZ	66/69
				derelict unconv., Tucson AZ	69/75
28704	A-26C	44-35425	N3427G	(to l'Armee de l'Air as 44-35425): BOC	6.4.54
	B-26B			based Indochina: ret. to USAF	31.8.54
				Aero Enterprises Inc	
				Pacific Flight Service Inc, Angwin CA	63/64
				James L. Shipley/Kem-Air, Worland WY	66/70
				(tanker #B27)	
				Lynch Air Tankers, Billings MT	73/76
				(tanker #B27, later #59)	
				crashed fire bombing, Grand Junction CO	8.8.76
28718 •	A-26C	**44-35439**		(to l'Armee de l'Air as 44-35439): BOC	6.4.54
	B-26B			based Indochina: ret. to USAF	4.9.54
			N74833	JPR Corp, Miami FL	.63/69
				John M. Sliker, Wadley GA	70/72
				John J. Stokes, San Marcos TX	77
				Lynch Air Tankers, Billings MT	4.5.79/90
				Evergreen Ventures Inc/	

				Evergreen Heritage Collection, Marana AZ	3.90/96
				(flies as "USAF 435439")	
28719 •	A-26C	**44-35440**		(to l'Armee de l'Air as 44-35345): BOC	16.2.54
	B-26B			based Indochina: ret. to USAF	22.10.55
				(open storage Clark AFB, Philippines 55/58)	
			N6838D	Rock Island Oil & Refining Co, Wichita KS	64/72
				Aero Union Corp, Chico CA	71
			CF-MSB	Conair Aviation Ltd, Abbotsford BC	6.71
				(tanker #325)	
			C-FMSB	Conair Aviation Ltd, Abbotsford BC	77/88
				USAFM, Travis AFB: del.	.88/96
				(displ. as "435440/BG-O")	
28723 •	A-26C	**44-35444**	N7656C	Vance Roberts, Seattle WA	63/70
	RB-26C		CF-TFB	Air Spray Ltd, Edmonton ALTA	71
			C-FTFB	Air Spray Ltd, Red Deer ALTA (tanker #4)	6.73/96
28735 •	A-26C	**44-35456**	N330WC	Western Contracting Corp, Sioux City IA	63/70
	RB-26C			Aero Union Corp, Chico CA	72
			CF-AGO	Conair Aviation Ltd, Abbotsford BC	7.72/80
				(tanker #326)	
				u/c collapsed landing, Fort St John BC	14.5.80
			C-FAGO	Air Spray Ltd, Red Deer ALTA	.83/96
				(tanker #36 "*Dragon Lady*")	
28736	A-26C	44-35457		(to l'Armee de l'Air as 457, 44-35457): BOC	4.9.56/66
	RB-26C			(conv. to RB-26P 11.61)	
	RB-26P		F-BMKT	Societe Carta, Creil: CofA issued	5.5.66
			ZS-ESX	International Aviation Services, Pretoria	26.1.67
			F-BLCN	ntu: stored at Creil, France	68
				broken-up Creil	c70
28745	A-26C	44-35466	N8019E	Madden & Smith Aircraft Corp, Miami FL	64
	TB-26B			Consolidated Air Parts Co, Los Angeles CA	66/72
				derelict, unconv., Tucson AZ	69/71
28762 •	A-26C	**44-35483**		(rebuilt as B-26K by On Mark)	29.1.65
	TB-26B	64-17666		retired, Hurlburt Field FL	1.70
	B-26K			USAFM, Hurlburt Field FL	22.1.70/96
	A-26A			(displ. on plinth: no marks)	
28772 •	A-26C	**44-35493**	N2852G	Dollar Lines Inc, San Francisco CA	
	RB-26C			Pacific Flight Service Inc, Angwin CA	64/69
				Arthur W. McDonnell, Lancaster CA	11.70/72
				Stencel Aero Engineering, Ashville NC	77
				Oklahoma Aircraft Sales, Yukon OK	84
				John MacGuire, El Paso TX	9.84/87
			N576JB	John MacGuire/War Eagles Air Museum,	
				Santa Teresa NM	17.2.87/96
				(see N94445: id. unknown at end of listing)	
28774	A-26C	44-35495	N501N	Northern Natural Gas, Denver CO	59/61
	B-26C		N507WB	Williams Bothers Co, Tulsa OK	22.5.61/63
				T. E. Mercer Trucking Co, Fort Worth TX	64
				Tradewinds Aircraft Supply, San Antonio TX	66/70
				Milt Stollak, Burbank CA	77
28776 •	A-26C	**44-35497**		trade school: instructional airframe	
	RB-26C		N3426G	Johnson Flying Service, Missoula MT	.61/70
				(del. to Missoula .61 in USAF black sc.,	
				conv. Missoula to fire tanker #A17)	
				Evergreen Air, Missoula MT (tanker #A17)	.75
				Lynch Air Tankers, Billings MT (tanker #56)	.77/92
				Air Spray Ltd, Edmonton ALTA	25.9.92

			C-FOVC	Air Spray Ltd, Edmonton ALTA (tanker #56)	20.1.93/96
28783 •	A-26C	**44-35504**		(to l'Armee de l'Air as 807C, 44-35504)	13.9.56/67
	B-26C			(conv. to B-26APQ13 radar trainer .62): wfu	4.67
				Chateaudun AB, France: gate guard	72/77
28784 •	A-26C	**44-35505**	**N4815E**	Rock Island Oil & Refining Co, Wichita KS	
	B-26C			Tallmantz Aviation Inc, Orange County CA	63/76
				Albert Redick, Chino CA	77
				On Mark Aviation, Knoxville TN	.78
				sale rep., Chino CA	84/96
28787 •	A-26C	**44-35508**		(to FA Colombiana as 2504)	.57/67
	RB-26C			Gomez Nino AB, Villavicencio: displ.	83
				Apiay AB, Colombia: displ.	90/96
28802 •	A-26C	**44-35523**	**N3428G**	Aero Atlas Inc, Red Bluff CA	
	B-26C			Rosenbalm Aviation Inc, Medford OR	63/72
				(tanker #F29; #29)	
				William A. Dempsay, East Wenatchee WA	72/77
				(tanker #108)	
				Kinney Air Tankers, Richey MT (tanker #108)	81
				Custom Farm Service of Montana, Richey MT	84
				William A. Dempsay/Central Air Service,	
				East Wenatchee WA	7.85/95
				Bonanzaville Eagles Aircraft Museum,	
				West Fargo ND: displ. as "435523"	94/96
28803 •	A-26C	**44-35524**	N9401Z	Donaire Inc, Phoenix AZ	64/69
	B-26C			Thomas W. Hammon, Phoenix AZ	70/72
			CF-CUI	reg.	72
			C-FCUI	Air Spray Ltd, Red Deer ALTA (tanker #12)	81/95
28820	A-26C	44-35541		(to l'Armee de l'Air as 44-35541): BOC	7.4.54
	B-26B			based Indochina: ret. to USAF	10.7.54
			N8032E	Madden & Smith Aircraft Corp, Miami FL	64
				Consolidated Air Parts Co, Los Angeles CA	66/95
				derelict unconv., Tucson AZ	69/72
28831 •	A-26C	**44-35552**	**N5544V**	Rosenbalm Aviation, Medford OR	63/72
	B-26C			William A. Dempsay, East Wenatchee WA	c72/77
				(tanker #104)	
				Kinney Air Tankers, Richey MT	6.81
				(tanker #104)	
				Duane D. Sly, Platte SD	2.85/96
28841 •	A-26C	**44-35562**	N707TG	Texas Gas Transmission Corp, Owensboro KY	61/66
	B-26C		**N7079G**	Natrona Service Inc, Casper WY	69/88
	On Mark			Conrad Yelvington, South Daytona FL	8.89/92
				op: Lady Barbel Abela, Len Perry, London UK	11.91/92
				(camouflage, "*Bar-Belle Bomber*",	
				visited UK, Europe & Russia 7.92)	
				Bar Belle Aviation Inc, Miami FL derelict by 96	7.92/96
28859	A-26C	44-35580	N74831	Madden & Smith Aircraft Corp, Miami FL	66/69
	B-26C			sale rep., USCR (probably bu 1960s)	78/95
28860	A-26C	44-35581	N3485G	Stahmann Farms Inc, Las Cruces NM	63/64
	B-26C			M. S. Jovenich, New York NY	66
				Hamilton Aircraft Co, Tucson AZ	69
				Aircraft Surplus Co, Tucson AZ	70/72
			C-GWJG	Air Spray Ltd, Red Deer ALTA	6.76/82
				(tanker #9)	
				crashed near Watson Lake, Yukon Territory	1.7.82

28865 •	A-26C B-26B CB-26 C-26B	**44-35586**		(to FA Brasileira as B-26B 5156): BOC (conv. to transport as CB-26 5156, C-26B 5156) FAB Academy Museum, Pirassunga, Sao Paulo (displ. as "FAB C-26B 5156") Parnamirim AB, Brazil (displ. as "FAB B-26B 5156")	.57/75 85/87 .87
28869 •	A-26C RB-26C	**44-35590**	**N3248G**	E. J. Quick Ray Karrels, Port Washington WI Earl T. Reinert/Victory Air Museum, Mundelein IL (displ. as "435590/Nightmare") Earl T. Reinert, Arlington Heights IL	 63/70 76/79 9.87/96
28875 •	A-26C RB-26C	**44-35596**	N5636V	Hawaii Public Trade & Instructional School, Honolulu Airport HI USAFM, Hickam AFB HI	 64/79 82/93
28880 •	A-26C B-26C	**44-35601**	**N202R**	B. S. Hagill Metropolitan Paving Co, Oklahoma City OK Harry Mallory, Oklahoma City OK Aero Industries Inc, Addison TX Texas Instruments Inc, Dallas TX Edward G. Counselman, Topeka KS Rodney G. Huskey, Grand Junction CO (flies as "USAF 202/*Miss Murphy*)	 63/64 66 69/70 72/77 .78 11.81/96
28886	A-26C RB-26C RB-26P	44-35607	 F-BNTN	(to l'Armee de l'Air as 607, 44-35607): BOC (conv. to RB-26P 7.61): wfu Societe Carta, Creil: CofA issued retired Creil, France: CofA expired broken-up Creil	9.56/66 2.66 7.2.67 25.2.68 c70
28896 •	A-26C RB-26C On Mark	**44-35617**	N600WB	Ridge Associates Inc, Flint MI Mid America Air Transport, Chicago IL Red Dodge Aviation, Anchorage AK John Steinmetz, Griffin GA Oklahoma Aircraft Corp, Yukon OK impounded US Customs: alleged drug running USAFM, Travis AFB CA: del. USAFM, Hill AFB UT: fitted 8-gun nose	61/63 66 69/72 77 7.82/87 c85 .87/91 92/93
28906 •	A-26C JB-26C	**44-35627**		displ. on pylon, Dodge City Airport KS	73/88
28910	A-26C RB-26C	44-35631	N91346	Acme Aircraft Parts, Compton CA: ex USAF Transit Equipment Co, New York NY Greg Board/Aero Associates Inc, Tucson AZ (to FA Portuguesa as 7103): del. (rebuilt Tucson by Hamilton Aircraft for FAP) wfu, abandoned Luanda, Angola	8.4.59/63 17.6.63/65 9.4.65 7.65/75 11.75
28916	A-26C B-26C	44-35637	N8040E	Madden & Smith Aircraft Corp, Miami FL Consolidated Air Parts Co, Los Angeles CA derelict, unconv., Tucson AZ	64 66/95 69/72
28919	A-26C B-26C Smith Tempo II	44-35640	N4204A	L. B. Smith Aircraft Corp, Miami FL (USAF disposal at Hanscom AFB MA 27.11.57) (rebuilt Miami as prototype Smith Tempo I & II, testflying commenced Miami 10.59/62) Pinellas Aircraft Inc, St. Petersburg FL Appliance Buyers Credit Corp, St. Joseph MI North Phoenix Aviation, Phoenix AZ A. Newton Ball, Dillingham AK	11.57/63 7.3.63 18.4.63/66 11.66/67 19.1.67

				Robert L. Carleton, North Hollywood CA	23.2.67/68
				University of Nevada, Reno NV	12.6.68/80
				crashed Nevada, on weather research flight	2.3.80
28922 •	A-26C	**44-35643**		(to l'Armee de l'Air as 44-35643): BOC	10.4.54
	RB-26C			based Indochina: ret. to USAF	22.10.55
	Monarch			(open storage Clark AFB, Philippines 55/58)	
			N6841D	Rock Island Oil & Refining Co, Wichita KS	63/69
				Hodge Laboratories Inc, Wichita KS	70
				William K. Mayfield, Halstead KS	72
				resident, Carman, MAN : del.	14.10.73
			C-GCES	resident, Carman, MAN	10.74/79
			N8015H	Confederate Air Force, Harlingen TX	6.79/84
			N226RW	Confederate Air Force, Harlingen/Midland TX	2.84/96
				(flies as "4435643/*Daisy Mae/A*")	
28940 •	A-26C	44-35661	N9996Z	Donaire Inc, Phoenix AZ (tanker #C11)	63/64
	B-26C			George H. Stell, Phoenix AZ (tanker #C11)	66/72
			CF-CBK	O. Huitikka, Fort Francis ONT	11.72
			C-FCBK	Air Spray Ltd, Red Deer ALTA (tanker #11)	79/96
28950	A-26C	44-35671		(to l'Armee de l'Air as 44-35671): BOC	6.4.54
	B-26B			based Indochina: ret. to USAF	31.8.54
			N8033E	Madden & Smith Aircraft Corp, Miami FL	64
				Consolidated Air Parts Co, Los Angeles	66/95
				derelict, unconv., Tucson AZ	69/72
28960	A-26C	44-35681	N60Y	Mechanical Products Inc, Jackson MI	54
	B-26C			Philips Petroleum	
				Amerada Petroleum Corp, Tulsa OK	64
			N168Y	Amerada Petroleum Corp, Tulsa OK	66
			CF-VPR	Survair Ltd, Ottawa ONT	.67/70
28961	A-26C	44-35682	N5181V	R. F. Todd	
	RB-26C			John M. Sliker, Wadley GA	63/64
			D-CADU	Walter Rall/Prakla-Seismos AG, Hanover	5.64/67
				(conv. for survey ops., CofA 19.9.64)	
				(survey ops. Africa, South America 67)	
				Trans-Peruana, Lima Peru	13.5.67
				noted in scrapyard as D-CADU, Lima	69/70
28975 •	A-26C	44-35696		(to l'Armee de l'Air as 44-35696): BOC	6.4.54
	B-26B			based Indochina: ret. to USAF	3.7.54
			N8036E	L. B. Smith Aircraft Corp., Miami FL	63
				Richard B. Almour, Tucson AZ	64
				William E. Strader, Fresno CA	66/77
				Dwight Reimer, Shafter CA	78/79
				(race #26/*Cotton Jenny*)	
				Courtesy Aircraft Inc, Rockford IL	84
				Collings Found., Stowe MA	9.85/96
				(flies as 435696/*Late Date/My Mary Lou*)	
				crashed on takeoff, Kankakee IL	22.6.93
28977	A-26C	44-35698		CIA: Cuba ops.	3.9.60
	B-26C		N5001X (2	CIA/Gulf Air Inc, Miami FL	.62/63
				CIA/Intermountain Aviation, Marana AZ	.63
				On Mark Aviation, Van Nuys CA	7.63/64
				(On Mark covert ops. mods. development aircraft)	
			N800V	CIA/Intermountain Aviation, Marana AZ	1.64/67
				rep. broken-up Norton AFB CA	.71
				(id. N5001X changed from 44-34620 .62)	
28987 •	A-26C	**44-35708**		(to l'Armee de l'Air as 44-35708): BOC	18.4.54
	B-26C			based Indochina: ret. to USAF	10.11.55

	On Mark			(open storage Clark AFB, Philippines 55/58)	
			N5530V	On Mark Engineering Co, Van Nuys CA	63/66
				Raytheon Manufacturing Co, Bedford MA	69/76
			C-GXGY	Air Spray Ltd, Red Deer ALTA (tanker #10)	12.76/95
28989 •	A-26C	**44-35710**	**N7705C**	Mayhew Supply Inc, Gulfport MS	63
	B-26C			Appliance Buyers Credit Corp, St Joseph MI	64/69
				Rusk Aviation, Kankakee IL	72
				Eugene H. Akers, San Diego CA	77/87
				Eugene H. Akers, Georgetown SC	88
				David C. Tallichet/MARC, Chino CA	89/94
				(open storage Chino 79/94)	
				Pacific Fighters Inc, Chino CA	.94/96
				(rest. to fly Chino CA 94/95 as 434220/13")	
29000 •	A-26C	**44-35721**	**N9425Z**	Central Oregon Airial Co Inc, Bend OR	63/64
	B-26C			Lynch Air Tankers, Billings MT (tanker #57)	66/92
				Robert J. Pond/Planes of Fame East,	
				Minneapolis-Flying Cloud MN	9.92/96
				(flew as "435721/*Fire Eaters-Always*",	
				rest. Chino .93 as "USN 435721/BP/*Invader*")	
29003 •	A-26C	**44-35724**	N7954C	J. E. Gardner	
	B-26C			Rosenbalm Aviation, Medford OR	63/64
				Flick Aviation, La Grande OR (tanker #83)	66/70
				Rosenbalm Aviation, Medford OR	72
				William A. Dempsay, East Wenatchee WA	73
				(tanker #83; later #106)	
				Central Air Service, East Wenatchee WA	1.80/83
				USAFM, Beale AFB CA	.83/93
				(displ. as "434517/*Monnie*)	
29004	A-26C	44-35725	N800W	James M. Cook, Jacksboro TX	63/64
	RB-26C			U.S. Dept of Commerce, Washington DC	64/69
	B-26C			MASDC, Davis-Monthan AFB, Tucson AZ	.65/69
				(stored as "N800W/35725") sold as scrap	
				Allied Aircraft Inc, Tucson AZ: del. ex MASDC	2.4.76
29012 •	A-26C	**44-35733**		USAFM, Wright-Patterson AFB, Dayton OH	9.57/90
	B-26C			(displ. as 435733/BC-733/*Dream Girl*)	
29031 •	A-26C	**44-35752**	N8627E	Rock Island Oil & Refining Co, Wichita KS	64/66
	B-26C			Donaire Inc, Phoenix AZ	69
				Thomas W. Hammon, Phoenix AZ	70/71
			CF-KBZ	Kenting Aircraft Ltd, Toronto ONT	6.72
				Conair Aviation Ltd, Abbotsford BC	8.73
				(tanker #327)	
			C-FKBZ	Conair Aviation Ltd, Abbotsford BC	79/86
				Canadian Warplane Heritage, Mount Hope ONT	15.1.88
				(del. ex Abbotsford 15.1.88)	
			N81797	Vern Rayburn/Courtesy Aircraft Inc,	
				Rockford IL	8.5.89/95
				Flying Tigers Warbird Museum,	
				Kissimmeee FL: loan, displ.	92/96
				(flies as "435752/*Rude Invader*")	
29038	A-26C	44-35759	N5588A	R. A. Firestone, Teterboro NJ	
	JTB-26C			William C. Powell, Dallas TX	63
				Appliance Buyers Credit Corp, St Joseph MI	64
				derelict, Miami FL	68/71
29057 •	A-26C	**44-35778**		(to FA Colombiana as 2519): BOC	25.11.57
	B-26C			Museo Aeronautico, Bogota-Madrid AB	72/96
29059 •	A-26C	**44-35780**	**N8021E**	Madden & Smith Aircraft Corp, Miami FL	63/64

	TB-26B			Consolidated Air Parts Co, Los Angeles CA	66/72
				Allied Aircraft Sales, Tucson AZ	10.74/96
				derelict unconv, Tucson AZ	69/92
				removed to storage yard, Tucson AZ by	95
29067 •	A-26C	**44-35788**	**N8058E**	L. B. Smith Aircraft Corp., Miami FL	
	B-26C			(open storage, Charlotte SC 62/72)	
				John J. Stokes, San Marcos TX	77/78
				Joe Mabee, Midland TX	81/82
				EAA Aviation Foundation, Oshkosh WI	11.82/96
				(rest. Troy AL .87/94, del. Oshkosh .94)	
29087	A-26C	44-35808	N8041E	Madden & Smith Aircraft Corp, Miami FL	64
	RB-26C			Consolidated Air Parts Co, Los Angeles CA	66/72
				derelict unconv., ("AR ANG") Tucson AZ	69/72
29089 •	A-26C	**44-35810**	N9403Z	Von Carstedt/Carstedt Air, Long Beach CA	64
	B-26C			Clifton H. Troxell, Arden NV	66/70
				Reeder Flying Service, Twin Falls ID	72/77
				(tanker #27)	
			C-GPUC	Air Spray Ltd, Red Deer ALTA (tanker #27)	4.81/96
29099 •	A-26C	**44-35820**		(rebuilt as B-26K by On Mark)	16.2.65
	TB-26B	64-17671		Davis Monthan AFB AZ: del. for storage	17.1.70
	B-26K			Florence Air & Missile Museum, Florence SC	.73/96
	A-26A			(displ. : on USAFM charge from 23.4.93)	
29136 •	A-26C	**44-35857**	N9300R	Madden & Smith Aircraft Corp, Miami FL	64
	B-26C			Consolidated Air Parts Co, Los Angeles CA	66/70
			CF-ZTC	Forest Patrol Ltd	7.71
			C-FZTC	J. D. Irving	79
				Air Spray Ltd, Red Deer ALTA	8.79/96
				(tanker #14, later #13 "Lucky Jack")	
29137	A-26C	44-35858	N8039E	Madden & Smith Aircraft Corp, Miami FL	64
	RB-26C			Consolidated Air Parts Co, Los Angeles CA	66/72
				derelict unconv., Tucson AZ	69/72
29138 •	A-26C	**44-35859**		(to l'Armee de l'Air as 44-35859): BOC	1.6.60/68
	B-26C			(conv. to B-26APQ13 radar trainer .60): wfu	1.67
				(open storage, Chateaudun AB 67/69)	
				Bordeaux-Merignac AB: displ.	78/94
29139	A-26C	44-35860	N8049E	Madden & Smith Aircraft Corp, Miami FL	64
	B-26B			Consolidated Air Parts Co, Los Angeles CA	66/72
				derelict unconv.,Tucson AZ	69/72
29146	A-26C	44-35867	N8035E	Madden & Smith Aircraft Corp, Miami FL	64
	B-26C			Consolidated Air Parts Co, Los Angeles CA	66/72
				derelict unconv., ("MO ANG") Tucson AZ	69/72
29149 •	A-26C	**44-35870**	N320	L. B. Maytag Aircraft Corp, Miami FL	63/64
	B-26C			National Bank, Tulsa OK	66/69
	Marksman			Trinity Industries Inc	69
				Confederate Air Force, Harlingen TX	.70/72
				struck-off USCR: rep. sold to South America	c75
			N99426	noted in ferry marks, Opa Locka FL	7.81
				F. J. Luytjes, Dalton PA	84
				T. K. Edenfield, Albuquerque NM	5.85
				C. H. Midkiff, San Antonio TX	9.86
				Outlaw Aircraft Sales Inc, Clarksville TN	4.87
				Wayne County Sheriff Dept, Detroit MI	7.88/90
				sale rep., Brooksville FL	92/96

29154 •	A-26C	**44-35875**	N4816E	Rock Island Oil & Refining Co, Wichita KS	
	B-26C		CF-PGF	DM Air Enterprises Ltd, Vancouver BC	.63/66
				Air Spray Ltd, Edmonton ALTA (tanker #1)	.70/78
			C-FPGF	Air Spray Ltd, Red Deer ALTA (tanker #1)	79/96
29159	A-26C	44-35880	N8048E	Madden & Smith Aircraft Corp, Miami FL	64
	B-26C			Consolidated Air Parts Co, Los Angeles CA	66/72
				derelict unconv., Tucson AZ	69/72
29167 •	A-26C	**44-35888**	**N4810E**	Rock Island Oil & Refining Co, Wichita KS	64/66
	B-26C			Consolidated Aero Export Co, Los Angeles	69/72
				David C. Tallichet/ MARC, Chino CA	.74/92
29170	A-26C	44-35891		(to l'Armee de l'Air as 44-35891): BOC	3.1.51/55
	B-26C			based Indochina: ret. to USAF	14.10.55
				(open storage Clark AFB, Philippines 55/58)	
			N34962	C. C. Moseley, Los Angeles CA	64/70
29171 •	A-26C	**44-35892**		(to l'Armee de l'Air as 44-35892): BOC	1.7.54
	B-26C			based Indochina: ret. to USAF	23.8.54
			N4811E	Rock Island Oil & Refining Co, Wichita KS	64/66
				Consolidated Aero Export Corp, Los Angeles	69/72
				Fred E. Weisbrod Aircraft Museum, Peublo CO	.72/93
29172 •	A-26C	**44-35893**	N4812E	Rock Island Oil & Refining Co, Wichita KS	64/66
	B-26C			Consolidated Aero Export Corp, Los Angeles	69/72
			C-GHCC	Conair Aviation Ltd, Abbotsford BC	6.74
				(tanker #331)	
				Air Spray Ltd, Red Deer ALTA (tanker #31)	.82/96
29175 •	A-26C	**44-35896**		(rebuilt as B-26K by On Mark)	15.6.64
	B-26C	64-17640		Davis Monthan AFB AZ: stored, del.	10.69/71
	B-26K		N267G	State of Georgia Forestry Comm., Macon GA	.71/77
	A-26A			(open storage unconv., Macon GA 72/77)	
				Airspray Ltd, Edmonton ALTA	.77
				(del. Macon-Billings MT, open storage Billings during certification dispute with DoT 77/78)	
				Arnie Carnegie, Edmonton ALTA	78
			N2294B	Arthur W. McDonnell, Mojave CA	7.78/80
				(stored unconv."IF/640", Mojave CA 79)	
				USAFM, Ellsworth AFB SD	3.10.80/96
				(fcd. landing near Casper WY during del. flight no dam; flown out to Ellsworth AFB)	
29177 •	A-26C	**44-35898**	N3328G	Lear Inc, Santa Monica CA	61/64
	B-26C			Lear Siegler Inc, Santa Monica CA	66
				Aerospace Modifications, Coatsville PA	69
			CF-PGP	Air Spray Ltd, Edmonton ALTA (tanker #2)	7.71/76
			C-FPGP	Air Spray Ltd, Red Deer ALTA (tanker #2)	76/96
29180 •	A-26C	**44-35901**	N91351	Greg Board/Aero Associates Inc, Tucson AZ	65
	TB-26C			(planned sale to FA Portuguesa: not completed)	
				Flight Enterprises Inc, Prescott AZ	66/69
				open storage derelict unconv., Tucson AZ	69/92
				removed to storage yard, Tucson AZ by	94/96
29190 •	A-26C	**44-35911**		(to l'Armee de l'Air as 44-35911): BOC	3.1.51
	B-26C			based Indochina: ret. to USAF	22.10.55
	Monarch			(open storage Clark AFB, Philippines 55/58)	
			N6840D	Rock Island Oil & Refining Co, Wichita KS	63/64
				Magnolia Homes Manuf. Corp, Vicksburg MS	66
				Aero Specialities Inc, Long Beach CA	69/70
				Westinghouse Credit Corp, Brynmawr PA	72
				Milt Slollak, Burbank CA	77
				Stephen L. Miles, Carmel Valley & Salinas CA	10.83/88

				Courtesy Aircraft Inc, Rockford IL	1.89/90
				Coleman Warbird Museum, Coleman TX	92/96
				(flies as 435911/*Bandido*)	
29192 •	A-26C	**44-35913**	N303W	On Mark Engineering Co, Van Nuys CA	
	B-26C		N303WC	Western Contracting Corp, Lincoln NE	63/69
	On Mark			Aero Industries Inc, Addison TX	70
				Texas Instruments Inc, Dallas TX	72/77
				Edward G. Counselman, Topeka KS	11.78/84
				USAFM, Dyess AFB TX	84/96
29197 •	A-26C	**44-35918**		Davis Monthan AFB AZ: sold as surplus	6.58
	B-26C		N7953C	Garwin inc, Wichita KS	60/62
				Beech Aircraft Corp, Wichita KS: lsd.	.61/62
				(used for air-to-air refuelling trials)	
				F. Daniel Bennett, Miami FL	8.5.62
				Pasnefom SA, San Jose, Costa Rica	8.6.62
				(ferried to San Jose 6.62, flown as "N79580":	
				planned bombing raids against Cuba 7.62;	
				impounded by Costa Rican Government 8.62)	
			TI-1040L	Frank Marshall , Costa Rica	.63
			HR-276	reg.	.69
				(to FA Hondurena as 276, later 510)	.69/82
				crashed landing, Toncontin AB (repaired)	16.3.71
			N2781G	David Zeuschel, Van Nuys CA	7.12.82/83
				ferried Tegucigalpa AB, Honduras - Kelly AFB	.83
				USAFM, Kelly AFB TX	.83
				USAFM, Lackland AFB TX	87/94
				(displ. as 435918/BC-918/*Versatile Lady*)	
29202	A-26C	44-35923		Aircraft Industries Museum, Louisville KY	.60/73
	TB-26C				
29216 •	A-26C	**44-35937**		(to FA Chile as FAC 846): BOC	3.58
	B-26B			Confederate Air Force, Harlingen TX: not del.	3.80
	B-26D			El Bosque AB, Santiago: open storage	92/96
				(see also 44-34741)	
29217	A-26C	44-35938	N4203A	G. C. Murphy Co, McKeesport PA	59/61
	RB-26C		N510X	G. C. Murphy Co, McKeesport PA	6.63/67
	On Mark		N510A		
			N516X	Ralph Tait	67/69
				Twin Cities Aviation Inc, Minneapolis MN	69
			D-BACA	Friederich Stetzler/Transport Dienst GmbH,	
				Dusseldorf	8.69/73
				wheels up landing, Stuttgart West Germany	11.8.70
				crashed landing, Zurich, Switzerland	23.2.73
				burnt for fire practice, Zurich	5.7.73
29227 •	A-26C	**44-35948**	N67164	Stanolind Oil & Gas Co, Tulsa OK	54
	B-26C		N1244	Pan American Petroleum Corp, Tulsa OK	61/64
				Standard Oil Co (Indiana), Chicago IL	31.5.65
			N910H	Nine Ten Corp, Chicago IL	4.8.65/66
			N161H	Motorola Inc, Scottsdale AZ	69/70
				Grumman Ecosystems Corp, Bethpage NY	72
			C-GHLX	Conair Aviation Ltd, Abbotsford BC	7.75/86
				(tanker #332)	
				Air Spray Ltd, Red Deer ALTA (tanker #32)	90/96
29231	A-26C	44-35952	N1S	Superior Oil Co, Lafayette LA	54
	B-26C			Ohio Valley Aviation, Wheeling WV	63
			N4984N	Ohio Valley Aviation, Wheeling WV	64
				DEC Aviation Corp, Madison WI	66/70

c/n	Type	Serial	Reg.	Owner/History	Date
29234 •	A-26C TB-26B	44-35955	**N8394H**	Kenlyn Petroleum Corp, Los Angeles CA Rodney G. Huskey, Grand Junction CO	63/70 6.81/96
29243	A-26C B-26C	44-35964	N4813E	Rock Island Oil & Refining Co, Wichita KS Aim Aviation Inc, Houston TX Environmental Protectection Agency, Las Vegas NV Edward G. Counselman/Combat Air Museum, Topeka KS (flew in camouflage sc.) crashed, Cimarron NM (Counselman killed)	63 66/70 77 84/88 26.6.88
29248	A-26C B-26C	44-35969	N8628E	Rock Island Oil & Refining Co, Wichita KS Hamilton Aircraft Co, Tucson AZ (to FA Brasileira as B-26C 5175): BOC (rebuilt Tucson .69 by Hamilton Aircraft for FAB) wfu, SOC FAB	64/66 68/69 6.69/75 12.75
29265 •	A-26C TB-26C GB-26C	**44-35986**	N6382T	Benjamin Davis Vocational School, Detroit MI (instr. airframe, Detroit-Metro Airport MI) USAFM, Selfridge ANGB MI (displ. as "5986")	.61/86 .86/96
29273 •	A-26C TB-26C	**44-35994**	N4822E	Rock Island Oil & Refining Co, Wichita KS Allied Aircraft Sales Corp, Tucson AZ stored, derelict (tanker #C32), Buckeye AZ 78/79	64/66 69
- •	A-26 LAS Super 26	-	 N5052N N52NM XB-SIJ C-GQPZ	(to FA Mexicana as 1302) unconf. Mesta Machine Co, Pittsburgh PA (rebuilt Ontario CA .60 by Lockheed Aircraft Service as prototype LAS Super 26) Westernair of Albuquerque, Albuquerque NM Aviation Equipment Corp, Washington DC Bruce Irwin, Scottsdale AZ "*Koba Wiki*" wfu San Antonio TX: spar and legal problems 6.79/80 Air Spray Ltd, Red Deer ALTA (for spares) del. San Antonio-Red Deer ALTA, then dism. (orig. mainplane XB-SIJ with Aero Nostalgia Inc, Stockton CA, for USAFM A-26 static rebuild 91) (note: FAA quote id. 1302)	 54/66 69 70 72 c75 81/92 81/92
- •	A-26B	-	N65121 XB-PEK	Westland & Son Inc, Los Angeles CA President of Mexico "Sierra Hermosa" (to FA Mexicana as 1300) wfu, open storage derelict, Mexico City Museo de Talleres de la FAM: rep. in store	49 9.49/62 .62 71/79
-	A-26	-	 N62290	(to FA Salvaderena as 60_) John J. Stokes, San Marcos TX: reg. res. not del., abandoned open storage Ilopango (FAA quote id. "3890")	 .74 74
- •	B-26B	-	 N99425	(to FA Nicaragua as 601) David C. Tallichet/ MARC, Chino CA (not del., abandoned stripped at Managua 77/78) (FAA quote id. "162")	 3.77/96
- • c/n 7	A-26C On Mark	-	N36B N36BB (1 N94445	 B. B. Ranch, Ventura CA Hughes Aircraft Corp, Culver City CA Ascher Ward, Van Nuys CA (ferried Culver City-Van Nuys .79 ex storage) A. Wally McDonnell, Mojave CA USAFM, Grand Forks AFB ND USAFM, Robins AFB GA	 63/64 66/70 .79 .79 85/93 96

				(displ. Grand Forks & Robins as "434220")	
				(this a/c has hiastory confused with c/28772/	
				ex 44-35493)	
- •	A-26	-		State of Tennessee, Memphis TN	
	Monarch			(conv. to exec. Monarch 26 abandoned)	
				John M. Sliker, Wadley GA (dism.)	
				John J. Stokes, San Marcos TX (dism.)	
				Lynch Air Tankers, Billings MT (dism.)	80/92
				Neil M. Rose, Vancouver WA (rest. project)	25.9.92/96
				(prev. incorrectly rep. as 44-35682)	
- •	A-26C	-		USAFM, Robins AFB GA	91/94
				(displ. as "USAF 435732")	
-	A-26	-	YV-E-IPV	noted, Caracas, Venezuela	1.74
- •	A-26C	-		(to FA Chile as FAC 8...)	
				El Bosque, Chile: gate guard as "FAC 848"	82
- •	A-26C			(to FA Chile as FAC 8..)	
				Cerro Moreno AB: gate guard as "FAC 863"	82/94
				(prob. actually FAC 824 ex 44-35753)	
- •	A-26B	-		(to Indonesian AF/AURI/TNI-AU as M-265)	.60/77
				Indonesian Air Force Academy Museum,	
				Jawa Tengah, Yogyakarta: del.	7.12.77/84
				(last flight of a military Invader, del. 7.12.77,	
				rep. displ. as "TNI-AU M-263")	
				Indonesian Air Force Museum, Yogyakarta	.84/94
				(displ. as "TNI-AU M-265")	
- •	A-26B	-		(to FA Salvedorena as ...)	
				Ilopango AB: static rest., to be gate guard	.91/94
- •	A-26B	-		(to FA Salvedorena as ...)	
				Ilopango AB: engineless, on junk heap	91/94

DOUGLAS AD SKYRAIDER

1930 •	XBT2D-1	**Bu09102**		Naval Historical Centre,	
	XAD-1			Washington Navy Yard, Washington DC: stored	79
				USMCM, Quantico MCAS VA	87/94
				displ. Oceana NAS, Virginia Beach VA	87/96
				(displ. as "F501", later "09102/AE500"	
1931 •	XBT2D-1	**Bu09103**		dism. in junkyard, Fairless Hills PA	65
	XAD-1			Walter Soplata Collection, Newbury OH	85
2085 •	AD-1	**Bu09257**		stored trucking yard, Oklahoma City OK	60/70
	AD-2			(rep. under rest., Dallas TX 74)	
			N2AD	Douglas W. Wood, Dallas TX	4.81/96
6933 •	AD-3	**Bu122811**		NATTC, NAS Memphis TN	
	A-1E			EAA Museum, Oshkosh WI	78/96
7133 •	AD-4	**Bu123827**		gate guard, DeKalb-Peachtree Airport GA	59/66
			N54162	David M. Forrest, Avondale Estates GA	.66/69
			N23827	David M. Forrest, Avondale Estates GA	78/87
				(ff 5.12.78 as 168B/*Navy Atlanta*)	
				James McMillan/FOAG Inc, Breckenridge TX	2.87/88
				Wiley C. Sanders, Troy AL	4.89/96

7392 •	AD-4W AEW.1	**Bu124086**		(to RN Fleet Air Arm as WV106) FAA Museum: stored RNAS Culdrose Helston Aero Park, Cornwall (displ. as "WV106/CU-427")	 70 78/96
7427 •	AD-4W AEW.1	**Bu124121**		(to RN Fleet Air Arm as WT983) FAA Museum: stored RNAS Culdrose Fleet Air Arm Museum, RNAS Yeovilton (displ. as "WT121/CU-415")	 .60/72 6.72/96
7449 •	AD-4N A-1D	**Bu124143**	 N91909 F-WZDP **F-AZDP**	(to l'Armee de l'Air as No.14) ntu: Jack Spanich, Detroit MI (to FA Gabonaise as 124143/TR-KFP) Jean Baptiste Salis, La Ferte-Alais: del. Amicale J-B Salis, La Ferte-Alais (flies as "24143/RM-205/USS Saratoga")	10.6.60 76 .77/84 20.7.84 12.85/96
7462 •	AD-4N A-1D	**Bu124156**	 **N91935**	(to l'Armee de l'Air as No.30) (to FA Gabonaise as 124156) recov. from Gabon by Gyra France Jack Spanich, Detroit MI del. Chateaudun AB to USA, via Dublin Jimmy McMillan/Breckenridge Tank Truck Inc William E. Harrison, Tulsa OK Wiley C. Sanders/West Indies Investments Ltd, Troy AL (flies as 24156/AK-404/*USS Intrepid*)	.60 c68/76 .76 1.77 9.3.77 3.83/87 .87/88 11.88/96
7609 •	AD-4N	**Bu125716**	 **F-AZFN**	(to l'Armee de l'Air as No.11) (to FA Chad as No.11) Didier Chable, Melun-Villaroche (trucked N'djamena, Chad to Niamey, Niger 9.88, rest., del. to France: arr. Melun 9.11.88) J. J. Joyeux, Aulnat (flies as "125716/22-DC")	 15.2.77 8.88/91 93/96
7632 •	AD-4N	**Bu125739**		Bradley Air Museum, Windsor Locks CT New England Air Museum, Windsor Locks CT (to be rest. with parts of Bu122312/122818, both recov. from crash burial sites NALF Charlestown RI)	11.70/81 .81/90
7677	AD-4NA A-1D	Bu126877		(to l'Armee de l'Air as No.21) noted in store, Chateaudun AB, France rep. scrapped	.61/77 6.77
7680	AD-4NA A-1D	Bu126880	 F-AZGA	(to L'Armee de L'Air as No.34) (to FA Chad as ......) Didier Chable, Melun-Villaroche (ferry permit: N'djamena, Chad to France 2.92) crashed on del., in sandstorm, Agades, Niger (id. also quoted as Bu126934)	.61/77 15.2.77 8.88/93 16.4.92
7682 •	AD-4NA A-1D	**Bu126882**	 **N91945**	(to l'Armee de l'Air as No.85) (to FA Gabonaise as 126882) recov. from Gabon by Gyra France Jack Spanich, Detroit MI (del. Chateaudun AB to USA, via Dublin 9.3.77) dam., landing accident Harry S. Doan/Doan Helicopters Inc, New Smyrna Beach FL (rebuilt, flew as "37543/AK-409/USS Intrepid") overturned landing, Titusville FL (Doan k.) rebuilt, offered for sale at Doan auction Sherman Aircraft Sales, West Palm Beach FL	.61 c68/76 .76 1.77/84 c82 85/92 4.4.92 30.10.92 95

c/n	Type	Identity	Reg.	Owner / History	Date
7712 •	AD-4NA	**Bu126912**		(to l'Armee de l'Air as No.41)	.60
	A-1D			(to FA Gabonaise as 126912): del.	8.2.76/85
				recov. by Jean Salis, La Ferte-Alais, France	4.85
				Robert Lamplough, North Weald : arr. by sea	3.88
				Pacific Fighters, Chino CA : shipped ex UK	17.9.90/91
			N4277P	Erickson Air Crane, Medford OR	9.5.91/96
				(stored unconv. Chino CA "22-DJ/MN" 90/95)	
7722 •	AD-4NA	**Bu126922**		(to l'Armee de l'Air as No.42)	60
	A-1D			(to FA Gabonaise as 126922/TR-K..): del.	8.2.76/85
				recov. by Aero Retro, St Rambert d'Albion	.85
				Aero Retro : arr. by ship, Le Havre	17.4.85
			F-AZED	Amicale Jean Baptiste Salis/Jean Francois	
				Perrin & Partners, Le Havre	27.8.86/91
				The Fighter Collection, Duxford UK	12.91/93
				(del. to Duxford 24.12.91 "26922/JS-937")	
			G-RAID	The Fighter Collection, Duxford	7.6.93/95
				(flies as "26922/AK-402")	
7724 •	AD-4NA	**Bu126924**		(to l'Armee de l'Air as No.19)	.60
	A-1D			(to FA Gabonaise as 126924): del.	8.2.76/85
				recov. by Jean Salis, La Ferte-Alais, France	.85/88
				Salis Collection : arr. by ship, Le Havre "RM"	17.4.85
				M. Etchetto, Le Havre	87/88
			N2096P	Jeffrey G. Thomas, Anchorage AK	11.89/90
			N924JT	Vintage Wings, Anchorage AK	2.90/96
7735 •	AD-4NA	**Bu126935**		(to l'Armee de l'Air as No.56)	11.1.61
	A-1D			(to FA Chad as No.56)	7.4.76
			F-AZFO	Didier Chable, Melun-Villaroche	8.88/89
				(trucked N'djamena, Chad to Niamey, Niger 9.88, rest., del. to France: arr. France 7.2.89)	
			N2088G	Richard Bertea, Corona del Mar CA	9.89/96
				(shipped Long Beach CA, del. to Chino 9.9.89; flies as "Marines/126935/HB-14")	
7756 •	AD-4NA	**Bu126956**		(to l'Armee de l'Air as No.45)	4.11.60
	A-1D			(to FA Gabonaise as 126956/TR-KMP): del.	8.2.76/84
			F-WZDQ	Aero Retro, St. Rambert-d'Albon: del.	.84
				Amicale Jean Baptiste Salis, La Ferte-Alais	7.84/85
			F-AZDQ	Aero Retro, St.Rambert-d'Albon	5.9.85/94
				(flies as "126956/RM3")	
7759 •	AD-4NA	Bu126959		(to l'Armee de l'Air as No.50)	7.12.60
	A-1D			(to FA Chad as No.50)	7.4.76
			F-AZFP	Didier Chable, Melun-Villaroche	8.88
				(trucked N'djamena, Chad to Niamey, Niger 9.88, rest., del. to France: arr. France 20.3.89)	
			N2088V	Chancellor Aviation, Costa Mesa CA	9.89/92
				(shipped Long Beach CA, del. to Chino 9.9.89)	
				Warbirds Associates Inc, Wilmington DE	6.95
7765 •	AD-4NA	**Bu126965**		(to l'Armee de l'Air as No.54)	.61
	A-1D			(to FA Chad as 16965)	7.4.76
				ret. to French AF, stored Chateaudun AB	79/83
				Musee de l'Air, Paris-Le Bourget (stored)	84/85
			F-ZVMM	reg. for del. to Belgium	.85
			OO-FOR	Eric Vormezeele, Brasschaat, Belgium: del.	27.6.85/92
				(CofA 26.11.85, flies as French AF "126965")	
7770	AD-4NA	Bu126970		(to l'Armee de l'Air as No.79)	.61
	A-1D		N91954	Jack Spanich, Detroit MI	1.77/84
				(del. Chateaudun AB to Detroit 26-28.5.77)	
				(flew in camouflage "AF 26-970/TC")	

				cr. mountain nr Culpepper VA (Spanich k.)	4.11.84
7779 •	AD-4NA	**Bu126979**		(to l'Armee de l'Air as No.53)	.61
	A-1D			Musee de l'Air, Paris-Le Bourget	78/96
				(displ. as "AdA No.53/MK")	
7796	AD-4NA	Bu126996		(to l'Armee de l'Air as No.38)	.60
	A-1D		N92023	ntu: Jack Spanich, Detroit MI	1.77
				noted in storage, Chateaudun AB, France	6.77
7797 •	AD-4NA	**Bu126997**		(to l'Armee de l'Air as No.78)	.61
	A-1D		N92053	Jack Spanich, Detroit MI	1.77
				(del. Chateaudun AB to Detroit 26-28.5.77)	
				Preston Parish, Kalamazoo MI	77/78
				Spanich Corp, Livonia MI	9.85
			N409Z	Landon J. Cullum, Dallas TX	7.86/91
				Cinema Air, Carlsbad CA	12.91/96
				(flies as "126997/JC-409/USS Intrepid")	
7798 •	AD-4NA	**Bu126998**		(to l'Armee de l'Air as No.37)	.61/77
	A-1D			(to FA Chad as No.37)	15.2.77
			F-WZKY	Didier Chable, Melun-Villaroche	.88
			F-AZKY	Didier Chable, Melun-Villaroche	8.88/93
				(del. to France ex N'djamena, Chad .88, flies as USN "Bu126937")	
7802 •	AD-4NA	**Bu127002**		(to l'Armee de l'Air as No.61)	.61
	A-1D			awaiting del. to USA, Chateaudun AB, France	76
			N91989	ntu : Jack Spanich, Detroit MI	1.77
				(to FA Gabonais as 127002/TR-LQE)	.77
				(recov. ex Gabon by Michel Gineste 1.92)	
			F-AZHK	Michel Gineste/Maurice Etchetto, Le Havre	1.92
				Flying Legends, Dijon-Longvic	.92/93
				Jean Salis/Salis Aviation, La Ferte-Alais	.93/96
				(flies as "USN 127002/G-618")	
7807 •	AD-4NA	**Bu127007**		USNAM: loan Patriots Point Authority SC	90/94
				USS Yorktown Museum, Charleston SC	90/94
				(displ. on board carrier USS Yorktown as "127007/M-505")	
7832	AD-4W	Bu126849		(to RN Fleet Air Arm as WT849)	.55
	AEW.1		SE-EBN	Svensk Flygtjanst AB, Bromma	9.69/71
				crashed Sundsvall	5.71
7850 •	AD-4W	**Bu126867**		(to RN Fleet Air Arm as WV181)	.55
	AEW.1		SE-EBK	Svensk Flygtjanst AB, Bromma: del.	15.5.63/84
			G-BMFB	Aces High Ltd, North Weald	16.9.85
				Coys of Kensington Ltd, North Weald:	24.9.85/89
				(arr. dism. North Weald 9.85, stored 85/90)	
				Pacific Fighters, Chino CA: shipped ex UK	17.9.90/91
			N4277N	Erickson Air Crane Co, Medford OR	9.5.91/96
				(rest. Chino CA, ff 2.94 as "Marines RM24")	
7903 •	AD-4NA	**Bu127888**		(to l'Armee de l'Air as No.65)	.61
			N92034	Jack Spanich, Detroit MI	1.77
				(del. Chateaudun AB to Detroit 26-28.5.77)	
				Preston Parish, Kalamazoo MI	28.4.77/88
				US Army TT contract, based Kalamazoo MI	78
				Southern Packing & Storage, Greenville TN	8.82
				Preston Parish/Kalamazoo Aviation History Museum, Kalamazoo MI	5.83/96
				(flies as " USN 127888/B")	

c/n	Type	Military ID	Civil reg.	History	Date
7909 •	AD-4NA	**Bu127894**		(to l'Armee de l'Air as No.68) SOC	6.8.76
				(to FA Gabonaise as 127894/TR-KFQ)	
			N92072	ntu : Jack Spanich, Detroit MI	1.77
				(not del., stored France 77/85)	
				SAAF Museum, Ysterplaat: shipped ex France	11.85/96
				(stored unrest., Capetown-D.F.Malan 92)	
7937 •	AD-4W AEW.1	**Bu127922**		(to RN Fleet Air Arm as WT987)	
			SE-EBL	Svensk Flygtjanst AB, Bromma: del.	19.6.63/84
				(del. to Save 11.77, retired for disposal)	
				David C. Tallichet/MARC, Chino CA	.84
				(shipped ex Sweden, arr. Linden NJ 7.6.84)	
			N5469Y	David C. Tallichet/MARC, Chino CA	8.84/89
				(open storage Linden NJ as SE-EBL 6.84/89)	
				National Warplane Museum, Geneseo NY	8.89/96
				(stored Geneseo NY 94 pending rest.)	
7946 •	AD-4W AEW.1	**Bu127931**		(to RN Fleet Air Arm as WT951)	.53
			SE-EBM	Svensk Flygtjanst AB, Bromma: del.	9.7.63/84
			G-BMFC	Aces High Ltd, North Weald	16.9.85
				Coys of Kensington Ltd, North Weald	24.9.85/89
				(shipped to UK, arr. dism. North Weald 9.85)	
				Pacific Fighters, Chino CA: shipped ex UK	17.9.90/91
			N4277L	Erickson Air Crane Co, Medford OR	9.5.91
				Cham S. Grill, Medford OR	9.91/96
				(stored, unconv. yellow "SE-EBM", Chino CA 92/93)	
				(also rep. as c/n 7964; plate confirms 7946)	
7957	AD-4W AEW.1	Bu127942		(to RN Fleet Air Arm as WT944)	
			SE-EBG	Svensk Flygtjanst AB, Bromma: del.	26.3.63/74
				wfu 4.10.74, later broken-up Malmo	
7960 •	AD-4W AEW.1	**Bu127945**		(to RN Fleet Air Arm as WT947)	
			SE-EBI	Svensk Flygtjanst AB, Bromma: del.	26.4.63/73
				wfu 15.8.73: stored for museum	8.73/84
				Flygvapenmuseum, Linkoping, Sweden	84/93
				(rep. as composite with Bu124777/WV185: plate confirms c/n 7960)	
7962 •	AD-4W AEW.1	**Bu127947**		(to RN Fleet Air Arm as WT949)	
			SE-EBB	Svensk Flygtjanst AB, Bromma : del.	10.62/74
				wfu 29.8.74, stored for museum	
				Luftfartsmuseet, Stockholm-Arlanda, Sweden	79/92
7963	AD-4W AEW.1	Bu127948		(to RN Fleet Air Arm as WT950)	
			SE-EBD	Svensk Flygtjanst AB, Bromma: del.	15.1.63/74
				wfu 28.9.74, later broken-up Malmo	
7965	AD-4W AEW.1	Bu127950		(to RN Fleet Air Arm as WT952)	
			SE-EBA	Svensk Flygtjanst AB, Bromma: del.	14.9.62/74
				wfu 13.1.74, later broken-up Malmo	
7969	AD-4W AEW.1	Bu127954		(to RN Fleet Air Arm as WT956)	
			SE-EBE	Svensk Flygtjanst AB, Bromma: del.	25.1.63/74
				wfu 4.9.74, later broken-up Malmo	
7970	AD-4W AEW.1	Bu127955		(to RN Fleet Air Arm as WT957)	
			SE-EBF	Svensk Flygtjanst AB, Bromma: del.	1.3.63/76
				crashed, landing Lulea-Kallax	25.2.76
7972	AD-4W AEW.1	Bu127957		(to RN Fleet Air Arm as WT959)	
			SE-EBH	Svensk Flygtjanst AB, Bromma: del.	29.8.63/68
				dest. by fire, Lulea	9.8.68

7975 •	AD-4W AEW.1	**Bu127960**		(to RN Fleet Air Arm as WT962)	
			SE-EBC	Svensk Flygtjanst AB, Bromma: del.	11.62/74
				wfu 27.5.74, stored for museum	
				Svedino's Bil Och Flygmuseum,Sloine, Sweden	79/96
8369 •	AD-4B	**Bu132261**		displ. Camp Barrett, nr MCAS Quantico VA	76
				USMC Museum, MCAS Quantico VA	83/96
8927 •	AD-5Q EA-1F	**Bu132532**		USNAM, NAS Pensacola FL	76/96
8929 •	AD-5Q EA-1F	**Bu132534**		stored NAS Quonset Point RI	70
				displ. Pawtucket Boys Club, Pawtucket RI	.72/78
				Gordon Newell, New Hartford NY	c80
				(stored derelict, Utica-Riverside Airport NY)	
				Wayne Jordan, Binghamton NY	.85
				Harry S. Doan, New Smyrna Beach FL	90/92
				(stored derelict, "USS Independence": for rest.)	
				offered for sale, Doan auction	31.10.92
8993 •	AD-5N A-1G	**Bu132598**		(to SVNAF as 132598)	
				(to USAF as 51-598: 1st SOW)	
				USAFM, Hurlburt Field FL	73/94
				(displ. as "USAF 51-598")	
9385 •	AD-5W EA-1E	**Bu132789**		EAA Museum, Oshkosh WI	76/96
9460 •	AD-5 NA-1E	**Bu132443**		USAFM, Confederate Air Force, Harlingen TX	72/79
				Military Marine Academy, Harlingen TX	82/85
				USMCM, MCAS Quantico VA	93/94
				Texas Air Museum, Rio Hondo TX: loan	94
9480 •	AD-5 A-1E	**Bu132463**		NASM, stored NAF Washington DC	.74/85
				USAFM, McClellen AFB CA	.85/96
				(del. by C-5A 29.10.85; displ. "USAF 32463/EC")	
9506 •	AD-5 A-1E	**Bu132649**		(to USAF as 32649/IZ)	
				USAFM, Wright-Patterson AFB, Dayton OH	.67/90
				(displ. as "32649/IZ")	
9540 •	AD-5 A-1E	**Bu132683**		(to SVNAF as 132683)	
				recov. ex Thailand by Yesterdays Air Force	.79
				(stored unconv., Long Beach CA 1.80/85)	
			N39147	David C. Tallichet/YAF, Chino CA	4.83/95
				USAFM, March AFB CA: loan	93
9701 •	AD-6 A-1H	**Bu134472**		(to SVNAF as 134472)	
				(to R Thai AF as 14/072)	
				R Thai AF Museum, Don Muang AB, Bangkok	85/96
				(displ. as 14/072/*The Proud American*)	
9917 •	AD-6 A-1H	**Bu135273**		Walter Soplata Collection, Newbury OH	65/85
				(incomplete, fire damaged)	
9944 •	AD-6 A-1H	**Bu135300**		USNAM, NAS Pensacola FL	76/96
9976 •	AD-6 A-1H	**Bu135332**		(to SVNAF as 135332)	
				recov. ex Thailand by Yesterdays Air Force	.79
				(stored unconv., Long Beach CA 1.80/88)	
			N32612	ntu: Yesterdays Air Force, Chino CA	9.82/86
			N39148	David C. Tallichet/MARC, Chino CA	4.83/96

10095 •	AD-5Q EA-1F	**Bu135018**		USAFM, Pima County Air Museum, Tucson AZ (displ. as USN "GD-703", later "VR-703")	.69/96
10229 •	AD-5W EA-1E	**Bu135152**		stored NAS Memphis TN ("NATTC Memphis")	75
				Harry S. Doan, New Smyrna Beach FL (recov. derelict ex Memphis, rest. New Smyrna Beach 91/92, ff .92)	89/92
			N65164	Doan Helicopters Inc, New Smyrna Beach FL	9.92
				offered for sale, Doan auction: 5hrs SMOH	30.10.92
				Richard Bertea, Chino CA (del. FL to Chino 13.2.93: rest., ff Chino 7.93)	10.92/93
				Avery's Antique Airplanes Inc, Morganton NC (flies as "35152/HA152")	4.95
10255 •	AD-5W EA-1E	**Bu135178**		Naval Aerospace Medical Institute	
				USMC Museum, MCAS Quantico VA, del.	18.6.71/74
			N62466	Doug Champlin Collection, Enid OK	74
				John Downing	75
				Don Hendrick SC	76/81
				Airlift Inc	83
				Paul O'Connell, Donna TX	7.83
				Peter W. Thelen, Fort Lauderdale FL	1.84/85
				Lone Star Flight Museum, Houston TX	4.86/87
				Peter W. Thelen, Fort Lauderdale FL	88/89
				Taylor Energy Co, New Orleans LA (flies as "Marines 31/MR")	10.89/96
10265 •	AD-5W EA-1A	**Bu135188**		Roy M. Stafford/Black Shadow Aviation, Jacksonville FL (recov. ex NAS China Lake CA to Chino CA 5.89)	.89
				USNAM, NAS Pensacola FL	90
			N188BP	Robert J. Pond/Planes of Fame East, Minneapolis-Flying Cloud MN (rest. Chino CA, ff 8.7.91 as "Marines 21/BP")	26.2.90/93
				Lone Star Flight Museum, Galveston TX	4.93/94
				Amjet Aircraft Corp, St Paul MN	2.94/96
10678 •	AD-6 A-1H	**Bu137602**		NAS Lemoore CA (displ. on pole as "USN 35300/401")	65/93
10838 •	AD-6 A-1H	**Bu139606**		(to SVNAF as 139606)	
				recov. ex Thailand by Yesterdays Air Force (stored unconv., Long Beach CA 1.80/87)	.79
			N3915B	David C. Tallichet/YAF, Chino CA	4.83/86
			N39606	Donald Douglas Museum, Santa Monica CA	7.88/95
				Museum of Flying, Santa Monica CA (rest. Chino .89, flies as "USN/D-606")	90/96
10897 •	AD-6 A-1H	**Bu139665**		(to SVNAF as 139665)	
				recov. ex Thailand by Yesterdays Air Force (stored unconv., Long Beach CA 1.80/88)	.79
			N39149	David C. Tallichet/YAF, Chino CA (stored unconv., Chino CA .88/94)	4.83/95

Notes

1883	B-18	37-022	N67931	Aero Dusters Inc, Chicago IL (ex War Assets)	23.7.46
				Michael C. Mahone/International Aircraft Industries, Compton CA	24.12.46
				Angel's Latin American Air Transport, Compton CA	25.2.47/48
				Garland E. Lincoln Air Service, Van Nuys CA	2.5.48/50
				Charlie Waller, Kent WA	19.9.50/54
				Palmer Cold Storage, Palmer AK	26.5.54/55
				Aero Enterprises Inc, Anchorage AK	11.55/70
1890 •	B-18 B-18B	**37-029**	NC52056	Smyrna Beach Aero, Miami FL	.45
			N52056	Anthony Stinis, Jamaica NY	54
				Christler & Avery, Greybull WY	
				Avery Aviation, Greybull WY (tanker #B20)	63/69
				Hawkins & Powers Aviation, Greybull WY	.69/81
				(tanker #B20) : open storage, Greybull WY	75/81
				USAFM, Castle AFB CA	10.81/96
				(del. ex Greybull 25.10.81: displ. as "USAAC R38")	
2469 •	B-18A	**37-469**	NC56847	G. H. Baldwin CA	.46
			N56847	Leo J. Demers, Salem OR	54
				Walter J. Martin, Long Beach CA	64/66
				Westernair of Albuquerque, Albuquerque NM	69/70
				(ex sprayer: open storage Tucson AZ 65/70, then stored Albuquerque NM)	
				Dennis Hock	
				(del. Albuquerque-Wright Patterson AFB)	
				USAFM, Wright-Patterson AFB, Dayton OH	72/92
				(rest., displ. as "USAAC R33")	
2505 •	B-18A	**37-505**	N67947	D. Eugene Walsh	8.54
				Tyler Flight Service, Westminster MD	54
				Tyler Flight Service, Long Island NY	
				Aero Service of Dalhart, Dalhart TX	63/66
			XB-LAJ	Federacion Regional de Sociedades Cooperativas de la Industria Pesquera de Baja California, Ensenada, Baja California	.66/67
				stored engineless, Ensenada, Baja California	10.69
			N18AC	ntu: Tucson Air Mus. Foundation, Tucson AZ	.71/72
				Pima County Air Museum, Tucson AZ	73/81
				USAFM: moved to MASDC (still as XB-LAJ)	19.5.81
				USAFM, McChord AFB WA: del. by C-5A	.83/96
				(displ. as USAAC "37-505")	
2561	B-18A	37-561	N66272	Jaime Paullada, Los Angeles CA	25.6.46
				Clifford Quesenberry, East Beckley WV	21.9.46
				Lawrence A. Mudgett, Bangor ME	31.3.47
				Cape Air Service Inc, Hyannis MA	12.48/50
				Tyler Flight Service, Long Island NY	7.3.50
				Tyley Flight Service, Westminster MD	54
				D. Eugene Walsh	8.54/55
				Marvin Kohn, Brooklyn NY	2.5.55
				Plains Aero Service Inc, Amarillo TX	13.5.55/66
			XB-LAW	Federacion Regional de Sociedades Cooperativas de la Industria Pesquera de Baja California, Ensenada, Baja California	.66/67
				noted derelict, engineless, Ensenada	10.69
				broken-up, Ensanada, Baja California	c72
2643 •	B-18A	**38-593**	N66267	Lynn W. Roberts, Reno NV	54
				Roberts Aircraft Co, Boise ID (tanker #D18)	58/70
				(wfu, open storage Phoenix-Litchfield AZ 69/76)	

				Pima Air Museum, Tucson AZ: arr. dism.	5.9.76/93
2673 •	B-18A	**39-025**		(to CAEC/Cuban AF as ....)	
			N62477	Leo J. Demers, Salem OR	54/55
				Roger Stedman, Miami FL: USCR	63/66
				impounded, Miami FL: rep gun running to Cuba	.58
				USAFM, Wright Patterson AFB, Dayton OH	61/74
				USAFM, Cannon AFB NM	85/88
				USAFM, Lowry AFB CO	93/96
				(displ. as USAAC "39-522")	

DOUGLAS B-23 DRAGON

2714	B-23	39-028	NC54584	Starling Airports Inc, MO	.46
				Daniel Peterkin, IL	.46/47
			N100P	National Distillers Products, New York NY	54/58
			N58091	Green Bay Packaging, Green Bay WI	59/66
				J & G Carlton Inc, Muskegon MI	69
				Lorenair Inc, Miami FL	70/72
2717 •	B-23	**39-031**	NC51436	Pan American Airways, New York NY	.46
			N400W	Pan American World Airways, New York NY	54
				(op. as executive transport by Juan Trippe)	
			N4000W	Pan American World Airways, New York NY	59/66
				Carolina Aircraft Corp, Miami FL	29.8.68
			HC-APV	Ecuatoriana, Quito	12.68/82
				(retired, open storage Quito 75/82)	
				Museo Aereo de FAE, Mariscal Sucre AB Quito	85/93
				(displ. in bogus FA Ecuatoriana scheme)	
2719 •	B-23	**39-033**	NR49548	Gar Wood Industries Inc MI	.45
			N747	Howard Hughes, Culver City CA	
				Rexall Drugs, Chicago IL	.50
				Food Machinery & Chemical Corp, McAllen TX	54/59
				FMC Corp, San Jose C	61/64
			N747M	Monarch Aviation Inc, Monterey CA	.66
				Douglas B-23 of Monterey Inc, Monterey CA	69/72
				Edward J. Daly/World Airways, Oakland CA	4.78/85
				Douglas Historical Foundation, Long Beach CA:	
				leased: displ. at Douglas plant, Long Beach	84/85
				Mike Bogue, Oakland CA	11.85/93
				(del. to Oakland 25.11.85, flies as "39-033")	
2722 •	B-23	**39-036**	NR52327	Paul Mantz, Burbank CA	.45
	UC-67		N52327	California Oil Co, New Orleans LA/Houston TX	.46/66
				Chevron Oil Co, Houston TX	69
				Westernair of Albuquerque, Albuquerque NM	70
				University of Washington, Seattle WA	.70/73
				Spurling Aviation, Seattle WA	77
				Puget Sound Helicopters Inc, Seattle WA	23.1.81
				University of Washington, Seattle WA	84
				damaged, landing at Kingman AZ	6.84
				Ascher Ward & Al HAnsen, Mojave CA	.84/85
				(rest. to military configuration, Mojave CA .85)	
				USAFM, McChord AFB WA	12.85/93
				(del. 12.12.85: displ. as USAAC "9-17B")	
2723 •	B-23	**39-037**	N41821	Union Oil Co. of California, Los Angeles CA	54
			N800L	Westinghouse Electric Corp	59
			N800N	A. J. Dewitt, Chatanooga TN	63/64
				Medical Electronics Inc, Camp Hill PA	66
				John H. Logsden, New Orleans LA/St Louis MO	69/72
				Robert P. Schlaefli, Fairbanks AK	77

				Florida Aircraft Leasing, Fort Lauderdale FL	10.81
				James W. Boy, Fort Lauderdale FL	84
				USAFM, Wright-Patterson AFB OH : del.	5.82/92
				(displ. as "9-17B")	
2724 •	B-23	**39-038**	NC56249	Henry J. Kaiser Co CA	.46
	UC-67		N56249	Standard Oil Co California, San Francisco CA	54
				General Electric Co, Schenectady NY	59
			N62G	John W. Mecom Co., Houston TX	63/72
				Confederate Air Force, Harlingen/Midland TX	10.73/96
				(del. 29.10.73: op by Cajun Wing, Lafayette LA;	
				rest. Harlingen: by road to Midland TX .93)	
2727	B-23	39-041	NC61666	General Motors Corp, Detroit MI	.46
			N61666	D. D. Feldman, Dallas TX	54
				General Electric Co, Schenectady NY	59/64
				Airlease Inc, Chicago IL	66
				Harris Trust & Savings Bank, Chicago IL	69/70
				rep. based Las Vegas, named *Dragonfly*	c71
				also rep. abandoned in Argentina during	60s
2730	B-23	39-044	NR49811	Hughes Tool Co, Culver City CA	.45
	UC-67		NC49811	Howard Hughes/Hughes Tool Co, CA	46/50
			N49811	National Supply Co, Pittsburg PA	54
			N141WD	Winn Dixie Stores	
			N777X	Madden & Smith Aircraft Inc, Miami FL	63/66
			N744Q	McDonald Lumber Inc, Minneapolis MN	.66
				Capitol Reserve Corp, Los Angeles CA	69/70
2732	B-23	39-046	NR53253	Gar Wood Industries Inc, MI	.45
			N53253	Tennessee Gas Transmission Co, Houston TX	54
				H. C. Price Co	59
				Amann Division Inc, San Antonio TX	64
				Gulf & Western Corp, Houston TX	66/70
				sale rep., USCR	78/92
2733 •	B-23	**39-047**	NR45361	United Rexall Drug Co, MA	45/47
	UC-67		N45361	General Electric Co, Schenectady NY	54
			N1G (2	General Tire & Rubber Co, Akron OH	
			N244AG	Aerojet General Corp, Azusa CA	59
			N8658E	L. B. Smith Aircraft Corp, Miami FL	
			N409ME	Inter Public Inc, New York NY	63/64
			N880L	Laboratory for Electronics, Boston MA	66/69
				Jenny Flight Engineering, Bedford MA	70/72
				Mickey Jones, Emmonak AK	77
				Leroy W. Richards, Chico CA	82
				USAFM, Castle AFB CA	.82/93
				(displ. as USAAC "39-047/112-MD")	
2737 •	B-23	**39-051**	NC61Y	Roscoe Turner	7.4.45/50
			N61Y	Great Lakes Carbon Corp	30.8.50
				Celanese Corp. of America, New York NY	1.53/54
			N34C	Consolidated Coal Co, Pittsburgh PA	63
			N534C	Consolidated Coal Co, Pittsburgh PA	64
			N230SU	Ohio State University, Columbus OH	66
			N534J	Air Lease Inc, Harvey LA	69/70
				USAFM, loan: Pima Air Museum, Tucson AZ	73/93
2739	B-23	39-053	NC58092	Lehman Brothers, New York NY	.46
			N58092	H. K. Porter Co, Pittsburgh PA	54/64
				Monarch Aviation Inc, Monterey CA	66
				Trans Aero Systems Inc, Miami FL	69/70
2743 •	B-23	**39-057**	NR33309	Pan American Airways, La Guardia NY	.45/46
				The Hearst Corp, New York NY	.46

			N400B	E. W. Scripps Co, Cincinnati OH	.48/54
			N4000B	E. W. Scripps Co, Cincinnati OH	63/69
				Purdue University	19.11.69
				Dennis M. Sherman,West Palm Beach FL	23.5.70
				Aviation Contractors Inc, American Fork UT	72
				Westair International Inc, Broomfield CO	73/75
				Tom Page/P & M Supply Co., Willoughby OH	75
				Texas Aerial Surveys Inc, Dallas TX	76
				Tom Page/P & M Supply Co., Willoughby OH	77/81
				National Jets Inc, Fort Lauderdale FL	11.83
				Weeks Air Mus., Tamiami FL	5.84/95
				(displ. in camouflage "USAAC 40/17B")	
				dam. Tamiami FL, Hurricane Andrew	24.8.92
2745 •	B-23	**39-059**	NR49891	Pan American Airways, La Guardia NY	.45
	UC-67		N49891	Esso Shipping Co, New York NY	54/58
			N86E	Chatham Chemical Corp	59
				Houston Chemical Corp	61
				John W. Mecom Co, Houston TX	63/72
				abandoned at Athens, Greece	69/86
2748	B-23	39-062	NR33310	Pan American Airways, La Guardia NY	.45/46
			NC33310	Col. Roscoe Turner	
			N33310	Fairbanks-Morse Company	
				General Electric Co, Schenectady NY	54/64
			N1755	Carolina Aircraft Corp, Fort Lauderdale FL	69
				Transport Leasing Corp, Miami FL	70
				impounded Tocumen, Panama	c71/75
				broken-up Tocumen, Panama by	78
2749 •	B-23	39-063	N47994	Esso Shipping Co, New York NY	54
			N777LW	Le Tourneau-Westinghouse Co	59
				Bruce McCreary Co, Grass Valley CA	66/70
				Robert P. Schlaefli, Fairbanks AK	77
				Robert P. Schlaefli/SLAFCO, Moses Lake WA	.84/91

DOUGLAS SBD DAUNTLESS

- •	SBD-2	**Bu02106**		ditched Lake Michigan,off carrier *Wolverine*	6.43
				USNAM, NAS Pensacola FL	93/96
				(recov. from Lake Michigan for USNAM, salvaged in excellent complete condition: static rest. at NAS Pensacola FL 93/95)	
1245 •	SBD-3	**Bu06508**		ditched Lake Michigan,off carrier *Wolverine*	23.11.43
				(recov. from Lake Michigan 23.10.90 for USNAM)	
				USNAM, NAS Pensacola FL	.90/94
				(static rest. GA 93: displ. Pensacola)	
- •	SBD-3	**Bu06583**		ditched Lake Michigan,off carrier *Wolverine*	30.10.43
				USNAM, NAS Pensacola FL	93
				(recov. from Lake Michigan for USNAM)	
- •	SBD-3	**Bu06624**		ditched Lake Michigan,off carrier "Wolverine"	19.9.43
				USNAM, NAS Pensacola FL	93/94
				(recov. from Lake Michigan c91 for USNAM)	
				Kalamazoo Aviation History Museum, Kalamazoo MI: loan for rest. & displ: arr.	9.10.93/96
1509 •	SBD-3	**Bu06694**		USNAM, NAS Pensacola FL	93/94
				(recov. from Lake Michigan c91 for USNAM)	
				USS Lexington Museum, Corpus Christi TX	93/94
				(displ. unrest. on board carrier 94)	

1708 •	SBD-4	**Bu06833**		(USN "B8"): ditched, Lake Michigan	16.9.44
				(recov. from Lake Michigan .91 for USNAM)	
				USNAM, NAS Pensacola FL	.91/94
				(displ. as recov.)	
- •	SBD-4	**Bu06900**		rep. USNAM, NAS Pensacola FL	93/94
				San Diego Aerospace Museum CA: loan	94
1858 •	SBD-4	**Bu06953**		(to RNZAF as NZ5037)	
				crashed Espiritu Santo, Vanuatu, South Pacific	11.2.44
				RNZAF Museum, Wigram AB NZ: stored	.87/95
				(hulk recov. from Vanuatu .87 by RNZAF C-130:	
				displ. as recov. in jungle diorama 95)	
2350 •	A-24A	**42-60817**	N9142H	City of Portland Mosquito Control, OR	58/65
				op. Aero Flight Inc, Troutdale OR : sprayer	
			N15749	USMC Museum, MCAS Quantico VA	.65
				USNAM, NAS Pensacola FL	.66/94
				(moved by road, Portland-Pensacola .66)	
				(displ. as SBD-3 "2-S-12", later "Bu6583")	
			N5254L	USNAM, NAS Pensacola FL: reg. candidate	8.10.92/94
				Roy M. Stafford/Black Shadow Aviation,	
				Jacksonville FL: reg. candidate	20.1.93
				Erickson Air Crane, Medford OR	5.93/95
2468 •	SBD-4	**Bu10508**		(to RNZAF as NZ5021)	
				Ross Jowitt, Auckland-Ardmore NZ	90/95
				(hulk recov. ex Pacific island: rest. project)	
2478 •	SBD-4	**Bu10518**		Warner Brothers Studio, Toluca Lake CA: hulk	
				Ed Maloney/The Air Museum, Claremont CA	c62/64
				Admiral Nimitz Museum, Fredericksburg TX	
				Bruce D. Roberts, New London Airport PA	75
				loan: Bradley Air Museum, Windor Locks CT	
			N4864J	Charles F Nichols/Yankee Air Corps, Chino CA	4.84/95
				(airworthy rest. Chino, but not flown,	
				using wings recov. from Guadalcanal by YAC)	
2565 •	SBD-4	**Bu10575**		ditched in Lake Michigan, off Chicago IL	14.9.44
				recov. from Lake Michigan by USNAM	.91
				USNAM, NAS Pensacola FL	.91/94
- •	SBD-4	**Bu10715**		ditched Lake Michigan, off carrier "Sable"	2.9.44
				(recov. from Lake Michigan by Ed Marshall c81)	
				Charles F Nichols/Yankee Air Corps, Chino CA	86
				(rest. project, using wings recov. from	
				Guadalcanal, South Pacific by YAC)	
				David C. Tallichet/MARC, Chino CA : unrest.	.87/91
				Museum of Flying, Santa Monica CA	.91
				(arr. Santa Monica dism. 7.91, rest. project)	
883 •	SBD-5	**Bu28536**		(to RNZAF as NZ5062): BOC 3.44: SOC	20.5.44
				ret. to USMC, Russell Field, South Pacific	10.5.44
				MGM Studios, Culver City CA (wind machine) 55/68	
				Ed Maloney/The Air Museum, Chino CA	.68/87
			N670AM	Planes of Fame, Chino CA	.87/96
				(rest. Chino .82/87, using wings recov. from	
				Guadalcanal, South Pacific: ff 2.7.87 as "S-4")	
812 •	SBD-5	**Bu36173**		ditched Lake Michigan, off carrier "Sable"	5.3.44
				(recov. from Lake Michigan .88)	
				Patriots Point Naval & Maritime Museum/	
				USS Yorktown Museum, Mount Pleasant SC	.88/96
				(rest., displ. on USS "Yorktown" as "36173/14")	

c/n	Type	Serial	Reg	Owner / History	Date
6119 •	SBD-6	**Bu54605**		Smithsonian Institute	.48/70
				stored Weeksville NC	5.48/61
				USMC Museum, MCAS Quantico VA	.70
				NASM, Washington DC	75/93
				(displ. as "VS-51/54605/109")	
17371 •	A-24B	**42-54532**	NL94513	Seaboard & Western Airlines,	
				San Francisco CA	.47
				(to FA Mexicana as .....)	
			XB-QUC	Compania Mexicana Aerophoto, Mexico City	60/63
				Tallmantz Collection, Orange County CA	.64
				The Air Museum, Ontario CA	.65/67
			N54532	Robert L. Griffin/CAF, San Antonio TX	.70/72
				Confederate Air Force, Harlingen/Midland TX	10.78/96
				(flies as SBD-3, "54532/2-B-4/B14")	
17421 •	A-24B	**42-54582**	N4488N	Marsh Aviation, Litchfield AZ	54
				City of Portland Mosquito Control, OR	60/70
				op: Aero Flight Inc, Troutdale OR : sprayer	
				Pacific Aeronautical Corp, Lake Oswego OR	.71/74
			N17421	Windward Aviation, Enid OK	3.74/75
				USMC Museum, MCAS Quantico VA	3.75/96
				(displ. as "SBD-5/USMC/S6")	
17432 •	A-24B	**42-54593**		MGM Studios, Culver City CA (wind machine)	
	RA-24B			Admiral Nimitz Museum, Fredericksburg TX	
				Trade Tech. School, Waco TX : to scrapyard	
				Nick Pocock, China Springs TX	75/91
				Kevin R. Smith, Fredericksburg VA	.91
				(fuse only, planned rest. to fly)	
17482 •	A-24B	**42-54643**		MGM Studios, Culver City CA (wind machine)	
				Admiral Nimitz Museum, Fredericksburg TX	72/74
				Bradley Air Museum, Windsor Locks CT: arr.	4.12.74/88
				Bruce Roberts, New London PA	.88
			N51382	Weeks Air Museum,	
				Tamiami FL (rest. project)	.88/96
17493 •	A-24B	**42-54654**		MGM Studios, Culver City CA (wind machine)	
				David C. Tallichet/MARC, Chino CA	79/93
				(rest. Akron-Canton Airport OH, for MARC 91)	
17521 •	A-24B	**42-54682**		(to FA Mexicana as .....)	
			XB-ZAH	Compania Mexicana Aerophoto, Mexico City	63
				(noted wfu, engineless, Mexico City 12.63)	
				Tallmantz Aviation/Movieland of the Air,	
				Orange County CA (displ. as USN SBD)	4.64
			N74133	Rosen-Novak Auto Co, Omaha NE	66/68
				remained on displ. Orange County: auctioned	29.5.68
				John McGregor, San Fernando CA	69/70
				Admiral Nimitz Museum, Fredericksburg TX	.72/94
				(rest. by Trade School, Waco TX 72, displ.	
				at museum as "SBD-3 5-B-1", later "MB-21")	
			N93RW	Air SRV Inc/Lone Star Flight Museum,	
				Galveston TX	2.9.94/96
				(arr. dism. Galveston 8.94: for rest.)	
17651	A-24B	42-54812	NX46472	Sperry Gyroscope Co, New York NY	45/47
	RA-24B		N46472	City of Portland Mosquito Control OR	56/65
				Aero Flight Inc, Kent WA	1.7.65
				Confederate Air Force, Mercedes TX	10.65
				crashed on del. flight, Brownwood TX	10.10.65
				rear fuselage noted on dump. Harlingen TX	76

- •	SBD-3	-	composite hulk, rep. recov. ex crash sites FL Harry S. Doan, New Smyrna Beach FL offered for sale, Doan auction (rest. project: QEC & most airframe components)	 87/92 30.10.92
- •	SBD-4	-	rep. recov. from Lake Michigan Weeks Air Museum, Tamiami FL (rest. project)	 90/96

FAIREY BATTLE

- •	Mk. I (T)	**L5306**	(to RCAF as 2139): BOC 10.4.42: SOC Tex LaVallee/LaVallee Cultural & Aeronautical Collection, St Chrysostome QUE Canadian Museum of Flight & Transportation, Vancouver BC: unrest. components	9.12.43 80 .80/96
-	Mk. I	L5340	(to RCAF as 1614): BOC 2.4.40: SOC recov. derelict from farm Canada Sir W. J. D. Roberts/Strathallan Aircraft Collection, Auchterader, Scotland RAF Museum Store, RAF Henlow RAF Museum, RAF St.Athan (components used in rest. of L5343)	16.2.45 .72 73/83 83/87
- •	Mk. I	**L5343**	forced landing, aband. Kaldadaranes, Iceland hulk recov. ex crash site by RAF Museum RAF Museum Store, RAF Henlow: stored (rest. begun RAF Leeming, then RAF Cardington) RAF Museum, RAF St.Athan (static rest. using fuse. L5340 completed 3.90) RAF Museum, Hendon (displ. as "L5343/S-VO")	13.9.40 8.72 73 .81/90 3.90/96
F.4139 •	Mk. I	**P2234**	(to RCAF as 1317): BOC 3.11.39: SOC Tex LaVallee/LaVallee Cultural & Aeronautical Collection, St Chrysostome QUE	12.9.40 88
- •	Mk. I (T)	**R3947**	(to RCAF as 1923) BOC 7.4.41: SOC Western Canada Aviation Museum, Winnipeg MAN: incomplete hulk (id. assumed, quoted as RCAF3947, a DH.82)	16.2.45 79/96
- •	Mk. I Mk. I TT	**R3950**	(to RCAF as 1899): BOC 7.4.41: SOC sold to farmer, MacDonald ALTA Tom Voll, Michigan (planned rest. to fly) Sir W. J. D. Roberts/Strathallan Aircraft Collection, Auchterader, Scotland Charles Church, Winchester loaned: Imperial War Museum, Duxford: arr. Historic Aircraft Collection Musee Royal de l'Armee, Brussels, Belgium (del. by C130 3.5.90; displ. as "R3950/HA-L")	16.2.45 .45/69 70/72 11.72/87 .87/89 15.10.87 .90/95
F.4848 •	Mk. I (T)	**R7384**	(to RCAF as R7384): BOC (stored for future museum use .46) Canadian National Aeronutical Collection, Rockcliffe AB ONT National Aviation Museum, Rockcliffe ONT (displ. as "RCAF R7384/35")	18.1.41 65/82 9.82/96
- •	Mk. I (T)	-	Koninklijk Legermuseum, Brussels Belgium (fuselage only)	92

Warbirds of Great Britain's Casa 2111 G-BDYA still wearing its last Spanish colour scheme at Blackbushe after being brought back from Spain for the Late Doug Arnold. **APN**

Lufthansa Junkers Ju52/3m 'D-AQUI' departs from the dockside London City Airport, destination Biggin Hill. This was the first time a Junkers had landed in central London, but not the first warbird at L.C.A. The Royal Navy's Swordfish beat them to it. **James Kightly.**

The best we were able to do to represent the Axis forces for many years was to have types such as the CASA 352 and Pilatus P2 (in this case owned by Aces High and Plane Sailing) putting on a fine show of agression at the 1986 Fighter Meet. **James Kightly.**

The Lockheed Hudson had a long ɔost war civilian career in Australia, being popular as an air-iner, newspaper and general freighter and a geo-survey nachine. Here A16-112 wears the egistation VH-AGS and colours of Adastra Aerial Surveys. **APN.**

Mark Hurd Aerial Surveys, Inc., it says on the hangar, and two seat P-38 N505MH is right at home. Now listed as N38EV, and it was seen (rarely) for a period as *Miss Behavin* in the U.K. when based at Biggin Hill with Warbirds of Great Britain. **APN.**

he Lockheed P2V-7 Neptune lways occupies an impressive hunk of airshow space, as well as osting a fair ammount to oper-te. Bob DeLa Hunty and Gordon ilynn's machine wears its original oyal Australian Navy colours, 89-273, and is regstered to them s VH-IOY. **Alan Scoot.**

c/n	Model	Serial	Civil Reg.	History	Dates
F.5607 •	Mk. 1	Z2033	SE-BRD	Svensk Flygtjanst AB, Stockholm-Bromma	3.49/64
	TT Mk. 1		G-ASTL	Peter Thomas/Skyfame Aircraft Museum,	
				Staverton: del.	5.5.64/78
				Imperial War Museum, Duxford	.78/96
				(displ. as Z2033/275/*Evelyn Tentions*)	
- •	FR Mk. I	DK560		(to RCN as DK560): BOC 1.6.46: SOC	1.3.54
				(to Ethiopian AF as DK560)	.54
				del. to Ethiopia on carrier HMCS Magnificent	.54
				Asmara AB, Ethiopia/Eritrea: open storage	70/93
				National Aviation Museum, Ottawa ONT	.93/96
				(airfreighted to Canada 10.93 by RCAF C-130)	
F.6071 •	Mk. 1	DT989	SE-BRG	Svensk Flygtjanst AB, Stockholm-Bromma	.50/69
	TT Mk. 1			(wfu, stored Stockholm-Arlanda 66/69)	
				Technical Museum, Arlanda, Stockholm	.69/85
				Bjorn Lowgren, Stockholm: rest. project	.85/90
F.6121 •	Mk. 1	PP392	SE-CAW	Svensk Flygtjanst AB, Stockholm-Bromma	.56/64
	TT Mk. 1			Malmo Technical Museum, Malmo	.65/80
				Flygvapenmuseum, Linkoping, Sweden	.80/96
- •	Mk. I	PP462		(to RCN as PP462): BOC 1.6.46: SOC	1.3.54
	FR Mk. I			(to Ethiopian AF as PP462)	.54
				del. to Ethiopia on carrier HMCS Magnificent	.54
				Asmara AB, Ethiopia/Eritrea: open storage	70/93
				CFB Shearwater Aviation Museum NS	.93/96
				(airfreighted to Canada 10.93 by RCAF C-130,	
				under static rest. at CFB Shearwater 96)	
F.6180 •	Mk. 1	PP469	SE-CAU	Svensk Flygtjanst AB, Stockholm-Bromma	.56/64
	TT Mk. 1			(fire training area, Midlanda Airport .64/85)	
				Bjorn Lowgren, Stockholm (rest. project)	.85/90
F.7402 •	Mk. 1	MB410		(to R Thai AF as SF11): del.	21.1.52
	FR. Mk. 1			R Thai AF Museum, Don Muang AB, Bangkok	66/96
F.8026 •	FR Mk. 4	VH127		RNAS Culdrose: stored	69
	TT Mk. 4			Fleet Air Arm Museum, RNAS Yeovilton	73/96
				(displ. as "VH127/E-209")	
F.8309 •	AS Mk. 5	VT409		Unimetal Ltd, Droysden: scrapyard	60/80
				Nick Grace, St.Merryn, Cornwall	82
				(hulk stored St.Merryn, with WD833)	
				North East Aircraft Museum, Sunderland	84/87
				(composite rest. project, with WD899)	
F.8420 •	AS Mk. 5	VX388		(to RAN as VX388): BOC	25.5.49/65
	TT Mk. 5			(arr. as deck cargo on carrier HMAS Sydney 25.5.49)	
				del. to Sydney-Bankstown NSW for disposal	3.3.65/66
				M. D. N. Fisher/Historical Aircraft	
				Preservation Society, UK: not collected	8.7.66
				Camden Museum of Aviation, Camden NSW	
				later Narellan NSW	.69/96
F.8497 •	AS Mk. 5	WB271		(to RAN as WB271): BOC	7.3.52/65
	TT Mk. 5			(arr. as deck cargo on carrier HMAS Sydney 3.52,	
				collected ex RNFAA NAS Sembawang, Singapore)	
				del. Sydney-Bankstown NSW for disposal	3.3.65/66
				RN Fleet Air Arm Museum, RNAS Yeovilton	8.2.66/72
				(shipped to UK on carrier *HMS Victorious* 4.67)	
				RN Historic Flight, RNAS Yeovilton	.72/96

				(rest., ff 21.9.72: flies as "RN WB271/204R")	
F.8646 •	AS Mk. 6	**WB518**		(to RAN as WB518): BOC	12.50/65
	TT Mk. 6			(arr. as deck cargo on carrier *HMAS Sydney* 12.50)	
				del. Sydney-Bankstown NSW for disposal	3.3.65/66
				Returned Services League, Griffith NSW: del.	2.67/91
				(displ. on pole as "WB518/903NW")	
				Classic Aviation Pty Ltd, Bankstown NSW	.91/94
				(partially rest. to fly Sydney-Bankstown,	
				using components from WD828 91/94)	
				Eddy Kurdizel, Fort Collins CO	4.94
				(left Bankstown in shipping container 4.94,	
				to be rest. to fly Fort Collins)	
F.8654 •	AS Mk. 6	**WD826**		(to RAN as WD826): BOC	11.3.53
	TT Mk. 6			(arr. deck cargo on carrier HMAS Vengeance 3.53)	
				NAS Schofields NSW: inst. airframe	.64/74
				Naval Aviation Museum, NAS Nowra NSW	12.74/86
			VH-NVU	RAN Historic Flight, NAS Nowra NSW	30.9.86/96
				(rest. Nowra,ff 4.10.86 as "RAN WD826/245K")	
F.8655 •	AS Mk. 6	**WD827**		(to RAN as WD827): BOC	12.50/56
				(arr. as deck cargo on carrier HMAS Sydney12.50)	
				Australian Air League, Blacktown NSW: displ.	2.11.56/73
				Moorabbin Air Museum, Moorabbin VIC	29.4.73/96
				(shipped ex Sydney, arr. Melbourne-Essendon 6.5.73:	
				parts used for airworthy rest. of WD828;	
				later displ. Moorabbin as "WD827/911NW")	
F.8656 •	AS Mk. 6	**WD828**		(to RAN as WD828): BOC	12.50/65
	TT Mk. 6			(arr. as deck cargo on carrier HMAS Sydney12.50)	
				del. Sydney-Bankstown NSW for disposal	3.3.65
				Moorabbin Air Museum, Melbourne VIC: del.	18.2.67/82
				(trucked to Essendon VIC 21.7.73: rest. to fly)	
			VH-HMW	Michael B. Wansey, Newcastle NSW	.82/89
				(rest. completed at Ballarat VIC, ff 28.9.84	
				as WD828/271K/*Mickey's Mouse*)	
				forced landing, near Camden NSW	4.12.87
				Classic Aviation Pty Ltd, Bankstown NSW	2.89/92
				(arr. Bankstown 1.90, for rebuild using WB518;	
				airframe WD828 rest. for static displ.)	
				Returned Services League, Griffith NSW	.91/95
				(displ. on pole, Griffith NSW as "WB518/903NW")	
F.8661 •	AS Mk. 6	**WD833**		(to RAN as WD833): BOC	12.50/65
				(arr. as deck cargo on carrier HMAS Sydney12.50)	
				NAS Hastings VIC: gate guard	60
				R. H. Grant Trading Co, Melbourne VIC	9.60/67
				(scrapyard advertising displ. as "WD833/910NW")	
				Tom B. King, Melbourne VIC	68/70
				Berwick Museum of Transport, Berwick VIC	72/74
				Sir W. J. D. Roberts/Strathallan Aircraft	
				Collection, Scotland : stored, unrest.	12.74/81
				E. Nick Grace, St Merryn, Cornwall	.81/84
				(stored St.Merryn, with parts VT409, 81/84)	
				Ward Wilkins/Unlimited Aero, Fort Collins CO	13.8.84/88
				(shipped ex Southampton to USA 15.4.86)	
			N833WD	Henry J. Schroeder, Danville IL: stored	11.89/94
				Wally Fisk/Amjet Aircraft Corp, St Paul MN	1.94/95
				(stored St Paul-Anoka County MN pending rest.)	
F.8668 •	AS Mk. 6	**WD840**		(to RAN as WD840): BOC	12.50/65
	TT Mk. 6			(arr. as deck cargo on carrier HMAS Sydney12.50)	
				del. Sydney-Bankstown NSW for disposal	3.3.65
				Jarman Aircraft Engine Overhaul Services,	

				Sydney NSW	7.66
				Ed Fleming/Skyservice Aviation, Camden NSW:	
				del. to Camden ex storage Bankstown	1.67/69
				resident of Carman MAN	.69/72
			CF-CBH	resident of Carman MAN	.72/75
				(ff Carman 17.9.72, Merlin 500 ex Avro York,	
				cockpit fitted out as 8-seater)	
			N810J	Jerry Barg, South Easton MA	.75
			N1840	Gene Fisher/Mid Atlantic Air Museum,	
				Middletown PA	5.82/84
				Don Knapp/DK Precision, Fort Lauderdale FL	89/90
				Lone Star Flight Museum, Galveston TX	.90/96
F.8724	AS Mk. 6	WD901		(to RAN as WD901)	11.3.53/65
	TT Mk. 6			(arr. deck cargo on carrier *HMAS Vengeance* 3.53)	
				del. Sydney-Bankstown NSW for disposal	3.3.65
				Casula Auto Wreckers, Casula NSW	8.7.66/67
				(advertising displ. in front of car wrecking yard)	
				William F. G. Gambella, Charleston SC	.67
				(shipped to USA on SS African Crescent .67)	
			N7469	John M. Sliker, Wadley GA	.68/71
			CF-BDH	Canadian Warplane	
				Heritage, Hamilton ONT	9.71/77
				(del. GA-Toronto 9.71; flew as "RCN BD-H")	
				crashed in Lake Ontario nr. Toronto (Ness k.)	2.9.77
F.8755 •	AS Mk. 6	**WH632**		(to RAN as WH632): BOC 14.8.53 : SOC	29.5.60
				(arr. as deck cargo on carrier *HMAS Sydney* 8.53)	
				Australian Air League, Marrickville NSW: arr.	3.6.60/66
				Camden Museum of Aviation, Camden NSW	17.6.66/78
				Canadian Warplane Heritage, Hamilton ONT	6.78/91
				(shipped ex Sydney to Canada 6.78)	
			C-GBDG	Canadian Warplane Heritage, Hamilton ONT	10.91/96
				(rest. Hamilton ONT & Victoria BC, ff 4.92 Victoria)	
				accident on takeoff for del. to CWH, Victoria BC	7.5.92
				(ff after rebuild late 95)	
F.8813 •	AS Mk. 6	**WJ109**		(to RAN as WJ109): BOC	11.3.53/63
	TT Mk. 6			(arr. deck cargo on carrier *HMAS Vengeance* 8.53)	
				NAS Nowra, NSW: gate guard	65/72
				Naval Aviation Museum, Nowra NAS, NSW	12.74/96
				(displ. as "WJ109/207K")	

FAIREY GANNET

F.9137 •	AS Mk. 1	**WN365**		(prototype T. Mk.2, ff Northolt 16.8.54)	
	T Mk. 2		G-APYO	Fairey Aviation Ltd, White Waltham	17.2.60/61
	T Mk. 5			(rebuilt as T.5, ff 3.3.60)	
				(to Indonesian Navy as AS-14): crew training	.60/61
				Westland Aircraft Ltd	20.6.61
				(wfu 10.61, stored White Waltham .61/66)	
				(to RN FAA as XT752): del.	8.66
				Fleet Air Arm Museum, RNAS Yeovilton	83/94
				(stored RNAS Culdrose 83/85, arr. RNAS	
				Lee-On-Solent for storage 4.10.85/94)	
				sold at Sotheby's auction	18.11.94
				AMJET, Minneapolis, shipped	95
				restoration to airworthy	
F.9451 •	AEW. 3	**XL482**		RNAS Culdrose: stored	.78/81
			N1350X	Nathaniel A. Kalt, San Antonio TX	10.81
				(rest., ff Culdrose 4.2.82, dep. on del. 15.2.82)	
				Dowty-Rotol, San Antonio TX	2.82/83

				Hamilton Standard, Stratford CT : del.	21.4.83/86
				New England Air Museum, Bradley CT : del.	8.9.86/93
				Kal Aero Service, Bonita CA	.93/96
F.9461 •	AEW. 3	**XL502**		RNAS Lossiemouth: ground trainer	78
				RNAS Leuchars: ground trainer	84/86
			G-BMYP	Neil Moffat/Moffat Aviation, Carlisle (wfu .89, stored)	16.9.86/89
				Gerry Cooper/Cooper Aerial Surveys, Sandtoft	.94/96

FAIREY SWORDFISH

- •	Mk. II Mk. IV	**W5856**		(to RCN as W5856): BOC 15.12.44: SOC	21.8.46
				Ernest K. Simmons, Tillsonburg ONT (open storage on farm, sold at auction 5.9.70)	.46/70
				owner Alabama USA: rest. commenced	76
				Sir W. J. D. Roberts/Strathallan Aircraft Collection, Auchterader, Scotland	8.77/85
			G-BMGC	Strathallan Aircraft Collection, Auchterader	10.85/90
				The Swordfish Heritage Trust (trucked to Brough 14.12.90 for rest., ff 12.5.93)	10.90/93
				op by RN Historic Flight, RNAS Yeovilton (flies as "RN W5856/A2A")	22.5.93/96
- •	Mk. II Mk. IV	**HS469**		(to RCN as HS469): BOC 2.9.43: BOC	17.8.46
				Ernest K. Simmons, Tillsonburg ONT (open storage on farm, sold at auction 5.9.70)	.46/70
				Jack Arnold Aviation Museum, Brantford ONT	
				Shearwater Aviation Museum, CFB Shearwater NS: rest. project	80/90
			C-GRCN	Shearwater Aviation Museum NS (rest. CFB Downsview ONT, rolled-out 25.8.90; airfreighted to CFB Shearwater, ff 13.4.94: displ. Shearwater as "RCN HS469")	8.90/96
- •	Mk. II Mk. IV	**HS503**		(to RCN as HS503): BOC 22.4.43: BOC	21.8.46
				Ernest K. Simmons, Tillsonburg ONT (open storage on farm, sold at auction 5.9.70)	.46/70
				Canadian National Aeronautical Collection, Rockcliffe AB ONT	5.9.70
				RAF Museum Store, RAF Henlow: airfreighted	10.70/90
				RAF Museum, RAF Cosford	93/96
-	Mk. II Mk. IV	**HS517**		(to RCN as HS517): BOC 29.4.43: SOC	21.8.46
				Ernest K. Simmons, Tillsonburg ONT (open storage on farm, sold at auction 5.9.70)	.46/70
				Grattons Weldwood Farm Museum, London ONT	5.9.70/79
- •	Mk. II Mk. IV	**HS554**		(to RCN as HS554): BOC 16.9.43: SOC	21.8.46
				Ernest K. Simmons, Tillsonburg ONT (open storage on farm, sold at auction 5.9.70)	.46/70
				Bob Spence & E. Sharpe, Muirkirk ONT	5.9.70/91
			C-GEVS	Robert Spence, Muirkirk ONT (rest. Muirkirk, ff 17.8.92 as "RN HS554")	30.8.91/96
- •	Mk. II	**HS618**		RNAS Manadon: inst. airframe	60/63
				Fleet Air Arm Museum, RNAS Yeovilton (displ. as "V6105", W5984/5H", later "P4139")	.63/96
- •	Mk. II	**LS326**		Fairey Aviation Co Ltd, Heston	9.45/47
			G-AJVH	Fairey Aviation Co Ltd, Heston (stored White Waltham .48/54, became derelict: trucked to Hamble .54 for rest., ff 10.55) (flew in film *Sink The Bismark* .58)	28.5.47/59

					donated to RNFAA as LS326	30.4.59
					Royal Navy Historic Flight, RNAS Yeovilton	10.60/96
					(flies as "RN LS326/L2")	
-	•	Mk. III	**NF370**		Imperial War Museum, Lambeth, London	65/86
					Imperial War Museum, Duxford: static rest.	.86/94
-	•	Mk. III	**NF389**		Royal Navy Fleet Air Arm: display flying	54/58
					(flew in film *Sink The Bismark* .58)	
					FAA Museum Store, RNAS Lee-on-Solent:	
					displ. as "NF389/5B"	60/93
					(spares source for LS326; pattern aircraft	
					for rest. of W5856 Brough 90/93)	
					Fleet Air Arm Museum, RNAS Yeovilton	94
					(full static rest., displ.)	
-	•	Mk. II	-		Ernest K. Simmons, Tillsonburg ONT	.46/70
		Mk. IV			(open storage on farm, sold at auction 5.9.70)	
				N2235R	Mira J. Slovak, Santa Paula/Ojai CA	2.83/95
					Museum of Flying, Santa Monica CA: loan	90/94
					(rest., displ. (no wings) as "RN HS164")	
-	•	Mk. III	-		Ernest K. Simmons, Tillsonburg ONT	.46/65
		Mk. IV			(open storage on farm 46/65)	
					Canadian National Aeronautical Collection,	
					Rockcliffe AB ONT: static rest.	.65/82
					National Aviation Museum, Rockcliffe ONT	9.82/93
					(displ. as "NS122/TH-M")	
-	•	Mk. II	-		Ernest K. Simmons, Tillsonburg ONT	.46/70
		Mk. IV			(open storage on farm, sold at auction 5.9.70)	
					Bob Spence & E. Sharpe, Muirkirk ONT	5.9.70/88
					Carl Enzenhofer, Vancouver BC	
					(stored dism. unrest. Pitt Meadows ONT 95)	
-	•	Mk. II	-		Ernest K. Simmons, Tillsonburg ONT	.46/70
		Mk. IV			(open storage on farm, sold at auction 5.9.70)	
					private owner, Waco TX	88
-		Mk. III	-		Ernest K. Simmons, Tillsonburg ONT	.46/70
		Mk. IV			(open storage on farm, sold at auction 5.9.70)	
					Jack Arnold, Brantford ONT	5.9.70
					Luther A Young, Lakeland FL	c73
-		Mk. III	-		Ernest K. Simmons, Tillsonburg ONT	.46/70
		Mk. IV			(open storage on farm, sold at auction 5.9.70)	
					Jack Arnold, Brantford ONT	3.9.70
					Luther A Young, Lakeland FL	c73
-		Mk. III	-		Ernest K. Simmons, Tillsonburg ONT	.46/65
		Mk. IV			(open storage on farm)	
					Age of Flight Museum, Niagara Falls ONT	68/70
					stored dism., unrest., Oshawa ONT	70

FIAT CR32/HISPANO HA-132

262	•	HA.132L	**C.1-262**		(to Spanish AF/Ejercito de l'Aire as C.1-262)	
					Museo del Aire, Cuatro Vientos AB, Madrid	78/96
					(displ. as "3-52")	
328	•	HA.132L	**C.1-328**		(to Spanish AF/Ejercito de l'Aire as C.1-328)	
					Museo Storico dell'Aeronautica Militaire	
					Italiana, Vigna di Valle AB	80/96
					(displ. as "Italian AF MM4667/V11-92")	

Fiat CR-42 Falco

326	•	CR-42	**MM5701**		"95-13": forced landing beach Orfordness UK (to RAF as BT474): flight trials RAF Duxford: packed for museum use RAF Air Historic Branch (stored RAF Stanmore Park 49/55, RAF Wroughton, RAF Fulbeck, RAF Biggin Hill 64) RAF Museum, RAF St Athan: static rest. RAF Museum, Hendon (displ. as "MM5701/95-13")	11.11.40 .41/43 12.43/60 46/65 .68/78 .78/95
921	•	CR-42 J-11			(to R Swedish AF as Fv2543): BOC SOC: to R Swedish AF Historical Collection Flygvapenmuseum, Linkoping, Sweden	20.5.41 14.3.45/84 .84/92
	•	CR-42			on rebuild in Italy for British collector	95/96
	•	CR-42			on rebuild in Italy	95/96

Fiat G-46

FIAT G.46

11		G.46-1B	MM52778	I-AEHP	Ministero di Fesa Aeronautica, Bari	64
14		G.46-1B	MM52781	I-AEHN	Ministero di Fesa Aeronautica, Gorizia Cof A expired	5.59/72 2.69
23	•	G.46-1B	**MM52790**	I-AEHL	Ministero di Fesa Aeronautica, Forli displ. on pole Forli, Italy as "MM52790"	3.62/64 88
32		G.46-1B	MM52799	I-AEHE	Ministero di Fesa Aeronautica, Bologna	11.59/72
43		G.46-3B	MM52800	I-AEHI	Ministero di Fesa Aeronautica, Rome-Urbe CofA expired 19.5.80: wfu at Urbe	10.58/77 80/87
44	•	G.46-3B	MM52801	I-AEHU **G-BBII**	Ministero di Fesa Aeronautica, Varese Hon. Patrick Lindsay, Booker (rest. Booker 73, "I-AEHU/MM52801")	7.59/72 13.9.73/78
45		G.46-3B	MM52802	I-AEHM	Ministero di Fesa Aeronautica, Capua	64
46		G.46-3B	MM52803	I-ADRO	Ministero di Fesa Aeronautica, Novi Ligune	10.58/76
69		G.46-3A	MM52805	I-AEKE	Ministero di Fesa Aeronautica, Medena	64
81		G.46-3A	MM52807	I-AELL	Ministero di Fesa Aeronautica, Belluno crashed Arezzo	64 24.9.67
85		G.46-3A	MM52811	I-AEKX	Ministero di Fesa Aeronautica, Bari	64
87		G.46-3A	MM52813	I-AEKU	Ministero di Fesa Aeronautica, Medena	64
91		G.46-3A	MM52817	I-AEKF	Ministero di Fesa Aeronautica, Ferrara crashed Bolognia	64 16.7.69
92		G.46-3A	MM52818	I-AEKP	Ministero di Fesa Aeronautica, Udine	64
93		G.46-3A	MM52819	I-AELA	Ministero di Fesa Aeronautica, Gorizia	8.60/64

				stored derelict, Gorizia, Italy	88
97	G.46-3A	MM52823	I-AEKQ	Ministero di Fesa Aeronautica, Vicenza	64
133	G.46-3B	MM53083	I-AEKJ	Ministero di Fesa Aeronautica, Catania	64
136	G.46-3B	MM53086	I-AEKK	Ministero di Fesa Aeronautica, Udine	10.59/76
				CofA expired	9.69
137	G.46-3B	MM53087	I-SGLL	Giuseppe Stifani, Milan	64
138	G.46-3B	MM53088	I-AEKD	Ministero di Fesa Aeronautica, Linate	64
140 •	G.46-3B	**MM53090**	I-AEHF	Ministero di Fesa Aeronautica, Ferrara	64
				Museo Storico dell'Aeronautica Militaire Italiana, Vigna di Valle AB: stored	84/88
141 •	G.46-3B	**MM53091**	I-AEHX	Ministero di Fesa Aeronautica, Padova	64
				(crated ex Padova, shipped to USA c70)	
			N46FM	Frank N. Marici, Roslyn Estates NY	6.72/95
				(noted airworthy Farmingdale NY 5.92)	
142 •	G.46-3B	**MM53092**	I-BIBY	Pietro Bosio, Brescia	2.61/77
				CofA suspended Brescia	17.1.85
				struck-off reg.	.91
143 •	G.46-3A	**MM53093**	I-AEHO	Ministero di Fesa Aeronautica, Padova	10.58/76
	G.46-4A			Eric Vormezeele, Brasschaat AB	84/92
152 •	G.46-3A	**MM53102**	I-AEKG	Ministero di Fesa Aeronautica, Turin	2.60/88
158	G.46-4B	MM53398	I-AEHV	Ministero di Fesa Aeronautica, Mantova	64
164 •	G.46-4B	**MM53404**	I-AEHJ	Ministero di Fesa Aeronautica, Reggio Emilia	64
				gateguard Bresso, Italy	78
				Association pour le Patromoine Aeronautique, Graulhet, France	92
165	G.46-4B	MM53405	I-AEHW	Ministero di Fesa Aeronautica, Fano	9.59/72
169	G.46-4B	MM53409	I-AEKB	Ministero di Fesa Aeronautica, Madena	64
171	G.46-3B	MM53411	I-AEHT	Ministero di Fesa Aeronautica, Vicenza	64
175	G.46-3B	MM53299	I-AEHD	Ministero di Fesa Aeronautica, Padova	11.59/72
178	G.46-4B	MM53302	I-AEHY	Ministero di Fesa Aeronautica, Venezia	64
179	G.46-4B	MM53303	I-AEHR	Ministero di Fesa Aeronautica, Firenze	11.59/72
180 •	G.46-4B	**MM53304**	I-AEKA	Ministero di Fesa Aeronautica, Gorizia	12.59/76
			I-LSBA	L. Sorlini, Montegaldella	11.89
			I-AEKA	G.Sorlini, Montegaldella	1.8.90
182	G.46-4B	MM53306	I-AEHG	Ministero di Fesa Aeronautica, Turin	64
183	G.46-4B	MM53307	I-AEHS	Ministero di Fesa Aeronautica, Brescia	64
184	G.46-4B	MM53308	I-AEHZ	Ministero di Fesa Aeronautica, Napoli	64
187	G.46-4B	MM53311	I-AEKC	Ministero di Fesa Aeronautica, Belluno	64
188	G.46-4B	MM53312	I-LEOR	Ministero di Fesa Aeronautica, Cagliari	64
189 •	G.46-4A	**MM53283**		Museo Storico dell'Aeronautica Militaire	

					Italiana, Vigna di Valle AB: displ.	80/88
190		G.46-4A	MM53284	I-AEHQ	Ministero di Fesa Aeronautica, Milan	64
192	•	G.46-4A	**MM53286**	I-AELM	Ministero di Fesa Aeronautica, Bologna Museo Storico dell'Aeronautica Militaire Italiana, Vigna di Valle AB: stored	64 80/88
193		G.46-4A	MM53287	I-AEKM	Ministero di Fesa Aeronautica, Bologna	64
197		G.46-4A	MM53291	I-AEKO	Ministero di Fesa Aeronautica, Brescia	64
198	•	G.46-4A	**MM53292**		Museo Storico dell'Aeronautica Militaire Italiana, Vigna di Valle AB: stored	 84/88
199	•	G.46-4A	**MM53293**	I-AEKI **OO-VOR**	Ministero di Fesa Aeronautica, Ferli Eric Vormezeele, Brasschaat AB (ff after rest. 6.79)	64 8.77/92
213		G.46-4B	MM53508	I-AEHH	Ministero di Fesa Aeronautica, Verona	64
216	•	G.46-4A G.46-6	**MM53491**	**I-AEKT**	Ministero di Fesa Aeronautica, Rome-Urbe Aero Club Roma, Rome-Urbe (flying at airshow Torino 5.86)	9.68 76/88
219		G.46-4A	MM53494	I-ARYA	Sergio Gomerio, Treviso Aero Club di Firenz crashed Petriolo, nr Florence	64 67 14.5.67
222		G.46-4A	MM53497	I-AEKZ	Ministero di Fesa Aeronautica, Fano (flew in camouflage sc. 75)	9.60/77
-	•	G.46-4B			airfreighted to RAF Northolt by IAF C118 (stored Shoreham 70) British Historic Aircraft Museum, Southend (displ. as Italian AF "FHE") Jeff Hawke/Visionair, Coventry: at auction Patrick Luscombe/British Air Reserve, Lympne (moved Southend-Lympne .85, stored) Aeroplane Restoration Co, Duxford (stored dism., "MM53211/ZI-4", rest. to fly abandoned: planned static rest. only) (rep. c/n 106 but unconf: given UK ident. BAPC79) new owner in France	.70 .71/83 10.5.83 .83/85 92/93 95/96

G-46 with Frasca Air Museum, Urbana IL (94/96) as G-55 replica (under conv.)

Fiat G-59

74	•	G.59-2A G.55 repl.	**MM53265**		Museo Storico dell'Aeronautica Militaire Italiana, Vigna di Valle AB: "RB-49" (under rest. Lecce 92, Torino 95, conv. to G.55 Centauro with DB601 engine)	 84/94
61	•	G.59-4B	**MM53276**		Museo Storico dell'Aeronautica Militaire Italiana, Vigna di Valle AB: displ.	 80/94
179	•	G.59-4B	**MM53772**	 N59B	Museo Storico dell'Aeronautica Militaire stored Practica d'Mare AB, Italy: "RS-25" auctioned, derelict, at Naples-Capo di Chinos Pino Valenti, Venice, Italy Guido Zuccoli, Darwin NT Australia (shipped Italy-USA for rest. Chino CA .84) Guido Zuccoli, Darwin Australia	70/80 70/82 11.83 11.83 11.83 31.7.87/89

				(ff Chino 2.9.87, flew in USA as *Ciao Bella*, shipped ex CA to Darwin, Australia 8.88)	
			VH-LIX	Guido Zuccoli, Darwin NT	5.9.89/95
				(flies as "Italian AF G59-B/*Ciao Bella*, rebuilt .94 as single seater)	
131 •	G.59B-4A	**MM53526**		Museo Storico, Spagnolia, Italy: "RR-80"	70/94
181 •	G.59B-4B	**MM53774**		Museo Storico dell'Aeronautica Militaire Italiana, Vigna di Valle AB: derelict "RR-76"	83
				auctioned, derelict, at Naples-Capo di Chinos	11.83
				Pino Valenti, Venice	11.83/91
			I-MRSV	Pino Valenti, Venice	.91/95
				(rest. Venice-Lido di Venezia 84/92, ff 25.5.92)	

FOCKE WULF FW190

Nr1227 •	Fw 190A-5		JG54 "DG+HO": crashed near Leningrad	.44
			complete intact recov. from crash site, Russia	.90
			arr. crated, Booker UK : rest. project	7.6.91
			Warbirds of GB Ltd,	91/92
			(arr. Biggin Hill 30.8.91: rest. project)	
			under active rebuild to fly U.K.	
Nr5476 •	Fw 190A-2		"Yellow 9": crashed Sogne Fjord, Norway	11.3.43
			wreck recov. by Norwegian AF Museum	.87
			Texas Air Museum: reg. candidate	7.7.92
		N6152P	Wade S. "Jay" Hanes, Anson TX	22.2.93/96
			Texas Air Museum, Rio Hondo TX: displ.	93/96
			(fully rest. Rio Hondo TX "Yellow 9" 93)	
			(also rep. as Fw190A-3 W.Nr 5467)	
Nr350177•	Fw 190A-8		"Blue 4": shot down over Norway	9.2.45
			Norwegan AF Museum: wreck recov.	
		N4247L	John W. Houston/Texas Air Museum, Rio Hondo TX	4.4.91/96
			(rest. project, Rio Hondo TX 93)	
Nr550214•	Fw 190A-6 /R6		III./NJG 11 "PN+LU" :	
			captured Leck-Holstein, Germany	.45
			(to RAF as AM 10)	.45/46
			del. Farnborough ex Schleswig, Germany	16.6.45
			shipped to Capetown, South Africa, arr.	6.11.46
			Dunnottar AB: displ.	
			Snake Valley AB: static rest.	71
			South African National Museum of Military History, Saxonwold, Johannesburg	.70/96
			(displ. as Luftwaffe "PN+LU")	
Nr550470•	Fw 190A-6	**N126JG**	Malcolm B. Laing, Lubbock TX	3.92/96
Nr584219•	Fw 190F-8 /U1		"Black 38": captured Grove, Denmark	.45
			(to RAF as AM 29)	.45
			del. Farnborough ex Schleswig, Germany	2.9.45
			RAF Air Historical Branch	5.46/70
			RAF Wroughton: crated for storage	7.46
			(stored Stanmore Park 49/55, Fulbeck 59, Henlow 64, Gaydon 70)	
			RAF Museum, RAF St Athan	.70/89
			(rest. RAF St Athan, regular engine runs)	
			RAF Museum, Hendon	90/96
Nr601088•	Fw 190D-9		JG26: captured at Flensburg	.45

			shipped to USA ex France on *HMS Reaper*	7.45
			(to USAAF as FE-120/T2-120)	.45/46
			Smithsonian Institute, stored Park Ridge IL	2.10.46
			NASM, Silver Hill MD	65/94
			USAFM, Wright-Patterson AFB OH: loan	68/96
Nr732070•	Fw 190A-8		"Blue 9": crashed Norway	.45
			Norwegian AF Museum: wreck recov.	
			John W. Houston/Texas Air Museum	
			Rio Hondo TX	90/96
Nr732183•	Fw 190A-3		"Black 3": crashed Norway	
			Kongelige Norsk Luftforssvaret Collection,	
			Bergen, Norway	84/91
		N90FW	Texas Air Museum,	
			Rio Hondo TX	8.88/95
			(rest. Rio Hondo for KNL Collection 88/91;	
			rest. fuselage to Gardermoen AB, Norway .91)	
			Norwegian AF Museum, Gardermoen: listed	.91/96
Nr733682•	Fw 190A-8 /R6		II KG/200: Mistel S3B (Ju-88H combination)	
			captured Tirstrup, Denmark	.45
			(Mistel combination ferried Schleswig, Germany	
			ex Tirstrup 30.7.45: Ju-88H scrapped)	
			(to RAF as AM 75): del. Farnborough	11.11.45
			RAF Cranwell: displ.	9.46/60
			(stored RAF Bicester 61, RAF Biggin Hill 62)	
			Imperial War Museum, Lambeth, London	64/96
			(rest. at Duxford .86/89, ret. Lambeth .89)	
Nr174013	Fw 190A-13		I./JG26 "Yellow 10": captured Flensburg	.45
Nr836017•	Fw 190D-13		shipped to USA ex France on HMS Reaper	7.45
			(to USAAF as FE-118/T2-118)	.45/46
			Georgia Institute of Technology, Atlanta GA	.46/68
			Nazi Museum, Santa Barbara CA (hulk)	.68/71
			(assembled Santa Barbara Airport .68)	
		N190D	Doug Champlin/Windward Aviation, Enid OK	.72/77
			(shipped to Germany .72 for rest. 72/79)	
			Champlin Fighter Museum, Mesa AZ	81/96
Nr930838•	Fw 190F-8		captured Zagreb-Pleso, Yugoslavia	.44
			(to Yugoslav AF as 43)	
			Yugoslav Aeronautical Museum, Belgrade	70/92
Nr931862•	Fw 190F-8		5./JG9 "White 1": shot down over Norway	9.2.45
			(recov from fjord for KNL Collection c84)	
			Kongelige Norsk Luftforssvaret Collection,	
			Bergen , Norway	84/88
			John W. Houston/Texas Air Museum	.88/92
		N91FW	Texas Air Museum, Rio Hondo TX	4.90/95
			(rest. Rio Hondo TX completed 92, using parts	
			from 4 other Fw190 wrecks recov. ex Norway)	
Nr640069	Fw 190A-7 Fw 190F-8 /R1		(Fw 190A-7 rebuilt 4.44 as Fw 190F-8/R1) Nr931884•	
			I./SG2 "Yellow 10": captured near Munich	
			shipped to USA on HMS Reaper	7.45
			(to USAAF as FE-117/T2-117)	
			Smithsonian Institute, stored Park Ridge IL	31.5.46
			NASM, Silver Hill MD	65/96
			(rest., rolled out 10.83 as "931884 White 7")	
Nr150003•	Ta 152H-1		JG301 "6": captured Tirstrup, Denmark	.45
			shipped to USA ex France on *HMS Reaper*	7.45
			(to USAAF as FE-112/T2-112)	.45

					Smithsonian Institute, stored Park Ridge IL	.46
					NASM, Silver Hill MD	72/96
No.62	•	NC 900A-8 (Fw190A-8)	**No.62**		(Armee de l'Air as No.62)	
					Musee de l'Air, Paris-Le Bourget	80/95
					(displ. as 'Luftwaffe 7298/13+-")	
-	•	Fw 190A-8			Zemun, Yugoslavia	88
-	•	Fw 190D-9			JG26 : crashed into Lake Schwerin	17.4.45
					Luftwaffen Museum, Uetersen AB, Hamburg	11.90/93
					(salvaged ex Lake Schwerin, East Germany 11.90: static rest. project)	
-		Fw 190A-3			recov. complete ex Sognefjord, Norway	6.88
					(salvaged by Norwegian Navy divers, rep. unrestorable due salt water immersion)	
-	•	Fw 190A			Specialty Aircraft Construction (NZ) Ltd, Wigram AB, Christchurch NZ	94/96
					(three airframes rep recov. ex crash sites Russia: three under rest. Wigram AB, to be powered by Russian built Shvetsov ASh-82 radials)	

GLOSTER GLADIATOR

-	•	Mk. I Mk. II	**K8042**		Marshalls of Cambridge: inst. airframe	
					RAF Air Historical Branch, RAF Biggin Hill	64
					RAF Museum Store, RAF Henlow	69
					RAF Museum, Hendon: displ. as "K8042"	73/94
-	•	Mk. I	**L8032**		Gloster Aircraft Ltd, Hucclecote	23.2.48/50
					(stored Hucclecote .44/50)	
					Air Service Training Ltd, Hamble	10.50/51
					(arr. by road, instructional airframe 13.10.50)	
					Vivian H. Bellamy/Flightways Ltd, Eastleigh	12.51/52
				G-AMRK	Vivian Bellamy/Flightways Ltd, Eastleigh: ff	13.6.52/53
					GlosterAircraft Ltd, Hucclecote: del.	20.8.53/60
					(flew as "K8032" later "L8032")	
					Shuttleworth Trust, Old Warden: del.	7.11.60/96
					(flies as "N2308/HP-B")	
-	•	Sea Gladiator I	**N5519**		Palace Armoury Museum, Valetta, Malta	9.43/73
					National War Museum, Fort St. Elmo, Valetta	73/96
					(fuse. only, displ. as "N5520 Faith")	
-	•	Mk. II	**N5579**		landed on ice, Lake Lesjaskogsvatn, Norway:	
					straffed & later sank	25.4.40
					remains recov. from lake	.72
					stored at Dovre, Norway	72/88
					(planned rest. for Armed Forces Museum, Oslo)	
-	•	Mk. II	**N5589**		landed on ice, Lake Lesjaskogsvatn, Norway:	
					straffed & later sank	25.4.40
					remains recov. from lake	.72
					stored at RAF Wildenrath, West Germany	72/88
-	•	Mk. II	**N5628**		landed on ice, Lake Lesjaskogsvatn, Norway:	
					straffed & later sank	25.4.40
					remains recov. from lake	.70
					RAF Museum, Hendon (fuselage only)	.72/95
-	•	Mk. II	**N5641**		dsm. on ice, Lake Lesjaskogsvatn, Norway	25.4.40
					Ludvig Hope: recov., stored in shed near lake	13.8.40/77

					Norwegian Defence Museum, Rygge AB	9.77/80
					Royal Norwegian Air Force Museum, Gardermoen AB (displ. as "N5641/HE-G")	90/93
-	•	Mk. II	**N5903**		Gloster Aircraft Ltd, Hucclecote (stored)	2.48
					Air Service Training, Ansty: arr. dism.	23.11.50
					Air Service Training, Hamble: inst. airframe	.51
					Vivian Bellamy/Flightways Ltd, Eastleigh	12.51/53
					Gloster Aircraft Ltd, Hucclecote	8.53/60
					Shuttleworth Trust, Old Warden	11.60/94
					Fleet Air Arm Museum, RNAS Yeovilton: loan (displ. as Sea Gladiator "N2276","N5226/H")	.78/94
					The Fighter Collection, Duxford (arr. Duxford 30.11.94: rest. to fly)	11.94/96
				G-GLAD	Patina Ltd	5.1.95
					rest to fly The Fighter Collection, Duxford	96
5/ 9066	•	Mk. I J 8A			(to R Swedish AF as Fv278): BOC (served in Finland 1.40 to 3.40)	9.6.38
					SOC: to R Swedish AF Historic Collection	30.6.45/84
					Flygvapenmuseum, Linkoping, Sweden (displ. in Finnish AF markings)	.84/96

GRUMMAN AF-2 GUARDIAN

	•	AF-2S	**Bu123088**	**N3143G**	Aero Union Corp, Anderson CA & Chico CA (conv. to tanker, but not into service)	6.62/95
					stored engineless, Chico CA (noted under rest., Chico 11.92)	77/91
4	•	AF-2S	**Bu123100**	**N3144G (2**	Aero Union Corp, Anderson CA & Chico CA (tanker #E30) (flew as "USN 123100/SK-30" 75/78)	.62/84
					USNAM, NAS Pensacola FL (displ. as "USN 123100/SK-30")	84/94
42	•	AF-2S	**Bu126731**	**N9993Z**	Bert Ferganchick, Avondale AZ	63/69
					Aero Union Corp, Chico CA (stored unconv., Chico CA 73/88)	70/88
					Confederate Air Force, Harlingen/Midland TX (stored unconv. orig USN sc., Mesa AZ 92/95)	8.88/95
96	•	AF-2S	**Bu126792**	**N9995Z**	Bert Ferganchick, Avondale AZ	63/69
					Aero Union Corp, Chico CA (tanker #E21)	70/77
					EAA Aviation Foundation Inc, Oshkosh WI	84/86
					Jimmy Leeward/Leeward Air Ranch/ Bahia Oaks Inc, Ocala FL (flies as "USN 126792")	.87/93
21	•	AF-2S	**Bu129233**	**N9994Z**	Bert Ferganchick, Avondale AZ	63/69
					Aero Union Corp, Chico CA (stored unconv. ("Akron 155"), Chico 72/88, static rest. Chico .90 as "N9995Z/#E21")	70/91
					Pima County Air Museum, Tucson AZ (displ. as tanker "N9995Z/#E21")	.91/93

656	•	F4F-3	**AL246**		(for French Navy/Aeronavale: not del.)	
		Martlet			(to RN Fleet Air Arm as AL246)	
		Mk. I			Loughborough College, Loughborough UK	.45/61
					RNAS Lossiemouth: stored for museum use	.61/63
					Fleet AirArm Museum, RNAS Yeovilton	.63/96
754	•	F4F-3	**Bu3872**		ditched Lake Michigan off carrier "Wolverine"	17.8.43
					USNAM, NAS Pensacola FL	.91/94
					(recov. from Lake Michigan by USNAM .91)	
					Patriots Point Naval & Maritime Museum,	
					Mt. Pleasant SC: loan	94
838	•	F4F-3A	**Bu3956**		ditched Lake Michigan off training carrier	30.11.43
					recov. from Lake Michigan	c91
					USNAM, NAS Pensacola FL	94
					San Diego Aerospace Museum, San Diego CA	.94
					(rest. project)	
851	•	F4F-3A	**Bu3969**		recov. from Lake Michigan	c87
					USNAM, NAS Pensacola FL	87/94
					Patriots Point Naval & Maritime Museum,	
					Mt. Pleasant SC: loan	87/90
					(static rest. by Grumman NY 92)	
					San Diego Aerospace Museum CA: loan	94
921	•	F4F-3	**Bu4039**		ditched Lake Michigan off carrier "Wolverine"	21.7.43
					USNAM, NAS Pensacola FL	.91/94
					(recov. from Lake Michigan by USNAM .91;	
					displ. unrest. Pensacola 94)	
3763	•	F4F-4	**Bu12068**		VMF-214, cr. Henderson Field, Guadalcanal	21.1.43
					War Museum, Honiara, Solomon Islands	.73/91
					(barged to Honiara .73, displ. as unrest. hulk)	
3809	•	F4F-4	**Bu12114**		NAS Sand Point WA: open storage	45/50
					Holgate Technical School/Seattle Community	
					College, White Centre, Seattle WA	55/68
					USMC Museum, MCAS Quantico VA	9.68/96
					(shipped Seattle-Quantico .68, stored:	
					static rest. 6.75/78, displ. as "12114/2")	
5920	•	F4F-3	**Bu12260**		ditched Lake Michigan off carrier *Wolverine*	1.5.44
					USNAM, NAS Pensacola FL	.91
					(recov. ex Lake Michigan 12.12.91)	
				N12260	Jim Porter & Dick Hansen/A & T Recovery Inc	
					Batavia IL	12.91/96
					(rest. Batavia IL, ff 18.7.94 as "12260/F-3")	
5956	•	F4F-3	**Bu12296**		ditched Lake Michigan, off carrier USS *Sable*	21.6.43
					USNAM, NAS Pensacola FL	.91
					(recov. ex Lake Michigan .91)	
				N3210D	A & T Recovery Inc: reg. candidate	12.91
					David P. Kensler/Warbirds Aircraft Restoration	
					& Salvage Inc, Waterford MI	12.91/96
					(rest. Pontiac MI 92/95, ff 20.6.95)	
5957	•	F4F-3	**Bu12297**		USNAM, NAS Pensacola FL, loan to:	
					Cradle of Aviation Museum, Garden City NY	88/96
					(no other details: pres. recov ex Lake Michigan)	
5980	•	F4F-3	**Bu12320**		ditched Lake Michigan, off carrier *USS Sable*	31.3.44
				N5254A	USNAM, NAS Pensacola FL	8.10.92/96

				(recov. ex Lake Michigan c91,	
				static rest. Jacksonville FL 92 for USNAM)	
				USMCM, MCAS El Toro CA: displ.as "6"	93/94
- •	FM-1	-		(to RN Fleet Air Arm as JV482)	
	Mk. V			882 Sqn: ditched Portmore Lough, Ireland	24.12.44
				Ulster Aviation Society, Castlereagh	4.84/95
				(recov. by chopper 30.4.84, static rest.)	
•	FM-1	**Bu14994**		ditched Lake Michigan, off USS"Woloverine"	1.45
				USNAM, NAS Pensacola FL	93/95
				Valiant Air Command, Titusville FL: loan	.94/96
				(under static rest. at Tico FL)	
01 •	FM-1	**Bu15392**		instruct. airframe Tech School, Norman OK	c47/c49
				NASM, Silver Hill MD: stored	c49/73
				(static rest. by Grumman Bethpage NY 74/75)	
				NASM, Washington DC: displ. as "USN E10"	75/93
288 •	FM-2	**Bu16089**		USNAM, NAS Pensacola FL: stored	93/94
				(no other details: pres. recov ex Lake Michigan)	
477 •	FM-2	**Bu16278**		ditched Lake Michigan, near Chicago IL	26.6.45
				recov. from Lake Michigan by USNAM	.91
				USNAM, NAS Pensacola FL	.91
020 •	FM-2	**Bu46867**		displ. service station, Palwaukee IL	61/65
				Victory Air Museum, Mundelein IL	68/76
				stored dism. Chino CA	
			N909WJ	Don Whittington/World Jet Inc,	
				Fort Lauderdale FL	2.8.89/91
				(rebuild to fly, Ft.Collins CO 89/90)	
				flown to Chino CA, shipped to UK : arr.	30.12.90
				Warbirds of GB Ltd,	12.90/92
				Iron Baron Corp, Dover DE	8.94/96
				(USCR quotes id. Bu16203)	
183 •	FM-2	**Bu47030**	N315E	Alexis I. DuPont, Wilmington DE	12.62/72
				Alexis (Lex) DuPont/Colonial Flying Field Mus.,	
				Toughkenamon PA	73/96
				(flies as "USN 47030/F-13")	
313 •	FM-2	**Bu47160**		Trade School MT: inst. airframe	50/56
				(sold to ag. operator .56, conv. to sprayer)	
			N2876D	Western Aerial Contractors, Eugene OR	63/64
				Robert J. Hartlaub, Summit NJ	66/69
				Air Sales Inc, Miami FL	70
				Keith J. Mackey, Opa Locka FL	70/72
				(flew as "USN 7")	
				Wings of Yesterday Flying Air Museum,	
				Santa Fe NM	77/84
			N551TC	John C. Hooper/Intracoastal Terminal Inc,	
				Harvey LA	5.84/91
				Lone Star Flight Museum, Galveston TX	8.91/96
				(flies as USN 7/*Old Fang*)	
045 •	FM-2	**Bu55404**		USNAM, NAS Pensacola FL: stored	93/94
				(no other details: pres. recov ex Lake Michigan)	
226 •	FM-2	Bu55585	**N681S**	Joe Speidel, Miami FL	61
				Lloyd P. Nolan/Confederate Air Force,	
				Mercedes TX	5.61/64
				Gerald Martin/CAF, Hereford TX	66/72
				(flew as "N6815" 66/70)	
				Confederate Air Force, Harlingen/Midland TX	2.2.72/96

				(flies as "USN 55585/F-15")	
3268 •	FM-2	**Bu55627**	N7906C	Ed Maloney/The Air Museum, Ontario CA	59/72
			N47201	James Nunn, Ontario CA	.76/77
				John V. Crocker, San Mateo CA	82/84
				The Fighter Collection, Duxford UK:	.82/86
				(del. USA to France, arr. 11.6.82,	
				based Duxford as "USN 47201/8")	
				Robert J. Pond/Planes of Fame East,	
				Minneapolis-Flying Cloud MN : shipped ex UK	6.85/96
				(id. also quoted as Bu03455)	
4312 •	FM-2	**Bu74120**		park war memorial, Windsor Locks CT	50/67
				Bradley Air Museum, Windsor Locks CT	25.5.67/80
				New England Air Museum, Windsor Locks CT	83/96
4353 •	FM-2	**Bu74161**		USNAM, NAS Pensacola FL	93/94
				Admiral Nimitz State Historical Park,	
				Fredericksburg TX: rest., loan	93/94
				(presumed recov. ex Lake Michigan)	
4704 •	FM-2	**Bu74512**		Edison Technical School, Seattle WA	50/60
				park playground, White Centre, Seattle WA	65/69
				Pacific Northwest Aviation History Museum,	
				Boeing Field WA	.69/83
				(static rest., Fairchild AFB WA 83)	
				Museum of Flight, Boeing Field, Seattle WA	.83/96
				(static rest., Paine Field WA 94)	
4752 •	FM-2	**Bu74560**	N90523	Air Service Kontrol Inc, West Bend WI	c50/60
				Frank G. Tallman, Orange County CA	60
				Wade R. Porter, Columbus IN	63/64
				Yankee Air Club Inc, Sunderland MA	66
				Damn Yankee Air Force, Turner Falls MA	66/69
				William C. Whitesell, Medford NJ	.69/70
				Windward Aviation, Enid OK	.71/79
				Champlin Fighter Museum, Mesa AZ	78/90
			N16TF	Cinema Air, Houston TX	12.90
			N29FG	Cinema Air, Carlsbad CA	7.91/95
				(flies as "USN 74560")	
5618 •	FM-2	**Bu86564**	**N4629V**	Frank Tallman, Riverside-Flabob CA	58
				Tallmantz Aviation/Movieland of the Air	
				Museum, Orange County CA	61/65
				Rosen Novak Auto Co, Omaha NB	66
				(remained at Tallmantz until auction 29.5.68)	
				F. R. Davis, Beaverton OR	29.5.68/70
				Yankee Air Corps/	
				Yanks Air Museum, Chino CA	6.83/96
5626	FM-2	Bu86572	N35MK	reg.	.54
				Lyman Rice, Laconia NH	59
				Hamilton Aircraft Co, Tucson AZ	63/64
				New London Airport, New London PA	66/69
				Jaques R. DuPont, Newcastle DE	72
			N35M	sale rep.	84/88
				struck-off USCR (pobably bu 1960s)	4.90
5635 •	FM-2	**Bu86581**	N86581	Gunther W. Balz, Kalamazoo MI	70/72
				Preston Parish, Kalamazoo Air Zoo MI	73
			N1PP	Preston Parish/Kalamazoo Aviation History	
				Museum, Kalamazoo MI	83/96
				dam. wheels-up forced landing MI (repaired)	22.7.94
				(flies as "86581/1")	

34	•	FM-2	**Bu86680**	NX55558	Richard R. Carlisle AL	.46
				N777A	Alfred T. Whiteside, Jacksonville FL	55/56
					(mod. to carry 4 passengers)	
				YV-T-OTO		1.62
				YV-T-HTJ	struck-off reg.	10.2.69
				N11FE	Frederick W. Edison, Kalamazoo MI	5.70/74
					crashed into Lake Michigan (salvaged)	29.6.75
					Richard Foote, Summerland Key FL	76/84
					Professional Aircraft Sales,	
					New Smyrna Beach FL	86/96
					(flies as "Bu5134 USS Tulagi")	
					(note: id. confusion with c/n 5835 which see:	
					USCR quotes 5734; also quoted as Bu86870)	
44	•	FM-2	**Bu86690**	N20HA	Don Underwood, Phoenix AZ (sprayer)	56/58
					S. S. Steele, Safford AZ	63/64
					James R. Freese, Fremont/Modesto CA	66/72
					Jack Lenhardt/Lenhardt Airpark, Hubbard OR	77/79
					(flew as "Marines/2")	
					USNAM, NAS Pensacola FL	.79/90
					(displ. as "86690/2")	
				N70637	World Jet Inc, Fort Lauderdale FL	8.93
					NA-50 Inc, New York NY	10.93/94
				N49JC	NA-50 Inc, New York NY	1.94/95
65	•	FM-2	**Bu86711**	**N4845V**	Dale P. Newton, Medford OR	64/70
					Eric G. Mingledorf, Monroe LA	9.75/95
					Chennault Air Museum, Monroe LA: displ.	
					The Fighter Collection, Duxford:	.92/96
					(rest. Chino CA, ff 14.1.93 as "USN 86711/84",	
					shipped to UK, arr. Duxford 15.4.93, ff 2.5.93)	
					(flies as "RNFAA/F")	
95	•	FM-2	**Bu86741**	N19K	E. J. Saviano, La Grange IL	64
					Alexis I. DuPont, Wilmington DE	66/84
					Alexis I. DuPont, Toughkenamon PA	86/88
					Weeks Air Museum, Tamiami FL	.88/90
				N222FM	Weeks Air Museum,	
					Tamiami FL (rest., ff .93 as "USN 4")	7.90/96
					(USCR quotes id. 5975: 5795 believed correct)	
04	•	FM-2	**Bu86746**	**N6290C**	California Polytechnic Institute CA	c47
					owner, Medford OR: stripped for spares	c52
					Forrest M. Watson, Wellington TX	64
					Robert L. Younkin, Fayetteville AR: hulk	
					owner, St. Louis MO: rest. project	
					Dick Lambert & Michael Rettke, Atlanta GA	2.66
					(trucked dism. St. Louis-Atlanta 4.66,	
					rest., ff 6.6.67 as "USN 86940/5")	
					Michael G. Rettke, Merritt Island FL	69
					Antiques & Classics Inc,	
					Champaign IL	2.70/96
					Rudy Frasca/Frasca Air Museum, Urbana IL	93/95
					(flies as "USN 5")	
05	•	FM-2	**Bu86747**	N68843	Charlie T. Jensen, Reno NV (sprayer)	56/72
					(wfu, stored Reno NV 55/73)	
					Kenneth Spiva, Tracy CA & Lovelock NV	.74/77
					(rest., flew as "USN/7")	
					USNAM, NAS Pensacola FL	81/96
					(displ. as "86747")	
08	•	FM-2	**Bu86750**	**N12371**	Robert L. Younkin, Fayetteville AR	67/77
					crashed, Houston-Lakeside Airport TX	14.10.83

c/n	Type	Bu No.	Reg.	Owner / History	Date
				Jack B. Barnett, Arabi TX	12.83/96
5812 •	FM-2	**Bu86754**	**N58918**	reg., sprayer	.55/58
				Ron Zerbel, Nyssa OR	63/64
				Spray Rite Inc, Oakley ID	66/70
				Don H. Novas, Blackfoot ID	77/90
				Erickson Air Crane, Medford OR	.90/96
5831 •	FM-2	**Bu86773**	**N1352N**	Butler Aviation, Redmond OR (sprayer)	58
				crashed, forced landing, Burns OR	c60
				Ron Zerbel, Nyssa OR (dam.)	c61
				Medford Air Service, Medford OR	63/70
				Robert L. Younkin, Fayetteville AR	77/92
				Bruce D. New London PA	7.94/96
5835 •	FM-2P	**Bu86777**	N90541	I. N. Burchinall Jr, Paris TX	12.74
			N5HP	Howard E. Pardue/Breckenridge Aviation Museum,	
				Breckenridge TX	12.80/96
				(flies as USN 5/*Kimberly Brooke*)	
				(id. confused with c/n 5734)	
5877 •	FM-2	**Bu86819**	N	Butler Aviation, Redmond OR (sprayer)	c57
				crashed while spraying	c58
				Ron Zerbel, Nyssa OR (dam.)	c60
				various owners under rebuild	
				Eugene Mahlon OR	73
				Yankee Air Corps, Chino CA	.81
			N5833	Yankee Air Corps, Chino CA	8.83/88
				CAF/Air Group One, Ramona CA	.86
				(trucked Chino-Ramona : rest., ff 24.4.87)	
				Confederate Air Force, Harlingen/Midland TX	1.89/96
				dam., undercarriage collapse, parked CA	.93
				(USCR quotes id. 5833, flies as "USN 86819")	
6014 •	FM-2	**Bu86956**	N18PK	E. J. Saviano, La Grange IL	63/64
			N18P	William D. Ross, Chicago IL	66/67
				Louis V. Gallo, Hillside IL	69/77
				Joseph G. Mabee, Midland TX	3.80/96
				(also rep. as Bu86960, flies as "Bu86960")	
- •	FM-2	-	**N6699K**	American Aviation Inc, Walnut Ridge AR	90/96
				(rebuild by Yankee Air Corps, Chino CA)	
				(USCR quotes id. "428B")	
- •	FM-1& FM2	-		Two aircraft ditched Lake Washington, near Seattle WA	
				Recovery Services Ltd, Bellevue WA: recov.	26.5.87
				Bruce D. Roberts, New London PA	.87/90

GRUMMAN F6F HELLCAT

c/n	Type	Bu No.	Reg.	Owner / History	Date
A-212 •	F6F-3	Bu08825	**N4965V**	Michael E. Coutches, Hayward CA	c62
				Wayne B. Fowler, Shaw Island WA: sprayer	64/66
				Charles F. Willis/Willisco Inc, New York NY	68/72
				(based Seattle-Paine Field WA, flown in	
				Alaska Airlines colours, "Little Nugget")	
				Willard Compton, Canby OR	75/91
				crashed and badly dam., Canby OR	12.6.77
				(long-term rebuild project)	
A-218	F6F-3	Bu08831		(VF-6/USS Intrepid) : BOC	5.11.43
				Chicago Vocational School, Chicago IL	47/69
				Earl Reinert/Victory Air Museum,	
				Mundelein IL : stored, incomplete	.69/79
				Ed Maloney/Planes of Fame Museum, Chino CA	.79

				(rear fus. used in rebuild of N4964W)	
				(centre-section to Charles F. Nichols/YAC,	
				Chino CA : used in rebuild of N100TF)	.80
				(prev. incorrectly rep. as Alex Vraciu's Bu40467)	
-1257 •	F6F-3	**Bu66237**		ditched, Pacific Ocean, near San Diego CA	12.1.44
				recov. from depth 3400ft, by USN	10.10.70
				San Diego Aero Space Museum, San Diego CA	72
				Pima County Air Museum, Tucson AZ	74/92
				(displ. as recov. "Z11")	
				USNAM, NAS Pensacola FL	92/96
				(static rest. Jacksonville FL 92)	
-2742 •	F6F-3	**Bu41476**		Walter E. Ohlrich, Norfolk VA	
			N41476	USMC Museum, MCAS Quantico VA	12.71/96
-3100 •	F6F-3K	**Bu41834**		NASM Store, Silver Hill MD	75/83
				NASM loan: Yorktown Assoc., Charleston SC	10.76/81
				(displ. on USS "Yorktown", Mt. Pleasant SC)	
				NASM Store, Silver Hill MD	.81
				rest. for displ. Grumman Corp, Bethpage NY	.83
				NASM, Washington DC	.87/88
				NASM Store, Silver Hill MD	89/96
				(displ. as "41834/37")	
-3196 •	F6F-3	**Bu41930**	N6096C	Wayne B. Fowler, Shaw Island WA: sprayer	63/64
				John Church, Monterey CA	.64/65
			N103V	Peter J. Brucia, Garden City NY: del.	11.65/70
				William Ross, Elk Grove Village IL	72
				Doug Champlin/Windward Aviation, Enid OK	.72/81
				Champlin Fighter Museum, Mesa AZ	81/90
				Cinema Air, Houston TX	.90
			N30FG	Cinema Air, Carslbad CA	7.91/96
				(flies as "41930/5K")	
-4140 •	F6F-3	**Bu42874**		USNAM, NAS Pensacola FL	79
				(recov. ex ocean ditching)	
				San Diego Aerospace Museum, San Diego CA	79/93
				(displ. as USN "42874/21")	
-4280 •	F6F-3	**Bu43014**		recov. from Boy Scout campground	
			N7537U	John R. Sandberg, Minneapolis MN	69/70
				David B. Robinson, Miami Springs FL	72/84
				(rest. project, Miami Airport 74/84)	
				Weeks Air Museum,Tamiami FL	8.84/96
				(id. prev. incorrectly rep. as Bu80167)	
-5597 •	F6F-5	**Bu70185**		ditched in sea off Martha's Vineyard MA	3.4.45
				(hulk salvaged from sea 3.12.93)	
				Quonset Air Museum, Quonset Point RI	12.93/95
				(planned static rest. project)	
-5634 •	F6F-5	**Bu70222**		derelict, Fergus Falls Airport MN	62
			N1078Z	John R. Sandberg, Minneapolis MN	.62/72
				Lloyd P. Nolan/CAF, Harlingen TX	.72/73
				Ed Messick/Confederate AF, Harlingen TX	9.4.73/90
				Confederate Air Force, Harlingen/Midland TX	90/96
				(id. prev. incorrectly rep. as Bu80166)	
-8867 •	F6F-5K	**Bu77722**		US Naval Reserve Base,Andrews AFB MD: del.	.65/93
				(displ. on pole as "USN 22")	
-9790 •	F6F-5	**Bu78645**	**N9265A**	Yankee Air Corps/	
				Yanks Air Museum, Chino CA	3.78/96
				(flies as "USN 45")	

A-10337•	F6F-5K	**Bu79192**		Bradley Air Museum, Windsor Locks CT: arr.	25.10.73
				(recov. from NAS China Lake CA .73)	
				dam. by tornado at museum	3.10.79
				New England Air Museum, Windsor Locks CT	83/96
				(rest. completed .92, displ. as "79192/S60")	
A-10738•	F6F-5K	**Bu79593**		Bradley Air Museum, Windsor Locks CT	73
				(recov. ex storage NAS China Lake CA .73)	
				USS Alabama Battleship Memorial, Mobile AL	76/91
				(displ. as "F6F-3 41476")	
				Patriots Point Naval & Maritime Museum,	
				Mount Pleasant SC	93/94
				(displ. on board USS Yorktown as "79593/00")	
A-10814	F6F-5N	Bu79669		NAS Moffett Field CA	65/72
				(displ. as "1158")	
A-10828•	F6F-5K	**Bu79683**	N7896C	John A. Ortseifen, Fort Lauderdale FL	63/77
				(retired, Chicagoland Airport IL 66/77)	
				Preston Parish, Kalamazoo MI	.79/81
			N4PP	Preston Parish/Kalamazoo Aviation History	
				Museum, Kalamazoo MI	7.81/95
				(rest. Kalamazoo, ff .81: flies as "USN 4")	
A-10924•	F6F-5 Mk. II	**Bu79779**		(to Royal Navy FAA as KE209)	
				RNAS Lossiemouth: stored for museum: del.	4.53/60
				Fleet Air Arm Museum, RNAS Yeovilton	65/96
A-11008•	F6F-5K	**Bu79863**		Grumman Aircraft Co, Bethpage NY	56/57
				USNAM, NAS Pensacola FL	.57/72
			N79863	Aerial Classics, Atlanta GA	.72/84
				Patriots Point Development Authority/	
				USS Yorktown Museum, Mount Pleasant SC	86/91
				(displ. on *USS "Yorktown*)	
				rep: Warbirds of GB Ltd.	.91/92
				Iron Baron Corp, Dover DE	8.94/96
A-11286•	F6F-5K	**Bu80141**	N80142	USMC Museum, MCAS Quantico VA	65/70
				W. C. Yarbrough, Marietta GA	72
			N100TF	Thomas H. Friedkin, Rancho Santa Fe CA	1.77/79
				crashed, forced landing, San Marcos CA	3.4.79
				Yankee Air Corps,Chino CA	.81/88
			N10CN	ntu: Charles F. Nichols, Chino CA	
				(rebuild Chino 85/88, using fuselage	
				center-section of Bu08831)	
			N100TF	David C. Tallichet/MARC, Chino CA	.88/89
				The Fighter Collection, Duxford	.89/91
				(ff Chino 7.89; shipped to UK, arr. 1.8.90)	
			G-BTCC	The Fighter Collection, Duxford	12.90/95
				(flies as USN "40467/19")	
A-11631•	F6F-5	**Bu93879**	**N4994V**	The Air Museum, Claremont CA	58/62
				The Air Museum, Ontario & Chino CA	62/95
				dam. landing, Elsinore Dry Lake CA (repaired)	.72
A-11955•	F6F-5	**Bu94203**	**N7865C**	Nicholas Parks, Hayward CA	64/70
				Thomas W. Short, Harlingen TX	70
				Aerial Classics, Atlanta GA	.70/72
				USNAM, NAS Pensacola FL	73/93
				(displ. as USN/*Minsi III*)	
A-11956•	F6F-5N	**Bu94204**		Normandie Iron and Metal Company	59
			N4998V	Eddie Fisher, Hollywood CA	

				The Air Museum, Ontario CA	67/70
				(unconv. "94204/FASRON 4/The Beguine")	
				Michael E. Coutches, Hayward CA	5.70/86
				loan: Wagons to Wings Museum, San Jose CA	10.74/86
				Lone Star Flight Museum,	
				Houston/Galveston TX	11.86/96
				(rest. Hayward CA, ff 4.5.89 as "USN 32")	
-12015•	F6F-5K	**Bu94263**		NAS Norfolk VA (stored)	65/70
				USMC Museum, MCAS Quantico VA	76/94
				(static rest. MCAS Cherry Point NC 78)	
				Cradle of Aviation Museum NY: loan	83/95
				(displ. as "94263/VMF-511/IM")	
-12137•	F6F-5	**Bu94385**	**N7861C**	Michael E. Coutches, Hayward CA	61
				Tom O'Connor/CAF, Victoria TX	9.61/66
				Henry L. Gardner/CAF, Victoria TX	69/70
				crashed, Victoria TX	7.69
				Michael E. Coutches, Hayward CA (wreck)	8.71/95
-12225•	F6F-5N	**Bu94473**		The Air Museum, Ontario CA	67/70
	F6F-5K			(displ. in red drone sc. "473"; then stored)	
				The Air Museum, Chino CA	70/84
				(rest. Chino 83/84, with parts Bu08831)	
			N4964W	Planes of Fame East,	
				Minneapolis-Flying Cloud MN	.84/95
				landing accident, Chino CA (repaired)	19.3.84
				(flies as "USN 58644/36")	
- •	F6F	-		Sea-Air-Space Museum, New York NY	91
				(displ. as "24803/39" on *USS Intrepid*)	
-	F6F-3	-		(to Royal Navy FAA as JV111)	
	Mk. I			"E-P": cr. into sea, Bay of Rosas, Spain	22.8.44
				salvaged by fishermen, off Cap Creuse	3.12.79
				hulk in scrapyard, Rosas 79/82; gone by	83
- •	F6F-3K	-		(to Uraguayan Navy as ....)	
				rep. stored awaiting displ., Montevideo	77

GRUMMAN F7F TIGERCAT

115 •	F7F-3	**Bu80373**	N7654C	Calvin J. Butler/Butler Farm Air Service,	
				Redmond OR (tanker #F18; later #18)	63/66
				TBM Inc, Tulare CA (tanker #E63)	69/80
				USNAM, NAS Pensacola FL	.80/96
				(displ. as "80373/12")	
116 •	F7F-3N	**Bu80374**	**N7629C**	Cal-Nat Airways Inc, Grass Valley CA	64/69
				(tanker #E62; later #E41)	
				Sis Q Flying Service, Santa Rosa CA	.69/81
				(tanker #E41)	
				USMC Museum, MCAS Quantico VA	.81/91
				Darryl Greenamyer, Ocala FL/Ramona CA	.91/94
				(del. Quantico to Ramona CA .93 still "E41")	
117 •	F7F-3E	**Bu80375**		NAS Anacostia	
	F7F-3N			USMC Museum, MCAS Quantico VA	76
				Pima County Air Museum, Tucson AZ	10.87/88
				(open storage, derelict unconv., "Marines")	
				Bill Klaers & Allan Wojciak, Rialto CA	90/96
				(rest. to fly, Rialto CA 91/95	)
124 •	F7F-3N	**Bu80382**		NAS Anacostia	

				USMC Museum, MCAS Quantico VA	75
				(trucked to USNAM via Norfolk VA .75)	
				USNAM, NAS Pensacola FL	.75/85
				Yankee Air Force Museum, Willow Run MI	88/89
				Planes of Fame Museum, Chino CA	.90/96
				(displ. in orig. sc "Marines/382")	
C.132 •	F7F-3N	**Bu80390**		NAS Litchfield Park AZ: storage: del.	4.49/58
	F7F-3P		**N6129C**	Kreitzberg Aviation, Salem OR	.58/59
				Wayne B. Fowler, Shaw Island WA	26.5.59/60
				Aero Enterprises, Elkhart IN	.60/61
				Johnson Flying Service, Missoula MT	.61/63
				(conv. to fire tanker at Salem OR .61)	
				Calvin J. Butler/Butler Farm Air Service,	
				Redmond OR (tanker #F16; later #16)	.63/66
				TBM Inc, Tulare CA (tanker #E62)	6.66/78
				Harold Beal/On Mark Aviation, Knoxville TN	11.78/81
			N700F	Preston Parish/Kalamazoo Aviation History	
				Museum, Kalamazoo MI	3.80
			N700FM	ntu: Air Training Inc, Knoxville TN	1.81
			N700F	Preston Parish/Kalamazoo Aviation History	
				Museum, Kalamazoo MI	.81/96
				(stored Knoxville TN 78/84, rest. 84/85:	
				del. to Kalamazoo 3.85, flies as "80390/D3")	
C.139	F7F-3	Bu80397	N6177C	S. V. Flying Service, Montague CA	63/64
				Sis Q Flying Service, Montague CA later	
				Santa Rosa CA (tanker #E31)	64/74
				crashed dest., Ukiah CA	31.8.74
C.146 •	F7F-3	**Bu80404**	**N7626C**	Aero Ads Inc (sky-writing)	58
				Cal-Nat Airways Inc, Grass Valley CA	63/69
				(tanker #E42)	
				Sis Q Flying Service, Santa Rosa CA	.69/84
				Macavia International Corp, Santa Rosa CA	6.85/86
				(tanker #E42)	
				Weeks Air Museum,	
				Tamiami FL:	.86/96
				dam. Tamiami, by Hurricane Andrew	24.8.92
				(rest. to fly, Rialto CA .93/94)	
C.152 •	F7F-3N	**Bu80410**	**N7627C**	Cal-Nat Airways Inc, Grass Valley CA	62/69
				gear folded landing, Grass Valley CA	31.8.62
				Sis-Q Flying Service, Santa Rosa CA (wreck)	.69/72
				Weeks Air Museum, Tamiami FL	88/89
				(stored dism., Ocotillo Wells CA 88/89)	
				USMCAM, Quantico MCAS VA	90/94
				static rest. Rialto CA .90/91 "Marines/80410")	
				Pima Air Museum, Tucson AZ: loan	.91/96
C.154 •	F7F-3N	**Bu80412**	N7628C	Cal-Nat Airways Inc, Grass Valley CA	62/69
				(tanker #E59)	
				accident landing, Ukiah CA	7.66
				Sis-Q Flying Service, Santa Rosa CA	.69/72
				(bought as wreck, stored Santa Rosa CA 72)	
				Weeks Air Museum, Tamiami FL	88/90
				(stored dism., Ocotillo Wells CA 88/89)	
				Klaers Aviation, Rialto CA: dism.	91
				Robert J. Pond/Planes of Fame East,	
				Minneapolis-Flying Cloud MN	.91/94
			N207F	Robert J. Pond, Palm Springs CA	20.5.94/95
				(rest. Chino CA .91/94, ff 13.7.94 as	
				USN 80411/BP7/*King of the Cats*)	
				(USCR quotes id. 80411)	

C.167 •	F7F-3P	**Bu80425**	**N7235C**	Calvin J. Butler/Butler Farm Air Service,	
				Redmond OR (tanker #F17; later #17)	63/66
				TBM Inc, Tulare CA (tanker #E64)	69/79
				David C. Tallichet/MARC, Chino CA	.82/94
				Combat Air Museum, Topeka KS: loan, del.	3.92/93
			NX7235C	The Fighter Collection, Duxford UK	.94/96
				(del. Topeka-Chino CA .94 for rest.)	
			GRUMT		
C.225 •	F7F-3	**Bu80483**	**N6178C**	George F. Kreitzberg, Salem OR	63/64
				Cal-Nat Airways, Grass Valley CA	.64/66
				(tanker #E43)	
				Sis-Q Flying Service, Santa Rosa CA	69/85
				Macavia International Corp, Santa Rosa CA	6.85/86
				(tanker #E43)	
				Weeks Air Museum,	
				Tamiami FL : stored Santa Rosa CA	87/88
				Lea Aviation (US) Inc, Tampa FL	.88/93
				op: Planesailing Air Displays, Duxford	.88/93
				(del. Duxford 13.11.88, flew as "USN JW/483")	
				Richard Bertea, Chino CA & Corvallis OR	5.93/96
				(del. UK-Ft. Wayne IN 5.93, del. Chino 11.9.93)	
C.236	F7F-3	Bu80494	N6179C	Fred J. Arnberg Inc, Yreka CA	63/64
				Sis-Q Flying Service, Montague CA later	
				Santa Rosa CA (tanker #E23)	.64/74
				crashed Rohnerville CA	26.9.74
C.245 •	F7F-3N	**Bu80503**		TBM Inc, Sequoia CA	60/80
				(stored dism., unconv. in hut, Sequoia CA 73)	
			N800RW	Lone Star Flight Museum,	
				Houston TX later Galveston TX	12.88/96
				(rest. Vintage Aircraft Fort Collins CO .88/89 ; flies as	
				Marines 80503/RW/*Big Bossman*)	
C.261	F7F-3	Bu80525	N7238C	Dick Gordon, Santa Rosa CA	63/64
				Cal-Nat Airways, Grass Valley CA	.64
				(tanker #E41)	
				Sis-Q Flying Service, Santa Rosa CA	66/74
				(tanker #E22)	
				crashed Rohnerville CA	21.10.74
C.268 •	F7F-3	**Bu80532**	**N7195C**	George F. Kreitzberg, Salem OR	10.57/63
				(del. Salem ex Litchfield Park NAS AZ 10.57,	
				conv. to sprayer, ff Salem 10.8.58)	
				Scotts Valley Flying Service, Etna CA: leased	2.7.60/63
				(conv. to tanker 5.60)	
				Sis-Q Flying Service, Santa Rosa CA	.63/79
				(tanker #E32, later #E40)	
				Gary H. Flanders & Mike Bogue, Oakland CA	8.79/96
				(flies as "Marines/VMP-254/80532")	

GRUMMAN F8F BEARCAT

D.10 •	XF8F-1	**Bu90446**		NASM: stored dism., Silver Hill MD	52/76
	F8F-1			Darryl G. Greenamyer, Van Nuys CA	.76
	F8F-1D			(exchanged with NASM for D.1020/ N1111L)	
			N99279	George Enhorning/Wolcott Air Service,	
				Wolcott CT	3.77/83
			N14HP	Howard E. Pardue, Breckenridge TX	3.83/96
				(flies as "USN 14P", race #14)	
D.18 •	F8F-1	**Bu90454**	N6624C	E. D. Weiner, Los Angeles CA	.59
			N3351	E. D. Weiner, Los Angeles CA	.59/63
				Vernon D. Jarvis, Decatur IL	.63

				R. E. Schreder, Bryan OH	.63/66
			N9G	Gunther W. Balz, Kalamazoo MI	.68/77
				(race #1, later #7)	
				Preston Parish/Kalamazoo Aviation History	
				Museum, Kalamazoo MI	9.77/96
				(flew as "R Thai AF/G", later "90454/3F8")	
D.205 •	F8F-1	**Bu94956**		(to R Thai AF as 15-178/98)	
				R Thai AF Museum, Don Muang AB, Bangkok	68/96
				(displ. as "RTAF 15-178/4312")	
D.527 •	F8F-1	**Bu95255**		(to l'Armee de l'Air as 95255)	
				(to SVNAF as 95255)	
				Tan Son Nhut AB, South Vietnam: displ.	67/87
				J. Salis Aviation, La Ferte-Alais France	
				Museum of Flying, Santa Monica CA	.90/95
			N65135	Liberty Aero Corp, Santa Monica CA	17.9.90/96
			N41089	Vintage Wings Inc, Anchorage AK	22.9.94
				Liberty Aero Corp, Santa Monica CA	3.95
				(rest. Santa Monica CA & Mojave CA 90/95,	
				ff Mojave 19.5.95)	
				(USCR quotes id. 95255 for N41089,	
				"001" for N65135)	
D.610 •	F8F-1	**Bu95338**		(to l'Armee de l'Air as 95338)	
				(to SVNAF as 95338)	
				Tan Son Nhut AB, South Vietnam: displ.	67/87
D.614 •	F8F-1	**Bu95342**		(to R Thai AF as ......)	
				Nakorn-Sawan AB, Thailand: displ.	85/87
D.628 •	F8F-1	**Bu95356**	N7247C	Vernon D. Jarvis, Decatur IL	63
				R. E. Schreder, Bryan OH	.63/64
				Ernest J. Saviano, Lombard IL	66/69
				John J. Mark, Hales Corners WI	69
				crashed Madison WI	.69
				Joe Tobul, Wexford PA (wreck)	82
			N4752Y	John J. Dowd, Syracuse KS	6.84/96
				(rest. to fly, using parts from Bu95089 &	
				Bu121470 recov. by NEAM from burial site	
				after crashes at NLAF Charlestown RI)	
D.641 •	F8F-1	**Bu95369**		(to l'Armee de l'Air as 95369)	
				(to SVNAF as 95369)	
				Nha Trang AB, South Vietnam: displ.	67/87
D.739A	G-58A		NX1201V	Gulf Oil Co: ff	23.7.47
	Gulfhawk IV		NL3025 (1	Gulf Oil Co/Al Williams: "Gulfhawk 4th": del.	10.48/49
				crashed, dest. by fire, New Bern NC	18.1.49
				(id. to Pioneer Aero, Chino CA for rebuild	
				of D.1081 which adopted id. D739A/N3025 .92)	
D.779 •	F8F-1B	**Bu122095**		(to R Thai AF as ......)	
				displ. outside Govt. offices, Bangkok	65/80
				Jean Salis Collection, La Ferte Alais, France	.86/87
				(shipped to France ex Thailand .87)	
				Stephen Grey/The Fighter Collection, Duxford	.87/92
				(arr. Duxford 6.88, stored dism. 88/92)	
			G-BUCF	The Fighter Collection, Duxford	18.2.92
				Yankee Air Corps, Chino CA	.92
				(arr. dism. Chino CA 4.92, rest. to fly 92/94)	
			N2209	Yanks Air Museum, Chino CA	24.8.93/95
D.804 •	F8F-1B	**Bu122120**		(to R Thai AF as .....): BOC 10.11.52: wfu	8.61

				Lop Buri AB, Thailand: gate guard	
				Foundation for the Preservation & Development of Thai Aircraft, Chiang Mai AB	91/96
				(arr. dism. USA 12.94 for rest. to fly by Grumman employees: to return to Thailand on completion)	
.862 •	F8F-1B	**Bu121488**		(to l'Armee de l'Air as 121488)	
				(to SVNAF as 121488)	
				Tan Son Nhut AB, South Vietnam: displ. "484"	71
.854 •	F8F-1B	**Bu121510**		(to l'Armee de l'Air as 121510)	
				(to SVNAF as G1510)	
				Bien Hoa AB, South Vietnam: displ. "G1510"	67/87
.902	F8F-2	Bu121528	N9886C	Kucera & Associates, Cleveland OH	63
			N212KA	Kucera & Associates, Cleveland OH	.63/70
				(race #99)	
				crashed, Lost Nations Airport OH (Kucera k.)	13.12.68
.963	F8F-2	Bu121589	N5171V	Norwood R. Hanson, Bloomington IN	.61/64
				(flew as *Last of The Red Hot Cats*)	
			N5555H	Norwood R. Hanson, New Haven CT	65/70
				struck mountain, dest., Scott NY (Hanson k.)	.70
.982	F8F-2P	Bu121608	N7700C	J. W. (Bill) Fornof, Houma LA	c60/71
				(purchased San Antonio TX, stored after frustrated sale to Cuba)	
				crashed, NAS Quonset Point RI (Fornof k.)	5.6.71
.988 •	F8F-2	**Bu121614**	**N7957C**	Bearcat & Co/CAF, Mercedes TX	.58/69
				Confederate Air Force, Harlingen TX	73/74
				crashed	5.74
				The Fighter Collection, Duxford UK	.87/91
				(stored dism., Chino CA)	
				Steve Hinton, John Maloney & Kevin Eldridge, Chino CA	92/94
				(rest.to fly Chino CA 92/96))	
.1020 •	F8F-2	**Bu121646**	N7699C	Antelope Valley Aerial Surveys, Palmdale CA	.59
			N1111L	Darryl G. Greenamyer, Mojave CA	.61/76
				(race #1/*Conquest*)	
				(piston eng. air speed record 483.041mph 16.8.69)	
				NASM, Silver Hill MD	.76/90
				(displ. as N1111L/*Buff*)	
.1053 •	F8F-2	**Bu121679**	N4992V	Bud Marquis, Marysville CA	59/63
				Larry Hamilton/Hamilton Aircraft,Sonoma CA	.63/64
				Michael E. Coutches, Hayward CA	6.64
			N818F	Michael E. Coutches, Hayward CA	.66/95
.1081 •	F8F-2	**Bu121707**	N1027B	Kaman Aircraft Corp, CT	c59/70
				(unconv., used as wind machine)	
				USMC Museum, MCAS Quantico VA	.70/78
				(trucked to Mojave c78 for rebuild by McDonnell Enterprises, for USMC Museum)	
				A. Wally McDonnell, Mojave CA	16.4.80
				Elmer F.Ward/Pioneer Aero, Chino CA: dism.	.81/92
				(rebuild Chino CA 81/92, using parts D.1261; adopted id. Gulfhawk D.739A upon completion)	
			N3025 (2	Elmer F. Ward/Pioneer Aero, Chino CA	7.92/95
				(ff Chino 27.7.92, flew as *Gulfhawk 4th*)	
				forced landing, Oshkosh WI	2.8.93
				(rebuild to fly, Chino CA 93/96)	
.1084 •	F8F-2P	**Bu121710**		Naval Training Station, Bainbridge MD	

				USNAM, NAS Pensacola FL	.64/94
				(rest. Jacksonville FL .93 as "USN B100")	
D.1088 •	F8F-2P	**Bu121714**	N4995V	Ed Maloney/The Air Museum, Claremont CA	.57/60
				Ed Maloney/The Air Museum, Ontario & Chino	60/72
			N1YY	Harold 'Bubba' Beal & Charles 'Chubb' Smith/	
				B & S Advertising Inc, Knoxville TN	.72
			N700H	B & S Advertising Inc, Knoxville TN	.77
			N700HL	B & S Advertising Inc, Knoxville TN	1.81/
				op: The Fighter Collection, Duxford UK	
				del. US to Geneva, arr.	3.6.81/96
				(flies as "VF-11/S-100")	
D.1105	F8F-2	Bu121731	N1028B	John Church/New Jersey Air Co,	
				Hackensack NJ	59/63
				Sky Service Inc, Linden NJ	.63/64
			N500B	Chester F. Christopher, New Shewsbury NJ	.66/68
			N5005	Judsen S. Smith, Lebanon NJ	.69
				Michael A. Geren, Kansas City MO	.70/71
				(race #14; #66; #44)	
				crashed, dest., San Diego CA (Geren k)	18.7.71
D.1122 •	F8F-2	**Bu121748**	N1029B	John Church/New Jersey Air Co,	
				Hackensack NJ	59/63
				Michael E. Coutches, Hayward CA	.63/64
			N618F	Michael E. Coutches/American Military	
				Aircraft Museum, Hayward CA	67
				Stanley M. Kurzet, Covina CA (race #7)	.69/75
			N200N	John Gury, St Louis MO	.75/79
				Harold Beal & Charles Smith, Knoxville TN	.79
				lsd:World Jet Inc, Fort Lauderdale FL	.82/87
D.1125	F8F-2	Bu121751	N9885C	William M. Stead, Reno NV	63/66
				(race #80/*Smirnoff*)	
				Moseley Aviation Inc, Tolleson AZ	66/68
				I. N. Burchinall Jr, Paris TX	69/72
				Mike Smith, Johnson KS : del.	11.72/77
				(race #41/*Lois Jean*)	
				Harold Beal & Charles H. Smith, Knoxville TN	.77/80
				crashed dest., Commerce GA (Smith k.)	18.6.80
D.1126 •	F8F-2	**Bu121752**	N7827C	John W. Dorr, Orinda CA	.58/64
				Thomas P. Mathews, Monterey CA	.64/68
				(race #10 *Tom's Cat*)	
				Walter E. Ohlrich, Norfolk VA	.68/72
				(race #10 *Miss Priss*)	
				John Herlihy, Montara CA	.72/73
				(race #8 *Sweet Pea)*	
			N2YY	Harold Beal, Knoxville TN	.73
			N800H	Harold Beal & Charles Smith/B & S Advertising	
				Knoxville TN (race #8 *Precious Bear*)	.75/77
				World Jet Inc,	
				West Palm Beach FL	.77/90
				(race #8 *Bearcat Bill)*	
				op Warbirds of GB Ltd	.90/92
				(shipped to UK, arr 30.12.90;	
				Iron Baron Corp, Dover DE	5.94/95
				Duxford by	11.95
D.1148 •	F8F-2	**Bu122619**		NAS Litchfield Park AZ: open storage	57/63
			N7958C	T. A. Underwood, Buckeye AZ	.63
				Frank Williams, Port Arthur TX	.63
				Larry Hamilton/Hamilton Aircraft,Sonoma CA	.63/65
				Aviation Amazement-Amusement Inc/	

				Confederate Air Force, Oklahoma City OK	.66/67
				Gardner Flyers/CAF, Brownwood TX	.68/72
				Max Hoffman,	c72
				Ken Boomhower	c72
				Harold Beal & Charles Smith, Knoxville TN	.73/75
			N700F	Harold Beal, Knoxville TN	.75/78
				Whittington Brothers Inc, Fort Lauderdale FL	.78/79
			N14WB	Don Whittington/World Jet Inc, FLL FL	9.79/80
				EAA Aviation Foundation, Oshkosh WI	.80/94
				(displ. as "USN 122619/Denver/P-14")	
D.1162 •	F8F-2	**Bu121776**	N1030B	Kaman Aircraft Corp, CT	c59/70
				(unconv., used as wind machine)	
				USMC Museum, MCAS Quantico VA: stored	.70/96
D.1170 •	F8F-2	**Bu122629**	N1031B	crashed at Valparaiso IN	.62
				Earl Reinert/Victory Air Museum,	
				Mundelein IL: wreck	68
				(stored Valparaiso IN, later Mundelein IL 62/68)	
			N777L	Lyle T. Shelton, Granada Hills CA	.68/96
				(rebuilt Long Beach CA, Wright R-3350, ff 9.69;	
				mod. racer #70, #77 *Able* later *Cat Rare Bear*;	
				world piston eng. speed record 528 mph 21.8.89)	
				minor dam. forced ldg., Reno NV (repaired)	9.92
D.1181	F8F-2P	Bu121787	N6821D	M. W. Fairbrother, Rosemount MN	.63/66
			N148F	John Church/New Jersey Air Co,	
				Hackensack NJ (race #11)	.66/68
				Walter (Budd) Fountain/Hawke Dusters,	
				Modesto CA (race #99; #24)	.68/73
				crashed and dest., Mojave (Fountain k.)	20.10.73
D.1190 •	F8F-2	**Bu122637**	N1033B	William Johnson, Miami FL	.63/65
				John Church/New Jersey Air Co,	
				Hackensack NJ	.66/68
				Sherman Cooper, Merced CA	.68/71
				John Church, Hackensack NJ	.71/73
			N198F	John Gury, St Louis MO	.73/80
				(flew as USN "G-98"; race #99; #11; #98)	
				John Herlihy, Montara CA	.80
				Cecil H. Harp, Canby OR	.81/84
				Cinema Air Inc, Houston TX	5.84/96
				(flies as "USN 122637/C98")	
D.1227 •	F8F-2P	**Bu122674**	N7825C	E. D. Weiner, Los Angeles CA	.58
				Leo J. Demers, Aurora OR	63
				Larry Hamilton/Hamilton Aircraft,Sonoma CA	.63/64
				Richard S. Tobey, Newport Beach CA	66
				Paul D. Finefrock, Hobart OK	69
				Gary R. Levitz, Long Beach CA/Avalon TX	.69/72
				Confederate Air Force, Harlingen/Midland TX	8.2.72/96
				(rest. Chino CA 88/91, ff 17.12.91 "122674")	
D.1261 •	F8F-2	Bu122708	N7701C	Rudolph Paslaski, Detroit MI	63/64
				Michael J. Devanny, Cincinatti OH	66
				Ronald E. Reynolds , Norwalk CT	69/72
				Jack M. Sliker, Wadley GA	73/75
				(race #4/*Escape II*)	
				crashed, Flagstaff AZ (Sliker killed)	16.9.75
				Elmer F. Ward, Chino CA (wreck)	85/96
				(parts used in rebuild of D.1081, Chino CA)	
D.1262 •	G-58B		**N700A**	Grumman Aircraft Eng. Corp: ff	7.1.50/59
	Gulfhawk			(op. by Roger Wolfe Kahn, Grumman President)	
	Redship			Cornell Aeronautical Lab., Buffalo NY	.59/66

					William Ross, Elk Grove Village IL	
					J. W. (Bill) Fornof, Houma LA	69/77
					Champlin Fighter Museum, Mesa AZ	.81/84
					Planes of Fame East,	
					Minneapolis-Flying Cloud MN	86/96
-	•	F8F-1	-		(to R Thai AF as ....)	
					Ta Khli AB, Thailand: gate guard	67/90
					(displ. as "RTAF 4000", later "43104")	
-	•	F8F-1	-		(to R Thai AF as 15-43/93)	
					displ. Air Force Academy, East Bangkok	85
					(additional aircraft to D.779)	

GRUMMAN JF/J2F DUCK

145	•	JF-1	**Bu9447**	**N1235N**	Intercoastal Aircraft Inc, Seattle WA	63/69
					(last FAA inspection 7.49)	
					Charles W. Kirk, Carson City NV	5.89/95
					(long-term rest. project)	
536	•	J2F-4	**Bu1649**	**N63850**	William F. Patterson, Miami FL	63/69
					(last FAA inspection 1.53)	
					William F. Floten, Seattle WA	12.91/95
-	•	J2F-6	**Bu32769**		(to USAF as 48-0563): 10th ARS, Alaska	
		OA-12			crashed landing, Chekatna Lake AK	25.8.48
					recov. from crash site by Ketch Ketchum	.76
				N4222U	Lindley H. Ketchum, Anchorage AK	2.81/84
				N8563F	Lindley H. Ketchum, Anchorage AK	84/95
					(long term rest. Lake Hood AK)	
					Alaska Aviation Heritage Museum,	
					Anchorage-Lake Hood: displ. during rest.	93
-	•	J2F-6	**Bu33549**	**N1214N**	Woodhouse Inc, Long Beach FL	63/69
					John C. Seidel, Sugar Grove IL	73/78
					Kermit A. Weeks/Weeks Air Museum,	
					Tamiami FL	4.82/95
					(flew as "1-J-7/*Candy Clipper*")	
					dam. Tamiami, Hurricane Andrew	24.8.92
					(rest. to fly, Kansas .93)	
-	•	J2F-6	**Bu33559**	N3960C	Ellsworth Hodges, Cherry Creek NY	63/64
					Jack R. Browne, San Juan PR	66/69
					Jack R. Browne, St Thomas USVI	72/74
					Crow Inc, Swanton OH	77/84
					crashed, landing Maumee River OH	12.7.80
					Steven T. Hamilton, Reno NV (hulk)	86/88
				N910CM	Charles M. Kirk, Carson City NV	5.89/93
				N3960C	Jack A. Erickson, Medford OR	2.93/95
					(long-term rest. project)	
-	•	J2F-6	**Bu33581**		NAS Norfolk VA: stored for USNAM	65/69
					USNAM, NAS Pensacola FL	.70/95
					(displ. as "USN 33581/149")	
-	•	J2F-6	**Bu33587**	**N67790**	Aircraft Specialties Inc, Mesa AZ	63/64
					(tanker #C07)	
					Hart Marine Inc, Lafayette LA	66/69
					Tallmantz Aviation Inc, Santa Ana CA	72/84
					Kermit A. Weeks/Weeks Air Museum,	
					Tamiami FL	.85/87
					USAFM, Wright-Patterson AFB, Dayton OH	.87/95

				(displ. as "USAF 8563")	
- •	J2F-6	**Bu33594**	**N1273N**	Wallace B. Pankratz, Brawley CA	63/74
				San Diego Aerospace Museum, San Diego CA	.74/95
				(displ. as "Bu33594")	
				(c/n quoted as A-633504)	
- •	J2F-6	**Bu33614**	**N55S**	Tres Americae Enterprises, Miami FL	63/69
				(retired Letica, Colombia: derelict by 70/81)	
				Lake Wales Air Services, Lake Wales FL	72/77
				claimed by resident of, Carman MAN	.81
				(dism. at Letica by Diemert, abandoned due ownership dispute .81)	
				recov. ex Letica by Kermit Weeks	.82
				Kermit A. Weeks/Weeks Air Museum, Tamiami FL: rest. project	12.82/95
- •	J2F-6	**Bu36976**	**N1196N**	C. E. Crosby, Bellingham WA	63
				Kay Barricklow, Arcola IL	.63/64
				I. N. Burchinall Jr, Honeygrove TX	66/69
				Tallmantz Aviation, Santa Ana CA	
				(flew in movie "Murphy's War")	
				Carl Mies Filter Products Inc, Louisville KY	72
				EAA Aviation Foundation, Oshkosh WI	76/95
				(rest. by Grumman, del. to Oshkosh .82, displ. as "USN F-J-1")	
- •	J2F-	-	OB-164	Verano Linguistic Institute "Amamta"	7.46
				(to Peru Navy as 164)	10.61/64
				displ. on lake Parque las Leyendas, Lima	65/77
- •	J2F-6	-	-	(to Mexican Navy as MV-08)	.47
				Museo de la Fuerza Aerea Mexicana, Santa Lucia : displ. as "MV-08"	67/78

GRUMMAN OV-1 MOHAWK

GRUMMAN V-1 MOHAWK

2 •	OV-1A	**59-2604**	**N4235Z**	Lortz & Son Manufacturing Co Inc	17.3.81
	JOV-1A			Thunderbird Aviation Inc, Deer Valley AZ	84/88
				Lone Star Flight Museum, Galveston TX	6.90/96
				(rest. San Marcos TX, flies as "Army 59604")	
4 •	OV-1A	**59-2606**	**N72606**	Richard A. Boulais, Glendale AZ	5.9.89/96
6 •	OV-1A	**59-2608**	**N2608**	Airmet Corp	10.89/92
15 •	OV-1A	**59-2617**	**N75207**	reg. res.	84/92
- •	OV-1A	**59-2631**		US Army: retired, stored Guthrie AAB	11.88/92
				US Army Aviation Museum	.88/92
			N4376U	Sanders Lead Co, Troy AL	16.3.92/96
21 •	OV-1A	**60-3722**	**N2623Q**	Moseley Aviation Inc, Phoenix AZ	29.11.82
				reg. pending	88/92
34 •	OV-1A	**60-3735**	**N75213**	Thunderbird Aviation Inc, Deer Valley AZ	77/83
- •	OV-1A	**60-3736**		Michael G. Langer, St Paul MN	.82/92
	JOV-1A			(stripped hulk ex Davis Monthan AFB AZ)	
			N134GA	American Wings Air Museum, St. Paul-Anoka County MN	7.92/95
				(rest. Anoka County, due to fly .96)	
- •	OV-1C	**60-3758**	**N6743**	Florida Military Aviation Museum,	

				Clearwater FL	94
- •	OV-1C	**62-5856**	**N6744**	struck-off USCR National Warplane Museum, Geneseo NY (rest. project)	1.90 2.90/95
-	OV-1B	**62-5866**	**N171**	US Geological Survey Department, Panama	.71/74
-	OV-1B	**62-5880**	**N512NA**	NASA, Langley Research Center, Hampton VA	84
48A •	OV-1A OV-1B	**63-13118**	**N75205**	reg. res.	84/92
49A •	OV-1A OV-1B	**63-13119**	 **N90788**	(to USN as 63-13119) based NAS Patuxant River MD reg. res.	 4.74 84/88
58A •	OV-1A	**63-13128**	**N87864**	Pittsburgh Institute of Aeronautics, Allegheny County Airport, Pittsburgh PA	 7.77/96
- •	OV-1B	**64-14243**	**N243KM**	reg. candidate	6.93
-	OV-1B	**64-14244**	**N637NA**	NASA, Lewis Research Center, Cleveland OH	74/77
- •	OV-1C OV-1D GOV-1D	**67-18906**	 **N906KM**	Fort Eustis VA: ground inst. airframe Kenosha Military Museum, Kenosha WI	 26.5.94/96
-	OV-1C	**67-18915**	**N928NA**	NASA	
- •	OV-1C	**68-15936**	**N134AW**	American Wings Air Museum, St. Paul-Anoka County MN (flies as "US Army 15936")	 27.8.92/95
- •	OV-1C OV-1D	**68-15939**	N70783 **N939MM**	McClain Museum Inc: reg. candidate McClain Museum Inc, Anderson IN	11.5.93 1.94/96
- •	OV-1D GOV-1D	**68-15958**	 **N10VD**	Fort Eustis VA: ground inst. airframe IN Museum of Military History, Indianapolis IN	 30.4.93/96
-	OV-1C	**68-16993**	 4X-JRB	(to Israeli IDFAF as 056): del. test reg. ret. to USAF	.74 .78
-	OV-1C	**69-17021**	 4X-JRA	(to Israeli IDFAF as 055): del. test reg. ret. to USAF American Wings Air Museum, St Paul MN	.74 .78 93/94

GRUMMAN TBF/TBM AVENGER

2734 •	TBF-1	**Bu0628**		ditched Lake Michigan of carrier "Sable" USNAM, NAS Pensacola FL (static rest.) (recov. from Lake Michigan by USNAM)	3.7.43 92
2781 •	TBF-1C	**Bu01747**		ditched Lake Michigan of carrier "Wolverine" USNAM, NAS Pensacola FL (static rest.) (recov. from Lake Michigan .91)	11.6.43 .91/94
4010 •	TBF-1C	**Bu05954**		ditched Lake Michigan, off USS "Wolverine" recov. from Lake Michigan: "USN T-14" Harland Avezzie, Westfield MA	12.43 .79 .90/92

			N5954A	Indiana Museum of Military History, Indianapolis IN	21.9.92
				(rest. to fly, Westfield MA 91/92)	
4045 •	TBF-1C	**Bu05997**		MGM Studios, Culver City CA	70
				Ed Maloney/The Air Museum, Chino CA	.70/72
				MARC, Chino CA	.72/82
				Yankee Air Corps/ Yanks Air Museum, Chino CA	83/93
				(stored unconv., orig. scheme, Chino CA)	
4968 •	TBF-1C	**Bu24085**		NASM, stored Silver Hill MD	65/91
5219 •	TBF-1C Mk. II	**Bu24336**		(to RNZAF as NZ2504)	.43/59
				Te Rapa AB NZ: gate guard	7.59/78
				RNZAF Museum, Wigram AB	.78/95
				(rest. to taxy condition 6.79, displ. as "NZ2521")	
5220 •	TBF-1C Mk. II	**Bu24337**		(to RNZAF as NZ2505)	.43/59
				Bennett Aviation, Te Kuiti: open storage	59
				in playground, Opunake, Taranaki NZ	60/69
				Silverstream Railway & Vintage Transport Museum, Hutt River, Wellington: displ. as "NZ2518"	73/78
				RNZAF Museum, Wigram AB: stored whole	92/95
5625 •	TBF-1C Mk. II	**Bu47859**		(to RNZAF as NZ2527): del.	1.44/59
				Bennett Aviation Ltd, Te Kuiti	12.59
			ZK-CBO	Barr Brothers Ltd, Ardmore, Auckland	18.3.62/63
				(crop sprayer conv. abandoned 3.63)	
				to playground, Kuirau Park, Rotorua	10.64/69
				Museum of Transport & Technology, Auckland	74/94
				Confederate Air Force (NZ Wing), Auckland-Dairy Flat: loan for static displ.	.81/96
5782 •	TBF-1C Mk. II	**Bu48016**		(to RNZAF as NZ2539)	
				Bennett Aviation, Te Kuiti: open storage	59
				in playground, Havelock North NZ	69/73
				Ken Jacobs, Auckland NZ: stored	92/95
746 •	TBM-3	**Bu23602**		NAS Mustim Field, Philadelphia PA : stored	47/75
				USNAM: displ. *USS "Intrepid*, Philadelphia	.76
				Bradley Air Museum, Windsor Locks CT	18.9.76/79
				badly damaged by tornado, Windsor Locks CT	3.10.79
				New England Air Museum, Windsor Locks CT	89/90
				(static rest., using parts from hulks of Bu53100 & Bu53527, recov. by NEAM from burial site after crashes at NALF Charlestown RI)	
2062 •	TBM-3	**Bu69323**	N7961C	Daro Inc, San Clemente CA	63/70
				(tanker #E92; later #24)	
				Sis-Q Flying Service, Santa Rosa CA	.70
			C-GLEJ	Evergreen Air Service Ltd, Roxboro QUE	12.74/78
				Forest Protection Ltd, Fredericton NB	78/95
				(tanker #24)	
2064 •	TBM-3U	**Bu69325**	N104Z	U. S. Forestry Service, Davis CA	.56/61
			N1044	Aero Insect Control Inc, Rio Grande NJ	63/66
			CF-XOM	Maritime Air Service Ltd, Moncton NB	6.69/70
				Hicks & Lawrence Ltd, Tillsonburg ONT	72/81
				(tanker #18)	
			N325GT	Syracuse Flying Service, Syracuse KS	10.85/88
				Stallion Aircraft Inc, Bensenville IL	8.89/95
				op: Air Classics Aircraft Museum, DuPage IL	95
				(flies as "USN T-88")	
				(note: CCAR quoted id. as "69324")	

2066 •	TBM-3S	**Bu69327**		(to RCN as 69327): BOC 27.9.50: SOC	5.7.60
	AS Mk. 3		CF-KCG	Skyway Air Services, Langley BC	61/69
				Conair Aviation Ltd, Abbotsford BC	.69/79
				(tanker #615)	
				Forest Protection Ltd, Fredericton NB	
				Warbirds of GB Ltd, Blackbushe	
				Imperial War Museum, Duxford UK	.77/96
				for American Air Museum in Britain	
2068 •	TBM-3U	**Bu69329**	N73642	Reeder Flying Service, Twin Falls ID	63/84
				(tanker #D23; later #23)	
				(open storage, derelict, Twin Falls ID 80/84)	
				Gary Wolverton, Twin Falls ID	84
			N700RW	Lone Star Flight Museum,	
				Houston/Galveston TX	10.86/96
				(flies as USN "69329/329RW")	
2083 •	TBM-3E	**Bu69344**	**N66475**	Ball Ralston Flying Service, Hillsboro OR	63/64
				AV Aircraft Co, Deming NM	66/70
				Hemet Valley Flying Service, Hemet CA	c71
				(stored Stockton CA 74)	
				sale rep: USCR	84/92
2094 •	TBM-3E	**Bu69355**	N7850C	Cisco Aircraft Inc, Lancaster CA	63
				Desert Aviation Service, Phoenix AZ	.63/64
				Aircraft Specialties, Mesa AZ	66
				R. E. Hyde/Ag Air Inc, Dos Palos CA	69/70
				Marom Ltd, Herzelia, Israel	.69
				(derelict at Herzelia as N7850C 74)	
				Israeli Air Force Museum, Hatzerim AB	89/96
				(rest., displ. in RNFAA scheme)	
2100 •	TBM-3E	**Bu69361**	N9596C	P & B Aviation, Oroville CA (tanker #E19)	63
				Aero Union Corp, Anderson/Chico CA	.63/63
				Air Tankers Inc, Newcastle WY/ Casper WY	66/72
			C-GOEG	Norfolk Aerial Spraying Ltd, Simcoe NB	5.75/78
				Reynolds Aviation Museum, Wetaskiwin ALTA	88/95
				(rest. to fly, Wetaskiwin 92/95)	
2113 •	TBM-3E	**Bu69374**	**N9650C**	Bill Wood, Imperial Beach CA (tanker #83)	63/72
				MARC, Chino CA	79/92
2114	TBM-3	**Bu69375**	N3965A	Nevadair, Tonopah NV	63/70
				Charlie T. Jensen, Tonopah NV	72/78
2198 •	TBM-3E	**Bu69459**	**N8397H**	Cisco Aircraft Inc, Lancaster CA	63
				Aerial Applicators Inc, Salt Lake City UT	.63/72
				Hillcrest Aircraft, Lewiston ID	77
				Paramount Leasing Corp, Bakersfield CA	84
				Northwest Warbirds Inc, Kimberly ID	86/87
				John MacGuire/War Eagles Air Museum,	
				Santa Teresa NM	3.88/96
2211 •	TBM-3	**Bu69472**	N9593C	Frontier Airways, Visalia CA	63/64
				op: Clayton V. Curtis, Boise ID (tanker #D5)	63
				Loening Air Inc, Boise ID	66
				Clayton V. Curtis, Boise ID	69/70
				Bill Dempsay/D & D Aero Spray, Rantoul KS	72
				James Levrett, Reno NV	77
				Pima County Air Museum, Tucson AZ	83/93
				(displ. as USN "69472/301")	
2241 •	TBM-3S	**Bu69502**		(to Royal Navy FAA as XB446)	.53

	AS. Mk. 4			Fleet Air Arm Museum, RNAS Yeovilton	.64/92
				(displ. as "XB446/992-CU")	
2270	TBM-3	Bu69531	N179Z	U. S. Forestry Service, Beltsville MD	63/64
			N17930	Seeley Flying Serv., Newcastle & Casper WY	66/69
				Air Tankers Inc, Casper WY	70/72
			C-GOBK	Norfolk Aerial Spraying Ltd, Simcoe NB	5.74/78
				crashed while spraying, Minto NB	30.5.78
2273 •	TBM-3	**Bu85454**		rep. Wings of History Museum, Santa Fe NM	91
2279 •	TBM-3S	**Bu85460**		(to RCN as 85460): BOC 22.7.50: SOC	5.7.60
	AS Mk. 3		N7032C	crashed on take-off, Idaho City ID	9.7.61
				Richardson Aviation, Yakima WA	63/72
				Marom Ltd, Herzelia, Israel: leased	67
				(noted spraying in Greece 68)	
			C-GFPS	Evergreen Air Service Ltd, Roxboro QUE	5.76
				Forest Protection Ltd, Fredericton NB	78/96
				(tanker #3, wfu stored Fredericton 94/95)	
2318	TBM-3	**Bu85499**	N9597C	Calvin J. Butler, Redmond OR	63
				Johnson Flying Service, Missoula MT	.63/72
				(tanker #A6)	
			C-GLEM	Evergreen Air Service Ltd, Roxboro QUE	4.75
				Forest Protection Ltd, Fredericton NB	78/80
				struck-off reg.	6.80
2325 •	TBM-3S	**Bu85506**		(to RCN as 85506): BOC 16.6.52: SOC	30.1.58
	AS Mk. 3		N6582D	Simsbury Flying Service, Simsbury CT	63/66
				Ag Air International, Dos Palos CA	.67
				Marom Ltd, Herzelia, Israel	.67/91
				(noted based Athens, spraying contract 7.68)	
				stored derelict, Herzelia, Israel as N6582D	74/91
2379 •	TBM-3	**Bu85560**	**N6830C**	Nevadair, Tonopah NV	63/70
				Charlie T. Jensen, Tonopah NV	72/77
				Western Aerospace Museum, Oakland CA	93/96
2413	TBM-3	Bu85594	N1366N	TBM Inc, Bakersfield/Tulare CA	59/74
				(tanker #E66 ; later #E60)	
				op: Aero Union Corp, Chico CA (tanker #E60)	73
				crashed Placerville CA	18.8.73
2416 •	TBM-3S	Bu85597		(to RCN as 85597): BOC 23.6.52: SOC	17.1.58
	AS Mk. 3		CF-IMK	Skyway Air Services, Langley BC	61/69
				Conair Aviation Ltd, Abbotsford BC	.69/76
				(tanker #602)	
			C-FIMK	Forest Protection Ltd, Fredericton NB	78/94
				(tanker #2, wfu stored Fredericton 90/95)	
				Jeff Thomas/Vintage Wings, Seattle WA	.94
				(trucked dism. ex Fredericton 7.94)	
			N704QZ	Byron D. Neely, Austin TX	22.7.94/96
2442	TBM-3S	Bu85623		(to Dutch Navy/MLD as 1-29; 037)	.55
				De Kooy NAS, Holland: displ.	70
2451 •	TBM-3E	**Bu85632**	N7002C	Plains Aero Service, Dalhart TX	63/64
				Air Tankers Inc, Newcastle WY	66/72
			C-GOBJ	Norfolk Aerial Spraying Ltd, Simcoe NB	5.74/79
				Forest Protection Ltd, Fredericton NB	85/89
				(tanker #B15)	
				Northwest Warbirds Inc, Kimberly ID	.89
			N81865	Wayne G. Rudd, Carbondale CO	13.6.89/96
				(del. ex Canada 28.6.89)	

2455	TBM-3E	Bu85636	N6823C	Sierra Aviation, Porterville CA (tanker #E45)	63
				Wen Inc, Porterville CA (tanker #E45)	.63/64
				Air Tankers Inc, Newcastle WY	66
2469 •	TBM-3E TBM-3W2	**Bu85650**		(to Dutch Navy/MLD as P-102; 16-102; 045)	9.53
				Anthony Fokker School, The Hague	68/72
				C. Honcoop, Veen, Netherlands	76
				Sir W. J. D. Roberts/Strathallan Collection, Auchterader, Scotland	5.76
			G-BTBM	Sir W. J. D. Roberts/Strathallan Collection	12.77/81
				Warbirds of GB Ltd, Blackbushe	14.7.81/85
				stored Blackbushe : struck-off reg.	20.4.82
				Aces High Ltd, Duxford	7.6.85
				sold in US: struck-off reg.	22.7.85
			N61BD	Edward A. Deeds, Charlotte VA	4.86/89
			N452HA	Herbert H. Avery, Morganton NC	7.89/91
				Avery's Antique Airplanes Inc, Morganton NC	12.91/96
2484	TBM-3S AS Mk. 3	Bu85665		(to RCN as 85665): BOC 8.6.50: SOC	30.1.58
			CF-IMV	Wheeler Airlines, St Jean QUE	58/65
				Wheeler Northland Airways Ltd, St Jean QUE	66/70
				Evergreen Air Service Ltd, Roxboro QUE	72/75
				crashed	9.6.77
2534 •	TBM-3	**Bu85715**	N1369N	TBM Inc, Bakersfield/Tulare CA (tanker #E36)	63/69
				Sis-Q Flying Service, Santa Rosa CA (tanker #E36; later #E27)	70/72
			C-GLEF	Evergreen Air Service Ltd, Roxboro QUE	4.75
				Forest Protection Ltd, Fredericton NB (tanker #8, wfu stored Fredericton 90/95)	78/94
				Jeff Thomas/Vintage Wings, Seattle WA (trucked dism. ex Fredericton 7.94)	7.94
			N65VC	Ozark Management Inc, Rolla MO	2.95
2536	TBM-3E	Bu85717		NAS Memphis TN: displ. on pole	65/73
				rep. scrapped	
2552 •	TBM-3E	**Bu85733**	N6824C	Wilson Aviation Industries, Lewiston ID	63
				Hillcrest Aircraft Co, Lewiston ID	.63/64
				Johnson Flying Service, Missoula MT (tanker #A12)	66/72
			C-GLEK	Evergreen Air Service Ltd, Roxboro QUE	4.75
				Forest Protection Ltd, Fredericton NB (tanker #14)	81/96
2606 •	TBM-3E	Bu85787	**N7000C**	Hillcrest Aircraft Co, Lewiston ID	63/70
				wreck, stored Twin Falls ID	80/93
2613 •	TBM-3E	Bu85794	**N7001C**		
				Central Air Service, Lewistown MT	.57/77
				Gordon B. Plaskett, King City CA	.80
				Alan Clark/Flytex Inc, Dallas TX	.83/84
				Alan Clark/Fighting Air Command, Dallas TX	86/87
				Coke V. Stuart, Valdosta GA	.88/92
				Richard D. Ervin, Indianapolis IN	4.93/96
2648	TBM-3S AS Mk. 3	Bu85829		(to RCN as 85829): BOC 19.10.50: SOC	30.1.58
			N6584D	Simsbury Flying Service, Simsbury CT	66
			CF-XON	Maritime Air Service Ltd, Moncton NB	6.69/72
				Hicks & Lawrence Ltd, Tillsonburg ONT	72/75
				struck-off reg.	5.75

2652	TBM-3S	Bu85833		(to RCN as 85833): BOC 30.6.50: SOC	26.3.58
	AS Mk. 3		CF-IMO	Forest Patrol Ltd, St John NB	65/71
				wfu: struck-off reg.	5.71
2655	TBM-3E	Bu85836	N7014C	Johnson Flying Service, Missoula MT	63/72
				(tanker #A11)	
			C-GLEP	Evergreen Air Service Ltd, Roxboro QUE	4.75
				Forest Protection Ltd, Fredericton NB	78/84
				crashed St Croix NB	10.6.84
2663	TBM-3U	Bu85844	N106Z	U. S. Forestry Service, Davis CA	.56/59
				struck-off USCR	8.59
			N3356G	Hemet Valley Flying Service, Hemet CA	63/70
				(tanker #E75)	
				crashed dest.	28.7.70
2673	TBM-3E	Bu85854	N7015C	Johnson Flying Service, Missoula MT	63/72
				(tanker #A7)	
			C-GLEQ	Evergreen Air Service Ltd, Roxboro QUE	4.75
				crashed	23.6.77
2680 •	TBM-3S	**Bu85861**		(to RCN as 85861): BOC 15.7.50: SOC	16.9.53
	AS Mk. 3			crashed in Bedford Bay, nr HMCS Shearwater	6.8.53
				(recov. from sea, static rest. for display)	
				CFB Shearwater NS : gate guard	.73/96
2688 •	TBM-3E	**Bu85869**	N9927Z	Aircraft Specialties Inc, Mesa AZ	63/77
				(tanker #C3; #E39; #C39)	
				Globe Air Inc, Mesa AZ	4.81/84
				Justus O. Jackson, Comstock TX	86/88
			F-AZJA	Didier Chable, Melun-Villaroche: del.	30.9.89/96
				(flies as "USN/SK-401")	
2701 •	TBM-3E	**Bu85882**	**N9584Z**	Cisco Aircraft Inc, Lancaster CA	63/64
				Loening Air Inc, Boise ID	66/70
				Ralph M. Ponte, Cedar Ridge CA	77
				Joseph G. Mabee, Midland TX	6.78/96
2702	TBM-3E	Bu85883	N6825C	Ralph M. Ponte, Visalia CA	63/66
				op: Cal-Nat Airways, Grass Valley CA	63/67
				(tanker #E37)	
				Hemet Valley Flying Service, Hemet CA	69/72
				(tanker #E37)	
				crashed Columbia CA	4.9.71
2705 •	TBM-3E	**Bu85886**	**N9586Z**	Cisco Aircraft Inc, Lancaster CA	63/64
				Loening Air Inc, Boise ID	66
				Hillcrest Aircraft, Lewiston ID	69/70
				G & M Investments, Lewiston ID	72
				Craig Aero Service, Buttonwillow CA	77
				Ralph M. Ponte, Grass Valley CA	.78
				Joe Dulvick	80/81
				Jack L. Kelley, Dallas TX	83/88
				TBF Inc, Tenafly NJ	90/94
				P O B Inc/Avirex, Tenafly NJ	7.94/95
				(flies as USN "85886/SL-401")	
2709 •	TBM-3E	**Bu85890**	N1952M	Georgia Forestry Commission, Macon GA	63/72
				USMC Museum, MCAS Quantico VA	74/94
				(static rest. MCAS Cherry Point NC .74/76,	
				airlifted under chopper to MCAS Quantico .76;	
				displ. as "85890/19")	
2747	TBM-3S	Bu85928		(to RCN as 85928): BOC 30.6.50: SOC	6.3.58
	AS Mk. 3		CF-IMW	Wheeler Airlines, St Jean QUE	65

				Wheeler Northland Airways Ltd, St Jean QUE	66/70
				Evergreen Air Service Ltd, Roxboro QUE	72/75
				crashed	10.6.75
2757 •	TBM-3E	**Bu85938**	**N7226C**	Sierra Aviation, Porterville CA	63
				(tanker #E44)	
				Wen Inc, Porterville CA	.63/64
				Whirly Birds Inc, Porterville CA	66/69
				Capitol Aire Inc, Carson City NV	70/72
				Craig Aero Service, Buttonwillow CA	77
				Stewart Aviation Inc, Moses Lake WA	84/88
				Summers Farm & Ranch Inc, Sugar City ID	5.90/96
2776 •	TBM-3E	**Bu85957**	**N9547Z**	Aero Crop Service Inc, Tolleson AZ	63/64
				(tanker #E80)	
				Reeder Flying Service, Twin Falls ID	66/84
				(tanker #E80)	
				Gary W. Wolverton, Kimberly ID	84
				Northwest Warbirds Inc, Twin Falls ID	3.86/96
2802 •	TBM-3S	**Bu85983**		(to RCN as 85983): BOC 29.5.52: SOC	26.3.58
	AS Mk. 3		N4039A	Simsbury Flying Service, Simsbury CT	64/72
				(stored unconv. Simsbury CT .58/72)	
			CF-BEG	Miramichi Air Service Ltd, Douglastown NB	5.74/75
				Hicks & Lawrence Ltd, Tillsonburg ONT	78
				(tanker #1/"Yogi Bear")	
			N28SF	Syracuse Flying Service, Syracuse KS	10.85/86
				C C Air Corp, Rialto CA	12.86/96
				(flies as USN "85983/X2")	
2839 •	TBM-3S	**Bu86020**		(to RCN as 86020): BOC 5.10.50: SOC	22.4.58
	AS Mk. 3		N7157C	Donald A. Goodman, Missoula MT	63/70
				(tanker #63)	
			C-GFPL	Evergreen Air Service Ltd, Roxboro QUE	5.76
				Forest Protection Ltd, Fredericton NB	78/96
				(tanker #22)	
2883	TBM-3E	Bu86064	N7161C	Jim Routh/Routh Aircraft, Paso Robles CA	63
				(tanker #E97; #C97)	
				Multiple Management Corp, Long Beach CA	.63/64
				Hemet Valley Flying Service, Hemet CA	66/72
				(tanker #E97)	
			C-GFPO	Evergreen Air Service Ltd, Roxboro QUE	5.76
				Forest Protection Ltd, Fredericton NB	81
				struck-off reg.	1.85
2909	TBM-3	Bu86090	N9434Z	F. H. Haradon, Goleta CA (tanker #E52)	63
				Sonora Flying Service, Columbia CA	.63/64
				Fire Flyers Inc, Reno NV	66
				Sis-Q Flying Service, Montague CA	
				Hemet Valley Flying Service, Hemet CA	68/72
				(tanker #E52)	
			C-GFPP	Evergreen Air Service Ltd, Roxboro QUE	5.76
				crashed	17.6.77
2910	TBM-3	Bu86091	N9307Z	Cisco Aircraft Inc, Lancaster CA	62/64
				(tanker#E82)	
				D & D Aero Spraying, Rantoul KS	66/69
			CF-AYL	Norfolk Aerial Spraying Ltd, Simcoe NB	.70/72
				crashed	17.6.73
2917	TBM-3S	Bu86098		(to RCN as 86098): BOC 8.7.50: SOC	30.1.58
	AS Mk. 3		CF-IMX	Wheeler Airlines, St Jean QUE	6.3.58/65
				Wheeler Northland Airways Ltd, St Jean QUE	66/70

				Evergreen Air Service Ltd, Roxboro QUE	72
937	TBM-3	Bu86118	N9860C	Jim Routh/Routh Aircraft, Paso Robles CA	63/64
				(tanker #E95)	
				Hemet Valley Flying Service, Hemet CA	66/70
				(tanker #E95)	
				crashed near Ramona CA	4.9.70
942 •	TBM-3R	**Bu86123**	**N6831C**	Charlie T. Jensen, Sacramento CA	62/63
				(tanker #E22)	
				Charlie T. Jensen/Nevadair, Tonopah NV	63/77
				Richard J. Dieter & Ray Stutsman,	
				South Bend IN	.79/83
				(rest. .80 as "86123/RB-123")	
				Tom A. Thomas, Oklahoma City OK	.84
				Ada Aircraft Museum, Frederick OK	7.84/95
				Mid America Air Museum, Liberal KS: loan	93/96
				(flies as "86123/RB-123")	
999 •	TBM-3S	**Bu86180**		(to RCN as 86180): BOC 19.10.50: SOC	5.7.60
	AS Mk. 3		CF-MUD	Skyway Air Services, Langley BC	61/69
				(tanker #12)	
				Conair Aviation Ltd, Abbotsford BC	.69/75
				(tanker #612)	
				ditched while spraying, Lake Nigault QUE	11.6.71
				Forest Protection Ltd, Fredericton NB	78/96
				(tanker #12, wfu stored Fredericton 94/95)	
014	TBM-3E	Bu86195	N7229C	Hemet Valley Flying Service, Hemet CA	59/71
				(tanker #E71)	
				crashed dest., Lake Piru CA	30.8.71
063	TBM-3E	Bu86244	N6826C	Sonora Flying Service, Columbia CA	63
				(tanker #C53)	
				John P. Lippott, Salmon ID	.63/66
				Idaho Aircraft Co, Boise ID	69/72
			CF-AGN	Conair Aviation Ltd, Abbotsford BC	4.72/76
				(tanker #607)	
			C-FAGN	Forest Protection Ltd, Fredericton NB	78/84
				struck-off reg.	11.87
099 •	TBM-3E	**Bu86280**	N7219C	Christopher G. Davis, Kansas City KS	63
				Thurman E. Yates, Gila NM (tanker #C50)	.63/66
				P. F. Flickinger, Bayard NM (tanker #C50)	69/70
				Maples Aviation Co, Vichy MO	72
			N86280	Thomas L. Wofford, Weiner AR	12.76/88
				Ron Maggard/Ronson Machine & Manufacturing Co,	
				Independence MO	89/91
				Combat Air Museum, Topeka KS: loan	90
				Cavanaugh Flight Museum,	
				Dallas-Addison TX	1.91/96
				(rest. San Marcos TX 91/92 "USMC 86280/54",	
				del. to Addison 12.12.92)	
134	TBM-3S	Bu53072		(to RCN as 53072): BOC 19.8.52: SOC	5.7.60
	AS Mk. 3M		CF-KCH	Skyway Air Services, Langley BC	.60/69
				Conair Aviation Ltd, Abbotsford BC	.69/74
				(tanker #606)	
				crashed : struck-off reg.	24.7.74
140	TBM-3S	Bu53078		(to RCN as 53078): BOC 29.5.52: SOC	14.5.58
	AS Mk. 3		CF-JJC	reg.	.58
			N68683	Ivan Gustin, Lewiston ID	66
				Hillcrest Aircraft Co, Lewiston ID	69/70
				G & M Investments, Lewiston ID	72

			CF-BEF	Miramichi Air Service Ltd, Douglastown NB	75
				(USCR quotes id. 6125) crashed	20.5.75
3181 •	TBM-3S AS Mk. 3M	Bu53119		(to RCN as 53119): BOC 29.5.52: SOC	9.5.58
				Simsbury Flying Service, Simsbury CT	
			N33BM	Baron Volkmer, Dallas TX	70/73
				Wilson C. Edwards, Big Spring TX	74/96
3201 •	TBM-3S AS Mk. 3	**Bu53139**		(to RCN as 53139): BOC 27.9.50: SOC	30.1.58
			CF-IMN	Skyway Air Services, Langley BC	61/69
				Conair Aviation Ltd, Abbotsford BC (tanker #605)	.69/76
				Forest Protection Ltd, Fredericton NB (tanker #5, wfu stored Fredericton 90/95)	78/94
				Jeff Thomas/Vintage Wings, Seattle WA (trucked dism. ex Fredericton 7.94)	7.94
			N6VC	Ozark Management Inc, Rolla MO	2.95
3262 •	TBM-3S AS Mk. 3	**Bu53200**		(to RCN as 53200): BOC 29.5.52: SOC	17.1.58
			N9010C	Hillcrest Aircraft, Lewiston ID (tanker #D6)	63/66
				Johnson Flying Service, Missoula MT (tanker #A13)	69/72
			C-GLEL	Evergreen Air Service Ltd, Roxboro QUE	4.75
				Forest Protection Ltd, Fredericton NB (tanker #13)	78/96
3271	TBM-3E	Bu53209	N7960C	Major Oil Corp, Tucson AZ	63
				Norman M. Poteet, Tucson AZ	.63/64
				Sonora Aviation Inc, Tucson/Carson City NV	66/69
			CF-AXS	Norfolk Aerial Spraying Ltd, Simcoe NB	6.71/79
				crashed near Serogle NB	15.6.79
3291 •	TBM-3	**Bu53229**	N7236C	Georgia Forestry Commission, Macon GA	.63/69
				MARC, Chino CA (stored MARC compound, Chino CA 87)	87/92
3303	TBM-3S AS Mk. 3	Bu53241		(to RCN as 53241): BOC 15.7.50: SOC	10.1.58
			CF-IMM	Skyway Air Services, Langley BC	61/69
				Conair Aviation Ltd, Abbotsford BC (tanker #604)	.69/73
				crashed spraying, Sussex NB	14.5.73
3318	TBM-3	Bu53256	N9592C	Aerial Applicators, Salt Lake City UT (tanker #D19)	63/70
			CF-ZYB	Hicks & Lawrence Ltd, Tillsonburg ONT	6.71
				crashed	1.6.71
3369	TBM-3	Bu53307	N9078Z	Daro Inc, San Clemente CA (tanker #E98)	63/70
				Sis-Q Flying Service, Santa Rosa CA (tanker #E26)	.70/72
			C-GLEI	Evergreen Air Service Ltd, Roxboro QUE	4.75
				crashed	8.5.75
3381 •	TBM-3 TBM-3R	**Bu53319**		USN BOC 17.5.45: stored 24.9.54: SOC	8.56
			N3966A	Nevadair, Tonopah NV	27.6.58/70
				Charlie T. Jensen, Tonopah NV	72/77
				stored unconv. ("RB-319"), Sacramento CA	58/80
				Aero Union Corp, Chico CA (del. Sacramento-Chico CA .81, stored unconv.)	.80/87
				Anthony Haig-Thomas, North Weald UK	5.87/91
				TBM Aircraft Inc, Holmdell NJ (shipped to UK 1.89, ff Ipswich 25.1.89)	88/91
			G-BTDP	Anthony Haig-Thomas, North Weald (flies as "53319/RB319")	5.2.91/95

3396	TBM-3S	Bu53334		(to RCN as 53334): BOC 17.10.50: SOC	22.4.58
	AS Mk. 3		CF-KPJ		
			N68663	Klamath Aircraft Inc, Klamath Falls OR	63/66
				Sis-Q Flying Service, Santa Rosa CA	69/72
				(tanker #E25)	
			C-GLEG	Evergreen Air Service Ltd, Roxboro QUE	4.75
				crashed	4.7.75
3399 •	TBM-3S	**Bu53337**		(to RCN as 53337): BOC 29.5.52: SOC	10.1.58
	AS Mk. 3		CF-IMI	Skyway Air Services, Langley BC	61/69
				Conair Aviation Ltd, Abbotsford BC	.69/76
				(tanker #601)	
				Forest Protection Ltd, Fredericton NB	78/94
				(tanker #1: wfu, open storage Fredericton 84/94)	
				Jeff Thomas/Vintage Wings, Seattle WA	.94
			N337GA	Warren Al Pietsch, Minot ND	9.94/96
				(del. to ND ex Fredericton 3.11.94)	
3413	TBM-3	Bu53351	N7411C	Harold Parkhurst, Managua, Nicaragua	63/70
			CF-ZTA	Miramichi Air Service Ltd, Douglastown NB	6.71/72
				crashed	21.7.74
3415 •	TBM-3	**Bu53353**	**N5264V**	Georgia Forestry Commission, Macon GA	.63/69
				Harry S. Doan, Daytona Beach FL	84/88
				Wiley C. Sanders, Troy AL	12.88/96
				(flies as "USN WS53")	
3465 •	TBM-3E	**Bu53403**		NAS Norfolk VA: stored	65
				USNAM, NAS Pensacola FL	.68/94
				Admiral Nimitz State Historical Park,	
				Fredericksburg TX: loan, displ.	93/96
3482 •	TBM-3S	**Bu53420**		(to RCN as 53420): BOC 19.10.50: SOC	5.7.60
	AS Mk. 3M		CF-KCM	Skyway Air Services, Langley BC	61/69
				Conair Aviation Ltd, Abbotsford BC	.69/76
				(tanker #616)	
			C-FKCM	Forest Protection Ltd, Fredericton NB	78/93
				(tanker #16, wfu stored Fredericton 90/94)	
				sold to USA: struck-off reg.	12.93
				Jeff Thomas/Vintage Wings, Seattle WA	.93/94
			N420GP	Vintage Wings, Anchorage AK	2.94/96
				(trucked dism. ex Fredericton 7.94)	
3516 •	TBM-3E	**Bu53454**	**N7030C**	Tom White/Idaho Air Tankers Inc, Boise ID	63/64
				(tanker #D13)	
				Reeder Flying Service, Twin Falls ID	66/84
				(tanker #13)	
				Gary Wolverton, Twin Falls ID	84
				Southeastern Aircraft Inc, Live Oak FL	86/87
				MARC, Chino CA	90
				USNAM, NAS Corpus Christi TX	.87/92
				(displ. as "53454/Gipsy III", later "X-2")	
				(rep at Dayton Air Show "N7030C Bu53454")	7.95
3541 •	TBM-3E	Bu53479	N9595C	reg.	.57
				Cisco Aircraft Inc, Lancaster CA	62/64
				(tanker #E67)	
				D & D Aero Spray, Rantoul KS	66/77
				sale rep., USCR	84/96
3551	TBM-3S	Bu53489		(to RCN as 53489): BOC 28.7.50: SOC	30.1.58
	AS Mk. 3		N6580D	Simsbury Flying Service, Simsbury CT	
				(derelict unconv., Simsbury CT 72/75)	
				Leonard Tanner, Barre MA	88/89

				Corwin H. Meyer Aviation Assoc, Ocala FL	.89/90
				(hulk moved to FL .89 for rest. to fly)	
				destroyed by fire	
3554	TBM-3	Bu53492	N9083Z	Riverside Aircraft Co, Riverside CA	62/64
				(tanker #E63)	
				Aero Union Corp, Chico CA (tanker #E28)	66/72
				crashed, Chester CA	2.8.73
3565 •	TBM-3S	**Bu53503**		(to RCN as 53503): BOC 30.6.50: SOC	1.1.58
	AS Mk. 3		N6583D	Simsbury Flying Service, Simsbury CT	63/70
				Joe E. Jones/CAF, Harlingen TX	.70/72
			N53503	Robert L. Wick/CAF, Harlingen TX	13.1.72/91
				Confederate Air Force, Midland TX	9.91/96
				(flies as "USN 82")	
3584 •	TBM-3E	Bu53522	N7410C	Stencel Aero Engineering, Ashville NC	63/72
				John J. Stokes, San Marcos TX	77/79
				Howard E. Pardue, Breckenridge TX	.79/80
			N88HP	Howard E. Pardue, Breckenridge TX	10.80/88
				John VanAndel/Flying Dutchman Marine Corp,	
				Wilmington DE (flies as "USN 88")	8.89/96
3616	TBM-3S	Bu53554		(to RCN as 53554): BOC 19.8.52: SOC	5.7.60
	AS Mk. 3M		CF-KCF	Skyway Air Services, Langley BC	61/69
				Conair Aviation Ltd, Abbotsford BC	.69/71
				(tanker #603)	
				crashed Winfield BC	8.8.71
3637 •	TBM-3E	Bu53575	**N6447C**	Sonora Aviation, Tucson AZ/Carson City NV	63/69
				(tanker #C47)	
				Capitol Aire Inc, Carson City NV	72
				Craig Aero Service, Buttonwillow CA	77
				Stewart Aviation Inc, Moses Lake WA	84
				Northwest Warbirds Inc, Kimberley ID	86/87
				Jack A. Erickson, Central Point OR	8.88/96
3654	TBM-3E	Bu53592	N5168V	Hemet Valley Flying Service, Hemet CA	63/72
				(tanker #E68)	
			C-GFPQ	Evergreen Air Service Ltd, Roxboro, QUE	6.76
				Forest Protection Ltd, Fredericton NB	78/82
				crashed near Edmunston NB	8.6.82
3655 •	TBM-3E	Bu53593	N6822C	TBM Inc, Tulare CA	.58/82
			N5567A	stored unconv. "USN/New York/141/N5567A",	
				Tulare-Sequoia CA	70/82
			N6822C	USNAM, NAS Pensacola FL : del. ex Sequoia	9.82/94
				(listed as both registrations: USCR 66/84)	
3669	TBM-3	Bu53607	N8398H	Cisco Aircraft Inc, Lancaster CA	63
				Aerial Applicators, Salt Lake City UT	64/69
				(tanker #D20)	
			CF-ZYC	Hicks & Lawrence Ltd, Tillsonburg ONT	5.71/75
				crashed	20.5.75
3672 •	TBM-3S	**Bu53610**		(to RCN as 53610): BOC 22.7.50: SOC	30.1.58
	AS Mk. 3		CF-IMR	Wheeler Airlines, St Jean QUE	6.3.58/65
				Wheeler Northland Airways Ltd, St Jean QUE	66/70
				Evergreen Air Service Ltd, Roxboro QUE	72/75
			C-FIMR	Forest Protection Ltd, Fredericton NB	78/96
				(tanker #23)	
3694	TBM-3S	Bu53632		(to RCN as 53632): BOC 25.7.50: SOC	5.7.60
	AS Mk. 3M		CF-MXN	Canadian Colleries Resources, Vancouver BC	65/66

				Skyway Air Services, Langley BC	69
				Conair Aviation Ltd, Abbotsford BC	.69/75
				(tanker #619)	
				crashed into river, Kamloops BC	31.7.71
				crashed, fire bombing, Moyie Lake BC	18.8.73
700 •	TBM-3S	**Bu53638**		(to RCN as 53638): BOC 19.8.52: SOC	5.7.60
	AS Mk. 3		**CF-KCL**	Skyway Air Services, Langley BC	61/69
				Conair Aviation Ltd, Abbotsford BC	.69/76
				(tanker #609)	
				Forest Protection Ltd, Fredericton NB	.77/78
				crashed Oromocto Lake NB	29.5.78
				Allan Rubin/International Vintage Aircraft, Hamilton ONT	86/96
				(under rest. to fly, Markham ONT 92/93)	
759	TBM-3S	Bu53697		(to RCN as 53697): BOC 25.7.52: SOC	5.7.60
	AS Mk. 3		N9711Z	Sierra Aviation, Porterville CA	.62/63
				(tanker #E46)	
				Wen Inc, Porterville CA (tanker #E46)	.63/64
				P & B Aviation, Red Bluff CA	66
				Sis-Q Flying Service, Montague CA	69
				(tanker #33)	
			C-GLEH	Evergreen Air Service Ltd, Roxboro QUE	4.75
				Forest Protection Ltd, Fredericton NB	78/86
				(tanker #11)	
				crashed landing, Brockway NB	18.5.84
788 •	TBM-3E	**Bu53726**	N7076C	Marsh Aviation Co, Litchfield Park AZ	63/64
				Reeder Flying Service, Twin Falls ID	66/84
				(tanker #56)	
				Gary Wolverton, Twin Falls ID	84
				Northwest Warbirds Inc, Twin Falls ID	87/88
				USMC Museum, MCAS El Toro CA	88/94
				(displ. as "Marines 53726")	
789	TBM-3	Bu53727	N9082Z	Hemet Valley Flying Service, Hemet CA	63/72
				(tanker #E73)	
				crashed firebombing, Bear Mountain CA	28.7.70
794	TBM-3S	Bu53732		(to RCN as 53732): BOC 8.6.50: SOC	5.7.60
	AS Mk. 3		CF-KCN	Skyway Air Services, Langley BC	61/69
				Conair Aviation Ltd, Abbotsford BC	.69/72
				(tanker #617)	
				crashed Angus Home Lake BC	27.8.72
322	TBM-3S	Bu53760		(to RCN as 53760): BOC 16.6.52: SOC	30.1.58
	AS Mk. 3		N6581D	Simsbury Flying Service, Simsbury CT	63/77
				Richard Foote/Professional Aircraft Sales Co, Willimantic CT & New Smyrna Beach FL	84/88
				crashed dest., Danielson CT	6.88
830 •	TBM-3U	**Bu53768**	N103Z	U. S. Forestry Service, Davis CA	.56/64
				(wfu, stored 58/64)	
			N10361	Seeley Flying Service, Newcastle WY	66/69
				(tanker #B18)	
				Air Tankers Inc, Casper WY	
1			C-GLDX	Norfolk Aerial Spraying Ltd, Simcoe NB	5.75/79
			N683G	Bob Odegaard/Odegaard Aviation, Kindred ND	9.85/96
				(flies as "53768/63")	
337	TBM-3E	Bu53775	N7028C	Hillcrest Aircraft Co, Lewiston ID	63/72
				(tanker #D7)	
			CF-ZTR	Miramichi Air Service Ltd, Douglastown NB	.71/75

3846	TBM-3	Bu53784	N9590C	Dennis G. Smilanich/Idaho Aircraft, Boise ID	63/72
				(tanker #D1)	
			CF-AGL	Conair Aviation Ltd, Abbotsford BC	72
				(stored, not operated by Conair)	
3847 •	TBM-3E	**Bu53785**	**N7075C**	Marsh Aviation Co, Litchfield Park AZ	63/64
				Reeder Flying Service, Twin Falls ID	66/77
				(tanker #55)	
				Dwight Reimer, Shafter CA	79/80
				(flew as *My Assam Dragon*)	
				Gordon Plaskett, King City CA	82
				Stephen Grey, Geneva, Switzerland: not del.	.82
				Robert J. Pond/Planes of Fame East,	
				Minneapolis-Flying Cloud MN	83/96
				(flies as "Royal Navy JR456/RP")	
3849 •	TBM-3E	**Bu53787**	N3969A	Edgar L. Thorsrud, Missoula MT	63/72
				Johnson Flying Service, Missoula MT	72
				(tanker #A21)	
			C-GFPT	Evergreen Air Service Ltd, Roxboro QUE	5.76
				Forest Protection Ltd, Fredericton NB	78/95
				(tanker #10, wfu stored Fredericton 94/95)	
3866 •	TBM-3S	**Bu53804**		(to RCN as 53804): BOC 19.8.52: SOC	5.7.60
	AS Mk. 3M		N9710Z	Columbia Flying Service, Hollister CA	63/64
				(tanker #E79)	
				George C. Abell, Topanga CA (tanker #E79) 66/69	
				Yesterdays Air Force,	
				Chino CA	.72/90
				USNAM, NAS Corpus Christi TX	90
				USNAM, USS Lexington, Corpus Christi TX	93/94
				(displ. on board carrier as "53804/X2")	
3880 •	TBM-3S	**Bu53818**		(to RCN as 53818): BOC 16.6.52: SOC	10.1.58
	AS Mk. 3		N9187Z	Columbia Flying Service, Hollister CA	63/64
				(tanker #E89)	
				Ewing Aviation Co, Sepulveda CA	63
				George C. Abell, Topanga CA	66/69
				Ralph M. Ponte, Grass Valley CA	75
				Leo Conavan, Fort Worth TX	77
			N93818	Leo Conavan, Fort Worth TX	4.79
				Wilbert R. Porter, Sacramento CA	84/92
				Wally Fisk/Amjet Aircraft Corp,	
				St Paul-Anoka County MN (flies as "USN 17")	9.93/96
3890 •	TBM-3S	**Bu53828**		(to RCN as 53828): BOC 16.6.52: SOC	17.1.58
	AS Mk. 3		N9014C	Vincent S. Buraas, Northwood ND	63/69
				(stored as derelict hulk, Northwood ID 74)	
				Minnesota Air & Space Museum, St Paul MN	87
			N28FB	Edwin E. Forsberg, Wilmington CA	1.89/92
				Carl W. Scholl, Chino CA	6.92/95
				(long-term rest. project)	
3891 •	TBM-3E	**Bu53829**	N9591C	Pete Fountain, Moscow ID	63/64
				Sonora Aviation, Carson City NV	66/69
				(tanker #55)	
			CF-AYG	Norfolk Aerial Spraying Ltd, Simcoe NB	7.71/79
			N293E	Odegaard Aviation, Kindred ND	9.85/88
				Tri State Warbird Collection,	
				Wahpeton ND	1.91/96
3897 •	TBM-3	Bu53835	N3967A	Nevadair, Tonopah NV	63/69
	TBM-3U			Charlie T. Jensen, Tonopah NV	72
				Maynard Lund, Ritzville WA	.78

				Skarda Flying Service, Hazen AR	1.84/96
				(flies as "USN 53835/GS-41")	
3904 •	TBM-3E	**Bu53842**	N7025C	Chris D. Stoltzfus & Assoc., Coatesville PA	63/64
			N603	New York Conservation Dept., Albany NY	66/75
			N60393	State of New York, Albany NY	.75/87
				Patriots Point Naval & Maritime Museum, Mt Pleasant SC	87/96
				(displ. on carrier USS Yorktown as "USN X-2")	
3919 •	TBM-3E	Bu53857	N7017C	Central Air Service, Lewistown MT	63/72
			C-GFPM	Evergreen Air Services Ltd, Roxboro QUE	5.76
				Forest Protection Ltd, Fredericton NB	78/96
				(tanker #21)	
3920 •	TBM-3E	**Bu53858**	N3357G	Hemet Valley Flying Service, Hemet CA	63/72
				(tanker #E72)	
			C-GFPR	Evergreen Air Service Ltd, Roxboro QUE	5.76
				Forest Protection Ltd, Fredericton NB	78/96
				(tanker #4,wfu stored Fredericton 94/95)	
3976 •	TBM-3E	**Bu53914**	N7029C	John E. Orahood, Rocky Ford CO	63
				Aerial Applicators, Salt Lake City UT	.63/72
				(tanker #D16)	
			CF-BQS	Hicks & Lawrence Ltd, Tillsonburg ONT	.72
				crashed in forest, Maine: abandoned at site	19.5.72
			N7029C	Rhode Island Aviation Heritage Association/ Quonset Air Museum, North Kingstown RI	3.91/94
				(recov. to NAS Quonset Point by helicopter 11.91, planned rest. to fly)	
				(USCR quotes id. as 6961)	
4015 •	TBM-3E	**Bu91110**	N6827C	TBM Inc, Tulare CA (tanker #E58)	63/72
				Hillcrest Aircraft, Lewiston ID	77/78
				Paramount Leasing Corp, Bakersfield CA	84
				Gro Pro Corp, Oklahoma City OK	86/88
				Merlin Aire Ltd, King City CA	88/92
				op: Old Flying Machine Co, Duxford	.88/92
				(shipped to UK, arr. 12.5.88; flew as "USN/X-2")	
				Alpine Fighter Collection, Wanaka NZ	.92
				(del. Duxford-Ipswich 1.10.92, shipped to NZ)	
			ZK-TBM	Alpine Deer Group, Wanaka	11.92/95
				(flies as "RNZAF NZ2518")	
4064	TBM-3	Bu91159	N3249G	Johnson Flying Service, Missoula MT	63/69
				(tanker #A14)	
			C-GLEN	Evergreen Air Service Ltd, Roxboro QUE	4.75
4076 •	TBM-3U	**Bu91171**	N107Z	U. S. Forestry Service, Davis CA	.56/59
			N7858C		8.59
				Parsons Airpark Inc, Carpinteria CA	63/64
				T. A. Underwood, Buckeye AZ	.64
				Aerial Applicators Inc, Salt Lake City UT	66/72
				(tanker #D17)	
			CF-BQT	Ag Air Inc, Dawson Creek BC	5.72
				Hicks & Lawrence Ltd, Tillsonburg ONT	75/79
			C-FBQT	Ag Air Inc, Dawson Creek BC	88
4093 •	TBM-3U	**Bu91188**	N108Z	U. S. Forestry Service, Davis CA	.56/64
				(tanker #08)	
			N108Q	Georgia Forestry Commission, Macon GA	66/69
				(tanker #2)	
				Dale F. Carter, Elsa TX	72
				George W. Clapp, Allegany NY	84
				Lance Aircraft Supply Inc, Dallas TX	86/88

				Georgia Historical Aviation Museum,	
				Stone Mountain GA (displ. in USN sc.)	89/96
4100 •	TBM-3R	Bu91195		(to JMSDF as 23...)	
				Tateyama AB, Japan: displ.	68/91
4169 •	TBM-3	**Bu91264**		NAF El Centro CA: ground handling airframe	50/58
			N7835C	The Air Museum, Claremont CA	.58/69
				later Ontario CA: static displ., derelict by	73
				Planes of Fame, Chino CA	77/96
				(rest. Chino CA, ff .76 as "USN Bu7154")	
				(USCR quotes id. as 7154)	
4194 •	TBM-3	Bu91289	N7833C	Hemet Valley Flying Service, Hemet CA	60/72
				(tanker #E56, #E74)	
			C-GFPN	Evergreen Air Service Ltd, Roxboro QUE	5.76
				Forest Protection Ltd, Fredericton NB	81/95
				(tanker #17, wfu stored Fredericton NB 94/95)	
4293 •	TBM-3E	**Bu91388**	N9564Z	Cisco Aircraft Inc, Lancaster CA	63
				Aircraft Specialties Inc, Mesa AZ	.63
				(tanker #C34)	
				Desert Aviation Service, Phoenix AZ: sprayer	.63/66
				Ontario Flight Service, Ontario OR	69
				crashed nr John Day OR: wreck abandoned	c71
				derelict hulk, Ironside OR	73/78
				Ralph M. Ponte, Grass Valley CA	12.83/88
				Taylor Energy Co, New Orleans LA	6.90/96
4331 •	TBM-3S	**Bu91426**		(to RCN as 91426): BOC 19.8.52: SOC	5.7.60
	AS Mk. 3M		CF-MUE	Skyway Air Services, Langley BC	61/69
				Conair Aviation Ltd, Abbotsford BC	.69/75
				(tanker #618)	
				Forest Protection Ltd, Fredericton NB	78/96
				(tanker #18, wfu stored Fredericton 94/95)	
4341 •	TBM-3	Bu91436	N9569Z	Cisco Aircraft Inc, Lancaster CA	63
				Desert Aviation Service, Phoenix AZ	.63/70
				Aircraft Specialties Inc, Mesa AZ: hulk	81
				(hulk stored Mesa AZ 81, USN sc., "Buehner")	
				Tom Reilly Vintage Aircraft, Kissimmee FL	89/96
				(hulk at Kissimmee FL, pending rest. 90)	
4355	TBM-3E	Bu91450	N7239C	Riverside Aircraft Co, Riverside CA	63/64
				Aero Union Corp, Chico CA	66/70
				David C. Tallichet/Yesterdays Air Force,	
				Chino CA	.72
			C-GCWG	Canadian Warplane Heritage, Hamilton ONT	6.78/92
				(flew as "RCN 91450/VG-ABG")	
				dest. by hangar fire, Hamilton ONT	15.2.93
				(USCR & CCR quote id. as 7340)	
4358 •	TBM-3E	Bu91453	N4170A	Reeder Flying Service, Twin Falls ID	63/77
				(tanker #D10; later #10)	
				Gary M. Wolverton, Kimberly ID	84
				James R. Williams, O'Brien OR/Berkeley CA	11.84/95
				(flies as "US Marines 91453/15")	
4426 •	TBM-3E	**Bu91521**	**N4171A**	Reeder Flying Service, Twin Falls ID	63/72
				(tanker #D11; later #11)	
				Louis Deterding, Havre MT	77
				Donald J. von Siegel, Parkin AR	84/87
				Corwin H. Meyer Aviation Assoc., Ocala FL	88/92
				Steve M. Hay, Lansing IL/Syracuse IN	.94/95

4470	TBM-3	Bu91565	N4168A	Reeder Flying Service, Twin Falls ID	63/72
				(tanker #D8; later #8)	
4491 •	TBM-3E	**Bu91586**	**N9433Z**	Sonora Flying Service, Columbia CA	63/64
				(tanker #C56)	
				Sonora Aviation Inc, Tucson/Carson City NV	66/69
				Capitol Aire Inc, Carson City NV	70/72
				(tanker #56)	
				Craig Aero Service, Buttonwillow CA	77
				Stewart Aviation, Moses Lake WA	84
				Northwest Warbirds Inc, Kimberly ID	86
				Friends for Long Is. Heritage, Muttontown NY	3.87/95
				(static rest. by Grumman, Bethpage NY 88/90)	
				Cradle of Aviation Museum, Garden City NY	91/95
				(displ. as VMTB-624 "113")	
4503 •	TBM-3E	**Bu91598**	**N9548Z**	Rector Air Service, Pacific Palisades CA	62/66
				(tanker #E76)	
				Hemet Valley Flying Service, Hemet CA	69/70
				(tanker #E76)	
				Reeder Flying Service, Twin Falls ID	71
				crashed Tuolomne CA	18.8.73
				(stored damaged, Stockton CA 74)	
				Ralph M. Ponte, Cedar Ridge CA, rebuilt	.76/84
				Weeks Air Museum,Tamiami FL	5.84/95
				(flew as USN "X-2")	
				dam. Tamiami, Hurricane Andrew	24.8.92
4542	TBM-3	Bu91637	N10164	Chris D. Stoltzfus & Assoc, Coatesville PA	59/70
				sale rep., USCR (probably bu 1960s)	72/92
4569 •	TBM-3E	Bu91664	**N9651C**	Cal-Nat Airways Inc, Grass Valley CA	62/70
				(tanker #E57)	
				USNAM, NAS Cecil Field FL	93/94
4619 •	TBM-3E	Bu91714	**N9429Z**	Reeder Flying Service, Twin Falls ID	62/84
				(tanker #E51, later #D12 ,#57,#12)	
				Charles T. Reeder, Twin Falls ID	88/91
				Jack S. Miller, Buchanan TN	6.91/96
4631 •	TBM-3E	Bu91726	**N5260V**	Riverside Aircraft Co, Riverside CA	62/64
				(tanker #E65)	
				Aero Union Corp, Chico CA	66/69
				Capitol Aire Inc, Carson City NV	72
				Bernard Hinman, Liberal KS	77
				Henry Oliver III, Santa Fe NM	84/86
				(rest. by Terry Morrison & James Seals,	
				Los Lunas NM as "USN 91726/32NE")	
				Ridge Grande Contract Furnishing,	
				Albuquerque NM	87/88
				Evergreen Ventures Inc/	
				Evergreen Heritage Collection, Marana AZ	2.89/95
				(flies as "91726/32")	
4638 •	TBM-3E	**Bu91733**	**N9590Z**	Cisco Aircraft Inc, Lancaster CA	62/63
				(tanker #E81)	
				Desert Aviation Service, Phoenix AZ	.63/64
				Aircraft Specialties Inc, Mesa AZ	66/77
				(tanker #C25)	
				Globe Air, Mesa AZ	4.81/84
				Collings Foundation, Stowe MA	5.86/96
4646 •	TBM-3U	**Bu91741**	**N6829C**	TBM Inc, Tulare CA	63/64
				Dan Agron/Ag Air International, Dos Palos CA	66/70

c/n	type	serial	reg	history	date
				op: Marom Ltd, Herzelia, Israel: del.	12.64/74
				(del. via Prestwick UK 15.12.64)	
				(open storage, derelict, Herzelia, Israel 74)	
				Israeli AF Museum, Hatzerim AB : stored	89/95
-	TBM-3	-	CF-ZTS	Miramichi Air Service Ltd, Douglastown NB	.71/72
				(id. quoted as 6822)	
- •	TBM-3E	-	**N4169A**	Reeder Flying Service, Twin Falls ID	63/81
				(tanker # 63; later #9)	
				Gary M. Wolverton, Kimberly ID	3.81/95
				(open storage unrest., Twin Falls ID 80/93)	
				(USCR quotes id. as 5653)	
- •	TBM-3E	-	**N4172A**	Aerial Applicators, Salt Lake City UT	63/72
				(tanker #D18)	
				Louis Deterding, Havre MT	77
				(stored derelict, Salt Lake City UT 77)	
				Tom Reilly Vintage Aircraft, Kissimmee FL	2.80/95
				(stored dism., Kissimmee FL 88/93)	
				(USCR quotes id. as 6810)	
-	TBM-3	-	**N4173A**	Hillcrest Aircraft Co, Lewiston ID	63/72
				(USCR quotes id. as 5708)	
-	TBM-3S2	-		(to JMSDF as 2344)	
				Kure AB, Hiroshima, Japan: displ.	68/72
-	TBM-3S2	-		(to JMSDF as 2347)	
				Shimofusa AB, Japan: displ.	68/72
-	TBF-1	-		recov. from Lake Michigan	c77
				Indiana Museum of Military History,	
				Indianapolis IN	88/90

GRUMMAN HU-16 ALBATROSS/CARIBBEAN

c/n	type	serial	reg	history	date
- •	SA-16A	**48-0607**		(to Philippine AF as 48607)	
	HU-16A			Philippine AF Museum, Villamore AB, Manila	.93
G32 •	SA-16A	**49-0074**		(to FA Brasileira as 6530)	.59
	HU-16A		PP-ZAS	Lindalvo de Carta	.91
			N97HU	Paragon Ranch Inc, Broomfield CO	4.10.94/96
G33 •	SA-16A	**49-0075**		(to FA Brasileira as 6531)	.59
	HU-16A		PP-ZAT	Lindalvo de Carta	.91
				noted Campo de Marte AB, Brazil	5.91
			N98HU	Paragon Ranch Inc, Broomfield CO	4.10.94/96
				(rest. Brazil 94 ex open storage, for del. USA)	
G37 •	SA-16A	**49-0079**		(to FA Brasileira as 6534)	.59
	HU-16A			Museu Aerospacial da Forca Aera Brasileira	85
				(displ. as "FAB 6529")	
G40 •	SA-16A	**49-0082**		(to FA Brasileira as 6538)	.59
	HU-16A		PP-ZAX	Lindalvo de Carta	.91
				(noted, Campo de Marte AB, Brazil 5.91)	
			N99HU	Paragon Ranch Inc, Broomfield CO	4.10.94/96
G53	SA-16A	49-0095		(to WGN as RE+507, 60+02)	
	HU-16B		N13047	Consolidated Aero Export Corp., Tucson AZ	6.72
G54	SA-16A	49-0096		(to WGN as RE+508, 60+03)	
	HU-16B		N13046	Consolidated Aero Export Corp., Tucson AZ	6.72/75

				(noted stored, Tucson AZ 9.75)	
G55 •	SA-16A HU-16B	**49-0097**		(to FA Chile as 566): del.	.58
				Confederate Air Force, Harlingen TX	.79
			N8064N	Resorts International Inc, Miami FL	10.79
				(stored, FAC camouflage, Opa Locka FL 81)	
				Dusemses Company Inc, Miami FL	84/87
				Dennis G. Buehn, Reno NV	9.87
				Air and Sea Service Inc, Miami FL	6.88/89
			N16HU (2	Westernair Inc, Albuquerque NM	6.89/90
			XB-FKX	Eloy S. Vallina, Chihuahua, Mexico	.90/93
				Rio Grande Yacht	
			N16HU (2	Westernair Inc, Albuquerque NM	7.95/96
G57 •	SA-16A HU-16D	**49-0099**		(to FA Chile as 567) : del.	.58/79
			N8497J	Resorts International Inc, Miami FL	10.80
				Grumman Aerospace Corp, St Augustine FL	84/88
				(stored St Augustine FL 88)	
				Island Flying Boats Inc, Miami FL	4.89
				Air Crane Inc, Opa Locka FL	7.89/90
				Thomas A. Quinn, Tulsa OK	92/96
G61 •	SA-16A HU-16A	**50-0174**		(to Italian AF/AMI as MM50-174) BOC	26.3.58
				Biella AB: displ.	10.79
G64 •	SA-16A HU-16A	**50-0177**		(to Italian AF/AMI as MM50-177) BOC	8.4.58
				Comune di Lampedusa: displ.	11.79
G66 •	SA-16A HU-16A	**50-0179**		(to Italian AF/AMI as MM50-179) BOC	26.3.58
				Italian AF Museum, Vigna di Valle AB: del	14.5.79/88
G69 •	SA-16A HU-16A	**50-0182**		(to Italian AF/AMI as MM50-182) BOC	13.6.58
				last flight 11.11.78; displ. Guidonia	11.78
G77 •	SA-16A HU-16B Conroy Turbo Albatross	**51-0004**	N459U	FAA, Atlantic City NJ	63/69
				Conroy Aircraft Corp, Santa Barbara CA	9.69/70
			N16CA	Conroy Aircraft Corp, Santa Barbara CA	2.70
				(conv. RR Darts, Santa Barbara CA ff 25.2.70)	
				Conroy Albatross Inc, Salisbury MD	77/95
				(open storage Salisbury MD 74/92)	
G79 •	SA-16A SA-16B HU-16B	**51-0006**		USAFM, Offutt AFB NE	74/94
G87 •	SA-16A HU-16D	**51-0014**		(to FA Chile as 569)	
			N8497N	Resorts International Inc, Miami FL	10.80
				Grumman Aerospace Corp, St Augustine FL	10.80/95
				(stored St Augustine FL 88)	
G89 •	SA-16A UF-1G HU-16E	**51-0016**		(to USCG as 1016)	
				Davis Monthan AFB AZ: arr. for storage	9.5.79
				Smithsonian Institute, Washington DC	88
				Davis-Monthan AFB AZ: storage	88
G92	SA-16A HU-16B	**51-0019**		stored unconv., Tucson AZ	73/75
			N5545	Diamond Aero Corp, Orange CA	76/79
				(to Philippine AF as 10019)	c10.78
			RP-R459	Trans Corp, Manila PI	.86/89
				struck-off reg.	.89
G96 •	SA-16A HU-16B	**51-0022**		USAFM, Pima County Air Museum, Tucson AZ	5.71/93
- •	SA-16A	**51-0025**		USAFM: Bradley Air Mus., Windsor Locks CT	73/79

(18B)	HU-16B			badly dam. by tornado at museum	3.10.79
				New England Air Museum, Windsor Locks CT	
			N7141S	Dennis G. Buehn, Carson City NV	4.90/96
- •	SA-16A	**51-0026**		(to USCG as 1026) :	
	UF-1G			Davis Monthan AFB AZ: arr. for storage	2.6.77
	UF-2G			Allied Aircraft Sales Inc, Tucson AZ/ behalf of	HU-16E
				Grumman Aerospace Corp, St Augustine FL	1.12.80
				(stored civil contractor yard DMAFB 88/90)	
			N7027T	Island Flying Boats Inc, Miami FL	2.89/93
				South FL Aviation Investments, Opa Locka FL	3.93/96
				Island Flying Boats Inc, Opa Locka FL	6.95
- •	SA-16A	**51-0030**		(to USCG as 1030)	
	UF-1G			Davis Monthan AFB AZ: arr. for storage	19.4.73
	UF-2G			Allied Aircraft Sales Inc, Tucson AZ/ behalf of	
	HU-16E			Grumman Aerospace Corp, St Augustine FL	3.2.81
			N7027L	Island Flying Boats Inc, Miami FL	2.89/93
				South FL Aviation Investments, Opa Locka FL	3.93/96
				(unconv. in contractors yards DMAFB 88/95)	
- •	SA-16A	**51-0035**		(to Italian AF/AMI as MM51-035) BOC	10.9.65
	HU-16A			Goriza AB: displ. as "15-8"	84
- •	SA-16A	**51-0043**	**N7049D**	Caribbean Flying Boats, Miami FL: reg. res.	11.88/92
	HU-16A			(unconv. in contractors yards DMAFB 88/95)	
G106 •	SA-16A			(to FA Argentina as BS-01)	.61
	SA-16B		**LV-RBJ**	Andes Aviacion: noted Don Torcuato	5.91
				(also re. as c/n G108)	
-	UF-1G	**USCG1243**		Davis Monthan AFB AZ: arr. for storage	1.6.73
	UF-2G			Allied Aircraft Sales Inc, Tucson AZ/ behalf of	
	HU-16E			Grumman Aerospace Corp, St Augustine FL	4.3.81
				reg. candidate	7.11.88
G116 •	UF-1G	**USCG1260**		Davis Monthan AFB AZ: stored	69
	UF-2G		**N4844**	Allied Aircraft Sales Inc, Tucson AZ	73
	HU-16E			Aircraft Surplus Co Inc, Tucson AZ	77
				sale rep., Tucson AZ	84/96
-	UF-1G	**USCG1265**		Davis Monthan AFB AZ: stored	73
	UF-2G			Allied Aircraft Sales Inc, Tucson AZ/ behalf of	
	HU-16E			Grumman Aerospace Corp, St Augustine FL	
				(stored civil contractor yard DMAFB 88)	
			N7027J	Island Flying Boats Inc, Miami FL	4.89/93
				South FL Aviation Investments, Opa Locka FL	3.93/95
				Island Flying Boats Inc, Opa Locka FL	6.95
- •	UF-1G	**USCG1272**		Davis Monthan AFB AZ: arr. for storage	15.12.76
	UF-2G			Allied Aircraft Sales Inc, Tucson AZ/ behalf of	
	HU-16E			Grumman Aerospace Corp, St Augustine FL	1.12.80
				(stored civil contractor yard DMAFB 88)	
			N7027F	Air Crane Inc, Opa Locka FL	1.89
				Island Flying Boats Inc, Miami FL	4.89
				Eugene R. Elzinga, Hollywood FL	9.89/96
- •	UF-1G	**USCG1280**		Davis Monthan AFB AZ: arr. for storage	71
	UF-2G			Consoliadted Aeronautics Corp, Tucson AZ by	73
	HU-16E			USAFM, Kirtland AFB NM	78/96
				(displ. as "USAF 10071")	
				(also rep. as c/n G428: above bel. correct)	
G146 •	SA-16A	**51-0067**	**N3395F**	Robert Bean, Hereford AZ	73/77

	HU-16B			(stored unconv., Tucson AZ 73/76)	
				Antilles Air Boats, St Croix USVI	79/81
				sale rep., Tucson AZ	84
				Lawrence D. Weerts, Tucson AZ	3.88
				Jerry L. Weaver, Carson City NV	6.90/96
G154	SA-16A	**51-0473**	**N6327**	stored unconv., Tucson AZ	73/75
	HU-16B			Aircraft Surplus Co Inc, Tucson AZ	77
				(to Philippine AF as 10473)	c78
G164 •	SA-16A	**51-5282**		USAFM, Wright-Patterson AFB, Dayton OH	74/90
	HU-16B				
G173 •	SA-16A	**51-5291**	N7049C	Caribbean Flying Boats, Miami FL: reg. res.	11.88/92
	HU-16B			Amleco Inc, Tucson AZ	4.94
			N291TC	Amleco Inc, Tucson AZ	7.94
				Western International Aviation, Tucson AZ	94/95
				Amleco Inc, Tucson AZ	5.95
G174 •	SA-16A	**51-5292**	N65135	Robert Bean, Hereford AZ	13.8.75
	HU-16B			Trans American Air Transport, Chicago IL	10.75
			N311MC	Trans American Air Transport, Chicago IL	77/80
			N211MC	Trans American Air Transport, Chicago IL	3.80
				Libardo Camargo, Bogota, Colombia	83
				(abandoned Grand Turk, Turks & Caicos 5.84/88)	
				sale rep., Wilmington DE	84/87
				Albert C. Hansen, Mojave CA	8.88/92
				Barnstormer's Import & Lsg, Scottsdale AZ	6.95
G185 •	SA-16A	**51-5303**		USAFM, Lackland AFB TX: displ.	.68/94
	HU-16B		**N41011**	Darryl Greenamyer/ILOC Corp, Ocala FL	21.7.94
				Ascher Ward, Van Nuys CA	.94/95
				(towed to Kelly AFB 11.8.94 for rest.,	
				dep. Kelly AFB on del. Van Nuys 28.1.95)	
				(noted, Van Nuys, USAF "Rescue/15303" 4.95)	
				Robert F. Carlson, East Walpole MA	7.95
G186 •	SA-16A	**51-5304**		(to Ejercito del Aire as AD.1B-8)	
	HU-16B			Museo del Aire, Cuatro Vientos AB, Madrid	.79/92
				(displ. on pond as "AD.1B-8/51-5304/SAR")	
G194 •	SA-16B	**51-7144**		USAFM, SST Aviation Museum, Kissimmee FL	74/79
	HU-16B			USAFM, Robins AFB GA	85/94
G201	SA-16B	51-7151	N7038	stored Tucson AZ	73/75
	HU-16B			Harlan Cross, Costa Mesa CA	77
				(to Philippine AF as 17151)	.78
G210	SA-16B	51-7160	N3398F	Robert Bean, Hereford AZ	73/84
	HU-16B			(stored unconv., Tucson AZ 73/76)	
				crashed, badly damaged, Tucson AZ	9.3.77
				struck-off USCR	4.85
G211 •	SA-16B	**51-7161**		(to Ejercito del Aire as AN.1B-11)	
	HU-16B		N29850	Westair International Inc, Broomfield CO	16.3.82/84
				(del. Madrid-Shannon 12.8.82, stored 82/85)	
			G-BMDX	Mike Little/Daedalus Aviation Ltd, London	26.9.85
			N23ML	Mike Little, Vancouver BC	15.2.86
				(arr. Guernsey 15.2.86, dep. on del. US 17.8.86)	
			N3JY	Corpcon Business Serv. Inc, Ft. Lauderdale FL	10.6.86/96
G212 •	SA-16B	**51-7162**		(to USN as Bu142428)	
	UF-1L		**N51025**	Grumman International Inc, St Augustine FL	1.88
	HU-16B			Howard W. Selby, Boulder CO	6.1.92/96

G213 •	SA-16B	**51-7163**		Pan American World Airways: leased	69/71
(50B)	HU-16B			(op. Mombassa-Mahe as "0-17163/Pan Am")	
			N70725	reg. candidate	10.77/90
				(open storage, Long Beach CA 84)	
				forced landing, Visalia CA as "0-17163"	.87
				USAFM, Castle AFB CA	.91/93
G214 •	SA-16B	**51-7164**		(to USN as Bu142429)	
	HU-16B		N5160W	Dennis G. Buehn, Reno NV	4.88/89
			N16HD	Lincoln Service Corp, Owensboro KY	10.90
				Vega Corp, Eugene OR	10.90/96
G218 •	SA-16B	**51-7168**		stored unconv., Tucson AZ	73/75
	HU-16B		N3385F	Antilles Air Boats, St Croix USVI	.76/81
	G-111			Flying Boat Inc/Chalks International Airline,	
				Miami FL	3.81/82
			N122FB	Flying Boat Inc, Miami FL	12.82/96
				(open storage Marana AZ 87/94)	
G219 •	SA-16B	**51-7169**		Michigan Military Air Museum, Saginaw MI	73/74
(86B)	HU-16B			museum closed, impounded by USAFM	.74
				BCM Aircraft Inc, Dallas TX	.74
			N24BM	BCM Aircraft Inc, Dallas TX	1.75
				(ferried Saginaw-Tri City to Dallas 26.3.75)	
				Antone Freitas, Lake Park FL	77
				Robert A. Sweetapple, Miami FL	10.84
				Aircraft Specialty Inc, Belle Chasse LA	2.87
				Robert K. Cabos, Keaau HI	7.87/90
				Richard L. Gooding, Broomfield CO	12.90
			N46RG	Richard L. Gooding, Broomfield CO	5.91/92
			N159JR	Fightertown Inc, Miami FL	7.95
G226 •	SA-16B	**51-7176**		Pate Museum of Transportation, Ft Worth TX	74/95
	HU-16B			(displ. as "USCG 7176")	
G228 •	SA-16B	51-7178	N160HV		
	HU-16B		N8988	A. R. Buckner, Albuquerque NM	72
				Westernair of Albuquerque, Albuquerque NM	73/74
			PK-OAH	Airfast Services Indonesia PT, Singapore	7.74/88
				(wfu, open storage Singapore-Seletar 86/88)	
				to fire practice area, Seletar	
G233 •	UF-1	**Bu131890**	**N1359Y**	Allied Aircraft Sales Inc, Tucson AZ	12.6.75
	HU-16C			Westernair of Albuquerque, Albuquerque NM	9.81/95
				(unconv. in contractors yard DMAFB 88)	
- •	UF-1	**Bu131892**		Allied Aircraft Sales Inc, Tucson AZ/behalf of	HU-16C
				Grumman Aerospace Corp, St Augustine FL	17.2.81
			N7141H	R. Simpson, Carson City NV	27.4.90/95
				(unconv. in contractors yards DMAFB 88/95)	
- •	UF-1	**Bu131896**		Allied Aircraft Sales Inc, Tucson AZ/ behalf of	
	HU-16C			Grumman Aerospace Corp, St Augustine FL	3.2.81
				(unconv. in contractor yard DMAFB 88/90)	
				reg. candidate	7.11.88
- •	UF-1	**Bu131904**		Allied Aircraft Sales Inc, Tucson AZ/ behalf of	
	HU-16C			Grumman Aerospace Corp, St Augustine FL	9.3.81
			N7026X	Air Crane Inc, Opa Locka FL	12.88
				Island Flying Boats Inc, Miami FL	4.89/93
				South FL Aviation Investments, Opa Locka FL	3.93
				Big Toe Inc, Incline Village NV	3.94/96
				(unconv. in contractor yards DMAFB 81/95)	

- •	UF-1	**Bu131905**		Allied Aircraft Sales Inc, Tucson AZ/ behalf of	
	HU-16C			Grumman Aerospace Corp, St Augustine FL	11.3.81
			N7026N	Air Crane Inc, Opa Locka FL	11.88
				Island Flying Boats Inc, Miami FL	4.89/93
				South FL Aviation Investments, Opa Locka FL	3.93
				Dennis G. Buehn, Carson City NV	2.95/96
				(unconv. in contractor yards DMAFB 81/95)	
269 •	UF-1	**Bu131906**		Davis Monthan AFB AZ: arr. for storage	8.5.68
	HU-16C			Allied Aircraft Sales Inc, Tucson AZ/ behalf of	
				Grumman Aerospace Corp, St Augustine FL	17.2.81
				(unconv. in contractor yard DMAFB 81/88)	
			N7026J	Air Crane Inc, Opa Locka FL	11.88
				Island Flying Boats Inc, Miami FL	4.89/92
				Richard G. Sugden, Wilson WY	1.93/94
				(rest. Tucson AZ 93/94 ex storage)	
			N3HU	Richard G. Sugden, Wilson WY	11.94/96
- •	UF-1	**Bu131910**		Allied Aircraft Sales Inc, Tucson AZ/ behalf of	
	HU-16C			Grumman Aerospace Corp, St Augustine FL	17.2.81
				(unconv. in contractor yard DMAFB 81/88)	
			N7025J	Air Crane Inc, Opa Locka FL	12.88
				Island Flying Boats Inc, Miami FL	2.89
				Stephen Ritland, Flagstaff AZ	6.89/96
- •	UF-1	**Bu131911**		Allied Aircraft Sales Inc, Tucson AZ/ behalf of	
	HU-16C			Grumman Aerospace Corp, St Augustine FL	9.3.81
			N89LH (1	Lynn C. Hunt, Santa Rosa CA	6.87/88
				(unconv. in contractor yard DMAFB 88)	
			N416C	Lynn C. Hunt, Santa Rosa CA	9.88/96
				(flies as "USN 131911")	
- •	UF-1T	**Bu131916**		Allied Aircraft Sales Inc, Tucson AZ/ behalf of	
	HU-16C			Grumman Aerospace Corp, St Augustine FL	10.3.81
			N916DB	Dennis G. Buehn, Reno NV	7.86/88
				Grumman Aerospace Corp, St Augustine FL	88/89
				(unconv. in contractors yard DMAFB 88)	
				Charles Glen Hyde, Roanoke TX	2.89/93
				Flight Data Inc, Carson City NV	9.93/94
			N55GH	Glen Hyde/Flight Data Inc, Carson City NV	10.94/96
- •	UF-1T	**Bu131917**		Allied Aircraft Sales Inc, Tucson AZ/ behalf of	
	TU-16C			Grumman Aerospace Corp, St Augustine FL	9.3.81
				(stored civil contractor yard DMAFB 88)	
			N7024Z	Air Crane Inc, Opa Locka FL	1.89
				Island Flying Boats Inc, Miami FL	4.89/93
				South FL Aviation Investments, Opa Locka FL	3.93/96
237	SA-16B	**51-7184**		(to USCG as 7184)	
	UF-2G		N7039	noted stored Tucson AZ	.73/75
	HU-16E			Aircraft Surplus Co Inc, Tucson AZ	77
				(to Philippine AF as 17184)	2.78
- •	SA-16B	**51-7186**		Davis Monthan AFB: stored	68
6B)	HU-16B			USAFM, Confederate Air Force, Harlingen TX	72/79
			N4478E	Wilkie Cameron, Lubbock TX	15.9.83/84
				Ada Aircraft Museum, Frederick OK	6.84/88
				Mid-America Air Museum, Liberal KS	.88/94
				Wally Fisk/Amjet Aircraft Corp, St Paul MN	4.95
244 •	SA-16B	**51-7187**	N48318	Robert Bean, Hereford AZ	3.11.76/77
	HU-16B			Robert Bean, Tucson AZ	84
			ZP-TWV	noted at Fort Lauderdale FL	4.85
			N48318	Jet Fleet Inc, Fort Lauderdale FL	4.85/89
				(noted FLL as 'N43818' and 'N4831B' 87/89)	

				US Marshals Service, Miami FL	4.90
				WCJB Corp, Los Angeles CA	5.91
				Ralph N. Smith, Maclean VA	92
				Aero Exchange Corp, Arlington VA	12.92/95
G246 •	SA-16B UF-1G UF-2G HU-16E	**51-7188**		(to USCG as 7188)	
				Davis Monthan AFB AZ: del. for storage	14.3.73
			N118DB	Dennis G. Buehn, Reno NV	11.85/88
				Grumman Aerospace Corp, St Augustine FL	.88
				(unconv. in contractors yard DMAFB 88)	
				Air Crane Inc, Opa Locka FL	12.88
				Island Flying Boats Inc, Miami FL	2.89/92
				G. A. Romero, Ciudad Juarez Mexico	10.8.92
				(to Mexican Navy as MP-429)	.92/94
G247	SA-16B HU-16B	**51-7189**	N16CE	Conroy Albatross Inc, Salisbury MD	73/79
				(planned Turbo Albatross conv. not commenced)	
				open storage, Salisbury MD	73/79
- •	SA-16B HU-16B	**51-7193**		USAFM, Confederate AF, Harlingen TX	72/84
				USAFM, Glenn Martin Airport, Baltimore MD	88
- •	SA-16B HU-16B	**51-7194**		(to Ejercito del Aire as AD.1B-13; to AN.1B-13)	
				Museo del Aire, Cuatro Vientos, Madrid	78/87
G254 •	SA-16B HU-16B	**51-7195**		Davis Monthan AFB AZ: del. for storage	23.4.68/76
				Desert Air Parts, Tucson AZ	4.6.76
			N7024S	Caribbean Flying Boats, Miami FL: reg. res.	11.88/90
				Darryl Greenamyer, Ocala FL	8.91
				National Diversified Services, Scottsdale AZ	11.91/92
				Western Aviation Contractors, Provo UT	6.92/95
G267 •	SA-16B HU-16B	**51-7200**		USAFM, Chanute AFB, Rantoul IL	79/94
- •	SA-16B HU-16B	**51-7204**		(to R Hellenic AF as 517204)	
				R Hellenic AF Museum, Tatoi AB Greece	95
G277 •	SA-16B HU-16B	**51-7206**	N16HU (1	Westernair of Albuquerque, Albuquerque NM	72/73
				H. L. Freedman, Albuquerque NM	.73/74
				Westernair of Albuquerque, Albuquerque NM	.74
				Continental Oil of Indonesia	9.74/88
				(wfu, open storage Singapore-Seletar 74/88)	
- •	SA-16B UF-1G UF-2G HU-16E	**51-7209**		(to USCG as 7209)	
				USAFM, Luke AFB AZ (displ. as "10047")	78/88
				USAFM, McClellan AFB CA: arr. by C-5A	25.3.88/93
				(displ. as "USCG 7209")	
- •	SA-16B HU-16B	**51-7212**		Florence Air & Missile Museum, Florence SC	74/95
G288	SA-16B UF-1G UF-2G HU-16E	51-7213		(to USCG as 7213)	
				Davis Monthan AFB AZ: displ. main gate	87
				Smithsonian Institution, Washington AZ	87/88
			N7029C	Darryl G. Greenamyer, Rancho Santa Fe CA	10.88/90
				Nol J. Pedrsen/Pacific Flying Fish Inc, Los Angeles CA/Manila PI	2.91
				cr. in sea off Hawaii, del. flight to Philippines	18.6.91
G289 •	SA-16B UF-1G UF-2G HU-16E	**51-7214**		(to USCG as 7214)	
				Grumman Aerospace Corp, St Augustine FL	1.82
			N1384D	Smithsonian Institution, Washington DC	8.82
				Grumman Aerospace Corp, St Augustine FL	2.83/88

				(stored St Augustine FL 88)	
				sale rep., West Hollywood FL	90/95
- •	SA-16B	**51-7215**		(to USCG as 7215)	
	UF-1G			George H. Baker/American Aviation,	
	UF-2G			New Smyrna Beach FL	85/92
	HU-16E			(stored dism. New Smyrna Beach, derelict)	
- •	SA-16B	**51-7216**		(to USCG as 7216)	
	UF-1G			Sea-Air-Space Museum, New York NY	84/92
	UF-2G			(displ. on deck of carrier USS Intrepid)	
	HU-16E				
- •	SA-16B	**51-7218**		(to USCG as 7218)	
	UF-1G			Davis Monthan AFB AZ: del. for storage	18.7.78
	UF-2G			Smithsonian Instution, Washington DC	88
	HU-16E		**N7029F**	Darryl G. Greenamyer, Rancho Santa Fe CA	10.88/94
				Wally Fisk/Amjet Aircraft Corp, St Paul MN	22.1.94/96
				(flies as "USCG 7218")	
311 •	SA-16B	**51-7226**		(to USCG as 7226)	
	UF-1G			Davis Monthan AFB AZ: del. for storage	22.11.77
	UF-2G			Smithsonian Institution, Washington DC	
	HU-16E		N5402G	Grumman Aerospace Corp, St Augustine FL	7.88
				(unconv. in contractors yard DMAFB 88)	
				Wilson C. Edwards, Big Spring TX	7.88
			N226CG	Wilson C. Edwards, Big Spring TX	3.89/96
				(flies as "USCG 7226/San Francisco")	
312 •	SA-16B	**51-7227**		(to USCG as 7227)	
	UF-1G			Davis Monthan AFB AZ: del. for storage	15.9.69
	UF-2G			Smithsonian Institution, Staurt FL	
	HU-16E			Grumman Aerospace Corp, St Augustine FL	88
			N70263	Aircrane Inc, Opa Locka FL	9.11.88
				Island Flying Boats Inc, Miami FL	2.89/92
				Aircraft Sales & Leasing, Daytona Beach FL	7.93/94
				Western Aviation Maintenance, Mesa AZ	5.10.94/95
				(stored unconv. derelict civil contractor yards, DMAFB 88/95, to Mesa AZ by 10.95 for conv. by Marsh Aviation to Garrett turbine tanker)	
313 •	SA-16B	**51-7228**		(to USCG as 7228)	
	UF-1G			USNAM, NAS Pensacola FL	80/83
	UF-2G			New England Air Museum,Windsor Locks CT	.83/88
	HU-16E			(arr. by barge ex Pensacola .83)	
314 •	SA-16B	**51-7229**		(to USCG as 7229)	
	UF-1G			Grumman Aerospace Corp, St Augustine FL	5.88
	UF-2G				
	HU-16E				
319 •	SA-16B	**51-7234**		(to USCG as 7234)	
	UF-1G			Davis Monthan AFB AZ: arr. for storage	21.3.78
	UF-2G		**N46978**	reg. res.	8.3.84/92
	HU-16E				
321 •	SA-16B	**51-7235**		(to R Thai Navy as 7235)	
	HU-16B			R Thai Navy Museum, Samut Prakhan AB	90
				displ. Sukhumvit Road, Bangkok Thailand	95
323 •	SA-16B	**51-7236**		(to USCG as 7236)	
	UF-1G			USNAM, NAS Pensacola FL	79/94
	UF-2G			(displ. as "USCG 7236")	
	HU-16E				

G325 •	SA-16B	**51-7238**		(to USCG as 7238)	
	UF-1G			A. Wally McDonnell, Mojave CA	.74
	UF-2G			dam. in windstorm, Mojave CA	30.12.74
	HU-16E			(stored dam., Mojave CA 74/84)	
			N4955E	reg. res.	4.84/90
			ZP-TWT	noted Opa Locka FL	10.84
G327 •	SA-16B	**51-7240**		(to USCG as 7240)	
	UF-1G			Davis Monthan AFB AZ: arr. for storage	69
	UF-2G		**N49115**	Wayne Williams, Addison TX	13.2.84
	HU-16E			Ronald W. Cox, Addison TX	12.84
				Jet Fleet Inc, Wilmington DE	2.86/90
				US Marshals Service: for sale at Dothan AL	7.91
				sale rep., Mojave CA	92
				Robert F. Carlson, Carson City NV	4.94
				South FL Aviation Investments, Opa Locka FL	11.94
				World Jet Inc, Fort Lauderdale FL	4.95
G331 •	SA-16B	**51-7243**		(to USCG as 7243)	
	UF-1G			Davis Monthan AFB AZ: arr. for storage	18.10.78
	UF-2G		N1048G	Grumman Aerospace Corp, St Augustine FL	14.12.79
	HU-16E			Smithsonian Institution, Washington DC	80 G-111
				Chalks International Airline, Miami FL	13.11.80
				Flying Boat Inc/Chalks International Airline	12.81
			N120FB	Flying Boat Inc/Chalks International Airline	11.82/95
				(wfu Marana AZ 88, in service Chalks 91/95)	
G332 •	SA-16B	**51-7244**		(to USCG as 7244)	
	UF-1G			USAFM, Oregon Museum of Science & Technology,	UF-2G
				Portland OR	73/75
	HU-16E		N55784	Flying Boat Inc/Chalks International Airline,	
	G-111			Miami FL	3.80
			N113FB	Flying Boat Inc, Miami FL	7.82/96
				(open storage Marana AZ 87/92)	
G333 •	SA-16B	**51-7245**		(to USCG as 7245)	
	UF-1G			Davis Monthan AFB AZ: arr. for storage	28.6.78
	UF-2G			Smithsonian Institution, Washington DC	
	HU-16E			Grumman Aerospace Corp, St Augustine FL	88
				(unconv. in contractors yard DMAFB 88)	
			N70262	Air Crane Inc, Opa Locka FL	11.88
				Island Flying Boats Inc, Miami FL	2.89/92
				South FL Aviation Investments, Opa Locka FL	3.93
				World Jet Inc, Fort Lauderdale FL	4.95
				Don R. Johnson, Riddle OR	5.95
G335 •	SA-16B	**51-7246**		(to USCG as 7246)	
	UF-1G			Davis Monthan AFB AZ: arr. for storage	13.1.76
	UF-2G			Desert Air Parts, Tucson AZ	21.8.81
	HU-16E		**N29853**	Westair International Inc, Monument CO	16.3.82/88
				JE Investments Inc, Opa Locka FL	3.89
				Island Flying Boats Inc, Miami FL	1.90/95
G336 •	SA-16B	**51-7247**		(to USCG as 7247)	
	UF-1G		N227S	Smithsonian Institute, Washington DC	8.79/90
	UF-2G			USCGAS Elizabeth City NJ: displ.	85
	HU-16E				
G339 •	SA-16B	**51-7249**		(to USCG as 7249)	
	UF-1G		N1043N	reg.	7.5.79
	UF-2G		N249S	Smithsonian Institute, Washington DC	8.79
	HU-16E			Resorts International Inc, Miami FL	13.11.80
	G-111			Flying Boat Inc/Chalks International Airline	6.81/82
			N121FB	Flying Boat Inc, Miami FL	7.82/96

				(open storage Marana AZ 87/88,	
				based Singapore 93/94)	
- •	SA-16B	**51-7250**		(to USCG as 7250)	
	UF-1G			last flying USCG HU-16, retired Cape Cod MA	3.83
	UF-2G			USCGAS Cape Cod/Otis ANGB MA: displ.	85/93
	HU-16E				
- •	SA-16B	**51-7251**		(to USCG as 7251)	
	UF-1G			USAFM, Dyess AFB TX	85/95
	UF-2G				
	HU-16E				
- •	SA-16B	51-7253		(to Italian AF as MM51-7253)	
	HU-16B			Museo dell'Aria, San Pelagio Castle, Padova	84/88
- •	UF-1G	**USCG1294**		Davis Monthan AFB AZ: arr. for storage	24.1.73
	UF-2G			Allied Aircraft Sales Inc, Tucson AZ	1.12.80
	HU-16E			Grumman Aerospace Corp, St Augustine FL	
				(unconv. in contractors yard DMAFB 88)	
			N7028L	Air Crane Inc, Opa Locka FL	1.89
				Island Flying Boats Inc, Miami FL	4.89/93
				South FL Aviation Investments, Opa Locka FL	3.93/95
				Island Flying Boats Inc, Opa Locka FL	6.95
351 •	SA-16A	**52-0124**		(to USCG as 2124)	
	UF-1G		**N16ZE**	Conroy Albatross Inc, Salisbury MD	27.2.92/95
	UF-2G				
	HU-16E				
352 •	SA-16A	**52-0125**		(to USCG as 2125)	
	UF-1G			Davis Monthan AFB AZ: arr. for storage	12.6.73
	UF-2G			Dross Metals Inc, Tucson AZ	4.9.79
	HU-16E			Grumman Aerospace Corp, St Augustine FL	
				(unconv. in contractors yards DMAFB 88/95)	
356 •	SA-16A	**52-0129**		(to USCG as 2129)	
	UF-1G			USS Alabama Battleship Commission,	
	UF-2G			Mobile AL	79/94
	HU-16E			(displ. as "USCG 2129")	
357 •	SA-16A	**52-0130**		(to USCG as 2130)	
	UF-1G			Davis Monthan AFB AZ: del. for storage	29.8.74
	UF-2G		**N1026A**	Andrews University, Berrien Springs MI	26.3.79/88
	HU-16E			Wilson C. Edwards, Big Spring TX	3.90/95
359 •	SA-16A	**52-0132**		(to USCG as 2132)	
	UF-1G			Davis Monthan AFB AZ: del. for storage	21.8.69
	UF-2G			Smithsonian Institute, Washington DC	88
	HU-16E			Davis-Monthan AFB AZ: storage	88
361 •	SA-16A	**52-0134**		(to USCG as 2134)	
	UF-1G			A. Wally McDonnell, Mojave CA	.74
	UF-2G			(stored unconv., Mojave CA 74/82)	
	HU-16E		**N4470W**	Caribbean Air Transport, St Croix USVI	10.83/88
				(noted stored unconv., Ft. Lauderdale FL 10.84)	
				Southwest Aviation Inc, Fairacres NM	2.89/92
				Airpower Inc, Lakeport CA	4.93/95
362 •	SA-16A	**52-0135**		(to USCG as 2135)	
	UF-1G			Davis Monthan AFB AZ: storage	69
	UF-2G			Allied Aircraft Sales Inc, Tucson AZ	73
	HU-16E			Grumman Aerospace Corp, St Augustine FL	
				(unconv. in contractors yard DMAFB 88)	
			N7025Y	Island Flying Boats Inc, Miami FL	4.89/93

				South FL Aviation Investments, Opa Locka FL	3.93/96
				Island Flying Boats Inc, Opa Locka FL	6.95
G373 •	UF-1	**Bu137900**		Allied Aircraft Sales Inc, Tucson AZ/ behalf of	
	UF-2			Grumman Aerospace Corp, St Augustine FL	9.3.81
	HU-16C		N901DB	Dennis G. Buehn, Reno NV	28.7.86/90
				Island Flying Boats, Miami FL	6.91/93
				South FL Aviation Investments, Opa Locka FL	3.93
G374 •	UF-1	**Bu137901**		Smithsonian Institution, Stuart FL	2.2.80
	UF-2		N2660L	Flying Boat Inc/Chalks International Airline,	
	HU-16C			Miami FL	12.82/83
	G-111		N124FB	ntu: Flying Boat Inc, Miami FL	12.83
			N2660L	Flying Boat Inc, Miami FL	12.83/96
				(open storage Marana AZ 84/92)	
G377 •	UF-1	**Bu137904**	N8523H	Grumman Aerospace Corp, St Augustine FL	9.4.81/88
	UF-2			(noted stored USNAM, Pensacola FL 6.82)	
	HU-16D			Smithsonian Institution, Washington DC	7.3.89
				Island Flying Boats Inc, Miami FL	3.89
				Air Crane Inc, Opa Locka FL	1.90/92
			XB-...	H. R. Ovalle, Ciudad Juarez Mexico	24.7.92
			N8523H	USNAM, NAS Pensacola FL	10.92
G381 •	UF-1	**Bu137908**		Davis Monthan AFB AZ: storage	.66/88
	HU-16C			disposal less undercarriage, engines, floats	.88
			N61406	Dross Metals Inc, Tucson AZ	12.91/92
				John & Joyce Proctor, Roseburg OR	7.93/94
				(rest., ff 3.93 as "USN 137908")	
			N4WT	John M. Proctor, Roseburg OR	4.94/95
				(began world tour 4.95: Alaska-Russia-Japan	
				-Australia, parked Nowra NAS NSW 11.95)	
G384 •	UF-1	**Bu137911**		Allied Aircraft Sales Inc, Tucson AZ/ behalf of	
	HU-16C			Grumman Aerospace Corp, St Augustine FL	9.3.81
				(stored civil contractor yard DMAFB 87/88)	
			N89LH (2	Lynn C. Hunt, Santa Rosa CA	
			N7027Z	Air Crane Inc, Opa Locka FL	1.89
				Island Flying Boats Inc, Miami FL	4.89/93
				South FL Aviation Investments, Opa Locka FL	3.93/96
G385 •	UF-1	**Bu137912**		Allied Aircraft Sales Inc, Tucson AZ/ behalf of	
	HU-16C			Grumman Aerospace Corp, St Augustine FL	9.3.81
				(stored civil contractor yard DMAFB 88)	
			N70270	Air Crane Inc, Opa Locka FL	1.89
				Island Flying Boats Inc, Miami FL	4.89/93
				South FL Aviation Investments, Opa Locka FL	3.93/96
G388 •	UF-1	**Bu137915**		Dross Metals Inc, Tucson AZ	20.1.82
(24B)	HU-16C		**N4796U**	Dross Metals Inc, Tucson AZ	3.84
	G-111			ACME, Shakopee MN	5.84/87
				Robert C. Mace, Globe AZ	10.88/95
G394 •	UF-1	**Bu137921**		Allied Aircraft Sales Inc, Tucson AZ/ behalf of	
	HU-16C			Grumman Aerospace Corp, St Augustine FL	17.2.81
			N7026Y	Air Crane Inc, Opa Locka FL	1.89
				Island Flying Boats Inc, Miami FL	4.89/93
				South FL Aviation Investments, Opa Locka FL	3.93
				Dennis G. Buehn, Carson City NV	5.94/96
				(unconv. in contractors yards DMAFB 88/95)	
G397 •	UF-1	**Bu137924**		Allied Aircraft Sales Inc, Tucson AZ/ behalf of	
	HU-16C			Grumman Aerospace Corp, St Augustine FL	9.3.81
				(stored civil contractor yard DMAFB 88)	

			N7028C	Air Crane Inc, Opa Locka FL	1.89
				Island Flying Boats Inc, Miami FL	4.89/93
				South FL Aviation Investments, Opa Locka FL	3.93/96
G399 •	UF-1	**Bu137926**		Allied Aircraft Sales Inc, Tucson AZ/ behalf of	
	HU-16C			Grumman Aerospace Corp, St Augustine FL	9.3.81
			N926DB	Dennis G. Buehn, Reno NV	7.86
				Melvyn L. Arthur, Phoenix AZ	8.87
			N888AC	Arthur Corp, Phoenix AZ	10.87/90
				(rest. Tucson AZ 85/90, ff .90)	
				Melvyn L. Arthur/American Aircraft	
				Management, Scottsdale AZ	11.90/96
				(dep. Scottsdale 10.9.92 on leisurely flight to	
				UK, Europe & S.Africa, ret. to USA 9.94)	
G400 •	UF-1	**Bu137927**		Allied Aircraft Sales Inc, Tucson AZ/ behalf of	
	HU-16C			Grumman Aerospace Corp, St Augustine FL	9.3.81
				Dennis G. Buehn, Reno NV	16.4.85
			N9722B	Dennis G. Buehn, Reno NV	9.85/96
				(flies as "USN 137927/Guantanamo")	
G401 •	UF-1	**Bu137928**		Allied Aircraft Sales Inc, Tucson AZ/ behalf of	
	HU-16C			Grumman Aerospace Corp, St Augustine FL	17.2.81
				(stored civil contractor yard DMAFB 88)	
			N7025E	Air Crane Inc, Opa Locka FL	1.89
				Island Flying Boats Inc, Miami FL	4.89
				Nevada Capital Equities Inc, Crystal Bay NV	11.89/90
				Roy Grossman, Chico CA	92
				Glen Johnson, Fort Worth TX	3.10.94
			N928J	Glen Johnson, Fort Worth TX	12.94/96
G403 •	UF-1	**Bu137930**		Allied Aircraft Sales Inc, Tucson AZ/ behalf of	
	HU-16C			Grumman Aerospace Corp, St Augustine FL	3.2.81
				(stored civil contractor yard DMAFB 87)	
			N70133	Dennis G. Buehn, Reno NV	6.88
				Robert H. Nottke, Barrington Hills IL	90
				Nevada Capital Equities Inc, Reno NV	9.90
				Desside Trading Co, Sparks NV	12.90/92
G405 •	UF-1	**Bu137932**		Allied Aircraft Sales Inc, Tucson AZ/ behalf of	
	HU-16C			Grumman Aerospace Corp, St Augustine FL	9.3.81
				(stored civil contractor yard DMAFB 88)	
			N70276	Air Crane Inc, Opa Locka FL	1.89
				Island Flying Boats Inc, Miami FL	4.89/90
			N44RD	Reid W. Dennis, Woodside CA	7.90/96
G406 •	UF-1	**Bu137933**		Allied Aircraft Sales Inc, Tucson AZ/ behalf of	
	HU-16C			Grumman Aerospace Corp, St Augustine FL	11.3.81
			N70275	Air Crane Inc, Opa Locka FL	1.89
				Island Flying Boats Inc, Miami FL	4.89/93
				South FL Aviation Investments, Opa Locka FL	3.93
				Dennis G. Buehn, Carson City NC	1.95
				(unconv. in contractors yards DMAFB 88/95)	
G407 •	UF-1G	**USCG1311**		Davis Monthan AFB AZ: arr. for storage	4.11.77
	UF-2G		N3790U	I. N. Burchinall Jr, Paris TX	15.7.80
	HU-16E			Western Aviation Contractors Inc,	
				American Fork UT	84
				sale rep., Mena AR	86
				sale rep., Mojave CA	88
				Wilson C. Edwards, Big Spring TX	10.89/90
				Flying Boat Inc, Fort Lauderdale FL	2.91
			N114FB (2	Flying Boat Inc/Chalks International Airline	
				Fort Lauderdale FL	7.91/96
				(op. by Chalks for pilot training only 91/95)	

G408 •	UF-1 UF-2S HU-16D	**Bu141261**	 **N13598**	Davis Monthan AFB AZ: arr. for storage reg. Allied Aircraft Sales Inc, Tucson AZ Westernair of Albuquerque, Albuquerque NM	21.9.68 11.78 21.8.81 10.81/96
G409	UF-1 HU-16C	**Bu141262**	 **N7025N**	Allied Aircraft Sales Inc, Tucson AZ/ behalf of Grumman Aerospace Corp, St Augustine FL (stored civil contractor yard DMAFB 88) Air Crane Inc, Opa Locka FL Island Flying Boats Inc, Miami FL South FL Aviation Investments, Opa Locka FL Urbano M. Dasilva, Tecumseh MI dam. collision with boat during water landing, St. Ignace, St. Helena Isle MI	 10.3.81 1.89 2.89/93 3.93 4.94/96 2.8.94
G412 •	UF-1 HU-16C	**Bu141265**	 **N7025V**	Allied Aircraft Sales Inc, Tucson AZ/ behalf of Grumman Aerospace Corp, St Augustine FL (stored civil contractor yard DMAFB 88) Air Crane Inc, Opa Locka FL Island Flying Boats Inc, Miami FL South FL Aviation Investments, Opa Locka FL (derelict unconv., Western International yard, Davis Monthan AFB AZ 95)	 9.3.81 1.89 2.89/93 3.93/95
G413 •	UF-1 UF-2 HU-16D G-111	**Bu141266**	**N693S**	USNAM, NAS Pensacola FL: reg. candidate Smithsonian Institute, Washington DC (noted stored USNAM, Pensacola 6.82) EAA Museum, Lakeland FL: displ.	79 1.80/88 88/94
G418 •	UF-1 HU-16C	**Bu141271**	 N70258	Allied Aircraft Sales Inc, Tucson AZ/ behalf of Grumman Aerospace Corp, St Augustine FL Air Crane Inc, Opa Locka FL Island Flying Boats Inc, Miami FL South FL Aviation Investment, Opa Locka FL (unconv. in contractors yards DMAFB 88/95)	 17.2.81 1.89 4.89/93 3.93/95
G423 •	UF-1 HU-16C	**Bu141276**	 **N43155**	(to Icelandic Coast Guard as 141276) Davis Monthan AFB AZ: arr. for storage Allied Aircraft Sales Inc, Tucson AZ/ behalf of Grumman Aerospace Corp, St Augustine FL Rick Grant, Oakland CA (stored civil contractor yard DMAFB 88) Grant Engineering, Richmond CA	66/70 9.9.70 4.3.81 10.87 5.91/96
G425 •	UF-1 UF-2S HU-16D	**Bu141278**	 **N20861**	Davis Monthan AFB AZ: del. for storage Smithsonian Institute, Washington DC Ascher Ward, Van Nuys CA: reg. candidate Flying Boat Inc, Fort Lauderdale FL (unconv. in contractors yards DMAFB 88/95)	10.12.69 88 11.93 1.94/96
G426 •	UF-1 UF-2S HU-16D	**Bu141279**	N8827	sale rep., USCR	5.73/95
G432 •	UF-1 UF-2S HU-16D G-111	**Bu141282**	N4253R **N125FB**	Grumman Aircraft Corp, St Augustine FL Flying Boat Inc/Chalks International Airline Miami FL (open storage Marana AZ 84/94)	16.2.80 9.83/96
-	UF-1G UF-2G HU-16E	**Bu141287**		(to USCG as 1316) Davis Monthan AFB AZ: arr. for storage (to Icelandic Coast Guard as 1316)	 23.8.68 .69

				Kolar Inc, Tucson AZ	31.5.74
G367 •	UF-1G UF-2G HU-16E	**Bu142360**		(to USCG as 1290) : returned to USN	
				Allied Aircraft Sales Inc, Tucson AZ/ behalf of	
				Grumman Aerospace Corp, St Augustine FL	4.3.81
				(stored civil contractor yard DMAFB 88)	
			N7026H	Air Crane Inc, Opa Locka FL	1.89
				Island Flying Boats Inc, Miami FL	2.89/92
				sold to Mexico	7.5.92
			N7026H	Robert F. Carlson, Carson City NV	10.94/95
				Amphib Inc, Wheeling IL	9.95
G368 •	UF-1G UF-2G HU-16C	**Bu142361**		(to USCG as 1291)	
				(to Icelandic Coast Guard as 142361)	
				(returned to USN as Bu142361)	.69
				Allied Aircraft Sales Inc, Tucson AZ/ behalf of	
				Grumman Aerospace Corp, St Augustine FL	4.3.81
			N143DB	Dennis G. Buehn, Reno NV	7.87/88
				Westholm Aviation Inc, Minden NV	10.89/92
				M. M. Inc, Newark DE	9.92/96
				(flies as "USN Kodiak/361")	
- •	UF-1G UF-2G HU-16C	**Bu142362**		(to USCG as 1292)	
				Allied Aircraft Sales Inc, Tucson AZ/ behalf of	
				Grumman Aerospace Corp, St Augustine FL	4.3.81
			N70252	Air Crane Inc, Opa Locka FL	1.89
				Island Flying Boats Inc, Miami FL	2.89/93
				South FL Aviation Investments, Opa Locka FL	3.93/96
				(unconv. in contractors yards DMAFB 88/95)	
- •	UF-1 UF-1G UF-2G HU-16C	**Bu142363**		(to USCG as 1293)	
				USAFM, March AFB CA	82/93
				(displ. as "USCG 1293", later "USAF 01280")	
-	UF-1L LU-16C HU-16C	**Bu142428**		Allied Aircraft Sales Inc, Tucson AZ/ behalf of	
				Grumman Aerospace Corp, St Augustine FL	3.2.81
				reg. candidate	7.11.88
-	UF-1G UF-1L HU-16C	**Bu142429**		(to USCG as ....) : ret. to USN	
				Allied Aircraft Sales Inc, Tucson AZ/ behalf of	
				Grumman Aerospace Corp, St Augustine FL	9.3.81
				reg. candidate	7.11.88
G444 •	UF-2S HU-16D	**Bu146426**		(to WGN as RE+501, SC+101, SC+301, 60+04)	
			N13048	Consolidated Aero Export Corp., Tucson AZ	.72
				Grumman Aerospace Corp, St Augustine FL	5.72/77
				(del. to USA, via Hamburg 7.7.72)	
				USNAM, NAS Pensacola FL	
				Smithsonian Institute, Washington DC	3.82
			N695S	Smithsonian Institute, Washington DC	7.82/90
				(*Smithsonian Marine Systems Lab* titles)	
				USNAM, NAS Pensacola FL: loan, displ.	90
				Mark Clark/Courtesy Aircraft, Rockford IL	91
				A & T Recovery Inc, Berwyn IL	2.91
				Flying Boat Inc, Fort Lauderdale FL	11.91/92
				Omni Engineering Inc, Wilmington DE	7.10.94/96
G445 •	UF-2S HU-16D	**Bu146427**		(to WGN as RE+502, SC+102, SC+302, 60+05)	
			N13045	Consolidated Aero Export Corp., Tucson AZ	.72
				Grumman Aerospace Corp, St Augustine FL	5.72/77
				(del. to USA, via Hamburg 25.7.72)	
				(to TNI-AU/Indonesian AF as PB-5..)	
			PK-VAB	Dirgantara Air Services PT, Jakarta	
				(operated for Conoco)	80/81

				struck-off reg.	10.10.81
				(to TNI-AL/Indonesian Navy as PB-5..)	
			N900DA	Four Square Ltd, Venice FL	12.5.93
				Norton Aero Ltd, Athol ID	4.95
G446 •	UF-2S	**Bu146428**		(to WGN as RE+503, SC+103, SC+303, 60+06)	
	HU-16D		N13044	Consolidated Aero Export Corp., Tucson AZ	.72
				Grumman Aerospace Corp, St Augustine FL	4.72/77
				(del. to USA, via Hamburg 28.6.72)	
				(to TNI-AL/Indonesian Navy as PB-5..)	
			N125DA	Four Square Ltd, Venice FL	12.5.93/95
G447	UF-2S	Bu146429		(to WGN as RE+504, SC+104, SC+304, 60+07)	
	HU-16D		N13043	Consolidated Aero Export Corp., Tucson AZ	.72
				Grumman Aerospace Corp, St Augustine FL	4.72/77
				(del. to USA, via Hamburg 5.6.72)	
				(to TNI-AL/Indonesian Navy as PB-5..)	
G448 •	UF-2S	**Bu146430**		(to WGN as RE+505, SC+105, SC+305, 60+08)	
	HU-16D		N13042	Consolidated Aero Export Corp., Tucson AZ	.72
				Grumman Aerospace Corp, St Augustine FL	5.72/77
				(to TNI-AL/Indonesian Navy as PB-5..)	
			N202DA	Four Square Ltd, Venice FL	12.5.93/95
-	CSR-110	**RCAF9301**	N9425	Grumman Aerospace Corp, St Augustine FL	.71
	G-111			(awaiting collection, Saskatoon SASK 10.71)	
				(to FA Chile as .....)	
G451 •	CSR-110	**60-9303**		(to RCAF as 9303)	
	G-111		N9427	Grumman Aerospace Corp, St Augustine FL	.71
				(awaiting collection, Saskatoon SASK 10.71)	
				(to FA Chile as 573)	
			N8497H	Resorts International Inc, Miami FL	10.80
				Grumman Aerospace Corp, St Augustine FL	84/86
				(to R Malaysian AF/TUDM as M35-01)	10.86/95
				(pres. Kuala-Lumpur Simpang AB)	93/95
G452 •	CSR-110	**60-9304**		(to RCAFas 9304)	
	G-111		N9380	Grumman Aerospace Corp, St Augustine FL	.71/77
				(awaiting collection, Saskatoon SASK 10.71)	
				Chalks International Airline, Miami FL	.77
				Flying Boat Inc/Chalks International Airline	3.81/82
			N118FB	Flying Boat Inc, Fort Lauderdale FL	3.82/95
				(open storage Marana AZ 87/92)	
G453	CSR-110	**60-9305**		(to RCAF as 9305)	
	G-111		N9386	Grumman Aerospace Corp, St Augustine FL	.71
				(awaiting collection, Saskatoon SASK 10.71)	
				(to Mexican Navy as MP-101)	.74
G454	CSR-110	**60-9306**		(to RCAF as 9306)	
	G-111		N9387	Grumman Aerospace Corp, St Augustine FL	.71
				(awaiting collection, Saskatoon SASK 10.71)	
				(to Mexican Navy as MP-102)	.74
G455	CSR-110	**60-9307**		(to RCAF as 9307)	
	G-111		N9388	Grumman Aerospace Corp, St Augustine FL	.71
				(awaiting collection, Saskatoon SASK 10.71)	
				(to Mexican Navy as MP-103)	8.3.74
G456 •	CSR-110	**60-9308**		(to RCAF as 9308)	
	G-111		N9392	Grumman Aerospace Corp, St Augustine FL	.71
				(awaiting collection, Saskatoon SASK 10.71)	
				Edward F. Dexter	72

				Chalks International Airline, Miami FL	11.72/82
			N119FB	Flying Boat Inc/Chalks International Airline	10.82/95
				(open storage Marana AZ 87/92)	
G457	CSR-110	**60-9309**		(to RCAF as 9309)	
	G-111		N9405	Grumman Aerospace Corp, St Augustine FL	.71
				(awaiting collection, Saskatoon SASK 10.71)	
				(to Mexican Navy as MP-104)	8.3.74
G458	CSR-110	**60-9310**		(to RCAF as 9310)	
	G-111		N9423	Grumman Aerospace Corp, St Augustine FL	.71
				(to FA Chile as 570)	.71
			N8497E	Resorts International Inc, Miami FL	10.80
				Grumman Aerospace Corp, St Augustine FL	84/86
				(to R Malaysian AF/TUDM as M35-02)	10.86
G460 •	UF-2S	**Bu148325**		(to JMSDF as 9052)	
	HU-16D		N3470F	Resorts International Inc/	
	G-111			Chalks International Airline, Miami FL	6.76/81
			N116FB	Flying Boat Inc/Chalks International Airline,	
				Miami FL	2.81/96
				(open storage Marana AZ 87/92)	
G461 •	UF-2S	**Bu148326**		(to JMSDF as 9053)	
	HU-16D		N3479F	Resorts International Inc/	
	G-111			Chalks International Airline, Miami FL	6.76/82
				Flying Boat Inc/Chalks International Airline	3.81/82
			N117FB	Flying Boat Inc, Miami FL	3.82/96
				(open storage Marana AZ 88,	
				in service with Chalks Ft Lauderdale 10.93/94)	
G462 •	UF-2S	**Bu148327**		(to JMSDF as 9054)	
	HU-16D		N88998	reg. candidate	10.77
	G-111		**N115FB**	Flying Boat Inc/Chalks International Airline,	
				Miami FL	2.81/96
				(open storage Marana AZ 87/88)	
G463 •	UF-2S	**Bu148328**		(to JMSDF as 9055)	
	HU-16D		N3469F	Resorts International Inc/	
	G-111			Chalks International Airline, Miami FL	6.76/77
			N112FB	Flying Boat Inc/Chalks International Airline	6.79/95
				(first G-111 in service with Chalks 1.81)	
				(open storage Marana AZ 87/92)	
G464 •	UF-2S	**Bu148329**		(to JMSDF as 9056)	.61
	HU-16D		N88999	reg. candidate	10.77
	G-111		N114FB (1	Flying Boat Inc, Miami FL	3.81
				Grumman Aerospace Corp, St Augustine FL	.81
				(rebuilt St. Augustine FL as G-111 .81)	
			PK-PAM	Pelita Air Service, Jakarta (op. for Conoco)	7.81/87
				CofA expired 16.9.87: wfu	9.87
			N26PR	Kirk Williams/Paragon Ranch, Broomfield CO	10.91/94
				Mirabella Yachts Inc, Palm Beach FL	28.6.94/96
- •	UF-1	**Bu149836**		Allied Aircraft Sales Inc, Tucson AZ/behalf of	
	HU-16C			Grumman Aerospace Corp, St Augustine FL	17.2.81
			N7026C	Air Crane Inc, Opa Locka FL	1.89
				Island Flying Boats Inc, Miami FL	4.89/93
				South FL Aviation Investments, Opa Locka FL	3.93/94
				Dennis G. Buehn, Carson City NV	17.11.94
				Tom Casey, Palm Beach FL	2.95
				(unconv. in contractors yards DMAFB 88/95)	
- •	SA-16B	**Bu151265**		(to R Thai Navy as 1265)	
	HU-16B			R Thai Navy Museum, U Taphao AB	90/93

-	UF-1	**PB-522**		(to TNI-AU/Indonesian Navy as PB-522)	.58
			PK-VAA	Dirgantara Air Services PT, Jakarta	3.78/82
				(op. for Conoco)	
- •	HU-16	-	HK-3642	Lineas Aereas del Amazonas - LAMA, Leticia	c8.91
- •	HU-16	-	HK-3643	Lineas Aereas del Amazonas - LAMA, Leticia	c8.91
- •	HU-16	-		(to FA Brasileira as FAB .....)	
			PP-ZAV	noted Campo de Marte, Brasil	5.91
- •	HU-16	-		(to FA Brasileira as FAB .....)	
			PP-ZAW	noted Campo de Marte, Brasil	5.91
- •	HU-16B	-		(to Chinese Nationalist AF as 11024)	
				Chung Cheng Museum, Taipei Airport, Taiwan	90/91
- •	UF-1	-		(to TNI-AU/Indonesian Navy as PB-...)	
				Indonesian AF Museum, Yogyakarta	93/96
				(displ. as "TNI-AU/IR-0117")	

GRUMMAN/COLUMBIA XJL

- •	XJL-1	**Bu31399**		prototype: ff	25.10.46
				stored NAS Norfolk VA 48/59: disposal	.59
			N54207	Herbert D. Scudder, Baltimore MD	63/69
				Bernard H. Ulbrich, Baltimore MD	72
				(rest. project Essex Skypark MD 72/73,	
				stripped hulk, Essex Skypark by 76)	
				sale rep., Lakeport CA	92
			N48RW	Richard W. Martin, Carlsbad-Palomar CA	4.93/96
				(rest. to fly, Carlsbad-Palomar CA 92/94)	
- •	XJL-1	**Bu31400**		stored NAS Norfolk VA 48/59: disposal	.59
			N54205	Greg R. Board, Michigan City IN/Tucson AZ	58/64
				(del. Tucson ex Philadelphia Navy Yard PA .61;	
				re-engined B-25 QEC/Wright R-2600;	
				open storage Ryan Field & Tucson AZ 66/85)	
				Aero American Corp, Tucson AZ	66/72
				Robert O. Hoover, Tucson AZ	1.75/95
				Pima County Air Museum, Tucson AZ	88/96

HANDLEY PAGE HALIFAX

- •	Mk. II	**W1048**		crashed Lake Hoklingen, Levanger, Norway	28.4.42
				(lost during attack on "Tirpitz")	
				recov. from lake by RAF Museum team	6.73
				RAF Museum Store, RAF Henlow	74
				RAF Museum, Hendon	83/95
				(unrest. hulk: displ. as recov., "W1048/TL-S")	
- •	Mk. II	**HR792**		crashed takeoff, Stornoway	13.1.45
				(fuse. to farm, Isle of Lewis, as chicken coop)	
				Yorkshire Air Museum, Elvington	5.84/96
				(fuselage recov. from farm, Isle of Lewis 5.84;	
				rebuild with parts LW687 & JP158, using	
				mainplane from Hastings TG556)	
				(partially rest. fuse mounted on mainplane, roll-out	
				Elvington 13.8.93 as LV907/*Friday the 13th*)	
- •	Mk. VIIa	**NA337**		shot down Lake Mjosa, Norway "2P-X"	13.4.45

				RCAF Memorial Museum, Trenton ONT (raised from lake, recov. 9-10.9.95, planned complete static rest. in Canada)	9.95

HANDLEY PAGE HAMPDEN

EEP/ 22522 •	Mk. I	**P1344**		shot down by Bf109s Petsamo, Finland/Russia	5.9.42
				Jeet Mahal, Vancouver BC (wreck recov. ex Russian crash site .90, hulk shipped to UK, arr. 4.9.91: "PL-K")	.90/92
				RAF Museum, RAF Cardington (planned rest. for static displ.)	8.92/96
FAL/ • CA/80	Mk. I	**P5436**		(to RCAF as P5436): BOC 6.1.42: SOC	1.12.42
				ditched, Patricia Bay, Vancouver Island BC	15.11.42
				Canadian Museum of Flight & Transportation, Vancouver BC: recov. from 600 ft. depth (static rest., using parts recov. from AN132 & AN136 ex BC crash sites: almost complete by 95)	.85/96
- •	Mk. I	**AE436**		recov. from Tsatsa Mountains, Sweden	.76
				RAF Museum Store, RAF Henlow: hulk	.76/87
				Flygvapenmuseum, Sweden: rear fuse.	88
				Brian Nicholls/Lincolnshire Aviation Heritage Centre, East Kirby: rest. project (rear fuse. arr. East Kirkby 16.1.89 ex Sweden)	.87/96

HAWKER FURY/SEA FURY

-	FB Mk.11	**TF956**		RNAS Lossiemouth: stored	60/63
				Hawker-Siddeley Aircraft Ltd, Dunsfold: del. (planned company historic flight: rest. commenced)	.63/70
				Fleet Air Arm Historic Flight, RNAS Yeovilton (rest. Yeovilton, ff 20.1.72 as "TF956/123/T")	.70/89
				cr. into sea off Prestwick, Scotland	10.6.89
41H/ 609972 •	FB Mk.11	**TG114**		(to RCN as TG114): BOC 24.5.48: SOC	2.10.56
			CF-OYF	Brian Baird, Toronto ONT	11.62
			N54M	J. W. ("Bill") Fornof, Houma LA	66/69
				crashed landing, Houma LA (stored dam. Mesa AZ, later rebuilt Phoenix AZ using parts from RCN VR918 & VR919)	c67
			N232J	Frank C. Sanders, Chino CA (conv. 2 seater, flew as "N232/232/0")	71/76
				Lloyd A. Hamilton, Santa Rosa CA	80
				William E. Sims, Charleston IL	.82/87
				Ronald M. Runyan, Springdale OH : USCR	5.88/92
				Robert J. Lamplough, North Weald UK (del. by air: arr North Weald 24.4.90)	.88/92
			G-BVOE	Aces High Ltd, North Weald	13.6.94/95
			N232J	Maruna Airplane Co, Akron OH	1.96
41H/ 609977 •	FB Mk.11	**TG119**		(to RCN as TG119): BOC	24.5.48/56
				Bancroft Industries	63
				Canadian National Aeronautical Collection Rockcliffe AB ONT	.63/82
				National Aviation Museum, Rockcliffe ONT (displ. as "RCN TG119/110")	9.82/94
- •	FB Mk.11	**VR930**		Hawker Siddeley Aircraft, Dunsfold: stored	64
				RAF Museum, RAF Colerne	65/75
				FAA Museum, RNAY Wroughton: stored	.75/86
				RN Historic Flight, RNAS Yeovilton: stored (trucked Yeovilton-Brough 6.94 for rest. to fly)	92/95

Continued on Page 218

Messerschmitt Bf109F-4 10132 here at AJD's facility in Suffolk, was recovered from Northern Russia in 1995, as detailed in W.W.33. **Mark Sheppard.**

Messerschmitt Bf109E wk.nr.3579 in Craig Charleston's workshop January 1993, complete, but needing a lot of work. The caption on the back of this photograph reads: "Dormant, certainly not dead!" **Chris Michell.**

Meserschmitt Bf109 163824 sat outside in Australia. A controversial machine due to its attempted export to Britain, it is now in store in Canberra. At least it put the issue of 'National Treasures' on the warbird agenda, for all nations to decide on their policy. **APN.**

Though the propeller blades were cropped, and other comprimises made, it was worth it to hear the sound of Messerscmitt Me410 even on a rainy Welsh saturday. Now the aircraft is silent and static at Cosford. When will the first Axis twin take to the air? **James Kightly.**

The Planes of Fame Mitsubishi J2M-3 'Raiden' is one of only two survivors, the other being in store with the National Air and Space Museum at Silver Hill. Given the Planes of Fame attitude towards unlikely restorations, it is just possible we may see the type back in the air one day. **Gary Robert Brown.**

Taxiied with elan, tail up (and off the runway) at the 1996 Warbirds over Wanaka show, the Nakajima Ki-43 Hayabusa 'Oscar' is a jewel in the New Zealand Fighter Pilot's museum. Though held to be counterproductive to restore to airworthy condition (due to the substitution of original parts) it is nevertheless displayed as activly as possible. **Ian Brodie.**

c/n	Model	Serial	Regn	History	Dates
- •	FB Mk.11	**VW232**		(to RAN as VW232): BOC	3.49/59
				(arr. deck cargo on carrier HMAS Sydney 25.5.49)	
				NAS Nowra NSW: ground inst. airframe	3.51/59
				Sydney Technical College, Ultimo NSW	9.3.59
				Museum of Applied Sciences, Sydney NSW	65/74
				(stored, Sydney Technical College, Ultimo NSW, painted as "RAN VX730")	
				Camden Museum of Aviation NSW : loan, arr.	11.74
				Australian War Memorial, Canberra ACT	82/95
				Naval Aviation Museum, Nowra NAS, NSW	8.87/91
				(loan: displ. as "RAN VX730/108K")	
- •	FB Mk.11	**VW623**		(to RAN as VW623): BOC	3.49
				(arr. deck cargo on carrier HMAS Sydney 25.5.49)	
				Nowra NAS, NSW: gate guard "102/K"	65/72
				Naval Aviation Museum, Nowra NAS, NSW	12.74/95
				(long-term rest. to fly Nowra, "VW623/102K")	
- •	FB Mk.11	**VW647**		(to RAN as VW647): BOC 3.49 SOC	15.11.59
				(arr. deck cargo on carrier HMAS Sydney 25.5.49)	
				Experimental Building Station, Ryde, Sydney	15.1.59/69
				(wind machine to test building materials)	
				Ed Fleming/Skyservice Aviation, Camden NSW	.69
				Camden Museum of Aviation, Camden later Narellan NSW	10.69/95
				(rest. as "VW647/127K", first engine runs 10.76)	
ES.3615 •	T Mk.20S	**VX281**		Hawker-Siddeley Aircraft Ltd, Langley	.57/63
			D-CACO	Federal Republic of Germany: del.	10.6.63/74
			G-BCOW	Warbirds of GB Ltd, Blackbushe	10.74/77
				(del. Blackbushe ex Germany 11.10.74)	
				Spencer R. Flack, Elstree	2.77/80
				(flew as "RNFAA 253")	
			N8476W	Dale Clarke, Gardena CA	7.80/84
				(dep. Blackbushe on del. USA 3.6.80, flew as race #40 *Nuthin Special*)	
				Liberty Aero Corp, Gardena CA	6.84/88
			N281L	Liberty Aero Corp, Santa Monica CA	3.88/92
				(flies as RN 281/*Dragon of Cymru*)	
				Wally Fisk/Amjet Aircraft Corp, St Paul MN	9.93/96
ES.8502 •	T Mk.20S	**VX300**		Hawker-Siddeley Aircraft Ltd, Langley	.57/58
			D-FAMI	Federal Republic of Germany: del.	29.8.58
			D-CAMI	Deutsche Luftfahrt-Berantungdienst, Colgne	4.59/74
			G-BCKH	Warbirds of GB Ltd, Blackbushe: del. ex Colne	9.8.74/77
			N46690	del. Blackbushe-Prestwick on del. to USA	19.6.77
			N62147	John J. Stokes, San Marcos TX	9.74
			N924G	Sanders Aircraft, Chino CA	78/95
				(race #88 Royal Navy 924)	
ES.3613 •	T Mk.20S TT Mk.20	**VX302**		Hawker-Siddeley Aircraft Ltd, Langley	.57/63
			D-CACE	Federal Republic of Germany: del.	5.4.63/74
			G-BCOV	Warbirds of GB Ltd, Blackbushe	10.74/76
				(del. Blackbushe ex Germany 11.10.74)	
				Michael W. Stow, Blackbushe	9.76/85
			N613RD	Richard S. Drury, Goleta CA : del to USA	6.85/87
				(flew as "RN VX302/43D/Iron Angel")	
			N51SF	Jerry C. Janes & Assoc. Inc, Rockford IL	8.87/94
				(Wright R3350, race #20 *Cottonmouth*)	
				Stan Musick/Musick Aircraft Corp, Brownwood TX (flies as *Sea Fuzzy*)	12.94/96
ES.8501 •	T Mk.20S	**VX309**		Hawker-Siddeley Aircraft Ltd, Langley	.57/58

c/n	Model	Serial	Reg	Owner / History	Date
	TT Mk.20		D-FIBO	Federal Republic of Germany: del.	29.8.58
			D-CIBO	Deutsche Luftfahrt-Berantungdienst, Colgne	63/72
				FAA Historic Flight, RNAS Yeovilton: hulk	.76
				RNAS Wroughton, Yeovilton: spares use	80/96
- •	FB Mk.11	**VX653**		RNAS Lossiemouth: stored	69
				RAF Museum, Hendon	.72/91
				The Fighter Collection, Duxford	11.91/92
				(arr. Duxford by road 24.11.91: stored)	
			G-BUCM	The Fighter Collection, Duxford	26.2.92/96
				(current rest. to fly)	
-	FB Mk.11	**VX715**		(to Kon Marine as 6-14)	
				inst. airframe Gilze-Riijen AB (stored)	74
				Lloyd A. Hamilton, Santa Rosa CA	4.74
				shipped to USA, stored Santa Rosa CA	.74/83
				(rebuilt with parts of WH589 and adopted that id.)	
ES.8503 •	T Mk.20S	**VZ345**		Hawker-Siddeley Aircraft Ltd, Langley	.57/58
			D-FATA	Deutsche Luftfahrt-Berantungdienst: del.	16.9.58
			D-CATA	Deutsche Luftfahrt-Berantungdienst, Colgne	63/74
				displ. Koln/Bonn	74
				(presented to RAF as VZ345)	10.74
				RAE/Aeroplane &Armament Experimental	
				Establishment (A&AEE), RAF Boscombe Down	10.74/92
				(del. 15.10.74, flew as "VZ345 CH/272")	
				landing accident RAE Boscombe Down	17.4.85
				(stored dam. RAE Boscombe Down 85/92)	
				RN Historic Flight, NAS Yeovilton: loan	.92/96
				(arr. Yeovilton dism. 11.92, stored;	
				trucked to Brough 6.94 for spares for VR930)	
ES.9505	T Mk.20S	VZ350		Hawker-Siddeley Aircraft Ltd, Langley	.57/59
			D-COCO	Federal Republic of Germany: del.	11.8.59/72
			N20SF (1	John J. Stokes/Warbirds of the World,	
				San Marcos TX	77/78
				William E. Harrison, Tulsa OK	.78
				(flew as "Royal Navy 52", race #3)	
				Robert Z. Friedman/Everco Industries, IL	12.78
				crashed on take-off Waukegan IL (Friedman k.)	16.12.78
				wreckage to Sanders Aircraft, Chino CA	79/95
				(id. tfd. to VZ368 for rebuild of N20SF(2)	
ES.9506 •	T Mk.20S	**VZ351**		Hawker-Siddeley Aircraft Ltd, Langley	.57/58
			D-CEDO	Federal Republic of Germany: del.	11.8.59/72
			OO-SFY	ntu: Eric Vormezeele, Braaschaat, Belgium	9.75/85
				(stored unrest. Braaschaat 75/85)	
				Jimmie Hunt, Memphis TN: shipped	10.85/87
				George H. Baker/American Aero Service,	
				New Smyrna Beach FL	.87/90
ES.3612	T Mk.20S	**VZ365**		Hawker-Siddeley Aircraft Ltd, Langley	.57/63
			D-CACA	Federal Republic of Germany: del.	28.3.63/72
				(noted derelict, Cologne WG 4.74)	
				Eric Vormezeele, Braaschaat, Belgium	9.75/85
				(stripped hulk: stored unrest. Braaschaat 75/85)	
				Jimmie Hunt, Memphis TN: shipped	10.85
				George H. Baker/American Aero Service,	
				New Smyrna Beach FL	.86/87
				(used in rebuild to *Skyfury* racer	
				of IAF 325/N30SF: which see)	87
- •	T Mk.20	VZ368		Hawker-Siddeley Aircraft Ltd, Langley	.57
				(to Burmese AF as UB-451)	
				Frank C. Sanders, Chino CA : stored dism.	.79/82

			N20SF (2	Sanders Aircraft, Chino CA (rebuilt Chino, ff 6.8.83 with P&W R4360, race #8 *Dreadnought*: adopted id. VZ350)	7.83/95
ES.8504 •	T Mk.20S	**WE820**		Hawker-Siddeley Aircraft Ltd, Langley	.57/58
			D-FOTE	Federal Republic of Germany: del.	9.58
			D-COTE	Deutsche Luftfahrt-Berantungdienst, Colgne	63/72
			N85SF	John J. Stokes, San Marcos TX	80
				Eric Lorentzen, Caldwell NJ (rebuilt as modified racer with Wright R3350, race #88 *Blind Man's Bluff*)	84/87
				Eric Lorentzen/Window Magic of Arizona Inc, Scottsdale AZ	8.87/88
				Steven A. Bolan, Scottsdale AZ	1.88/89
				Bill Woods/Western Wings Aircraft Sales Co, Oakland OR	10.89/90
				dam. landing gear-up, Reno NV (race #90)	9.90
				Tom A. Dwelle, Auburn CA (trucked Reno-Auburn CA 2.91for rebuild, ff Auburn 4.9.93 as #10 *Critical Mass*)	2.91/95
ES.3611	T Mk.20S	WE824		Hawker-Siddeley Aircraft Ltd, Langley	.57
			D-CABY	Federal Republic of Germany: del.	7.3.63/70
				crashed, written-off	3.3.70
41H/ 636292 •	FB Mk.11	**WG565**		(to RCN as WG565): BOC 28.8.51: SOC	18.4.57
				Southern Alberta Inst. of Technology, Calgary	4.57/66
				CFB Tecumseh, Calgary: gate guard	5.66/84
				Aero Space Museum of Calgary ALTA	84
				Naval Museum of Alberta, CFB Tecumseh	.88/91
				Calgary Aerospace Museum ALTA: stored	94
41H/ 636294 •	FB Mk.11	**WG567**		(to RCN as WG567): BOC 28.8.51: SOC	8.2.57
			CF-VAN	Robert P. Vanderveken, Pierrefonds QUE	9.61/65
			N878M	Michael D. Carroll, Long Beach CA (conv. to mod. racer #87)	.65/69
				Sherman Cooper, Merced CA (race #87 *Miss Merced*)	.69/72
				forced landing, near Mojave CA	11.71
				James A. Mott, South Gate CA (rebuilt Chino 80/88: race #42 *Super Chief*)	1.76/95
ES.3617 •	FB Mk.11 FB Mk.50	**WG599**		(to R Netherlands Navy/Kon Marine.......)	
			D-CACY	Federal Republic of Germany, Bonn	12.64/72
				Luftwaffen Museum, Uetersen AB, Germany	6.73/95
				Old Flying Machine Co, Duxford: arr. (airlifted by German Army CH-53 ex Uetersen)	22.5.95/96
- •	FB Mk.11	**WG630**		(to RAN as WG630): BOC 7.3.52: SOC (arr. deck cargo on carrier HMAS Vengeance 3.52)	15.11.59
				Experimental Building Station, Ryde NSW (wind machine to test building materials)	11.59/86
				Australian War Memorial, Canberra ACT	8.86
				Naval Aviation Museum, Nowra NAS, NSW (long-term rest. to fly, Nowra "WG630/110K")	8.87/95
ES.8509	T Mk. 20	WG652		Hawker-Siddeley Aviation Ltd, Langley	.57
			D-CAFO	Federal Republic of Germany, Bonn: del.	23.5.60/74
			G-BCKG	Warbirds of GB Ltd, Blackbushe (del. Blackbushe ex Germany 15.8.74)	30.7.74
			N62143	Merryl D. Schulke, Orlando FL (del. USA by Schulke, via Prestwick 20.10.74)	9.74
				John J. Stokes/Warbirds of the World, San Marcos TX	.74/77

				Lloyd A. Hamilton, Santa Rosa CA	5.77
				(conv. to single-seater .79)	
				Jimmy R. McMillan, Breckenridge TX	84
				Arthur W. McDonnell, Mojave CA	5.84/88
				(race #106/*JR-106*")	
				dest. in hangar fire, Shafter CA	7.88
				reg. pending, Palos Park IL	96
ES.3616 41H/ 636070 •	T Mk.20S	**WG655**		Hawker-Siddeley Aviation Ltd, Langley	7.57/63
			D-CACU	Federal Republic of Germany, Bonn: del.	7.8.63/76
				(donated to RN/FAA as WG655)	6.76
				RN Historic Flight, RNAS Yeovilton: del.	23.6.76/90
				crashed, fcd. ldg. near Yeovilton	14.7.90
				Rural Aviation Ltd, Auckland NZ: wreck	91
				(wreck sold to Chicago IL, wing folding gear removed, fitted to Fury ZK-SFR)	
			N20MD	Charles Greenhill, Mettawa IL	17.8.93/96
41H/ 636334 •	FB Mk.11	**WH587**		(to RAN as WH587): BOC 7.3.52: SOC	23.9.63
				(arr. deck cargo on carrier HMAS Vengeance 3.52)	
				G. Greig, Sydney	.63/64
				Lord Trefgarne, Sydney NSW	64
				(del. Bankstown NSW 11.63, shipped to USA .64)	
			N260X	Grant Weaver, San Jose CA (race #33)	5.65/67
				Stan Booker, Fresno CA (race #33)	67
				James R. Fugate, Aurora OR	69
				Sherman Cooper, Merced CA	.71/72
				Westernair of Albuquerque, Albuquerque NM	.72
				Ellsworth Getchell, San Jose CA	7.75/96
				(flies as "RAN WH587/105")	
41H 636335 •	FB Mk.11	**WH588**		(to RAN as WH588): BOC 7.3.52: SOC	23.9.63
				(arr. deck cargo on carrier *HMAS Sydney* 3.52)	
				Lord Trefgarne, Sydney-Bankstown NSW: del.	11.63
				Fawcett Aviation, Bankstown NSW	64/65
			VH-BOU	Fawcett Aviation, Sydney-Bankstown NSW	11.65/69
				(target-tug mods Bankstown, ff 16.9.66)	
				Arnold J. Glass, Sydney NSW	71/72
			N588	Lloyd A. Hamilton, Santa Rosa CA: shipped	4.72/95
				dam., fcd. landing nr. Santa Rosa (repaired)	5.5.74
				(race #16 RAN WH588/16K/*Baby Gorilla*)	
41H 636336 •	FB Mk.11	WH589		(to RAN as WH589): BOC 7.3.52: SOC	23.9.63
				(arr. as deck cargo on carrier *HMAS Sydney* 3.52, collected ex RNFAA NAS Sembawang, Singapore)	
				Lord Trefgarne, Sydney-Bankstown NSW: del.	11.63
				Fawcett Aviation, Bankstown NSW	64/69
				Ormond A. Haydon-Baillie, Vancouver BC	1.69
				(open storage Bankstown 63/69, shipped Sydney to USA on *USS Coral Sea* .69)	
			CF-CHB	Ormond A. Haydon-Baillie, Vancouver BC	.70
				(del. Vancouver-Southend: arr. 23.11.73)	
			G-AGHB	Ormond A. Haydon-Baillie, Southend	9.5.74/78
				(flew as camouflaged "WH589/O-HB")	
				Spencer R. Flack, Elstree	.79
				crashed Osnabruck, West Germany	24.6.79
				Angus McVitie, Cranfield UK (wreck)	80/83
				Craig Charleston, Colchester UK (wreck)	90
			N4434P	Lloyd A. Hamilton, Santa Rosa CA	10.83/96
				(rebuilt as mod. racer with P&W R4360, race #15 *Furias*: composite rebuild of VX715 & WJ290, using fuse. of WH589: adopted id. WH589)	
- •	FB Mk.11	**WJ231**		Fleet Air Arm Museum, RNAS Yeovilton	8.65/96
				(displ. as "WE726", later "WJ231")	

c/n	Version	Serial	Registration	History	Date
41H/ 642111	FB Mk.11	**WJ244**		RNAS Lossiemouth: del. for storage	19.5.60/64
				Hawker Siddeley Aircraft, Dunsfold: del.	16.4.64
				Malcolm D. N. Fisher/Historic Aircraft Preservation Society, Biggin Hill	.66
				Historic Aircraft Museum, Southend: dism.	68/78
			G-FURY	Spencer R. Flack, Elstree	5.7.78/81
				(rest. Elstree, ff 6.80)	
				crashed & dest. near RAF Waddington	2.8.81
				Ted Sinclair, Milton Keynes: wreck	85
				(planned composite rest. project)	
41H/ 696792 •	FB Mk.11	**WJ288**		RNAS Lossiemouth: del. for storage	9.5.61/63
				Hawker Siddeley Aircraft Ltd, Dunsfold: del.	12.3.63/66
				Malcolm D. N. Fisher/Historic Aircraft Preservation Society, Biggin Hill: arr. dism.	2.9.66
				Historic Aircraft Museum, Southend: arr.	6.5.67/83
				Patrick Luscombe: at museum auction	10.5.83
			G-SALY	Patrick Luscombe/British Air Reserve, Lympne/Duxford (rest. Lympne 86)	12.7.83/88
				Warbirds of GB Ltd, Biggin Hill	.88/89
				Ed Stanley, Portland OR: shipped to Chino CA	.90
			N15S	Edwin Stanley, Portland OR	6.91/93
				David W. Peeler, Columbus OH & Memphis TN	12.93/9
-	FB Mk.11	WJ290		Hawker Siddeley Aircraft Ltd, Langley	.57
				Delft Technical School, Netherlands	
				Lloyd A. Hamilton, Santa Rosa CA	80
				(used in rebuild of VX715 as N4434P)	
37542 •	FB Mk.11	**WJ293**		(to Iraqi AF as 302)	
			N39SF	Ed Jurist & David C. Tallichet, Orlando FL	.79
				(recov. ex Iraq, stored dism. Orlando FL)	
				Ed Jurist/Vintage Aircraft Intnl., Nyack NY	8.79
				Henry Haigh/Haigh Industries, Howell MI	12.81/96
				(rebuilt Breckenridge TX with Wright R3350, ff .90 as camouflaged "HH")	
37721 •	FB Mk.11	**WM483**		(to Iraqi AF as 304)	
			N42SF	Ed Jurist & David C. Tallichet, Orlando FL	.79
				(recov. ex Iraq, stored dism. Orlando FL)	
				Ed Jurist/Vintage Aircraft Intnl., Nyack NY	8.79/90
				Richard Bertea, Chino CA	11.90/95
				(rest. Chino CA 92/93, Wright R3350 with 4 blade prop: ff 12.93 as "RCN 14B")	
37755 •	FB Mk.11	**WM484**		(to Iraqi AF as 305)	
			N59SF	Ed Jurist & David C. Tallichet, Orlando FL	.79
				(recov. ex Iraq, stored dism. Orlando FL)	
				Ed Jurist/Vintage Aircraft Intnl., Nyack NY	8.79/87
				Tom Reilly, Kissimmee FL	2.88/95
37757 • 41H/ 65816	FB Mk.11	**WN480**		(to Iraqi AF as ...)	
			N60SF	Ed Jurist & David C. Tallichet, Orlando FL	.79
				(recov. ex Iraq, stored dism. Orlando FL)	
				Ed Jurist/Vintage Aircraft Intnl., Nyack NY	8.79
				John D. Rodgers, St Charles IL	81/91
				(rest. Chicago-Landings as "RN FAA 757/JR")	
				Don Crowe, Delta BC/ Crew Concepts Inc, Boise ID	2.91/95
				forced landing, Reno NV	9.93
				(trucked to Victoria BC: Centaurus replaced)	
				(flies as RCN 181/*Simply Magnificent*)	

37528	FB Mk.11	WN482		(to Iraqi AF as 310)	
			N19SF (1	Ed Jurist & David C. Tallichet, Orlando FL	.79
				John Williams, Tampa FL	.79/81
				(rest. Live Oak FL, ff 13.7.79 as "RCN 121")	
				crashed dest., Harlingen TX (Williams k.)	9.10.81
				(id. tfd. to rebuild project .94: see N19SF(2	
41H/ 656803 •	FB Mk. 11			(to RCN as ....)	
				Frank C. Sanders, Chino CA	c70/90
				(parts used in other Sanders rebuild projects: hulk rebuilt Chino 90/94: adopted id. N19SF)	
				Sanders Aircraft Inc, Chino CA	90/94
			N19SF (2	Sanders Aircraft, Chino CA	20.7.94/96
				(rebuilt Chino CA with Wright R3350, ff 30.7.94 as race #19)	
37514 • (ISS20)	Fury FB.10			(to Iraqi AF as 250)	
			N21SF	Ed Jurist & David C. Tallichet, Orlando FL	.79
				(recov. ex Iraq, stored dism. Orlando FL)	
				Ed Jurist/Vintage Aircraft Intnl., Nyack NY	8.79
				Michael H. Mock & Robert del Valle/ International Ship Repair Service, Tampa FL	3.80/85
				(rest. Tampa FL as "RAN DM/369")	
				Russ Francis, Wallingford VT	7.86/88
				Wiley Sanders/Sanders Truck Lines, Troy AL	10.88/96
				landing accident Troy AL	7.7.90
				(rebuilt with Wright R3350, Breckenridge TX)	
37517 •	Fury FB.10			(to Iraqi AF as 313)	
			N24SF	Ed Jurist & David C. Tallichet, Orlando FL	.79
				(recov. ex Iraq, stored dism. Orlando FL)	
				Ed Jurist/Vintage Aircraft Intnl., Nyack NY	8.79/88
				Sonoma Valley Aircraft Inc, Vineburg CA	7.88
				Milton C. (Chuck) Leshe, Chandler AZ	2.89/96
				(rest. Breckenridge TX 90/92, Wright R3350; mod. racer #8)	
37522 •	FB Mk.11	**WJ298**		(to Iraqi AF as 303): del. ex Langley	9.7.52
			N26SF	Ed Jurist & David C. Tallichet, Orlando FL	.79
				(recov. ex Iraq, stored dism. Orlando FL)	
				Ed Jurist/Vintage Aircraft Intnl., Nyack NY	8.79/84
				John J. Dowd, Syracuse NY	1.88/96
37525 • 41H/ 656823	Fury FB.10			(to Iraqi AF as 325)	
			N30SF	Ed Jurist & David C. Tallichet, Orlando FL	.79
				(recov. ex Iraq, stored dism. Orlando FL)	
				Ed Jurist/Vintage Aircraft Intnl., Nyack NY	8.79/84
				George H. Baker/American Aero Services, New Smyrna Beach FL	11.86/89
				(rebuilt as *Sky Fury* with Wright R3350 using parts of VZ365/D-CACA : ff .90, race #71)	
			N71GB	George H. Baker, New Smyrna Beach FL	8.89/96
37534 • (ISS13)	Fury FB.10			(to Iraqi AF as 243): del. ex Langley	23.9.49
			N28SF	Ed Jurist & David C. Tallichet, Orlando FL	.79
				(recov. ex Iraq, stored dism. Orlando FL)	
				Ed Jurist/Vintage Aircraft Intnl., Nyack NY	8.79
				Guido Zuccoli, Darwin NT : shipped	1.82
			VH-HFX	Guido Zuccoli, Darwin NT	22.4.85
				Bruce Andrews, Melbourne VIC	11.85/91
				(flew as "RAN WH589/115NW")	
			G-BTTA	The Old Flying Machine Company, Duxford	
				shipped, arr. Duxford	25.7.91/96
37536 •	Fury FB.10			(to Iraqi AF as 255)	

(ISS25)		N34SF	Ed Jurist & David C. Tallichet, Orlando FL	.79/82
			(recov. ex Iraq, stored dism. Orlando FL)	
			Ed Jurist/Vintage Aircraft Intnl., Nyack NY	8.79/84
			Howard Pardue/Breckenridge Aviation Museum, Breckenridge TX	4.86/88
		N666HP	Breckenridge Aviation Museum TX	2.88/96
			(rest. Breckenridge TX with Wright R3350, flies as race #66 *Fury*)	
37537 •	Fury FB.10		(to Iraqi AF as 254)	
(ISS24)		**N35SF**	Ed Jurist & David C. Tallichet, Orlando FL	.79
			(recov. ex Iraq, stored dism. Orlando FL)	
			Ed Jurist/Vintage Aircraft Intnl., Nyack NY	8.79/94
			Vernon C. McAllister, Del Norte CO	.94/96
			(under rest. to fly)	
37539 •	Fury FB.10		(to Iraqi AF as 315)	
		N36SF	Ed Jurist & David C. Tallichet, Orlando FL	.79/82
			(recov. ex Iraq, stored dism. Orlando FL)	
			Ed Jurist/Vintage Aircraft Intnl., Nyack NY	8.79/88
			Coleman Warbird Museum, Coleman TX	7.89/90
			(rest. Coleman TX, ff 4.91: shipped to UK 9.91)	
			John Bradshaw, Wroughton/Benson UK	2.8.90/96
			(flies as "Dutch Navy/RAN 361")	
37541 •	Fury FB.10		(to Iraqi AF as 314)	
		N38SF	Ed Jurist & David C. Tallichet, Orlando FL	.79
			(recov. ex Iraq, stored dism. Orlando FL)	
			Ed Jurist/Vintage Aircraft Intnl., Nyack NY	8.79/95
37703 •	Fury FB.10		(to Iraqi AF as 253) : del. ex Langley	21.11.49
(ISS23)		N40SF	Ed Jurist & David C. Tallichet, Orlando FL	.79
			(recov. ex Iraq, stored dism. Orlando FL)	
			Ed Jurist/Vintage Aircraft Intnl., Nyack NY	8.79/82
			Guido Zuccoli, Darwin NT: shipped	1.82
		VH-HFA	Ted Allen, Proserpine QLD	25.1.84/88
			(incorrect id. "WJ231" quoted, flew as RAN 253/K/*Magnificent Obsession*)	
			John MacGuire,Abilene TX: shipped ex Darwin	11.88
		N57JB	John MacGuire/War Eagles Air Museum, Santa Teresa NM: displ. as "RAN 253/K"	13.2.89/95
37723 •	Fury FB.10		(to Iraqi AF as 326)	12.53
41H/ 643827		N43SF	Ed Jurist & David C. Tallichet, Orlando FL	.79
			(recov. ex Iraq, stored dism. Orlando FL)	
			Ed Jurist/Vintage Aircraft Intnl, Nyack NY	8.79/84
		ZK-SFR	Grant Biel & Robbie Booth/ NZ Sea Fury Syndicate, Auckland-Ardmore	11.2.87/93
			(airfreighted to NZ by RNZAF C130, rest. Ardmore, ff 12.3.88 as "RN WJ232/O")	
			(fitted wing-folding mechanism ex WG655 .91)	
			Flightwatch Services Ltd, Auckland-Ardmore	94/96
37724 •	Fury FB.10		(to Iraqi AF as 312)	
		N45SF	Ed Jurist & David C. Tallichet, Orlando FL	.79
			(recov. ex Iraq, stored dism. Orlando FL)	
			Ed Jurist/Vintage Aircraft Intnl., Nyack NY	8.79
			Sonoma Valley Aircraft Inc, Glen Ellen CA	6.83/96
			(rest., flying by 89)	
37726 •	Fury FB.10		(to Iraqi AF as 318)	
		N46SF	Ed Jurist & David C. Tallichet, Orlando FL	.79
			(recov. ex Iraq, stored dism. Orlando FL)	
			Ed Jurist/Vintage Aircraft Intnl., Nyack NY	8.79/96

37727 •	Fury FB.10		(to Iraqi AF as 252)	
(ISS22)		N48SF	Ed Jurist & David C. Tallichet, Orlando FL	.79
			(recov. ex Iraq, stored dism. Orlando FL)	
			Ed Jurist/Vintage Aircraft Intnl., Nyack NY	8.79/87
37729 •	FB Mk.11		(to Iraqi AF as 308)	
41H/		N54SF	Ed Jurist & David C. Tallichet, Orlando FL	.79
65802			(recov. ex Iraq, stored dism. Orlando FL)	
			Ed Jurist/Vintage Aircraft Intnl., Nyack NY	8.79/82
			Guido Zuccoli, Darwin NT : shipped	1.82
		VH-HFG	Guido Zuccoli, Darwin NT	9.11.83/95
			(rest. Darwin, ff 14.11.83 as RAN 308/K)	
			dam., fcd. ldg. nr. Toowoomba, QLD (repaired)	24.3.84
			(id. orig. quoted as c/n 37522/N26SF: which see)	
37731 •	Fury FB.10		(to Iraqi AF as 249) : del. ex Langley	23.9.49
(ISS19)		N54SF	Ed Jurist & David C. Tallichet, Orlando FL	.79
			(recov. ex Iraq, stored dism. Orlando FL)	
			Ed Jurist/Vintage Aircraft Intnl., Nyack NY	8.79/82
		VH-HFR	ntu: Rob H. Poynton, Toodyay WA: shipped	1.82/92
		VH-ISS	Robert H. Poynton, Perth WA: reg. res.	15.9.92/96
			(rest. to fly, Toodyay/Cunderdin/Jandakot WA, as Iraqi AF 249)	
37733 •	Fury FB.10		(to Iraqi AF as 316)	
		N56SF	Ed Jurist & David C. Tallichet, Orlando FL	.79
			(recov. ex Iraq, stored dism. Orlando FL)	
			Ed Jurist/Vintage Aircraft Intnl., Nyack NY	8.79
			John D. Rodgers, St Charles IL	12.81/95
			op: Air Classics Aircraft Museum, DuPage IL	95/96
			(flies as Royal Navy 737/JR)	
37734	Fury FB.10		(to Iraqi AF as 324)	
41H/	(2 seat)	N58SF	Ed Jurist & David C. Tallichet, Orlando FL	.79
623271			(recov. ex Iraq, stored dism. Orlando FL)	
			Ed Jurist/Vintage Aircraft Intnl., Nyack NY	8.79/80
			Weeks Air Museum, Tamiami FL	.80/95
			dam. in hangar fire, Rockford IL	19.7.89
		N1324	Buddy Bryan/Utilco Inc, Tifton GA	7.90/93
			Neil J. McClain, Salt Lake City UT	11.93/96
			(note: N1324 rep. as rebuild project of N58SF but USCR quotes N1324 id. as 41H-623282)	
87953 •	Fury		(to Iraqi AF as 327)	
		N62SF	Ed Jurist & David C. Tallichet, Orlando FL	.79
			(recov. ex Iraq, stored dism. Orlando FL)	
			Ed Jurist/Vintage Aircraft Intnl., Nyack NY	8.79/96
87954 •	Fury		(to Iraqi AF: rep. as spare airframe)	
		N63SF	Ed Jurist & David C. Tallichet, Orlando FL	.79
			(recov. ex Iraq, stored dism. Orlando FL)	
			Ed Jurist/Vintage Aircraft Intnl., Nyack NY	8.79/96
(ISS4)	Fury FB.10		(to Iraqi AF as 234)	
			(to R Moroccan AF as.....)	4.2.60
			stored, Rabat, Morocco	.78
			rep. via French broker to USA	
(ISS11) •	Fury FB.10		(to Iraqi AF as 241)	
		N64SF	Ed Jurist & David C. Tallichet, Orlando FL	.79
			(recov. ex Iraq, stored dism. Orlando FL)	
			Ed Jurist/Vintage Aircraft Intnl., Nyack NY	8.79/87
(ISS29)	Fury FB.10		(to Iraqi AF as 259)	

				(to Moroccan AF as .....)	4.2.60
				stored, Rabat, Morocco	.78
				rep. via French broker to USA	
- •	FB Mk. 11	-		(to FA Cubana as 541)	.58
				Bay of Pigs Museum, Playa Giron, Cuba	76/96
- •	FB Mk. 11	-		(to FA Cubana as 542)	.58
				Museo de la Revolucion, Havana, Cuba	80/96
6310 •	FB Mk.50 (Fokker)	06-43		(R Netherlands Navy/Kon Marine as 06-43)	
				Delft Technical School, Delft, Netherlands	.59/71
				Aviodome Museum, Amsterdam-Schiphol	.71/93
				Militaire Luchtvaart Museum, Soesterberg AB	93/96

HAWKER HURRICANE

W/0 5422 •	Mk. I	**L1592**		dam. forced landing, near Croydon	18.8.40
				(repaired: stored for future museum use)	
				RAF Air Historical Branch, Stanmore	54
				Science Museum, South Kensington, London	62/96
41H/ 11096 •	Mk. I	**N2394**		(to Finnish AF as HU-452, later HC-452)	.40
				Finnish AF Museum: stored Vesivehmaa AB	69
				Aviation Museum of Central Finland, Luonetjarvi AB, Tikkakoski	72/92
- •	Mk. I	**P2617**		RAF Kenley, for movie "Reach For The Sky"	.55
				RAF Air Historical Branch, Stanmore	.55
				RAF Rufforth: stored, derelict	58
				RAF Bicester: travelling exhibit	65/71
				(taxy scenes, film *Battle of Britain* 68)	
				RAF Museum, Hendon	11.72/96
				(displ. as "P2617/AF-F")	
- •	Mk. I	**P2902**		crashed Dunkirk, France.	31.05.40
				(hulk recov. ex sand dunes, Dunkirk .88)	
			G-ROBT	Richard A. Roberts, Billinghurst	19.9.94/96
				(rest. to fly, Suffolk 94)	
				(rest. to fly as P2902/DX-X)	
- •	Mk. I	**P3175**		shot down by Bf110 near North Weald	31.8.40
				RAF Museum, Hendon	79/96
				(displ. unrest. as wartime wreck)	
- •	Mk. I Mk. IIa	**P3351** **DR393**		(to RAF as P3351): crashed Prestwick	21.7.40
				(rebuilt as Mk. IIa DR393)	
				(to Soviet AF as DR393): shipped	5.41
				rep. crashed near Murmansk	.43
				recov. ex crash site Russia	
				Jim Pearce, Shoreham UK: hulk arr.	9.92/93
				(wings carry RAF roundel & Russian star, Polish chequerboard emblem on each cowling)	
			ZK-TPL	Alpine Fighter Collection, Wanaka NZ	.93/95
				Hawker Restorations UK 94/95: shipped to NZ 9.95 for completion)	
				(rest. to fly as P3351/TP-K)	
- •	Mk. I	**V6846**		(to Indian AF as V6846)	6.44
				Patna AB, India: displ.	66/73
- •	Mk. IIb	**Z5053**		(to Soviet AF as Z5053)	1.42
				rep. shot down in combat, Archangel, Russia	8.43

C/n	Type	Serial	Reg.	History	Date
				recov. from crash site, Welikoe, Oneshakij	
				Swiss purchaser: planned rest. in Hungary	
				Historic Flying Ltd, Audley End: arr UK	7.94/95
			G-BWHA	Historic Flying Ltd, Audley End	23.8.95
				Richard A. Roberts, Billinghurst	96.
- •	Mk. IIb Trop	**Z5207**		Shipped to Russia. 151Wing.	08.41
				Flew off *HMS Argus*	07.09 41
				handed over to Russian Airforce. 72 IAP	17.10.41
				recov. from crash site, Kola Peninsula, Russia	
				Swiss purchaser: planned rest. in Hungary	
				Historic Flying Ltd, Audley End: arr UK	7.94
				Richard A. Roberts, Billinghurst	96.
				(id. believed correct, unconfirmed)	
- •	Mk. IIb Trop	**Z5227**		Shipped to Russia. 151Wing.	08.41
				Flew off *HMS Argus*	07.09 41
				handed over to Russian Airforce. 72 IAP	17.10.41
				recov. from Murmansk region. Russia	95
				Greg Herrich. USA.	95/96
				(planned restoration to fly).	
-	MkIIb Trop	**Z5252**		Shipped to Russia. 151 Wing.	08.41
				Assembled Archangel and test flown	13.09.41
				Presentation aircraft '01' with Russian stars.	
				General Kouznetzov. Commander Russian	
				Air forces. Kola Region.	25.09.41
				Stored in Military Musreum. Russia.	
				rep Jim Pearce, Shoreham UK: arr.	96.
				rep H. Taylor.	
				(planned restoration to fly).	96.
CCF/41H/ 4013 •	Sea Hurr. Mk. 1b	**Z7015**		Loughborough Tech. College: inst. airframe	11.43/61
				Shuttleworth Trust, Old Warden: by road21.2.61/83	
				(static displ. Old Warden 61/75; taxy scenes	
				in film *Battle of Britain* .67/68;	
				rest. to fly begun .75 Staverton, to Duxford .81)	
			G-BKTH	Shuttleworth Trust/Imperial War Museum 24.5.83/95	
				(long-term rest. Duxford .81/94,	
				ff Duxford 16.9.95 as "RNFAA Z7015/7-L")	
CCF/41H/	Sea Hurr.	**AE977**		recovered from crash site. SW England	88
				Alpine Fighter Collection, Wanaka NZ	94
			G-TWTD	Tim Wallis & Tony Ditheridge/	
				Hawker Restorations Ltd, Milden	21.4.94
				(rest. to fly, Suffolk 94)	
- •	Mk. IIc	**BH229**		(to Soviet AF as ......)	
				recov. ex crash site Russia	
				Jim Pearce, Shoreham UK: hulk arr.	9.92/93
				Alpine Fighter Collection, Wanaka NZ: shipped.93/94	
- •	Sea Hurr. Mk. XIIa	**BW841**		(to RCAF as BW841): BOC 18.12.41: SOC	16.10.42
				Jack Arnold, Brantford ONT	90/92
				Jack Arnold, Titusville FL	93/94
				(hulk recov. ex farm ONT, rest. to fly)	
CCF/ R30019 •	Sea Hurr. Mk. XIIa	**BW853**		(to RCAF as BW853): BOC 17.12.41: SOC	12.10.44
				crashed, Bagotville QUE: major dam.	1.8.44
				Anthony J. Ditheridge, Suffolk UK	88
			G-BRKE	AJD Engineering, Milden	6.10.89/94
				(rest. to fly, Suffolk)	

CCF/ R30028 •	Sea Hurr. Mk. XIIa	BW862		(to RCAF as BW862): BOC 30.12.41: SOC	12.10.44
				crashed forced ldg., Lac St. Jean QUE	6.7.44
				Tex LaVallee/LaVallee Cultural & Aeronautical Collection, St Chrysostome QUE	80
				(incomplete hulk recov. ex junkyard QUE)	
				Canadian Museum of Flight & Transportation, Surrey BC, later Langley BC: stored	.80/96
- •	Sea Hurr. Mk. XIIa	**BW873**		(to RCAF as BW873): BOC 19.1.42: SOC	15.8.44
				Jack Arnold Aviation Museum, Brantford ONT	88/92
				Jack Arnold Aviation Museum, Titusville FL	93/94
				(rest. project: with parts RCAF5301, 5381)	
CCF/ R32007 •	Sea Hurr. Mk. XIIa	**BW881**		(to RCAF as BW881): BOC 22.1.42: SOC	28.9.44
				Jack Arnold, Brantford ONT: recov. ex farm	
				Matt Sattler, Carp ONT	88
				Anthony J. Ditheridge, Suffolk UK	12.88/94
				(rest. to fly, Suffolk 94/95)	
			G-KAMM	M. Hammond, Eye, Suffolk	23.2.95
- •	Mk. IV	**KX829**		Loughborough Tech. College: inst. airframe	7.3.46/61
				Museum of Science & Industry, Birmingham	.61/96
				(displ. as "KX829/JV-I", later "P3395")	
- •	Mk. IV	**KZ321**		(to Yugoslav AF as ....)	
				(to IDFAF as ....)	
				Warbirds of GB Ltd, Blackbushe	.83/89
				(hulk recov. from scrapyard Jaffa, Israel .83)	
			G-HURY	Warbirds of GB, Biggin Hill 31.3.89/91	
				(rest. project, stored Biggin Hill 89)	
				The Fighter Collection, Duxford	.91/95
				(rest. to fly, Duxford 95)	
- •	Mk. IIc	LD619		(to SAAF as 5285)	4.44
				South African National Museum of Military History, Saxonwold, Johannesburg	5.50/92
41H/ 368368 •	Mk. IV	**LD975**		(to Yugoslav AF as 9539)	
				Yugoslavian Aviation Museum, Belgrade	68/96
				(displ. as "LD975")	
41H/ 469290 •	Mk. IIc	**LF363**		RAF Air Historical Branch, Stanmore	54
				RAF Kenley: for movie "Reach for the Sky"	.55
				RAF Battle of Britain Memorial Flight	6.57/95
				(flew in movie *Battle of Britain* .68)	
				forced landing, burned, RAF Wittering	11.9.91
				(burnt-out wreck arr. Audley End 6.10.94 ex RAF Coningsby for rest. to fly for BBMF)	
- •	Mk. IIc	**LF658**		(to Belgium AF as LF658): BOC	2.9.46
				Musee Royal de l'Armee, Brussels	68/95
				(displ. as "LF345/ML-B", later "LF345/ZA-P")	
- •	Mk. IIc	**LF686**		RAF Bridgenorth	62
				RAF Museum, RAF Colerne	65/69
				NASM, Silver Hill MD	69/96
				(static rest. Silver Hill 92/95 using parts ex UK)	
- •	Mk. IIc	**LF738**		RAF Biggin Hill: displ.	54/84
				(stored Rochester 85/93, static rest. .93/95)	
				RAF Museum, RAF Cosford:	96
- •	Mk. IIc	**LF751**		RAF Waterbeach	

				RAF Bently Priory: gate guard (static scenes, "Battle of Britain" .68) (arr. Rochester 21.3.85 for static rest. 85/88)	54/85
				RAF Manston: displ. as "BN230/FT-A"	4.88/95
- •	Mk. IIc	**PZ865**		last Hurricane built: ff. Langley	27.7.44
				Hawker Aircraft Ltd, Langley (stored .46/50, rest. Langley, ff 13.5.50)	8.44/50
			G-AMAU	Hawker Aircraft Ltd, Dunsfold	1.5.50/72
				Hawker Siddeley Aviation Ltd, Dunsfold (flew in *Battle of Britain*.68)	7.63/72
				RAF Battle of Britain Memorial Flight (flew as PZ865 *Last Of The Many)*	29.3.72/96
42012	Mk. IIb Mk. XII	RCAF5377		RCAF BOC 16.6.42: SOC	13.7.46
				Jim Roy, Portage la Prairie MAN (to farm ex RCAF surplus, became derelict)	.46/64
				resident, Carman, MAN	.64/66
			CF-SMI	resident, Carman, MAN (rest. Carman, flew as "RCAF 5585") (shipped UK .67 for movie "Battle of Britain" .68)	.66/68
			G-AWLW	N. A. W. (Tony) Samuelson, Elstree 10.7.68/69	
				Sir W. J. D. Roberts, Shoreham	12.69/72
				Sir William Roberts/Strathallan Collection, Auchterader, Scotland (flew as "P3308/UP-A")	3.72/84
			C-GCWH	Canadian Warplane Heritage, Hamilton ONT (del. to Hamilton by RCAF C-130: ff 4.6.84, flew as "P3069/YO-A")	5.84/93
				dest. in hangar fire, Hamilton ONT	15.2.93
42015 •	Mk. IIb Mk. XII	**RCAF5380**		RCAF BOC 16.6.42: crashed 29.9.42: SOC	11.2.43
				rep. under rest., Ontario, Canada	88
42024 •	Mk. IIb Mk. XII	**RCAF5389**		RCAF 23.6.42: SOC	20.8.46
				Air Museum of Canada, Calgary ALTA	69/72
				Calgary Air & Space Museum, Calgary ALTA (displ. during static rest.)	88/94
42025 •	Mk. IIb Mk. XII	RCAF5390		RCAF BOC 30.6.42: SOC	4.4.44
				crashed into sea	7.2.44
				Bob Schneider/RRS Aviation, Hawkins TX	88
				USAFM, Wright Patterson AFB OH : arr. (static rest., displ. as RAF "Z3174")	9.90
- •	Mk. IIb Mk. XII	**RCAF5400**		RCAF BOC 18.1.44: SOC	3.7.47
				Don Bradshaw, Saskatoon SASK	85
				Weeks Air Museum, Tamiami FL (rest. project)	.85/94
- •	Mk. IIb Mk. XII	**RCAF5409**		RCAF BOC 20.7.47: SOC	20.8.46
				Neil M. Rose, Vancouver WA (rest. project)	89
44013 •	Mk. IIb Mk. XII	**RCAF5418**		RCAF BOC 5.8.42: SOC	20.8.46
				Reynolds Pioneer Museum, Wetaskiwin ALTA c73/86	
				Reynolds Aviation Museum,Wetaskiwin ALTA (rest., engine runs 12.88 as "RCAF 5418")	87/94
44019	Mk. IIb Mk. XII	**RCAF5424**		RCAF BOC 18.8.42: SOC	15.8.46
				Air Museum of Canada, Calgary ALTA	69/70
				Rem Walker, Regina SASK: rest. project	.70/82
46002 •	Mk. IIb Mk. XII	**RCAF5447**		RCAF BOC 29.9.42: SOC	20.8.46
				Harry Whereatt, Assiniboia SASK	88/93

c/n		Mark	Serial	Reg	History	Date
-	•	Mk. IIb	**RCAF5455**		RCAF BOC 12.9.42: crashed 28.1.44: SOC	30.5.44
		Mk. XII			Harry Whereatt,	
					Assiniboia SASK	72
					(*Stardust*, recov. derelict ex farm,	
					Stewart Valley, SASK)	
-	•	Mk. IIb	**RCAF5461**		RCAF BOC 12.9.42: SOC	30.6.47
		Mk. XII			Commonwealth Air Training Plan Museum,	
					Brandon MAN	88/89
60372	•	Mk. IIb	**RCAF5481**		RCAF BOC 7.10.42: SOC	29.11.44
		Mk. XII			Jack Arnold Aviation Museum, Brantford ONT	84
					(recov. derelict ex farm: complete except wings)	
					Charles Church (Spitfires) Ltd, Sandown UK	.86/89
					arr. crated ex Davidstown, Canada	6.86
				G-ORGI	Charles Church Displays Ltd, Micheldever	11.89/91
					(rebuilt Micheldever, ff 8.9.91)	
				N678DP	Liberty Aero Corp/	
					Museum of Flying, Santa Monica CA20.2.91/95	
					(shipped to Chino CA, arr. 1.3.92:	
					ff Chino CA 17.4.92 as "P2970/US-X")	
52019	•	Mk. IIb	**RCAF5584**		RCAF BOC 6.11.42: stored for museum use	46
		Mk. XII			Canadian National Aeronautical Collection,	
					Rockcliffe AB ONT	.64/82
					National Aviation Museum, Rockcliffe ONT	9.82/96
					(displ. as "RCAF 5584/A")	
52024	•	Mk. IIb	**RCAF5589**		RCAF BOC 6.11.42: SOC	1.10.46
		Mk. XII			Harry Whereatt, Assiniboia SASK	
					(recov. derelict ex farm, Saskatoon SASK)	
					Brian Angliss/Autokraft Ltd, Brooklands	88/90
				G-HURR	Brian Angliss/Autokraft Ltd, Brooklands30.7.90/92	
					(rest. Brooklands as "BE417/AE-K", due to fly .92)	
52025	•	Mk. IIb	**RCAF5590**		RCAF BOC 6.11.42: SOC	3.7.47
		Mk. XII			rest. project, Ontario, Canada	89
-		Mk. IIb	**RCAF5625**		RCAF BOC 26.1.43: SOC	26.10.46
		Mk. XII			Rae Reid/Reid's Flying Service, Guelph ONT	10.46/56
					(del. ex surplus Rockcliffe ONT-Guelph 19.10.46)	
					CofA refused; used as airport gate-guard	47/56
					derelict, to scrapyard Guelph ONT	
					Rem Walker, Regina SASK: hulk	80/82
					(used in rest. of RCAF 5711: que se)	
-	•	Mk. IIb	**RCAF5627**		RCAF 18.11.42: SOC	2.2.44
		Mk. XII			rest. project, Ontario, Canada	89
56021	•	Mk. IIb	**RCAF5666**		RCAF BOC 3.2.43: SOC	20.12.44
		Mk. XII			crashed, forced ldg. Moosehead Lake ME	29.10.44
					Tex LaVallee/LaVallee Cultural & Aeronautical	
					Collection, St Chrysostome QUE	80
					(incomplete hulk recov. ex scrapyard QUE)	
					Ed & Rose Zalesky, Surrey BC: stored	.80/96
56022	•	Mk. IIb	**RCAF5667**		RCAF BOC 3.2.43: SOC	1.10.46
		Mk. XII			derelict on farm, Saskatchewan	48/65
				N2549	Neil M. Rose, Vancouver WA	6.65/96
					(recov. ex farm SASK 6.65,	
					long-term rest. Vancouver WA, ff 10.5.94)	
					dam. landing Yakima WA	22.5.94
72036	•	Mk. IIb	**RCAF5711**		RCAF BOC 8.1.43: SOC	3.7.47

	Mk. XII			Air Museum of Canada, Calgary ALTA	70
				Rem Walker, Regina SASK	75/82
				(rest. project, composite rebuild using parts	
				from RCAF 5625, 5547 & 5424: que se)	
				B. J. S. Grey, Duxford: shipped UK ex Canada 12.82	
			G-HURI	The Fighter Collection, Duxford	9.6.83/96
				(rest. Coventry & Coningsby, arr. Duxford	
				30.1.88 for final work, ff 1.9.89 as "Z7381/XR-T")	
1H-	Mk. IIc	-		(to Soviet AF as ......)	
08549 •				recov. ex crash site Lov Ozero, N. Russia	c85
				rest., displ. on pylon Revda, Russia: dedicated1.9.89/94	
0182 •		-		(to Soviet AF as ......)	
				hulk recov. ex crash site Russia	
				Kolair Inc, Roswell GA	94
				(one of three centre-section wrecks offered for sale	
				as rest. project)	
- •	Mk.II	-		(to Soviet AF as ......)	
				recov. ex crash site Russia	
				The Fighter Collection, Duxford	92
				Imperial War Museum, Duxford	.92
				(to be rest. Duxford for static displ., using parts	
				from a second wrecked airframe ex Russia)	
- •	Mk. IIb	-		(to Indian AF as ....)	
				Indian AF Museum, Palam AB, New Dehli	67/91
				(displ. as "AP832")	
- •	Mk. IV	-		(to IDFAF as ....)	
				Robs Lamplough, Duxford UK	.83/89
				(wreck recov. from scrapyard Jaffa, Israel .83)	
				(rest. project: Fowlmere 85, North Weald 89)	
- •	Mk. IIb	-		(to RCAF as ....)	
	Mk. XII			Duane Egli, Fabens TX	72
				(recov. swamp near Gander, trucked TX .72)	
				Len Tanner, New Baintree CT : rest. to fly	88/91
			N68RW	Lone Star Flight Museum, Galveston TX	8.91/94
				(rest. Fort Collins CO 91/95, due to fly .96;	
				id. quoted as "CCF-96")	
- •	Mk. IIb	-		(to RCAF as ....)	
	Mk. XII			Bob Schneider/RRS Aviation, Hawkins TX	89
				(five derelict airframes recov. ex farms, Canada)	
- •	Mk. IIb	-		(to Soviet AF as .....)	
				recov. from crash sites Russia	
				Ben Kolotilin/ Kolair Inc, Roswell GA	95
				Ed & Rose Zalesky, Surrey BC: arr.	11.95
				(3 crash hulks: composite rest. project)	

HAWKER TEMPEST

- •	Mk. V	**EJ693**		Technical High School, Delft, Netherlands	63/67
				RAF Museum Store, RAF Henlow	68/88
				Tangmere Flight, Tangmere	89/92
				Cantor International Ltd	
				Weeks Air Museum, Tamiami FL	9.92/93
			N7027E	Kermit A. Weeks, Tamiami FL	26.4.93/95
				(rest. to fly Hull UK 93, Booker .93/96)	
- •	Mk. II	**LA607**		prototype Tempest Mk. II: ff	18.9.43
				College of Aeronautics, Cranfield	48/66

				Skyfame Museum, Staverton & Duxford	7.66/83
				(displ. as "LA607/J-DN")	
				Kermit A. Weeks FL: Duxford auction	14.4.83
			N607LA	Weeks Air Museum, Tamiami FL	11.83/96
				(stored Tamiami FL, pending rest.)	
12177 •	Mk. II	**MW376**		(to Indian AF as HA564)	.47
				recov. by Warbirds of GB Ltd, Blackbushe	.79/80
				(arr. crated Blackbushe ex India .79)	
				Tangmere Flight, Tangmere	.80
				Chris P. Horsley, Chichester	.88
				Syndicate, Stamford	90
			G-BSHW	David Martin, London	10.6.91/93
				estate of David Martin	93
				(rest. to fly, Spanhoe Lodge 88/92; rest. ceased, trucked to Audley End 25.10.93: project for sale)	
				North Weald	5.96
1181 •	Mk. II	**MW401**		(to Indian AF as HA604)	.47
				recov. by Warbirds of GB Ltd, Blackbushe	.79/80
				(arr. crated Blackbushe ex India .79)	
				Tangmere Flight, Tangmere	.80
				Autokraft Ltd, Brooklands	.88
			G-PEST	Autokraft Limited, Brooklands	9.10.89/96
				(rest. to fly, Brooklands)	
- •	Mk. II	**MW404**		(to Indian AF as HA557)	.47
				recov. by Warbirds of GB Ltd, Blackbushe	.79/80
				(arr. crated Blackbushe ex India .79)	
				Tangmere Flight, Tangmere	.80
				Chris P. Horsley, Chichester	.88
- •	Mk. II	**MW741**		(to Indian AF as HA622)	.47
				open storage, airfield decoy, Poona AB, India	69
				rep. still stored in India	88
- •	Mk. II	**MW758**		(to Indian AF as HA580)	.47
				open storage, airfield decoy, Poona AB, India	69
				recov. by Warbirds of GB Ltd, Blackbushe	.79/80
				(arr. crated Blackbushe ex India .79)	
				Tangmere Flight, Tangmere	.80
420 •	Mk. II	**MW763**		(to Indian AF as HA586)	.47
				recov. by Warbirds of GB Ltd, Blackbushe	.79
				(arr. crated Blackbushe ex India .79)	
				Tangmere Flight, Tangmere	.80
				Autokraft Ltd, Brooklands	88
			G-TEMT	Autokraft Ltd, Brooklands	9.10.89/96
				(rest. to fly, Brooklands)	
- •	Mk. II	**MW810**		(to Indian AF as HA591)	.47
				recov. by Warbirds of GB Ltd, Blackbushe	.79/80
				(arr. crated Blackbushe ex India .79)	
				Tangmere Flight, Tangmere	.80/86
				New England Air Museum, Windsor Locks CT	1.7.86/90
				rep. sold	.90
- •	Mk. II	**MW848**		(to Indian AF as HA623)	.48
				Indian AF Museum, Palam AB, New Dehli	68/91
- •	Mk. V	**NV778**		RAF Proof & Experimental Establishment,	
				Foulness Island, Essex	58
				RAF Middleton St. George: displ. as "SN219"	61/62
				RAF Museum, RAF Cosford: displ. as "NV778"	67/69

					RAF Museum, Hendon	.72/91
					RAF Museum Store, RAF Cardington	11.91/94
-	•	Mk. II	**PR538**		(to Indian AF as HA457)	
					airfield decoy, Poona AB, India	69
					recov. by Warbirds of GB Ltd, Blackbushe	.79/80
					(arr. dism. Blackbushe ex India .79)	
					Tangmere Flight, Tangmere	.80/87
					RAF Museum Store, Cardington	.87
					(composite static rest. Duxford for RAFM 90/91)	
					RAF Museum, Hendon	11.91/95
					(arr. Hendon 10.11.91, displ. as "PR536/OQ-H")	
					(id. also quoted as PR536)	

HAWKER TYPHOON

-	•	Mk. IB	**MN235**		(to USAF for trials, Wright Field as T2-491)	3.44
					Smithsonian Institute/NASM: stored	53/68
					Museum of Science & Industry, Chicago: loan	
					RAF Museum, Hendon	4.68/96
					(airfreighted to RAF Shawbury .68 for rest.)	
-	•		-		Phil Earthy/Classic Warbirds, Norfolk UK	91/96
					(rest. project, using components ex scrapyard)	

HEINKEL HE111/CASA2.111

Nr1526	•	He 111P-1			(Luftwaffe "33+C25"; later KG4 "5J+CN")	
					shot down by RNFAA Skua, crashed in	
					mountains near Lesjaskog, Norway	26.4.40
					Norwegian AF Museum, Gardermoen AB	.76/92
					(wreck recov. ex mountains 7.76,	
					fully rest. Gardermoen: displ. as "5J+CN")	
Nr2940	•	He 111E-1			(to Legion Condor, Spain): del.	3.38
					(to Ejercito del Aire as B.2-82): wfu	.56
					Museo del Aire, Cuatro Vientos AB, Madrid	65/93
					(displ. as "B.2-82/14-16")	
Nr701152	•	He 111H-20			"NT+SL": captured by USAAF in Germany	.45
					del. to Cherbourg, France: planned shipping to	
					USA; but del. Cherbourg-USAAF Boxted UK	2.7.45
					RAF Air Historical Branch: dism., packed	5.47/64
					(stored dism. Stanmore Park 54, Wroughton,	
					Fulbeck, Biggin Hill 60, St Athan 67)	
					RAF Henlow: for film *Battle of Britain*	.67/68
					RAF Museum, RAF St Athan	70/78
					RAF Museum, Hendon	.78/95
					(displ. as "701152/NT+5L")	
-		CASA-2.111	DBR2.1-10	N99260	Dolph D. Overton, Kenley NC	2.77
				G-BFFS	Warbirds of GB Ltd, Blackbushe	4.11.77
					crashed on del., near Escorial, Spain (N. Williams k)	11.12.77
535	•	CASA-2.111	**DBR2.1-14**		Museo del Aire, Cuatro Vientos AB, Madrid	78/80
					Air Classik, Frankfurt-Rhein Main: displ.	81/96
-	•	CASA-2.111	**DBR2.1-129**		Musee de l'Air, Paris-Le Bourget	75/93
-	•	CASA-2.111	**EB.21-27**	**N99230**	Dolph D. Overton, Kenley NC	2.77/83
					(del. to USA,via Prestwick, Scotland 11.10.77)	
					displ. Wings & Wheels Museum, Orlando FL	81
					MARC, Chino CA	7.83/95
					Combat Air Museum, Topeka KS: loan	90/96

c/n		Type / Mil. ID	Reg.	Owner / Operator	Date
				(flies as "Luftwaffe 9K+EZ")	
167	•	CASA-2.111 **DB.21-37**		T. G. Mahaddie, Tablada, Spain	.67/68
			G-AWHB	T. G. Mahaddie/Spitfire Productions Ltd,	
				Duxford (for film *Battle of Britain*)	21.5.68/69
				T. G. Mahaddie: stored West Malling	2.69/72
				Historic Aircraft Museum, Southend	3.72/83
				(displ. as "6J+PR")	
				Paul Raymond/London War Museum (dism.)	10.5.83/85
				Kermit A. Weeks, Tamiami FL: at auction	5.6.85
				(remained stored dism., Royston, Herts 83/88)	
				Aces High Ltd, North Weald UK	.88/96
				(arr. dism. North Weald 2.88: stored dism.,	
				under static rest. North Weald .93/94)	
				(also rep. as B.21-57, c/n 049 & c/n 186!)	
025	•	CASA-2.111 **DB.21-77**		T. G. "Hamish" Mahaddie, Tablada, Spain	.67/68
			G-AWHA	T. G. Mahaddie/Spitfire Productions Ltd,	
				Duxford (for film *Battle of Britain*)	14.5.68/69
				displ. West Germany for film promotion	.69/70
			D-CAGI	reg.	20.8.70
				noted at Saarbrucken WG	8.70
				Deutsches Museum, Munich ("6J+PR")	72/85
				Flugwerft Schleissheim Deutsches Museum,	
				Oberschleissheim, Munich	92/93
				(also rep. as B.21-166, B.21-177 & c/n 166!)	
-	•	CASA-2.111 **BB.21-82**		Auto und Technik Mus., Sinsheim, Germany	92/94
				(displ. as "Luftwaffe 5J+GN")	
108	•	CASA-2.111 **EB.21-97**			
		CASA-2.111 **BT.8B-97**		Museo del Aire, Cuatro Vientos AB, Madrid	.72/93
				(displ. as "T.8B-97/462-04")	
-	•	CASA-2.111 **BB.21-103**		Ejercito del Aire, Tablada AB, Seville	
				displ.	75/95
				Old Flying Machine Co, Duxford UK	.95
				awaiting shipment	96
-	•	CASA-2.111 **EB.21-117**		Luftwaffen Museum, Uetersen AB, Hamburg 73/93	
				(displ. as "Luftwaffe GI+AD")	
-	•	CASA-2.111 **ET.8B-124**	G-BDYA	Warbirds of GB Ltd, Blackbushe	21.5.76
				(del. Blackbushe 18.6.76 ex Madrid)	
			N72615	Confederate Air Force, Harlingen; later	
				Midland TX	8.77/96
				(del. to USA via Prestwick 24.9.77, flew as	
				Luftwaffe 1H+GS, later "7053/9K+WS)	
				dam. takeoff, Harlingen TX (repaired)	12.10.89
				(flies as Luftwaffe 7052/9K+GS)	
-	•	CASA-2.111D		USAFM Wright-Patterson AFB, Dayton OH	73/96
				(under rest. for static displ. 89)	

HENSCHEL HS293

c/n		Type	Reg.	Owner / Operator	Date
Nr21816	•	Hs 293A-1		Kongelige Norsk Luftforssvaret Collection,	
				Gardermoen AB, Norway	78/84
				Forsvarsmuseet, Akershus Castle, Oslo	84/93
Nr242886	•	Hs 293A-1		Vojenske Muzeum, Kbely AB, Czechoslovakia	84
-	•	Hs 293A-1		Luftwaffen Museum, Uetersen AB, Hamburg	84/93

Ilyushin IL-2

303560 •	Il-2-m3M	3560	(Soviet AF 3560) fcd. ldg. on frozen Lake Sennegress, Norway Norwegian Air Force Museum Collection (recov. from lake .88, static rest. in Norway & Revda, Russia 88/89) Sor-Varanger Museum, Kirkenes, Norway (displ. as Soviet AF "2")	 22.10.44 .88 10.89/92
- •	Il-2-m3		(to Soviet AF as Red 38) Czechoslovak Museum, Kbely AB, Prague	 73/94
- •	Il-2		(to Soviet AF as ....) Jeet Mahal, Vancouver BC (static rest. Russia: offered for sale rest. 94) NASM, Silver Hill MD: arr. dism.	 94 4.95
- •	Il-2-m3		Aviation Museum of Central Finland, Luonetjarvi AB : fuse. only, stored	 80/92
- •	Il-2-m3		Museum of the 16 Luftarmee, Wunsdorf AB Germany: displ.	 92
- •	Il-2-m3		(to Polish AF as ....) Polish Army Museum, Warsaw: displ.	 83/93
- •	Il-2		(to Bulgarian AF as 425) Plovdiv Museum, Bulgaria: displ.	 95

Ilyushin IL-10

•	Il-10		Yuri Gagarin Air Force Academy, Monino AB Moscow, Russia: displ. complete	 91/94
- •	Il-10		Beijing Aeronautical Institute, Beijing China	87
- •	Il-10		People's Liberation Army Air Force Museum, Changping, China: stored dism. as "25"	 93/94
- •	Il-10		People's Liberation Army Air Force Museum, Changping, China: displ. as "33"	 93/94
- •	Il-10		People's Liberation Army Air Force Museum, Changping, China: stored dism. as "56"	 93/94
- •	Il-10		People's Liberation Army Air Force Museum, Changping, China: stored dism. as "80"	 93/94
- •	Il-10		People's Liberation Army Air Force Museum, Changping, China: displ. as "1219"	 93/94
- •	Il-10UTI		People's Liberation Army Air Force Museum, Changping, China: displ. as "10"	 93/94
- •	Il-10 (Avia)		(to Polish AF as "4") Polish Army Museum, Warsaw Museum of Aircraft & Astronautics, Krakow	 68/74 83/92
B33-502•	Il-10 (Avia B33)		(to Czech AF as 5502) Letecka Expozice Vojenskeho Muzea,Kbely AB, Prague, Czechoslovakia (displ. as "Czech AF DD-39")	 73/94
- •	Il-10		Zruc Museum, Pilsen, Czech Republic	95

Nr4043 •	Ju 52 /3mge	D-ABIS	Deutsche Lufthansa *Kurt Wolfe*	
		PP-CAX	Syndicicato Condor *Gurupira*	
		LQ-ZBD	Museo Nacional de Aeronautica, Buenos Aires (displ. as FA Argentina T-149, later T-158/LADE, Rio Negro)	67/95
Nr4145 •	Ju 52 /3mge		(to Spanish AF as T.2B-108)	
			Verkehrsmuseum, Munich WG : del. (displ. Munich as D-2201 7.65)	.65
			stored RAF Gatow, West Germany (rest. for static display .74 as D-2201)	.67/93
			Berlin Senat Transport Museum	74
			Museum fur Verkehr und Technik, Berlin (displ. as D-AZAW)	84/93
Nr5489 •	Ju 52 /3mg2e	D-AQUI	Lufthansa (ff 6.4.36): del. *Fritz Simon*, operated on floats	10.4.36
		LN-DAH	DNL-Norwegian Airlines, Oslo *Falken*	1.7.36/40
			seized by German Army in Norway	4.40
		D-AQUI	Lufthansa *Kurt Wintgens*	10.40/45
			(to Norwegian Air Force as ...)	.45
		LN-KAF	DNL-Norwegian Airlines, Oslo *Askeladden* (floatplane: rebuild 11.47, used fuselage ex Luftwaffe Ju52/3mg8e Nr130714)	18.5.46
			Scandinavian Airlines System: floatplane	.47/56
			Kapitan Christian Drexel, Ecuador	.56
			wfu 10.56 Oslo Harbour, sunk in harbour (salvaged, rebuilt as landplane)	.56
		HC-ABS	Transportes Aereos Orientales SA, Quito (*Amazonas*: shipped ex Oslo 30.7.57, wfu .63, open storage Quito .63/70)	7.57/63
		N130LW	Lester F. Weaver, Polo IL (ff Quito 10.11.70; del. Dixon IL 22.11.70)	5.69/71
			Cannon Aircraft	74
		N52JU	Martin Caidin Productions, Cocoa Beach FL (del. Tico FL 5.3.75, rest. 11.76, BMW radials replaced by P&W R1340's: flew as *Iron Annie*)	.74/84
			dam. accident, Gainesville FL (repaired)	17.7.80
		D-CDLH	Lufthansa Traditionsflug, Hamburg (del. USA-Hamburg 13/28.12.84, rest. Hamburg, ff 1.4.86 as Lufthansa D-AQUI) (airfreighted to USA for flying tour 6.90-2.91)	12.84/96
-	Ju 52 /3mg3e		(to FA Portuguesa as 103, later 6303)	.37
			childrens playground Evora, Portugal	69/85
Nr5596 •	Ju 52 /3mg3e		G6+OM: crashed Kirkenes, Lapland	19.10.44
			wreck located Lapland	73
			planned recov. by Finnish Air Force	
Nr5661 •	Ju 52 /3mg3e		(to FA Portuguesa as 104, later 6304)	.37
			Portugal dos Pequeninos, childrens playground, Coimbra, Portugal	69/82
			Museu do Ar, Alverca AB, Lisbon (open storage, dism.)	87/92
Nr5664 •	Ju 52 /3mg3e		(to FA Portuguesa as 106, later 6306)	.37
			Museo do Ar, Alverca AB, Lisbon (open storage, dism.)	72/93
-	Ju 52		(to FA Portuguesa as 6300)	.37

	/3mg3e		Museo do Ar, Alverca AB, Lisbon (open storage, dism.)	73/93
-	Ju 52 /3mg3e		(to FA Portuguesa as 101, later 6301) Museo do Ar, Alverca AB, Lisbon (open storage, forward section badly damaged)	.37 73/93
Nr5670 •	Ju 52 /3mg7e	 **OO-AGU**	(to FA Portuguesa as 109, later 6309) Museo do Ar, Alverca AB, Lisbon Musee Royal de l'Armee, Brussels SABENA Old Timers, Brussels (loan) (shipped to Brussels, arr. 24.4.85; rest. to fly Zaventem: tailplane of FAP 6310)	.37 .72/85 .85/95 25.8.87/95
Nr6134 •	Ju 52 /3mg4e		"CO+EI" landed on ice, Lake Hartvigvannet, Norway ice melted, sank Lake Hartvigvannet Kongelige Norsk Luftforssvaret Collection, Gardermoen AB, Oslo Norway (recov. from Lake Hartvigvannet by KNL .86)	.39 13.4.40 5.40 .86/93
Nr6580 •	Ju 52 /3mg4e	 HB-HOS **HB-HOS**	(to Swiss AF as A-701) reg. for international flights (returned to Swiss AF as A-701) Friends of Dubendorf Museum/Ju-Air, Dubendorf AB crashed landing Winningen, West Germany (rebuilt Altrenheim, ff 6.10.88 as "A-701")	.39/82 13.9.48 3.9.59/82 26.8.82/93 29.5.87
Nr6595 •	Ju 52 /3mg4e	 HB-HOT **HB-HOT**	(to Swiss AF as A-702) reg. for international flights (returned to Swiss AF as A-702) Friends of Dubendorf Museum/Ju-Air, Dubendorf AB (flies as "A-702")	.39/85 27.3.51 3.9.59/85 29.7.85/93
Nr6610 •	Ju 52 /3mg4e	 HB-HOP **HB-HOP**	(to Swiss AF as A-703) reg. for international flights (returned to Swiss AF as A-703) Friends of Dubendorf Museum/Ju-Air, Dubendorf AB (flies as "A-703")	.39/82 9.5.47 3.9.59/82 10.82/93
Nr6657 •	Ju 52 /3mg4e		III./KGzbV 102: "CA+JY" landed on ice, Lake Hartvigvannet, Norway ice melted, sank Lake Hartvigvannet Kongelige Norsk Luftforssvaret Collection, Gardermoen AB, Oslo: recov. ex lake (displ. Oslo-Fornebu Airport "CA+JY" 84; under static rest. Gardermoen AB 86/93)	30.8.39 13.4.40 5.40 10.6.83/93
Nr6693 •	Ju 52 /3mg4e		"DB+RD" landed on ice, Lake Hartvigvannet, Norway ice melted, sank Lake Hartvigvannet Kongelige Norsk Luftforssvaret Collection, Gardermoen AB, Oslo: recov. ex lake Luftwaffen Museum, Wunstorf AB (rest. Wunstorf, rolled-out 15.8.87 "DB+RD")	.39 13.4.40 5.40 .86 .86/93
Nr6791 •	Ju 52 /3mg4e		"VB+UB" landed on ice, Lake Hartvigvannet, Norway ice melted, sank Lake Hartvigvannet Kongelige Norsk Luftforssvaret Collection, Gardermoen AB, Oslo, Norway (recov. from Lake Hartvigvannet by KNL .86) Technikmuseum Speyer, Speyer, Germany (static rest. completed, displ. as "VB+UB")	.39 13.4.40 5.40 .86/91 93

Nr55657 •	Ju 52 /3mg4e		"IZ+BY" landed on ice, Lake Hartvigvannet, Norway ice melted, sank Lake Hartvigvannet Kongelige Norsk Luftforssvaret Collection, Gardermoen AB, Oslo Norway (recov. from Lake Hartvigvannet by KNL .86)	.39 13.4.40 5.40 .86/93
Nr501196•	Ju 52 /3mg7e		(to R Norwegian AF as Y-AC) (to FA Portuguesa as 111: later 6311) displ. Aero Clube de Viseu, Viseu Portugal Museo do Ar, Alverca AB, Lisbon (open storage)	.45/50 9.50 77/82 83/93
Nr501219•	Ju 52 /3mg7e		(to R Norwegian AF as Y-AB): (to FA Portuguesa as 110: later 6310): del. Museo do Ar, Alverca AB, Lisbon	 9.50 73/93
- •	Ju 52 /3mg4e		(to FA Colombiana as FAC 625) FA Colombiana Museum, Bogota-El Dorado AB	.34 67/95
No.053 •	Amiot AAC.1 No.053		(to FA Portuguesa as 6320): del. Ota AB, Portugal: displ. Hugo Junkers Kaserne, Hohn AB WG (airfreighted by WGAF Transall to Hohn AB .75, displ. as "Luftwaffe IZ+IK")	26.11.60 72/75 .75/92
No.205 •	Amiot AAC.1 No.205		(to FA Portuguesa as 6315) Museo do Ar, Alverca AB, Lisbon (open storage)	2.12.60 69/93
No.216 •	Amiot AAC.1 **No.216**		(to Aeronavale as DK-2, 55S.32, No.216) wfu, stored Villacoublay AB Musee de l'Air, Paris-Le Bourget (rest., displ. from 5.78 as "334/DG") Musee des Tradition de l'Aeronautique Navale, Rochefort-Soubise AB	 c65/75 .75/91 .91/93
No.222 •	Amiot AAC.1 **No.222**	**F-BBYB**	Societe Transatlantique Aerienne (to JRV/Yugoslav AF as 7208) Yugoslav Aeronautical Museum, Belgrade (open storage Belgrade Airport 69/80, then displ.)	26.8.46/48 .50/60 7.69/92
No.363 •	Amiot AAC.1 **No.363**		(Armee de l'Air as No.363) Deutsches Museum, Munich	 28.3.58/93
- •	Amiot AAC.1		(to FA Portuguesa as 6316) Imperial War Museum, Duxford: arr. dism. (static rest., displ. as "Luftwaffe 1Z+NK")	11.60 6.9.73/95
50 •	CASA 352L **T.2B-140**	N9012P	David C. Tallichet/MARC, Chino CA (stored Cuatro Vientos AB, Madrid 78/83, del. via France and WG to Stansted UK, arr. 27.8.83) op. Keith May/Ju52 Flight Ltd, Rochester UK (flew as Luftwaffe "IZ+EK") dep. Rochester to West Germany struck-off USCR	10.78/92 83/85 .85 11.8.92
- •	CASA 352L **T.2B-142**	**N9012N**	David C. Tallichet/MARC, Chino CA (arr. Biggin Hill on del. ex Spain 12.9.79, operated by Jeff Hawke, Biggin Hill 79/82) (dep. Biggin Hill for USA 19.11.82 but grounded Dublin 25.11.82, stored Dublin 82/86) Auto und Technik Museum, Sinsheim WG	10.78/92 .86/91

					Svedinos Bil Och Flygmuseum, Sloinge, Sweden	92/93
54	•	CASA 352L	**T.2B-144**	N88927	reg.	
				D-CIAS	Kurfiss Aviation/Air Classik, Stuttgart: del.	4.74
					Air Classik, Frankfurt Airport: del. (displ. airport terminal as "D-CIAS")	14.9.74/93
-	•	CASA 352L	**T.2B-148**	N99234	Dolph D. Overton, Kenley NC (del. to USA, arr. Strathallen, Scotland 14.7.78, continued via Reykjavik 20.6.79)	2.77/82
					displ. Wings & Wheels Museum, Orlando FL	.79/82
				C-GARM	Western Canada Avn. Mus. Winnipeg MAN (dep. Orlando on del. flight to Canada 11.5.82) (conv. to Ju-52cao/ce at Winnipeg, rolled-out 1.4.85, displ. as Canadian Airways CF-ARM)	25.1.82/91
-		CASA 352L	**T.2B-163**		stored derelict, Cuatro Vientos AB	74
					childrens playground, Cuatro Vientos	77
121	•	CASA 352L	**T.2B-165**	D-CIAK	Air Classik: displ. Bonn-Wahn, del.	26.4.75/76
					Air Classik: displ. Dusseldorf, del. (displ. Dusseldorf Airport as "D-CIAK", later as "Lufthansa D-ADAM")	19.5.76/85
					Ikarus Flugverkehsmuseum, Marl WG (displ. as "Lufthansa D-ADAM")	87
					moved to Bochum WG, for displ. (adv. for sale, dism. 8.92)	.89/92
				HB-HOY	Friends of Dubendorf Museum/Ju-Air, Dubendorf AB (trucked to Dubendorf for rest., due to fly .96)	.93/94
67	•	CASA 352L	**T.2B-176**	N99059	Confederate Air Force, Harlingen TX (del. to USA via Biggin Hill 5.9.79/9.7.80)	.77/80
				N352JU	Confederate Air Force, Harlingen/Midland TX (del. Harlingen 19.7.80, flies as 1Z+AR)	10.80/95
-	•	CASA 352L	**T.2B-181**		displ. Murcia-Alcantrilla AB, Spain (displ. as T.2B-181/721-10)	83/91
-	•	CASA 352L	**T.2B-209**		displ. El Avion restaurant, Plasencia Spain	84
					rep. sold to West Germany by	88
					Auto und Technik Museum,Sinsheim Germany (displ. as Lufthansa D-AQUI)	92/94
102	•	CASA 352L	**T.2B-211**		Museo del Aire, Cuatro Vientos AB, Madrid (rest. Cuatro Vientos, ff 19.4.88; flies as "T.2B-211/911-16")	.73/93
103	•	CASA 352L	**T.2B-212**	G-BECL	Warbirds of GB Ltd, Blackbushe (del. Blackbushe 30.7.76, flew as "N9+AA")	27.6.76/85
					Keith May/Ju52 Flight Ltd, Rochester (stored Blackbushe 81/85, ferried to Coventry 8.10.85 for open storage 85/90	24.5.85
				F-AZJU	Amicale J-B Salis, La Ferte Alais : del. (flies as Luftwaffe N9+AA) (also rep. as c/n 24, built 1.47)	1.6.90/93
128	•	CASA 352L	**T.2B-237**		noted stored Cuatro Vientos AB, "461-4"	10.77
				D-CIAD	Air Classik, Dusseldorf (del. from Barcelona to Dusseldorf 18.2.81)	10.80/82
					Flugausstellung Museum,Hermeskeil Germany (del. Saarbrucken 23.8.82, by road to museum) (also rep. as T.2B-127, c/n 37)	8.82/93

c/n		Type	Military ID	Civil ID	Owner / history	Date
135	•	CASA 352L	**T.2B-244**		USAFM, Wright-Patterson AFB, Dayton OH (displ. in Spanish AF sc. 901-20, later displ. in Luftwaffe camouflage scheme)	.71/92
137	•	CASA 352L	**T.2B-246**		Museo del Aire, Torrejon AB, Madrid (displ. as T.2B-246/792-20	77/91
145	•	CASA 352L	**T.2B-254**		Museo del Aire, Cuatro Vientos AB, Madrid (displ. as T.2B-254/721-14, later D-2521)	.73/93
146	•	CASA 352L	**T.2B-255**	G-BFHD	Warbirds of GB Ltd, Blackbushe (del. Blackbushe 4.7.78, flew as N9+AA)	11.77/82
					Brian Woodford/Wessex Aviation & Transport Ltd (arr. dism. Bournemouth 9.85 : stored)	7.3.85/87
					Aces High Ltd, North Weald	25.6.87
					NASM, stored Washington-Dulles Airport MD (displ. as D-ODLH/*Deutsche Luft Hansa*)	.87/91
148	•	CASA 352L	**T.2B-257**	**D-CIAL**	Air Classik: displ. Stuttgart Airport, del. (displ. as Lufthansa D-ADAM) (moved to Malsheim airfield for storage 2.9.85)	7.4.75/85
					Auto und Technik Museum,Sinsheim Germany (displ. on pole as D-2527)	.86/94
155	•	CASA 352L	**T.2B-262**	**G-BFHG**	Warbirds of GB Ltd, Blackbushe (del. Blackbushe 6.78 ex Spain)	11.77/84
					Aces High Ltd, Duxford/North Weald (del. Blackbushe-Duxford 11.84, flew as "D2+600", "VK+AZ", "D-TABX" & "VZ+NK")	11.84/92
					Fantasy of Flight, Polk City FL (trucked dism. ex storage North Weald 9.94, shipped to Port Everglades FL, arr. 10.94) (c/n also quoted as 153, plate shows 155)	10.92/94
163	•	CASA 352L	**T.2B-272**		RAF Museum, RAF Cosford (del. ex Spain, arr. Biggin Hill 18.5.78) (displ. as British Airways G-AFAP)	5.78/95
164	•	CASA 352L	**T.2B-273**	G-BFHE	Warbirds of GB Ltd, Blackbushe	11.77/81
					dam. in gales Cuatro Vientos AB, Madrid (del. Blackbushe 4.7.80 ex Spain)	.77
					South African Airways, Johannesburg (del. Blackbushe-Bremen WG 12.5.81, then shipped to Johannesburg)	.81/83
				ZS-UYU	South African Airways, Johannesburg (rebuilt Johannesburg, ff 14.1.84 as "ZS-AFA")	11.8.83
				ZS-AFA	SAA *Jan van Riebeeck*	10.86/93
166	•	CASA 352L	**T.2B-275**	**G-BFHF**	Warbirds of GB Ltd, Blackbushe (del. Blackbushe 6.78, flew as "N7+AA")	11.77/85
					Keith May/Ju52 Flight Ltd, Rochester (arr. by road Coventry ex Blackbushe 9.85, stored dism.; dep. for WG 30.1.86)	24.5.85
					Auto und Technik Museum, Sinsheim WG (displ. as Luftwaffe "RJ+NP")	1.86/94

JUNKERS JU87 STUKA

c/n	Type	Owner / history	Date
Nr2883	Ju 87D-5	"R1+JK" : held RAF Sealand	1.46
Nr494083•	Ju 87G-2	RAF Air Historical Branch: stored (stored RAF Stanmore Park, RAF Wroughton, RAF Fulbeck, RAF Biggin Hill)	.46/60

(8474M)

		RAF Museum, RAF St Athan: "W8+A" RAF Henlow: for movie "Battle of Britain" .67/68 RAF Museum, Hendon: displ. as "R1+JK"	.60/78 .78/95
Jr5856 •	Ju 87R-2	3/St G.5 "L1+BL": crashed near Murmansk 2.7.42 recov. ex crash site Murmanska, Russia (hulk arr. Suffolk UK 7.94, stored pending rest.) Alpine Fighter Collection, Wanaka NZ 94/95 (shipped to NZ .95, to be rest.)	 .92
Ir5954 •	Ju 87B-2 /Trop	1/St G.1 "A5+HL" : captured in Libya Museum of Science & Industry, Chicago IL EAA Air Museum, Hales Corner WI: loan Museum of Science & Industry, Chicago IL 88/94 (displ. as "A5+HL")	 65/67 /76
Ir6234 •	Ju 87R-4	3/St G.5 "L1+FW" crashed near Murmansk 24.04.42 recov. from crash site Russia Jim Pearce, Shoreham UK (remains only)92/93 Alpine Fighter Collection, Wanaka NZ:shipped.93/95 (stored Wanaka NZ, to be rest. Wigram AB)	
Ir16970 •	Ju 87	recov. from Mediterranean, near Malta National War Museum, Valetta, Malta (parts only)	 85/92
- •	Ju 87B	Auto und Technik Museum,Sinsheim Germany (recov. ex lake: derelict, incomplete)	92/94
- •	Ju 87B-2	Yugoslavian Aviation Museum, Belgrade (stored : incomplete fuselage)	88/92
- •	Ju 87	Specialty Aircraft Construction (NZ) Ltd, Wigram AB, Christchurch NZ (2 airframes recov. ex crash sites Russia)	 94/95

JUNKERS JU88

JNKERS Ju 88

r1379 •	Ju 88A-4	forced landing frozen Lake Tornetrask, Sweden (later sank) Auto und Technik Museum,Sinsheim Germany (recov. from Lake Tornetrask .86, rest., displ. as Luftwaffe 4H+UV)	 2.5.45 .86/94
r4588 •	Ju 88A-4	II./KG3 5K+AC recov. from crash site Russia Archangel Museum (remains only)	 92
r0881033 •	Ju 88C-0	I./KG30 4D+FH recov. from crash site Norway, by RNoAF Norwegian AF Museum, Gardermoen AB Oslo	 .82 .82/93
r0881478 •	Ju 88A-4	..+BH : recov. from crash site by RNoAF Norwegian AF Museum, Gardermoen AB Oslo	.82 .82/93
r360043 •	Ju 88R-1	IV./NJG3 "D5+EV" del. RAF Dyce ex Norway by defecting pilot (to RAF as PJ876): trials Farnborough, ff dism. for future museum use: stored Air Historical Branch Collection, Stanmore (stored RAF Wroughton 56, later RAF Fulbeck) RAF Air Historical Branch, RAF Biggin Hill RAF Henlow: for film *Battle of Britain*	 9.5.43 26.5.43/45 11.45 49/54 62/64 .67/68

			RAF Museum Store, RAF Henlow: dism.	68/73
			RAF Museum, RAF St Athan: arr.	8.73/78
			(rest., displ. as 360043/D5+EV)	
			RAF Museum, Hendon	.78/95
Nr430650	•	Ju 88D-1 /Trop	(to Romanian AF as 430650)	
			del. RAF Limassol, Cyprus by defecting pilot	22.7.43
			(to RAF as HK959): overhaul at Heliopolis	10.43
			(to USAAF as FE-1598): del. Cairo-USA	10.43
			(36 hrs. flight trials Wright Field OH .43/44)	
			stored Davis-Monthan AFB AZ	8.46/60
			USAFM Wright-Patterson AFB, Dayton OH	1.60/95
			(displ. as F6+AL, later Romanian AF 105)	
-	•	Ju 88A-4	(to Finnish AF as JK-260)	
			Paimion Paroni Automuseo, Hevonpaa, Finland:	
			planned recov. from lake St.Petersburg	.93
-	•	Ju 88	planned recov. ex crash sites by RNoAF for	
			Norwegian AF Museum, Gardermoen AB Oslo	90
			(total 3 aircraft)	

Index of Advertisers

The Editor wishes to thank all our Advertisers for their support in the production of this publication.

Left: A fearsome and unique grin, and a regular resident at La Ferte Alais for many years, on North American T6G F-AZBQ. **Thierry Thomassin.**

Below: Four Harvards in formation has not been that rare in South Africa, but is well worth us picturing nevertheless. **Greg Pullin.**

Bottom: North American B-25 Mitchell N908 was not the first or the last to be used as a camera ship, but it was certainly an unusual adittion to the film *633 Squadron* in front of the cameras. **APN.**

WARBIRDS
WORLDWIDE

Fly *Crazy Horse*, The Dual Cockpit, Dual Control TF-51 Mustang

Patrick Bunce

Complete Checkout Training

Just like the U.S. Navy Test Pilots that we train twice yearly, you'll experience everything there is in a P-51 from basic turns, stalls and aerobatics to dynamic maneuvering, spins and vertical rolls and enough systems, procedure and landings to qualify you for an FAA Mustang Letter of Authorization.

Familiarization/Pleasure Flights

Strictly for fun. Plan your own hour or more of aerobatics, low level 'sight seeing', air combat maneuvers, landing circuits - whatever you've dreamed of doing in a Mustang and regardless of your experience, you'll fly it yourself - supervised by an experienced Instructor Pilot.

- Orientation Flights
- Complete Check Out Training
- LOA's (P-51)
- Airshows
- Filmwork
- All Aerobatics
- Air Combat Tactics
- Tactical Formation
- Video of your flight available

Stallion 51 Corporation

804 N. Hoagland Blvd., Kissimmee, FL 34741, U.S.A.

Phone (407) 846 4400 Fax: (407) 846 0414

A Great Gift Idea! Expensive........But Well Worth It!

Stallion 51 Corporation is endorsed by Warbirds Worldwide

Stallion 51

Above: The famous (in warbird circles) and yet rarely photographed Hawker Sea Fury on display in Cuba; how long will it remain there? It would be different to have one of the many flying Sea Furies around in Cuban Air Force colours. **Rod Kenward**. **Right:** Converted two-seater Hawker Sea Fury T20 N85SF *Critical Mass* catches the late evening Reno sun in 1994. Obvious here is the minimal visibility avaliable to the pilot of this machine who occupies the rear of the two original positions. **Thierry Thomassin. Below:** One of the most tragic losses of recent years was the destruction of the Canadian Warplane Heritage's Hawker Hurricane 'P3069' in the hangar fire of Feburary 15th 1993. **Thierry Thomassin**.

Call or fax World Jet -

Telephone: 954-772-7444
Fax: 954-772-7451

These Aircraft are For Sale

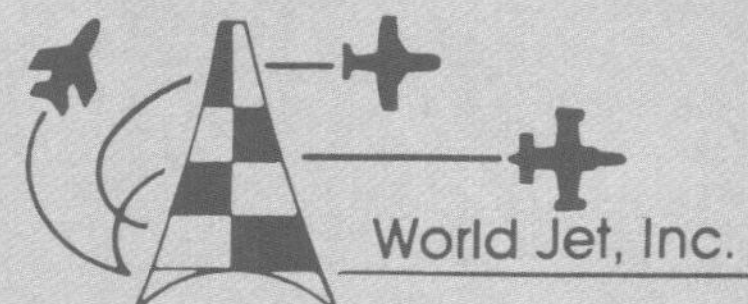

Largest Hamilton Standard Inventory

IN THE WORLD!

WE SERVICE WHAT WE SELL

Propellers ● Timers Governors ● Switches ● De-Icer Equipment ● Relays
Synchronisers ● Spare parts ● Propeller Control & Brush Pad Assemblies
Tools & Test Equipment ● Control Boxes ● Fuel Control Electronics ● Air Conditioning
for...● BEECH ● BOEING ● CESSNA ● CONVAIR ● DE HAVILLAND ● DOUGLAS ● LOCKHEED ● MARTIN ● PIPER

SPECIALIZING IN:

C-130 P-3 BUFFALO G-222

WARBIRDS

● CHANDLER EVANS ● PESCO ● WOODWARD GOVERNOR
● MCCAULEY ● HARTZELL ● SENSENCIH ● SAFEWAY
JAA APPROVED ● JAR-145 APPROVED
APPROVED FAA REPAIR STATION NO. AZ4R068M

P.O. BOX 15819-ZIP 91615-5819
8101 LANKERSHAM BLVD.,
NO. HOLLYWOOD, CA 91605 U.S.A

PHONE: 213-877-2104 OR 818-765-9086
FAX: 818-767-5140 TWX 910-498-2210 CA

JOIN EAA WARBIRDS OF AMERICA® & Keep 'em Flying

If you love military aircraft then you belong with EAA Warbirds of America...an organization of people who rally around the motto Keep 'em Flying.

For only $40.00* you can belong to a very prestigious group of aviation enthusiasts by becoming a member of EAA WARBIRDS OF AMERICA. Your one-year membership includes eight colorful, photo filled issues of WARBIRDS magazine and four informative Warbird Division newsletters. Your membership will also include an embroidered jacket patch and decals for your car or airplane.

Join Today!!!

For Information Call

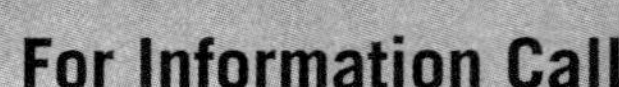

414-426-4800

EAA WARBIRDS OF AMERICA
P.O. Box 3086
Oshkosh, WI 54903-3086
U.S.A.

** U.S. funds. Plus $6.00 postage. Cost includes membership in Experimental Aircraft Association and EAA Warbirds of America Division*

Covington Aircraft Engines Inc.

FAA REPAIR STATION 212-23

Major Overhauled Engines

Specializing in Pratt & Whitney

- **R-985-AN1 or 14B**
- **R-1340-AN1**
- **R-1340-S1H1-G**

"We strive to produce the very best engine possible"

Paul Abbott, President, Covington Aircraft Engines Inc.

Impellers and shafts being dynamically balanced before blowers are assembled at the Covington facility (left). All engines go through a test programme before release in the Test cell at Covington's (right)

Covington Aircraft Engines Inc.,
P.O. Box 1344, Municipal Airport,
Okmulgee, OK 74447, USA

Telephone 918 756 8320 Fax 918 756 0923
Telex 3791814

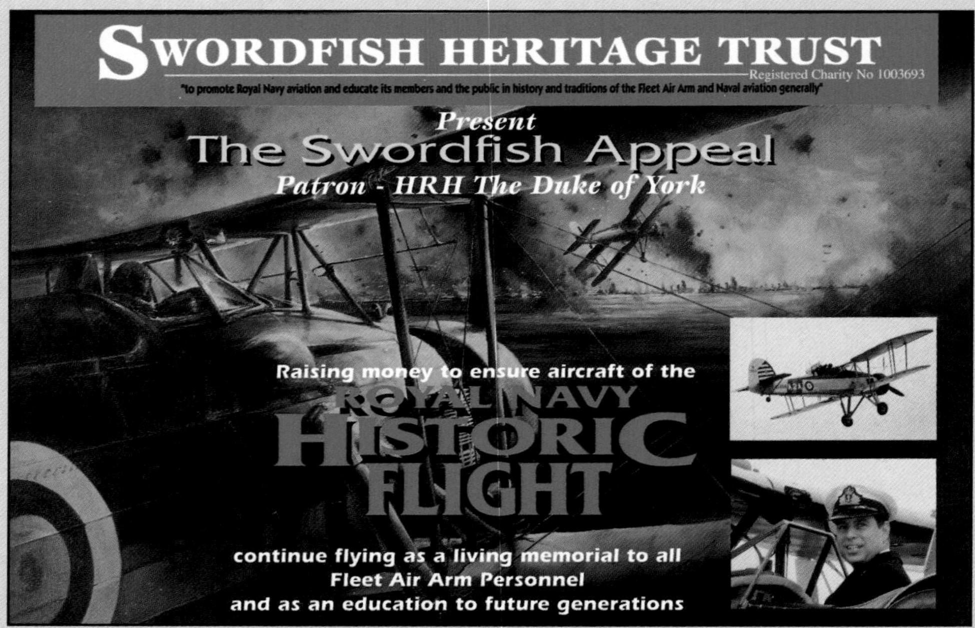

As a registered educational charity, the Swordfish Heritage Trust is a custodian of Fleet Air Arm Heritage, promoting Royal Navy Aviation history through educational projects, particularly to young people.Veterans and supporters saving history for their future. A vital part of that aim is to ensure aircraft of the Royal Navy Historic Flight are not disbanded and their aircraft not sold, whilst increasing access by the public to the experience of their fine flying displays. The unique Swordfish display, with the crew saluting the crowd whilst proudly flying the white ensign, has been enjoyed by millions of people at airshows, commemorative events and on TV, for over 20 years.

This famous Royal Navy Squadron now invites your full involvement to help raise the vital funds required to ensure they continue long into the future and expand the educational aims of the Swordfish Heritage Trust. Expansion of educational projects and public access to these historic aircraft is a priority, to demonstrate the proud history of British Naval Aviation and the heroic heritage. Your direct help will also bring you many FREE exciting and valuable educational visits, gifts, incentives and rewards along with access to, and full involvement with, the aircraft.

Donate or raise a minimum of £15.00 for the Swordfish Appeal to gain FREE membership of the Royal Naval Historic Flight Support Group

with FREE draw entry for a flight in the Swordfish or a BOND helicopter and FREE model kit of RNHF Swordfish, Firefly, Sea Hawk or Sea Fury from AIRFIX. Raise a little more to receive VIP treatment at airshows and special event tickets. Corporate sponsors can gain unique entertainment and high profile opportunities

Contact the Swordfish Appeal Director, Ian Lauder Tel 01403 753736 Fax 01403 752403

Space Donated by Warbirds Worldwide Ltd

Talk to really experienced craftsman about your future requirements. Access to and stockists of the largest quantity of World War I accessories and hardware in the U.K. and approved timber stock is always commercially available. Work is undertaken on behalf of all the major U.K. national museums and collectors in addition to projects displayed at international locations e.g. Nieuport 28 at Fort Rucker, Alabama and the Bristol F2B at the Brussels Military Museum.

The foremost European World War I and Pre-1940's multi wing aeroplane manufacturing and restoration company. We are, by far and away, the highest standard of commercial restoration available. Vast knowledge with unsurpassed innovative originality to return your priceless historic exhibit to the air, or museum.

SkySport was recently described by a U.K. based national museum as being 'the only Company actually conserving historically significant airframes for the future on a commercial basis.

SkySport Engineering has completed more than 30 major restoration and overhauls in the past 15 years. Some of the aeroplane work undertaken includes the following: 3 new aeroplanes - 2 Sopwith Pups, 1 Sopwith Dove - all flown, Sopwith Triplane, 2 Camels, 2 Bleriots (1989 Channel re-run), BE2C,BE2E, SE5A, 4 Bristol Fighters, Nieport 28, Fiesler Storch, 2 Westland Wallace, a Hawker Demon, HP Gugnunc, nine Stampe SV4Cs, 4 Tiger Moths, Valmet Viima, Stearman, DC-3, Sunderland, Jungmeister, Jungmann, DH84 Dragon, DH89 Rapide, DH90 Dragonfly, DH106 Comet, Comper Swift, Thruxton Jackaroo, and 2 Miles Falcons.

CAA Approved Company

TOTAL honesty is a way of life at

SkySport Engineering Ltd.

AEROPLANE MANUFACTURING CO.

Rotary Farm, Thorncote Green, Nr. Hatch, Sandy, Beds SG19 1PU, England

Tel: 01767 627375 Facsimile: 01767 627718

Hawker Restorations Limited

Hawker Restorations can offer the following services from their new 10,000 sq. ft. facility at Earls Colne Airfield in the U.K.:

- Extensive Hawker Hurricane restoration facilities with 3 Hurricanes currently under restoration
- 2 Hurricane projects for sale with extensive history
- Complete finished aircraft including guns and period detail at a fixed price
- Specialised Warbird maintenance team with experience on Hurricanes, Mustang, Spitfire, Yak and various other aircraft. Maintenance at a competitive price.
- The manufacture of detail and machine components
- Spray-bake painting facility
- Specialist work on vintage wood and fabric aircraft.

All the above are based at an historic World War II licensed airfield with a 900m strip and extensive leisure facilities including Golf course and overnight accommodation etc.

Hawker Restorations has A8-20,M5, and E4 CAA approvals

Contact Mr. Paul Mercer, Chief Engineer at either:

Moat Farm, Milden,
Ipswich, Suffolk
Tel: 01449 741496
Fax: 01449 741584

Earls Colne Airfield, Earls Colne,
Colchester, Essex
Tel: 01787 224773
Fax: 01787 224774

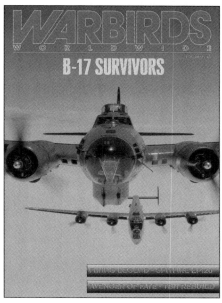

Kawanishi K1N Kyofu

514	•	N1K1 Floatplane	44	NAS Patuxent River MD: evaluation	46
				NASM, Silver Hill MD: stored	60/96
562	•	N1K1 Floatplane	45	NAS Norfolk VA: stored	65
				Admiral Nimitz State Historical Park, Fredericksburg TX: displ.	77/96
565	•	N1K1 Floatplane		NAS Willow Grove PA	58/96
				(displ. as "121", later "44")	

Kawanishi N1K2 Shiden-Kai 'George'

5128	•	N1K2-J		(to USAAF as FE-306/T2-306): shipped	.45
				Naval Research Laboratory,Washington DC	57
				(derelict in childrens playground)	
				USNAM, NAS Norfolk VA	60/94
				Bradley Air Mus., Windsor Locks CT: loan	12.75/81
				(trucked ex NAS Norfolk, arr. Bradley 4.12.75)	
				New England Air Museum, Windsor Locks CT	81/96
5312	•	N1K2-J	**62387**	City of San Diego CA	59
				USAFM, Wright Patterson AFB OH: arr.	27.9.59/91
				(displ. as "343-A-II")	
5341	•	N1K2-J		NAS Patuxent River MD: evaluation	46
				NAS Willow Grove PA	12.46/73
				NASM, Silver Hill MD: displ. as "A/3-15"	87/91
				Champlin Fighter Museum, Mesa AZ: loan	92/96
				(static rest. Mesa completed .94 as "343-35")	
-	•	N1K2-J		USNAM, NAS Pensacola FL	94
				(under rest. by Georgia Metal Shaping GA 94)	
				ex stored in crate: prob. the Willow Grove aircraft)	

Kawasaki Ki 61 Hien 'Tony'

195		Ki-61		crashed Borpop Strip, New Ireland	c42
				recov for local displ., New Ireland	.74/79
379	•	Ki-61-IIb		Roy Worcester, Wewak PNG	72/74
				recov. ex Cape Wom strip, near Wewak	c70
				Cliff Cummins, California	79
				(arr. Chino CA .79 for planned rest. to fly)	
				Frank Taylor, Bakersfield CA	
				Weeks Air Museum, Tamiami FL (crated ex Chino .86)	.86/96
				(displ. dism. in museum, tailplane ex 640)	
				dam. by Hurricane "Andrew", Tamiami FL	24.8.92
640	•	Ki-61		Air Museum of PNG : salvage rights	75
				National Museum, Port Moresby PNG	.84/96
				(recov. from crash site .84, arr. dism. Port Moresby 26.11.84 : stored)	
-	•	Ki-61		Bruce Fenstermaker CA	90
				(recov. from Babo Island, Indonesia c90)	
				Museum of Flying, Santa Monica CA	.91/93
				(hulk arr. Santa Monica 6.91, for static rest.)	
-	•	Ki-61		Kamikaze Museum, Chiran, Kyushu, Japan	87/91

-	•	Ki-61			Kawaguchiko Motor Museum, Yamanashi Prefecture, Japan	91

LAGG 11

-	•	LAGG-11	-		Aero Trader, Chino CA: arr. dism.	1.89/90
-	•	LAGG-11	-		Aero Trader, Chino CA: arr. dism.	1.89/90
-	•	LAGG-11	-		Aero Trader, Chino CA: arr. dism.	1.89
					Weeks Air Museum,Tamiami FL	89

LAVOCHKIN LA-9

-	•	LA-9			Central Military Museum, Bucharest, Bulgaria	90/95
-	•	LA-9			Beijing Aeronautical Institute, Beijing China (displ. as "7504")	87/91
-	•	LA-9			People's Liberation Army Air Force Museum, Changping, China: displ. as "06"	91/94
-	•	LA-9			China	87/91
					Old Flying Machine Company Duxford for rebuild to fly shipped ex China	3.96
-	•	LA-9UTI			People's Liberation Army Air Force Museum, Changping, China	91/94

LAVOCHKIN LA-11

-	•	LA-11	-		(to Soviet AF as 20)	
					Russian Armed Forces Museum, Monino: displ.	
					The Fighter Collection, Duxford UK (arr. dism. Duxford 5.93, rest. to fly)	.93/95
10142	•	LA-11	-		(to Chinese AF as ....)	
					China Xinxing Corp	
				N2276Y	Aero Trader Inc, Chino CA	5.94
					Weeks Air Museum, Tamiami FL	10.94/95
-	•	LA-11	-		(to Chinese AF as ....)	
					Beijing Aeronautical Institute, Beijing China (displ. as "7505")	87/91
-	•	LA-11	-		(to North Korean AF as 24)	
					People's Liberation Army Air Force Museum, Datangshan: displ. as "24"	91/94
-	•	LA-11	-		(to AURI as F-911)	
					Indonesian AF Museum, Adisutjipto AB, Yogyakarta	.86/96

NOTES

1930 •	B14L		NX21771	Sperry Gyroscope Co, New York NY	42/45
				University of Southern California, Santa Maria-Hancock Field CA	48/54
				(inst. airframe)	
			N21771	Santa Maria Junior Technical College, Santa Maria CA	66/69
				reg. pending (listed in USCR as L.18)	77/87
2405	Mk. II	T9370	NX28991	Sperry Gyroscope Co, New York NY	45/47
				Dante S. Pinelli, Princeton NJ	54 L.18
				(rebuilt into L.18 Lodestar, with new id. "2626", by Hamilton Aircraft Co, Tucson AZ c55)	Learstar
				PacAero Engineering Corp, Santa Monica CA	.57
			D-CABO	Helmut Horten GmbH, Dusseldorf: del.	11.57/61
			N211L	Learjet Corp, Wichita KS	5.61/69
				Carolina Aircraft Corp, Ft Lauderdale FL	8.69/72
				crashed and dest., Lake Okeechobee FL	12.5.72
3826 •	Mk. IIIa	**V9241**		(to RNZAF as NZ2013): BOC 9.41 SOC	5.49
				J. W. Clarke, Oamaru, Maheno NZ	50/74
				(fuse. used on farm in chicken run)	
				Oamaru Air Training Corps: rest. project	
				RNZAF Museum, Wigram AB	.89/96
				(complete static rest)	
3854 •	Mk. III	**AE499**		(to RNZAF as NZ2031): SOC 10.41 SOC	5.49
				W. & T. Garr, Dunedin NZ	
				Barrie East: loan to	
				Museum of Transport & Technology, Auckland	73/95
3858 •	Mk. III	**AE503**		(to RNZAF as NZ2035): SOC 10.41 SOC	5.49
				Warwick Birt NZ: rest. project	65/71
				Ferrymead Museum of Science & Technology, Christchurch NZ (stored dismantled)	.71/95
6034 •	A-28 Mk. IVA	**41-23175**		(to RAAF as A16-105): BOC	12.41/47
				European Air Transport, Sydney NSW	9.47
			VH-BKY	Curtis Madsen Aircrafts Pty Ltd, Sydney NSW	10.49/50
			VH-EWB	East West Airlines, Tamworth NSW	12.50/58
				Cathedral City	
			VH-EWS	East West Airlines, Tamworth NSW	3.58/62
			VH-SMO	John Fairfax & Son, Sydney NSW	10.62
				lsd. Adastra Aerial Surveys, Sydney NSW	10.62/67
			VH-AGP	Adastra Aerial Surveys Pty Ltd, Sydney NSW	5.67/76
			VH-FXF	Malcolm J. Long, Melbourne VIC	11.76/95
				(rest., flew as A16-105/FX-F)	
				displ. Air World, Wangaratta VIC	.86/96
6041 •	A-28 Mk. IVA	**41-23182**		(to RAF as BW363)	
				(to RAAF as A16-112): BOC	12.41/47
				Stanley Godden, Sydney NSW	9.47
			VH-BNJ	East West Airlines, Tamworth NSW	12.49
			VH-EWA	East West Airlines, Tamworth NSW	3.51
				"Peel River"	
			VH-AIU	Adastra Aerial Surveys Pty Ltd, Sydney NSW	7.53
			VH-AGS	Adastra Aerial Surveys Pty Ltd, Sydney NSW	1.56/76
				wfu; stored Tamworth: struck-off reg	4.72/76
				Malcolm J. Long, Melbourne VIC	3.76/93
				(del. Tamworth-RAAF Pt. Cook 26.3.76; by road to Moorabbin VIC, rest. to fly 83/93)	
			VH-KOY	Malcolm J. Long, Coolangatta QLD	4.93/95

				(ff Moorabbin 10.4.93 as "A16-112/KO-Y")	
6051 •	A-28	**41-23192**		(to RAAF as A16-122): BOC	12.41/47
	Mk. IVA			Gregory R. Board, Sydney NSW	7.47
			VH-AGX	Adastra Aerial Surveys Pty Ltd, Sydney NSW	11.54/73
				crashed, Horn Island QLD	21.12.73
				Robert L. Eastgate, Melbourne VIC	.76/95
				(recov. and shipped to Melbourne VIC 2.77)	
				(stored, rest. RAAF Point Cook VIC 77/94)	
6124 •	A-29	**41-23307**		(to RAF as BW445): surplus in Canada	
	Mk. IIIA		CF-ESJ	Arctic Airlines, Edmonton ALTA	54
			N4980V	Gordon B. Hamilton Co, Tucson AZ	5.54
				Thomas H. Peterson, Tucson AZ	11.54/55
				Giddings & Lewis Machine Tool Co	11.55/59
				(rebuilt by Hamilton Aircraft Co, Tucson AZ	
	Lodestar			as L.18 Lodestar)	12.56
				Jack Adams Aircraft Sales	1.60
				Edward L. Stringfellow Jr, Leeds AL	1.60/64
				(conv. to exec windows, tailcone 9.64 by	
				Aerodyne Engineering)	
				Stringair Corp, Leeds AL	3.61/64
			N880V	Stringair Corp, Leeds AL	9.64/65
				Robert I. Ingalls Jr	7.65
				Jefferson County Board of Education	.65/66
				Lackey Aero Corp	1.66
				James W. Gentle & Ernest L. Jordan	2.66
				McMartin Industry, Omaha NE	2.66/72
				Duncan Aviation Inc	4.72
				Hawkins & Powers Aviation, Greybull WY	8.72/96
6378	A-29	41-23561		(to RAF as BW699) surplus in Canada	
	Mk. IIIA		CF-ESI	Arctic Airlines, Edmonton ALTA	
			N4969V	Hamilton Aircraft Co, Tucson AZ	.54
	Lodestar			(rebuilt as L.18 Lodestar, by Hamilton	
				Aircraft Co, Tucson AZ)	
				trucked to Santa Monica CA	
	Learstar			(rebuilt by Lear Inc, Santa Monica CA)	
			N34L		
			N141PA		
			N777W	Walsh Construction Co, New York NY	60/69
			N7041N	Transair Inc, Linden NJ	72
			N100DK	International Fruit Produce Co, Manila PI	75
				crashed Puerto Princes, Philippines	4.7.75
6448 •	A-29	**41-23631**		(to RAF as BW769): surplus in Canada	
	Mk. IIIA		CF-CRJ	Canadian Pacific Airlines, Vancouver BC	5.46
				Photographic Survey Corp	5.49
				Kenting Aviation Ltd, Toronto ONT	56/64
				Field Aviation, Oshawa ONT	
				displ. on pole, Gander NFLD	.67/90
				(unveiled as "T9422" by AVM D.C.T. Bennett 10.67)	
6464 •	A-29A	**41-36975**		(to RAF as FH174)	
	MK. IIIA			(to RAAF as A16-199): BOC	4.42/47
				McQuarie Grove Flying School NSW	9.47
			VH-SMM	Herald Flying Service, Sydney NSW	12.50/66
				lsd. Adastra Aerial Surveys, Sydney NSW	59/66
			VH-AGJ	Adastra Aerial Surveys Pty Ltd, Sydney NSW	12.66.73
				M. J. Whittington, Sydney NSW	4.73
				Sir W. J. Roberts/Strathallan Collection,	
				Auchterader, Scotland	4.73
				(del. ex Sydney 19.4.73-10.5.73)	
			G-BEOX	Sir W. J. Roberts/Strathallan Collection,	

				Auchterader, Scotland	25.3.77/81
				RAF Museum, Hendon	14.7.81/96
				(displ. as "A16-199/SF-R")	
465 •	A-29A	**41-36976**		(to RAF as FH175)	
	Mk. IIIA			(to RNZAF as NZ2049): BOC 4.42 SOC	12.47
				John R. Smith, Mapua, Nelson NZ	69/95
			(rest. project)		
608 •	A-29A	**41-37119**		(to RAF as FH318): surplus in Canada	
	Mk. IIIA		CF-EZJ	Arctic Airlines, Edmonton ALTA	
			N4934V	Gordon B. Hamilton Co, Tucson AZ	.54
				(rebuilt as L.18 Lodestar, by Hamilton Aircraft Co,	
	Lodestar			Tucson AZ)	
	H.250		N230B	(conv. by Howard Aero to Howard 250)	61
			CF-CPL	Canadian Packers Ltd	65
				Atlantic Aviation of Canada Ltd	70
			N19PA	Penn-Aire Aviation, Franklin PA	10.70/73
				Frank Pacale	12.73
				Edsel R. Hensley	28.2.75/79
				Aircraft Sales Inc	7.8.79
				Morgan Rourke Aircraft Sales,Bartlesville OK	29.1.80/95
618 •	A-29A	**41-37129**		(to RAF as FH328)	
	Mk. IIIA			(to RNZAF as NZ2059): SOC	5.49
				Asplins Supplies, Hamilton NZ	69/73
				(fuselage noted: reported to collector)	
716 •	A-29A	**41-37227**		(to RAF as FH426)	
	Mk. IIIA			Museo del Aire, Cuatro Vientos AB, Madrid	93
				(recov. ex crash site, displ. unrest.)	
725 •	A-29A	**41-37236**		(to RAF as FH435)	
	Mk. IIIA			(to RNZAF as NZ2084)	
				K. Pennel, Katangaroa NZ	
				RNZAF Museum, Wigram AB	94
				(fuse. stripped for parts to rest. NZ2013)	
942 •	A-28A	**42-47022**		(to RAF as FK466): disposal Greenwood NS	.45
	Mk. VI			L.W. Layton Salvage, Canning NS (dism.)	.80
				Atlantic Canada Aviation Museum, Halifax NS	.88/91
- •	Mk. I	-		(to RAAF as A16-22): BOC	9.2.40
				Guinea Airways Ltd, Adelaide SA: for parts	27.2.46
				Harry Parrott, Belair SA: dism.	.46/72
				(fuselage used as hut, Belair SA 50/63)	
				Pearce Dunn/Warbirds Aviation Museum,	
				Mildura VIC: displ. as unrest. fuselage	11.72/83
				(trucked to Mildura ex Belair SA 12.11.72)	
				Malcolm J. Long, Melbourne VIC: fuse only	88/96
				(trucked Moorabbin-Pt.Cook for parts for	
				rest. of VH-AGX 11.91)	

Lockheed P2 Neptune

044 •	P2V-5	**Bu124904**	**N126Z**	US Forest Service, Redding CA (tanker #D1)	.69/84
	EP-2E			(first P-2 tanker, conv. Medford OR .69/70)	
				Evergreen Helicopters Inc, Marana AZ	10.84
				(wfu stored Marana AZ 79/92, derelict)	
			N208EV	Evergreen Helicopters Inc, Marana AZ	10.85/96
192 •	P2V-5	**Bu128346**	**N96264**	Black Hills Aviation, Alamogordo NM	11.76/93
	SP-2E			(tanker #12)	
				Neptune Inc, Alamogordo NM (tanker #12)	9.93/96

Continued on Page 274

Republic test-pilot Mr Glen Bach waves from the (then) Republic Corporation owned P47 N5087V which was on a tour of Europe and the Paris Airshow in 1963 to counterpoint the new Thunderbolt II. On the nose are the flags of the countries which used the Thunderbolt during W.W.II. **W.W. Collection.**

Bearing a rather hybrid scheme Republic P47 G-BLZW at Blackbushe. This aircraft was one of Doug Arnold's which appeared with hastily applied D-Day stripes in the little seen film *The Eye of the Needle* albeit static only. **Gary Robert Brown Collection.**

For a brief period, while at Chatham, Kent, the nomadic Short Sunderland G-BJHS (ML418) was painted with the Ryanair logo and the name *Spirit of Foynes* which was where the aircraft was intended to operated from. This deal fell through, and the aircraft recrossed the Atlantic to join the Fantasy of Flight Museum. **James Kightly.**

are, and static, but included here, ne Tachikawa Ki-36 "Ida" is one of ne many unique types to be seen in ne Thai Air Force museum in angkok, making it an essential visit or any aviation enthusiasts passing nrough. **Roger Wallsgrove.**

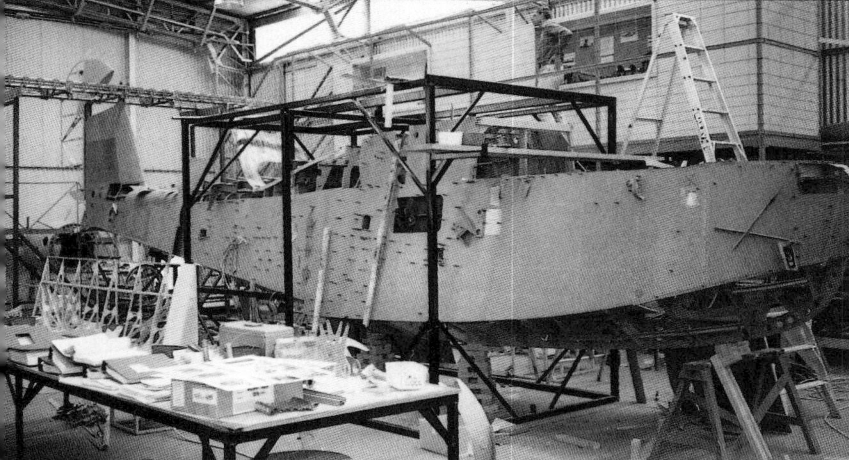

From the same drawing board as the Spitfire, the Supermarine Walrus is another type undergoing a slow renassance. While the R.A.F. Museum has the Australian Seagull Mk.V A2-4, the R.A.A.F. Museum has a Walrus recovered from (of all places) Antarctica, and it is currently (as seen here at the end of 1995) undergoing restoration to taxiing condition. **Roger Wallsgrove.**

ne of the very few large biplane ying boats left, Supermarine tranraer CF-BXO is seen here in ueen Charlotte Airways ownership, efore its transfer to the R.A.F. Museum, Hendon. Q.C.A. was also nown as 'Queer Collection of ircraft' in their day. **APN**

5212 •	P2V-5 SP-2E	**Bu128366**	**N205EV**	W. A. Bishop, Cleveland TN Evergreen Helicopters Inc, Marana AZ (stored unconv. Marana AZ, became derelict) Evergreen Heritage Collection, Marana: listed	7.3.77 .77/96 92
5224 •	P2V-5 SP-2E	**Bu128378**	**N204EV**	W. A. Bishop, Cleveland TN Evergreen Helicopters Inc, Marana AZ (stored unconv., Marana AZ, now derelict)	25.2.77 .77/96
5228 •	P2V-5 SP-2E	**Bu128382**	**N203EV** (tanker #142)	W. A. Bishop, Cleveland TN Evergreen Helicopters Inc, Marana AZ	18.2.77 .77/96
5268 •	P2V-5 SP-2E	**Bu128422**	 **N1386C**	Consolidated Aeronautics Corp, Tucson AZ Black Hills Aviation, Alamogordo NM Neptune Inc, Alamogordo NM (open storage stripped, Alamogordo 85/95, under conv. to tanker Alamogordo 10.95)	20.10.76 3.82/93 9.93/96
5291 •	P2V-5 SP-2E	**Bu131410**	**N88487**	Allied Aircraft, Tucson AZ International Mailing & Printing Corp, Fort Lauderdale FL (brown & cream sc.) ESI Financial Services Corp, Miami FL Dennis H. Callahan, Neptune Beach FL (wfu open storage, Kissimmee FL 90/92) USNAM, NAS Jacksonville FL (displ. as "Bu131410")	27.10.76 84 87/90 92 8.93/96
5305 •	P2V-5 SP-2E	**Bu131424**	 **N1386K**	Consolidated Aeronautics Corp, Tucson AZ Black Hills Aviation, Alamogordo NM Neptune Inc, Alamogordo NM (stored unconv. derelict, Alamogordo 85/94)	20.10.76 3.82/93 9.93/96
5315 •	P2V-5 SP-2E	**Bu131434**	**N96271**	Black Hills Aviation, Alamogordo NM (tanker #07) Neptune Inc, Alamogordo NM (tanker #07)	5.11.76/92 94
5326 •	P2V-5 SP-2E	**Bu131445**	**N9855F**	Granek Co, Tucson AZ Black Hills Aviation, Alamogordo NM (tanker #06) Neptune Inc, Alamogordo NM (tanker #06)	5.11.76 77/93 9.93/96
5337 •	P2V-5 SP-2E	**Bu131456**	**N88484**	Allied Aircraft, Tucson AZ Aircraft Surplus Co, Tucson AZ AMCEP Inc, Tucson AZ ntu: Air Atlantique, Coventry UK Instone Airline Inc, Redondo Beach CA (stored unconv., Tucson AZ 90/92)	26.10.76 11.77/84 87 6.87 7.87/96
5340 •	P2V-5 SP-2E	**Bu131459**	**N96278**	Black Hills Aviation, Alamogordo NM (tanker #05) Neptune Inc, Alamogordo NM (tanker #05)	10.76/93 9.93/96
5344 •	P2V-5 SP-2E	**Bu131463**	 **N13859**	Consolidated Aeronautics Corp, Tucson AZ Black Hills Aviation, Alamogordo NM Neptune Inc, Alamogordo NM (stored, derelict unconv., Alamogordo 85/95)	20.10.76 3.82/93 9.93/95
5363 •	P2V-5 SP-2E	**Bu131482**	**N206EV**	W. A. Bishop, Cleveland TN Evergreen Helicopters Inc, Marana AZ (tanker #145)	10.3.77 .77/96
5383 •	P2V-5 P2V-5F	**Bu131502**	**N202EV**	W. A. Bishop, Cleveland TN Evergreen Helicopters Inc, Marana AZ	9.2.77 .77/96

	SP-2E			(tanker #141)	
387 •	P2V-5	**Bu131506**		Consolidated Aeronautical Corp, Tucson AZ	20.10.76
	SP-2E		**N13852**	Black Hills Aviation, Alamogordo NM	3.82/93
				Neptune Inc, Alamogordo NM	9.93/96
				(stored derelict unconv., Alamogordo 85/95)	
421 •	P2V-5	**Bu131540**	**N51796**	reg. candidate	1.78/92
	SP-2E				
031 •	P2V-7	**Bu135588**	**N4846N**	Tanana Valley Community College,	
	SP-2H			Fairbanks AK	6.85/90
				Hans M. Vandermeer, Anchorage AK	2.91/96
				(stored unconv., Greybull WY 92)	
039 •	P2V-7	**Bu135596**	**N9AU**	Aero Union Corp, Chico CA	7.86/96
	SP-2H				
057 •	P2V-7	**Bu140154**	**N8056D**	David Brady, Cartersville GA	23.3.89/91
	SP-2H			Reva J. Brady, Carterville GA	92
				Hawkins & Powers Aviation, Greybull WY	3.93/96
065 •	P2V-7	**Bu140963**	N963LH	Allied Aircraft Sales, Tucson AZ	.86
	SP-2H		N142DP	Aero Union Corp, Chico CA	2.4.86
	Firestar		N703AU(1	ntu: Aero Union Corp, Chico CA	3.87
			N702AU	Aero Union Corp, Chico CA	8.87/88
			N90YY	Aero Union Corp, Chico CA	12.88
			N716AU(2	Aero Union Corp, Chico CA (tanker #16)	4.89/96
074 •	P2V-7	**Bu140972**	**N2215G**	Hawkins & Powers Aviation, Greybull WY	16.1.90/96
	SP-2H			(stored unconv., Greybull 91/93)	
082 •	P2V-7	**Bu140980**	**N980AP**	Aerospace Products Inc, North Hollywood CA	13.8.86/88
	SP-2H			North American Warbirds Mus., Gibsonia PA	1.88/94
				Aero Union Corp, Chico CA	15.9.94/96
102 •	P2V-7	**Bu140443**	N8063S	David Brady, Cartersville GA	23.3.89
	SP-2H		**N140HP**	Hawkins & Powers Aviation, Greybull WY	12.89/95
				(tanker #140)	
109 •	P2V-7	**Bu140450**	N4765X	reg. res.	3.84
	P-2H		**N117SR**	MBB Corp, Westchester PA	12.84
129 •	P2V-7	**Bu143173**	N173AM	AMCEP Inc, Tucson AZ	24.7.87
	SP-2H			(noted Wilmot Metals yard, Tucson AZ 11.87)	
				Consolidated Avn. Enterprises, Burlington VT	4.88/90
				Air Atlantique, Coventry UK	.88
				noted awaiting del., Burlington VT	90
				Hawkins & Powers Aviation, Greybull WY	5.91/95
				(stored unconv., Greybull 91)	
158 •	P2V-7	**Bu144681**	**N4235N**	Black Hills Aviation, Alamogordo NM	26.3.81/93
	SP-2H			(tanker #10)	
				Neptune Inc, Alamogordo NM (tanker #10)	9.93/96
165 •	P2V-7	**Bu145903**	N903LH	Allied Aircraft Sales, Tucson AZ	24.10.86
	SP-2H			Aero Union Corp, Chico CA	11.86
			N713AU	Aero Union Corp, Chico CA	3.87/96
				(stored unconv. Chico 89/90, tanker conv. .92)	
167 •	P2V-7	**Bu145905**	**N7060Y**	Hawkins & Powers Aviation, Greybull WY	12.88/96
	SP-2H			(stored unconv., Greybull 92/93)	
168 •	P2V-7	**Bu145906**	N8064A	David Brady, Cartersville GA	23.3.89
	SP-2H		**N139HP**	Hawkins & Powers Aviation, Greybull WY	2.90/96

				(tanker #139)	
7180 •	P2V-7S SP-2H	**Bu145915**	**N45309**	Mid Atlantic Air Museum, Middletown PA (flies as USN 145915/PL-9)	8.11.83/96
7184 •	P2V-7 SP-2H	**Bu145917**	**N720AU**	Aero Union Corp, Chico CA	20.7.87/96
7186	P2V-7 SP-2H	Bu145918	N918AP	Aerospace Products Inc, North Hollywood CA Black Hills Aviation, Alamogordo NM Neptune Inc, Alamogordo NM (tanker #04) crashed dest., firebombing, Missoula MT	13.8.86/87 4.88/93 9.93/95 5.8.94
7190 •	P2V-7 SP-2H Firestar	**Bu145920**	N920AU **N701AU**	Aero Union Corp, Chico CA Aero Union Corp, Chico CA (tanker #01) (prototype Firestar tanker conv. .88)	3.4.86 9.86/95
7191 •	P2V-7 SP-2H	**Bu145921**	**N54317**	AMCEP Corp, Tucson AZ Aero Corp Inc, Lodi CA Aero Corp Pty Ltd, Perth, Western Australia (ferried Tucson to Perth WA, arr. 17.11.88; tanker conv., stored Perth Airport 92/95)	10.88 5.8.88 .88/96
7183 •	P2V-7 SP-2H	**Bu147566**	 N8187Z **VH-LRR**	(to Aeronavale as 147566) Robert De La Hunty, Sydney NSW (del. ex Tahiti 7.89, based Nowra NAS NSW) Robert De La Hunty, Sydney NSW	 .89/91 10.91/96
7198 •	P2V-7 SP-2H	**Bu147948**	**N80232**	Central Air Service: reg. res. (noted unconv. in yard AMARC, Tucson AZ 9.90, partial tanker conv., Tucson AZ .91) Central Air Service, East Wenatchee WA (open storage Avra Valley AZ 93/95)	4.4.89/92 4.92/96
7199 •	P2V-7 SP-2H	**Bu147949**	**N949RR**	Classics in American Aviation, Reno NV Aviation Classics Ltd, Reno NV	7.89/91 2.91/96
7200 •	P2V-7 SP-2H	**Bu147950**	**N22154**	Hawkins & Powers Aviation, Greybull WY (stored unconv., Greybull 91/93)	16.1.90/96
7207 •	P2V-7 SP-2H	**Bu147957**	**N7060X**	Hawkins & Powers Aviation, Greybull WY (stored unconv., Greybull WY 94)	5.12.89/96
7209 •	P2V-7 SP-2H	**Bu147959**	**N959LH** **N717AU**	Allied Aircraft Sales, Tucson AZ Aero Union Corp, Chico CA Aero Union Corp, Chico CA	10.86 11.86 7.87/96
7211 •	P2V-7 SP-2H	**Bu147961**	**N299MA**	Minden Aircraft Corp, Tucson AZ (tanker #99)	10.4.91/96
7214 •	P2V-7S SP-2H Firestar	**Bu147964**	N964L **N718AU**	Allied Aircraft Sales, Tucson AZ Aero Union Corp, Chico CA Aero Union Corp, Chico CA (tanker #18)	10.86 11.86 6.87/96
7216	P2V-7 SP-2H	Bu147966	N4602X	reg. res. stored Bobs Air Park, AZ; for Aero Union, by	1.84/92 9.86
7217 •	P2V-7S SP-2H Firestar	**Bu147967**	N967LH N702AU(1 **N703AU(2**	Allied Aircraft Sales, Tucson AZ Aero Union Corp, Chico CA ntu: Aero Union Corp, Chico CA Aero Union Corp, Chico CA (Firestar tanker #03)	10.86 11.86 3.87 8.87/96
7218 •	P2V-7S	**Bu147968**	N968L	Allied Aircraft Sales, Tucson AZ	10.86

	SP-2H			Aero Union Corp, Chico CA	11.86
			N716AU(1	Aero Union Corp, Chico CA	7.87/89
			N702AU(2	Aero Union Corp, Chico CA	2.89/96
223 •	P2V-7	**Bu148338**	N22166	Hawkins & Powers Aviation, Greybull WY	16.1.90
	SP-2H		**N138HP**	Hawkins & Powers Aviation, Greybull WY	6.90/96
				(tanker #138)	
224 •	P2V-7	**Bu148339**	N339L	Allied Aircraft Sales, Tucson AZ	10.86
	P-2H			Aero Union Corp, Chico CA	11.86
			N714AU	Aero Union Corp, Chico CA	8.87/96
225 •	P2V-7	**Bu148340**		Davis Monthan AFB AZ: wfu, stored	22.7.76/92
	SP-2H		**N6165Y**	USNAM, NAS Pensacola FL	12.92/96
226 •	P2V-7	**Bu148341**	**N2216K**	Hawkins & Powers Aviation, Greybull WY	16.1.90/96
	SP-2H			(stored unconv., Greybull 91/93)	
227	P2V-7	Bu148342	N70600	Hawkins & Powers Aviation, Greybull WY	5.12.88/92
	SP-2H			crashed in snowstorm, Dixon WY, during del.	
				flight from Davis Monthan AFB to Greybull	8.2.92
228 •	P2V-7	**Bu148343**	N343RR	University of Nevada Systems, Reno NV	4.85/87
	SP-2H			Aero Union Corp, Chico CA	7.87
			N715AU	Aero Union Corp, Chico CA	6.88/96
229 •	P2V-7	**Bu148344**	**N355MA**	Minden Air Corp, Tucson AZ (tanker #55)	4.96
	SP-2H			(conv. to tanker at Tucson AZ 4.95)	
231 •	P2V-7	**Bu148346**	**N2216S**	Hawkins & Powers Aviation, Greybull WY	16.1.90/96
	SP-2H			(stored unconv., Greybull 91/93)	
232	P2V-7S	Bu148347	N48347	Dept. of Interior, Anchorage AK	11.74/76
	SP-2H				
236 •	P2V-7S	**Bu148351**	**N148RR**	University of Nevada/Desert Research Inst.,	
	SP-2H			Reno NV	18.3.85/88
	DP-2H			sale rep., USCR	90/95
				Minden Air Corp, Tucson AZ	96
				(stored unconv. contractors yard DMAFB 95,	
				due to be conv. to tanker .95)	
243 •	P2V-7	**Bu148355**	**N2218A**	Hawkins & Powers Aviation, Greybull WY	16.1.90/95
	SP-2H			(stored unconv., Greybull 91/93)	
246 •	P2V-7	**Bu148356**	**N2218E**	Hawkins & Powers Aviation, Greybull WY	16.1.90/95
	SP-2H			(stored unconv., Greybull 91/93)	
247 •	P2V-7S	**Bu148357**	**N4692A**	Mid Atlantic Air Museum, Middletown PA	20.1.84/95
	SP-2H			(flies as USN "148357/PL-6")	
250 •	P2V-7S	**Bu148358**	**N4619N**	Indiana Museum of Military History,	
	SP-2H			Indianapolis IN	6.1.84
			N14835	Indiana Museum of Military History	7.85/93
				(flew as USN 148358/PL-6)	
				Neptune Inc, Alamogordo NM	9.93/96
255 •	P2V-7	**Bu148359**	**N2218Q**	Hawkins & Powers Aviation, Greybull WY	16.1.90/96
	SP-2H			(stored unconv., Greybull 91/93)	
256 •	P2V-7S	**Bu148360**	**N360RR**	University of Nevada Systems, Reno NV	4.85
	SP-2H			Military Heritage Command, Denver CO	7.87/92
				J. W. Duff Aircraft Parts, Denver CO	4.93/96
260 •	P2V-7S	**Bu148362**	**N362RR**	University of Nevada Systems, Reno NV	4.85/96

	SP-2H			(open storage unconv., Chico CA 89/93)	
7273 •	P2V-7	**Bu149073**		(to RAAF as A89-273) : BOC	3.62/78
	SP-2H			disposal ex RAAF Townsville QLD: for scrap	8.6.78
	M.R.4		**VH-IOY**	Peter Rundle, Townsville QLD	2.79/88
				(rest. Townsville QLD: ff 9.5.81)	
				Robert De La Hunty, Sydney NSW	.88/96
				(flies in midnight blue sc. as RAAF A89-273)	
7281 •	P2V-7	**Bu149081**		(to RAAF as A89-281) : BOC	3.62/78
	SP-2H			disposal ex RAAF Amberley QLD	8.6.78
	M.R.4			Chewing Gum Field Air Museum,	
				Tallebudgera QLD : displ. as "A89-281"	.78/89
			VH-NEP	Alan Wilson/Australian Flying Museum,	
				Brisbane-Archerfield QLD: reg. res.	.89/96
				(trucked to Archerfield QLD .90, rest. to fly)	
7282 •	P2V-7S	**Bu150279**	**N3767U**	reg. res.	88/92
	SP-2H				
7284 •	P2V-7S	**Bu150281**	N281RR	University of Nevada Systems, Reno NV	4.85/87
	SP-2H			Aero Union Corp, Chico CA	.87
			N719AU	Aero Union Corp, Chico CA	10.88/96
7285 •	P2V-7S	**Bu150282**	**N4235T**	Black Hills Aviation, Alamogordo NM	26.3.81/93
	SP-2H			(tanker #09)	
				Neptune Inc, Alamogordo NM (tanker #09)	9.93/96
7286 •	P2V-7S	**Bu150283**	N283RR	University of Nevada Systems, Reno NV	4.85/87
	SP-2H			Aero Union Corp, Chico CA	7.87
			N712AU	Aero Union Corp, Chico CA	6.88/96
8010 •	P2V-7	**RCAF24110**	CF-MQV	ntu: Flying Fireman Ltd, Victoria BC	72
	P-2H		**N14447**	Johnson Flying Service, Missoula MT	.72/75
				Black Hills Aviation, Alamogordo NM	.75/93
				(tanker #11)	
				Neptune Inc, Alamogordo NM (tanker #11)	9.93/96
8013	P2V-7	RCAF24113	CF-MQW	ntu: Flying Fireman Ltd, Victoria BC	72
	P-2H		N14448	Johnson Flying Service, Missoula MT	.72/75
				(tanker #A16)	
				Black Hills Aviation, Alamogordo NM	.75
				(tanker #A16)	
				crashed, dest., Wenatchee WA	.75
8025	P2V-7	RCAF24125	CF-MQX	ntu: Flying Fireman Ltd, Victoria BC	71
	P-2H		N65170	Johnson Flying Service, Missoula MT	.72/75
				(tanker #A17)	
				Black Hills Aviation, Alamogordo NM	.75/90
				(tanker #17, #08)	
				crashed firebombing, Montesano WA	30.9.90
				(note: N65170 #08 at Pima Air Museum AZ	
				92/95: different aircraft, id. unknown)	

LOCKHEED PV VENTURA

4184 •	Mk. II	**AE841**		(to SAAF as 6066)	
				W. Frewen, Saxonwold : derelict on farm	.51/78
				SAAF Museum, Snake Valley AB: open storage	.78/94
				SAAF Museum, Swartkop AB: storage	.94/95
4385	Mk. II	AJ247		(to RCAF as AJ247): BOC 18.1.43: SOC	20.3.47
	Howard			War Assets Corporation (sold for $100)	10.47

	Super Ventura			W. E. Colpitts, Moncton NB	20.10.47
			NL5770N	Hunter C. Moody/Decatur Aviation Co, Decatur IL	12.48/51
			N5770N	Frederick B. Ayer/Trade-Ayer Co, Linden NJ	21.4.51
				Arthur O. Meurer Company Inc	11.6.51
			N18M	Fairbanks Morse & Co, Chicago IL	13.6.51/59
				(civil executive conv. completed 6.52)	
			N92U	W. B. Willis	9.2.59
				Howard Aero Inc, San Antonio TX	10.59/60
				(conv. to Super Ventura completed 15.4.60)	
			N200JW	Jim Walter Corp, Tampa FL	15.4.60/67
			N208JW	Jim Walter Corp, Tampa FL	7.9.67/68
			N570FT	Florida Tile Industries Inc	15.4.68/69
				Hydros Inc, St Petersburg FL	8.11.69/70
				Friedkin Enterprises Inc	5.10.70/71
				Marine Investment Inc	16.6.71/75
				Rotor-Aire Inc/Helicopter Enterprises Inc	21.7.75
				Sea-Air Corp	10.75/77
				Equipment Specialists Inc, Jacksonville FL	9.2.77
				crashed, dest. Tenerife-Magdalen, Colombia	13.4.77
401 •	Mk. II Howard Super Ventura	**AJ263**		(del. to USAAF as Model RB-37: AJ263)	
			NL9774H	J. W. Slager	29.4.46/51
				(purchased ex War Assets Admin: $2100)	
			N1491V	ntu	4.51
			N9774H	Clyde Sturgell Jr	30.7.50
				Irwin Hansen	5.51
				AiResearch Aviation Service Co	9.7.51/53
				Mark Hurd Aerial Surveys, Minneapolis MN	30.6.53/55
				Northern Natural Gas Co, Omaha NE	9.12.55/59
			N502N (1	Northern Natural Gas Co, Omaha NE	1.6.59/60
				(conv. to Super Ventura completed 19.8.60)	
			N963B (2	Northern Natural Gas Co, Omaha NE	8.9.60/61
				Blount Bros Construction Co, Montgomery AL	13.3.61/68
				University of Alabama, Tuscaloosa AL	23.8.68/69
				Maurice R. Smith, Midland TX	18.9.69/73
				Ruth M. Richards/Onyx Aviation, Miami FL	10.73/74
				Ernest Stern & George Stern, Pittsburgh PA	22.8.74/76
				Francis J. Puppio, Brigantine NJ	5.11.76/78
				Larry Jones	24.2.78
				James L. Stankowitz, Anchorage AK: USCR	12.78/96
				(impounded Bogota, Colombia, 76/89)	
449 •	Mk. II	**AJ311**		(del. to USAAF as Model 37: AJ311)	
				(allocated to FA Brasileira as AJ311)	
				Lightning Transients Research Inc, St Paul MN	65/70
				(unconv. RAF scheme: used for static tests for lightning strike research)	
				USAFM: under rest. St Paul MN	73
				Fred E. Weisbrod Aircraft Museum, Pueblo CO	86/96
607 •	Mk. II	**AJ469**		(to SAAF as 6130)	
				W. Frewen, Saxonwold : derelict on farm	.51/78
				SAAF Museum, Ysterplaat, Capetown	.78/83
				RAF Museum Store, RAF Henlow/RAF Cosford	.83/95
633 •	Mk. II	**AJ495**		(to SAAF as 6075)	
				W. Frewen, Saxonwold : derelict on farm	.51/78
				SAAF Museum, Ysterplaat AB, Capetown	10.78/94
				(open storage, unrest., Ysterplaat 92)	
642 •	Mk. II	**AJ504**		(to SAAF as 6112)	
				W. Frewen, Saxonwold : derelict on farm	.51/78
				SAAF Museum, Snake Valley AB: open storage	2.76/94
				SAAF Museum, Swartkop AB: storage	.94/96

4646 •	Mk. II	**AJ508**		(to SAAF as 6120)	
				W. Frewen, Saxonwold : derelict on farm	.51/78
				SAAF Museum, Snake Valley AB: open storage	2.76/94
				SAAF Museum, Swartkop AB: storage	.94/96
4676	B-34	41-38020		(to RAF as FD568: not del.)	
	Mk. IIA			(to USAAF as FD568)	
	RB-34			FA del Ejercito de la Revolucion Americana/	
				Caribbean Legion, Cayo Confites, Cuba	47
				(to FA Ejercito de Cuba as FAEC 214)	8.47/51
			N1489V	Babb Co, Newark NJ	10.51/54
				(adv. for sale Babb Co 5.53: unconv. ex military)	
	Howard			D. U. Howard, San Antonio TX	56
	Super Ventura		CF-MFL	Massey Ferguson Ltd	.59
				Dominion Tar & Chemical Ltd, Montreal QUE	65
				Canadian Inspection & Testing Co, Montreal	66/70
			N1489V	Hill Aircraft & Leasing, Atlanta GA	72
			N8GW	Hill Aircraft Leasing, Atlanta GA	.72
				William T. Hayes	.74
				Frank A. Hill, Fort Lauderdale FL	76
				World Photography Corp, Fort Lauderdale FL	12.77/79
				crashed dest., Belle Glade FL	11.4.79
4688 •	B-34	**41-38032**		(to RAF as FD580: not del.)	
	Mk. IIA			(to USAAF as FD580)	
	RB-34			FA del Ejercito de la Revolucion Americana/	
				Caribbean Legion, Cayo Confites, Cuba	47
				(to FA Ejercito de Cuba as FAEC 215)	8.47/51
			N1527V	The Babb Co Inc, New York NY	10.7.51
				Ayercraft Inc/Trade Ayer Inc, Linden NJ	25.2.52/57
				Mechanical Products, Jackson MI	19.11.56
			N1000X	Mechanical Products, Jackson MI	26.6.57/62
				Robert V. Kamensky & Leo L. Yoder	14.6.63
				Mabel C. Harris, Fort Lauderdale FL	22.3.65/72
				Samuel E. McConnell	9.10.72
				D & D Supply Inc, Miami FL	5.12.77/86
				Bush Aviation Inc, Fort Lauderdale FL	4.3.86
				(adv. for sale, with bomb doors intact)	
				Southwest Aviation Inc, Fairacres NM	6.3.86/92
				(open storage, Fort Lauderdale 86/91)	
				Aero Nostalgia Inc, Stockton CA	94
				USNAM, NAS Pensacola FL	15.9.94/96
4773 •	RB-34	**41-38117**		(to RAF as FD665)	
	Mk. II			(to RNZAF as NZ4600): BOC 6.43: SOC	12.11.47
				M. Russ, Nelson: trucked to farm	.47/71
				Museum of Transport & Technology, Auckland	.71/96
				(recov. from farm, shipped to Auckland 9.71,	
				static rest., displ. as "RNZAF NZ4600")	
5162 •	PV-1	**Bu33153**		(to RCAF as 2165): BOC 20.5.43: SOC	4.10.49
	GR. V			The Babb Co (Canada) Ltd	16.4.49
	Howard		N5768N	Hunter C. Moody/Decatur Aviation Co,	
	Super Ventura			Decatur IL	20.10.50
				Sinclair Refining Co, Tulsa OK/New York NY	5.1.51/58
				Dallas Aero Services, Dallas TX	3.4.58
			N131A	Ada Oil Co, Houston TX	3.6.58/66
				(conv. to Super Ventura completed 10.9.58)	
				Clarks Aerial Service, Brownfield TX	19.1.68/77
				Brownfield Aerial Inc, Brownfield TX	7.10.77
5170 •	PV-1	**Bu33161**		(to RCAF as 2174): BOC 29.5.43: SOC	19.3.57
	GR.V		CF-HBW	Spartan Air Services Ltd, Ottawa ONT	56

	Howard		N4968C		
	Super Ventura		N18N	Volusia Locations Inc, Saratoga WY	59/65
				(conv. Howard 500 prototype .63)	
	Howard		N365N	Husky Aviation Co, Cody WY	.65/66
	500		CF-WKG	Pacific Petroleums Ltd, Calgary ALTA	.67/69 (
	c/n 500-101)		N500B	Dee-Howard Co, San Antonio TX	.70
				Rawcon de Costa Rica, San Jose, Costa Rica	.70/74
				Dee-Howard Co, San Antonio TX	
			C-GLOM	Futura Airlines, Vancouver BC	12.80
				Owen Sound Air Services, Toronto ONT	.81
			PJ-LLZ	Lucht Land Zee NV, Aruba	5.5.83
				derelict, impounded Nassau, Bahamas	88/89
5173	PV-1	**Bu33164**		(to RCAF as 2205): BOC 25.6.43: SOC	22.1.47
	GR.V			Lionel Verreault	48
				W. C. Siple/Siple Aviation Ltd	22.6.48
			N64005	Hunter C. Moody/Decatur Aviation Co,	
				Decatur IL	30.7.48
				Wings Inc	20.10.49
				Sun Oil Co, Philadelphia PA	29.3.50/55
				(conv. to executive aircraft Islip NY 3.50)	
				Trade Ayer Inc, Linden NJ	19.8.55/58
			N1958S	F. B. Ayer & Associates Inc, New York, NY	3.3.58/61
				Hugh M. Pierce, Scarsdale NY	29.6.61/64
				K & S Aircraft Inc	17.4.64/65
				Leon H. Patin	25.2.65
				P. J. Mathews & C. Mandina	26.8.65/68
				Drew National Leasing Corp, New York NY	12.68/71
				Frank A. Hill/Hill Air, Fort Lauderdale FL	27.7.71
				sale rep., USCR	72/96
				(last noted at Fort Lauderdale FL 9.70)	
258 •	PV-1	**Bu33249**		(to RCAF as 2180): BOC 29.5.43: SOC	11.8.50
	GR.V			Douglas W. Siple/Siple Aviation Ltd	53
	Howard			Universal Trading Corp, New York NY	25.11.53
	Super Ventura		N10485	Howard Aero Service, San Antonio TX	13.12.54
				(conv. to Super Ventura completed 31.10.56)	
			N1212	Fruehauf Trailer Co, Detroit MI	11.56/60
			N2020	Reserve Mining Co, Silver Bay MN	20.5.60/63
				University of Minnesota, Minneapolis MN	12.63/64
			N8020	Andre J. Andreoli/Associated Developments	14.8.64/67
			N4005	Cathedral of Tomorrow Inc, Cuyahoga OH	18.9.67/72
				Unit Electric Control Inc	10.7.72/73
				Billy C. Hayes	19.9.73
				Robert Harrison (sale not completed)	.75
				sale rep., USCR	84/96
267	PV-1	Bu33258		(to RCAF as 2185): BOC 10.6.43: SOC	28.2.51
	GR.V			Spartan Air Services Ltd, Ottawa ONT	55
	Howard		N10473	Howard Aero Services, San Antonio TX	14.6.55
	Super Ventura			(conv. to Super Ventura completed 18.2.57)	
			N2600	Socony Mobil Oil Co, New York NY	18.2.57/62
	Howard		N9211R	Socony Mobil Oil Co, New York NY	.62/64
	350			Maverick Equipment Co	24.6.64/65
			N544B	Bovaird Supply Co, Tulsa OK	17.6.65/69
				Dee Howard Aircraft Sales, San Antonio TX	4.6.69/70
				Buddy Lee & Richard Blake	25.5.70
				George Nowlan/Danny Davis, Brentwood TN	26.5.71/73
				Basler Flight Service, Oshkosh WI	12.6.73/74
				Bronco Mines Inc	23.5.74/75
				Onyx Aviation Inc, Miami FL	31.1.75
				Marion County Sheriff FL: seized	9.75
				Aeromedia Inc	12.75/76
				Kentucky Trust Oil Corp, Miami FL	26.5.76/78
				US Customs, Fort Lauderdale FL: seized	11.76

			H & H Inc	3.3.78
			US Customs, Savannah GA: seized	6.3.78
			Marian Air Spray, Savannah GA	17.7.78/79
			Triple D Transport Co, Fort Lauderdale FL	24.2.79
			crashed dest., nr. Guantanamo, Cuba	27.4.79
5269 •	PV-1 **Bu33260**		(to RCAF as 2186): BOC 10.6.43: SOC	11.8.50
	GR.V		D. W. Siple/Siple Aircraft Ltd	55
	Howard	N75384	Universal Trading Corp, New York NY	11.8.55
	Super Ventura		Howard Aero Service, San Antonio TX	5.12.55/57
			(conv. to Super Ventura completed 12.12.57)	
		N9060	Cluett Peabody & Co, New York NY	12.57/63
			Rita Corp	3.7.63
			Fairchild Stratos Corp	3.7.63/64
			Chemical & Industrial Corp, Cincinatti OH	27.4.64/68
			William C. Whitesell/ Flying W Airways,	
			Fort Lauderdale FL & Medford NJ	11.68/72
			R. Cornell Co	3.3.72/73
			Lomax Corp	14.6.73/74
			Hydro Development International Ltd SA	11.1.74/77
			Onyx Aviation Inc, Oklahoma City OK	10.77/78
			Southern Aero Traders, Miami FL	11.78/89
			Oklahoma Aircraft Corp, Yukon OK	90/96
			(open storage, Yukon OK 80/82)	
5272	PV-1 Bu33263		(to RCAF as 2189): BOC 10.6.43: SOC	11.8.50
	GR.V		D. W. Siple/Siple Aircraft Ltd	53
	Howard		Universal Trading Corp, New York NY	11.53/54
	Super Ventura	N10486	Howard Aero Service, San Antonio TX	12.54/60
			(conv. to Howard Pressurised Super Ventura	
	Howard		completed 15.4.60)	
	500	N721N	Nationwide Mutual Insurance, Columbus OH	20.4.60/69
(c/n 500-102)			(further conv. by Howard .62; although allocated	
			c/n 500-102 full conv. to H.500 not completed)	
			Howell Instrument Inc, Fort Worth TX	29.8.69/76
			Waggoner Aircraft Inc	25.8.78/79
			Aggadir Ltd, New York NY	14.6.79
			ditched in sea off Aruba, Antilles	7.7.79
5274	PV-1 Bu33265		(to RCAF as 2217): BOC 7.7.43: SOC	22.1.47
	GR.V	N5761N	conv. to executive config. by Spartan Aero	c53
	Howard	N3031 (1	Republic Steel Corp, Cleveland OH	53/64
	Super Ventura	N8081		
		N730EG	Purdue Aero Corp, Lafayette IN	66
			Edwin J. Gould, New York NY	.67/72
			Home Interiors & Gifts Inc	73
			Dallas Chapter, Dallas TX	.75/76
			crashed Culican, Mexico	1.4.75
5275	PV-1 Bu33266		(to RCAF as 2190): BOC 10.6.43: SOC	28.2.51
	GR.V	N10475		
	Howard	CF-KEH	Spartan Air Services, Ottawa ONT	59
	Super Ventura	N101MC	International Minerals & Chemical Corp	61
			Commonwealth Plan Inc, Boston MA	63
	Howard 350	N361MC	Commonwealth Plan Inc, Boston MA	.63/66
			Aviation Properties Inc, Dallas TX	69/70
			Executive Leasing Services Inc	.70
			Mor Pon Inc, Dallas TX	.71/72
			crashed dest., landing Philadelphia PA	15.10.72
5277	PV-1 **Bu33268**		(to RCAF as 2214): BOC 7.7.43: SOC	22.1.47
	GR.V	N64007	Hunter C. Moody/Decatur Aviation Co,	
			Decatur IL	49
			Bacon Corp, Santa Monica CA	54

c/n	Type	Bu No.	Reg.	History	Date
				(executive aircraft, advertised for sale 10.54)	
			XB-REX	President Aleman of Mexico, Mexico City	
			N5399N	Los Angeles Air Service, Las Vegas NV	55/56
				Howard Aero Inc, San Antonio TX	61/72
5280	PV-1	**Bu33271**		(to RCAF as 2191): BOC 10.6.43: SOC	8.6.53
	GR.V			Kenting Aviation Ltd, Toronto ONT	52
	Howard		N1506V	Louise Bartlett	7.7.52
	Super Ventura			Lockwood, Kessler, Bartlett Inc, New York NY	11.52/54
				(civil. conv. by Spartan Aero completed 6.2.53)	
				Mark Hurd Aerial Surveys, Minneapolis MN	1.2.54
				Plymouth Oil Co, Pittsburgh PA	26.10.54
				(conv. to Super Ventura completed 10.9.55)	
			N11P	Plymouth Oil Co *The Wildcatter*: del.	9.55/62
				Ohio Oil Co, Findlay OH	3.4.62/64
				George H. Bailey Co, Fort Wayne IN	22.5.64/68
				Ronald C. Witt, St Paul MN	9.4.68/73
				Onyx Aviation Inc, Miami FL	14.5.73
				Pan American Development Co, Long Beach CA	12.73
				sale rep., Long Beach CA : USCR	90/95
5283	PV-1	Bu33274		(to RCAF as 2196): BOC 15.6.43: SOC	10.3.51
	GR.V		N1504V	Standard Oil Co, Chicago IL	56
	Howard		N234YU	Ebco Manufacturing Co, Columbus OH	4.56/72
	Super Ventura			crashed Atlantic City NJ	1.2.75
5324 •	PV-1	**Bu33315**		(to RCAF as 2195): BOC 14.6.43: SOC	10.3.51
	GR.V		**CF-FAV**	Spartan Air Services Ltd, Ottawa ONT	53
				forced landing and abandoned, 50 miles north Yellowknife NWT	14.8.53
				Tony Jarvis/Ventura Memorial Flight Association, Edmonton ALTA	.88/91
				(recov. by helicopter 17.6.88)	
				Edmonton Aviation Heritage Society, Edmonton-Industrial Airport ALTA	92
				(rest. to fly, CFB Namao ALTA)	
5331 •	PV-1	Bu33322		(to RCAF as 2202): BOC 22.6.43: SOC	11.8.50
	GR.V		N5776N	Douglas W. Siple/Siple Aircraft Ltd	51
	Howard			Hunter C. Moody/Decatur Aviation Co, Decatur IL	15.11.51
	Super Ventura			Northern Natural Gas Co, Omaha NE	10.3.53/59
	Howard			(exec. conv. by Spartan Aero, Tulsa OK 2.54)	
	350		N507N	Northern Natural Gas Co, Omaha NE	25.3.59/61
				(conv. to Super Ventura completed 31.3.59)	
				wheels up landing, Omaha NE	24.7.60
			N507H	Husky Aviation Co, Cody WY	1.1.61/64
				Willis C. Walker, Saratoga WY	12.64/66
				(conv. by Business Aircraft Corp, San Antonio to BAC/Howard 350 completed 18.4.66)	
				Husky Aviation Co, Cody WY	22.4.66/67
				Penn Aire Aviation	13.2.67/68
				Brads Machine Products, Gadsden AL	12.68/71
				Cessna Finance Corp, Wichita KS	4.1.71/72
				Hawkinson Enterprises Inc	12.72/73
				M. Lane Powers	15.6.73/75
				Paul D. Finefrock & Ken Whetzel, Hobart OK	16.7.75
				US Drug Enforcement Agency: seized	8.75
				held by US Customs Service, New Orleans LA 76	
				USNAM, NAS Pensacola FL	81/83
5332 •	PV-1	**Bu33323**		(to RCAF as 2197): BOC 15.6.43: SOC	22.1.47
	GR.V		N64008		
			N164H	M. A. Hanna Mining Co, Cleveland OH	54/64
				(civil conv. by Spartan Aero, Tulsa OK .55)	

c/n	Type	Mil. ID	Reg.	Owner / History	Date
				Purdue Aeronautics Corp, Lafayette IN	.64
				James E. McDaniel	.65
				Gulf & Western, Houston TX	.66
				Pinellas Central Bank & Trust Co	.67
				Clarks Aerial Service, Brownfield TX	69/77
				Brownfield Aerial Inc, Brownfield TX	11.77
				E. R. Meither	4.78
5333	PV-1	Bu33324		(to RCAF as 2200): BOC 15.6.43: SOC	7.2.52
	GR.V			Kenting Aviation Ltd, Ottawa ONT	
			N3948C		
			N44R	Rockwell Manufacturing Co, Pittsburgh PA	53/59
			N401M	Howard Aero Inc, San Antonio TX	61
			N45CK	Chun King Corp, Duluth MN	63/64
				Jenno F. Paulucci, Duluth MN	.66
				University of Minnesota, Minneapolis MN	.67/69
				Clarks Aerial Service, Brownfield TX	.69/72
				crashed while spraying, Union Springs AL	4.5.73
5334	PV-1	Bu33325		(to RCAF as 2209): BOC 5.7.43: SOC	20.3.52
	GR.V			Kenting Aviation Ltd, Ottawa ONT	.52
			N3950C	Albert J. Leeward/Leeward Aeronautical Services, Fort Wayne IN	29.2.52
			N52K	Kraft Foods Co, Chicago IL	2.7.52/56
				(civil conv. by Spartan Aero Repair, Tulsa OK to executive config, completed 14.1.53)	
			N33DP	Daniel Peterkin/Morton Salt Co, Chicago IL	11.56/63
			N322PN	Powernail Corp, Prairie View IL	.63/66
			N922PN	Powernail Corp, Prairie View IL	12.65/70
5336 •	PV-1	**Bu33327**		(to RCAF as 2198): BOC 15.6.43: SOC	22.1.47
	GR.V			Lionel Verreault	.48
	Howard			W. C. Siple/Siple Aircraft Ltd	22.6.48
	Super Ventura		N64004	Hunter C. Moody/Decatur Aviation Co, Decatur IL	30.7.48
	Howard			(conv. to executive config by Aero Trades Inc, MacArthur Airport NY)	350
				Triangle Conduit & Cable, New Brunswick NJ	12.50/56
				Howard Aero Service, San Antonio TX	15.5.56/58
			N234P	Northern Pump Co, Minneapolis MN	1.1.58/79
				(conv. to Super Ventura completed 7.7.58)	
				North Star Sales & Leasing Inc	2.2.79/80
				Summit Quarries Inc, Summit Station PA	22.7.80/83
				Pacific Northwest Lumber, Spokane WA	11.83
				seized by police, New Smyrna Beach FL	8.10.84/86
				Doan Helicopter Inc, New Smyrna Beach FL	10.86/92
				(offered for sale, Doan auction 30.10.92: type Howard 350: ferriable, executive interior)	
				James A. McNally, Belthesda MD	5.94/96
5355 •	PV-1	**Bu33346**		wreck located in Alaska	
			N57HA	US Historical Aircraft Preservation Museum Inc, Anchorage AK	87/88
5371	PV-1	Bu33362		(to RCAF as 2211): BOC 5.7.43: SOC	28.2.51
	GR.V		N75381		
			N5C	Champlin Oil & Refining Co	61
			N175S	Skelly Oil Co, Tulsa OK	63/68
				B. B. Saxon Co	.68
				Gen Aero Inc, San Antonio TX	69
				Sparlinco Corp, Dallas TX	70
				Frank Armstrong, Dallas TX	.71/72
				Pioneer Ventures Inc	72
				crashed, alleged drug flight, Chimichagua, Colombia	15.4.73

5372	PV-1	Bu33363		(to RCAF as 2210): BOC 5.7.43: SOC	22.9.52
	GR.V		CF-HBX	Spartan Air Services Ltd, Ottawa ONT	56
	Howard		N4969C	Howard Aero Inc, San Antonio TX	61
	500		N511YP	Petan Co, Santa Barbara CA	61/69
(c/n 500-103)				(conv. Howard 500 .64)	
			N511Y	McMahons Inc, Santa Barbara CA	.69/72
				Darrell A. Tomblin Corp	73
				Lonnie Russell Lsg. & Rental, Birmingham AL	.74/76
			N127LR	Lonnie Russell Lsg. & Rental, Birmingham AL	.76
				Oklahoma Aircraft Corp, Yukon OK	.78
				crashed Key Largo FL	4.1.78
5375	PV-1	Bu33366		(to RCAF as 2232): BOC 28.7.43: SOC	28.2.51
	GR.V		CF-FSL	Spartan Air Services Ltd, Ottawa ONT	56
	Howard		N4970C		
	500		N420L	Avco Distributing Co, New York NY	61/64
	(c/n 500-104)			(rep. conv. to full Howard 500 not completed)	
			N4201		.65
			N3031 (2	Republic Steel Corp, Cleveland OH	.66
			N8031	Republic Steel Corp, Cleveland OH	.67
			YV-P-AEK	Mene Grande Oil Co	1.69
			N8033	reg.	4.71
			N80BD	F. J. Boutell Driveaway Inc, Flint MI	72
				Red River Ranch, Fort Lauderdale FL	76
				rep. crashed	
				struck-off USCR as exported	11.77
5378 •	PV-1	**Bu33369**		(to RCAF as 2221): BOC 17.7.43: SOC	11.8.50
	GR.V			disposal ex RCAF Vulcan ALTA	.53
			N1590V	Universal Trading Corp, New York NY	1.12.53/54
				(civil conv. to executive aircraft by Spartan	
				Aircraft Co, Tulsa OK 4.12.53 - ff 10.8.55)	
				Trade-Ayer Inc, Linden NJ	9.3.54/58
				Spartan Aircraft Co, Tulsa OK	1.7.58/61
			N159V	Spartan Aircraft Co, Tulsa OK	11.61/64
			N159U	Spartan Aircraft Co, Tulsa OK	24.8.64/69
				Clark's Aerial Service, Brownfield TX	25.2.69/76
				Brownfield Aerial Inc, Brownfield TX	7.10.77
				Aristera Co, Lubbock TX	15.12.77
				Juan D. Perez, Tampa FL	2.10.78/83
				Hill Air Company Inc, Fort Lauderdale FL	26.9.83/85
				(open storage Ft. Lauderdale FL 80/86)	
				Jim Ricketts/Aero Nostalgia Inc, Stockton CA	2.7.85/88
				(del. Stockton 26.9.86 ex Ft. Lauderdale,	
				rest. to mil. config: del. to Australia 7.88)	
			VH-SFF	RAAF Museum, RAAF Point Cook VIC: del.	13.7.88/96
				(flies as "RAAF A59-67/SF-F")	
5379	PV-1	Bu33370		(to RCAF as 2222): BOC 17.7.43: SOC	22.9.52
	GR.V		N456 (1	Pure Oil Co, Chicago IL	56/61
				undercarriage collapsed, landing Hobbs NM	26.3.61
			N456G	rereg.	12.10.62
				Howard Aero Inc, San Antonio TX	63
				Business Aircraft Corp, San Antonio TX	64/70
5489	PV-1	Bu34599		(to RCAF as 2230): BOC 22.7.43: SOC	11.8.50
	GR.V		N10484		
	Howard		N4900	Mid Continental Leasing Co, Amarillo TX	63/66
	Super Ventura			King Resources Inc, Denver CO	.68/70
				Lee Matherne	.70
5490	PV-1	Bu34600		(to RCAF as 2223): BOC 17.7.43: SOC	4.6.52
	GR.V			Spartan Air Services Ltd, Ottawa ONT	
			N9318H	Albert J. Leeward/Leeward Aeronautical	

				Services, Fort Wayne IN	
			N31J	Southern Aero Inc, Atlanta GA	56
				C. F. Johnson, Palm Beach FL	61/64
				Business Aircraft Corp, San Antonio TX	.64/70
5492 •	PV-1	**Bu34602**		(to RCAF as 2226): BOC 22.7.43: SOC	28.2.51
	GR.V			Spartan Air Services Ltd, Ottawa ONT	55
	Howard		N10476	Howard Aero Service, San Antonio TX	14.6.55/57
	Super Ventura			(conv. to Super Ventura completed 16.10.57)	
			N100P	National Distillers Corp, New York NY	10.57/59
			N130P (1	National Distillers Corp, New York NY	22.10.59
			N130PL(1	Pacific Lumber Co, San Francisco CA	11.59/61
			N430PL	Pacific Lumber Co, San Francisco CA	11.61
			N183PL	Pacific Lumber Co, San Francisco CA	12.61/64
				Fontaine Truck Equipment C, Birmingham AL	11.4.64/67
				Robert B. Hodgson	22.1.68/69
				Scotts Inn Development Co, Columbus OH	11.4.69/71
				James V. & Marlyn S. Pike	10.72/74
				Aero Union Corp, Chico CA	1.2.74/96
				(wfu, open storage Chico CA 78/95)	
5494 •	**PV-1**	**Bu34604**		(to RCAF as 2231): BOC 22.7.43: SOC	22.8.52
	GR.V			Spartan Air Services Ltd, Ottawa ONT	54
	Howard		N10483	Howard Aero Service, San Antonio TX	24.9.54/56
	Super Ventura		N101P	Howard Aero Service, San Antonio TX	8.6.56/57
			N711R	Howard Aero Service, San Antonio TX	31.1.57
	Howard			E. Cockrell/Cockrell Corp, Houston TX	27.5.57/70
	350			(conv. to Super Ventura completed 27.5.57)	
				(conv. to Howard 350 completed 8.2.65)	
			N815G	Robert B. Phillips/Phillips Advertising Co	9.4.70/73
				Executive Aviation Ltd	2.4.74/75
				CAVU of Miami Inc, Miami Beach FL	23.5.75/78
				impounded for drug running, Teterboro NJ	22.3.76
				Jerry Langer & H. Rosenburg	3.5.78
				Air Carriers Inc, Miami FL	16.8.78/96
5495	PV-1	Bu34605		(to RCAF as 2227): BOC 22.7.43: SOC	19.3.57
	GR.V			Spartan Air Services Ltd, Ottawa ONT	
	Howard		N5390N	Howard Aero Inc, San Antonio TX	55/59
	Super Ventura			(prototype 'Super Ventura': demonstrator) ff	5.55
			N46F	Hunt Oil Co, Dallas TX	61/69
			N4680	Clarks Aerial Service, Brownfield, TX	70/76
				struck-off reg.	.77
5497 •	PV-1	**Bu34607**		(to RCAF as 2228): BOC 22.7.43: SOC	28.2.51
	GR.V			Spartan Air Services Ltd, Ottawa ONT	24.9.52/55
	Howard		N75382	Howard Aero Service, San Antonio TX	14.6.55
	Pressurised		N100M	ntu: Signal Oil & Gas Co	8.59
	Ventura		N510N	Howard Aero Service, San Antonio TX	11.59/60
	Howard			(conv. to Pressurised Ventura completed 27.1.60)	
	400			Northern Natural Gas, Omaha NE	15.1.60/61
			N501N	Northern Natural Gas, Omaha NE	22.5.61/65
				Nello L.Teer Co, Durham NC	17.3.65/72
				Dee Howard Co, San Antonio TX	31.1.72
				A. P. St.Philip Inc	2.6.72/75
				Casey Aviation Inc	1.75/76
				Transecutive Aviation, Pittsburgh PA	8.76/77
			N2ES	Transecutive Aviation, Pittsburg PA	7.77/84
			N52ES	Transecutive Aviation, Pittsburgh PA	2.6.84
				R. M. Richards/Onyx Aviation, Miami FL	10.84
				Clifton F. Albright	29.10.84
				Edwin B. Dearborn (sale not completed)	12.11.84
				sale rep., Kenner LA : USCR	90/96

5500 •	PV-1 Howard 500	**Bu34610**		(to RAF as FP552)	
				(to SAAF as 6409)	44/59
(c/n 500-111)				Howard Aero Inc, San Antonio TX	.59/61
				(stripped airframe shipped ex S.Africa 12.59, rebuild as H500 completed 19.9.61)	
			N456 (2	Pure Oil Co, Palatine IL	20.9.61/65
				Union Oil Co of California, Palatine IL	23.8.65
			N749G	Union Oil Co of California, Palatine IL	11.11.66
				Carrier Corp, Syracuse NY	31.8.67/69
				Kimbell Properties Inc, Fort Worth TX	1.12.69/76
			N696JB	Dolph Briscoe, Uvalde TX	24.9.76/79
			N896JB	Oklahoma Aircraft Corp, Yukon OK	6.9.79/81
				Dixon Hyckes Inc, Memphis TN	7.11.81/84
				Aviall of Texas Inc, Dallas TX	12.10.84
				Brinson Air Inc, Miami FL	7.5.85
				Harmer Inc, Miami FL	10.85/86
				Foxtrot Romeo Inc, Miami FL	12.9.86/89
				Nighthawk Air Systems Inc, Miami FL	11.9.89/95
				(open storage, Tamiami FL 88/92)	
				dam. by Hurricane Andrew, Tamiami FL	9.92
5535 •	PV-1	**Bu34645**		(to RNZAF as NZ4522)	
				crashed landing, Talasea strip, New Britain	9.9.44
				(still in situ, largely complete: stripped for parts by MoTaT Auckland, for c/n 4773/NZ4600)	
5551 •	PV-1 Howard 500 (c/n 500-105)	**Bu34661**		(to RAF as FP570)	
				(to SAAF as 6414)	
			N74022	Howard Aero Inc, San Antonio TX	.59
				(stripped airframe shipped ex S.Africa 12.59, rebuilt San Antonio as Super Ventura)	
			N20S (2	Storer Broadcasting	23.1.61
			N500Y	Howard Aero Inc, San Antonio TX	61/63
				(conv. to Howard 500 completed 11.7.63)	
				Natural Gas Pipeline Co, Chicago IL: del.	11.7.63/66
				Dayton Steel Foundry Co, Dayton OH	10.6.66/68
				Southwest Forest Industries, Phoenix AZ	24.5.68
			N4362F	Southwest Forest Industries, Phoenix AZ	10.69/72
				J. E. Rose	12.9.72
				N. Marshall Seeburg & Sons Inc	17.11.73
				James K. Leeward/Bahia Oaks Inc, Ocala FL	17.3.75/77
				Chuck Larson	8.4.77/78
				Atlas Aircraft Corp, Long Beach CA	8.6.78
			N500HP	Atlas Aircraft Corp, Long Beach CA	2.4.79/80
				Mathias B. Velasco	12.80/82
				Trailblazer Leasing Corp, Las Vegas NV	10.82/84
				V. E. Kuster Co Inc, Long Beach CA	6.8.84/95
				loan: Nevada Air Museum, Reno-Stead NV	87
5560 •	PV-1 Howard Super Ventura Howard 500	**Bu34670**		(to RAF as FP579)	
				(to SAAF as 6417)	44/60
				Howard Aero Inc, San Antonio TX	.59/61
				(stripped airframe shipped ex S.Africa 12.59, rebuilt as Super Ventura, later H500)	
(c/n 500-113)			N539N	Charles A. Steen/Utex Exploration Co	15.12.61
				Business Aircraft Corp, San Antonio TX	22.10.62
			N200G (2	Green Construction Co, Owensboro KY	8.11.62/66
			N206G	American Machinery & Foundry Co, Shreveport LA	4.1.66/72
			N381RD	Bird Corp, Sandpoint ID ("Bluebird II")	30.6.72/78
				Forrest M. Bird	11.1.78
			N500LN	Western Aviation Leasing, Wilmington DE	14.6.78/95
				lsd. Duncan Baker/Baker Petroleum Co, Coventry UK: del.	6.10.78/96

5591 •	PV-1 **Bu34701**		(to RCAF as 2236): BOC 12.8.43: SOC	22.9.52
	GR.V		Spartan Air Services Ltd, Ottawa ONT	54
	Howard	N5393N	Howard Aero Service, San Antonio TX	17.9.54/56
	Super Ventura	N345 (1	ntu	5.6.56
	Howard	N111M (1	Howard Aero, San Antonio TX	31.8.56/57
	350		(conv. to Super Ventura completed 11.1.57)	
			Gamble Skogmo Inc, Minneapolis MN	12.1.57/61
		N191N	Gamble Skogmo Inc, Minneapolis MN	12.6.61/65
			(conv. to Howard 350 completed 23.4.62)	
			Simpson Timber Co, Seattle WA	28.5.65/69
		N593EW	R. H. Bentley	1.4.69
			Sealy Mattress Co, Houston TX	16.5.69/71
			Austin Management Co	12.71/73
			Mobile Housing Inc	11.6.73/74
			Raymond F. Johnson	21.8.74/76
			Drug Enforcement Agency, San Antonio TX	21.7.76
			US Customs Air Support Unit	28.7.76/80
			Georgia Historical Aviation Museum, Stone Mountain GA	1.8.80
			Oklahoma Aircraft Corp, Yukon OK	21.12.81
			Graham L. Kendall, Oklahoma City OK	8.11.82/96
5598	PV-1 Bu34708		(to RCAF as 2248): BOC 18.9.43: SOC	22.1.47
	GR.V	N5065N	conv. to executive config. by Spartan Aero	
	Howard	N3030 (1	Republic Steel Corp, Cleveland OH	49/59
	Super Ventura	N3060	Republic Steel Corp, Cleveland OH	
	Howard		Wings Leasing Corp, Reno NV	63/64
	700	N30606 (1	rereg.	.64
		N16777 (2	Dee Howard Co, San Antonio TX	.66
			Interstate Aircraft Leasing, Columbus OH	.67/69
			Scoa Industries Inc, Columbus OH	69/70
			Lease Air Inc	.70/71
		N25YC (1	Youngstown Cartage Co	71
			crashed, dest., Philadelphia PA	11.9.71
5599 •	PV-1 **Bu34709**		(to RCAF as 2244): BOC 25.8.43: SOC	3.10.46
	GR.V	N1206	Fruehauf Trailer Co, Detroit MI	56
	Howard	N5034F	Firestone Tire & Rubber Co, Akron OH	61/66
	Super Ventura		AiResearch Aviation, Los Angeles CA	.68
	BA400	N1970H	University of Southern California, Los Angeles CA	69
		N197RD	Rowan Drilling Co, Houston TX	70/72
		N100LR	Lamb Industries Inc	.73
		N400MC	B. B. McCormick & Sons Inc, Jacksonville FL	76
		YV-183CP	reg.	11.77
			ATRAMAR, Colombia	11.91/94
5649 •	PV-1 **Bu34759**		(to RAF as FP607)	
	GR. V		(to SAAF as 6432)	
			South African Airways Apprentice Training School, Johannesburg-Jan Smuts	
			Edenvale Veterans Association, South Africa	92/94
5650 •	PV-1 **Bu34760**		(to RAF as FP608)	
	Howard		(to SAAF as 6433)	44/60
	Super Ventura	N127N	Howard Aero Inc, San Antonio TX	.59
	Howard		(stripped airframe shipped ex S.Africa 12.59, rebuilt San Antonio as Super Ventura)	
(c/n 500-109)	500	N90N	Natural Gas Pipeline Co, Chicago IL	.61/66
			(conv. to Howard 500 completed 4.12.63)	
		N137U	United Industrial Corp	6.12.67/68
			Industrial Flights Inc, New York NY	11.6.68/72
			Nello L. Teer Co, Durham NC	31.1.72/83
			Soundair Corp, Toronto ONT	22.6.83/90

				Kog Classics Inc/Red Bird Aero	12.11.90
				Graves Aircraft Inc, El Reno OK	22.11.90
				Barbary Coast Airways, Watsonville CA	92
				Edward A. Mueller, Belmont CA	6.93/96
				(open storage Ft Lauderdale-Executive FL 95)	
5655	PV-1	Bu34765		(to RAF as FP613)	
	Howard			(to SAAF as 6427)	
	500			Howard Aero Inc, San Antonio TX	.59
(c/n 500-107)				(stripped airframe shipped ex S.Africa 12.59,	
				rebuild San Antonio as H500 completed 10.63)	
			N3030 (2	Republic Steel Corp, Cleveland OH	61/66
			N3031 (2	Republic Steel Corp, Cleveland OH	72
			N303L	United Founders Life Insurance Co	
				Ward International Aircraft, Dallas TX	22.12.75
				Advance Aviation	
				dam. wheels-up landing, Dallas TX	1.4.77
				Robert L. Curtis	.79
			C-GKFN	Kelowna Flightcraft Ltd, Kelowna BC	3.81
				crashed, dest., Toronto ONT	9.7.81
5694 •	PV-1	**Bu34804**		(to RCAF as 2246): BOC 13.9.43: SOC	18.3.57
	GR.V			Spartan Air Services Ltd, Ottawa ONT	
	Howard		N10481	D. U. Howard, San Antonio TX	56
	Super Ventura			Howard Aero Service, San Antonio TX	5.3.56/57
				(conv. to Super Ventura completed 1.4.57)	
			N28C	Kudner Agency Inc	1.4.57/58
			N20S (1	Storer Broadcasting	9.6.58/61
				dam. when Jato bottles fired on ground,	
				La Guardia NY	5.9.58
			N208S	Storer Broadcasting	23.1.61
				Oral Roberts Evangelistic Assoc., Tulsa OK	1.12.61/69
				ground collision with DC-7 N632C, Denver CO	24.1.65
				Camp Meeting Revival, Arlington TX	4.2.69/75
				Church of Compassion, Dallas TX	.75/78
				Aircraft Associates	12.9.78/79
				impounded, alleged drug running, Polk County FL	28.3.79
				Don M. Hendricks/Hendricks Aero Service	1.4.81/82
				Airlift Inc	5.2.82
				Skyrider Airfreight, Tulsa OK	22.2.82/96
5696	PV-1	Bu34806		(to RCAF as 2245): BOC 13.9.43: SOC	18.3.57
	GR.V			Spartan Air Services Ltd, Ottawa ONT	
	Howard		N10480		
	Super Ventura		N711Z	Triangle Conduit & Cable, Morristown NJ	56/61
				ran off runway, Morristown NJ	13.5.59
				Commonwealth Plan Inc, Boston MA	63
			N9221R	Commonwealth Plan Inc, Boston MA	.64
				C.C. Leasing Corp	
				Dee Howard Co, San Antonio TX	.67
			N446DD	Coral Drilling Inc, Midland TX	.68/69
				Aviation Services Inc, Little Rock AR	.70/72
				crashed, Austin TX	3.8.72
5697 •	PV-1	Bu34807		(to RCAF as 2247): BOC 16.9.43: SOC	11.8.50
	GR.V			Douglas W. Siple/Siple Aircraft Ltd	52
			N5779N	Hunter C. Moody/Decatur Aviation Co,	
				Decatur IL	3.4.52/53
				Ohio Oil Co, Findlay OH	27.6.53/57
				(conv. to civil executive aircraft by Ohio	
				Aviation Co, completed 2.8.54)	
				Trans International Airlines, Oakland CA	3.1.57/62
			N151V	Raymond J. Leeward/Trans International	
				Airlines, Miami FL	10.9.62/63
				Angels Inc, Tampa FL	12.63/66

				John W. Debaun, Hewitt NJ	8.10.66/70
				Clarks Aerial Service, Brownfield TX	23.1.70/76
				Brownfield Aerial Inc, Brownfield TX	7.10.77
				I. N. Burchinall Jr/Flying Tigers Air Museum, Paris TX	11.78/83
				James P. MacIvor, Miami FL	14.2.83
				USMC Museum, MCAS Quantico VA (stored)	20.6.83/96
5700 •	PV-1	**Bu34810**		(to RCAF as 2255): BOC 30.9.43: SOC	22.9.52
	GR.V		N5392N	D. H. Braman, Victoria TX	56
	Howard		N539	undercarriage collapsed, San Antonio TX	7.5.59
	Super Ventura			Utex Exploration Co	61
			N350S	Business Aircraft Corp, San Antonio TX	63/64
	Howard				
				French Oil Co, Odessa TX	.64/69
	350			Financial South Leasing Corp, New Orleans LA	69/72
				Tom Hill	73
				Onyx Aviation Inc, Miami FL	.74
			N555JM	United Engines Inc	.74
			N855JM	Onyx Aviation Inc, Miami FL	.76
				B. L. Skidmore, Miramar FL	.77
5702	PV-1	Bu34812		(to RCAF as 2254): BOC 24.9.43: SOC	18.3.51
	GR.V			Spartan Air Services Ltd, Ottawa ONT	
	Howard		N10479		
	Super Ventura		N200P (1	National Distillers Corp	
			N200G (1	Green Construction Co, Owensboro KY	61
			N539N	Business Aircraft Corp, San Antonio TX	63/64
				Reading-Bates Offshore Drilling, Tulsa OK	.64/69
				Dee Howard Sales Inc, San Antonio TX	70/72
				L. M. Adamson Construction Co	.73
				struck-off USCR	.76
5705 •	PV-1	**Bu34815**		(to RCAF as 2253): BOC 23.9.43: SOC	22.9.52
	GR.V		N5394N	D. U. Howard, San Antonio TX	56
	Howard		N685	D. U. Howard, San Antonio TX	.57
	Super Ventura			Standard Oil Co, Chicago IL	61/65
			N910V	Nine Ten Corp, Chicago IL	1.6.65/72
				IMC Mint Corp	.73
				Sky High Inc	.75
				John A. O'Connell	
				Indiana Board of Pharmacy, Indianapolis IN	6.78
				Hendry County Sheriff FL: seized with drugs	.79
				Southern Aero Traders, Opa Locka FL	7.80
				(last noted Opa Locka 7.81): struck-off USCR	11.83
5770	PV-1	Bu34880		(to RAF as FP641)	
	Howard			(to SAAF as 6441)	
	500		N1424	Howard Aero Inc, San Antonio TX	.59/61
(c/n 500-108)				(stripped airframe shipped ex S.Africa 12.59, rebuild San Antonio as H500 completed 12.63)	
				John W. Galbreath, Columbus OH	.61/66
			N14241	John W. Galbreath, Columbus OH	.66
			N941S	Wheaton Glass Corp, Millville NJ	67/68
			N227W	Wheaton Glass Corp, Millville NJ	.68/72
				Subter Realty Corp	.73
			N500BY	Alexandria Inc	12.73/74
				Navarro Ranches Inc, Vicksberg MI	8.75/77
				FA Mexicana: impounded in Mexico	
5784	PV-1	Bu34894		(to RAF as FP642)	
	Howard			(to SAAF as 6444)	
	500		N963B (1	Howard Aero Inc, San Antonio TX	.59/60
	(c/n 500-106)			(stripped airframe shipped ex S.Africa 12.59,	

				rebuilt San Antonio as Howard 500)	
			N502N (2	Howard Aero Inc, San Antonio TX	8.9.60/61
				Northern Natural Gas, Omaha NE	.61/64
			N21W (2	Transcontinental Gas Pipeline Corp, Houston TX	.65/70
			N621W	Seeburg Enterprises Inc, Chicago IL	.71
				crashed Santa Lucia, Mexico	14.9.73
				Aircraft Parts Inc (wreck)	.73
				Premiere Corp, Dayton OH (wreck)	74/76
				broken-up for spares by Premier Corp.	
5793 •	PV-1 Howard 500	**Bu34903**		(to RAF as FP649)	
				(to SAAF as 6488)	
(c/n 500-110)			N74028	Howard Aero Inc, San Antonio TX	.59/64
				(stripped airframe shipped ex S.Africa 12.59, rebuild San Antonio as H500 completed 8.4.64)	
			N515 (2	Marathon Oil Co, Findlay OH	8.4.64/65
			N277T	Trunkline Gas Co, Houston TX	23.7.65
			N277J	Trunkline Gas Co, Houston TX	30.12.66
			N277X	Panhandle Eastern Pipeline, Kansas City MO	28.2.67/68
				Fabricated Products Co, Indianapolis IN	2.11.68/69
				Dillon Companies Inc, Hutchinson KS	25.7.69/73
				Continental National Bank, Fort Worth TX	24.4.73/78
			N217BT	Luxury Flight Inc	6.4.78
			N71BT	ntu: Luxury Flight Inc	2.7.78
			N217BT	Luxury Flight Inc	7.78/80
			C-GTIP	Owen Sound Air Services/Soundair Corp, Toronto ONT	16.9.80/85
			N5831Y	Inversiones Tetela S.A., Cuernava, Mexico	2.4.85
				Jeronimo Weber/Inversiones Tetela S.A., Wetmore TX	11.9.85/92
				Westernair Inc, Albuquerque NM: reg. res.	9.6.92
				Lone Star Flight Museum, Galveston TX	11.92/96
5841 •	PV-1 Howard 500	**Bu34951**		(to RAF as FP668)	
				(to SAAF as 6506)	
(c/n 500-116)			N74882	Howard Aero Inc, San Antonio TX	.59
				(stripped airframe shipped ex S.Africa 12.59, rebuild San Antonio as H500 completed .63)	
			N239R	J. Ray McDermott Co, Houston TX	63/72
			N11CP	rereg.	
			N11QP	Jack E. Kemp	
				Hardin E. Miller, Azle TX	.76
				F & A Western Hemisphere Inc	.78
				Graham L. Kendall, Oklahoma City OK	84
5854 •	PV-1 Howard 500	Bu34964		(to RAF as FP681)	
				(to SAAF as 6454)	
(c/n 500-112)				Howard Aero Inc, San Antonio TX	.59/61
				(stripped airframe shipped ex S.Africa 12.59, rebuild San Antonio as H500 completed 8.11.61)	
			N111M (2	Gamble Skogmo Inc, Minneapolis MN	8.11.61/66
			N686M	Gamble Skogmo Inc, Minneapolis MN	10.1.66/67
			N8020	Andre J. Andreoli/Associated Developments	7.8.67
			N25YC (2	Buckeye Leasing Corp, Youngstown OH	10.71/74
				op: Youngstown Cartage Co	
				American Aircraft Sales	18.1.74
			N65PC	Premiere Corp, Dayton OH	18.1.74/77
				Onyx Aviation, Miami FL	20.5.77
				Advance Aviation Inc	9.9.77/78
				DR & M Inc	26.5.78/80
				Overseas Investment Lease Corp, Miami FL	5.2.80/95
				Juan P. Media, Caracas, Venezuala	10.6.81
				(rep. to be the camouflaged Howard 500 op. in Nicaragua by CIA/Contras c84)	

c/n	Type	Serial	Reg	Owner / History	Date
5855 •	PV-1	**Bu34965**		(to RAF as FP682)	
	GR. V			(to SAAF as 6447)	
				South African Airways Apprentice Training	
				School, Johannesburg-Jan Smuts: "TS303"	79/88
				SAAF Museum, Ysterplaat AB: arr.	11.88/96
				(rest., displ. as "SAAF 6447/V")	
5857 •	PV-1	**Bu34967**		(to RAF as FP684)	
	GR. V			(to SAAF as 6453)	
				Howard Aero Inc, San Antonio TX	.59
				South African Airways Apprentice Training	
				School, Johannesburg-Jan Smuts	
				SAAF Museum: stored Johannesburg-Rand	88/94
				Field Aviation, Germiston, S.Africa: dism.	93/96
5880	PV-1	Bu34990		(to RCAF as 2258): BOC 23.11.43: SOC	22.1.47
	GR.V		N64002	Hunter C. Moody/Decatur Aviation Co,	
				Decatur IL	49
				(conv. to executive config. by Spartan Aero c53)	
			N21W (1	Transcontinental Gas Pipeline Corp,	
				Houston TX	54/64
				wing fire on engine start, Atlantic City NJ	9.9.62
			N216Q	rereg.	
			N216U	Florida Aircraft Leasing Corp, Miami FL	.65
				Miami Aviation Corp, Opa Locka FL	66
				Palm Coast Agency Inc, Freeport Bahamas	.67/70
5887	PV-1	Bu34997		(to RCAF as 2256): BOC 16.11.43: SOC	18.3.57
	GR.V			Spartan Air Services Ltd, Ottawa ONT	
	Howard		N10478	Howard Aero Inc, San Antonio TX	61
	Super Ventura		N5033F	Firestone Tire & Rubber Co, Akron OH	.61/66
				Aircraft Trading Co, San Antonio TX	.68/69
				Coastal States Gas Producing Co, Houston TX	69/70
				Karen Corp	
				ground looped and dam., Lakeville MN	10.7.72
				collided on approach, crashed Tucumcari NM	3.12.72
5890 •	PV-1	**Bu48654**		(to RCAF as 2262): BOC 3.12.43: SOC	5.3.52
	GR.V			Kenting Aviation Ltd, Toronto ONT	52
			N3949C	Albert J. Leeward/Leeward Aeronautical	
				Service, Fort Wayne IN	22.2.52
			N165H	M. A. Hanna Mining Co, Cleveland OH	1.12.52/65
				(civil exec conv. by Spartan Aero, Tulsa OK 7.53)	
				Ohio State University, Columbus OH	18.10.65
				Westernair of Albuquerque, Albuquerque NM	11.6.66
				William C. Whitesell/Thunderbird Airways	6.12.66/68
				William C. & James P. Whitesell/	
				Flying W Airways, Medford NJ	28.5.68
				Concare Aircraft Leasing Corp	10.6.68
				Clarks Aerial Service, Brownfield TX	10.68/77
				(conv. to sprayer/seeder config. 3.3.69)	
				Brownfield Aerial Inc, Brownfield TX	7.10.77/79
				Oklahoma Aircraft Corp, Yukon OK	21.3.79
				John J. Rutkosky/Flagler Beach Aero	7.12.79
				Almeckair Inc, Miami FL	12.2.82/84
			N367	ntu:Audrey S. McPherson, Fernadina Beach FL	5.12.83/84
			N165H	PV-1 Ventura Corp, Weston MA	6.11.84/90
				(planned rest. to military PV-1 as warbird)	
				Airplane Sales International Corp,	
				Beverly Hills CA (sale rep. not completed)	6.2.90
5891	PV-1	Bu48655		(to RCAF as 2265): BOC 9.12.43: SOC	11.8.50
	GR.V			Douglas W. Siple/Siple Aircraft Ltd	53

	Howard			Universal Trading Corp, New York NY	11.53/54
	Super Ventura		N10487	Howard Aero Service, San Antonio TX	12.54/57
			N515 (1	Ohio Oil Co, Findlay OH	21.1.57/61
				(conv. to Super Ventura completed 13.6.57)	
			N511U	Howard Aero, San Antonio TX	11.61/62
				Ohio Oil Co, Findlay OH	1.6.62
				Marathon Oil Co, Findlay OH	23.8.62/63
			N151LS	Lone Star Steel Co, Dallas TX	12.63/67
			N1514S	Lone Star Steel Co, Dallas TX	10.4.67/68
				Hunsaker Truck Lease Inc, Carrollton TX	6.2.68/73
				Dee Howard Aircraft Sales, San Antonio TX	25.9.73
				Vernon R. Shurmon	2.11.73
				Reagan & Co	31.1.74/75
				Millwood Aviation, New York NY	24.4.75/78
				Ventura Air Inc	5.5.78/79
				Inter Island Shipping, West End, Bahamas	8.3.79
				crashed into swamp, Dania FL	26.5.79
5892	PV-1	Bu48656		(to RCAF as 2263): BOC 3.12.43: SOC	16.10.53
	GR.V		N5549N	Leeward Aero Sales Inc, Fort Wayne IN	56
	Howard		N18N		
	Super Ventura		N181V	Volusia Locations, Saratoga WY	61
				International Aircraft Service, Oakland CA	63/64
	Howard			Business Aircraft Corp, San Antonio TX	.64
	350		N510RA	Robbins Aviation Corp	
			N510R	G.W. Corp, Chicago IL	.65/66
			N350Q	Westernair Inc, Albuquerque NM	.68/69
				Capitol Florida Associates Inc, Alexandria VA	70
				crashed, dest. by fire, Opa Locka FL	18.8.70
5894	PV-1	Bu48658		(to RCAF as 2264): BOC 3.12.43: SOC	18.3.57
	GR.V			Spartan Air Services Ltd, Ottawa ONT	
	Howard		N10482	reg.	
	Super Ventura		N99G	noted RATO equipped	57
			N36R	Ryder System Inc	59/61
	Howard			JAR Corp	61
	350		N236R	dam. heavy landing Washington DC	23.7.62
				Butler Co, Chicago IL	63/64
				Russell Stover Candies Inc, Lincoln NE	.64/66
				Robertson Aircraft Co, Dallas TX	.68/70
				Dan Futrell, Nashville AR	.71/72
			N10TP	Tassero Petroleum Inc	.73
				International Fruit & Produce Co, Manila, PI	.73
				crashed on landing, Iloilo, Philippines	22.6.73
5939	PV-1	Bu48703		(to RAF as JS923)	
	Howard			(to SAAF as 6465)	
	500			Howard Aero Inc, San Antonio TX	.59/61
(c/n 500-115)				(stripped airframe shipped ex S.Africa 12.59,	
				rebuild San Antonio as H500 completed .63)	
			N139W	J. Ray McDermott Co, Houston TX	63/69
			N86W	El Paso Products Co, Odessa TX	.70/72
			N44HH	L. A. Grelling	.75
				Lew Childre & Sons, Foley AL	10.76/77
				Intercontinental Oil Co TX	6.77
				landing collision, dest., Pawhuska OK	13.8.77
5958 •	PV-1	**Bu48722**		(to RAF as JS942)	
	Howard			(to SAAF as 6458)	
	500			Howard Aero Inc, San Antonio TX	.59
(c/n 500-114)				(stripped airframe shipped ex S.Africa 12.59,	
				rebuild San Antonio as H500 completed 8.5.64)	
			N130PL (2	Pacific Lumber Co, San Francisco CA	63
				U.S. Metals Refining Co, New York NY	63/64
			N130P (2	US Metals Refining Co, New York NY	8.5.64/68

				Aero International Associates Inc	8.11.68/69
				Southern Minerals Corp, Corpus Christie TX	17.1.69/70
				Dee Howard Sales Inc, San Antonio TX	2.10.70/71
				Dan J. Harrison, Houston TX	12.3.71/78
				Coffee Intercontinental Inc/Blair Aviation	1.2.78/79
				Pine Crest Development Inc	22.6.79
				Northwest Precast Concrete Co Inc	10.10.79
				Nevada Airlines, Las Vegas NV: leased	4.80
				Stan Booker/ Nevada Airlines, Las Vegas NV	9.9.80/81
				Western Heritage Thrift & Loan, Bountiful UT	11.81/96
				(open storage, derelict, Chandler AZ 87/95)	
5988	PV-1	Bu48752		(to RCAF as 2273): BOC 19.1.44: SOC	4.6.52
	GR.V			Spartan Air Services Ltd, Ottawa ONT	
	Howard		N9319H	Henry J. Kaiser Co, Oakland CA	
	350			Thatcher Glass Manufacturing Co, Elmira NY	56
			N60TG	Thatcher Glass Manufacturing Co, Elmira NY	
				Howard Aero Inc, San Antonio TX	61
			N350K	Panhandle Eastern Pipeline, Kansas City MO	63/66
				South Texas Natural Gas Gathering Corp	.67
				350 Corp, Indianapolis IN	.68/72
				Holiday Aero, Clearwater FL	73/76
6011 •	PV-1	**Bu48775**		(to RAF as JS956)	
	GR. V			(to SAAF as 6534)	
				Fort Klapperkop Military Museum, Pretoria	70/84
				SAAF Museum	
				Field Aviation, Germiston, South Africa	93/96
6152 •	PV-1	**Bu48906**		(to RAAF as A59-73): BOC 13.3.44: SOC	12.10.45
				dam. by fire, Gove airstrip NT, abandoned	6.8.45/88
				(static displ., Gove Airport .88/95)	
				shipped to RAAF Darwin NT for complete rest.	7.95
6219 •	PV-1	**Bu49403**		(to RAF as JT861)	
	GR. V			(to SAAF as 6487)	
				Voortrekkerhoogte, Snake Valley	
				SAAF Museum, Lanseria AB	.73/96
6290 •	PV-1	**Bu49474**		(to RAF as JT867)	
	GR. V			(to SAAF as 6498)	
				South African Airways Technical School,	
				Johannesburg-Jan Smuts: "TS306"	79/88
				SAAF Museum, Swartkop AB: arr.	11.88/94
6371 •	PV-1	**Bu49555**		(to RAAF as A59-96): BOC 1.6.44: SOC	25.2.49
				RAAF disposals, Evans Head NSW	2.49
				fus. recovered from farm, Byron Bay NSW	4.78
				Chewing Gum Field Air Museum,	
				Tallebudgera QLD (fuselage only)	.81/91
				Queensland Air Museum, Caloundra QLD	.91/95
6442	PV-1	Bu49626		Sherman Machine & Iron Works, Clinton OK	.47/48
	Howard			(purchased ex War Assets Admin. for $1250)	
	Super Ventura		NL5055N	Spartan Aircraft Co, Tulsa OK	23.1.48
				(civil conv. by Spartan; CofA 10.7.48)	
			N5055N	Dresser Industries Inc, Cleveland OH	12.7.48/59
				Purdue Aeronautics Corp	20.8.59/60
			N435T	Chicago Tribune Corp, Chicago IL	10.60/66
				(conv. to Super Ventura completed 20.1.61)	
			N16777 (1	Chicago Tribune Corp, Chicago IL	30.4.66
			N30306 (2	D. U. Howard, San Antonio TX	15.8.66
			N3524	Armour & Co Corp, Chicago IL	11.66/71
				Falcon Aircraft Conversions, San Antonio TX	17.6.71/73

				John S. Burns/Burns Aviation	14.3.73
				Northeast Aircraft Sales, Stratford CT	6.74/95
				impounded Barranquilla, Colombia: derelict by	76

LOCKHEED P-38 LIGHTNING

5266	P-38E RP-38E	41-2048		Lockheed Aircraft Co, Burbank CA (test aircraft, mod. cockpit area)	43/46
			NX91300	Lockheed Aircraft Co, Burbank CA (test aircraft for Lockheed XF-90 programme)	3.46/54
			N91300	Hycon Aerial Surveys, Ontario CA (survey conv. Ontario CA .54: P-38L engines & components, extended survey nose; magnetometer survey ops. in South America) (last FAA inspection 11.57, wfu, open storage Las Vegas NV 59/62)	8.54/62
				Don M. May, Phoenix AZ	25.6.62
				Kucera & Associates, Cleveland OH: not del.	10.62
				crashed on takeoff, Phoenix AZ (May k.)	24.10.62
5757 •	P-38F	**41-7630**		forced landing Greenland, on del. to England (with 5 other P-38s & B-17: all buried by snow)	15.7.42
				Pat Epps/Greenland Expedition Society (recov. from under 260 feet of ice .90/92)	.81/94
			N5757	Greenland Expedition Society, Atlanta GA (recov. completed 1.8.92, rest. began 10.92 at Middlesboro-Bell County Airport KY: rest to fly as 17630/*Glacier Girl*)	12.1.94/96
7081 •	P-38F	**42-12647**		National Museum, Port Moresby PNG ("34" recov. from swamp, nr. Pt Moresby 11.78) (long-term rest. project, using parts recov. from 42-12857, 42-12847, 42-66868 crash sites)	11.78/96
7518 •	P-38F F-5A	**42-13084**		National Museum, Port Moresby PNG (recov. ex swamp, nr. Port Moresby PNG 11.78) derelict hulk : parts for rest. of 42-12647	11.78/96
7834 •	P-38G	**42-13400**		crashed Attu, Aleutians, abandoned	1.1.45
			N55929	US Historic Aircraft Preservation Museum, Anchorage AK: purchased in-situ from USAF	9.8.84/88
				American Vets Memorial Museum, Denver CO	88/96
1362 •	P-38H	**42-66851**		forced landing Brahmin, Madang PNG	20.9.43
				Gary R. Larkins, Auburn CA (intact hulk recov. ex Faita PNG .92)	92
				Jack A. Erickson, Medford OR (rep impounded by PNG Govt on wharf, Lae PNG 5.92)	.92
				National Museum, Port Moresby PNG (stored Lae .92/93)	.92
1417 •	P-38H	**42-66905**		crashed near Dobodura PNG: abandoned	12.43
				National Museum, Port Moresby PNG: listed (*Japanese Sandman II*: not recov. ex crash site)	79/88
2054 •	P-38J F-5C	**42-67543**		Ragsdale Flying Service, Austin TX	64
				Marvin L. Gardner/CAF, Mercedes TX (derelict hulk recov. ex Austin-Buehler Field TX, stored Mercedes TX .64/87)	.64/87
				Stephen Grey, Duxford UK (stripped hulk trucked Mercedes-Chino CA .87)	.87/92
			N3145X	Fighter Rebuilders, Chino CA	1.92/95
				op: The Fighter Collection, Duxford UK (rest. Chino, ff 11.1.92; shipped to Duxford 3.92, flew as 67543/*Happy Jack's Go Buggy*,	1.92/95

				later 67543/KI-S/*California Cutie*)	
				landing accident , Lydd UK (repaired)	6.9.92
				(flew for film 6.94 as French AF 228223)	
2273 •	P-38J	**42-67762**		USAAF Museum Collection, Freeman Field IN	9.10.45/46
				NASM, Park Ridge IL: stored	16.8.46/60
				NASM, Silver Hill MD	.60/96
2922 •	P-38J	**42-104088**		Interstate Aircraft Corp	
				Dale M. Myers	
			N5260N	ntu: Clarence Page/Page Airmotive, Yukon OK	
				(not flown, stored: stripped hulk by 73/77)	50/73
				Gary R. Levitz, Dallas TX	.69/73
				Confederate Air Force: stored Yukon OK	75/77
			N38LL (2	Confederate Air Force, Harlingen/Midland TX	18.2.76/96
				(airlifted by chopper Yukon to England AFB LA 9.77,	
				rest. commenced, later to Lafayette LA;	
				to San Marcos TX .81/92, ff 28.2.92	
				as *Scatterbrain Kid II*: Hycon survey nose)	
				badly damaged, forced landing, Breckenridge TX	28.5.95
				(under rebuild, San Marcos TX 95)	
-	P-38L	**43-50281**	NX33638	Fairchild Aerial Surveys, Van Nuys CA	.46/47
(-VN)	F-5G			(purchased ex surplus, Kingman AZ .46)	
				(to FA Boliviana as FAB....): not del.	.49
				(stored Washington-National DC 49/50)	
				Jack P. Hardwick, El Monte CA	.50
				(del. Washington to CA .50: conv. for survey)	
			N33638	Fairchild Aerial Surveys, Los Angeles CA	51/63
				Luther O. Eldridge, Monrovia CA	63
				(noted with camera nose, Van Nuys CA 7.64)	
				Darryl G. Greenamyer, Burbank CA	9.63/66
			N138X	Darryl G. Greenamyer, Burbank CA	67
				(race #1 *Yippie*: photo nose)	
				Revis Sirmon & Paul A. Fournet, Abbeville LA	6.68/74
			N38LL (1	Revis G. Sirmon/Coastal Chemical Co,	
				Abbeville LA	.69/74
				(fighter nose, race #1, #38 *Scatterbrain Kid*)	
				crashed dest. landing, Lafayette LA	19.10.74
4318 •	P-38J	**44-23314**		Hancock College of Aeronautics,	
	TP-38J			Santa Maria CA: inst. airframe	46/54
			N29Q	Jack P. Hardwick, El Monte CA	4.54/59
				(open storage, Lavern-Brackett Field CA 54/59)	
				Ed Maloney/The Air Museum, Claremont CA,	
				later Ontario & Chino CA	12.59/88
				(flown 61, static displ. 62/87, rest. Chino 87/88,	
				ff 22.7.88, flies as 423314/*Joltin Josie*)	
				Robert J. Pond, Spring Park MN	88/89
			N38BP	Robert J. Pond/Planes of Fame East,	
				Minneapolis-Flying Cloud MN	10.89/96
4806	P-38L	44-23802	NX68394	Howard S. Gidovlenko (race #25)	48/49
				(mod. racer, clipped wings)	
				Wilson V. Newhall, Chicago IL	50
				(noted Chicago-Municiple 4.50)	
6790 •	P-38L	**44-25786**		Yugoslavian Aviation Museum, Belgrade	89/92
				(stored : incomplete airframe)	
7765 •	P-38L	44-26761	NL5054N	Everett L. Moore, Tulsa OK	10.47 F-5G
				(ex War Assetts Admin., Altus OK 10.47 $800)	
				Clark Smith, Cumberland PA	2.48
				Luis Struck, Mexico	49/51

			CF-GKE	Kenting Aerial Surveys, Toronto ONT	.51
				Spartan Air Services Ltd, Ottawa ONT	8.51/56
			N6190C	Hycon Aerial Surveys, Ontario CA	5.56
				(wfu 12.59, stored Las Vegas NV 59/61)	
				Bruce & Gunn Inc, Dallas TX	12.60/62
				Kucera & Associates Inc, Cleveland OH	11.62/68
				(survey contract Bolivia, Colombia, Paraguay)	
				dam. gear collapse, Ascuncion Paraguay	5.1.65
				(abandoned: open storage, Asuncion 65/72)	
				Ronald Bryant, Jacksonville FL	1.68
				I. N. Burchinall Jr, Paris TX	.68/70
				William E. Padden, Los Angeles CA	71/72
				resident, Carman, MAN	72/74
				('dismantled'. Ascuncion, shipped to Richmond VA .72)	
				Dick Lambert, Plainfield IL: stored dism.	2.74/81
				Kermit A. Weeks, Tamiami FL	.81/82
			N2897S	Weeks Air Museum, Tamiami FL: displ. dism.	3.82/95
7965 •	P-38L F-5G	44-26961		(to Costa Rica Military AF as G.C.R-01): del.	11.48/49
				(to FA Guatelmateca as ....)	12.49/51
				(not flown by FAG, stored La Aurora AB)	
				(to FA Hondurena as 504)	53/60
			N74883	Bob Bean Aircraft, Blythe CA	31.3.60
				Ed Maloney/The Air Museum, Ontario CA	65/67
				(static displ. as "FAH504")	
				G. E. (Larry) Blumer/Air Maintenance Inc,	
				Puyallup WA (race #59 "*Scrap Iron IV*")	69/72
			N38DH	Don Hull, Houston TX	76
				Friends of Harbor Island Inc, San Diego CA	.77
			N6961	John G. Deahl, Denver CO	7.77/81
				crashed dest. Salt Lake City UT (Deahl k.)	9.4.81
				Lester Friend, Palomar CA: wreck	.88
				Planes of Fame, Chino CA: wreck	93
7973 •	P-38L F-5G	**44-26969**	NX53753	Aero Exploration Co Inc, Tulsa OK	5.46/48
				(ex War Assets Admin., Kingman AZ 3.46, $1250)	
			N53753	Mark Hurd Mapping Co, Minneapolis MN	.49/56
				Mark Hurd Aerial Surveys, Minneapolis MN	8.56/58
			N503MH	Mark Hurd Aerial Surveys, Santa Barbara CA	3.58/66
				(wfu, open storage, Santa Barbara CA 68)	
				Bruce L. Pruitt, Livermore CA	6.12.68/94
				(long-term rest. to fly 68/90: 8-gun nose)	
				to Jack Erickson OR for rebuild	96
8000 •	P-38L F-5G	**44-26996**		Aero Exploration Co, Tulsa OK	22.3.46
				(ex War Assets Admin, Kingman AZ 3.46 $1250)	
			NX53752	Aero Exploration Co Inc, Tulsa OK	10.5.46/48
			NL53752	Aero Exploration Co Inc, Tulsa OK	.48/51
				(wfu, Tulsa OK by 7.49/51)	
			CF-GCH	Spartan Air Services Ltd, Ottawa ONT	12.51/56
			N5596V	Hycon Aerial Surveys, Ontario CA	8.11.56/62
				(wfu, open storage Las Vegas NV 12.59/62)	
				Don E. May, Phoenix AZ	25.6.62/63
				Ben W. Widtfeldt/Desert Aviation Inc,	
				Phoenix AZ	19.6.63
				Aero Enterprises, La Porte IN	9.9.63
				Laurel Walsh, Birmingham MI	11.11.63
				(last annual FAA inspection 1.58)	
				J. W. Bohmier/New London Airport,	
				New London PA	6.12.63/64
				Jim Cullen/Westair Co, Westminster CO	2.11.64/65
				Troy G. Hawkins, Wichita Falls TX	9.9.65/67
				J. L. Ausland/Sports Air, Seattle WA	20.4.67/68
				William E. Padden, Los Angeles CA	20.4.68/70
				I. N. Burchinall Jr, Paris TX	19.8.70/73

				landing accident, struck trailer, Paris TX	24.5.71
				David M. Boyd/ Eagle Aviation, Tulsa OK	2.4.73/79
				(wreck, stripped for parts, Paris TX 71/79)	
				John P. Silberman, Key West FL	4.1.79/89
				(rest. Live Oaks FL, ff 9.85: camoufl. "985")	
				Museum of Flying, Santa Monica CA	10.89/90
				(rest. fighter nose Santa Monica .90 as "7985")	
				William Lyons/Martin Aviation, Santa Ana CA	20.5.90/95
				dam. landing accident, Winslow AZ (repaired)	8.92
				Museum of Flying, Santa Monica CA	.95/96
				(USCR quote id. as 7985)	
8026	P-38L	44-27022	N1219N	R. A. Wardell & R.W. Martin, Portland OR	.46
	F-5G			(ex War Assets Admin., Kingman AZ 4.46 $1250)	
				crashed, dest.	25.5.48
8087 •	P-38L	**44-27083**		Russell C. Reeves, Tulsa OK	8.4.46
	F-5G			(ex War Assets Admin., Kingman AZ, $1250)	
				Raymond H. Miller, Tulsa OK	11.4.46/47
			NX75551	Raymond H. Miller, Wenatchee WA	9.1.47/48
			N75551	Mark Hurd Mapping Co, Minneapolis MN	7.2.48/56
				Mark Hurd Aerial Surveys, Minneapolis MN	8.56/57
			N502MH	Mark Hurd Aerial Surveys, Santa Barbara CA	30.1.57/68
				(open storage derelict, Santa Barbara 66/68)	
				Bruce L. Pruitt, Livermore CA	6.12.68/94
				(stored, long-term rest. project)	
			N2114L	Jack A. Erickson, Medford OR	5.95
8091 •	P-38L	**44-27087**	NX65485	Russell C. Reeves, Tulsa OK	4.46/50
	F-5G			(purchased ex War Assets Admin., Kingman AZ)	
				Tennessee Valley Authority TN: survey ops.	11.50/53
				Aero Service Corp, Philadelphia PA: survey	7.53/57
				op: World Wide Surveys Inc (fleet #2)	54/55
				(ferried via Prestwick, Scotland 5.54 & 10.55)	
			N345	James M. Cook, Dallas TX: weather research	1.57/69
				Gary R. Levitz/Confederate AF, Dallas TX	6.69/83
				(race #55; #38 *Double Trouble*)	
				(dam., u/c collapse, Reno NV 9.83)	
			N345DN	Invader Aviation, Wilmington DE	11.83/84
				John MacGuire, MacGuire Ranch, El Paso TX	.84/87
			N577JB	John MacGuire, El Paso TX	4.87/94
				War Eagles Air Museum,	
				Santa Teresa NM: del.	.90/96
				(displ. glossy black, N345/*Relampago*)	
8187 •	P-38L	**44-27183**		Kargl Aerial Surveys, Midland TX	13.5.46
	F-5G		NC62441	Kargl Aerial Surveys, Midland TX	17.5.46/47
				Aero Exploration Co, Tulsa OK	12.47/53
			N62441	Mark Hurd Aerial Surveys, Minneapolis MN	2.1.53/58
			N501MH	Mark Hurd Aerial Surveys, Minneapolis MN	3.58/65
				Byers Airways, Seattle WA	4.65
				Pacific Aerial Surveys, Seattle WA	24.5.65
			N517PA	Pacific Aerial Surveys, Seattle WA	12.65/69
				Wally D. Peterson, Manson WA	21.5.69/71
				I. N. Burchinall Jr, Paris TX	27.8.71/73
				David M. Boyd, Tulsa OK	3.4.73/81
				(rest. Tulsa OK .73/81, P-80 nose fitted)	
			N517PA	N. Merrill Wein, Fairbanks AK	28.2.81/90
				(del. ex Tulsa 3.3.81 to be based Chino CA)	
			N718	Yankee Air Corps,	
				renamed Yanks Air Museum, Chino CA	13.3.90/95
8235 •	P-38L	44-27231	NX79123	James L. Harp, Aurora IL (race #95)	7.46
	F-5G			(purchased ex War Assets Admin., Altus OK 7.46,	

				del. by Harp from Altus to Joliet IL 22.7.46)	
			N79123	J. E. Howard, Champaign IL	11.46/48
				Ray Reinert, Arlington IL	.48/50
				Carl C. Hughes, San Antonio TX	.50/54
				Joseph P. Jacobson, Stilwell KS	.54
				Jack P. Hardwick, El Monte CA	.55
				(stored Hardwick's yard, El Monte 60/76)	
				David C. Tallichet/Yesterdays Air Force, Chino CA	3.77/87
				(rest. Tulsa OK & Chino CA 84/91)	
				David C. Tallichet/MARC, Chino CA	10.87/95
				(rest. completed Chino 6.92 210993/*Marge*)	
8270 •	P-38L F-5G	44-53015	NX57492	Rex H. Mays, CA	.46/47
				(ex War Assets Admin., Kingman AZ 3.46 $1250)	
				(race #55 *MacMillan Meteor*)	
				Robert B. Utterbeck, Costa Rica	12.48/51
			N9957F	Edward C. Waterman	17.10.51
				Hycon Aerial Surveys, Ontario CA	11.55/62
				(wfu 12.59, stored Las Vegas NV 60/62)	
				Tallmantz Movieland of the Air Museum, Orange County CA: displ.	.62/66
				Rosen Novak Auto Co, Omaha NE	.66/67
				(remained displ., Orange County CA)	
				Walter H. Erickson, Minneapolis MN	68/70
				David C. Tallichet/Yesterdays Air Force, Chino CA	.70/80
				(fitted fighter nose, flew as "453015/KI-W")	
				Gary R. Larkins/RMP Aviation, Colfax CA	.80/81
				USAFM, McGuire AFB NJ	.81/94
				del. by Tallichet, dam. landing Memphis TN	3.81
				(repaired, del. to McGuire AFB 4.5.81)	
				(displ. on pedestal as "*Pudgy* (V)/131")	
8342 •	P-38L P-38M	44-53087	NX62887	Forrest M. Bird/Bird Airways, Long Beach CA	25.3.46
				David A. Bishop, Green Bay WI	13.6.46
				Ralph B. Lenz, De Pere WI	14.8.46/47
				R. C. Allwon, Wichita KS	26.5.47/48
				George L. Harte, Denton TX	25.6.48
				Spartan Air Services Ltd, Ottawa ONT	.51/52
			CF-GDS	Spartan Air Services Ltd, Ottawa ONT	6.52/56
				dam. landing, Island Airport QUE (repaired)	19.4.53
			N1107V	Hycon Aerial Surveys Inc, Ontario CA	23.5.56/58
				Vern W. Cartwright/ Cartwright Aerial Surveys, Sacramento CA	12.5.58/59
			YV-C-BAR	Cartwright Aerial Surveys, Caracas	9.59
			N1107V	Cartwright Aerial Surveys,Sacramento CA	61
				Marvin L. Gardner & Lloyd P. Nolan/ Lightning & Co, Mercedes TX	12.9.61/64
				Robert H. Kucera/Kucera & Associates Inc, Cleveland OH (South America survey ops.)	3.4.64/67
				A. G. Wilson/Al Wilson Flight Training Center, Kansas City KS	12.1.67
				Mark Hurd Aerial Surveys, Santa Barbara CA	22.3.67/68
				(wfu, open storage Santa Barbara CA 67/68)	
				Wilson Flight Training Center, Kansas City KS	23.2.68/69
				(op. on survey contract, South America)	
				Peter W. Kahn/Corporate Air Motive, San Jose CA	3.7.69/70
			N3800L	Peter W. Kahn, Danville IL	7.70/73
				(rest., fitted P-38E nose ex MGM Studio CA)	
				Jack Flaherty/Flaherty Factors, Monterey CA	27.3.73
				Wilson C. Edwards, Big Spring TX	4.9.73/81
				EAA Aviation Foundation, Oshkosh WI	7.12.81/95
				(displ. as Richard Bong's 2103993/*Marge*)	

8350 •	P-38L	44-53095	NL67745	R. A. Wardell & R. W. Martin, Jacksboro OR	47
	P-38M			(to FA Hondurena as 503, later 506): del.	.48/60
			N9005R	Bob Bean Aircraft, Blythe CA	2.2.60/69
				(stored unconv., Blythe CA 60/70)	
				William Ross, Elk Grove Village IL	.69/86
				(del. Blythe-DuPage County Airport IL .70,	
				flew as "453095/Der Gabelschwanz Teufel")	
				Lone Star Flight Museum,	
				Houston, later Galveston TX	11.86/96
				(flies as *Putt Putt Maru*/100")	
8352 •	P-38L	**44-53097**		R. A. Wardell & R. W. Martin, Jacksboro OR	47
	P-38M		NX67861	(to CAEC/Cuban AF as ....)	
				(to FA Hondurena as 503): del.	.54/60
			N9011R	Bob Bean Aircraft, Blythe CA	2.2.60/68
				(stored unconv., Blythe CA 60/71)	
				Carl Kidd/Aviation Service Co, Atlanta GA	.68/69
				Herbert L. Sander, Atlanta GA	70/71
				Al Hicks, Carlsbad-Palomar CA	
			N7TF	Tom Friedkin, Carlsblad-Palomar CA	.71/74
				(arr. Van Nuys CA ex Blythe storage .71,	
				rest., ff Van Nuys 9.72 as "453097/F")	
			N3JB	John P. Bolton, Orlando FL	.74/76
				John J. Stokes, San Marcos TX	.76/77
				Cecil Harp & Robert Ennis, Modesto CA	.78/83
				Champlin Fighter Museum, Mesa AZ	7.83/95
				(conv. to P-38L, flies as "53097/4-JS")	
8441 •	P-38L	**44-53186**	NL62350	Kargl Aerial Surveys, Midland TX	22.3.46/47
	F-5G			(ex War Assets Admin., Kingman AZ $1250)	
				Aero Exploration Co, Tulsa OK	12.47/52
			N62350	Mark Hurd Aerial Mapping Co, Minneapolis MN	11.52/58
				(noted at Prestwick & Naples 10.57-6.58)	
			N505MH	Mark Hurd Aerial Surveys, Santa Barbara CA	3.58/67
				(wfu, open storage Santa Barbara CA 63/67)	
				Harrah's Club Automobile Collection, Reno NV	4.1.67/82
				(del. Reno .68: static displ. as "453186")	
				Frank Taylor, Reno NV	c82
				John D. Pearl/Rudulphs Flying Circus,	
				Chino CA	11.6.82/85
				David C. Tallichet/ MARC, Chino CA	10.1.85/87
				(rest. Reno NV, Casper WY & Chino CA)	
			G-MURU	ntu: Warbirds of GB, Biggin Hill	10.87/90
				(del. Biggin Hill 16.5.89, flew as "Miss Behavin")	
				Evergreen Ventures Inc, McMinnville OR	8.2.90/92
				(dep. Biggin Hill on del. Marana AZ 9.7.90)	
			N38EV	Evergreen Heritage Collection, Marana AZ	6.90/95
				(rest. Marana & Ft Collins CO 90/95 "453186")	
8448	P-38L	44-53193	NX34993	Nadine B. Ramsey, KS	.46
	F-5G		N34993	Aero Service Corp, Philadelphia PA	51/60
			CF-NMW	Bradley Air Services, Carp ONT	60/61
				(flew last Canadian P-38 survey mission 9.61)	
				Age of Flight Museum, Niagara Falls ONT	.61/65
			N3005	Aidair Museum, Wilmington DE	.69
				Colonial Flying Corps Museum, New Garden	
				Flying Field, Toughkenamon PA	72/76
				Peter S. Sherman, Maitland FL	7.77
				(rest., fitted fighter nose *Glamorus Glyness*)	
			N38PS	Peter S. Sherman, Maitland FL	22.7.78
				crashed nr.White House OH (Sherman killed)	7.78
				(prev. incorrectly rep. as 5747/44-24743)	

8487 •	P-38L F-5G	**44-53232**	NX66678	J. Yandell (race #11 *Country Boy II*") James L. Bledsoe, Miami FL (to FA Hondurena as 505) Bob Bean Aircraft, Blythe CA (del. Honduras-Kelly AFB TX .60, stored 60/61) USAFM, Wright-Patterson AFB OH: del. (displ. as P-38J "267855/KI-W") (NX66678 prev. rep. as 8414/44-53159)	46 47 .48/60 31.3.60 27.5.61/96
8491 •	P-38L	**44-53236**		Richard I. Bong Memorial, Poplar WI (del. Duluth MN 7.12.48, to Polar by road 7.49, rest. 55, displ. on poles 5.55 as "2103993", later 423964/*Marge*)	7.49/94
8497 •	P-38L F-5G	**44-53242**	NX57496 N57496	M. E. Jenkins, CA (race #47) Tom P. Mathews (race #47) Ball-Ralston Inc, Hillsboro OR California Electric Power Company Weather Modification Co, Redlands CA crashed, forced landing near Bishop CA Joel Bishop: wreck recov. ex crash site Museum of Flying, Santa Monica CA Tom Reilly Vintage Aircraft, Kissimmee FL	.46 47 .48 3.48/55 9.55/69 c58 90 .90/91 10.91/96
8502	P-38L F-5G	44-53247	NX90813 N90813	Wesley M. Gray, Long Beach CA (ex War Assets Admin., Kingman AZ 2.46) Robert M. Love & Nancy Harkness-Love, DE Cecil W. Kenyon (avionics testing) Aero Service Corp, Philadelphia PA Virgil Kaufman Foundation, Philadelphia PA Bob Bean Aircraft, Blythe CA (stored Blythe CA 61/70) USAFM, Pima County Museum, Tucson AZ (displ. as "453247") Musee de l'Air, Paris-Le Bourget, France dest. in museum hangar fire, Le Bourget	.46 .46 10.46 5.51/60 12.60/61 5.61/72 .72/89 26.5.89/90 17.5.90
8509 •	P-38L F-5G	**44-53254**	NX25Y **N25Y**	Lilee Products Co, Chicago IL (ex War Assets Admin., Kingman AZ $1250) J. D. Reed Co, Houston TX (mod. racer, fighter nose, #14 *Sky Ranger*) Hugh Wells, Baltimore MD Sylvan Lair & Vernon Thorpe, Yukon OK Marvin L. Gardner & Lloyd P. Nolan/ Confederate Air Force, Mercedes TX Joe Henderson/CAF, Brownwood TX Marvin L. Gardner, Harlingen & Austin TX (race #25 ; later #13 "*White Lightnin*") (USCR quotes id. 5339, ie. 44-24335)	4.46 9.46/53 .53 .62/63 .63/70 72 77/96

Lockheed PV-2

15-1073•	PV-2	**Bu37107**	**N7261C**	Ralph S. Johnson/Master Equipment Co, Cheyenne WY Westco Interservice Group, St Helens OR Quarry Products Inc, Richmond CA Neil M. Rose, Vancouver WA	 .57/84 .84 6.87/92 12.92/96
15-1095•	PV-2	**Bu37129**	**N7268C**	Aircraft Specialties Inc, Mesa AZ Globe Air Inc, Mesa AZ Southwest Aviation Inc, Fairacres NM Quarry Products Inc, Richmond CA (open storage, Mesa AZ 81/95)	66/81 4.81/84 1.86/87 4.88/96
15-1125•	PV-2	**Bu37159**	**N6853C**	Ben Whitney Trading Co, Calexico CA	61

				Thomas E. Herrod, Billings MT	63/66
				D & D Aerial Spraying, Rantoul KS	.68/76
				Kinney Air Tankers, Richey MT	.82
				sale rep., Tucson AZ	87
				Quarry Products, Richmond CA	7.87/89
				American Air Museum Society, Richmond CA	3.89/92
				(open storage, Schellville CA 88/91)	
				Richard T. Mitchell/Round Engine Operations, Broussard LA	7.92/95
				Richard T. Mitchell/Combat Aircraft Museum, Lafayette LA	93/96
15-1137•	PV-2	**Bu37171**	**N7249C**	Ralph S. Johnson/Master Equipment Co, Cheyenne WY	.57/78
				Ralph S. Johnson/RALCO Inc, Cheyenne WY	2.79
				Westco Interservice Group, St Helens OR	84
				Quarry Products, Richmond CA	6.87/92
				Neil M. Rose, Vancouver WA	12.92/95
15-1150•	PV-2	Bu37184	**N7253C**	Ralph S. Johnson/Master Equipment Co, Cheyenne WY	.57/79
				Ralph S. Johnson/RALCO Inc, Cheyenne WY	2.79
				substantial damage, Humble City NM	26.6.79
				Dawson Aviation Inc, Glendive MT	2.86/95
15-1156•	PV-2	**Bu37190**	**N6856C**	Ralph S. Johnson/Master Equipment Co, Cheyenne WY (tanker #C38; #38)	.57/79
				Ralph S. Johnson/RALCO Inc, Cheyenne WY	2.79
				Ronald K. Gary, Douglas AZ	1.80/89
				T & G Aviation, Chandler AZ: leased (tanker #38)	81/82
				John W. Hirth/Hirth Air Tankers, Dothan AL & Buffalo WY (tanker #C38)	6.89/95
15-1168•	PV-2	**Bu37202**	**N7483C**	Henry R. Birmingham, Phoenix AZ	66
				Dothan Aviation Corp, Dothan AL	.67/81
				Hugh W. Wheelless, Dothan AL	3.80
				Aircraft Specialties Inc, Mesa AZ	.81/95
				(open storage, Mesa AZ 81/95)	
15-1177•	PV-2	**Bu37211**	**N7273C**	Aircraft Specialties Inc, Mesa AZ	66/81
				Globe Air Inc, Mesa AZ	4.81/84
				sale rep., USCR	87/95
				(open storage, Mesa AZ 81/95)	
15-1182•	PV-2	**Bu37216**	**N7256C**	Ralph S. Johnson/Master Equipment Co, Cheyenne WY	.57/79
				damaged in noseover, Torrington WY	24.6.77
				Ralph S. Johnson/RALCO Inc, Cheyenne WY	2.79
				Westco Interservice Group, St Helens OR	.84
				Quarry Products Inc, Richmond CA	6.87/92
				(open storage, Schellville CA 88/91)	
				Earl R. Benedict, Fairfield CA	4.95
15-1185•	PV-2	**Bu37219**	N7254C	Ralph S. Johnson/Master Equipment Co, Cheyenne WY	.57/81
				ran off runway, landing Tupelo MS	11.10.65
				derelict stripped, Bainbridge GA	81
15-1191	PV-2	Bu37225	N7266C	Ralph S. Johnson/Master Equipment Co Cheyenne WY	.57/66
				Clyde R. Mallory, Catskanie OR	.67/70
15-1196•	PV-2	**Bu37230**	**N7459C**	noted at Houston TX (ex USMC sc.)	.57

c/n	Type	Mil. ID	Reg.	Owner	Dates
	PV-2T			H. E. Connor	61
				Rogue Flying Service, Medford OR	63
				Aero Ag Inc, Medford OR (tanker #30)	64/66
				Clarks Aerial Services, Brownfield TX	.68/76
				Oklahoma Aircraft Corp, Yukon OK	.79
				Louis Minkoff, Ypsilanti MI	84
				sale rep., Columbus NE	87/89
				John W. Hirth/Hirth Air Tankers, Dothan AL & Buffalo WY: sprayer	8.89/95
15-1200•	PV-2 PV-2T	**Bu37234**	**N7458C**	Quintana Petroleum Corp, Houston TX	61/66
				Clarks Aerial Services, Brownfield TX	.68/76
				Brownfield Aerial Inc, Brownfield TX	.77
				Oklahoma Aircraft Corp, Yukon OK	.77
				Louis Minkoff, Ypsilanti MI	84
				Arrow Aircraft Inc, Toledo OH	1.86/87
				John W. Hirth/Hirth Air Tankers, Dothan AL & Buffalo WY: sprayer	5.88/96
15-1216•	PV-2	**Bu37250**	**N6857C**	Riverside Aircraft Co, Riverside CA	63/64
				Rosenbalm Aviation, Medford OR	.65/66
				Dothan Aviation Corp, Dothan AL	.67/76
				Hugh W. Wheelless, Dothan AL	.80
				Aircraft Specialties Inc, Mesa AZ	4.80/88
				Quarry Products Inc, Richmond CA	8.88/90
				Richard T. Mitchell/Combat Aircraft Museum, Lafayette LA	12.90/95
				(open storage, Mesa AZ 81/90, del. Mesa to Broussard LA 5.11.90 for rest., ff 10.91 as USN/*Fat Cat Too*)	
				dam. undercart collapse on takeoff (repaired)	.94
15-1220•	PV-2	**Bu37254**	N7248C	Ralph S. Johnson/Master Equipment Co, Cheyenne WY	.57/79
				Ralph S. Johnson/RALCO Inc, Cheyenne WY	2.79/85
				Southwest Aviation Inc, Fairacres NM	5.85
			N2PV	Southwest Aviation Inc, Fairacres NM	2.86/96
15-1223•	PV-2	**Bu37257**	N7255C	Ralph S. Johnson/Master Equipment Co, Cheyenne WY	.57/70
				Pima County Air Museum, Tucson AZ	12.75
				(derelict, unconv."USN/E-181" Douglas AZ 70/82, moved to Pima by road ex Douglas AZ 30.3.82)	
				Pima Air Museum, Tucson AZ	.82/93
				(stored unconv: fitted parts of N6856C)	
15-1228	PV-2 Howard Cargo	Bu37262	N7428C	F. J. Perillo, Tucson AZ	61/64
				Jewell Foilage Co, San Antonio TX	.66/69
				Clarks Aerial Service, Brownfield TX	70/76 conv.
				Brownfield Aerial Inc, Brownfield TX	.77
				I. N. Burchinall Jnr, Paris TX	.79/80
				Eagle Air Service, Lauderhill FL	80/84
				Richard T. Mitchell/Acadiana Aero Restoration Society, Broussard LA	.86/87
				(flew as "USN/Fat Cat")	
				Confederate Air Force, Harlingen TX	1.88/90
				crashed on takeoff, dest. by fire, Conroe TX	16.9.90
15-1231•	PV-2	**Bu37265**		disposal ex NAS North Island CA	12.8.57
			N3247G	L. B. Smith Aircraft Corp, Miami FL	12.8.57
				Ben T. Jones, Miami FL	16.8.57/62
			LV-PKC	Norsur, Buenos Aires	
			N3247G	Master Equipment Co, Cheyenne WY	11.7.62
				Henry Birmingham, Phoenix AZ	3.8.62/67
				(civil conv. as ag. sprayer completed 27.8.63)	

				Dothan Aviation Corp, Dothan AL	8.3.67/83
				(derelict at Wheeless Airport, Dothan 78/85)	
				Globe Air, Mesa AZ	1.4.83/85
				Richard T. Mitchell/Acadiana Aero Restoration	
				Society, Broussard LA	10.85/88
				Rose's Raiders, Vancouver WA	28.9.88/95
				(dism. for rest. to fly, Dothan AL)	
15-1236•	PV-2	**Bu37270**	**N7257C**	Ralph S. Johnson/Master Equipment Co,	
				Cheyenne WY	.57/79
				Ralph S. Johnson/RALCO Inc, Cheyenne WY	2.79/95
				(open storage, Chandler AZ 87/95)	
15-1242•	PV-2	**Bu37276**	**N7272C**	Appliance Buyers Credit Corp, St Joseph MI	64
				Donaire Inc, Phoenix AZ	.64
				Clarks Aerial Services, Brownfield TX	.66/77
				Brownfield Aerial Inc, Brownfield TX	.77
				Oklahoma Aircraft Corp, Yukon OK	.79
				R & R Land & Investment	3.80
				Arbor Air, Columbus NE	7.81/88
				John W. Hirth/Hirth Air Tankers,	
				Dothan AL & Buffalo WY: sprayer	5.88/96
15-1247	PV-2	Bu37281	N7263C	Ralph S. Johnson/Master Equipment Co,	
				Cheyenne WY	.57/74
				crashed while spraying, Winslow AZ	12.6.74
15-1330	PV-2	Bu37364	N7434C	F. J. Perillo, Tucson AZ: USCR	61/64
			CP-649	R. Rollano	9.58
				Aero Rutas Oriente: "Santa Rosa"	71
				noted wfu derelict, La Paz, Bolivia	3.71
15-1352•	PV-2	**Bu37386**		disposal ex NAS North Island CA	12.8.57
			N7264C	Ralph S. Johnson/Master Equipment Co,	
				Cheyenne WY	12.8.57/79
				(civil conv. to ag. sprayer completed 4.4.60)	
				Ralph S. Johnson/RALCO Inc, Cheyenne WY	1.2.79/96
				(FAA quote id. 15-1552, which was not built)	
15-1362•	PV-2	**Bu37396**	**N7265C**	Ralph S. Johnson/Master Equipment Co,	
				Cheyenne WY	.57/79
				Ralph S. Johnson/RALCO Inc, Cheyenne WY	2.79/86
				Historical Aircraft Memorial Foundation,	
				Tyler TX	1.86/89
				American Military Heritage Foundation,	
				Indianapolis IN	1.90/95
				(flies as Navy 37396)	
15-1385•	PV-2	**Bu37419**	N7486C	Kay Barricklow, Arcola IL	66/69
				Tallmantz Collection, Orange Co CA	
				(displ. unconv.,"NAS Norfolk/S")	65/67
				Aircraft Specialties Inc, Mesa AZ	68/81
				(civil conv. to sprayer, Mesa AZ .68)	
				Globe Air Inc, Mesa AZ	4.81/84
				Carson Air Foto, Miami FL	4.86/87
				Quarry Products Inc, Richmond CA	8.87/96
				(open storage, Schellville CA 88/91)	
15-1410•	PV-2	Bu37444	**N7086C**	Robert L. Larrabee, Seattle-Boeing Field WA	62/64
				(noted as fire tanker #D20 5.62)	
				Central Aircraft Maintenance/D & D Aero,	
				Rantoul KS (tanker #F43, #43)	.66/72
				John E. Hamersley, Walker MO	73/76
				Ralph S. Johnson/RALCO, Cheyenne WY	.77/79

				(tanker #43)	
				Valley Ag Inc, Douglas AZ	.80/84
				dam. landing, Philipsburg PA	2.5.80
				T & G Aviation Inc, Chandler AZ : lsd	81/83
				(tanker #112)	
				David C. Tallichet/MARC, Chino CA	87/96
				(open storage, Chandler AZ 87/95)	
15-1415	PV-2	Bu37449	N6718C	John B. Rosenthal Inc	61
				Aircraft Specialties Inc, Mesa AZ	63/80
				(last noted Mesa AZ 10.79)	
15-1428•	PV-2	**Bu37462**	**N7414C**	R. J. Harlow	61
				Purico Foods Corp, San Juan PR	63/64
				Corsair Air Services Co	.64
				George H. Stell, Phoenix AZ	.66
				Airfleet Leasing Inc, Gainsville FL	.68/70
				Dothan Aviation Corp, Dothan AL	.71/80
				Hugh W. Wheelless, Dothan AL	3.80
				Aircraft Specialties Inc, Mesa AZ	4.80/84
				Southwest Aviation Inc, Fairacres NM	3.86/88
				Joseph L. Davis, Fresno CA	7.88/96
15-1432•	PV-2	**Bu37466**	**N6855C**	McCullough Tool Co, Houston TX	61/64
				Aircraft Specialties Inc, Mesa AZ	66/81
				Globe Air Inc, Mesa AZ	4.81/84
				Southwest Aviation Inc, Las Cruces NM: USCR	2.86/95
				(stored Las Cruces NM)	
				John Bilyeu, Rialto CA	.92/95
				(being rest. Rialto to military config. 93/95)	
				Larry Rose, Imperial CA	.95
15-1438•	PV-2	**Bu37472**	**N7670C**	George H. Stell, Phoenix AZ	66
				Airfleet Leasing Inc, Gainsville FL	.68/70
				Dothan Aviation Corp, Dothan AL	.71/76
				Robert F. Yancey, Klamath Falls OR	4.78
				Eino W. Waara, Columbus NE	82/87
				John W. Hirth/Hirth Air Tankers, Dothan AL	
				& Buffalo WY: sprayer	88/96
15-1439•	PV-2	**Bu37473**		(to FA Portuguesa as 4620)	
				Museu do Ar, Alverca AB, Lisbon: stored	87/92
15-1456	PV-2	Bu37490	N6852C	O.J. McCullough/McCullough Tool Co,	
				Houston TX	61/64
				Aircraft Specialties Inc, Mesa AZ	66/76
				(last noted Mesa 10.78) struck-off USCR	11.83
15-1458•	PV-2	Bu37492	N7270C	W. F. Patterson Jr	61
				Flight Investment Corp, Miami FL	63/64
				John B. Miller	.64
			HK-......	Coperative Militares en Retiro, Colombia	.64
			N72707	Aircraft Specialties Inc, Mesa AZ	69/4.81
				Globe Air Inc, Mesa AZ	4.81/84
				Consolidated Aviation Enterprises,	
				East Middlebury VT	.85
				Classic Aviation International, Rosharon TX	12.86/89
				Aircraft Acquisition Service Inc,	
				Silver Spring MD (flew as "USN/171UP")	90/92
				Early Flying Inc, Arlington GA	5.94/95
				dam. landing, Houston-Southwest TX	7.94
15-1465•	PV-2	**Bu37499**	**N7080C**	Howard Aero Inc, San Antonio TX	61/63
				Business Aircraft Corp, San Antonio TX	64
				Ralph S. Johnson/Master Equipment Co,	

				Cheyenne WY (tanker #C39; #39)	66/79
				Ralph S. Johnson/RALCO Inc, Cheyenne WY	2.79
				T & G Aviation Inc, Chandler AZ : leased	81/83
				Russell G. Comstock, Danville CA	84/89
				John W. Hirth/Hirth Air Tankers, Dothan AL	
				& Buffalo WY (tanker #C39)	11.89/95
15-1468•	PV-2	**Bu37502**	**N7269C**	Aircraft Specialties Inc, Mesa AZ	69/85
				(stored unconv. in compound, Mesa 69/81:	
				"NAS Glenview/ Grosse Ile/ Los Alamitos")	
				Confederate Air Force WI Wing (spares use)	3.85/87
				(arr. Milwaukee by road ex Mesa 5.5.85)	
				Phil Cooper, New Bedford MA : by road	2.87/91
				(spares use for PV-2 N86493 and	
				PV-1 N165H rest. projects)	
15-1473•	PV-2	**Bu37507**		disposal ex NAS North Island CA	12.8.57
			N6643D	Trade Ayer Inc, Linden NJ	12.8.57/60
				D. U. Howard, San Antonio TX	9.2.60/62
				Robert A. Gallaher, Tucson AZ	25.10.62
			N86492	Ralph S. Johnson/Master Equipment Co,	
				Cheyenne WY	10.62/79
				(conv. from military config. to sprayer 8.63)	
				Ralph S. Johnson/RALCO Inc, Cheyenne WY	2.79/87
				Quarry Products Inc, Richmond CA	21.4.87/92
				(open storage Mesa AZ 86/93, under rest. 95)	
				Randsburg Corp, Portland OR	4.95
15-1478•	PV-2 Howard Super Harpoon	Bu37512		disposal ex NAS North Island CA	29.5.57
			N7453C	Commercial Cotton Co Inc	29.5.57
				William N. Byrd & Mobley M. Milam	5.7.57
				Quintana Petroleum Corp, Houston TX	13.7.57
			N144X	Quintana Petroleum Corp, Houston TX	7.8.58/67
				(civil conv. by Howard completed 19.2.59)	
				(wings rebuilt & modified by Oakland Airmotive,	
				Oakland CA; under-wing drop tanks: 9.63)	
			N1448	Arkansas Travel-Aires Inc, Pine Bluff AR	28.4.67
				Astro Airways Corp, Pine Bluff AR	12.68/73
				Ralph S. Johnson/RALCO, Cheyenne WY	6.9.73/77
				Aire Sales & Service Inc, Phoenix AZ	18.10.76
				Schaf-Air Inc	18.3.77/78
				Oil Investment Lease Corp	13.4.79
				Old South Agriculture Service Inc	13.12.79
				Christopher P. Ridout, Pembroke Pines FL	25.3.80/81
			N144CR	ntu: Christopher P. Ridout, Pembroke Pines FL	9.80
			N1448	G & S Enterprises, Beverly Hills CA	1.6.81/87
				Timothy A. Seidl, West Palm Beach FL	28.7.87
				sale rep., West Palm Beach FL: USCR	90/95
15-1488	PV-2	Bu37522	N6647D	Trade Ayer Inc, Linden NJ	61/69
				dam. hurricane, Belize, British Honduras	c64
				wreck noted near Belize Airport	72/76
15-1489•	PV-2	**Bu37523**	**N6634D**	Trade Ayer Inc, Linden NJ	61
				Skyways Inc, Cody WY	63/64
				Dothan Aviation Corp, Dothan AL	.66/76
				Bert Popek, McAllen TX	11.77/80
15-1490•	PV-2	**Bu37524**	**N7262C**	Ralph S. Johnson/Master Equipment Co,	
				Cheyenne WY	.57/79
				Ralph S. Johnson/RALCO Inc, Cheyenne WY	2.79/84
				Westco Interservice Group, St Helens OR	84
				Quarry Products Inc, Richmond CA	6.87/92
				(open storage, Schellville CA 88/91)	

				Earl M. Benedict, Fairfield CA	4.95
5-1496	PV-2	Bu37530	N6649D	Trade Ayer Inc, Linden NJ	61/64
			N86491	Ralph S. Johnson/Master Equipment Co, Cheyenne WY	64/73
				crashed, La Grange GA	10.10.73
5-1501•	PV-2D	**Bu37535**	N7079C	E. D. Weiner, Los Angeles CA	27.3.57/58
				(disposal ex NAS North Island CA 27.3.57)	
			N83L	E. D. Weiner, Los Angeles CA	10.58/59
				William E. Rosenbalm/Medford Air Service, Medford OR	3.12.59/61
				William E. Rosenbalm/Rosenbalm Aviation, Medford OR (tanker #29)	61/65
				Dothan Aviation Corp, Dothan AL	8.4.65/83
				(derelict, Dothan-Wheeless Airport AL 76/83)	
				Globe Air Inc, Mesa AZ	1.4.83/85
				Richard T. Mitchell/Acadiana Aero Restoration Society, Broussard LA	10.85/88
				Rose's Raiders, Vancouver WA	28.9.88/95
			N11559	ntu: Neil M. Rose, Vancouver WA	9.91
				(rest. Dothan-Wheeless 88/91: flies as *Rose's Raiders*, 8 gun nose)	
5-1503•	PV-2D	**Bu37537**	N6651D	Trade Ayer Inc, Linden NJ	61
				Wenairco, Wenatchee WA (tanker #E40)	63/72
				Central Air Service, East Wenatchee WA (tanker #E40)	.74/76
				Kinney Air Tankers, Richey MT (tanker #103)	2.81
				S. I. Verschoot, Richey MT: USCR	2.84/95
				Gary R. Larkins, Auburn CA	
				USNAM, NAS Pensacola FL: displ.	84/91
				USS Lexington Museum, Corpus Christi TX	93/94
				(displ. on board carrier as "Bu37537")	
5-1516•	PV-2D	Bu37550	**N7251C**	Southwest Aircraft, Fort Worth-Meacham TX	61/63
				Ralph Johnson Flying Service, Cheyenne WY	64/79
				Ralph S. Johnson/RALCO Inc, Cheyenne WY	2.79
				Aafchan Air, Chandler AZ	7.87/96
				(open storage, Chandler AZ 87/95)	
5-1597	PV-2D PV-2T	Bu37631	N7455C	(rep. in ex USMC scheme, Houston TX 57)	
				William N. Byrd, Brawley CA	61
				William H. Bird/Bird & Sons Inc, Seattle WA	61/70
				(flown on CIA contract work Laos)	
5-1598	PV-2D	Bu37632	N7969A	Ben T. Jones, Miami FL	61
				William C. Rogers, Miami FL: USCR	64/70
			LV-PKB	Norsur, Buenos Alres	
5-1599•	PV-2D PV-2T	**Bu37633**	**N7454C**	William N. Byrd, Brawley CA	61/64
				Aircraft Specialties Inc, Mesa AZ	.64/81
				Globe Air Inc, Mesa AZ	4.81/84
				Collings Foundation, Stowe MA	1.86/96
				(open storage, Mesa AZ 81/95)	
5-1600•	PV-2D	**Bu37634**	**N6655D**	Stahmann Farms, Las Cruces NM	61/84
				Thomas J. Newell, Colorado Springs CO	87/89
				Lone Star Flight Museum, Galveston TX (flies as USN "37634")	90/96
5-1603	PV-2D	Bu84059	N7427C	Zelair Corp, Defiance OH	61/64
			N230Z	Zelair Corp, Defiance OH	65
				California Aircraft Eng. Co, San Lorenzo CA	.65/66

				Aircraft Specialties Inc, Mesa AZ	69/72
				crashed on take off, Addison TX	28.4.75
				scrapped: struck off USCR	3.10.75
15-1604•	PV-2D	Bu84060	N6656D	Trade Ayer Inc, Linden NJ	12.8.57/60
				(disposal ex NAS North Island CA 12.8.57)	
				D. U. Howard, San Antonio TX	9.2.60/62
				Robert A. Gallaher	25.10.62
			N86493	Ralph S. Johnson/Master Equipment Corp, Cheyenne WY	10.62/79
				(conv. from military config. to sprayer 4.64)	
				Ralph S. Johnson/RALCO Inc, Cheyenne WY	2.79
				Big Iron Inc, Belton MO	84
				Confederate Air Force,Waukesha WI	9.85/95
				(del. Belton-Waukesha 2.10.85, under rest. to military config., parts ex N7269C & N7415C)	
15-1605	PV-2D	Bu84061	N7250C	Ralph S. Johnson/Master Equipment Co, Cheyenne WY	12.8.57/79
				(disposal ex NAS North Island CA 12.8.57; conv. ex military to granular ant-bait spreader 3.66)	
				Ralph S. Johnson/RALCO Inc, Cheyenne WY	1.2.79/85
				Douglas M. Lacey, San Rafael CA	11.86/88
				Fred L. Austin, Reno NV	6.12.88/90
				(op. by Lacey, flew as USN "FP/178")	
				crashed into Clear Lake CA (Lacey k.)	29.9.90
15-1606•	PV-2D	**Bu84062**	**N6657D**	Wenairco Inc, Wenatchee WA	61/72
				William A. Dempsay/Central Air Service, East Wenatchee WA (tanker #101)	.74/76
				Kinney Air Tankers, Richey MT (tanker #101)	.79
				S. I. Verschoot, Richey MT	.84
				Albert L. Hoover, Twin Falls ID	.87/88
				Quarry Products Inc, Richmond CA	8.88/96
15-1608•	PV-2D	**Bu84064**	**N7415C**	Zelair Corp, Defiance OH	61/66
				Aircraft Specialties Inc, Mesa AZ	69/81
				Globe Air Inc, Mesa AZ	4.81/84
				Confederate Air Force, Waukesha WI	.85
				crashed at Mesa, on test flight	1.5.85
				sold as wreck, Dennis Hill, Richey MT	10.85/87
				S. I. Verschoot, Richey/Glendive MT	3.88/96
				(stored dism. Ocotillo Wells CA 88/94: components used in rest. of N86493)	
- •	PV-1 Howard 500	-	**CP-1975**	noted at Opa Locka FL	3.85/9.85
				noted Bogota	93

MACCHI MC200 SAETTA

- •	MC.200	**MM8307**		Museo Aeronautico Caproni di Taliedo, Milan	75
				Museo Storico dell'Aeronautica Militaire Italiana, Vigna di Valle AB	80/96
- •	MC.200	**MM8146**		"372-5": captured Benghazi, North Africa	11.42
				(shipped to USA for war bonds tours)	
				Princeton Auto Museum, Oxford MA: derelict	50/60
				Gene Zimmerman PA: hulk	65
				Bradley Air Museum, Windsor Locks CT: hulk	11.65/80
				New England Air Museum, Windsor Locks CT	83/89
				Jeet Mahal, Vancouver BC	.89/92
				(shipped to Venegono, Italy arr. 4.12.89: rest. by Aermacchi, rolled-out 12.91 as "MM8146/372-5")	
				USAFM, Wright Patterson AFB, Dayton OH	10.92/96

Macchi MC202 Folgore

- •	MC.202	-		(to USAAC as EB-300/FE-300)	43
				Wright Field OH: flight trials	43/44
				(to USAAF as FE-498/T2-498)	45/46
				Smithsonian Institute: stored Park Ridge IL	8.46
				NASM, Silver Hill MD: displ. as "FE-498"	72
				NASM, Washington DC: displ. as "MM9476"	74/96
- •	MC.202	**MM9546**		Museo Storico dell'Aeronautica Militaire	
				Italiana, Vigna di Valle AB	80/96
	MC205V repl.			(conv. to MC205V config .50,	
				displ. as MC.205V Veltro "MM9345")	
- •	MC.202	**MM9667**		Museo Storico dell'Aeronautica Militaire	
				Italiana, Vigna di Valle AB	84/96
				(displ. as "MM7844")	

Macchi MC205V Veltro

665 •	MC.205V	**MM91818**		Malignani Technical Institute, Udine	60/79
				rest. to fly Venegono by Aermacchi	.79/80
			I-MCVE	Soc. Aeronautica Macchi, Venegono	12.80/87
				(ff Venegono 9.12.80, flew as "MM92214"	
				later "MM9327")	
				dam. taxy accident, Venegono	23.7.86
				(rebuilt by Aermacchi for static displ. 82/87	)
				National Museum of Science & Technology,	
				Milan, Italy (displ. as "MM92215")	.87/96
- •	MC.205V	**MM92166**		(to Egyptian AF as 1243)	
				National Museum of Science & Technology,	
				Milan, Italy	77/82
				Aeronautica Macchi, Venegono	.82/96
				(rest. to fly Venegono, using parts of MM91818)	

Martin AM Mauler

- •	AM-1	**Bu122259**		Alan Sparks/Pate Transport Museum	90
				(rep. recov. ex Aberdeen Proving Ground MD,	
				stored dism. "259")	
				Harry S. Doan/Doan Helicopters Inc,	
				New Smyrna Beach FL	92
				offered for sale at Doan auction 259	30.10.92
				(rest. project: complete fuse., 4 wings)	
				(id. also rep. as Bu122403)	
3920 •	AM-1	**Bu22260**		Aberdeen Proving Ground MD: target use	73
				New Mexico Institute of Mining & Technology,	
				Sirocco NM	79
			N5586A	Confederate Air Force, Brownfield TX	10.3.80/96
				(ff 3.84 as USN 151/*Able Mable*)	
				crashed Brownfield TX, on second test flight	.84
- •	AM-1	**Bu22275**		Aberdeen Proving Ground MD: target use	70/79
				Bradley Air Museum, Windsor Locks CT : arr.	28.4.79
				New England Air Museum, Windsor Locks CT	83/90
			N7163M	Jack Erickson/Erickson Air Crane,	
				Medford OR	7.90/96
- •	AM-1	**Bu122397**		Aberdeen Proving Ground MD: target use	

				USNAM, NAS Pensacola FL: stored	.72/94

MARTIN B-26 MARAUDER

-	B-26	40-1426		rep. recov. from Trobriand Island SWPA no further information	c74
- •	B-26	**40-1459**		forced landing Smith River BC	16.1.42
				David C. Tallichet/Yesterdays Air Force, Chino CA (recov. ex Smith River 9-11.71)	.71/91
			N4299K	David C. Tallichet/MARC, Chino CA (stored dism., MARC yard, Chino CA 72/91)	6.91/93
				lsd: Air Heritage Inc, Beaver Falls PA (stored dism. Beaver Falls, planned rest. to fly)	.91/92
				Empire State Aerosciences Museum, Schenectady NY: static rest. project	93
- •	B-26	**40-1464**		forced landing Smith River BC	16.1.42
				David C. Tallichet/Yesterdays Air Force, Chino CA (recov. ex Smith River 9-11.71)	.71/91
			N4297J	David C. Tallichet/MARC, Chino CA (rest. Chino 75/92, ff 18.4.92)	6.91/94
				USAFM, March AFB CA: loan	92/93
				Fantasy of Flight Museum, Polk City FL	7.9.94/96
- •	B-26	**40-1501**		forced landing Smith River BC	16.1.42
				David C. Tallichet/Yesterdays Air Force, Chino CA (recov. ex Smith River 9-11.71)	.71/91
			N4299S	David C. Tallichet/MARC, Chino CA (rest. project)	4.91/95
- •	B-26B	**41-31773**		(322nd BG/ 449th BS/ PN-O/"Flak Bait")	
				Smithsonian Institution	.49
				NASM, Silver Hill MD & Washington DC (nose displ. Washington DC: remainder stored)	60/96
-	B-26B	41-31856		Mr. Patterson, Pacific Palisades CA (stored at house, planned conv. to camper van)	c49/c75
				David C. Tallichet/Yesterdays Air Force, Chino CA (nose section only) (from same source: nose of "42-35075")	c75
2253	B-26C TB-26C	41-35071	N5546N	United Airlines	9.9.46
				Leland H. Cameron/Allied Aircraft Co, North Hollywood CA	29.3.48
				Leland H. Cameron/Advance Industries, North Hollywood CA (race #24 "Valley Turtle")	1.6.49
				S. Murray, Oakland CA	5.4.50
				Tennessee Gas Transmission Co, Houston TX	29.8.51/54
	B-26C-T			(conv. to B-26C-T executive model by AiResearch Aviation Service, Los Angeles CA c53: official date 5.6.58)	
			N500T	Tennessee Gas Transmission Co, Houston TX	28.3.57
			N5546N	Tennessee Gas Transmission Co, Houston TX	22.7.57/59
				William C. Wold & Assoc, New York NY	23.9.59/61
				California Airmotive Corp, Van Nuys CA	15.4.61
				Bacon Aircraft Co, Santa Monica CA	7.9.61
			XB-LOX	Ing. Jorge Mendez/PEMEX Corp, Mexico	11.9.61
				Ace Norris, Chatanooga TN	10.65
			N5546N	Ace Norris/Aero Carpet, Chatanooga TN	17.11.65
				Carolina Aircraft Corp, Fort Lauderdale FL	24.2.66

	Type	Serial	Reg.	History	Date
				Westernair of Albuquerque, Albuquerque NM	2.3.66
				W. Meller Associates (for engine testing)	11.9.66/67
				State Bank of Greeley, Greeley CO	10.11.67
				Confederate Air Force, Harlingen/Midland TX	11.67/95
				u/c collapsed during engine run Harlingen TX	.69
				(rest. Harlingen commenced 10.75, ff 11.9.84)	
				nose gear leg collapsed Harlingen (repaired)	12.10.85
				(flew as 135071/N/*Carolyn*)	
				crashed and dest., Odessa TX	28.9.95
- •	B-26G	**43-34581**		(to l'Armee de l'Air as 334581)	
				Air France Apprentices School, Vilgenis	.51/65
				USAFM, Wright-Patterson AFB, Dayton OH	6.65/92
				(airfreighted by C-124 ex Chateauroux AB	
				France 6.65; rest., displ. as 334581/TZ-G	
				later 295857/FW-K/*Shootin-in*)	
- •	B-26G	**44-68219**		(to l'Armee de l'Air as 468219)	
				Air France Apprentices School, Vilgenis	.51/65
				Musee de l'Air: stored dism. Villacoublay	.65/90
				Musee de l'Air: Paris-Dugney AB: stored	5.90/95
				(note: id. prev. incorrectly rep. as 42-85857)	
- •	B-26	-		David C. Tallichet/MARC, Chino CA	c76/90
				(recov. ex movie studio: nose section only, "2P1")	
				Carl Scholl/Aero Trader, Chino CA	.90/94
				(planned rest. of nose section as static displ.,	
				stored Ocotillo Wells CA 94 with another nose)	

Martin JRM Mars

	Type	Serial	Reg.	History	Date
- •	JRM-1	**Bu76820**		(USN "Philippine Mars"): ff 21.7.45: del.	28.7.45/56
	JRM-3			wfu NAS Alameda CA, open storage 11.56/59	
			CF-LYK	Forest Industries Flying Tankers Ltd,	
				Sproat Lake, Vancouver Island BC	12.59/75
				(conv. to water bomber at Victoria BC .62)	
			C-FLYK	Forest Industries Flying Tankers Ltd	77/95
- •	JRM-1	**Bu76823**		(USN "Hawaii Mars"): del.	5.46/56
	JRM-3			wfu NAS Alameda CA, open storage	11.56/59
			CF-LYL	Forest Industries Flying Tankers Ltd,	
				Sproat Lake, Vancouver Island BC	12.59/75
				(conv. to water bomber at Victoria BC .64)	
			C-FLYL	Forest Industries Flying Tankers Ltd	77/95

Martin PBM Mariner

	Type	Serial	Reg.	History	Date
- •	PBM-5A	**Bu122071**	**N3190G**	Bacon Aircraft Co, Riverside-Thermal CA	64/66
				IPICSA Inc, Hollywood CA	69/70
				(planned tropical fish transp. from S. America,	
				stored unconv., Thermal CA 60/72)	
				NASM, Washington DC	.71/93
				Pima County Air Museum, Tucson AZ: loan	.72/96
-	PBM-5A	-		(to Uruguayan Navy as A-81_): del.	.56
				Aviacion Naval Uruguaya, Montevideo: displ.	76

Nr790	•	Bf 109E-3		(to Condor Legion as "6•106"2/J88)	c37
				(to Spanish AF as 6-106)	c39
				Deutsches Museum, Munich	c55/93
				(displ. as "Nr2804 AJ+YM")	
Nr1010	•	Bf 109B-2		Messerschmitt GmbH: trials aircraft V10	38/40
			D-IAKO	Oberpfaffenhofen AB: inst. airframe	45
				buried in ditch, Oberpfaffenhofen, Munich	.45
				hulk recov. .93, displ. Obserschleisseim	.93
				planned static rest.	
Nr1185	•	Bf 109E-6		Messerschmitt Werke GmbH	
		'Me209V1'		World speed record breaker	c39
			D-INJR	Muzeum Lotnictwa I Astronautyki, Krokov	79
				(rep fuselage and major components)	
Nr1190	•	Bf 109E-6		II/JG26 "White 4"	
				forced landing Eastdown, Sussex	30.9.40
				(shipped to Canada, displ. Canada & USA	
				during wartime donation tours)	
				Canadian Civil Defence College,	
				Arnprior ONT: derelict	65
				Peter Foote, Hurn UK	.66/89
				(static rest. using parts from crash sites)	
Nr1289	•	Bf 109E-3		I/JG26 "Black 2": "SH+FA"	
				crashed in sea off Udimore, Sussex	28.11.40
				shipped to South Africa for war loan tours	.42/44
				South African National Museum of Military	
				History, Saxonwold, Johannesburg	.44/92
				(displ. in crashed condition)	
Nr 1342	•	Bf109E-3		4/JG51	
				crashed onto beach at Wissant	29.07.40
				recovered from beach.	88
				Charleston Aviation Services	92/96
				(rest. to fly UK)	
Nr 1407	•	Bf109E-3		5/JG77 'Black ?	
				belly landing on Hitra.	27.10.40
				Issued to Stab II/JG77	
				handed over to I/JG77	06.41
				2//JG77 'Black 8'.	
				shot down in combat	17.07.41
				recovered from lake	93.
				Believed stored in Hungary.	95.
Nr 1983	•	Bf109E		No further information	
Nr2242	•	Bf 109E-3		(to Swiss AF as J-355)	.40
				Swiss Air Force Museum, Dubendorf AB	68/96
				Swiss Transport Museum, Lucerne: loan	77
Nr3535	•	Bf 109E		recov. ex crash site Russia	
				Ben Kolotilin/Kolair Inc, Roswell GA	94
				(offered for sale as rest. project:	
				Ed & Rose Zalesky, Surrey BC: arr. crated 11.95	
				(id. quoted as Bf109G 109582-001G)	
Nr3579	•	Bf 109E-1		I (Jagd)/LG2 'White 14'	
				damaged in emergency landing	02.09.40
				rebuilt as Bf109 E7	40

		I/JG77 damaged in emergency landing	07.12.41
		4/JG5 "White 7" presumed lost	02.08.42
		recov. from crash site Russia	92
		Museum of Flying,	
		Santa Monica CA	92/96
		(rest. to fly UK)	
Nr4101 •	Bf 109E-3	2/JG51 "Black 12": forced landing Manston 27.11.40	
		(to RAF as DG200): repaired, ff Hucknall	25.2.41
		RAF Stafford: stored for museum use	.43
		RAF Air Historic Branch	47/65
		(stored RAF Stanmore Park 49, RAF Wroughton,	
		RAF Fulbeck, RAF Biggin Hill 60/69)	
		(displ. various locations as "12+GH")	
		RAF Henlow: for movie "Battle of Britain"	.67/68
		RAF Museum, RAF St.Athan: rest.	.69/76
		RAF Museum, Hendon	.78/96
		(displ. as "4101/Black 12")	
Nr7108 •	Bf 109F-4	"NE+ML" : recov. ex Northern Russia	.49
		Aviation Museum of Central Finland,	
		Luonetjavvi AB, Tikkakoski, Finland: stored	92/96
Nr8347 •	Bf 109F-4	6/JG54 "Yellow 10"	
		fcd. ldg. in woods, Lubjan, nr. Leningrad	13.3.42
		(stripped hulk recov. ex crash site .92)	
		arr. West Sussex UK: rest. project	12.92
		(id. also quoted as Nr.8147)	
Nr10132 •	Bf 109F-4	Stab II/JG5	
		shot down Motowka, Northern Russia	12.8.42
		recov., displ. Russian museum	
		AJD Engineering, Suffolk UK	.95
		to be restored for static exhibition	
Nr14141 •	Bf 109G-1 /R2	2/JG5 'Black 6'. engine fire & ditching.	11.10.43
		hulk recov. 28miles West Egersund. Norway.15.88.88	
		Flyhistorisk Museum, Sola AB, Norway	91/93
		(long-term static rest. using parts from other	
		salvaged wrecks: displ. as "6")	
Nr14798 •	Bf 109G-2	"Black 1": recov. from crash site Russia	c90
		(present location unknown)	
Nr31010 •	Bf 109F-2 /Trop	I/JG27 "White 6"	
		captured by SAAF at Marble Arch, Libya	.43
		(to SAAF as 777)	
		shipped to South Africa for war bond tours	.43
		South African National Museum of	
		Military History, Saxonwold	.44/96
		(rest., displ. as "White 6")	
Nr10639 •	Bf 109G-2 /Trop	III/JG77 "Black 6": captured Gambut Main	
		airfield, Libya by 3 Squadron, RAAF	13.11.42
		(flown as "RAAF CV-V", del. to Egypt 2.12.43)	
		flown by RAF on trials Lydda, Palestine	12.42/43
		(to RAF as RN228): shipped to UK	12.43
		(ff RAF Collyweston 19.2.44: flight trials)	
		RAF Sealand: packed for displ. use	4.46
		RAF Air Historical Branch: display use	.46/65
		(stored RAF Stanmore Park 49/54,	
		RAF Wroughton, RAF Fulbeck)	
		RAF Wattisham: rest. project	.61/72
		RAF Henlow: for film *Battle of Britain*	.67/68
		RAF Lyneham: rest. to fly commenced	.72/75

			RAF Northolt: rest., DB605A engine	.75/83
			RAF Benson: rest. continued	.83/91
		G-USTV	Imperial War Museum, Duxford	10.90/96
			(ff RAF Benson 17.3.91, flies as "Black 6")	
Nr14792 •	Bf 109G-6		(to Yugoslav Air Force as 9663)	
			Yugoslavian Aviation Museum, Belgrade	70/90
			(note: see Nr610824 below)	
Nr19310 •	Bf109G-4		BH+XN 4/JG52 'White 3.	
			engine problems & ditching Black Sea	20.03.43
			hulk recovovered Black Sea	c77
			rep in italy	95.
			(long-term static rest. using parts from other salvaged wrecks: displ. as "6")	
Nr151591	Bf 109G-10		recov. ex crash site, Czechoslovakia	.82
			Hans Dittes, Speyer Germany	93/96
			(fuse. & parts rep used in rebuild of D-FEHD)	
Nr160163 •	Bf 109G-6		rep. captured Italy	7.44
			(to USAAF as FE-496/T2-496): shipped	.44
			Smithsonian Institute, stored Park Ridge OH	5.46
			NASM, Washington DC	65/96
			(rest. 73/74, displ. as "White 2")	
Nr163824 •	Bf 109G-14 /U-2		captured Eggebek airfield, Schleswig	.45
			selected for museum use: trucked out dism.	4.9.45
			RAF Sealand: packed for shipping	1.46
			Australian War Museum, Canberra: shipped	6.46/63
			(stored RAAF Laverton VIC, later stored dism. Duntroon ACT for AWM: never displ.)	
			Brian Wetless, Bankstown NSW	.63
			Sid Marshall, Sydney-Bankstown NSW	64/75
			(displ. in Marshall Airways hangar 64/75)	
			Jack P. Davidson, Bankstown NSW	75/79
			Warbirds of Great Britain Ltd, Blackbushe	10.12.79
			export difficulty: seized Customs, Sydney	20.12.79
			(stored RAAF Stores Depot, Sydney .79/87)	
			Australian War Memorial, Canberra ACT	87/95
			(stored dism. AWM Mitchell Annexe ACT)	
Nr165227 •	Bf 109G-6		(to Finnish AF as MT-452)	
			Suomen Ilmailumuseo, Utti AB	.70/87
			displ. Santa Hamina	65/80
Nr167271 •	Bf 109G-6		(to Finnish AF as MT-507) : last flight	13.3.54
			Utti AB: displ.	57/70
			(rest. for engine runs Rissala AB .70/71)	
			Suomen Ilmailumuseo, Luonetjarvi AB	72/79
			Aviation Museum of Central Finland, Luonetjarvi AB, Tikkakoski, Finland: displ.	6.79/93
Nr610824 •	Bf 109G-6		(to Bulgarian AF as ....)	
			(to Yugoslav AF as 9664)	
			Yugoslav Aeronautical Museum, Belgrade	84
			Warbird of GB Ltd, Bitteswell	.85/88
			Warbirds of GB Ltd, Biggin Hill	.89/90
		N109MS	Evergreen Ventures Inc, McMinnville OR	5.90/95
			(rest. to fly, Fort Collins CO 91/95)	
			(id. also rep. as ex YAF 9663: see Nr14792)	
Nr610937 •	Bf 109G-14		captured near Munich	.45
			shipped to USA ex France on HMS Reaper	7.45

			(to USAAF as FE-124/T2-124)	.45
			Georgia Institute of Technology, Atlanta GA	49/60
			(became derelict, wings scrapped)	
			John W. Caler, Sun Valley CA	67/70
			(rest. project, using Avia built wings)	
		G-SMIT	Warbirds of GB Ltd, Blackbushe	79/90
			(stored Blackbushe, Bitteswell, Biggin Hill 79/90)	
		N109EV	Evergreen Ventures Inc, McMinnville OR	5.90/96
			(rest. to fly, Fort Collins CO 91/95)	
r611943 •	Bf 109G-10 /U-4		"Yellow 13": captured near Munich	.45
			shipped to USA ex France on HMS Reaper	7.45
			(to USAAF as FE-122/T2-122): not flown	.45
			Wright Field OH: displ.	46
			University of Kansas, Lawrence KS : displ.	47/48
			Eddie Fisher, Kansas City KS	.48/58
			Ed Maloney/The Air Museum, Claremont CA .58	
			Ed Maloney/The Air Museum, Ontario CA	65/70
			Planes of Fame Museum, Chino CA	74/96
			National Air Race Museum, Sparks NV: loan 4.93	
			(displ. as "611943/13")	
r784993 •	Bf 109G-14 /AS		JG53 "White 13"	
			crashed near Oberfellsberg, Germany	1.45
			(stripped hulk buried on farm)	
			Raymond Wagner, Saarlouis, Germany	.87/96
			(excavated .87: rest. project using parts recov. from Czechoslavakia)	
6 •	HA-1112-K1L **C.4J-10**		Museo del Aire, Cuatro Vientos AB, Madrid	.65/93
			(displ. as "94-28")	
7 •	HA-1112-M1L **C.4K-31**		T. G. "Hamish" Mahaddie, Tablada AB, Spain	7.66/68
		G-AWHE	T. G. Mahaddie/Spitfire Productions Ltd, Duxford (for movie "Battle of Britain")	14.5.68
		N109ME	Wilson C. Edwards, Big Spring TX	20.2.69
			Confederate Air Force, Harlingen TX later Midland TX (flies as "Luftwaffe 14")	17.2.71/95
- •	HA-1112-M1L **C.4K-64**		USAFM Wright-Patterson AFB, Dayton OH	.67/93
			(static rest. Robins AFB GA .82 as Bf-109G-5, DB.605 engine installed)	
- •	HA-1112-M1L	N6109	Jack Hardwick, El Monte CA	70
			Robert Murphy, Quantico VA	78/84
			(FAA quote id. as "8-109-116-137")	
39 •	HA-1112-M1L **C.4K-75**		T. G. "Hamish" Mahaddie, Tablada AB, Spain	7.66/68
		G-AWHG	T. G. Mahaddie/Spitfire Productions Ltd,	
			Duxford : for film *Battle of Britain*	14.5.68/69
			dam. on take off Le Havre, France	1.69
			(during del. UK to Spain for film "*Patton*")	
			Paul Jameson, Betchworth UK: arr dism.	7.70
			Fairoaks Aviation Services, Blackbushe UK	21.2.73/74
		N3109G	Merryl D. Schulke, Orlando FL	8.74
			(crated ex Blackbushe .74, stored Sanford FL)	
			David C. Tallichet Chino CA	25.10.74
		N3109	MARC, Chino CA	5.86/95
			(rest. Casper WY 84/86)	
			crashed, test flight, Casper WY	28.5.86
			R. Bastet, La Ferte-Alais, France	.94/95
			(under rest. 95 with DB.605 engine)	
			(USCR quotes id. "8-109-116-40")	
7 •	HA-1112-M1L **C.4K-99**		T. G. "Hamish" Mahaddie, Tablada AB, Spain	7.66/68

			G-AWHM	T. G. Mahaddie/Spitfire Productions Ltd, Duxford (for film "*Battle of Britain*")	14.5.68
			N90604	Wilson C. Edwards, Big Spring TX (stored Big Spring TX)	20.2.69/96
171	•	HA-1112-M1L **C.4K-100**		T. G. "Hamish" Mahaddie, Tablada AB, Spain	7.66/68
			G-AWHJ	T. G. Mahaddie/Spitfire Productions Ltd, Duxford (for film *Battle of Britain*)	14.5.68
			N90605	Wilson C. Edwards, Big Spring TX	20.2.69/80
				rep. crashed Oxfort CT (stored Big Spring TX)	28.2.75
				Kalamazoo Aviation History Museum, Kalamazoo MI	1.78/87
			N76GE	Kalamazoo Aviation History Museum (painted as C.4K-19/*Hapi*)	.87/96
172	•	HA-1112-M1L **C.4K-102**		T. G. "Hamish" Mahaddie, Tablada AB, Spain	7.66/68
			G-AWHK	T. G. Mahaddie/Spitfire Productions Ltd, Duxford (for film *Battle of Britain*)	14.5.68
			N9938	Wilson C. Edwards, Big Spring TX	10.68
				Confederate Air Force, Harlingen TX	71/91
				CAF, Detroit MI : static displ.	87/93
				American Airpower Heritage Flying Museum, Midland TX	9.91/93
				Old Flying Machine Company (arr. dism. Duxford UK 25.5.93, rest. to fly)	2.93/96
145	•	HA-1112-M1L **C.4K-105**		T. G. "Hamish" Mahaddie, Tablada AB, Spain	7.66/68
			G-AWHH	T. G. Mahaddie/Spitfire Productions Ltd, Duxford (for film *Battle of Britain*)	14.5.68
			N6036	Wilson C. Edwards, Big Spring TX (stored . Big Spring TX)	10.68/95
166	•	HA-1112-M1L **C.4K-106**		T. G. "Hamish" Mahaddie, Tablada AB, Spain	7.66/68
			G-AWHI	T. G. Mahaddie/Spitfire Productions Ltd, Duxford (for film *Battle of Britain*)")	14.5.68/69
			N90607	Wilson C. Edwards, Big Spring TX (stored Big Spring TX)	20.2.69/96
170	•	HA-1112-M1L	C.4K-107	T. G. "Hamish" Mahaddie, Tablada AB, Spain	7.66/68
				(taxiing scenes at Tablada, for film *Battle of Britain*)	68)
				Victory Air Museum, Mundelein IL	.68/76
			N170BG	BG Aero Inc, King City CA	84/86
				Tangmere Flight: shipped	.86/88
			G-BOML	E. Nick Grace, St Merryn (shipped ex USA 11.86 partly rest., rest. completed St. Merryn 86/88, ff 6.5.88)	15.4.88
				Old Flying Machine Co, Duxford	11.88/95
				dam. landing Duxford (rebuild Duxford .9)	10.93
40/2	•	HA-1112-K1L **C.4K-112** (2 place)		T. G. "Hamish" Mahaddie, Tablada AB, Spain	7.66/68
			G-AWHC	T. G. Mahaddie/Spitfire Productions Ltd, Duxford (for film *Battle of Britain*))	14.5.68/69
			N1109G	Wilson C. Edwards, Big Spring TX (stored Big Spring TX)	20.2.69/96
183	•	HA-1112-M1L **C.4K-114**		T. G. "Hamish" Mahaddie, Tablada AB, Spain	7.66
				T. G. Mahaddie/Spitfire Productions Ltd, RAF Henlow: as spares source by (static views in film *Battle of Britain*)	5.67/68
				Canadian National Aeronautical Collection, Rockcliffe AB ONT	.68/82

				National Aviation Museum, Rockcliffe ONT	9.82/96
				(displ. as C4K-114/471-39)	
				(note: NAM quote id. 164)	
78	•	HA-1112-M1L **C.4K-121**		T. G. "Hamish" Mahaddie, Tablada AB, Spain	7.66/68
				(taxiing scenes at Tablada AB, for film *Battle of Britain*)	
				Victory Air Museum, Mundelein IL	.68/76
				Don Knapp, Fort Lauderdale FL	87/90
				William C. Anderson, New York NY	.90/92
				(rebuild to fly, Geneseo NY: DB.605 engine)	
86	•	HA-1112-M1L **C.4K-122**		T. G. "Hamish" Mahaddie, Tablada AB, Spain	7.66/68
			G-AWHL	T. G. Mahaddie /Spitfire Productions Ltd,	
				Duxford (for film *Battle of Britain*)")	14.5.68/69
				A. C. Shire/20th Century Fox Films	12.68/69
				(flew UK-Spain 1.69 as "P-51B 714112",	
				for film *Patton*)	
				(displ. West Germany: movie promotion 69/70)	
				Luftsportverein Hellertal, Siegerland WG	9.70
				(displ. Siegerland airfield, JG54 scheme 70/73)	
			N109J	Doug Champlin/Windward Aviation, Enid OK	.73/81
				(conv. to Bf109E standard with DB.601 engine	
				at Augsberg WG .73/76: shipped to US)	
				Champlin Fighter Museum, Mesa AZ	81/96
				(USCR quotes id. "392", Champlin "J-392")	
90	•	HA-1112-M1L **C.4K-126**		T. G. "Hamish" Mahaddie, Tablada AB, Spain	7.66/68
			G-AWHD	T. G. Mahaddie /Spitfire Productions Ltd,	
				Duxford (for film *Battle of Britain*))	14.5.68/69
			N90603	Wilson C. Edwards, Big Spring TX	20.2.69/96
				(stored Big Spring TX)	
99	•	HA-1112-M1L **C.4K-127**		T. G. "Hamish" Mahaddie, Tablada AB, Spain	7.66/68
			G-AWHO	T. G. Mahaddie /Spitfire Productions Ltd,	
				Duxford (for film *Battle of Britain*))	14.5.68/69
			N90601	Wilson C. Edwards, Big Spring TX	20.2.69/78
				Experimental Airplane Association WI	80/83
				(trucked ex TX, rest. Franklin WI 80/82)	
			N109BF	EAA Aviation Museum, Oshkosh WI	2.83/95
93	•	HA-1112-M1L **C.4K-130**		T. G. "Hamish" Mahaddie, Tablada AB, Spain	7.66/68
			G-AWHN	T. G. Mahaddie /Spitfire Productions Ltd,	
				Duxford (for film *Battle of Britain*))	14.5.68
			N90602	Wilson C. Edwards, Big Spring TX	20.2.69/88
				Erickson Air Crane, Medford OR	89/96
01	•	HA-1112-M1L **C.4K-131**		T. G. "Hamish" Mahaddie, Tablada AB, Spain	7.66/68
				(taxiing scenes at Tablada AB, for film *Battle of Britain*)	
				Victory Air Museum, Mundelein IL	.68/76
				Jimmy Hunt, Memphis TN	85
				Eric Vormezeele, Braaschaat: arr. dism.	3.10.85
			OO-MAF	Eric Vormezeele, Braaschaat	21.5.91/96
				(rest. Brassachatt, ff 8.8.94)	
				(prev. rep. as C.4K-201 c/n 182)	
94	•	HA-1112-M1L **C.4K-134**		T. G. "Hamish" Mahaddie, Tablada AB, Spain	7.66/68
				(taxiing scenes at Tablada AB, for film *Battle of Britain*)	
				Victory Air Museum, Mundelein IL	.68/76
				Wittmundhafen AB, West Germany: displ.	88
95	•	HA-1112-M1L **C.4K-135**		T. G. "Hamish" Mahaddie, Tablada AB, Spain	7.66/68
				(taxiing scenes at Tablada AB, for film *Battle of Britain*)	
				Victory Air Museum, Mundelein IL	.68/75
				MBB Aircraft, Manching West Germany	.75/91
				(rebuilt with DB.605 engine, as Bf109G-6;	

c/n		Model / Identity	Reg.	History	Date
				ff Manching 23.4.82 as "FM+BB")	
			D-FMBB	MBB Aircraft/Flugzeug-Union Sud GmbH	4.82/94
				crashed on takeoff, Neuberg AB, WG	3.6.83
				(rebuilt .86 Manching, using HA1112 fuselage	
				c/n 156 acquired in France)	
				dam. groundloop, Manching, WG	27.10.86
				(rebuilt, new Permit to Fly 13.5.87)	
				Fliegendes Museum, Augsburg: loan	92
				(rest., ff Ingolstadt AB Germany 18.11.93)	
208		HA-1112-M1L C.4K-144		T. G. "Hamish" Mahaddie, Tablada AB, Spain	7.66/68
			G-AWHP	T. G. Mahaddie /Spitfire Productions Ltd,	
				Duxford (for film *Battle of Britain*))	14.5.68/69
			N8575	Wilson C. Edwards, Big Spring TX	20.2.69
				Confederate Air Force, Harlingen TX	28.4.70/87
				crashed Harlingen TX	19.12.87
213	•	HA-1112-M1L **C.4K-...**		Tablada AB, Spain: inst. airframe	
				Hans Dittes, Speyer near Mannheim WG	.80/86
				(id. quoted as "40", rep. C.4K-40:	
				rest. Mannheim, ff .86 in Luftwaffe scheme)	
			D-FEHD	Hans Dittes, Speyer	29.8.86/95
				(rebuild at Saarlouis, Germany .91/95 using	
				fuse. & parts of WNr151951, DB.605 engine,	
				fuse of c/n 213 rep to France	
				ff 22.3.95 Mannheim as "Luftwaffe 2+-")	
			D-HDME	Hans Dittes, Speyer	.95/96
				op: Old Flying Machine Co, Duxford UK: del.	8.5.95
220	•	HA-1112-M1L **C.4K-152**		T. G. "Hamish" Mahaddie, Tablada AB, Spain	7.66/68
			G-AWHR	T. G. Mahaddie /Spitfire Productions Ltd,	
				Duxford (for film *Battle of Britain*))	14.5.68
			N4109G	Wilson C. Edwards, Big Spring TX	10.68/96
				(stored Big Spring TX)	
-	•	HA-1112-M1L **C.4K-156**		Musee de l'Air, Paris-Le Bourget	73/96
				(displ. as C4K-156/471-28)	
226	•	HA-1112-M1L **C.4K-158**		Museo del Aire, Cuatro Vientos AB, Madrid	.65/93
				(displ. as "471-23")	
-	•	HA-1112-M1L **C.4K-162**		Museo del Aire, Tablada AB, Spain	78/85
				Jean-Michel Goyat & Rene Meyer/	
				Association Aeronautique Provencale Victor Tatin,	
				Le Plessis-Belleville, France	7.85/96
				(long-term rest. with DB.605 engine)	
234	•	HA-1112-M1L **C.4K-169**		T. G. "Hamish" Mahaddie, Tablada AB, Spain	7.66/68
			G-AWHT	T. G. Mahaddie/Spitfire Productions Ltd,	
				Duxford (for film *Battle of Britain*))	14.5.68
			N9939	Confederate Air Force, Harlingen TX	10.68/88
				dam. groundloop landing, Harlingen TX	10.76
				Confederate Air Force, Dallas TX : rebuild	87
				Harold E. Kindsvater, Clovis CA	.88
			N109W	Harold E. Kindsvater, Clovis CA	1.90/96
				(rest. to fly, Clovis CA .90)	
228	•	HA-1112-M1L **C.4K-170**		T. G. "Hamish" Mahaddie, Tablada AB, Spain	7.66/68
			G-AWHS	T. G. Mahaddie /Spitfire Productions Ltd,	
				Duxford (for film *Battle of Britain*)	14.5.68
				20th Century Fox Films	1.69
				(del. UK to Spain 1.69 as "P-51B 743652"	
				for film *Patton*)	

				displ. West Germany for movie promotion	69/70
				Andre Weise/Technical University,	
				Aachen, West Germany: arr. dism.	7.10.71/83
				(rest. as Bf109G, with DB.605D engine)	
				Auto und Technik Museum, Sinsheim WG	87/96
				Technikmuseum Speyer, Germany: loan	93
				(displ. as "Luftwaffe 4")	
35 •	HA-1112-M1L	**C.4K-172**		T. G. "Hamish" Mahaddie, Tablada AB, Spain	7.66/68
				(taxiing scenes at Tablada AB, for movie	
				"Battle of Britain" .68)	
				Victory Air Museum, Mundelein IL	.68/76
			N48157	William E. Harrison, Tulsa OK (rest.)	77/78
				crashed, groundloop, Waco TX	10.77
				Robs Lamplough, Duxford: arr dism.	7.78
			G-BJZZ	Robert Lamplough, Duxford	30.3.82/83
				(rebuilt Duxford, ff. 3.4.82 as "Yellow 14")	
				dam. accident, Biggin Hill	15.5.82
				Paul Raymond/Whitehall Theatre of War	.83/85
				Robs Lamplough, Duxford: at auction	5.6.85
				Ray Mulqueen, Wanaka NZ (sale aborted)	.85
				Charles Church, Micheldever	.86
			G-HUNN	Charles Church (Spitfires) Ltd, Sandown	29.4.87/90
				(rebuilt Sandown, ff. 15.8.87 as red "14")	
				op: Dick Melton Aviation, Winchester	90/91
			N109GU	Sherman Aircraft Sales,	
				West Palm Beach FL: shipped ex UK	10.91/94
				Cavanaugh Flight Museum, Dallas TX	12.94/95
- •	HA-1112-M1L	**C.4K-....**	N700E	Harold Beale/On Mark Aviation, Knoxville TN	
			N109DW	Harold Beale, Knoxville TN	80/81
				(race #109; #5): crashed Reno NV	18.9.81
			N700E	Planes of Fame Museum, Chino CA	9.81/96
				(trucked Reno-Chino 9.81; rebuilt, ff 19.5.89)	
				(USCR quotes id. "577")	
-	HA-1112-M1L	**C.4K-....**		Bradley Air Museum, Windsor Locks CT	78/80
				New England Air Museum, Windsor Locks CT	82
- •	HA-1112-M1L	**C.4K-....**			
				Luftwaffenmuseum, Uetersen AB, Hamburg	72/93
				Luftwaffenmuseum, Marseille Kaserne AB	91
				(displ. in Luftwaffe sc.)	
99565•	Avia CS-199	**UC-26**		Vojenske Muzeum, Kbely AB, Prague	
				Czechoslovakia	73/94
99178•	Avia S-199	**UF-25**		Vojenske Muzeum, Kbely AB, Prague	
				Czechoslovakia (rest. project)	84/94
82358•	Avia CS-199			(to Czechoslovakia AF as .....)	
				(to IDFAF as ....)	.48
				Be'er Sheva AB, Israel : displ.	81
				Israeli AF Museum, Hazerim AB	87/96
				(static rest. .89, displ. as "112.T")	
- •	Bf-109E-3			recov. ex lake, Northern Russia	.93
				good condition, offered for sale in West	.93
- •	Bf-109E	**6•88**		(to Legion Condor as 6•88)	c37
				(to Spanish AF as C.4E-88)	c39
				Robert J. Lamplough, Duxford UK	1.83/85
				(recov. ex fire dump Leon AB, Spain .83)	
				loaned: Tangmere Aviation Museum UK	87/89

- •	Bf-109F-1	Ailes Anciennes Marseille-Escadrille Pegase, Vinon-sur-Verdon, France: composite	 93
- •	Bf-109G-2	recov. ex Mediterranean Sea Luftfahrtmuseum, Laatzen, Hannover: displ. (static rest. completed for museum opening 11.92)	 91/93
- •	Bf-109G-6	forced landing on frozen lake, later sank recov. ex Lake Swiblo, Russia trucked to Moscow-Tuschino airfield	2.44 4.90 .90
- •	Bf-109	recov. ex crash site Russia Ben Kolotilin/ Kolair Inc, Roswell GA (offered for sale as rest. project: Ed & Rose Zalesky, Surrey BC: arr. crated (id. quoted as Bf109G 109631-0604)	 94 11.95

MESSERSCHMITT BF110

Nr3115 •	Bf 110C	1(Z)JG77: recov. from crash site in Russia hulk stored in UK (id. unconfirmed)	 92
Nr3084 **Nr4502**	Bf 110C-1 Bf 110E-2	Started life as C W.Nr. 3084 - never completed. Completed as E-2 'CD+MV' Stab/ZG76 as"M8+ZE" collected for 6(Z)JG5, flies as 'M8+ZE' 06.02.42 Shot down in combat 40m W Murmanschi. 11.3.42 (recov. from crash site by helicopter 1.92) Jim Pearce/Sussex Spraying Service, Shoreham UK (arr. Hull Docks ex Russia 18.2.92) Alpine Fighter Collection, Wanaka NZ .93/95 (shipped to NZ, arr. 4.94, rest. to fly NZ)	 07.41 08.41 2.92/93
Nr3154	Bf110 D-0	'NO+DS' 3/ZG76 damaged in combat. force landed frozen Lake Upmasjaure.25.05.40 attempted salvage Aircraft salvaged. Location unknown	 c46. 95. 95.
Nr3235 •	Bf 110C-4	1(Z)JG77 "LN+ER" (recov. from crash site in Northern Russia) Jim Pearce, Shoreham UK: shipped, arr. Alpine Fighter Collection, Wanaka NZ 93/95 (hulk shipped to NZ, arr. 4.94, rest. to fly Wigram AB NZ 95)	 12.92/93
Nr5052 •	Bf 110F-2	13(Z)JG5 "LN+NR" fcd. landing frozen Lake Pyavozero, Russia (sank: recov. from lake, Murmanskaja, Northern Russia by helicopter .92) Jim Pearce Shoreham UK Alpine Fighter Collection, Wanaka NZ .93/95 (shipped to NZ, arr. 4.94, rest. to fly Christchurch NZ 95)	 12.1.43 .92/93
Nr730301 •	Bf 110G-4 /R-3	I./NJG3 "D5+RL": captured Grove, Denmark .45 (to RAF as AM 34) del. Farnborough ex Schleswig, Germany 3.8.45	 .45

c/n		Type	Reg.	History	Date	
				RAF Air Historical Branch		5.46/64
				RAF Wroughton: dism. for storage	8.46	
				(stored RAF Stanmore Park 49)		
				RAF Andover: displ.		
				(stored RAF Biggin Hill 62, RAF Henlow 69)		
				RAF Museum, RAF St.Athan	77/78	
				RAF Museum, Hendon	.78/95	
				(displ. as "730301/D5+RL")		
		(8479M)				
-	•	Bf 110F-2		Flyhistorisk Museum, Sola AB, Norway 93		
				(wreck: wings, tail & fuse. parts: "LN+DR")		
-	•	Bf 110G-2		shot down by P-38 over Austria 23.4.44		
				recov. from Neusiedlersee Lake, Austria c79		
				Amt der Burgenlandischen Landesregierung,		
				Eisenstadt, Austria : rest. project	79/84	
				Osterreichisches Luftfahrtmuseum,		
				Thalerhof, Austria: rest. for static displ.	87/93	

MESSERSCHMITT ME410

c/n		Type	Reg.	History	Date	
Ir420430	•	Me 410A-1		"3U+AK": captured Vaerlose, Denmark	4.44	/U2
				(to RAF as AM 72): del. to Farnborough	13.10.45	
				RAF Air Historical Branch	5.46/60	
				RAF Wroughton: packed for storage	8.46	
		(8483M)		(stored RAF Stanmore Park 49,		
				RAF Wroughton 57, RAF Fulbeck 60)		
				RAF Museum, RAF Cosford	.61/85	
				RAF Museum, RAF St Athan	11.85/89	
				RAF Museum, RAF Cosford	.89/96	
Ir10018	•	Me 410A-3		2(F)/122 "F6+WK": captured Trapini, Sicily	.43	
				shipped USA for trials as EB-103	.44	
				(to USAAF as FE-499/T2-499)	.45/46	
				Smithsonian Institute, stored Park Ridge IL	.46.	
				NASM, Silver Hill MD	65/94	

MITSUBISHI/NAKAJIMA A6M3 ZERO

c/n		Type	Reg.	History	Date
148	•	A6M3-32		John Sterling, Boise ID: rest. project	94
				(rep. salvaged ex Pacific island,	
				shipped to USA .91)	
318	•	A6M3		John Sterling, Boise ID: stored	94
				(rep. hulk salvaged ex Pacific island,	
				shipped to USA .91)	
412	•	A6M2		War Memorial Park, Kieta PNG	80/94
				displ. on pole "3412"	
618	•	A6M2		W. G. Chapman/Air Museum of PNG	.68/72
				(recov. from Buin, Bougainville .68)	
				Australian War Memorial, Canberra ACT	.72/90
				arr. RAAF Wagga NSW for rest.	10.82/92
844	•	A6M2-22		captured by RNZAF at Kara strip,	
				South Bougainville: "2-182"	9.45
				(to RNZAF as NZ6000)	
				(shipped to NZ 10.45: flown Hobsonville 12.45)	
				Hobsonville AB: displ.	46/53
				(stored Auckland-Ardmore 53/58)	
				Domain War Memorial Museum, Auckland NZ	.58/95
869	•	A6M2	N6582L	reg. res.	92

c/n		Type	Id	Regn	History	Date
4043	•	A6M5			Japanese surrender aircraft:	
					flew Rabaul-Jacquinto Bay strip: abandoned	18.9.45
					N. M. Armstrong, Auckland NZ	
					(salvage rights: Jacquinot Bay, New Britain)	
					RAAF Museum, RAAF Point Cook VIC	.77
					(recov. ex Jacquinot Bay .77)	
					RAAF Point Cook ; arr. for storage	6.77/82
					Australian War Memorial, Canberra ACT	.82/92
					(arr. RAAF Wagga 10.82, stored unrest. 88)	
4323	•	A6M5-52			captured Yokosuka, Japan	.45
					shipped to USA on carrier USS Barnes	11.45
					NASM, Silver Hill MD	65/93
					Bradley Air Mus., Windsor Locks CT: loan	79
					dam. at museum by tornado	3.10.79
					San Diego Aerospace Museum, CA: loan	3.81/94
					(rest. completed 4.84, displ. as "3-143")	
					(c/n also quoted as 23186)	
4340	•	A6M5-52			captured Aslito airfield, Saipan	18.6.44
					shipped to USA on carrier USS Copahee	7.44
					NAS Anacostia: trials as "TAIC7/Tokyo Rose"	
					(to USAAF as FE-130/T2-130)	.45/46
					Smithsonian Institute: stored Park Ridge IL	3.46/53
					NASM, Silver Hill MD: stored	.53/65
					NAS Willow Grove PA: displ. as "31"	58
					USMC Museum, MCAS Quantico VA: loan	66/71
					NASM, Washington DC: displ. as "61-131"	76/94
4400	•	A6M5-52	**82020**		captured Truk, shipped US: "HK-102"	.44
					sold for scrap, wings cut off	
					Ed Maloney/The Air Museum, Claremont CA	c50
					Ed Maloney/The Air Museum, Ontario CA	.65/70
					Ed Maloney/Planes of Fame Museum, Chino	75/93
					(shipped to Japan for displ. 2.80, ret. 5.80)	
					(static rest., displ. as "HK-102")	
4461	•	A6M5		**N62175**	Keat E. Griggers, Tucson AZ	76
5349	•	A6M2			Darwin Aviation Museum, Darwin NT	90/93
					("BII-124", hulk only, first enemy aircraft	
					shot down over Australia 2.42)	
5357	•	A6M5-52	**61-120**		captured Aslito airfield, Saipan	18.6.44
					shipped to USA on carrier USS Copahee	7.44
					(190 hrs flight trials by USN as TAIC5 at	
					NAS Anacostia & Patuxent River 44/45)	
					Ed Maloney/The Air Museum, Claremont CA	50/65
					(static rest., displ. as "V101")	
					The Air Museum, Ontario CA & Chino CA	.65/78
				N46770	Ed Maloney/Planes of Fame Museum, Chino	78/95
					(rest. Chino, original Sakae engine, ff. 28.6.78	
					as "61-120"; tour of Japan 7.78/79)	
					dam. landing Chino CA (repaired)	25.6.82
					(tour of Japan: shipped ex Chino 3.95)	
					(USCR quotes id. "82020": see below)	
					(id. also rep. as 5347)	
5358	•	A6M2-21			resident, Carman MAN	.68/85
					(recov. ex Ballale Island, Bougainville .68,	
					airfreighted to Canada by RCAF C130 1.69:	
					put together Carman MAN, using parts from several	
					wrecks recov.ex Pacific: fitted P&W R1830)	

		N58245	Confederate Air Force, Harlingen TX	
			later Midland TX	.80/95
			Museum of Flying, Santa Monica	96
			(ff Carman MAN 12.8.85, del. to Harlingen .85; flies as "EII-102", "EII-142")	
			(USCR quotes id. "807", CAF quotes 5365; also rep. as A6M5-52, id. 5356 or "842")	
5359 •	A6M5-52		resident Carman MAN	.68/82
			(recov. ex Ballale Island, Solomons .68, airfreighted to Canada by RCAF C130 1.69)	
			ff Carman MAN, rep dam. on landing	20.9.73
			USMC Museum, MCAS Quantico VA	82/91
			(displ. as "136")	
			Liberal Air Museum, Liberal KS: loan	89/91
			USNAM, NAS Pensacola FL	92/96
			(rest. Jacksonville FL 92, displ. as EII-140)	
			(id. also quoted as 5450, type A6M2-21)	
5784 •	A6M2		Admiral Nimitz State Historical Park Foundation, Fredericksburg TX	.73
			(recov. from Gasmata strip, New Britain .73, stored Port Moresby PNG .73/75: not del.)	
			Australian War Memorial, Canberra ACT	.74/95
			(stored RAAF Point Cook VIC .77)	
			(arr. RAAF Wagga NSW for static rebuild 10.82)	
			completed, displ. as "V-173"	.88/96
			stored AWM Mitchell Storage Facility ACT	
51593 •	A6M2-21		displ. unrest., Kavieng, New Britain "13"	65/68
			Papua New Guinea War Memorial Trust	
			Tom B. King, Melbourne VIC	68/70
			USAFM, Wright Patterson AFB, Dayton OH	.70/96
			(crated RAAF Pt.Cook VIC .71, shipped to US; stored dism., awaiting rest. 88)	
			(USAFM quotes id. as 11593)	
- •	A6M	**N72584**	reg. res.	87/92
			(USCR quotes id. 4306)	
- •	A6M2-21		US War Bond tour	c44
			sold for scrap	.45
			Atlanta Museum Antique Store, Atlanta GA	.45/91
			(open storage, derelict)	
- •	A6M2-21 2 place		Geoff Pentland & Barry Coran, Melbourne	.72
			(recov. from sea near Rabaul, New Britain 8.72)	
			rest. Essendon Airport VIC: arr. by sea	23.9.72/75
			National Science Museum, Tokyo, Japan	.75/96
			(displ. as "53-122")	
- •	A6M5-21		Malmaluan Coastwatchers Memorial Lookout, Rabaul, New Britain : displ. on pole	68/96
			(recov. ex Tobera strip, Rabaul)	
- •	A6M5-52		(recov. ex Babo airstrip, West Irian .76)	
			Indonesian AF Museum, Adisutjipto AB, Yogyakarta	.84/96
			(rest., displ. as "30-1153")	
- •	A6M5-52		Military Museum of the Chinese People's Revolution, Beijing	87/91
- •	A6M5		JMSDF Museum, Hamamatsu City Japan	78/91
			recov. ex Guam, rest. as "43-188"	

-	•	A6M5-52		Air and Space Museum, Nagoya Airport, Aichi, Japan: displ. as "Y2-128"	91
-	•	A6M7-63		Kyoto-Arashiyama Museum, Kyoto Japan (displ. as "210-118B")	91
-	•	A6M5-52		Gifu AB, Japan: displ.	91
-	•	A6M2-52		shot down, crashed in sea, New Britain	11.11.43
				American War Aces Assoc., San Diego CA (recov. from sea, Rabaul, New Britain .71 by Jim French & Eugene Valencia, Bakersfield CA; airfreighted to USA .71)	.71
				USAFM: loan San Diego Aerospace Museum (displ. unrest. as recov. 71/77)	73/77
-	•	A6M2-32		Bruce Fenstermaker CA (recov. ex Babo Island, Indonesia c90)	90
				Museum of Flying, Santa Monica CA (hulk arr. Santa Monica 6.91: rest. to fly)	.91/93
-	•	A6M2-21		John Sterling : shipped to USA (recov. ex Pacific Island)	2.91
				Caldwell Air Museum, Caldwell ID	91
-	•	A6M2-32		John Sterling : shipped to USA (recov. ex Pacific Island)	2.91
-	•	A6M2-32		John Sterling : shipped to USA (recov. ex Pacific Island)	2.91
-	•	A6M5-52		Paimon Paroni Automuseo, Hevonpaa, Finland: planned recov. ex Estonia	.92
-	•	A6M2-21		Blayd Corp, Carman MAN Major project based on wings & parts ex resident, Carman MAN: 3285, 3471, 3753, 5459, 7830)	1.90/96

MITSUBISHI BETTY

1502	•	G4M2		Beijing Aeronautical Institute, Beijing	
				Military Museum of the Chinese People's Revolution, Beijing	87/91
3041	•	G4M3		shipped ex Yokosuka to USA on USS Core (to USAAF as FE-2205/T2-2205)	12.45
				Smithsonian Institute: stored Park Ridge IL	9.46/50
				NASM, Silver Hill MD: incomplete, stored	87/96
-	•	G4M1		Bruce Fenstermaker CA (recov. ex Babo Island, Indonesia c90)	90
				Museum of Flying, Santa Monica CA (hulk arr. Santa Monica 6.91 for static rest.)	.91/93
-	•	G4M	-	Kawaguchiko Motor Museum, Yamanashi Prefecture, Japan	91

NAKAJIMA KI 43 HYABUSA 'OSCAR'

6	•	Ki-43-IIb	**62387**	(to USAAF as FE-6430/T2-6430)	
				Smithsonian Institute: stored Park Ridge IL	22.7.46/50
				Kirtland AFB NM: displ.	50/55

				NASM, Silver Hill MD	58/94
				EAA Museum, Hales Corner WI, later Oshkosh WI: loan, displ. as "13"	70/94
4950 •	Ki-43-II	**750**		found hidden near Vunakanau strip, Rabaul	9.45
				taken over by RAAF at Rabaual	25.9.45
				RAAF: held by 2AD RAAF Richmond NSW	49
				Australian War Memorial, Canberra ACT	3.8.49
				R. G. Curtis, Sydney NSW : sold for scrap	.53
				Sid Marshall, Sydney-Bankstown NSW (open storage, later displ. in hangar)	62/80
				Jack Davidson, The Oaks NSW	80/85
				Col Pay/Pays Air Service, Scone NSW	.85/94
				planned sale to Japan: not completed	11.92
			ZK-OSC	Alpine Fighter Collection, Wanaka NZ (dep. Scone 27.5.94 for shipping to NZ, rest. Wanaka, first engine runs 27.9.95)	.94/95
- •	Ki-43-II			Indonesian AF Museum, Adisutjipto AB, Yogyakarta: displ. as "H45" (recov. ex Babo airstrip, West Irian)	.87/93
5465 •	Ki-43			Australian War Memorial, Canberra ACT (complete airframe recov. ex Alexishhafen PNG .84: static rest. project)	.84/94
				The Fighter Collection, Duxford UK: arr. (stored Duxford pending rest. to fly)	4.94/95
-	Ki-43			Roy Worcester, Wewak PNG	72
-	Ki-43			Clark AFB Philippines: displ. on pole	50/60
				scrapped	.60

NANCHANG CJ-6

NANCHANG CJ-6/YAK -18

232003 •	CJ-6A	-		(to Chinese AF as 85)	
				Paramac Enterprises Pty Ltd, Perth WA (arr. by ship, Fremantle WA 11.95)	.95/96
232012 •	CJ-6A	-		(to Chinese AF as 68)	
				Paramac Enterprises Pty Ltd, Perth WA (arr. by ship, Fremantle WA 11.95)	.95/96
0232019•	CJ-6A	-		(to Chinese AF as ....)	
			N31103	Starfighter Aerospace Co, Mineral Wells TX	7.91/92
				Thomas R. Hatchell, Timmonsville SC	11.93/96
0532007•	CJ-6A	-		(to Chinese AF as .....)	
			N18YA	reg.	14.5.90
				Alan L. Buchner, Fresno-Chandler Field CA	12.90/96
532009 •	CJ-6A	-		(to Chinese AF as ....)	
				Paramac Enterprises Pty Ltd, Perth WA (arr. by ship, Fremantle WA 10.95)	.95
0532021•	CJ-6A	-		(to Chinese AF as .....)	
			N41845	Starfighter Aerospace Co, Mineral Wells TX	3.91/92
			C-FOTJ	Rolf A. Yri, Fort Langley BC	12.92
1032007•	CJ-6A	-		(to Chinese AF as .....)	
			N7039Y	reg.	11.88

				Ron Weaver/Silverwest Aviation,Buckeye AZ	.91
				op: Yak USA Ltd, Buckeye AZ	.91
				Daniel H. Feil, East Wenatchee WA	1.94/96
				(flies as "Chinese AF 76")	
1032011•	CJ-6A	-		(to Chinese AF as ....)	
			G-BVFW	Elmair Ltd, Southend	9.11.93
				C. Noon, B. Richardson & F. Cheung, Slinfold UK	95
1032012•	CJ-6A	-		(to Chinese AF as ....)	
			N45YK	Richard R. Hoss, Ramona CA	7.4.95
1032013•	CJ-6A	-		(to Chinese AF as ....)	
			N613R	Red Star Warbirds Inc, Oklahoma City OK	22.7.94/96
1032015•	CJ-6A	-		(to Chinese AF as ....)	
			N615R	Red Star Warbirds Inc, Oklahoma City OK	22.7.94/95
1032018•	CJ-6A	-		(to Chinese AF as ....)	
			N9278F	reg.	19.7.95
1032022•	CJ-6A	-		(to Chinese AF as ....)	
			N3104D	reg.	7.91
				Monty R. Yancey, Klamath Falls OR	92
				GSC Corp, Lake Oswego OR	4.95
1232003•	CJ-6A	-		(to Chinese AF as .....)	
			N285CJ	reg.	19.8.95
1232004•	CJ-6A	-		(to Chinese AF as .....)	
			N457AB	reg.	19.8.95
1232010•	CJ-6A	-		(to Chinese AF as .....)	
			N59WT	reg.	23.8.95
1232027•	CJ-6A	-		(to Chinese AF as 84)	
				Paramac Enterprises Pty Ltd, Perth WA	.95
				(arr. by ship, Fremantle WA 11.95)	
1232028•	CJ-6A	-		(to Chinese AF as .....)	
			N5182C	reg.	10.92
				struck-off USCR	3.93
			C-GYAC	Lorne E. Fleming, Pincher Creek ALTA	30.7.93
1232046•	CJ-6A	-		(to Chinese AF as 62)	
				Paramac Enterprises Pty Ltd, Perth WA	.95
				(arr. by ship, Fremantle WA 11.95)	
1332008•	CJ-6A	-		(to Chinese AF as .....)	
			N4184G	Starfighter Aerospace Co, Mineral Wells TX	3.91
				Mike A. Rhodes, Corbett OR	1.92/95
1332010•	CJ-6A	-		(to Chinese AF as .....)	
			N99YK	Variety Aircraft Inc, Los Animas CO	10.91/92
				Gene Forester, Dallas TX	6.92/95
1332012•	CJ-6A	-		(to Chinese AF as .....)	
			N51800	Starfighter Aerospace Co, Mineral Wells TX	10.92
			C-FXMI	John L. Northey, Port Moody BC	9.11.94
1332013•	CJ-6A	-		(to Chinese AF as ....)	
			N3110S	Starfighter Aerospace Co, Mineral Wells TX	7.91/92
			C-GYAK	Joseph C. Howse, Duncan BC	6.92/95

1332014•	CJ-6A	-		(to Chinese AF as ....)	
			N3110W	Starfighter Aerospace Co, Mineral Wells TX	7.91/95
1332015•	CJ-6A	-		(to Chinese AF as ....)	
				Paramac Enterprises Pty Ltd, Perth WA	.95
				(arr. by ship, Fremantle WA 10.95)	
1332042•	CJ-6A	-		(to Chinese AF as ....)	
				Paramac Enterprises Pty Ltd, Perth WA	.95
				(arr. by ship, Fremantle WA 10.95)	
1432020•	CJ-6A	-		(to Chinese AF as 78)	
				Paramac Enterprises Pty Ltd, Perth WA	.95
				(arr. by ship, Fremantle WA 11.95)	
1432023•	CJ-6A	-		(to Chinese AF as .....)	
			N357AB	reg.	19.8.95
1432030•	CJ-6A tailwheel	-		(to Chinese AF as .....)	
				Warren Sessler/China Technologies Inc, USA	
				Jim Gardner, Sacramento CA	.88
			N7013S	James A. Gardner, Sacramento CA	5.89
			N18YK	James A. Gardner, Windsor CA	7.89/95
1432049•	CJ-6A	-		(to Chinese AF as ....)	
			N3104U	reg.	7.91
				Frank M. Land, Klamath Falls OR	92
				Planes & Things Inc, Surfside Beach SC	1.94/95
1432050•	CJ-6A	-		(to Chinese AF as ....)	
			C-FTQU	Joe Howse/Joal Holdings Ltd, Duncan BC	8.12.94
1532006•	CJ-6A	-		(to Chinese AF as ....)	
			N3105M	reg. res.	7.91/92
1532008•	CJ-6A	-		(to Chinese AF as ....)	
			G-BVFX	Elmair Ltd, Southend	9.11.93
				C. Noon, B. Richardson & F. Cheung, Slinfold	95
1532010•	CJ-6A	-		(to Chinese AF as ....)	
			N10EB	Lloyd A. Epperly, Mesa AZ	10.5.95
1532013•	CJ-6A	-		(to Chinese AF as ....)	
			C-FTLE	Lannon Aviation Ltd, Oliver BC	11.10.94
1532014•	CJ-6A	-		(to Chinese AF as ....)	
			C-FTGZ	J. Sam, Delta BC	23.9.94
1582004•	CJ-6A	-		(to Chinese AF as 26)	
			ZK-OII	Nanchang Syndicate, Auckland-Ardmore	12.94/95
1732037•	CJ-6A	-		(to Chinese AF as ....)	
			C-FTQW	Joe Howse/Joal Holdings Ltd, Duncan BC	8.12.94/95
1832003•	CJ-6A	-		(to Chinese AF as 52)	
				Paramac Enterprises Pty Ltd, Perth WA	.95
				(arr. by ship, Fremantle WA 11.95)	
1832039•	CJ-6A	-		(to Chinese AF as 78)	
			N4183E	Starfighter Aerospace Co, Mineral Wells TX	3.91
				Ivan O. Rasmussen, Glendale AZ	92
				Danny R. Linkous/Warbirds Ltd, Hickory NC	11.3.93/95
				(flies as "Soviet AF 1778")	
1832040•	CJ-6A	-		(to Chinese AF as ....)	

			N3110Q	Starfighter Aerospace Co, Mineral Wells TX	7.91/92
				Lone Star Warbirds Inc, Oklahoma City K	10.93/95
1832041•	CJ-6A	-		(to Chinese AF as 88)	
				Paramac Enterprises Pty Ltd, Perth WA	.95
				(arr. by ship, Fremantle WA 11.95)	
1832043•	CJ-6A	-		(to Chinese AF as 63)	
			N4184W	Starfighter Aerospace Co, Mineral Wells TX	3.91
				Ivan O. Rasmussen, Glendale AZ	11.91/95
				(id. also quoted as 1332043)	
2032007•	CJ-6A	-		(to Chinese AF as .....)	
			N5180W	Starfighter Aerospace Co, Mineral Wells TX	10.92
				struck-off USCR	3.93
			C-GYKK	Peter Longcroft, Sidney/Saanichton BC	19.8.93/95
2032008•	CJ-6A	-		(to Chinese AF as .....)	
			N5183F	Starfighter Aerospace Co, Mineral Wells TX	10.92
				Thomas R. Hatchell, Timmonsville SC	11.93/95
2032011•	CJ-6A	-		(to Chinese AF as 82)	
			N4182C	Starfighter Aerospace Co, Mineral Wells TX	3.91
				Ivan O. Rasmussen, Glendale AZ	11.91/95
2032015•	CJ-6A	-		(to Chinese AF as ....)	
			N31101	W. R. Laws, Placerville CO	7.91/95
				op: Coleman Warbird Museum, Coleman TX	92/95
2032016•	CJ-6A	-		(to Chinese AF as 61)	
				Paramac Enterprises Pty Ltd, Perth WA	.95
				(arr. by ship, Fremantle WA 11.95)	
2032018•	CJ-6A	-		(to Chinese AF as .....)	
			N41836	Starfighter Aerospace Co, Mineral Wells TX	3.91
				W. R. Laws, Placerville CO	92
				Douglas R. Putney, Wolfboro NH	4.93/95
2032020•	CJ-6A	-		(to Chinese AF as ....)	
			N3110U	Starfighter Aerospace, Mineral Wells TX	7.91
				Richard A. Cunningham, Pekin IL	12.91/95
2132048•	CJ-6A	-		(to Chinese AF as 24)	
			VH-NNA	Brian Candler/Lampa Holdings, Canberra ACT	7.90/91
				(arr. dism. Bankstown NSW 7.90, ff 11.90)	
				Naloura Pty Ltd, Griffith NSW	22.10.90
				Emalec Pty Ltd, Canberra ACT	93/95
2232005•	CJ-6A	-		(to Chinese AF as ....)	
				Paramac Enterprises Pty Ltd, Perth WA	.95
				(arr. by ship, Fremantle WA 10.95)	
2232009•	CJ-6A	-		(to Chinese AF as ....)	
			N3210N	Milo S. Turner, Fort Myers FL	12.91/92
				struck-off USCR	13.12.93
			C-GWDC	Dan Christian, Stratford ONT	14.3.94
2232013•	CJ-6A	-		(to Chinese AF as 61668)	
			N4350D	Starfighter Aerospace Co, Mineral Wells TX	2.92
				(noted Deer Valley Airport AZ 6.91)	
				Ivan Rasmussen, Glendale AZ	6.92/95
2232028•	CJ-6A	-		(to Chinese AF as ....)	
				(noted Fishburn-Margans Field, Sunderland 6.94)	

			G-BVVF	Yak China Ltd, Bishop Auckland	10.10.94
2232036	CJ-6A	-		(to Chinese AF as ....)	
			N3210R	Marcus L. Bates, Odessa TX	12.91
				Barclay C. Imle, Spring TX	1.92
				crashed, dest., Richmond TX (Imle k.)	6.5.92
				(id. also quoted as 2332036)	
2432001•	CJ-6A	-		(to Chinese AF as ....)	
			N5148C	Elmo Franklin, Fort Lauderdale FL	11.92/95
2432002•	CJ-6A	-		(to Chinese AF as ....)	
			N5199Y	Daniel G. Williams, Quinby VA	16.9.92/95
2432013•	CJ-6A	-		(to Chinese AF as 01)	
				Paramac Enterprises Pty Ltd, Perth WA	.95
				(arr. by ship, Fremantle WA 11.95)	
2432051•	CJ-6A	-		(to Chinese AF as ....)	
			N31107	Starfighter Aerospace, Mineral Wells TX	7.91
				David A. Rieder, Glendale AZ	11.91/95
2432060•	CJ-6A	-		(to Chinese AF as ....)	
				China Air Corp	
			N556TR	Thomas E. Rowe, Glendale AZ	3.94
2432061•	CJ-6A	-		(to Chinese AF as ....)	
			N8181C	GSC Corp, Portland OR	20.6.95
2432062•	CJ-6A	-		(to Chinese AF as ....)	
			N8181E	GSC Corp, Portland OR	20.6.95
2432066•	CJ-6A	-		(to Chinese AF as ....)	
			C-FTLU	David H. Sproule, Edmonton ALTA	12.10.94
2432072•	CJ-6A	-		(to Chinese AF as ....)	
			N257BP	Brooks C. Petersen, Long Beach CA	3.95
2432073•	CJ-6A	-		(to Chinese AF as ....)	
			N333MP	Michael M. Plecenik, Las Vegas NV	19.5.95
2532044•	CJ-6A	-		(to Chinese AF as 71887)	
			N4184S	Starfighter Aerospace	3.91
				John Crothers, Prescott Valley AZ	12.91/96
2532045•	CJ-6A	-		(to Chinese AF as .....)	
			N41839	Starfighter Aerospace Co, Mineral Wells TX	3.91
				Frank M. Land, Klamath Falls OR	6.91/96
2532049•	CJ-6A	-		(to Chinese AF as ....)	
			N3112A	Starfighter Aerospace Co, Mineral Wells TX	7.91/96
2532051•	CJ-6A	-		(to Chinese AF as .....)	
			N42952	Robert B. Caldwell, Williams CA	9.91/92
				Camden Aircraft Co, Wilmington DE	4.95
2532059•	CJ-6A	-		(to Chinese AF as ....)	
				China Air Corp	
			N21710	Brett G. Trossell, Tempe AZ	25.3.94
				James E. Goolsby, Crescent City FL	11.94/96
2532060•	CJ-6A	-		(to Chinese AF as .....)	
			N4294X	Robert B. Caldwell, Williams CA	9.91/93
				Caldwell Flying Service, Williams CA	4.93/96

2532061•	CJ-6A	-		(to Chinese AF as .....)	
			N4295C	Robert B. Caldwell, Williams CA	9.91/93
				Caldwell Flying Service, Williams CA	4.93/96
2532064•	CJ-6A	-		(to Chinese AF as .....)	
			C-FTKL	John R. Amy, Abbotsford BC	3.10.94
2532078•	CJ-6A	-		(to Chinese AF as .....)	
				China Air Corp	
			N100YK	Douglas E. Sapp: reg. candidate	25.2.94
				Douglas E. Sapp, Omak WA	2.95
2632034•	CJ-6A	-		(to Chinese AF as ....)	
			N66YK	Variety Aircraft Inc, Los Animas CO	10.91/96
2632035•	CJ-6A	-		(to Chinese AF as ....)	
			N64YK	David J. Stadler, Wenatchee WA	25.8.93/96
2632060•	CJ-6A	-		(to Chinese AF as ....)	
			C-FYAC	Dumoret's 3-Bar-J Ranch, Oliver BC	12.7.95
2632079•	CJ-6A	-		(to Chinese AF as 82)	
				Paramac Enterprises Pty Ltd, Perth WA	.95
				(arr. by ship, Fremantle WA 11.95)	
2751214•	CJ-6A	-		(to Chinese AF as .....)	
			N92401	reg.	23.8.95
2751219•	CJ-6A	-		(to Chinese AF as ....)	
				(noted Fishburn-Margans Field, Sunderland 6.94)	
			G-BVVG	Yak China Ltd, Bishop Auckland UK	10.10.94
2751231•	CJ-6A	-		(to Chinese AF as ....)	
			N10YK	Mary Jo Ann Bates, Odessa TX	18.2.93/96
2751232•	CJ-6A	-		(to Chinese AF as 46)	
			N46YK	Clayton Harrell/Rensselaer Learning Systems,	
	"Super CJ-6B"			Rochester NY	11.1.93/96
				(mod. larger radial, flies as "Soviet AF 46")	
2751234•	CJ-6A	-		(to Chinese AF as ....)	
			N2086F	reg. res.	11.93
			N666RW	Randol B. Webb, Abilene TX	2.94/95
2751239•	CJ-6A	-		(to Chinese AF as ....)	
			N39YK	Sam E. Holloman, Odessa TX	28.4.93/95
2751248•	CJ-6A	-		(to Chinese AF as 76)	
				Brian Candler/Lampa Holdings, Canberra ACT	7.90/93
				(arr. dism. Bankstown NSW 7.90)	
			VH-NNC	Lampa Holdings, Canberra ACT	10.93/95
2851246•	CJ-6A	-		(to Chinese AF as ....)	
			C-FSPY	JN International Trade & Technique Ltd,	
				New Westminster BC	9.6.94
2851253•	CJ-6A	-		(to Chinese AF as .....)	
			N92863	reg.	23.8.95
2851262•	CJ-6A	-		(to Chinese AF as .....)	
			N92352	reg.	23.8.95
2851272•	CJ-6A	-		(to Chinese AF as ....)	
			C-FSQC	North Country Sports Ltd, Smithers BC	14.7.94

2951207•	CJ-6A	-		(to Chinese AF as ....)	
			N3210M	Marcus L. Bates, Odessa TX	12.91/92
				CCS Concrete Construction, Keego Harbour MI	9.92/95
2951208•	CJ-6A	-		(to Chinese AF as 46)	
				Brian Candler/Lampa Holdings, Canberra ACT	7.90/91
			VH-NNB	Lampa Holdings, Canberra ACT	12.4.91/95
				(arr. dism. Bankstown NSW 7.90, ff 4.91)	
3051201•	CJ-6A	-		(to Chinese AF as ....)	
			N53HM	Harold Middleton, Austin TX	11.92/95
3051202•	CJ-6A	-		(to Chinese AF as ....)	
			N56YK	Rensselaer Learning Systems, Rochester NY	13.1.93
				Jerry M. Broughton, Charlotte NC	1.93/95
3051216•	CJ-6A	-		(to Chinese AF as ....)	
				Paramac Enterprises Pty Ltd, Perth WA	.95
				(arr. by ship, Fremantle WA 10.95)	
			VH-CJX	Brian J. Black, Witchcliffe WA	13.10.95
3151202•	CJ-6A	-		(to Chinese AF as 52)	
				Paramac Enterprises Pty Ltd, Perth WA	.95
				(arr. by ship, Fremantle WA 11.95)	
3151207•	CJ-6A	-		(to Chinese AF as ....)	
			N3210G	Marcus L. Bates, Odessa TX	12.91/95
3532023•	CJ-6A	-		(to Chinese AF as ....)	
			N28YK	Mary Jo Ann Bates, Odessa TX	2.93/95
3632001•	CJ-6A	-		(to Chinese AF as 74)	
				Paramac Enterprises Pty Ltd, Perth WA	.95
				(arr. by ship, Fremantle WA 11.95)	
3632022•	CJ-6A	-		(to Chinese AF as ....)	
			N24AD	reg.	18.9.92
				John S. Thigpen, Alexandra LA	10.93/96

NORTH AMERICAN ROCKWELL OV-10 BRONCO

300-3	YOV-10A	**Bu152881**	**N718NA**	NASA, NAS Moffett Field CA	74
305-1 •	OV-10A	**Bu155390**	**N636NA**	NASA	6.84/88
				George J. Rivera	
				reg. candidate	12.93
305-7 •	OV-10A	**Bu155396**	N627NA	NASA	6.84
	YOV-10D		N637NA	NASA	86/88
				George J. Rivera	
				reg. candidate	12.93
305-11 •	OV-10A	**Bu155400**	**N429DF**	US Department of Agriculture: reg. candidate	12.93
305-12 •	OV-10A	**Bu155401**		US Department of Agriculture: reg. candidate	12.93
305-13 •	OV-10A	**Bu155402**	**N413DF**	US Department of Agriculture: reg. candidate	12.93
305-16 •	OV-10A	**Bu155405**	**N414DF**	US Department of Agriculture: reg. candidate	12.93
305-17 •	OV-10A	**Bu155406**	**N617NA**	NASA, Cleveland OH	12.94/95
305-20 •	OV-10A	**67-14612**	**N95LM**	US Department of Interior, Boise ID	8.7.92/95

305-21 •	OV-10A	Bu155410	N471AW	American Warbirds Inc, Gaithersburg MD	10.94/95
305-23 •	OV-10A	67-14615	N93LM	US Department of Interior, Boise ID	8.7.92/95
305-24 •	OV-10A	67-14616	N97LM	US Department of Interior, Boise ID (USCR quotes id. "305-66M.37")	8.7.92/95
305-28 •	OV-10A	Bu155417	N472AW	American Warbirds Inc, Gaithersburg MD	10.94/95
305-38 •	OV-10A	Bu155427	N415DF	US Department of Agriculture: reg. candidate	12.93
305-39 •	OV-10A	Bu155428	N418DF	US Department of Agriculture: reg. candidate	12.93
305-44 •	OV-10A	-	N70161	reg. candidate	6.93
305-47 •	OV-10A	67-14639	N615NA	NASA, Cleveland OH	18.4.94/95
305-56 •	OV-10A	Bu155445	N419DF	US Department of Agriculture: reg. candidate	12.93
305-65 •	OV-10A	Bu155454	N400DF	State of California, Sacramento CA	3.93/95
305-68 •	OV-10A	Bu155457	N401DF	State of California, Sacramento CA	3.93/95
305-70 •	OV-10A	Bu155459	N402DF	State of California, Sacramento CA	3.93/95
305-72 •	OV-10A	67-14664	N685	US Department of Interior, Boise ID (id. assumed: USCR quotes "305-72M.40")	5.93/95
305-76 •	OV-10A	Bu155465	N80AD	Washington State DoT A.Div, Seattle WA	11.93/95
305-78 •	OV-10A	Bu155467	N403DF	State of California, Sacramento CA	3.93/95
305-82 •	OV-10A	Bu155471	N410DF	US Department of Agriculture/ State of California, Sacramento CA	 10.93/95
305-86 •	OV-10A	Bu155475	N407DF	State of California, Sacramento CA	3.93/95
305-91 •	OV-10A	Bu155480	N408DF	State of California, Sacramento CA	3.93/95
305-95 •	OV-10A	67-14687	N524NA	NASA, Langley Research Center, Hampton VA	8.93/95
305-97 •	OV-10A OV-10D	Bu155486	N473AW	American Warbirds Inc, Gaithersburg MD	10.94/95
305-99 •	OV-10A	Bu155488	N474AW	American Warbirds Inc, Gaithersburg MD	10.94/95
305-107•	OV-10A	Bu155496	N421DF	US Department of Agriculture/ State of California, Sacramento CA	 12.93
305-109•	OV-10A	Bu155498	N475AW	American Warbirds Inc, Gaithersburg MD	10.94/95
305-112•	OV-10A	Bu155501	N476AW	American Warbirds Inc, Gaithersburg MD	10.94/95
305-113•	OV-10A	Bu155502	N477AW	American Warbirds Inc, Gaithersburg MD	10.94/95
321-137•	OV-10A	68-03811	N91LM	US Department of Interior, Boise ID	8.7.92/95
321-142•	OV-10A	68-03816	N94LM	US Department of Interior, Boise ID	8.7.92/95
321-151•	YOV-10A	68-03825	N646	US Department of Interior, Boise ID	90/92 .8.7.92/95
338-9 •	OV-10B	Bu158300	D-9553	Rhein Flugzeughbau GmbH, Lubeck (to Luftwaffe as 99+24)	76 6.84
			F-....	Amicale les Avions Anciens, Montelimar	.91

For the recentU.K. T.V. programme *Over Here* made in 1995, Spitfire PR.XI Pl965 donned temporary fighter camoflage and joined veteran film star LF.IXe MH434. 'WO' now joins 'AI' 'CD' and 'NE' as famous film codes. **Richard Paver.**

Historic Flying rebuilt Spitfire Mk.IX TE566 which made the long journey back to its former domicile Czechoslovakia in 1994 delighting airshow goers who had not previously had the opportunity to see such a machine in the air since the immediate post-war period. It now wears the the R.A.F. roundels over the 'tripartite' Czech insignia previously worn, as well as D-Day stripes. **Richard Paver.**

After many years of trying to gain access to data plates, Spitfire historian Peter Arnold has tracked down the history of of the Burmese Spitfires. Spitfire Mk.IX UB421 (serialled in the TE5XX range) is an ex-Czech and Israeli airframe; one of four Spitfires and three Seafires now gathered together from around Burma and collected in one hangar at Miwlaladon in Jan '95. **Peter Arnold.**

NORTH AMERICAN AVIATION AT6 TEXAN/SNJ

CANADIAN CAR FOUNDRY HARVARD

14-130 •	AT-16	**42-593**		(to RCAF as FE396): BOC 5.8.42: SOC	26.6.47
	Mk. IIb		CF-FJE		
			LV-RTN		
			N50JD	James W. (Bill) Dorris, Leeward Air Ranch FL	9.91/93
14-186	AT-16	42-649		(to RCAF as FE452): BOC 12.9.42: SOC	12.11.46
	Mk. IIb			(to IDFAF as .....)	
			4X-ARA	Avitor Ltd, Tel Aviv	.63/72
14-190	AT-16	42-653		(to RCAF as FE456): BOC 12.9.42: SOC	12.11.46
	Mk. IIb		PH-UEI	Rijksluchtvaartdienst/Government Flying School	
				Gilze-Rijen AB, later Eelde	13.6.50/60
				sold to Belgium, struck-off reg.	23.9.60
			OO-JBW	COGEA Nouvelle, Ostend	8.65/66
				J. Thiel, Wevelgem	15.2.66/69
				C. Honcoop, Veen, Netherlands	7.70
				struck-off reg.	8.70
				displ. bicycle shop, Boxmeer, Netherlands	.71/80
14-201 •	AT-16	**42-664**		(to RCAF as FE467): BOC 17.9.42: SOC	23.12.46
	Mk. IIb			(to Swiss AF as U-332)	
				Museum de Schweizerischen Fliergertruppe,	
				Dubendorf AB, Switzerland	79/90
14-205	AT-16	42-668		(to RAF as FE471): shipped to India	2.43
	Mk. IIb			dam. overshoot, Amabala, India	13.5.46
			VT-CQN	F. J. Mobsby	12.47
				Baroda Rayon Corp, Juhu	
				crashed near Boisar, India	3.9.77
14-233 •	AT-16	**42-696**		(to RAF as FE499): del. to Canada	10.42
	Mk. IIb			(to RCAF as FE499): BOC 13.10.42: SOC	23.12.46
				Charles Babb Co, Montreal QUE	.47
				(to Chinese AF as .....)	
				Beijing Aeronautical Institute, Beijing, China	90
14-245 •	AT-16	**42-708**		(to RCAF as FE511): BOC 13.10.42: SOC	11.12.46
	Mk. IIb			Charles Babb Co, Montreal QUE	.47
	Sk.16A			(to R Swedish AF/Flygvapnet as Fv16128)	.47
				inst. airframe, Stockholm-Bromma Airport	
				Luftfartmuseet, Stockholm-Arlanda Airport	75/87
				Par Erixon, Angerod, Sweden: rest. to fly	.87/96
14-299 •	AT-16	**42-762**		(to RCAF as FE565): BOC 3.11.42: SOC	7.12.46
	Mk. IIb			Charles Babb Co, Montreal QUE	.47
	Sk.16A			(to R Swedish AF/Flygvapnet as Fv16030)	.47
				High Chaparral Wild West Village,	
				Hillerstorp, Sweden: derelict	85/96
14-324 •	AT-16	**42-787**		(to RCAF as FE590): BOC 3.11.42: SOC	9.9.46
	Mk. IIb			Charles Babb Co, Montreal QUE	.47
				(to Swiss AF as U-322)	
			G-AXCR	Mrs. L.A. Osborne, Blackbushe	27.3.69
				(del. Switzerland to Gatwick 13.4.69)	
			D-FHGK	Flugzeug-Handels GmbH, Karlsruhe	9.69/71
				G. Roth, Neckarelz, later Monchengladbach	.71/87
				Walter Eichhorn, Breitscheid/Bad Camberg	91/96
14-355 •	AT-16	**42-818**		(to RCAF as FE621): BOC 14.11.42: SOC	11.2.46
	Mk. IIb			Sola AB, Stavanger:"RCAF BE-M" incomplete	89
14-366 •	AT-16	**42-829**		(to RCAF as FE632): BOC 14.11.42: SOC	11.12.46
	Mk. IIb			Charles Babb Co, Montreal QUE	.47

	Sk.16A			(to R Swedish AF/Flygvapnet as Fv16109)	12.46
				Flygvapenmuseum, Malmslatt AB, Sweden	79/92
14-372 •	AT-16	**42-835**		(to RCAF as FE638): BOC 21.11.42: SOC	15.11.46
	Mk. IIb			Charles Babb Co, Montreal QUE	.47
	Sk.16A			(to R Swedish AF/Flygvapnet as Fv16074)	
				High Chaparral Wild West Village,	
				Hillerstorp, Sweden: derelict	92
14-426 •	AT-16	**42-889**		(to RCAF as FE692): BOC 15.12.42: SOC	26.6.47
	Mk.IIb			Charles Babb Co, Montreal QUE	.47
	Sk.16A			(to R Swedish AF/Flygvapnet as Fv16126)	6.47
				Dansk Veteranflysamlung, Stauning, Denmark	85/87
14-429 •	AT-16	**42-892**		(to RCAF as FE695): BOC 15.12.42: SOC	26.6.47
	Mk. IIb			Charles Babb Co, Montreal QUE	.47
	Sk.16A			(to R Swedish AF/Flygvapnet as Fv16105)	.47
				Hasslo Flygteknikcentrum: inst. airframe "8"	70/89
				The Fighter Collection, Duxford: arr. dism.	7.89
			G-BTXI	Patina Ltd/ op The Fighter Collection, Duxford	10.91/96
				(rest. to fly, Duxford 92/96)	
14-460	AT-16	42-923		(to RCAF as FE726): BOC 7.1.43: SOC	26.6.47
	Mk. IIb			Charles Babb Co, Montreal QUE	.47
	Sk.16A			(to R Swedish AF/Flygvapnet as Fv16092)	.47
			SE-FUY	S. H. Hansson, Hoganas	6.72/76
				crashed during air display, Arboga Sweden	25.5.76
14-486 •	AT-16	**42-949**		(to RCAF as FE752): BOC 22.1.43: SOC	15.11.46
	Mk.IIb			Charles Babb Co, Montreal QUE	.47
	Sk.16A			(to R Swedish AF/Flygvapnet as Fv16068)	.47
				Flygvapenmuseum, Malmslatt AB, Sweden	92/96
14-526 •	AT-16	**42-12279**		(to RCAF as FE792): BOC 2.2.43: SOC	11.12.46
	Mk. IIb			Charles Babb Co, Montreal QUE	.47
	Sk.16A			(to R Swedish AF/Flygvapnet as Fv16144)	.47
			SE-FUZ	Sterner Aero AB, Borliange	2.73/78
				B. O. Lowgren, Bromma	.78/80
				Olaf Lindelov	93/96
14-543 •	AT-16	**42-12296**		(to RCAF as FE809): BOC 7.2.43: SOC	12.11.46
	Mk. IIb			Charles Babb Co, Montreal QUE	.47
				(to R Netherlands AF as B-181)	.47/72
				Deelen AB: instructional airframe	72
				Anthony Fokker School, Hague: rest. to fly	.77/85
				Stichting Vliegsport, Gilze-Rijen AB	91/96
				(stored dism. Gilze-Rijen 91: rest. to fly)	
14-545 •	AT-16	**42-12298**		(to RCAF as FE811): BOC 7.2.43: SOC	2.10.46
	Mk. IIb			Charles Babb Co, Montreal QUE	.46
				(to Swiss AF as U-328)	
				Museum de Schweizerischen Fliergertruppe,	
				Dubendorf AB, Switzerland	79/85
14-555 •	AT-16	**42-12308**		(to RCAF as FE821): BOC 8.2.43: SOC	2.10.46
	Mk. IIb			(to R Netherlands AF as B-164)	.46/66
				(to R Netherlands Navy/MLD as 099): del.	30.3.66/68
				wfu, retired by MLD: stripped for parts	7.11.68
				Auto und Technik Museum, Sinsheim, Germany	92/96
				(displ. as RAF "FT454")	
14-565 •	AT-16	**42-12318**		(to RCAF as FE831): BOC 9.2.43: SOC	15.11.46
	Mk. IIb			Charles Babb Co, Montreal QUE	.46
	Sk.16A			(to R Swedish AF/Flygvapnet as Fv16010)	
				Luftfartmuseet, Stockholm-Arlanda, Sweden	79/85
14-639 •	AT-16	**42-12392**		(to RCAF as FE905): BOC 23.3.43: SOC	27.11.46
	Mk. IIb			(to R Danish AF as 31-329, later 329)	9.49/60
			LN-BNM	Snorr S. Kjetilson/Fjellfly, Skien	5.1.61/73
				CofA exp. 31.12.68: struck-off reg.	29.1.73

				British Historic Aircraft Museum, Southend	.72/83
				(shipped to Felixstowe Docks 5.72,	
				displ. Southend as "USAF 93584/LTA-584",	
				later "12392/LTA-392")	
				Paul Raymond/Whitehall Theatre of War	10.5.83/85
				RAF Museum Store, RAF Cardington: arr.dism	3.85/94
				(static rest. RAF Cardington for RAFM 88/91)	
				Newark Air Museum: loan	92/94
14-641 •	AT-16 Mk. IIb	**42-12394**		(to RAF as FE907): based Canada: BOC	23.3.43/46
				(shipped to UK, via USAAF Fort Dix 22.3.44)	
				(to R Netherlands AF as B-64)	8.46
				(to R Netherlands Navy/MLD as L-6)	27.8.46/48
				(to R Netherlands AF as B-64)	14.9.48/72
				(stored Woensdrecht AB 70/72, awaiting tfr.	
				to Deelan AB to become instructional airframe)	
			PH-FAR	ntu: Gilze-Rijen Aero Club, Gilze-Rijen AB	8.76
				(flew for film *A Bridge Too Far* .76 as	
				Fw190 "5+", P-47 "43-12394",	
				& Typhoon; further film flying 9.76	
				as replica Fokker D-XXI "219")	
				Militaire Luchtvaart Museum, Soesterberg AB	79/92
				(displ. as replica Fokker D.XXI "219")	
			PH-LSK	MLM/op: Stichting Vliegsport, Gilze-Rijen AB	30.3.88/92
14-664 •	AT-16 Mk. IIb	**42-12417**		(to RCAF as FE930): BOC 26.3.43: SOC	12.11.46
				Charles Babb Co, Montreal QUE	.46
				(to R Netherlands AF as B-163)	11.6.49/62
				SOC: beyond economic repair 15.11.62; sold	9.66
				displ. car yard Takken in Haarlem	11.66/67
				C. Honcoop, Veen, Netherlands	
				(stored at dairy farm near Weesp, Netherlands)	
				derelict hulk in scrapyard, Amsterdam	80
				Harry van de Meer, Amsterdam	.80/86
				(hulk stored Nyverdal .80/83 with B-168,	
				stored Aviodome Amsterdam-Schiphol 11.83/86)	
				Anthony E. Hutton, North Weald UK	.86/87
				(trucked dism. to North Weald .86: spares use)	
				Gordon King, Windsor, Berks	87
				Thameside Aviation Museum UK	.92
				(rep. id. confused with 14A-1184/B-59: que se)	
14-718 •	AT-16 Mk. IIb	**42-12471**		(to RCAF as FE984): BOC 26.4.43: SOC	2.10.46
				Charles Babb Co, Montreal QUE	.46
				(to R Netherlands AF as B-168)	.46/70
				C. Honcoop, Veen, Netherlands	
				(stored at dairy farm near Weesp, Netherlands)	
				derelict hulk in scrapyard, Amsterdam	80
				Harry van de Meer, Amsterdam	.80/86
				(hulk stored Nyverdal .80/83 with B-163)	
				Anthony E. Hutton, North Weald UK	.86/87
				(trucked dism. to North Weald .86: spares use;	
				fuse. stored Duxford 95)	
14-719 •	AT-16 Mk. IIb	42-12472		(to RCAF as FE985): BOC 26.4.43: SOC	2.10.46
				Charles Babb Co, Montreal QUE	.46
				(to R Netherlands AF as B-176)	.46
			PH-NID	Schreiner Aero Contractors, Texel	30.7.57/60
				(Dutch Navy target towing contract)	
				(ret. to RNAF as B-176): struck-off reg.	22.1.60
				Militaire Luchtvaart Museum, Soesterberg AB	77/85
				Pioneer Hangaar Collection, Lelystad	92
				(PH-NID officially quoted as 14-765/B-175,	
				also rep. as 14A-807/B-179)	
14-720 •	AT-16 Mk. IIb	42-12473		(to RCAF as FE986): BOC 26.4.43: SOC	2.10.46
				Charles Babb Co, Montreal QUE	.46
				(to R Netherlands AF as B-174)	.46/70

c/n	Type	Serial	Reg.	History	Date
				Fargo Air Service, Nashua NH	70
				(unconv., RNAF sc., Nashua NH 10.70)	
			N8994	Marylin Francis, Dawson GA	76
				Smithville Dusting Service, Smithville GA	77/86
				John R. Smith, Greensboro GA	7.86/95
				(flies as "USN 66-2814/JS")	
				(USCR quotes id. 66-2814 which was NZ948: above believed correct)	
14-725 •	AT-16 Mk.IIb Sk.16A	**42-12478**		(to RCAF as FE991): BOC 26.4.43: SOC	15.11.46
				Charles Babb Co, Montreal QUE.	46
				(to R Swedish AF/Flygvapnet as Fv16028)	
				Svedino's Bil Och Flygmuseum, Sloinge, Sweden: displ. as "16028/92"	75/92
14-726 •	AT-16 Mk. IIb Sk.16A	**42-12479**		(to RCAF as FE992): BOC 26.4.43: SOC	15.11.46
				(to R Swedish AF/Flygvapnet as Fv16047)	2.47/72
				(op. U.N. Observer Group in Lebanon: arr. Lebanon 1.7.58; ret. Sweden 14.10.58)	
				Jan Murer, Oslo, Norway: ex R Swedish AF	30.3.72
			LN-MAA	Jan Murer, Oslo	12.9.72/75
			G-BDAM	D. G. Jones, Cardiff: del. to Booker	23.3.75/78
				Roger H. Reeves, Manchester	7.78/81
				M. Victor Gauntlett/Pace Petroleum, London	7.81/85
				Victor Gauntlett, Norman A. Lees & Euan C. English, North Weald	15.4.85/96
14-733 •	AT-16 Mk. IIb	**42-12486**		(to RCAF as FE999): BOC 26.4.43: SOC	2.10.46
				Charles Babb Co, Montreal QUE	.46
				(to R Netherlands AF as B-177)	
				Militaire Luchtvaart Museum, Gilze-Rijen AB	77/85
				MLM, Woensdrecht AB: gate guard	92
14-739 •	AT-16 Mk. IIb	**42-12492**		(to RCAF as FH105): BOC 30.4.43: SOC	2.10.46
				Charles Babb Co, Montreal QUE	.46
				(to R Netherlands AF as B-178)	
				displ. on pole Maasbracht, Netherlands	72/89
14-748 •	AT-16 Mk. IIb	**42-12501**		(to RAF as FH114): shipped to UK	.43/46
				(to R Danish AF as 31-306)	12.46
				J. Utzon, Hellebeek	31.5.61/69
				Dansk Veteranflysamling, Stauning, Denmark	79/92
14-764 •	AT-16 Mk. IIb	**42-12517**		(to RCAF as FH130): BOC 30.4.43: SOC	2.10.46
				Charles Babb Co, Montreal QUE	.46
				(to R Netherlands AF as B-165)	
				(stored Woensdrecht AB 70/72, awaiting tfr. to Deelan AB to become instructional airframe)	
				Anthony Fokker School, Den Haag: "PH-AFS"	72/92
14-765 •	AT-16 Mk. IIb	**42-12518**		(to RCAF as FH131): BOC 30.4.43: SOC	2.10.46
				Charles Babb Co, Montreal QUE	.46
				(to R Netherlands AF as B-175)	
				Militaire Luchtvaart Museum, Soesterberg (stripped fuselage displ.)	77/93
14-770 •	AT-16 Mk. IIb	**42-12523**		(to RCAF as FH136): BOC 30.4.43: SOC	2.10.46
				Charles Babb Co, Montreal QUE	.46
				(to R Netherlands AF as B-193)	
				Westerschouwen, Schelse Estuary, Holland	92/96
14-772 •	AT-16 Mk.IIb Sk.16A	**42-12525**		(to RCAF as FH138): BOC 30.4.43: SOC	15.11.46
				(to R Swedish AF/Flygvapnet as Fv16033)	
				Svedino's Bil Och Flygmuseum, Ugglarp, Sweden: displ. as "16033/72"	75/96
14-787 •	AT-16 Mk. IIb	**42-12540**		(to RCAF as FH153): BOC 30.4.43: SOC	9.9.46
				Charles Babb Co, Montreal QUE	.46
				(to R Netherlands AF as B-158)	.46
			PH-HTC	ntu: C. Honcoop/Honcoop Trading Co, Veen	.71

			PH-PPS	J. Daams, Loosdrecht	12.72/73
			G-BBHK	T. D.L. Rose, Shoreham	7.9.73/74
				Robs Lamplough, Duxford	19.6.74/79
				Robert F. Warner, Exeter/Cardiff	21.1.80/96
14A-808 •	AT-16 Mk. IIb	**43-12509**		(to RCAF as FS668): BOC 3.6.43: SOC	4.12.46
				Charles Babb Co, Montreal QUe	.46
				(to R Netherlands AF as B-182)	
				Deelen AB: inst. airframe	72
				Militair Luchtvaart Museum, Soesterberg AB	77/94
				Aviodome Museum, Amsterdam-Schiphol: loan	.75/87
				(represented P-47 for film, displ. at Aviodome as P-47 repl. "WM-X" 77)	
			PH-TBR (2	J. A. Thuring/Militaire Luchtvaart Museum	2.3.94
14A-868 •	AT-16 Mk. IIb	**43-12569**		(to RAF as FS728): shipped to UK: BOC	9.43/47
				(to R Netherlands AF as B-104)	11.47
			PH-SKL	J. Daams, Loosdrecht	10.2.70/72
			G-BAFM	Hon. Patrick Lindsay, Booker	10.72/78
				(del. via Gatwick as PH-SKL 21.8.72)	
				John Parkes, Hamble/Sandown IOW	9.8.83/86
				Richard Parker/Parker Airways Ltd, Denham	10.86/92
				Neil Moffatt/Moffatt Aviation, West Sussex	6.92/96
				(prev. incorrectly quoted as B-105/FT210)	
14A-927 •	AT-16 Mk. IIb	**43-12626**		(to RAF as FS787): shipped to India: BOC	10.43/47
				(to Indian AF as HT291)	9.47
				Indian Air Force Museum, Palam AB	68/90
14A-966 •	AT-16 Mk. IIb	**43-12667**		(to RAF as FS826): shipped to UK: BOC	9.43/47
				(to R Danish AF as 31-309)	9.47
				Flyvevabnets Museum, Vaerlose AB, Denmark	79/92
				Danmarks Flyvemuseum, Billund: loan	10.86/92
14A-1020	AT-16 Mk. IIb	43-12721		(to RAF as FS880): shipped to UK: BOC	9.43/46
				(to R Netherlands AF as B-135)	10.46
			PH-BKT	Messrs Broek, Kevenaar & J. Thuring, Breda	14.6.71/80
				op: Gilze-Rijen Aero Club, Gilze-Rijen AB	76/78
				(flew for film *A Bridge Too Far* .76 as Fw190 "5+-", P-47 "43-12885/MX-W", & Typhoon "HF-J"; further movie work 9.76 as Fokker D-XXI "234")	
				Mrs. H. Toren, Hilversum	4.9.80/86
				crashed, dest., Keiheuval airfield, Belgium	4.2.90
14A-1055•	AT-16 Mk. IIb	**43-12756**		(to RAF as FS915): shipped to UK: BOC	9.43/46
				(to R Netherlands AF as B-41)	10.46/68
				Fargo Air Service, Nashua NH	70
				(noted unconv., RNAF sc., Nashua 10.70)	
			N8993	John P. Silberman, Savannah GA	72
				Ryman Ennis Kay, Jackson MS	76
				John M. Yates, Scottsdale AZ	84/88
				Thomas R. Martin, Wasilla AK	3.88/96
				(USCR quotes id. 66-2709, ie. RCAF2976: SOC 19.5.41 due major accident 26.4.41: above believed correct)	
14A-1057•	AT-16 Mk. IIb	**43-12758**		(to RAF as FS917): shipped to UK: BOC	9.43
				to Norwegian Training Base	6.45
				(to R Danish AF as 31-310)	5.47
			LN-BNN	Snorr S. Kjetilson/Fjellfly, Skien	5.1.61/71
				CofA lapsed 31.12.68, struck-off reg.	14.6.71
				(stored: to playground Sweden 71)	
				High Chaparral Wild West Village, Hillerstorp, Sweden: displ.	85/92
14A-1100•	AT-16 Mk. IIb	**43-12801**		(to RCAF as FS960): BOC 1.9.43: SOC	2.10.46
				Charles Babb Co, Montreal QUE	.46

C/n	Type	Serial	Reg	History	Date
				Fokker Aircraft Co, Amsterdam	.46
				(to R Netherlands AF as B-184)	.47
				Militaire Luchtvaart Museum, Soesterberg	68/93
			PH-TBR (1	ntu: Stichting Vliegsport Gilze-Rijen AB	.90
				(rest. to fly Gilze-Rijen AB 91)	
				Dutch Spitfire Flight, Deelen AB: loan	92
				ntu: J. Thuring/Militaire Luchtvaart Museum	9.6.93
14A-1106•	AT-16 Mk. IIb Sk.16A	**43-12807**		(to RCAF as FS966): BOC 4.9.43: SOC	7.12.46
				Charles Babb Co, Montreal QUE	.46
				(to R Swedish AF/Flygvapnet as Fv16077)	.46
				Flygvapenmuseum, Malmslatt AB: stored	
			VH-NZI	res: Pearce Dunn/Warbirds Air Museum, Mildura VIC: rest. project	.81/93
				(shipped on *MV Tombarra*, arr. Adelaide 9.8.81, container trucked to Mildura 11.8.81)	
				Robert H. Poynton/Panama Jack's Aircraft Service, Perth-Jandakot WA: rest. project	.93
			VH-JHP	John H. Poynton, Perth WA	5.11.93/96
				(rest. Jandakot WA, ff .95 "RSwAF 77/16")	
				John G. Reyner, Melbourne VIC: del.	9.12.95
14A-1184•	AT-16 Mk. IIb	**43-12885**		(to RAF as FT144): shipped to UK: BOC	11.43/46
				(to R Netherlands AF as B-59)	8.46
				(to R Netherlands Navy/MLD as L-5)	27.8.46/49
				(to R Netherlands AF as B-59)	14.4.49/74
				Deelan AB: inst. airframe	72
			PH-KLU	J. A. Thurling, Breda	23.8.74/78
				op: Gilze-Rijen Aero Club, Gilze-Rijen AB	76/78
				(flew for film "*A Bridge Too Far*" .76 as Fw190 "7+-", P-47 "43-12885/MX-W" & Typhoon "HF-S"; further film work 9.76 as Fokker D-XXI "234")	
				A. C. Groeneveld, Lelystad	12.78/89
				Cor de bly	81/93
				Henk Martens	93
				Pionier Hangaar Collection, Lelystad	92/96
				(officially quoted as id. 14-664/B-163: que se)	
14A-1188•	AT-16 Mk. IIb	**43-12889**		(to RAF as FT148): shipped to UK: BOC	11.43/46
				(to R Netherlands AF as B-82)	8.46
				Leeuwarden AB; on dump	63/82
				Aviodome collection: stored Badhoevedorp	83
				Aviodome, Amsterdam-Schiphol: displ.	92/96
14A-1192•	AT-16 Mk. IIb	**43-12893**		(to RAF as FT152)	
				(to Yugoslav AF as FT152)	3.45
				National Aviation Museum, Belgrade	92
14A-1216•	AT-16 Mk. IIb	43-12917		(to RAF as FT176): shipped to UK: BOC	11.43/46
				(to R Netherlands AF as B-56)	8.46
			PH-SAZ	ntu: Schreiner Aerocontractors: reg. appl.	12.6.64
				(to R Netherlands Navy/MLD as 043)	25.1.65
				retired by MLD: final MLD Harvard	31.3.71
			PH-KMA	C. Honcoop/Honcoop Trading Co, Veen	9.11.71/74
				(del. to Gilze-Rijen AB, civil conv. .71)	
				J. Daams/Skylight NV, Loosdrecht	20.2.74/78
				ground collision with Spitfire AB910, Bex, Switzerland	20.8.78
				wreck stored Hilversum: struck-off reg.	9.10.78
				(stored Nieuw Loosdrecht pending rebuild 92)	
14A-1263•	AT-16 Mk. IIb	**43-12964**		(to RAF as FT223): shipped to UK: BOC	1.44/47
				(to R Netherlands AF as B-69)	7.47
				Anthony Fokker School, The Hague	81
				National War & Resistance Museum, Overloon, Netherlands (displ. as "12964")	85/96
				(composite static rest: parts B-179 & B-199)	
14A-1268•	AT-16	**43-12969**		(to RAF as FT228): shipped to UK: BOC	1.44/47

	Mk. IIb			(to R Netherlands AF as B-73)	7.47
				Aviodome Museum, Amsterdam-Schiphol	77/87
				Wings of Victory Museum,Veghel, Netherlands	88/96
14A-1269•	AT-16 Mk. IIb	**43-12970**		(to RAF as FT229): shipped to UK: BOC	1.44/47
				(to R Netherlands AF as B-45): BOC	14.5.47/68
				C. Honcoop, Veen, Netherlands	.69
			PH-SKM	J. Daams/Skylight NV, Loosdrecht	10.2.70/71
			G-AZKI	Fairoaks Aviation Services Ltd/ Warbirds of Great Britain, Blackbushe	8.12.71/73
				(del. to Blackbushe ex Holland 30.11.71, flew as "FT239", later "FT229")	
				Anthony E. Hutton, Wroughton/Duxford	11.73/81
				Terry S. Warren, Sandown	11.81/82
				Andrew D. M. Edie, Shoreham	10.82
				Noblair/Fabricair, Pontoise, France	12.82/86
			F-WZDS	Tony Handley, Montpellier	7.86/87
			F-AZDS	C. Handley/S. L. C. A, Montpellier-L'or	12.87/89
				J. Moselius Dreyer, Avignon	90
				Assoc. French Rech. Maint. en Vol Avions Historiques, Le Castellet	93/96
14A-1363•	AT-16 Mk. IIb	**43-13064**		(to RAF as FT323): shipped to UK: BOC	1.44/46
				(to R Netherlands AF as B-19): BOC	28.11.46
				C. Honcoop, Veen, Netherlands	.69
			PH-SKK	J. Daams/Skylight NV, Loosdrecht	10.2.70
				sold to USA (not del.): struck-off reg.	19.11.71
			PH-SKK	R. N. Rijken	5.1.72
				sold to Switzerland (not del.): struck-off reg.	14.1.72
			G-AZSC	Fairoaks Aviation Services	7.4.72/76
				(del. Fairoaks ex Holland 12.1.72, flew as "RAF FT830" later "FT323")	
				Michael W. Stowe, Blackbushe	2.11.77/81
				Warbirds of Great Britain, Blackbushe	5.1.81/84
				Machine Music Ltd, Fairoaks later White Waltham/North Weald/Duxford	28.2.84/96
				rebuild	95/96
14A-1415•	AT-16 Mk. IIb	43-13116		(to RCAF as FT375): BOC "received in error"	22.12.43
				(to RAF as FT375): shipped to UK: BOC	4.3.44
				RAE/A&AEE, Farnborough/Boscombe Down	.46/94
14A-1420•	AT-16 Mk. IIb	**43-13121**		(to RCAF as FT380): BOC "received in error"	22.12.43
				(to RAF as FT380): shipped to UK: BOC	4.3.44/47
				(to RDAF as 31-324)	1.47
				Egeskov Veteranmuseum, Kvaerndrup	69/85
				Historiske Forening Museet, Karup, Denmark	92/96
14A-1422•	AT-16 Mk. IIb	**43-13123**		(to RCAF as FT382): BOC "received in error"	22.12.43
				(to RAF as FT382): shipped to UK: BOC	4.3.44/47
				(to R Netherlands AF as B-66)	6.47/68
				Fargo Air Service, Nashua NH	70
				(unconv., RNAF sc., Nashua 10.70)	
			N8992	David F. Goodwin, Manchester NH	72/76
				Edward Jacobs, Greenfield Park NY	84
				Carl A. Best, Dallas TX	7.85/96
				(USCR quotes id. 66-2637, ie. RCAF2904: SOC 18.10.60: but above believed correct)	
14A-1431•	AT-16 Mk.IIb	**43-13132**		(to RCAF as FT391): BOC "received in error"	15.12.43
				(to RAF as FT391): shipped to UK: BOC	4.3.44/47
				(to R Netherlands AF as B-97): BOC	29.10.47
				C. Honcoop, Veen, Netherlands	.69
			PH-HON	C. Honcoop, Veen	10.7.70/71
				Sir W. J. D. Roberts, Shoreham: del.	7.6.71
			G-AZBN	Sir W. J. D. Roberts/Strathallan Collection	13.7.71/81
				Colt Executive Aviation, Staverton	14.7.81/86
				Ashbon Associates Ltd, Duxford	5.9.85

c/n	type	id	reg	history	date
				Tudor Owen/op. Old Flying Machine Company, Duxford	26.2.87
				J. N. Carter/Swaygate, Hove	92
14A-1444•	AT-16 Mk. IIb	**43-13145**		(to RAF as FT404): shipped to UK: BOC	2.44/47
				(to R Netherlands AF as B-71)	7.47/72
				Deelen AB: inst. airframe: outer wings cut	72
				Militaire Luchtvaart Museum, Soesterberg AB	73/85
			PH-MLM	MLM/op: Stichting Vliegsport, Gilze-Rijen AB	5.7.85/92
				(at airshow Scheveningen, Netherlands 6.91)	
14A-1459•	AT-16 Mk. IIb	**43-13160**		(to RAF as FT419): shipped to UK: BOC	2.44/47
				(to R Netherlands AF as B-103)	11.47
				Anthony Fokker School, The Hague	
				KLM Apprentice School: inst. airframe	.72/85
				Militaire Luchtvaart Museum, Soesterberg	11.85/96
				(to Valkenburg AB 10.86/87 for rest., displ. Soesterberg 95 as "Marine 099")	
14A-1462•	AT-16 Mk. IIb	**43-13163**		(to RAF as FT422): shipped to UK: BOC	2.44/47
				(to R Netherlands AF as B-67)	6.47/72
				Deelen AB: instructional airframe	72
				Musee Royal de l'Armee, Brussels, Belgium	.87/91
				(stored Tieln Belgium, pending rest.)	
14A-1467•	AT-16 Mk. IIb	**43-13168**		(to RAF as FT427): shipped to UK: BOC	2.44/47
				(to R Netherlands AF as B-118)	10.47/72
				Deelen AB: instructional airframe	72
			PH-TOO	ntu: Gilze-Rijen Aero Club, Gilze-Rijen AB	8.76
				(flew for film *A Bridge Too Far*.76 as Fw190, P-47, & Typhoon "HF-L"; flew for movie 9.76 as Fokker D-XXI "241")	
			PH-IIB	H. B. van Meelis, Gilze-Rijen AB	31.7.79
				Stichting Vliegsport, Gilze-Rijen AB	90/96
14A-1494•	AT-16 Mk. IIb	**43-13195**		(to RAF as FT454): shipped to UK: BOC	3.44/47
				(to R Netherlands AF as B-84)	7.47/66
				(to R Netherlands Navy/MLD as 098)	30.3.66/69
				(open storage, wings removed, De Kooy AB 71)	
				C. Honcoop/Honcoop Trading Co, Veen	72
				(stored unconv. Veen 72)	
			OO-DAF	Eric Vormezeele, Brasschaat	4.8.72/92
14A-1745•	AT-16 Mk. IIb	**43-34859**		(to RAF as FX442): shipped to UK: BOC	6.44
				Avex Engineering: sold for scrap: SOC	12.56
				Skylines Scrap Metal, Sandhurst "SI-B"	55/63
				Bill Hamblen, Bournemouth: rest. project	84/86
				RAF Air Training Corps, Ringwood & Fordingbridge, Hampshire: static rest.	95
14A-1884•	Mk. IIb	**KF183**		shipped to UK: BOC RAF	5.44/90
				A&AEE, Farnborough/Boscombe Down	.47/96
14A-2014	Mk. IIb	KF314		shipped to UK: BOC RAF	7.44/82
				A&AEE, Farnborough/Boscombe Down	.49/82
				crashed nr. RAF Boscombe Down	22.2.82
14A-2103•	Mk. IIb	**KF403**		(to RNZAF as NZ1100): BOC	11.44
				(to RNZAF inst. airframe INST149)	
				retired, stored	4.49/59
				Bennett Aviation, Te Kuiti NZ: open storage	.59
				childrens playground, Takapau NZ	65/88
				(recov. ex playground .88, stored Ardmore)	
				Bruce Black, Paraparaumu NZ/Townsville QLD	.88/93
				(shipped Auckland to Townsville 12.88; under rest. to fly Townsville QLD .88/91)	
14A-2110•	Mk. IIb	**KF410**		(to RNZAF as NZ1102)	10.44
				(to inst. airframe INST138)	
				RNZAF Museum, Wigram AB : fuse, stored	92/96

14A-2123	Mk. IIb	KF423		shipped to UK: BOC RAF	.44/57
				Aviation Traders, Southend: sold for scrap	6.57
				Skylines Scrap Metal, Sandhurst UK	80/85
				Booker Aircraft Museum, Booker UK	.85/86
				(acquired as fuselage only: static rest.)	
14A-2135•	Mk. IIb	**KF435**		shipped to UK: BOC RAF	.44/57
				Skylines Scrap Metal, Sandhurst: as scrap	9.57/85
				Barry Parkhouse, Camberley: arr. dism.	1.85/87
				(acquired as fuselage only: static rest.)	
				Booker Aircraft Museum, Booker: arr. dism.	29.2.87/96
				(composite static rest: stbd wing FX350,	
				port wing ex R. Netherlands AF)	
14A-2268•	Mk.IIb	**KF568**		shipped to UK: BOC RAF	.44/49
				(to Belgian AF as H58)	10.49/58
			OO-AAR	H. de Paepe, Borgerhout	1.10.58/59
				sold to West Germany, struck-off reg.	11.9.59
			D-FIBU	RM Overseas Motorsales GmbH, Frankfurt	12.59
				Bundesrepublik Deutschland	
				(op. for Luftwaffe, used in Portugal)	
				(to FA Portuguesa as 1794)	.62/78
				US dealer: was to be broken-up for parts	.78
				Anders K. Seather, Oslo, Norway: del. Oslo	3.79
			LN-TEX	J. Murer & Partners, Oslo	3.8.79
				Morten Andreassen/Warbirds of Norway,	
				Gardermoen AB, Oslo	92/96
55-1605	BC-1A	39-855	NC58478	G. J. Degarmo, NH	.46
				Standard Aerial Surveys Inc, NJ	.46
			N58478	Agricultural Aviation Academy, Minden NV	63/64
				derelict, dism. at Minden NV	73
59-1938 •	AT-6	**40-2112**	NC90632	Bruce A. Gimbel, CT	.46
			N90632	Eastern Truck Rentals, Lowell MA	63
				Leopold Palliardi, Andover CT	.63/70
				Bradley Air Museum, Windsor Locks CT: arr.	18.5.74
				New England Air Museum, Windsor Locks CT	85/91
				(dism., open storage 74/90)	
			N6665Y	Connecticut Aeronautical Historical Association/	
				New England Air Museum, Windsor Locks CT	9.91/96
59-1945 •	AT-6	**40-2119**	**N56737**	Forest M. Bird, San Francisco CA	.46
				George Pulse, Pendleton OR	63/84
				Elizabeth P. & Alex Koleda, Prineville OR	9.86/95
59-1948 •	AT-6	**40-2122**	NC63625	Charles E. Compton, IL	.46
			N63625	Stoltzfus & Associates, Coatesville PA	63/64
				USMC Museum, Quantico VA	86/94
				Minneapolis ANGB MN: loan	86/94
				(displ. as "BC-1 USAAC 798")	
65-1999 •	SNJ-2	**Bu2010**	NC52900	Southern Airways Co, AL	.46
			N52900	Stinis Air Service, Flushing NY/Cypress CA	63/76
				Skytypers East Inc, Flushing NY	.77/86
				SNJ-2 Corp, Flushing NY	1.87/96
65-2000 •	SNJ-2	**Bu2011**	**N55729**	Stinis Air Service, Flushing NY/Cypress CA	63/77
				Skytypers Inc, Los Alamitos CA	84/87
				Gunnell Aviation, Santa Monica CA	92
				Bruce Redding/National Diversified Services,	
				Scottsdale AZ	92
				Donald S. Anklin/CrossroadsAir Enterprises,	
				Skaneateles NY	8.92/96
65-2009 •	SNJ-2	**Bu2020**	**N87613**	Stinis Air Service, Flushing NY/Cypress CA	63/77
				Skytypers Inc, Los Alamitos CA	84/87

				Thomas A. Leatherwood, Paso Robles CA	91/92
				Jim Goff/Seminole Air Centre, Seminole OK	4.95/96
65-2014 •	SNJ-2	**Bu2025**	**N61563**	Stinis Air Service, Flushing NY/ Cypress CA	63/77
				Skytypers Inc, Los Alamitos CA	84/87
				SNJ-2 Corp, La Guardia Airport NY	1.87/90
				Bruce Redding/National Diversified Services, Scottsdale AZ	8.90/96
65-2016 •	SNJ-2	**Bu2027**	N63641	Aero Enterprises Inc, Elkhart IN	63/64
			N2137E	Dell L. Shady, Huntsville AL	66/84
				(open storage, derelict, Huntsville AL 72/82)	
			N40HS	Hangar 6 Inc, Cincinatti-Lunkin Airport OH	8.90/92
				Neal T. Schaefer/SSS Inc, Cincinatti OH	9.92/96
				(rest. project, ff .93 as "USN 2027")	
65-2021 •	SNJ-2	**Bu2032**	NC60734	Stanley H. wioodward, PA	.46
			N60734	Stinis Air Service, Flushing Airport NY	63/72
				Stinis Air Service, Cypress CA	76
				Skytypers East Inc, Flushing NY	.77/86
				SNJ-2 Corp, Flushing NY	1.87/96
65-2023	SNJ-2	Bu2034		noted unconv., in USMC sc., Salisbury MD	73
65-2026 •	SNJ-2	**Bu2037**	N66082	Stinis Air Service, Flushing NY/ Cypress CA	63/77
				Skytypers Inc, Los Alamitos CA	84/92
				Mark D. Dilullo, Charlotte Court VA	4.92/95
65-2028 •	SNJ-2	**Bu2039**	**N62382**	Stinis Air Service, Flushing Airport NY	63/70
				Skytypers East Inc, Flushing NY	.77/86
				dam. landing, Flushing NY (repaired)	23.4.82
				SNJ-2 Corp, Flushing NY	1.87/96
65-2029 •	SNJ-2	**Bu2040**	**N52033**	Stinis Air Service, Flushing NY/Cypress CA	63/76
				Skytypers East Inc, Flushing NY	.77/86
				SNJ-2 Corp, Flushing NY	1.87/96
66-2265 •	Mk.II	**RCAF2532**		BOC 4.8.40: to RCAF Historical Collection	
				Canadian National Aeronautical Collection, Rockliffe ONT	79/82
				National Aviation Museum, Rockliffe ONT	9.82/93
66-2290	Mk.II	RCAF2557		RCAF BOC 30.8.40: SOC	10.5.60
			CF-MGZ	resident, Carman MAN	65/72
				Klaus Lawrenz, Pine Falls MAN	75/83
66-2313 •	Mk.II	**RCAF2580**		RCAF BOC 30.9.40: SOC	6.11.46
			N5848N	B & F Aircraft Supply, Oaklawn IL	63/96
66-2316 •	Mk. II Mk. IIR	**RCAF2583**		RCAF BOC 30.9.40: SOC	11.10.60
			C-GAYD	D. Currie & Associates, Toronto ONT	8.79
				Chris S. McLean, Calgary ALTA	81/83
				struck-off reg.	1.89
			N214RL	John F. Loerch, Tulsa OK	9.3.89/96
6-2324	Mk. II	RCAF2591		RCAF BOC 9.10.40: SOC	7.9.60
			CF-MTA	Glen Fetterly, Chilliwack BC	65/66
				Philip Kalnin & W. M. Bagocsi, Nanaimo BC	68/83
6-2325	Mk. II	RCAF2592		RCAF BOC 9.10.40: SOC	18.1.47
				Canadian War Museum, Ottawa ONT	78
				(displ. on pole as "2592")	
6-2401	Mk. II	RCAF2668		RCAF BOC 16.11.40: SOC	11.10.60
			N9435H	Squadron 3 Flying Club, Buffalo NY	63/64
				Wing & Anchor Club, Buffalo NY	66/69
				Austin W. Wadsworth, Geneseo NY	70/80
66-2425•	Mk. II	**RCAF2692**		RCAF BOC 29.11.40: SOC	1.11.60
			N9788Z	Edwin R. Walker, Edcouch TX	63/70

				sale rep. USCR	84/95
66-2488 •	Mk. II	**RCAF2755**		RCAF BOC 6.1.41: SOC	8.8.60
			CF-MSQ	Rainer Development Co, Strathmore ALTA	65/66
			C-FMSQ	McClain Flight Service Ltd, Cayley ALTA	31.7.91
			N2755Z	Jim Goff/Seminole Air Centre, Seminole OK	4.92/96
66-2499 •	Mk. II	**RCAF2766**		RCAF BOC 16.1.41: SOC	11.10.60
				displ. on pole Dunnville ONT	.64/93
66-2510 •	Mk. II	**RCAF2777**		RCAF BOC 14.1.41: SOC	11.10.60
				(tfd. to R Canadian Navy as 2777)	2.5.56
				CFB Shearwater NS: gate guard	84/96
66-2513 •	Mk. II	**RCAF2780**		RCAF BOC 15.1.41: SOC	1.11.60
			N9785Z	Franks Crop Dusting Service, Crystal City TX	63/64
				Billy J. Taylor, Brady TX	66
				Inez K. Taylor, Brady TX	69
				Ernest L. Opp, Bethalto IL	70/72
				Willis L. Webb, Fort Valley GA	76/85
			N88RT	Apex Associates Inc, Canby OR	10.85/86
				Bruce Redding/Apexxco Inc, Canby OR/ Scottsdale AZ	7.86/95
				(race #88 *Bumpin Dunkin 4*)	
66-2517 •	Mk. II	**RCAF2784**		RCAF BOC 17.1.47: SOC: Mutual Aid France	23.1.58
				(to Armee de l'Air as .....)	.58
			N203V	Ben W. Hall, Seattle WA	68/72
				(race #76 *Killer Too*)	
				Robert B. Dilbeck, Keller TX	76
				Milton Connell, Harlingen TX	77
				Fred E. Thompson, Richmond TX	84/87
			N8BP	Joseph Peterson, Dearborn MI	4.89
				Shellie Barnes/Trapline Inc, Boyne City MI	90/92
				Wally Fisk/Amjet Aircraft Corp, St Paul MN	8.93/96
				(flies as "SNJ-3 Marines 66-2517")	
66-2521 •	Mk. II	**RCAF2788**		RCAF BOC 6.1.41: SOC	8.8.60
			N3647G	David E. Bourassa, Salem OR	63/66
				James D. Wasson, Portland OR	69
				Kenneth E. Higginbotham, Beaverton OR	70/72
				Norman G. Hayden, Kent WA	76/92
				Bill Bailey, Seattle WA	94
				Charles R. King, Brownwood TX	9.94/96
66-2565	Mk.II	RCAF2832		RCAF BOC 29.1.41: SOC	1.11.60
			N9787Z	E. J. Payne, Weslaco TX	63/69
				(noted derelict on dump, Harlingen TX 7.76)	
66-2583 •	Mk. II	**RCAF2850**		RCAF BOC 4.2.41: SOC	20.5.60
			CF-MIV	Ranier Development Co, Strathmore ALTA	65/66
			N28500	Cal Nat Airways, Grass Valley CA	69
				Michael E. Coutches, Hayward CA	70/84
				Jim Mills, Livermore CA	86
				Michael E. Coutches, Hayward CA	5.89/96
66-2611 •	Mk. II	**RCAF2878**		RCAF BOC 14.2.41: wfu 4.56: SOC	21.6.60
			CF-MML		
			N6558D	Alden W, Young, Port Washington NY	63/66
				Robert A. Greacen, Merchantville NJ	69/76
				Stephen J. Roberts, Newark DE	84/86
				Joseph Natoli, Port Orange FL	
				Gary R. Alpert, State College PA	5.90/96
66-2633 •	Mk. II	**RCAF2900**		RCAF BOC 20.2.41: SOC	18.10.60
			N92871	William Lohse, Carter MT	63/64
				H. C. Palmer, Harrisburg AR	66
				Robert L. Younkin, Fayetteville AR	69/92

				T-6 Inc, Earl AR	9.94/96
66-2638 •	Mk. II	**RCAF2905**		RCAF BOC 20.2.41: SOC	8.8.60
			CF-NDF	T. Craven & R. Lidstone, Tillsonburg ONT	65/66
				Robert D. Gray, Burlington ONT	68
			N3270	Richard D. Sprague, Lake Grove NY	70
				William E. Riddle, Suffern NY	74/77
				T & R Aviation, Orlando FL	84
				Scott A. Sherman, Meridian MS	84
				James E. Kaylor, Ocala FL	7.85/96
				(flies as "RCAF3270")	
66-2647	Mk. II	RCAF2914		RCAF BOC 27.2.41: SOC	16.9.60
			N7808C	Robert V. Coffman, Littleton CO	63/64
				Hutton C. Smith, Salt Lake City UT	66
				Aero Inc, Broomfield CO	69
			N194A	Aero Inc, Broomfield CO (race #94)	70/72
				Sky Prints Corp., St Louis MO	76/77
				Red Baron Flying Service, Idaho Falls ID	
				(race #44 *Miss Behavin*)	
				John C. Mosby, Cuba MO	84
				Alan Preston Racing Team, Dallas TX	.84/86
			N44ZZ	Gifford Foley & Garson Fields/	
				Hanover Aero International, Nashua NH	6.87/90
				crashed into Lake Erie (Foley k.)	1.7.90
66-2651 •	Mk. II	**RCAF2918**		RCAF BOC 21.2.41: SOC	28.4.60
				Toronto Board of Education, Toronto ONT	80/85
				(inst. airframe, painted in civil sc. 85)	
			C-FNAH	Leslie Balla, Toronto ONT	2.11.94
66-2660 •	Mk. II	**RCAF2927**		RCAF BOC 5.3.41: SOC	1.11.60
			N9786Z	Leon Maxwell, Coalville UT	63/64
				Westair Co, Westminster CO	66/70
				Glenn T. Shaw, McCloud OK	76/77
				Tom A. Thomas, Oklahoma City OK	6.84
			N711XX	Tom A. Thomas/Thomas Concrete Products/	
				Ada Aircraft Museum, Oklahoma City OK	10.84/95
66-2670 •	Mk. II	**RCAF2937**		RCAF BOC 5.3.41: SOC	31.8.60
				Western Canada Aviation Museum	90
66-2684 •	Mk. II	**RCAF2951**		RCAF BOC 11.3.41: SOC	11.12.46
			N99839	Avery Aviation, Greybull WY	69
				Hawkins & Powers Aviation, Greybull WY	.69/75
			C-GDJC	D. Currie & Assoc., Toronto ONT	12.75
				Canadian Warplane Heritage, Hamilton ONT	79
				USAFM, Castle AFB CA	93
				(displ. as "USAAC 02684")	
66-2689 •	Mk. II	**RCAF2956**		RCAF BOC 11.3.41: SOC	13.9.60
			CF-SDK	Gary L. Oates & Mike Malagies, Weston ONT	68
			N2956	Frank J. Ciccolella, Tewksbury MA	69/86
				Ronald H. Gertsen, Kinnelon NJ	12.91/96
66-2690 •	Mk. II	**RCAF2957**		RCAF BOC 17.3.41: SOC	28.3.60
			CF-MFK	Ranier Development Co, Strathmore ALTA	65/66
				E. S. Fossen, Abbotsford BC	68/72
				Dave I. Heaps, Sardis BC	72/73
			N47079	Charles Landells, Kennewick WA	12.75/95
66-2703 •	Mk. II	**RCAF2970**		RCAF BOC 17.3.41: SOC	18.10.60
			N9799Z	Jack Briggs, Prineville OR	69/72
			N97GM	Gary J. Meermans, Long Beach CA	76/86
				(at Reno 9.85 #97)	
			N97AW	Bruce Redding/Apexxco Inc, Canby OR	8.86
				Tom Dwelle, Auburn CA	.87
				(race #97 *Tinkertoy*)	
				James W. Bennett, Euless TX	87/96

66-2711 •	Mk. II	**NZ918**		(to RNZAF as NZ918)	5.41
				(to RNZAF inst. airframe INST 135)	
				Bennett Aviation, Te Kuiti NZ: open storage	.59
				childrens playground Pahiatua NZ	76
				displ. on pole, Pahiatua NZ	90/96
66-2742	Mk. II	RCAF3009		RCAF BOC 31.3.41: SOC	21.10.60
				Canadian Military Aviation Museum,	
				Vancouver BC	83
66-2757 •	Mk. II	**AH195**		(to RNZAF as NZ944)	5.41
				(to RNZAF inst. airframe INST153)	
				Bennett Aviation, Te Kuiti NZ: open storage	.59
				Museum of Transport & Technology, Auckland	69/95
66-2759 •	Mk. II	**AH197**		(to RNZAF as NZ946)	
				(to RNZAF inst. airframe INST144)	
				Bennett Aviation, Te Kuiti NZ: open storage	.59
				to playground, Mathven NZ	c65
				fuse. stored on farm, Methven NZ	94
75-3048 •	Mk. II	**RCAF3134**		RCAF BOC 28.5.41: SOC	1.11.60
				(tfd. to R Canadian Navy as 3134)	5.5.50
			N9793Z	Colts Neck Flying Service, Colts Neck NJ	63
				Brian G. Vooght, Alexandria/McLean VA	.63/95
				(flies as "RCAF 471")	
75-3439 •	Mk. II	**RCAF 3165**		RCAF BOC 9.6.41: SOC Mutual Aid to Italy	11.10.57
				(to Italian AF as MM.........)	
				J. K. Kavanaugh	
			N3231H	Dennis G. Buehn, Reno NV: reg. candidate	16.11.94
75-3441 •	Mk. II	**RCAF3167**		RCAF BOC 11.6.41: SOC	16.3.60
				(tfd. to R Canadian Navy as 3167)	15.11.52
			CF-MEQ	M. C. Hurdle, Winnipeg MAN	65/68
				James D. Springer, Thunder Bay ONT	69/72
			C-GMEQ	Hugh G. Jervis-Read, Edmonton ALTA	9.74/75
				Jeremy I. Milsom, Calgary ALTA	78/88
			N99NS	Bob L. Nestor, Chubbuck ID	9.88/96
75-3462	Mk. II	RCAF3188		RCAF BOC 23.6.41: SOC	25.10.60
				(tfd. to R Canadian Navy as 3188)	15.7.54
			CF-MWJ	Kinniburg Spray Service Ltd,	
				Purple Springs ALTA	65/83
75-3465 •	Mk. II	**RCAF3191**		RCAF BOC 25.6.41: SOC	26.9.60
			CF-MTX	Harold A. Engel, Waterloo ONT	65/66
				Kenneth Gamble Ltd, Hamilton ONT	68
				Stanley Castle, Toronto ONT	68/75
				Robert Hewitt, Woodstock ONT	78/92
			C-FMTX	Bob Hewitt, Norman Beckham, Len Fallowfield/	
				Canadian Harvard Aircraft Association,	
				Woodstock ONT	78/92
			N3191G	Jim Goff/Seminole Air Centre, Seminole OK	4.92/96
75-3473 •	Mk. II	**RCAF3199**		RCAF BOC 25.6.41: SOC	21.10.60
	Mk. IIR		CF-MZI	Ranier Development Co, Strathmore ALTA	65/66
			N16730	Cal Nat Airways, Grass Valley CA	66
				Keefe Corp, Pacific Palisades CA	70
				Edward J. Modes, Burbank CA	72/86
				Richard T. Sykes, Toluca Lake CA	86
				Ray F. Schutte, Valencia/Redding CA	9.86/96
				(race #11 *Race Eleven*)	
75-3496 •	Mk. II	**RCAF3222**		RCAF BOC 8.7.41: SOC	25.8.60
			CF-MKA	N. F. Beckham & R. Hewitt, Woodstock ONT	.69/83
			C-FMKA	Norm Beckham/Canadian Harvard Aircraft	
				Association, Woodstock ONT	85/94

c/n	Model	Identity	Reg.	History	Date
75-3497 •	Mk. II	**RCAF3223**		RCAF BOC 2.7.41: SOC	27.6.47
				Charles Babb Co, Montreal QUE	.47
				(to R Swedish AF/Flygvapnet as Fv16145)	
				Jamtlands Flyghistoriska Museum,	
				Ostersund, Sweden	93
76-3553 •	Mk. II	**AJ583**		(to RCAF as AJ583): BOC 29.7.41: SOC	21.6.60
			CF-HWX	Alex Kennedy, Three Rivers QUE	65
				John S. Cowan, Toronto ONT	66/86
			C-FHWX	Pete Spence/Canadian Harvard Aircraft	
				Association, Woodstock ONT: del.	4.86/96
76-3556	Mk. II	AJ586		(to RCAF as AJ586): BOC 29.7.41: SOC	11.10.60
			N4657T	Robert H. Horn, Plainwell/Parchment MI	66/84
76-3586	Mk. II	AJ616		(to RAF as AJ616): shipped direct to Rhodesia	9.42
			N160JN	George O'Brien, Pontiac MI	66/69
				Myke H. Baar, Steamboat Springs CO	70/72
76-3658 •	Mk. II	**AJ688**		(to RCAF as AJ688): BOC 22.8.41: SOC	8.8.60
			N3646G	Charles McQueary, Rawlins WY	63/66
				Helen B. Matteri, Santa Rosa CA	69/70
				Robert E. Saucci, Santa Rosa CA	72
				Eugene F. Bowlin, Brookings OR	76/77
				Larry R. Thomas, San Mateo CA	3.81/96
76-3663 •	Mk. II	**AJ693**		(to RCAF as AJ693): BOC 25.8.41: SOC	31.1.44
				crashed into Lake Ontario	24.1.44
				(salvaged from Lake Ontario .83)	
				displ. on pole, Kingston Airport ONT "AJ693"	90
76-3701	Mk. II	AJ731		(to RCAF as AJ731): BOC 9.9.41: SOC	1.11.60
			N9789Z	Henry L. Gardner, Kenedy TX	63/69
				George H. Sanders, Higley AZ	70
				Frank C. Sanders, Santa Ana CA	72
				Steve Fowler, Seattle WA	76/77
				R. A. Kerley Ink Engineers, Broadview IL	84/86
				struck-off USCR	23.4.91
76-3762•	Mk. II	AJ792		(to RCAF as AJ792): BOC 16.10.41: SOC	18.10.60
			N3652G	Columbus L. Woods, Lewistown MT	63/64
				Arthur Osburnsen, Winnifred MT	66/69
				sale rep. USCR	84/95
76-3802 •	Mk. II	**AJ832**		(to RCAF as AJ832): BOC 16.10.41: SOC	18.10.60
			N9798Z	Neil M. Rose, Vancouver WA	63/69
			N832N	Neil M. Rose, Vancouver WA	70/71
				Barrie Simonson, Mercer Island WA	73/77
				Robert L. Ferguson, Wellesley MA	84
				Robert J. Colman, Quincy MA	9.85/96
76-3834 •	Mk. II	**AJ864**		(to RNZAF as NZ977)	1.42
				(recov. from crash site, NZ South Island)	
				Greg Ryan, Auckland-Ardmore: rest. project	88/95
				(under rest. Ardmore 95 using parts from NZ989	
				ex crash site & fuse. section of NZ1038: que se)	
			ZK-XII	NZ977 Syndicate, Papakura	28.5.90/96
76-3905 •	Mk. II	**AJ935**		(to RCAF as AJ935): BOC 19.10.42: SOC	18.10.60
				crashed on del. flight to Canada: rebuilt	.42
			N9796Z	Lee J. Hertwig, Oconto Falls WI	63/64
				Francis J. Moran, Franksville WI	1.67/95
76-3924	Mk. II	AJ954		(to RCAF as AJ954): BOC 9.2.42: SOC	1.11.60
			N9794Z	Gardner Brothers, Crystal City TX	63/84
76-3938 •	Mk. II	**AJ968**		(to RCAF as AJ968): BOC 14.1.42: SOC	1.11.60
			CF-MWV		
			N4802E	John J. Shinkunas, North Sioux City IA	63/64

				Joseph Lanctot, Sioux City IA	63
				Raymond E. Peterseon, Swanville MN	66
				George M. Szymeczek, Mason City IA	69/70
				Robert E. Behrens, Council Bluffs IA	76/84
				Husker Aircraft Repair Inc, Omaha NE	86
				Wayne Meylan, Oklahoma City OK	87
				David L. Fayman, Lawrence KS	1.88/95
77-3962 •	AT-6A	**41-153**	N94444	Lewis A. Gayle, Sylmar CA	66/72
				Paul Gaines, Salt Lake City UT	76/77
				John C. Harrison, Sacramento CA	80/85
				Darrell D. Dorman/Eagles Nest of the Ozarks Inc, Springfield MO	.85/96
77-4176 •	AT-6A	**41-217**		(to FA Portuguesa as 1608)	
			G-BGGR	Euroworld International Ltd, Biggin Hill	17.1.79
			D-FOBY	Air Classik GmbH, Dusseldorf: del.	9.4.79/87
				(displ. Dusseldorf Airport as *Firebird*)	
				Albatros Flugmuseum, Stuttgart Airport	92/95
				(displ. on airport roof)	
77-4183 •	AT-6A	**41-224**	NC57458	Trevelyn G. Keeley, CA	.46
			N57458	Travel Associates Inc, Leominster MA	63/70
			N57451	Paul A Harris, Friendswood TX	84/87
				Alan G. Zabowski, Washington NJ	92/95
77-4201 •	AT-6A	**41-242**	NC57493	Willis R. Bailard, CA	.46
			N57493	Willis R. Bailard, Ventura CA	63/69
				Ron B. Reed, Redwood City/Half Moon Bay CA	76/95
77-4215 •	AT-6A	**41-256**		Gerald S. Beck/Tri-State Aviation Collection, Wahpeton ND	.90/94
				(ex inst. airframe "T170": stored dism.)	
77-4360	SNJ-3	Bu6782	N55829	Eugene W. Lemire, Miami FL	63/84
77-4500	SNJ-3	Bu6822	N69334	Anthony Stinis, Jamaica NY	66/84
77-4579 •	AT-6A	**41-540**	**N94506**	Hardwick Aircraft Co, El Monte CA	66/69
				Charles Brooks, Los Angeles CA	72
				sale rep., USCR	84/96
77-4601 •	AT-6A	**41-552**	N2802D	Donald F. Welsh, Utica IL/San Diego CA	66/72
				James P. Price, San Diego CA	76
			N39RH	Robert H. Nottke, Barrington Hills IL	3.77
	Super Texan			(rest. Compton CA c78 as mod. Super Texan)	
				crashed in Canada	9.80
			N78RN	Robert H. Nottke, Barrington Hills IL	8.81/87
				Lone Star Flight Museum, Houston TX, later Galveston TX	4.88/96
77-4607 •	AT-6A	**41-558**	N96465		
			N48BC	Romaine A. Collins, Buckley WA	76/77
				Andrew W. Dibrino, Hillsboro OR	84
				Bruce Redding, Reno NV	85
				(race #48 *Bumpin Dunkin*)	
				Charles K. Theis, Reno NV	1.86/96
77-4698 •	AT-6A	**41-629**	NC61344	Vest Aircraft & Finance Co, Denver CO	.46
				Mountain States Aviation Inc, CO	.46
				(to SAAF as 7661)	70/94
			ZU-AOY	Harvard Club of South Africa	3.11.94/96
78-6098	SNJ-3	Bu6911	N66233	George A. Englehardt, North Hatfield MA	63/64
				(last FAA annual inspection 6.49)	
				William H. Laurence, Lisbon NY	66/70
				Alexander Dyko, Belmont MA	72/84

'8-6101	SNJ-3	Bu6914	N52230	Tom R. Burns, Washington DC	63/84
'8-6384	AT-6A	41-16056	PH-UBO	Rijksluchtvaartdienst/Government Flying School	
				Gilze-Rijen AB, later Eelde	17.9.46/60
				collided with PH-UBD, Gilze-Rijen (repaired)	8.5.50
				wfu, struck-off reg.	23.9.60
				stored complete Hornhuizen, Netherlands	76/78
				scrapped Hornhuizen	.78
'8-6394	AT-6A	41-16066	N9043Y	Kirk R. McKee, Sacramento CA	1.79
			N144KM(2	Kirk R. McKee, Sacramento CA	4.79/95
				crashed LeMoore NAS CA	5.5.85
'8-6445 •	AT-6A	**41-16107**		(to FA Venezolana as .....)	
				Museo Aeronautico, Maracay AB, Venezuala	90/96
				(displ. as "FAV E-71")	
'8-6616	AT-6A	41-16238	N4004B	Aircraft Parts & Supply Co, New Orleans LA	63/84
'8-6629	AT-6A	41-16251	N62081	Morris P. Woolley, Honolulu HI	63/84
'8-6632 •	AT-6A	**41-16254**	**N18J**	Earl C. Gibbs, Cleveland OH	63/77
				A. P. Rosnick, Omaha NE	84/86
				Donald J. Czaplicki, Omaha NE	87/92
				Jim Goff/Seminole Air Centre, Seminole OK	5.93/95
'8-6661	AT-6A	41-16283		(to FA Mexicana as .....)	
			N65512	S. D. Rorem, Oklahoma City OK	63/72
				(last FAA annual inspection 7.56)	
				I. N. Burchinall Jnr, Paris TX	76
				S. D. Rorem, Oklahoma City OK: USCR	84
'8-6680 •	AT-6A	**41-16302**	NC57318	Robert T. Green, CA	.46
			N57318	A. D. Drum, Fallon NV	63/69
				Lahontaw Valley Dusters, Fallon NV	70
				A. D. Drum, Fallon NV (race #39 "Ruthie")	72
				Donald A. Webb, Los Angeles CA	84
				Randall S. Difani, Long Beach CA	5.84/96
				(race #18 *Thunderbolt*)	
'8-6698 •	AT-6A	**41-16320**		(to FA Portuguesa as 1620)	
			G-TIDE	Euroworld International Ltd, Biggin Hill	28.3.79/80
			N3762J	Jimmie R. McMillan, Breckenridge TX	5.80
				Robert E. Richeson, Graham TX	84/89
			N42DQ	Robert E. Richeson, Graham TX	8.89/90
				(race #42 *Dairy Queen Blizzard*)	
			N77TX	William P. Lear Jnr, Los Altos Hills CA	9.90/92
				Gregory Hiser/Aero Concepts Inc, Wichita KS	4.93/96
'8-6821 •	AT-6A	**41-16443**		(to R Swedish AF/Flygvapnet as Fv16269)	
	Sk.16b		**SE-CHP**	Svensk Flygtjanst AB, Stockholm	10.58/63
				O. H. Ahnstrand, Vallingby	70
				B. O. Lowgren, Bromma	.71/96
'8-6992 •	AT-6A	**41-16614**		(to R Swedish AF/Flygvapnet as Fv16291)	
	Sk.16b		OY-DYE	A. P. Botved, Copenhagen	26.5.55
			D-IGAL	Deutscher Luftfahrt-Beratungsdienst,	
				Wiesbaden	.56/58
			D-FGAL	Deutscher Luftfahrt Beratungsdienst	1.58/61
			PH-NKD	J. Daams, Loosdrecht	16.6.61/76
				NV Skylight, Eelde, Netherlands	23.6.76/93
			N13FY	Western Associates, Portland OR	11.93/95
				op: NV Skylight, Eelde, Netherlands	11.93/96
'8-6999 •	AT-6A	**41-16621**		(to R Swedish AF as ......)	
			N766CA	Service Insurance Agency Inc, Rockford IL	4.83
				Dennis G. Buehn, Reno/Carson City NV	84/92
				Lars Ljungqvist, Gasten OR/Vancouver BC	8.92/95
'8-7005	AT-6A	41-16627		(to FA Brasileira as FAB T-6 1506)	

			PT-KVG	reg.	.76
				Alvir J. Batista	77
				Jose Aurelia, Lima Redig, Belo Horizonte	83/88
78-7018 •	AT-6A	**41-16640**	**N7991C**	Richard C. Fernalld, Pendleton OR/Yelm WA	10.84/95
78-7094 •	AT-6A	**41-16716**		(to FA Paraguaya as 0106)	
				World Wide Aeronautical Industries CA	9.2.91
				(purchased auction, Asuncion, Paraguay 9.2.91,	
				shipped, arr. dism. Santa Paula CA 9.91)	
			N6069H	World Wide Aeronautical Industries,	
				Moorpark CA: reg. candidate	19.9.91
				James Morgan, Aumsville OR	11.92/94
				Robert H. Poynton & Dave Saunders/	
				Western Warbirds, Perth-Jandakot WA	4.94
				(shipped ex Oregon, arr. Jandakot 15.6.94)	
			VH-WWA	Adrian F. Thomas, Perth WA	4.8.94/96
78-7095 •	AT-6A	**41-16717**		(to FA Paraguaya as 0103)	
				World Wide Aeronautical Industries CA	9.2.91
				(purchased auction, Asuncion, Paraguay 9.2.91,	
				shipped, arr. dism. Santa Paula CA 9.91)	
			N61167	World Wide Aeronautical Industries,	
				Moorpark CA: reg. candidate	19.9.91
				James Morgan, Aumsville OR	12.92/94
				Robert H. Poynton & Dave Saunders/	
				Western Warbirds, Perth-Jandakot WA	4.94
				(shipped ex Oregon, arr. Jandakot 15.6.94)	
78-7140 •	AT-6A	**41-16762**		(to SAAF as 7643)	
			ZU-AOX	Harvard Club of South Africa	3.11.94
78-7147	AT-6A	41-16769	NC57495	James E. Markell, CA	.46
			N57495	Ted E. Strode, Reedley CA	63/84
78-7228 •	AT-6A	**41-16850**		(to FA Mexicana as 797)	
			N7055D	Texas Turbo Jet Inc, Dallas TX	1.89
				John M. Foster, Alamogordo NM	5.90/96
78-7233	AT-6A	41-16855		(to FA Brasileira as FAB 1497)	
			PT-KSZ		80
78-7245 •	AT-6A	**41-16867**	NC61970	Joe Conn, OH	.46
				Robert Patterson, OH	.46
				(to IDFAF as 1165)	
				Ha-aretz Sciences & Technology Museum,	
				Tel Aviv, Israel	75/90
				(open storage 75 as "IDFAF 65", derelict)	
78-7266 •	AT-6A	**41-16888**		(to USN as Bu05437)	
	SNJ-3		**N547W**	Wings N Wheels Inc, Houston TX	2.4.92/96
78-7375 •	AT-6A	**41-16997**	NC90629	Louis J. Petritz, CA	.46
			N90629	H. A. Matteri, Santa Rosa CA	63/69
				John D. Molin, Santa Rosa CA	70
				Allan D. Pratt, Boulder Creek CA	72
				Mid-Continent Aircraft Corp, Hayti MO	.77
				Wesley D. Tolle, Knights Landing CA	79
				Nolan L. Cooper, Midland TX	84
			N814MN	Cooper & Associates, San Antonio TX	12.84/87
			N90629	Robert E. Ford, Aurora CO/Abilene TX	8.87/96
79-3988 •	SNJ-2	**Bu2553**	NC58224	Reading Batteries Inc, Reading PA	.46
			N58224	Manvel Corp, Kansas City MO	63/64
				Anthony Stinis, Flushing Airport NY	66/72
				Stinis Air Service, Cypress CA	76
				Skytypers East Inc, Flushing NY	.77/86
				SNJ-2 Corp, Flushing NY	1.87/96

79-3993 •	SNJ-2	**Bu2558**	**N60645**	Anthony Stinis, Jamaica NY	63/64
				Stinis Air Service, Flushing Airport NY	66/72
				Stinis Air Service Inc, Cypress CA	76/77
				Skytypers Inc, Los Alamitos CA	84/87
				Bruce Redding, Scottsdale AZ	90
				Darryl G. Greenamyer, Ocala FL	92
				Classic Aviation International Inc, Ocala FL	92
				Samuel Lauff, Ocala FL	5.93/96
79-3997 •	SNJ-2	**Bu2562**	NC65370	Henry L. Seale, TX	.46
			N65370	Stinis Air Service Inc, Flushing Airport NY	63/76
				Skytypers East Inc, Flushing NY	.77/86
				SNJ-2 Corp, Flushing NY	1.87/95
79-4003 •	SNJ-2	**Bu2568**	NC60833	Charlie W. Loyd, VA	.46
			N60833	Stinis Air Service, Flushing Airport NY	63/72
				Stinis Air Service, Cypress CA	76/77
				Skytypers Inc, Los Alamitos CA	84/87
				SNJ-2 Corp, La Guardia Airport NY	92
				sale rep., Miami FL	92
				John A. Kordenbrock, Cincinatti OH	3.94
81-4013	Mk. II	RCAF3019		RCAF BOC 12.4.41: SOC	16.9.48
			C-GAPE	R. Ratcliffe, St.Mary's ONT	8.85
81-4038 •	Mk. II	**RCAF3771**		RCAF BOC 22.4.41: SOC	14.12.60
			CF-TSV	F. Grindl & Colin A. Clark, Scarborough ONT	3.70/72
				Colin A Clark, Toronto ONT	72/75
			C-FTSV	Forest Protection Ltd, Fredericton NB	78/83
			N90541	Red S Aircraft Sales, Salinas CA	24.3.87
				Jim Lenahan, Colorado Springs CO	90/92
				Robert S. Haun, Westminster CO	11.92/96
81-4043	Mk. II	RCAF3776		RCAF BOC 23.4.41: SOC	26.9.60
			CF-PST	R. Hewitt & R. Pfefferle, Stoney Creek ONT	65
				J. D. Pile & B. E. Rowe, Brooklin ONT	66
				Herbert J. Vear, Toronto ONT	68/75
				Kinmer Farms Ltd, Fort Sasaktoon SASK	78/83
				op: Canadian Warplane Heritage, Hamilton ONT	74/79
81-4087 •	Mk. II	**RCAF3820**		RCAF BOC 8.5.41: to Mutual Aid France: SOC	21.10.57
				(to Aeronavale as 3820)	.57
				Musee des Traditions de l'Aeronautique Navale, Rochefort AB, France	88/90
				(displ. as "Aeronavale 820")	
81-4097 •	Mk. II	**RCAF3830**		RCAF BOC 10.5.41: SOC	11.10.60
			CF-RWN	Hicks & Lawrence Ltd, St. Thomas ONT	66/75
				John Gilvesy, Tillsonburg ONT	78/83
			C-FRWN	Don Nightingale, Kingston ONT	88/94
81-4099 •	Mk. II	**RCAF3832**		RCAF BOC 13.5.41: SOC	1.11.60
			CF-NIA	Lester C. Abbey, North Surrey BC	65/75
			N96281	Richard D. Benner, Anchorage AK	76/77
				Confederate Air Force, Harlingen/Midland TX	5.2.79/96
81-4107 •	Mk. II	**RCAF3840**		RCAF BOC 17.5.41: SOC	17.10.61
				Canadian National Aeronautical Collection, Rockliffe ONT	66/82
				Canadian War Museum, Ottawa: displ. on pole	
				National Aviation Museum, Rockcliffe ONT	9.82/90
81-4121 •	Mk. II	**BW196**		(to RCAF as BW196): BOC 20.5.41: SOC	18.10.60
				J. Sveinungsen	
			N3176U	Carl J. Terrana, Seattle WA	10.91/92
			N196FC	Carl J. Terrana, Seattle WA	1.92/96
				(flies as "T-6F 52-2196/WASH ANG 02196")	
81-4128 •	Mk. II	**BW203**		(to RCAF as BW203): BOC	20.5.41/58

				to Mutual Aid France: SOC	23.1.58
				(to l'Armee de l'Air as BW203)	.58
				(to FA Venezuela as .....)	
			N20240	Leeward Aeronautical Inc, Ocala FL	7.78
				struck-off USCR	12.80
84-7412 •	AT-6B	41-17034	N62510	Norman G. Bodet, Helotes TX	63/64
				Esther I. Carter, Cushing OK	66
				M. Sirmons, Atoka OK	69
				Hugh C. Alexander, Louisville GA	70
			N30HA	Hugh C. Alexander, Louisville GA	72
				(race #30 *Stewball*)	
				James Powell, Clarksdale MS	76/77
				William L. Reid/Warbirds of Arkansas Inc, Pine Bluff AR	4.78/96
84-7478	AT-6B	41-17100	N63481	John B. Rosenthal, San Mateo CA	63/84
84-7505 •	AT-6B	**41-17127**	PT-LDQ	Mael Bordados Ind. Com. Confeccoes Ltda, Santos Dumont	15.3.91
84-7640 •	AT-6B	**41-17262**		(to R Saudi AF as 17262)	
				Saudi AF Museum Collection, Riyadh	79
				Saudi AF Academy Collection, Riyadh: stored	87/90
84-7648 •	AT-6B	**41-17270**		(to SAAF as 7689)	
			ZU-ACV	S. D. Davidson, Newton Park	22.10.92
				sold to USA: struck-off reg.	22.11.93
			N544Q	James E. Beasley, Philadelphia PA	2.94
			N7859B	Andrew J. Stern, Lafayette Hill PA	2.95
84-7699 •	AT-6B	**41-17321**	NC61360	John A. Peacock, WA	.46
			N60690	reg.	11.92
				Wesley E. Labagh, Middletown NY	1.94/96
84-7748 •	AT-6B	**41-17370**	NC57418	Raymond J. Kasper, CA	.46
			N57418	Arthur W. Herron, Sacramento CA	63/69
				(last FAA annual inspection 5.54)	
				Claude E. Morey, San Rafael CA	70
				Richard T. Sykes, Toluca Lake CA (race #14)	6.83/96
84-7750 •	AT-6B	**41-17372**	N96224	reg. res.	84/92
				USAFM, Chanute AFB IL	93/96
84-7800 •	AT-6B	**41-17422**	N62144	Norman G. Bodet, Helotes TX	63/64
				Confederate Air Force, Mercedes TX	66
			N11171	Confederate Air Force, Harlingen/Midland TX	69/96
				(conv. to Zero lookalike., flies as "AI-115")	
07-6 •	Mk. IIb	**RCAF3039**		RCAF BOC 3.5.41: SOC	25.11.60
				(tfd. to R Canadian Navy as 3039)	29.6.55
			CF-NDB	Stan N. Fitzner & J.E. Simpson, Hamilton ONT	.60/79
			C-FNDB	Bob & David Hewitt, Norm Beckham/Canadian Harvard Aircraft Association, Woodstock ONT	6.79/96
07-15 •	Mk. IIb	RCAF3048		RCAF BOC 20.5.41: SOC	1.11.60
			N9790Z	Lloyd P. Nolen, Mercedes TX	63/70
				Confederate Air Force, Harlingen/Midland TX	72/95
				(flies as USAAC AT-6A 1110/41)	
07-30 •	Mk. IIb Mk. IV T-6H	RCAF3064		RCAF BOC 5.8.41: SOC: Mutual Aid Italy	11.10.57
				(rebuilt by CCF as Harvard IV)	
				(to Italian AF as T-6H-2M MM54137)	12.57/74
				last flight 14.6.74 "RM-12", stored Bergamo	6.74/81
				Robs Lamplough, Duxford UK	.81
				(arr. dism. Southampton docks 21.11.81, stored Botley, later Woolston 82/83)	
			G-BKWZ	ntu:	.81/83

					Tim Lane, Dorchester	22.4.83
				G-CTKL	C. T. K. Lane, Dorchester	11.83/87
					(rest. Dorchester 83/87, ff Dunkeswell 10.6.87, flew as USN 54137/69)	
					Jeff A. Carr, Dunkeswell	8.9.87
					Gavin Keegan, North Weald	91/96
07-36		Mk. IIb	RCAF3070		RCAF BOC 9.8.41	
					(tfd. to R Canadian Navy as 3070)	7.9.54
				CF-MSZ	Skyway Air Services Ltd, Langley BC	65/72
07-62	•	Mk. IIb	**RCAF3096**		RCAF BOC 5.9.41: SOC	3.6.60
					(tfd. to R Canadian Navy as 3096)	8.6.50
				CF-MGO	Fundy Industrial Transport Ltd, Lancaster NB	65
					William Chahley, Ltd, Lancaster NB	66
					Stanley Tucker, St. Johns NFLD	68/69
					Noel Clement, Summerside, Prince Edward Isl.	70/75
				C-FMGO	Miramichi Air Service Ltd, Douglastown NB	78/79
					Don McQuinn, Moncton NB	
					Byron Reynolds/Reynolds Aviation Museum, Wetaskiwin ALTA	82/96
07-144	•	Mk. IIb	**RCAF3275**		RCAF BOC 5.2.42: SOC	12.4.60
					(tfd. to R Canadian Navy as 3275)	15.11.52
				CF-MGI	Sky Harbour Air Services, Goderich ONT	65
					I. H. Petersen, Don Mills ONT	66
					Gary McCann, Stratford ONT	68/75
					Rolf A. Yri, Surrey BC	.75/86
				N9750M	Courtesy Aircraft Co, Rockford IL	2.7.86/87
				C-FGME	B. D. Beard, Langley BC	10.89
07-145		Mk. IIb	RCAF3276		RCAF BOC 5.2.42: SOC	14.12.60
					(tfd. to R Canadian Navy as 3276)	15.11.52
				CF-OHG	Fred Grindl & Frank McInnes, Brantford ONT	65/66
					Robert C. Smith & Assoc. Ltd, Toronto ONT	68/70
				N3276K	Max R. Hoffman, Fort Collins CO	72
07-166		Mk. IIb	RCAF3297		RCAF BOC 9.3.42: SOC	18.10.60
					(tfd. to R Canadian Navy as 3297)	29.6.55
				CF-MWP	Vance E. Molsberry, Edmonton ALTA	65/66
					Gail J. Schmidt, Edmonton ALTA	68/72
07-184	•	Mk. IIb	**RCAF3318**		RCAF BOC 18.3.42: SOC	14.12.60
					(tfd. to R Canadian Navy as 3318)	15.11.52
				CF-MMT	Robert M. Miller, Edmonton ALTA	65
					Vincent Clothier, Edmonton ALTA	66/83
				C-FMMT	struck-off reg.	9.87
				N92019	Jan C. Mueller, Northville MI	10.87/95
07-190	•	Mk. IIb	**RCAF3323**		RCAF BOC 24.3.42: SOC	8.8.60
					Canadian Harvard Aircraft Association, Woodstock ONT (rest. project)	88/90
07-191	•	Mk. IIb	**RCAF3324**		RCAF BOC 24.3.42: SOC	18.10.60
					(tfd. to R Canadian Navy as 3324)	2.6.54
				N3653G	Lockhart Leasing Corp, Salt LAke City UT	63/64
					Hilton D. Hobbs, Wendover UT	66
					Russell R. Lewis, Wendover UT	69/70
					Lance J. Johnson, Denver CO	76
					Clifford Branch, Temple Bar AZ	77
					George W. Coombes, Midland TX	84/95
					(flies as "USN SNJ-3 3324")	
07-202	•	Mk. II	**RCAF3327**		RCAF BOC 28.3.42: SOC	29.9.60
				CF-MTW	Walter Eichhorn, Toronto ONT	65/66
					Robert Allard, Toronto ONT	68
					V. L. Brown, Toronto ONT	69/70
					John T. Faichney, Milliken ONT	72/75
					Robert Arend, Toronto ONT	78/79
					Blain Fowler/J. L. Seagull & Associates,	

				Camrose ALTA	81/96
07-203 •	Mk. IIb	**RCAF3336**		RCAF BOC 8.4.42: SOC	12.8.49
	Mk. IIa		CF-NWH	Leonard F. Ross, Niagara Falls ONT	65/72
			N9113A	reg. res.	10.87
			N9115A	Samuel F. Spencer, Troy OH	6.88/96
88-9110 •	SNJ-4	**Bu05603**	N9560C	Plains Aero Service, Dalhart TX	63/70
				Eagle Field Museum, Firebaugh CA: derelict	93
88-9263 •	AT-6C	**41-33157**		(to RAF as EX184)	
	Mk. IIa			(to RNZAF as NZ1006): shipped direct to NZ	9.42
				Joe DrageDrages Historical Aircraft Museum,	
				Wodonga VIC	6.78
				F. William Pike, Sydney NSW	.78/82
				(shipped: stored unconv. Albury NSW .78/79)	
				Randal W. McFarlane, Nowra NAS NSW	82/86
			VH-TEX	Randal W. McFarlane, Bankstown NSW	2.5.86/88
				Chris P. Sperou, Adelaide SA	2.7.88/90
				Arthur A. Schmidt, Alice Springs NT	26.4.90/95
				(flies as "SNJ-4/Bu33157/GTNO BAY")	
88-9264 •	AT-6C	**41-33158**		(to RAF as EX185)	
	Mk. IIa			(to RNZAF as NZ1007): shipped direct to NZ	9.42
				(to RNZAF inst. airframe INST188)	
				Engine Support Inc, Sebring FL	.78
				Auckland Preservation Society, Auckland NZ	.80/81
				Robert Greinert & Phil Heesch/Historical Aircraft	
				Restoration Society, Sydney NSW	.81/87
				(stripped airframe, shipped to Sydney:	
				rest. project Scheyville NSW)	
			VH-HAR	Bruce Simpson/Classic Aviation,	
				Sydney-Bankstown NSW	22.4.87/96
				(rest. Bankstown, ff 3.87 as "NZ1007")	
88-9266 •	AT-6C	**41-33160**		(to RAF as EX187)	
	Mk. IIA			(to RNZAF as NZ1009): shipped direct to NZ	9.42
				(to RNZAF inst. airframe INST211)	
				Woodbourne AB NZ: stored	78
				RNZAF Historic Flight: reserve aircraft	92/96
				(stored Wigram AB NZ 92)	
88-9269 •	AT-6C	**41-33163**		(to RAF as EX190)	
	Mk. IIa			(to RNZAF as NZ1012): shipped direct to NZ	9.42
				Aviation Historical Society of NZ, Ashburton	.78
				(displ. complete, "NZ1012" Ashburton 78)	
				Ashburton Aviation Museum: displ.	92/95
88-9272 •	AT-6C	**41-33166**		(to RAF as EX193)	
	Mk. IIa			(to RNZAF as NZ1015): shipped direct to NZ	9.42
				(shipped to NZ ex USA on SS "Waiotapu" 7.42)	
				Woodbourne AB: maintained airworthy	77/79
				Wigram AB: stored	.79/85
				RNZAF Historical Flight, Wigram & Ohakea AB	8.85/96
88-9283 •	AT-6C	**41-33177**		(to RAF as EX204): shipped direct to S Africa	11.42
	Mk. IIa			(to SAAF as 7059)	
			ZU-AOR	Harvard Club of South Africa: reg. res.	3.11.94
				Harvard Club of South Africa, Springs : reg.	8.8.95
88-9351 •	SNJ-4	**Bu09836**	NC318	CAA, Washington DC	12.7.46/48
				returned to US Navy	6.4.48
			N9589C	Rogers Air Service, Chester CA (tanker #8)	58/60
				P & B Aviation, Red Bluff CA (tanker #8)	.60/63
				French Aviation Co, Bakersfield CA: sprayer	.63/70
				Frank E. Howerton, Long Beach CA	76/84
				struck-off USCR	.77
				Marshall W. Best, Indianapolis IN: readded	2.11.94/96

88-9352 •	SNJ-4	**Bu09837**		(to FA Paraguaya as 0148, 0111)	
				World Wide Aeronautical Industries CA	9.2.91
				(purchased auction Asuncion, Paraguay 9.2.91, shipped, arr. dism. Santa Paula CA 9.91)	
			N3172N	World Wide Aeronautical Industries, Moorpark CA	19.9.91/92
				James Morgan, Aumsville OR	94
				Robert H. Poynton & Dave Saunders/ Western Warbirds, Perth-Jandakot WA	4.94
				(shipped ex USA, arr. Jandakot 15.6.94)	
				Peter Gardiner, Capalaba QLD	7.94/96
				(trucked Brisbane ex Jandakot, arr. 19.7.94: rest. project Caboolture QLD)	
				(USCR quotes id. 417210: orig NAA plate shows BuAer 09837)	
88-9360	SNJ-4	Bu09845		(to FA Brasileira as ....)	
			PT-KTH	reg., conv. for agricultural ops.	.76
				Serrna SA de Aviacao, Agricola, Sao Paulo	83
				struck-off reg.	.87
88-9419 •	SNJ-4	**Bu09904**	N6063C	Joann F. Kopeky, San Diego CA	63/64
				Bar Aero, National City CA	66
				Richard B. Ferguson, Chula Vista CA	9.68/72
			N211RF	Richard B. Ferguson, Overton NV	76/95
88-9437 •	SNJ-4	**Bu09922**	N5286N	Mark Britt, Stone Mountain GA	63/64
				Cox Sky Ranch, Knoxville TN	66
				Jessie Q. Bristow, Greenville MS	69
				Stanley Bright, Sumner MS	70/72
				Mid Continent Aircraft Corp, Hayti MO	76/77
				(at Oshkosh 8.82)	
				crashed, during aerobatics	3.6.83
				Tan Air Industries, North Granby CT	1.84/96
88-9450 •	SNJ-4	**Bu09935**	NC367	CAA, Washington DC	18.9.46/48
				ret. to US Navy	6.4.48
			N101X	Lloyd Longmire, Seattle WA	63/66
				Courtesy Aircraft Ltd, Loves Park IL	69
				Philip W. Stumm, Pasadena TX	70
				Gulf Coast Flyers Inc, Pasadena TX	72
				John K. Kohlhaas, Corpus Christi TX	76/84
				Confederate Air Force, Harlingen/Midland TX	86/94
88-9544 •	SNJ-4	**Bu09985**	NX55941	pilot Helen McBride, Apopka FL: (Cleveland race #91: stock 48, mod. to single-seater for 49 race: #49 "The Mike"	48/49
			N55941	Grover T. Parks, Miami FL	63
				Walter R. Griffin, Summerfield NC	.63/77
				(open storage, mod. single seater, Greensboro NC 74/77)	
				Ag-Central Aircraft Inc, Lubbock TX	84
				Zero lookalike Steven Miles, Carmel Valley CA	6.85/95
				(noted Oakland CA 9.88, single-seat, Zero sc.)	
88-9551 •	SNJ-4	Bu09992	**N5287N**	Robert Kuhn, Morristown NJ	63/64
				Hemodynamics Research Inc, Morristown NJ	66
				Henry A. Rapone, Hauppauge NY	69
				Sabre Aviation Ltd, Hauppauge NY	70/77
				Firebird Enterprises, Middlefield OH	84/88
				Frederick P. Hosking & Robert B. Mitchell, Sedona AZ	7.91/96
				(flies as "51642/87")	
88-9556	SNJ-4	Bu09997	NC365	CAA, Washington DC	23.9.46/48
				returned to US Navy	6.4.48
			N9565C	Cloud Modification Service, Minot ND	63
				Ralph E. Minor, Stanford MT	.63/72

88-9589	SNJ-4	Bu10030	NC340	CAA, Washington DC	.46/48
				returned to US Navy	6.4.48
				(to FA Brasileira as FAB T6D 1406)	
			PT-KVD	reg.	.76
				Fauzzi Faud Bunduck, Sao Paulo	83
				dest., struck-off reg.	6.89
88-9696	AT-6C Mk. IIa	41-33253		(to RAF as EX280)	
				(to SAAF as 7333): shipped direct to S.Africa	6.43/69
				(to FA Portuguesa as 1523)	.69/78
			G-TEAC	Trans Europe Air Charter Ltd, Hurn	18.1.79/83
				(flew as "RAF MC280")	
				Euan C. English, Bourn/Wyton/North Weald	12.7.83/95
				crashed, dest., Woodham Walter (English k.)	4.3.95
				(flew as "EX280", later "88-9696/USAF688")	
88-9723 •	AT-6C Mk. IIa	**41-33260**		(to RAF as EX287)	
				(to SAAF as 7168): shipped direct to S.Africa	2.43/69
				(to FA Portuguesa as 1560)	.69/79
			G-RCAF	Euroworld International, Biggin Hill	6.3.79/80
			N42BA	William Arnot & D. Wigley, Breckenridge TX	14.7.80/84
				William G. Arnot, Abilene TX	86/96
				(race #1 "Silver Baby")	
88-9725 •	AT-6C Mk. IIa	**41-33262**		(to RAF as EX289)	
				(to SAAF as 7183): shipped direct to S.Africa	2.43/69
				(ret. to RAF as EX289): shipped to UK, arr.	10.46
				SOC RAF: sold for scrap	8.50
				(to FA Portuguesa as 1535)	.69/79
			G-TSIX	Dan Taylor/Loughborough & Leicester Aircraft Museum, East Midlands	19.3.79
				(del. via Hurn 6.10.79, displ. as "EX289/G-T6")	
				Auto Alloys (Foundries) Ltd	83
				Dan Taylor, Tatenhill later Gamston, Notts	91/94
				John Zemlick, Wakefield	5.7.94/96
				(flies as "111836/JZ6")	
88-9728 •	AT-6C Mk.IIa	**41-33265**		(to RAF as EX292)	
				(to SAAF as 7182): shipped direct to S.Africa	2.43
				(ret. to RAF as EX292): shipped to UK, arr.	10.46
				(to Belgian AF as H39)	3.47
				Musee Royal de l'Armee, Brussels	79/90
				Eric Vormezeele, Brasschaat, Belgium	92
88-9753 •	AT-6C Mk. IIa	**41-33273**		(to RAF as EX300)	
				(to SAAF as 7082): shipped direct to S.Africa	11.42/93
				Stuart D. Davidson, Port Elizabeth	.93
			ZS-VAI	Aircraft Bureau, Syferfontein	28.5.93
88-9755 •	AT-6C Mk. IIa	**41-33275**		(to RAF as EX302)	
				(to SAAF as 7084): shipped direct to S.Africa	11.42/69
				(to FA Portuguesa as 1545)	.69/80
			G-BICE	Colin M. L. Edwards, Ipswich	3.9.80/92
				dam. on ground by storm, Ipswich (repaired)	10.87
88-9796 •	SNJ-4	**Bu10092**	NC352	CAA, Washington DC	27.6.46/48
				returned to US Navy	6.4.48
			N47040	Donald H. Marshall, Ferriday LA	76/86
				sale rep., Wilmington DE	92/95
88-9830 •	SNJ-4	**Bu10116**		(to R Swedish AF as ....)	
				(to Paraguay Navy as ....)	
			N5984A	ntu	
			N75964	William T. Nightingale, Alta Loma CA	10.5.93
				(rest. Chino CA .93 as USN/917/*Boll Weevil*)	
88-9922 •	AT-6C Mk. IIa	**41-33327**		(to RAF as EX354)	
				(to SAAF as 7156): shipped direct to S.Africa	12.42/94

			ZU-AOT	Harvard Club of South Africa: reg. res.	3.11.94
88-9958 •	AT-6C Mk. IIa	**41-33328**		(to RAF as EX355)	
				(to SAAF as 7024): shipped direct to S.Africa	12.42/94
			ZU-AOO	Harvard Club of South Africa: reg. res.	3.11.94
				Harvard Club of South Africa, Springs : reg.	8.8.95
88-10008•	AT-6C Mk. IIa	**41-33338**		(to RAF as EX365):	
				(to SAAF as 7152): shipped direct to S.Africa	10.42/94
			ZU-AOS	Harvard Club of South Africa	3.11.94
88-10108	AT-6C Mk. IIA	41-33365		(to RAF as EX392)	
				(to SAAF as 7185): shipped direct to S.Africa	12.42/69
				(to FA Portuguesa as 1554)	.69/79
			G-BGOU	Euroworld International Ltd, Biggin Hill	28.3.79/80
				(del. via Dinard-Lydd 23.8.79)	
				A. Peter Snell & P.A. Wood, Audley End	7.10.80/83
				A. Peter Snell, Audley End	21.1.83/85
				(flew as "SAAF7185")	
				crashed dest., Bourn (Snell k.)	7.9.85
88-10117•	SNJ-4	Bu10148	NC363	CAA, Washington DC	4.9.46/48
				returned to US Navy	6.4.48
			N6411D	Hale H. Clark, Shaker Heights OH	63/64
				Nathaniel Hawthorne College, Antrim NH	66
				Anita L. Saunders, Bedford MA	69
				Robert D. Saunders, Atlanta GA	70
				Lynda W. Saunders, Avondale Estates GA	72
				Airmen Inc, Norman OK	76/77
				Confederate Air Force, Harlingen/Midland TX	31.1.78/96
88-10185•	SNJ-4	**Bu10206**	N90650	Arnold Lindberg, Cut Bank MT	63/64
				David Younkin, Fort Collins CO	66/69
				Richard E. Demars, Loveland/Fort Collins CO	84/86
				(race #94 *Nuthin Fancy*)	
			N119DP	Daniel L. Petersen, Lincoln NE/Ellisville MO	5.86/93
				Roman B. Oser, Jasper IN	11.93/96
88-10203•	AT-6C Mk. IIa	**41-33380**		(to RAF as EX407)	
				(to SAAF as 7203): shipped direct to S.Africa	3.43
				SAAF Museum, Swartkop AB	93/96
88-10252•	AT-6C Mk. IIa	**41-33395**		(to RAF as EX422)	
				(to RNZAF as NZ1023): shipped direct to NZ	2.43/78
				(to RNZAF inst. airframe INST189)	
				Engine Support Inc, Sebring FL	.78
				Aircraft Preservation Society, Auckland NZ	.78
				Joe Drage/Drages Historical Aircraft Museum, Wodonga VIC	6.78
				Ken Orrman, Shepparton VIC: stored dism.	.82/85
				Aero Technics, Canberra ACT: arr. dism.	4.85
				Brian J. Candler, Canberra ACT	11.86
			VH-CRC	Brian J. Candler, Canberra ACT	8.2.88/92
				(rest. Canberra 86/88, ff 2.88 as "USAF 23"	
				dam. landing, Canberra ACT (repaired)	9.7.89
				D. R. Cordy, Marong VIC	10.92/96
88-10253•	AT-6C Mk. IIa	**41-33396**		(to RAF as EX423)	
				(to RNZAF as NZ1024): shipped direct to NZ	2.43/78
				Joe Drage/Drage Historical Aircraft Museum, Wodonga VIC: shipped, static displ.	.78/80
				Joe Drage/Drage Air World, Shepparton VIC	82/89
				Doug Hamilton, Whorouly VIC	.90/91
			VH-XNZ	Doug S. Hamilton, Whorouly VIC	27.2.91/96
				(rest. Albury NSW, ff 2.91 as "NZ1024")	
				(note: CAA quote c/n 88-13188: NAA & USAAF plates of NZ1039/88-13188 fitted to NZ1024 during RNZAF service.)	
88-10254•	AT-6C	**41-33397**		(to RAF as EX424)	

	Mk. IIa			(to RNZAF as NZ1025): shipped direct to NZ	2.43/78
				Engine Support Inc, Sebring FL	.78
				David M. Diamond & Jim M. Sullivan, Otaio	.78
			ZK-ENN	David M. Diamond & Jim M. Sullivan, Timaru	30.6.80/87
				John Greenstreet, Auckland	90
				crashed, mid-air collision with ZK-ENE,	
				near Ardmore NZ	25.2.90
				John Greenstreet, Auckland (wreck, stored)	92
88-10271•	SNJ-4	**Bu10266**	NC269	CAA, Washington DC	2.5.46/48
				returned to US Navy	6.4.48
			N7093C	Stephen W. Pahs, Denver CO	63/70
				J. W. Duff, Denver CO: reappeared USCR	2.91/96
88-10278•	SNJ-4	**Bu10273**	N7413C	Central Valley Aviation, Fresno CA	63/70
				reappeared USCR	4.84
				Peter A. Crown, Gillette WY & Waianae HI	86/95
88-10293•	SNJ-4	**Bu10288**	NC273	CAA, Washington DC	10.4.46/48
				returned to US Navy	6.4.48
				(to FA Portuguesa as .....)	
			N3747X	Arthur D. Medore/Banaire, Hemet CA	23.1.80/84
				Paul D. Reese, Sissonville WV	2.86/96
88-10537 •	AT-6C	**41-33417**		(to RAF as EX444)	
	Mk. IIa			(to SAAF as 7028): shipped direct to S.Africa	1.43/94
			ZU-AOP	Harvard Club of South Africa	3.11.94/96
88-10560 •	AT-6C	**41-33440**		(to RAF as EX467)	
	Mk. IIa			(to SAAF as 7039): shipped direct to S.Africa	1.43/69
				(to FA Portuguesa as 1551)	.69/79
			G-BGOT	Euroworld International Ltd, Biggin Hill	28.3.79/80
				not del. UK: sold to USA, struck-off reg.	16.4.80
			N37642	Victor C. Bilbo, Dallas TX	6.80/88
				Norman V. Lewis, Louisville KY	92
				Larry G. Perry, Andover KS	5.92/96
88-10569	AT-6C	41-33449		(to RAF as EX476)	
	Mk. IIa			(to SAAF as 7295): shipped direct to S.Africa	4.43/46
				(ret. to RAF as EX476): shipped to UK, arr.	11.46
				(to Belgian AF as H8): BOC 25.2.47 SOC	27.8.58
			F-BJBE	Air France, Cormeilles/Toussous-le-Noble	21.5.59/64
				Air France, Vilgenis: inst. airframe	
				Christain Martin, St.Rambert-d'Albon	.83/85
			F-AZDK	C. Martin/Aero Retro, St.Rambert-d'Albon	7.3.85/89
				rep. crashed, France	7.89
88-10571•	AT-6C	41-33451		(to RAF as EX478)	
	Mk. IIa			(to SAAF as 7166)	
			ZU-AOU	Harvard Club of South Africa: reg. res.	3.11.94
				(note: SAAF quotes 7166 as EX277)	
88-10589•	AT-6C	**41-33469**		(to RAF as EX496)	
	Mk. IIa			(to SAAF as 7255): shipped direct to S.Africa	3.43/69
				(to FA Portuguesa as 1538)	.69/79
			N4995A	Jack Seale, Dallas TX	11.12.79
				David E. Henry, Houston TX	84/86
				Dennis G. Buehn, Reno NV	86
				Peter H. McMillan, San Fancisco CA	.86/90
				(flew in England-Australia Air Race 3.90	
				as 42495/*Spirit of San Francisco*)	
			VH-LJQ	Ray McWilliams/Sales Direction Pty Ltd,	
				Sydney NSW	4.12.90/93
				(Australian CofA, ff Sydney-Bankstown 12.90)	
				Doug Lennon, Toowoomba QLD	.92/96
				(rest. Oakey QLD 93/94 as "SAAF 7023")	
88-10633•	AT-6C	**41-33513**		(to RAF as EX540)	

	Mk. IIa			(to SAAF as 7270): shipped direct to S.Africa	4.43/47
				(ret. to RAF as EX540): shipped to UK, arr.	1.47/50
				sold for scrap, SOC	8.50
				(to Spanish AF as C.6-166)	
			N7044J	Courtesy Aircraft Inc, Rockford IL	12.88
				NA-50 Inc, Long Island City NY	92
				Thomas A. Sterling, Bandon OR	8.94/96
88-10677•	AT-6C Mk. IIa	**41-33557**		(to RAF as EX584)	
				(to SAAF as 7244): shipped direct to S.Africa	3.43/69
				(to FA Portuguesa as 1522)	.69/78
			G-RBAC	G. R. B. Aviation Co Ltd, Biggin Hill	25.1.79/80
				(del. to Biggin Hill 15.5.79)	
			G-BHXF	ntu	6.80
			G-VALE	Kayvale Finance Ltd, Shobdon	17.9.80/81
				(flew as USAF "8810677/LTA-584")	
				John Powell, Shobdon	85
			N36CA	Courtesy Aircraft Inc, Rockford IL	11.85/86
				Wally Braun, Chicago IL	86/88
				Confederate Air Force (MI Wing), Gary IN	88
				Leslie J. Raffel, Gurnee IL	12.89/96
88-10712•	SNJ-4 T-6C	**Bu26548**		(to USAF as T-6C 48-1343)	
			N99292	reg. res.	3.77/92
88-10727	SNJ-4	Bu26563	N52231	Tom R. Burns, Washington DC	63/84
88-11041•	SNJ-4	**Bu26667**		(to FA Portuguesa as ....)	
			N37477	Arthur D. Medore/Banaire, Hemet CA	23.1.80/95
88-11083	SNJ-4	Bu26669	N9530C	Eugene H. Lobdell, Los Angeles CA	63/64
				Robert M. McCoy, Orange/Inglewood CA	66/84
88-11104•	SNJ-4	**Bu26690**		(to JMSDF as .....)	
			N89015	reg. candidate	10.77
				Charles Landells, Kennewick WA	84/86
				Dennis G. Buehn, Carson City NC	92
				Joe A. Carcioppolo, Lyndhurst OH	4.95
88-11170•	AT-6C	**41-32815**	**N5WS**	Willie G. Walker/Walker Screws, Abilene TX	5.92/95
88-11198•	SNJ-4	**Bu26714**	N5299N	MN Vocational Education Board, St Paul MN	63/69
				(last FAA annual inspection 10.56)	
				MN Air & Space Museum, Minneapolis MN	88
88-11385•	AT-6C T-6G	**41-32950** **50-1279**		(rebuilt by NA (Fresno CA) as T-6G)	
				USAFM, Wright Patterson AFB OH	66/96
				(displ. as "AT-6A USAAC 41-279")	
88-11452•	SNJ-4	**Bu26808**	N9541C	Joe L. Meyers, Colfax WA	63
				Ward A. Clemmo, Puyallup WA	.63/64
				William J. Lewallen, Arizona City AZ	66/69
				Charles E. Keough, Tucson AZ	70
			N26808	K. R. Wynn, Houston TX	72
				Lee Groff, Jacksonville FL	76/77
				WWII Enterprises, Watchung NJ	84/86
				Wings of Eagles Inc, Readington NJ	9.91/95
88-11723•	SNJ-4	**Bu26904**	N9529C	A. W. Hecht, Redlands CA	63/64
				N. D. Adams, Brownwood TX	66
				Gardner Flyers Inc, Brownwood TX	69/70
			N4419T	Greg J. Babcock, Whapato WA	8.92/95
88-11731•	SNJ-4	**Bu26912**	N9522C	Lewis Aircraft Service, Pampa TX	63/64
				Roy C. Word, Pampa TX	66
				D & D Aero Spraying, Rantoul KS	69/86
				(mod. ag. conv: single rear seat)	
				Aero Tech Services Inc, Fayetteville AR	92
			N16JG	James T. Greeson, Tecumseh MI/Lebanon TN	6.92/96

88-11732•	SNJ-4	Bu26913	**N7059C**	Columbia Mold & Die Co, Bedford OH	63/72
				sale rep., USCR	84/96
88-11825•	SNJ-4	**Bu26966**		(to Argentine Navy/Armada as 0442/4-G-75)	
				Museo de la Aviacion Naval Argentina,	
				Espora NAS, Bahia Blanca: dam., stored	92
88-11850•	SNJ-4	**Bu26991**	**N6413D**	H. L. Webb, Berkeley MO	63/92
				Monte Zema, Colville WA	93/94
				(rest. project 92/94, completed .94)	
				Thomas E. Duzan, Kennewick WA	.94/95
88-11851•	SNJ-4	**Bu26992**	**N269WB**	reg.	12.12.80
				Edward A. Maslon/Eddies Aero Service,	
				San Diego-Gillespie CA	1.81/95
				(rest. 84/90, ff c91 San Diego-Gillespie CA	
				as "USAF/26992/LTA-269")	
88-11959•	SNJ-4	**Bu27060**	**N6414D**	Samuel N. Sweet, New Bedford MA	63/64
				Arthur J. Foster, West Palm Beach FL	66
				William W. Curtis, Windham Centre CT	69/70
				Victor R. Loranger, Sanford ME	72
				sale rep., USCR	84/96
88-11970•	SNJ-4	**Bu27071**	**N5850N**	B & F Aircraft Supply, Oaklawn IL	63/96
88-12013•	SNJ-4	**Bu27114**		Arthur Medore, Hemet CA: reg. candidate	30.6.93
88-12018•	SNJ-4	**Bu27119**	**N60380**	Salvatore Martino, Bradenton FL	63/64
				Romaine A. Collins, Vancouver WA	66/70
				Low Level Dusting Co., La Salle CO	11.71/96
88-12032•	AT-6C	**41-33561**		(to RAF as EX588)	
	Mk. IIa			(to RNZAF as NZ1033): shipped direct to NZ	5.43/78
				Stan G. Quill, Palmerston North	.78
			ZK-SGQ	Stan G. Quill/ NZ Sport & Vintage Aviation	
				Society, Masterton	24.2.81/96
88-12033•	AT-6C	**41-33562**		(to RAF as EX589)	
	Mk. IIa			(to RNZAF as NZ1034): shipped direct to NZ	5.43
				(to RNZAF inst. airframe INST210)	
				Ohakea AB: rest. as camoufl. "NZ1034/7-FE"	78
				RAAF Museum, RAAF Point Cook VIC	12.88/96
				(mod. as Mk.II for displ. as "RNZAF NZ947")	
88-12036•	AT-6C	**41-33565**		(to RAF as EX592)	
	Mk. IIa			(to RNZAF as NZ1037): shipped direct to NZ	5.43/78
			ZK-ENA	John Mathewson, Ardmore/Ranfurly	20.6.78/95
88-12044•	AT-6C	**41-33573**		(to RAF as EX600)	
	Mk. IIa			(to SAAF as 7382): shipped direct to S.Africa	6.43/69
				(to FA Portuguesa as 1559)	.69/79
			G-BGOV	Euroworld International Ltd, Biggin Hill	28.3.79/80
				(del. via Dinard-Lydd 23.8.79)	
				Aces High Ltd, North Weald	5.11.80/83
			N4434N	June Mourad, Old Rebel Field, Mercedes TX	11.8.83/96
88-12046•	AT-6C	**41-33575**		(to RAF as EX602)	
	Mk. IIa			(to SAAF as 7384): shipped direct to S.Africa	6.43/46
				(ret. to RAF as EX602): shipped to UK, arr.	10.46
				(to Belgian AF as H30): BOC	27.2.47/59
			F-BJBJ	Air France, Cormeilles	29.4.59/66
				Air France Technical School, Vilgenis	90/96
88-12054•	AT-6C	**41-33583**		(to RAF as EX610)	
	Mk. IIa			(to SAAF as 7303): shipped direct to S.Africa	7.43/94
			N9272C	reg.	8.95

88-12070•	AT-6C Mk. IIa	**41-33599**		(to RAF as EX626)	
				(to SAAF as 7306): shipped direct to S.Africa	7.43/94
			ZU-AOV	Harvard Club of South Africa: reg. res.	3.11.94
88-12122•	SNJ-4	**Bu27179**		(to FA Portuguesa as ......)	
			N8539B	Arthur D. Medore/Banaire, Hemet CA	4.11.80/95
88-12127•	AT-6C Mk. IIa	**41-33606**		(to RAF as EX633)	
				(to SAAF as 7349): shipped direct to S.Africa	6.43/46
				(ret. to RAF as EX633): shipped to UK, arr.	11.46
				(to Belgian AF as H29)	2.47/59
			F-BJBI	Air France, Cormeilles	25.6.59/63
				P. Mercier, Cormeilles	11.63/64
			F-WJBI	rereg.	.69
			F-BJBI	Aero Club de Neuilly, Les Mureaux	2.74/77
				Salis Collection, La Ferte-Alais	79
			F-AZBE	Amicale J-B Salis, La Ferte-Alais	8.80/96
				(flew as Aeronavale NA-64 "41-F-4", conv. single seat F6F lookalike. "USN RM/27" 84)	
88-12150•	AT-6C	**42-4071**		(to FA Mexicana as 791)	
			N7055H	Texas Turbo Jet Inc, Dallas TX	1.89
			N416JB	Jimmy Boshears, Bakersfield CA	12.89
			N7055H	Richard S. Fields, Fullerton CA	3.90/95
88-12151•	AT-6C	**42-4072**		(to FA Mexicana as 709)	
			N7054X	Texas Turbo Jet Inc, Dallas TX	1.89
				John M. Foster, Alamogordo NM	5.90/96
88-12281•	SNJ-4	**Bu27245**	**N24554**	Banaire Enterprises Inc, Hemet CA	76/77
				Mid Atlantic Air Museum, Middletown PA	2.83/96
88-12289•	SNJ-4	**Bu27253**	**N48119**	sale rep.	76
				Grand Canyon Ventures, Las Vegas NV	84/86
				Brandon D. Kunicki, Chino CA: rest. project	4.92/96
88-12291•	SNJ-4	**Bu27255**	N9528C	Richard W. Wheaton, Hollywood CA	63/64
				Anthony P. Colitti, Granada Hills CA	66/69
				Ronald E. Taylor, Glendale CA	70
				Bob Van Oosterhout, Las Vegas NV	72
			N86WW	Robert C. Forbes, Porterville CA	76
				Charles E. Beck, Los Angeles CA	10.76/95
				(race #2 *Honest Entry*)	
88-12326•	AT-6C Mk. IIa	41-33633		(to RAF as EX660)	
				(to SAAF as 7309): shipped direct to S.Africa	7.43/46
				(ret. to RAF as EX660): shipped to UK, arr.	9.46
				(to Belgian AF as H4)	2.47/59
			F-BJBC	Air France, Cormeilles	25.6.59/64
				Ste. Avions Meyer et Air Cameroun, Douala	11.64/71
				J. Dere, Douala, Camerouns	9.71
				struck-off reg.	.77
				Aero Retro, St. Rambert D'Albon, France	86/89
88-12349•	SNJ-4	**Bu27293**	**N9523C**	Transaire Spraying Co, Canyon TX	63/64
				Robert Tobacco, Colts Neck NJ	66/72
				John J. Stokes, San Marcos TX	76/77
				Phil B. Dear, Jackson MS	84
				McGehee Air Inc, McGehee AR	86
				Paul S. Farber, Great Neck NY	12.87/96
				(owner quotes this is a CCF Harvard Mk.4 rebuilt from SNJ-4 Bu27293)	
88-12407•	SNJ-4	**Bu27307**	**N9525C**	Richard T. Sykes, North Hollywood CA	7.61/95
88-12427•	SNJ-4	**Bu27327**	**N2269N**	Arthur D. Medore/Banaire, Hemet CA	7.78/92
				Gene F. Burrill, Prospect OR	92/95
				(3 year rest. project, ff 21.12.94)	
				crashed landing, near Portland OR	8.4.95

88-12472•	AT-6C	**42-4224**		(to FA Brasileira as FAB T6D-1264)	.43
			PT-KTA	reg., conv. for agricultural ops.	.76
				Caio Antonio dos Santos, Piracununga	83/84
			N88NR	Nelson E. Regner, Miami FL	3.10.84
			N310JH	Jones B. Hanson, Ft Lauderdale FL	6.85
				Wayne Dorman, Pompano Beach FL	86/91
				Michael A. Halem, New York NY	7.90/96
88-12507	SNJ-4	Bu27351	N9534C	Edward A. Ulco, New Milford PA	63/64
			N9543C	Edward A. Ulco, Hallstead PA	66/72
				Chester Siepiela, Hawley PA	76
				Clark Motor Co Inc, State College PA	.77/84
88-12508•	SNJ-4	**Bu27352**	**N7058C**	Columbia Mold & Die Co, Bedford OH	63/72
				Cherokee Corp, Encampment WY	76
				Cherokee Corp, Monument CO	4.83/86
				Jerome A. Flesher, Colorado Springs CO	91/96
88-12533•	SNJ-4	**Bu27377**	**N6416D**	Bernard E. Brown, Corona NY	63/64
				Carpenter & Dunn Inc, Manlius NY	66/69
				Jasta Aviation, Syracuse NY	70/72
				Ernest Enos, Bridgewater MA	76/77
				George H. Baker, Daytona Beach FL	84/92
				Steve C. Collins & Ray E. Fowler, Atlanta GA	9.93/96
				(flies as "USAF 2533/TA533")	
88-12619•	SNJ-4	**Bu27383**	**N2269S**	Arthur D. Medore/Banaire, Hemet CA	7.78/86
				Raymond G. Sanders, Kalispell MT	92
				(rest. project Ennis MT, ff 10.92)	
				Ervin F. Lyon, Lexington MA	.92/96
88-12622•	SNJ-4	**Bu27386**	**N7061C**	Robin E. Williamson, Santa Barbara CA	63/64
				Patrick H. Shiel, Lancaster CA	66/69
				Mike Sayan, Thousand Oaks CA	70/72
				Intnl. Recruiting Services Inc, Van Nuys CA	76/84
				Jim Furlong/Furlong-Gates Inc, Van Nuys CA	1.86/96
88-12640•	SNJ-4	**Bu27404**	**N7412C**	Edward G. Peters, Shafter CA	63/64
				John M. Percival, San Jose CA	66
				Joseph J. Andrade, San Mateo CA	69/70
				Curtis S. Turner, Modesto CA	72
				Wheeler Ridge Aviation, Bakersfield CA	5.76/96
88-12709	SNJ-4	Bu27433	N9536C	W. H. Horchheimer, Eloy AZ	63/64
				Kenneth L. Burmeister, Seattle WA	66
				National Aerial Advertising, Reading MA	69/72
				Rosie O'Grady's Warehouse Inc, Pensacola FL	76/77
			N711SQ	Rosie O'Grady's Flying Circus, Orlando FL	.77/87
				dest. midair collision Cessna 340, Orlando FL	2.5.87
88-12712	SNJ-4	Bu27436	N9542C	Robert A. Hodges, San Diego CA	63/69
				Charles C. Clevenger, San Francisco CA	70/72
88-12758•	AT-6C Mk.IIa	**41-33665**		(to RAF as EX692)	
				(to SAAF as 7321): shipped direct to S.Africa	8.43/49
				(to S Rhodesian AF as SR50)	3.49
				New Sarum AB: displ. on parade ground	60/67
				removed from display, stored	68
			ZS-WEJ	A. J. Watson, Honeydew	31.1.89
				(rest. Honeydew, using parts from	
				SAAF 7048 & 7651: nearly complete 9.89)	
88-12817•	SNJ-4	**Bu27481**	**N48153**	Banaire Enterprises Inc, Hemet CA	76/77
				sale rep., Homosassa Springs FL	1.81/96
88-12821•	SNJ-4	**Bu27485**	YV-ARA		
			N113MC	Mark L. Chamlis, Tallahassee FL	2.93/96

38-12827•	SNJ-4	**Bu27491**		(to FA Hondurena as 202)	
			N2781P	B & G Aero, King City CA: candidate	12.82
				(del. Tegucigalpa AB to CA .83)	
				B & G Aero, King City CA	6.83
			N127VF	Eddie L. van Fossen, Bakersfield CA	2.84/96
				(rest. Shafter-Minter Field .84 as	
				Marines 27491, race #27 *Miss TNT*)	
38-12841•	SNJ-4	Bu27505	**N2269T**	Arthur D. Medore/Banaire, Hemet CA	7.78/96
38-12847•	SNJ-4	Bu27511		(to FA Portuguesa as ....)	
			N3747Z	Arthur D. Medore/Banaire, Hemet CA	23.1.80/84
				Danny G. Kinker, Lawrence KS/Houston TX	8.90/96
38-12848	SNJ-4	Bu27512	N7056C	Edward H. Smith, Chicago IL	63/69
				Aerospace Dynamics, Thief River Falls MN	70/72
				crashed, aerobatics, Thief River Falls MN	6.7.72
38-12850•	SNJ-4	**Bu27514**	**N2269U**	Arthur D. Medore/Banaire, Hemet CA	7.78
				Charles E. Beck, Los Angeles CA	10.83/96
38-12858•	SNJ-4	**Bu27522**	CF-JXJ	reg.	.57
				Beverley G. Willison, Akron OH	65/79
			N8475S	reg. res.	7.80
			N934JT	Joseph O. Tobul, Pittsburgh PA	2.81/96
38-12929•	SNJ-4	**Bu27533**	N6861C	Dogwood Inc, Summit NJ	63/64
				Newton H. Smith, Edison NJ	66/76
				Har Ran Aircraft Sales, Tulsa OK	.77
				John M. Ware, Atlanta GA	84
				William F. Kramer, New Hyde Park NY	86
				Robert C. Beckman, Ashville OH	3.89/92
			N51562	Robert C. Beckman, Ashville OH	12.92/96
				(flies as "SNJ-4 USN/51562")	
38-12932•	SNJ-4	**Bu27536**	**N7038C**	Choteau Flying Service, Choteau MT	63/64
	SNJ-4C			Gordon Slusser, Richvale CA	66
				James W. Wirtz, Gridley CA	69/70
				Dimitry V. Prian, Long Beach CA	76
				Dennis G. Buehn, Reno NV	84/86
				Edward H. Wachs, Waukegan IL	8.90/95
38-12945•	SNJ-4	**Bu27549**		Tallmantz Collection/Movieland of the Air,	
				Orange County CA	68
			N80714	W. R. Klaers, D. Spears & A J. Wojciak	8.89
				NA-50 Inc, Tenefly NJ	92
				Seminole Air Centre, Seminole OK	6.92/95
38-12956•	SNJ-4	**Bu27560**	**N30CE**	Kal Aero Service Inc	14.1.86
				Carl Schmieder, Phoenix AZ	.86/87
				(rest. 86/90 lookalike N.A. P-64, ff 28.10.90)	
				Lone Star Flight Museum, Galveston TX	9.91/92
				(del. 15.10.91, flies as P-64 "USAAC 12596")	
				Tango Corp, Washington DC	7.94/96
38-13037•	SNJ-4	**Bu27581**		(to FA Portuguesa as ....)	
			N37474	Arthur D. Medore/Banaire, Hemet CA	23.1.80/95
38-13041•	SNJ-4	**Bu27585**	N7438C	Donald D. Walter, Phoenix AZ	63/64
				Moseley Aviation, Tolleson AZ	66
			N224X	Harry B. Marioneaux, Shreveport LA	69/72
				Confederate Air Force, Harlingen/Midland TX	3.5.75/95
38-13067•	SNJ-4	**Bu27611**		(to FA Paraguaya as .....)	
			N7437C	William C. Castleberry, Miami FL	63/66
				Walter H. Cooper, Cordele GA	69/70
				Harry Roth, Houma LA	76
				John S. Thigpen, Franklinton LA	.77/84
				reappeared USCR	8.87
				MGH Enterprises, Wilmington DE	92

				Morris W. Ray & David Peeler, Memphis TN	94/95
				7437 Charlie Inc, Memphis TN	3.95
88-13072•	SNJ-4	**Bu27616**	N7065C	William J. Whitfield, Davis CA	63/64
				Sutter Butte Dusters Inc, Live Oak CA	66
				Clifford D. Baker, Eudora AR	69
				Lee C. Abide, Greenville MS	70/84
				readded USCR	5.88
				Kenneth Day, Coleman TX	90/91
				(race #22 *Catch 22*)	
			N22KD	Kenny Day & William Laws/	
				Coleman Warbird Museum, Coleman TX	5.91/94
				Musick Aircraft Corp, Brownwood TX	6.95
88-13081•	SNJ-4 Sk.16 SNJ-4	**Bu27625**	**N1624M**	East Coast Airmotive Inc, Miami FL: USCR	63/70
				(to R Swedish AF as Fv16221)	54/57
				(to Argentine Navy/Armada as 0503/1-E-225,	
				later reserialled 0503/EAN-225)	5.57/70
				Museo de la Aviacion Naval Argentina,	
				Espora NAS, Bahia Blanca, Argentina: arr.	3.5.88/92
				(planned rest. to fly, displ. as 1E225)	
88-13164•	SNJ-4	**Bu27668**	N7070C	Arthur D. Binns, Harleysville PA	63/64
				Laurel Aero Leasing Corp, Laurel DE	66
				David W. Guernsey, Wellesley MA	69/84
				reappeared USCR	3.90
				Frank M. Land, Klamath Falls OR	92
				James V. Ferlaak, Elk River MN	5.94/96
88-13166•	SNJ-4	**Bu27670**	**N67003**	Silver State Construction Co, Fallon NV	63/69
				Mary Salerno, Las Vegas NV	76/86
				Marvin E. Hetzel, Riverside IL	11.86/96
88-13171•	SNJ-4	**Bu27675**	**N7062C**	Charles W. Robertson, Redondo Beach CA	63
				Lester D. Friend, San Diego CA	.63/64
				Jack W. Julian, North Edwards CA	66
				20th Century Fox Film Corp, Hollywood CA	68/71
				(conv. to Kate replica at Long Beach CA .68	
				for film "Tora Tora Tora"; open storage	
				Long Beach CA 69/71, sold at auction 2.71)	
				Brooks A. Moore, Bethany OK	84
				Richard E. Foote/Professional Aircraft Sales Co,	
				New Smyrna Beach FL	86
				Hugh C. & Mike Conley, College Park GA	7.88/96
				(flies as Japanese Kate BII-310)	
88-13187•	AT-6C Mk.IIa	**41-33714**		(to RAF as EX741)	
				(to RNZAF as NZ1038): shipped direct to NZ	8.43/78
				Mike Nortier, Auckland NZ: airframe only	.78
				G. Stan Smith/Warbirds, Dairy Flat NZ: fuse.	.78
				(fuse. used in rest. of NZ977 (76-3834) .90;	
				hulk stored incomplete Auckland 92)	
				Col Pay, Scone NSW: dism., rest. project	84
				(rest project: fuse NZ1086/INST176,	
				wings and parts from NZ1038)	
				Robert H. Poynton, Toodyay WA	8.84/92
				(moved by road Scone-Toodyay 8.84)	
			VH-AYO	Robert H. Poynton, Perth-Jandakot WA	19.3.92/96
				(rest. Jandakot WA ff 11.7.92)	
				adopted id. of NZ1038): see 88-16325	
88-13189•	AT-6C Mk.IIa	**41-33716**		(to RAF as EX743)	
				(to RNZAF as NZ1040): shipped direct to NZ	8.43/78
				Engine Support Inc, Sebring FL	.78
				Silverstream Railway & Vintage Transport,	
				Hutt Valley NZ	.78
				(planned static displ., stored Blenheim 79)	
			ZK-REB	Confederate Air Force (NZ Wing): reg. res.	92/95

				(under rest. Auckland-North Shore 94)	
8-13190•	AT-6C Mk.IIa	**41-33717**		(to RAF as EX744)	
				(to RNZAF as NZ1041): shipped direct to NZ	8.43
				Air New Zealand, Auckland: inst. airframe	10.71/92
8-13193•	AT-6C Mk.IIa	**41-33720**		(to RAF as EX747)	
				(to RNZAF as NZ1044): shipped direct to NZ	8.43
				Air New Zealand, Christchuch: inst. airframe	10.71/92
8-13243•	SNJ-4	**Bu27687**	N7839B	Gordon Wagner, Miami FL	63
				Charles I. Bernard, North Bay Village FL	.63/64
				Simon Crites, Vienna VA	66
				Harold F. Beal, Knoxville TN	69
			N55A	Jack R. Flanary, Reno NV	72
				Sierra Enterprises, Reno NV	76
				Har Ran Aircraft Sales, Tulsa OK	.77
				Samuel B. Saxton, Allentown PA	84/86
				Herman Bayerdorfer, Guilford ME	90
				James E. Thompson, Plainfield NH	92
				Bruce L. Moore, Canaan NH	9.93/95
8-13345•	SNJ-4	**Bu27729**	**N7407C**	Abbott Aviation, Challis ID	63/70
				(last FAA annual inspection 4.58)	
				Alex Koleda, Prineville OR	86
				Cinema Air Inc, Carlsbad CA	1.91/95
8-13364•	SNJ-4	**Bu27748**	**N10597**	Harold Baker, Chesterfield MO	63/66
				Horst K. Heiles, St. Louis MO	69
				George Banjak, Wester Groves MO	70/72
				Livesays Flying Service, Weldon AR	76/84
				Lee Maples, Vichy MO (race #70 "Show Me")	86/88
				C. E. Schmidt, Vichy MO	10.89/95
8-13369•	SNJ-4	**Bu27753**	**N6419D**	Walter R. Griffin, Greensboro NC	63/70
				Jack W. Reddick, Pleasant Garden NC	72
				damaged Julian NC	.73
				(stored, dam., Julian-Causey Airport NC 76)	
				sale rep., USCR	76/96
8-13370•	SNJ-4	**Bu27754**	**N7090C**	Boyd E. Quate, Scottsbluff NE	63
				Anthony Salvador, Lancaster CA	.63/64
				Joseph W. Kilgore, Inyokern CA	66
				Peter A. Dallas, Grand Canyon AZ	69
				David N. Walters, Phoenix AZ (race #38)	70
				Midway Mobile Homes Inc, Phoenix AZ	72
				Douglas Sellix, Springtown PA	76
				Harvey Gillman Aircraft, Brookville OH	.77
				Philip M. Robins, Garretson SD later Minneapolis MN	8.83/96
				(flies as 13370/370)	
8-13372•	SNJ-4	**Bu27756**	N7067C	Torbet Aircraft Inc, Orange County CA	63/64
				John W. Trueblood, Costa Mesa CA	66
				Arvin W. Pliss, Monterey CA	69/70
			N13372	Arvin W. Pliss, San Jose CA	76/86
				Paul Mace, Ashland OR	2.89/96
8-13374•	SNJ-4	**Bu27758**	**N6420D**	Robert Graf, Clinton CT	63
				David C. Terhune, Guilford CT	.63/66
				John Crumblish, Brewster NY	69/72
				Warbirds Inc, Miami FL	84
				Vincent Tirado/Classic Warbirds, Miami FL	86/92
				damaged by Hurricane Andrew	24.8.92
				Tri-State Aviation, Wahpeton ND	6.95
8-13376•	SNJ-4	**Bu27760**	**N7077C**	Fran D. Valenzuela, Encino CA	63
				Theodore Janozarek, Thousand Oaks CA	.63/64
				John McGregor, Los Angeles CA	66/70
				Lawrence B. Klaers, Fontana CA	76/87

				Eugene A. Zeiner, Santa Monica CA	1.91/96
88-13384•	SNJ-4	**Bu27768**	N5208V	James M. Dewey, Santa Paula CA	63/64
				Ward A. Clemmo, Puyallup WA	66
				James A. Williams, Palo Alto CA	69/72
				Frank G. Compton, Redondo Beach CA	76/79
			N101VT	Frank G. Compton, Torrance CA	4.79/84
				(flew as "SNJ-2/VN-3DB/USN101")	
				sale rep., Palos Verdes CA	86
				Gary Anderson IL	88
				Dennis Jankowski, Elgin IL	92
				Jeff Koenig/Koenig Farms Inc, Yuma CO	8.93/96
				(flies as"SNJ-2 27768")	
88-13386•	SNJ-4	**Bu27770**	**N6421D**	Madison Flying Club, Tallulah LA	63/64
				(last FAA annual inspection 8.60)	
				Robert Speed/Caprock Flying Svce, Vega TX	76/96
88-13391•	SNJ-4	**Bu27775**	N7003C	H. B. Cook, Joliet IL	63
				Aero Enterprises Inc, Elkhart IN	.63/64
				Ohio Valley Aviation, Wheeling WV	66
				Ehrick C. Goolsby, Okeechobee FL	69
				Davu Aviation, Sarasota FL	70
			N99DA	Davu Aviation, Sarasota FL	72
				David D. Allyn & Henry Oliver/	
				Wings of Yesterday Inc, Santa Fe NM	76/96
88-13466•	AT-6C	**42-43973**	N7405C	Boyd E. Quate, Scottsbluff NE	63
				Montie S. Miller, Lancaster CA	.63/64
				Joseph E. Bathancourt, Schenectady NY	66
				David P. Tonery, Mount Kisco NY	69
				Anthony Aguanno, Denville NJ	70
			N33CC	Anthony Aguanno, Denville NJ	76/77
				US Aeronautical Museum of Science,	
				Cleveland OH: displ.	
				Stanley P. Kavrik, Tucson AZ	86
				Evergreen Ventures Inc/	
				Evergreen Heritage Collection, Marana AZ	5.86/96
88-13478•	SNJ-4	**Bu27782**	**N6422D**	Richard P. Gazinga, Meriden CT	63
				Joseph A. Russo, Haddam CT	.63/64
				Philip Ditillo, Oakville CT	66/77
				Tan-Air Industries Inc, Granby CT	12.81/96
88-13509•	SNJ-4	**Bu27813**	**N6171Q**	Twin D Enterprises Inc, Hemet CA	17.5.93/96
88-13517•	SNJ-4	**Bu27821**	**N7024C**	Ray M. Roberts, New Orleans LA	63/66
				Spremich Enterprises Inc, New Orleans LA	69
				Charles I. Tucker, Ferriday LA	70/76
				Confederate Air Force, Harlingen/Midland TX	17.9.82/95
88-13519•	SNJ-4	**Bu27823**	**N6423D**	McCollum Aviation, Tampa FL	63/64
				Fred O. Eiler, Tarentum PA	66/92
				reg. pending, Radium Springs NM	96
88-13568•	SNJ-4	**Bu27832**	**N6171C**	Twin D Enterprises Inc, Hemet CA	17.5.93
				Joel M. McMillian, Birmingham AL: rest.	8.94/96
88-13581•	SNJ-4	**Bu27845**		(to Spanish AF as AE.6-157, C.6-157 "744-157")	
			N29910	Combat Aircraft Inc, Elkhart IN	5.82
			N822TH	ntu: Tom Hill, Dallas TX	9.83
			N29910	Glen Aviation Systems, Dallas TX	84
				Robert D. Smith, Irving TX	12.84/96
88-13583•	SNJ-4	**Bu27847**	**N4136A**	Harry B. Caldwell, Greensboro NC	63
				J. W. Morgan, High Point NC	.63/64
				George W. Lancaster, Wilmington NC	66
				Frank M. Sweet, Wake Forest NC	69/72

				Robert E. Wright, Brighton CO	76/77
				sale rep., Vernon TX	84/96
88-13584•	SNJ-4	**Bu27848**	**N4137A**	Louis Sylvestri, San Bruno CA	63
				Walt Auringer, San Francisco CA	.63/84
88-13585•	SNJ-4	**Bu27849**		(to FA Portuguesa as .....)	
			N8540Z	Arthur D. Medore/Banaire, Hemet CA	4.11.80/84
				Robert Mitchell & David Bruce/	
				Anderson Racing Inc, Belgrade MT	88/93
				(#4 "DashOne", later #55 "Slo Thunder")	
				Ralph Twombley/WW2 Warbirds Inc,	
				Orchard Park NY	9.93/95
				midair collision with N7404C during race,	
				crashed, Reno NV (Ralph Twombley k.)	18.9.94
				(USCR quotes id."88-13585": see next entry)	
88-13585•	SNJ-4	**Bu27849**		(to FA Portuguesa as .....)	
			N6171A	Twin D Enterprises Inc, Hemet CA	17.5.93
				Robert S. Haun, Westminster CO	10.94
88-13586•	SNJ-4	**Bu27850**	**N6463C**	Seventh Day Adventist Inc, Phoenix AZ	63/64
	SNJ-7			Power Plant Supply Co, Phoenix AZ	66
				James Rolfe, New Brighton MN	69/70
				James M. Landeen, Laurel MS	76/77
				Tim T. Cullum, Dallas TX	84
				Charles D. Arnet, Daphne AL	86
				Normand B. McAllister, Mobile AL	2.89/96
88-13587•	SNJ-4	**Bu27851**	N4138A	Lee Sherwood, Willows CA	63/69
				Tom Riessen, Red Bluff CA	72
			N97TR	Tom Riessen, Red Bluff CA	
				Aero Enterprises Inc, Seattle WA	76
				William Lamberton, Mercer Island WA	.77
				N. S. (Bud) Granley/Royal Eagle Squadron Inc,	
				Bellevue WA	4.78/96
88-13625•	SNJ-4	**Bu51358**	**N4140A**	Edward Mahler, Ozone Park NY	63/69
				George T. Moore, Whyattsville MD	70
				Howard W. Bennett, Salisbury MD	10.70/96
88-13627•	SNJ-4	**Bu51360**	N6424D	Franklin Machine Shop, Franklin NC	63/70
				Jack W. Ivey, Albany GA	76/84
				George O. Colvin, Big Cabin OK	86
			N694US	Air With Flair Inc, Athol ID	7.88
				(race #69 *Taylor Maid* #19 *Silverwood)*	
				Keith Antcliff, Athol ID	90
				William Droessler, McFarland WI	92
				Steven Hay, Syracuse IN	9.92/96
88-13630•	SNJ-4	**Bu51363**		(to FA Portuguesa as .....)	
			N22518	Arthur D. Medore/Banaire, Hemet CA	5.78/86
				Thomas A. Dodson, Tulsa OK	8.90/96
88-13635•	SNJ-4	**Bu51368**	N7098C	Charlotte Aircraft Corp, Charlotte NC	63/66
				(to Spanish AF as C.6-156 "912-55")	
			N26592	Dwane N. Natoli, Nokesville VA	2.82
				Dwane A. Shank, Greensburg KS	84/86
			N29BS	TTM Inc, Oklahoma City OK	4.88
				Thomas M. Shelton, Miami FL/Asheville NC	90/92
				Jack Mitchard/Tracom Aviation,	
				Beaver County PA	11.93/96
88-13640•	SNJ-4	**Bu51373**	**N7034C**	Byron R. Jacquot, National City CA	63
				Glenn A. O'Neal, Las Vegas NV	.63/72
				Roland J. Harrington, Abbeville LA	3.74/96
88-13763•	SNJ-4	**Bu51381**	N6425D	West Michigan Aviation, Muskegon MI	63
				Sherman Aircraft Sales, Fort Wayne IN	.63/64
				Jay C. Seiler, Tower City PA	66/72

				Aerotech Inc, Pontiac MI	76/77
				Veryl Fenlason, St Cloud MN	84/86
				Jerrold E. Wannenacher, Monument CO	5.86/96
88-13779	SNJ-4	Bu51397	N7007C	Aero Enterprises Inc, Elkhart IN	63/64
				Carl Vik, Harvey IL	66
			N173V	Carl Vik, Villa Park IL	69/72
88-13780 •	SNJ-4	**Bu51398**		NASM, Silver Hill MD	66/88
88-13784•	SNJ-4	**Bu51402**	**N7008C**	*Red River* titles; crop sprayer	50s
				Dean J. Lewis, Pampa TX: sprayer	63/66
				D & D Aero Spraying, Rantoul KS	69/92
88-13796•	SNJ-4	**Bu51414**	N5209V	F. B. Quinn, Van Nuys CA/Atlanta GA	63/66
				(op. Condor Squadron, Van Nuys CA 68)	
				James R. Levrett, Glendale CA	70/72
			N156	Leeroy E. Whitehead, Carpinteria CA	4.74/96
88-13805•	SNJ-4	**Bu51423**	**N7011C**	Transaire Spraying Co, Canyon TX	63/70
				John Green, Grenada MS	76
				Courtesy Aircraft Inc, Rockford IL	.77
				James C. Over, Grand Junction CO (race #71)	5.83/95
88-13891•	SNJ-4	**Bu51429**	N7439C	Charles H. Johnes, Delano CA	63/66
	SNJ-6C			William S. Cooper, Merced CA	69/70
				Jack W. Flaherty, Monterey CA	72
			N51428	C. Bruce Ashenfelter, Agincourt ONT	76
				Lynn Crouch, Whitehouse TN	.77
				Jack L. Kersetter, Wakeman OH	84/87
				C. Bruce Ashenfelter, Hartford WI	3.87/96
88-13892•	SNJ-4	**Bu51430**	**N7013C**	Transaire Spraying Co, Canyon TX	63/70
				Williams Flying Service, Tutwiler MS	73
				(open storage, derelict, Tutwiler MS 73)	
				Harland Avezzie, Westfield MA: rest. project	88
				Phillip J. Godlewiski, New Castle DE	90/92
				(rest. project Cape May NJ 90/94)	
				Richard M. Oliver, Mickleton NJ	.92/96
88-13907•	AT-6C	**41-33766**		(to RAF as EX793)	
	Mk. IIa			(to RNZAF as NZ1050): shipped direct to NZ	8.43
				(to RNZAF inst. airframe INST207)	
				Wigram AB: mounted on pole as gate guard	6.73/79
				RNZAF Museum, Wigram AB: displ. on pole	88/95
88-13908•	AT-6C	**41-33767**		(to RAF as EX794)	
	Mk. IIa			(to RNZAF as NZ1051): shipped direct to NZ	8.43/78
				Mike Nortier, Auckland NZ: airframe only	.78
				Stan Smith/Warbirds, Dairy Flat NZ: fuse	.78
				(rest. project, Auckland 92)	
88-13909•	AT-6C	**41-33768**		(to RAF as EX795)	
	Mk. IIa			(to RNZAF as NZ1052): shipped direct to NZ	8.43/78
				Museum of Transport & Technology, Auckland	78
			ZK-MJN	M. J. Nicholls, Ohakea	2.6.87
				Keith Skilling/Harvard 1052 Syndicate,	
				Auckland-Ardmore	90/96
				(rest. Auckland-Ardmore, ff .92 as "NZ1052")	
88-13910•	AT-6C	**41-33769**		(to RAF as EX796)	
	Mk. IIa			(to RNZAF as NZ1053): shipped direct to NZ	8.43/78
				Don Subritisky, Auckland NZ: airframe only	.78
				Jim Pavitt, Auckland	94/96
				(under rest. Auckland-Ardmore 94)	
88-13948	SNJ-4	Bu51466	N7099C	Paul E. Davis, Pittsburgh PA	63
				AT-6 Club, Niles OH	.63/64

			N630X (2	Dean Ortner, Wakeman OH	66/84
38-14025	SNJ-4	Bu51483	N6426D	Thomas F. Twomey, Weymouth MA	63/84
				(last FAA annual inspection 6.59)	
				noted dism. at house, Weymouth MA	9.80
38-14047•	SNJ-4	Bu51505	N7083C	Mark Britt, Stone Mountain GA	63
				David R. Heaton, Decatur GA	.63/66
				J. R. Adams, Forest Park GA	69/70
				Edward L. Bankston, Griffin GA	72
				Kent Jones, Dallas TX	76/77
				William J. Nelson/WJN Corp, El Paso TX	84/86
				Fred C. Sorenson, Aiea HI/Yelm WA	92/94
				Kosta Asselanis/Silver Inc, Eden Prairie MN	8.94/96
38-14048	SNJ-4	Bu51506	N9735Z	Ted Lacara, Los Angeles CA	63/69
				Joseph W. Quinn, Saugus CA	70
38-14124•	SNJ-4	**Bu51542**	**N7404C**	Adger W. McGinty, Fort Lauderdale FL	63
				Dick Dillon, Fort Lauderdale FL	.63/64
				Leon L. Gillett, Miami FL	66
				Antonio J. Muguria, Key West FL	69
				Key West Flyers Inc, Key West FL	70/72
				Brownings Inc, Roberts ID	76/77
				Jerry D. McDonald, San Joaquin CA	10.78/95
				(race #5 *Big Red*)	
				dam. midair collision with N8540Z, Reno NV	18.9.94
38-14177•	AT-6C Mk. IIa	**41-33800**		(to RAF as EX827)	
				(to RNZAF as NZ1056): shipped direct to NZ	9.43/78
			ZK-ENL	Don G. Reidpath, Auckland: reg. for del.	12.10.78
				Australian Aircraft Restoration Group/	
				Moorabbin Air Museum, Moorabbin VIC	.78/80
				(arr. Melbourne-Essendon on del. ex NZ 20.5.79)	
				Alec Encel, Melbourne VIC	82
				(del. to Melbourne-Moorabbin VIC 12.2.82	
				for certification, ex storage Berwick VIC)	
			VH-NAH	Alan Pay/Mt Carli Pty Ltd, Mount Beauty VIC	9.2.84/96
38-14178•	AT-6C Mk. IIa	**41-33801**		(to RAF as EX828)	
				(to RNZAF as NZ1057): shipped direct to NZ	9.43/78
				Engine Support Inc, Sebring FL	.78
				Silverstream Railway & Vintage Transport,	
				Hutt Valley NZ: static displ.	.78
				C.d'Arby, Ardmore NZ	89
				Richard Page, Auckland NZ	90/91
				(rest. to fly, Auckland-Ardmore 90/96)	
38-14226•	SNJ-4	**Bu51584**	**N1395N**	Angus C. Fox, San Fernando CA	63/64
				Al J. Gannon, Ventura CA	66
				Sky Prints Corp, St. Louis MO	69/72
				Brull Interstate Aircraft Co, Higginsville MO	76/77
				Gary Wilson Aircraft Inc, Independence MO	84
				USAFM, Lackland AFB TX	93/94
				(displ. as "USN Bu51584")	
38-14253•	SNJ-4	**Bu51611**		(to FA Portuguesa as ....)	
			N22519	Arthur D. Medore/Banaire, Hemet CA	5.78
				Loyal H. Diehl, Parker CO	84
				Gordon E. Pedron, Merrill OR/Groveland CA	5.85/96
38-14317•	SNJ-4	**Bu51629**	**N6427D**	Raymond H. Phillips, Mexia TX	63/64
				World Weather Inc, Bay City TX	66
				Donald L. Sundin, Heath OH	69/70
				Clifford Baker, Eudora AR	76/77
				sale rep., Eudora AR	84/86
				Tee Six Inc, Casper WY	4.91/96
38-14342•	SNJ-4	**Bu51654**	CF-LQQ	H. W. McKay/McKay Airways, Merlin ONT	65/68
				David L. McDonald, Petrolia ONT	69/70

			N7406C	Donald Ayers, Oklahoma City OK	76/77
				Wilson Dahlgren Corp, Oklahoma City OK	84/86
				John M. Reynolds, Aspen CO	8.87/95
88-14362•	SNJ-4	**Bu51674**	N58917	George Pulse, Pendleton OR	63/66
				Roy S. Sharp, Glendale CA	69/77
				Bob E. Amyx, Oklahoma City OK	84
				Roy Porter, Yukon OK	86
			N674N	Continental Petroleum Corp, Dallas TX	6.87
				Greg Morse, Dallas-Addison TX	88/89
				Scott A. Morse/Morse Aviation, Plano TX	9.92/96
88-14423•	AT-6D	**42-44450**		North Weald Aircraft Restoration Flight	
				North Weald: rest. as "483009"	81/86
			G-BPSE	Aces High Ltd, North Weald	20.4.89
88-14425•	SNJ-5	**Bu51677**	N6975C	GHS Aircraft Group, Phoenix AZ	63/64
				Richard T. Gregory, Phoenix AZ	66/72
				Ronald T. Montayne, Phoenix AZ	.74/95
88-14426•	SNJ-5	**Bu51678**	N6975S	Lennart C. Strand, Sonora CA	63/64
				Rose C. Gratrix, San Mateo CA	66
			N3579	Rose Gatrix & Jack C. Hovey, San Mateo CA	69/72
				James D. Smith, Mercer WA	4.73/96
88-14434•	SNJ-5	**Bu51686**	N9058Z	Frank L. Simmerman, Hollywood CA	63/66
				James R. Levrett, Glendale CA	69
			N913D	James R. Levrett, Glendale CA	72
				Donald R. Alderson, Hidden Hills CA	76/84
				Gary G. Stearns, Camarillo CA	3.85/96
88-14445•	SNJ-5	**Bu51697**	**N3195G**	Robert Contreras, San Diego CA	63/72
				Confederate Air Force, Harlingen/Midland TX	84/96
88-14446•	SNJ-5	**Bu51698**	**N7986C**	450 Corp, Denver CO	63/64
				John E. Adams, Phoenix AZ	66
				20th Century Fox Film Corp, Hollywood CA	.68/71
				(conv. to Zero replica at Long Beach CA .68 for movie "Tora Tora Tora"; open storage Long Beach CA 69/71, sold at auction Long Beach 2.71)	
				EAA Aviation Foundation, Oshkosh WI	72/84
				sale rep., Dallas TX	86
				Rudy A. Frasca, Champaign IL	7.87/96
				(flies as 'Japanese Zero' 147)	
88-14491•	AT-6D Mk. III	**41-33838**		(to RAF as EX865)	
				(to RNZAF as NZ1058): shipped direct to NZ	11.43
				Ferrymead Aviation Society, Christchurch NZ	76/92
				(static rest., using parts from NZ1080)	
				Ferrymead Museum of Science & Technology, Christchurch: displ.	92/96
88-14493•	AT-6D Mk. III	**41-33840**		(to RAF as EX867)	
				(to RNZAF as NZ1060): shipped direct to NZ	11.43/77
				RAAF Museum, RAAF Point Cook VIC	11.77/88
				(airfreighted by C130 NZ to Pt Cook 11.77)	
				(trucked to Bankstown for rest. to fly 9.88)	
			VH-SFY	R. Tayles/RAAF Museum, Point Cook VIC	28.9.88/96
				(flies as "RNZAF NZ934")	
88-14494•	AT-6D Mk. III	**41-33841**		(to RAF as EX868)	
				(to RNZAF as NZ1061): shipped direct to NZ	11.43/78
			ZK-ENH	W. R. Greville, Broken Hill NSW, Australia	2.8.78/80
				(del. via Sydney NSW 16.4.79)	
			VH-PEM	Warwick R. Greville, Broken Hill NSW	1.7.80/88
				Walcha Aerial Services, Walcha NSW	16.4.88/96
88-14510•	AT-6D	**42-44467**	F-BJBM	Air France, Cormeilles	10.59/67

c/n	Type	Serial	Reg	Owner / History	Dates
				Societe Gle d'Exploitation Aeronautique-SOGEA,	
				Troyes	.67/76
				wfu, struck-off reg.	.70
				Collection Robert Denizot, Pont-sur-Yonne	.76/90
				(stored, pending rest.)	
88-14518•	SNJ-5	**Bu51730**	**N4745C**	Ralph L. Horner, South Bend IN	63
				Linden Krousop, Van Wert OH	66
				Joe Binder, Fremont OH	10.68/96
88-14552•	AT-6D Mk. III	**41-33854**		(to RAF as EX881)	
				(to SAAF as 7424): shipped direct to S.Africa	11.43/69
				(to FA Portuguesa as 1506)	.69/78
			G-SUES	Mark Campbell Airfreight Charters Ltd,	
				Biggin Hill	18.1.79/81
				(del. via Nantes, France to Biggin Hill 16.6.79,	
				B. Willmot, Biggin Hill	2.6.81
				Peter W. Leaney, Biggin Hill	18.6.81/84
				(flew as "USAF EX881", later "USN 133854")	
				sold to Norway, struck-off reg.	10.2.84
			LN-LFW	ntu	.84
			LN-WNH	Nordic Air Service, Sandefjord/Torp	11.7.86
				op: Warbirds of Norway, Dalbo	86/93
				Morten Andreassen, Bodalen	93/95
				(flies as "RNoAF FS907/AJ")	
88-14555•	AT-6D Mk. III	**41-33857**		(to RAF as EX884)	
				(to SAAF as 7426): shipped direct to S.Africa	11.43/69
				(to FA Portuguesa as 1513)	.69
				rep. stored Portugal	80
				Sandy Topen/Vintage Aircraft Team, Bushey	84/85
				Vintage Aircraft Team, Cranfield: arr. dism.	2.85/87
				(used for film crash scene "FT323" .85)	
88-14618•	SNJ-5	**Bu51764**	N7973C	Farmers Crop Dusters, Rapid City SD	63/64
				Snedigar Flying Service, Rapid City SD	66
				Donald O. Koehmstedt, Overly ND	69/72
			N15WS	Waldon D. Spillers, Versailles OH	76/77
				Georgia Historical Aviation Museum,	
				Stone Mountain GA	5.82/96
88-14642•	SNJ-5	**Bu51788**	**N3643F**	Heislers Inc, Willard OH	63
				Heck Flying Service, Willard OH	.63/64
				O. B. Carlisle, Atlanta GA	66
				Hinds Junior College, Raymond MS	69/70
				James V. Ricks, Greenwood MS: readded	11.83/96
88-14643•	SNJ-5	**Bu51789**	**N5488V**	Herbert E. Olson, Seattle WA	63/69
				Robert D. Morrow, Salem OR	70
				James E. Gardner, Salem OR	72
				Cascade Ditching Co, Salem OR	76/86
				Thomas C. Payne, Leesburg VA	90/94
				Paul D. Faltyn, North Towawanda NY	6.94/96
88-14659•	AT-6D Mk. III	**41-33865**		(to RAF as EX892)	
				(to SAAF as 7431): shipped direct to S.Africa	11.43/69
				(to FA Portuguesa as 1529)	.69
			G-BGOS	ntu: Euroworld International Ltd, Biggin Hill	3.79/80
			N3770D	Jack R. Jenkins, Breckenridge TX	6.80
				Charles Lacy, Breckenridge TX	84
				Havins Jewellers Inc, Fort Stockton TX	86
				Jack Hall/Pony Corp, Abilene TX	87/92
				Joseph W. Dorman, Boynton Beach FL	8.93/96
88-14661	AT-6D Mk. III	41-33867		(to RAF as EX894)	
				(to SAAF as 7441): shipped direct to S.Africa	11.43/69
				(to FA Portuguesa as 1504)	.69/78
			G-ELLY	Elly Sallingboe/Euroworld Ltd, Biggin Hill	17.1.79
				(del. to Biggin Hill 15.5.79)	
				E.D. Sallingboe, Biggin Hill	4.9.80

				(flew as "USAF 133867")	
				crashed, dest. Rabat, Malta	22.6.82
88-14672•	AT-6D Mk. III	**41-33878**		(to RAF as EX905)	
				(to RNZAF as NZ1066): shipped direct to NZ	1.44/78
			ZK-ENE	M. C. Christopherson, Mt. Maunganui	20.6.78
				Paul Leuch, Ardmore	.78
				G. M. Porter, R. J. Booth, P. J. Adams, Auckland-Ardmore	87/93
				dam. collision ZK-ENN Ardmore: landed safely	25.2.90
				Wanaka Harvard Syndicate, Wanaka	94/95
88-14674•	AT-6D Mk. III	**41-33880**		(to RAF as EX907)	
				(to RNZAF as NZ1068): shipped direct to NZ	1.44/78
				(to RNZAF inst. airframe INST172)	
				Phillip Burns, Christchurch NZ	78
				John R. Smith, Mapua NZ: stored	.78/96
88-14675•	AT-6D Mk. III	**41-33881**		(to RAF as EX908)	
				(to RNZAF as NZ1069): shipped direct to NZ	1.44/78
				(to RNZAF inst. airframe INST173)	
				sold as surplus by RNZAF	.72
				Don Subritzki, Auckland: rest. project	78
				(rest. project, stored Auckland 92)	
				E. Billman, Auckland	95
88-14704•	SNJ-5	**Bu51810**	**N3269G**	Emilio Nervino, Santa Cruz CA, later Brownsville TX	4.60/96
88-14705•	SNJ-5	**Bu51811**		(to Spanish AF as C.6-142)	
			N3931S	Combat Aircraft Inc, Elkhart IN	13.5.83
				Donald J. Von Siegel, Parkin AR	84
				Gene McNeely/McNeely Charter Service, Earle AR (race #17 "Miss Iris")	87/92
				accident Earle AR	17.6.89
			N5FJ	Herbert J. Johnson, Cordova TN	10.93/96
88-14713•	SNJ-5	**Bu51819**	N7804B	Henry F. Wallace, Miami FL	63/64
				Richard E. Bowlby, Miami FL	66
				D & J Enterprises Inc, Miami FL	69
				Ben R. Bradley, Fort Lauderdale FL	70
				Russell Boy, Plantation FL	76/77
				Ron Runyan Aviation Co, Hamilton OH	84
				Sam Andrews, Bennett CO	85
				Richard D. Bobbitt, Aspen CO	86
			N155DB	Richard D. Bobbitt, Aspen CO	6.86
			N7804B	Red S Aircraft Sales, Jenks OK	7.87
				B. L. "Swamp" Smith, De Ridder LA	8.87/96
				(note: id. the same as next entry)	
88-14713• 2	SNJ-5	**Bu51819 (2)**		(to Spanish AF as C.6-162)	
			D-FIII	ntu: Hans Dittes, Mannheim West Germany	11.81
			N2965S	David Martin, Leimen WG	4.82
				David M. Reeves, Leimen WG	84
				Claus C. Stegman, Congers NY	86
				Heribert Somweiber, Lechaschau, Austria	90
				Oekonta Inc, Snellville GA	92
				Plane Fun Inc, Grossostheim, Germany	10.8.92/96
				(note: id. the same as entry above)	
88-14722•	AT-6D Mk. III	**41-33888**		(to RAF as EX915)	
				(to SAAF as 7439): shipped direct to S.Africa	11.43/69
				(to FA Portuguesa as 1502)	.69/78
			G-JUDI	Norfolk Aerial Spraying Ltd, Foulsham	11.78/80
				(del. via Dinard to Biggin Hill 29.11.78, flew as "RAF FX301")	
				Anthony Haig-Thomas, Duxford/Ipswich	10.1.80/89
				Anthony A. Hodgson, Clywd, Wales	91/92

88-14748•	AT-6D Mk. III	42-44554		(to RN FAA as FT971)	.44/56
				(to FA Portuguesa as 1661)	3.56/78
			G-BGOW	Euroworld International Ltd, Biggin Hill	28.3.79/80
				sold to USA: struck-off reg.	16.4.80
				Euroworld California Inc: US reg. candidate	7.80
			N13HP	Howard E. Pardue/Breckenridge Aviation Museum, Breckenridge TX	8.80/96
88-14780•	AT-6D	42-44586		(to FA Brasileira as 1320)	
				Museu Aerospacial, Campo dos Afonsos, Rio	90
				US reg. candidate	5.8.91
			N205SB	reg.	8.95
88-14806•	SNJ-5	Bu51828	N7972C	Robert G. Abrams, Chula Vista CA	63/69
			N711RA	Robert G. Abrams, Chula Vista CA	.69/77
				(noted San Diego-Gillespie Field 11.69)	
				Michael R. McCrae, Lemon Grove CA	1.79/96
88-14847•	SNJ-5	Bu51849		USNAM, NAS Pensacola FL	90/94
				(displ. as "51849/49")	
88-14880•	AT-6D Mk. III	41-33908		(to RAF as EX935)	
				(to SAAF as 7504): shipped direct to S.Africa	12.43/69
				(to FA Portuguesa as 1508)	.69/78
			G-BGOR	Euroworld International Ltd, Biggin Hill	28.3.79/80
				P. Mercer, Hurn	10.80/82
				Martin L. Sargeant, Headcorn/Rochester	11.82/96
				(note: plate quotes 88-14863/EX935)	
88-14889•	AT-6D Mk. III	41-33917		(to RAF as EX944)	
				(to RNZAF as NZ1065): shipped direct to NZ	12.43/78
			ZK-ENF	Messrs. E. J. Adams, W. S. Bell, D. J. Phillips, M. C. Christopherson & R. O. Dahlberg, Mount Maunganui	20.6.78
				M. R. Broadbent & R. F. Duncan, Ardmore	87/92
				Harvard 65 Syndicate, Auckland-Ardmore	93/96
88-14893•	AT-6D	42-44629	N6983C	Ernest W. Beechler, West Covina CA	63/64
				George E. Rauch, Salinas CA	66
				Dale B. Davis, Fort Wolters TX	69/70
				Thomas L. Camp, San Francisco CA	72
				Paul H. Poberezny/EAA Aviation Foundation, Oshkosh WI	76/94
				(displ. EAA Museum as "SNJ-3-NT USN/83")	
				Ozark Management Inc, Jefferson City MD	4.95
88-14905•	AT-6D	42-44641	N75342	Eldon P. Harvey, El Paso TX	63/77
				Roger A. Stout, El Paso TX	84/86
				S. Frank Sublett, Alexandria VA	88/96
88-14913•	SNJ-5 SNJ-5C	Bu51875		Morey Darznieks/Lance Aircraft Supply, Dallas TX	.88
				Chesapeake Airways Corp: candidate	3.4.89
			N3JC	William J. Crone, Beach City OH: rest.	3.4.89/96
88-14918•	SNJ-5	Bu51880	N7991C	Bob Dyer & Associates, Dallas TX	63
				A. R. Dillard, Wichita Falls TX	.63/64
				Julian R. Sirmons, Atoka OK	66/70
				Robert A. Ashworth, Farmer City IL	76/84
				Richard C. Fernalld, Pendleton OR/Yelm WA	10.84/95
88-14920•	SNJ-5	Bu51882	N3676F	Stencel Aero Engineering Corp, Ashville NC	63/66
				Milton S. Cooper, Prospect KY	69/72
				William R. Wobbe, Louisville KY	6.76/95
88-14934•	SNJ-5 SNJ-5C	Bu51896		Lance Aircraft Supply Inc, Dallas TX	
			N5632F	William J. Crone, Beach City OH	22.8.94/95
88-14949•	AT-6D	41-33932		(to RAF as EX959)	

	Mk. III			(to SAAF as 7509): shipped ex US, arr.	1.1.44/47
				(ret. to RAF as EX959): shipped to UK, arr.	10.46
				(to Belgian AF as H9): BOC 25.2.47: SOC	27.8.58
			F-BJBF	Air France, Cormeilles/Toussous	19.8.59/65
				Gaston Urbain, Cannes-Mandelieu	5.65/71
			G-AZJD	Sir W. J. D. Roberts/Strathallan Collection	8.71/72
				(del. ex France 27.11.71)	
				Gladaircraft Co Ltd, Biggin Hill	23.8.77/83
				Meridian Drilling Co, Biggin Hill	6.7.83
			F-WZDU	Guy J. C. Robert, Laval	10.84
			F-AZDU	Guy J. C. Robert, Laval	13.6.85/96
88-14950•	AT-6D Mk. III	**41-33933**		(to RAF as EX960)	
				(to SAAF as 7506): shipped direct to S.Africa	12.43
				SAAF Museum, Swartkop AB	22.4.90/96
				(recov. ex Stilfontein: stored .)	
88-14989•	AT-6D	**42-44675**	N75286	William L. Anderson, Houston TX	63/64
				Robert V. Weaver, Houston TX	66
				B. R. Coleman, Houston TX	69
				Coleman Flying Service, Spring TX	70
			N83H	Mary Diane Card, Houston TX	72
				James L. Irwin, Mineral Wells TX	76/77
				Ralph C. Parker, Wichita Falls TX	84/86
				Ozarks Auto Show, Branson MO	6.88/96
88-15006•	SNJ-5	**Bu51903**	N3196G	Paul W. Trist, Glendale CA	63/64
			N3605	George A. Cordingly, Beverly Hills CA	69/70
			N51903	Ed Messia CA	73
				Lester D. Friend, San Diego CA	76
				Joe Arnold, Eudora AR	.77
				Clarence M. Rittelmeyer, Pine Bluff AR	6.80/96
88-15011•	SNJ-5	**Bu51908**	N8209E	James D. Brew, Washington DC	63
				John F. Mount, Washington DC	.63/64
				Cecil L. Kephart, Hagerstown MD	66
				Stuart T. Garrison, Hockessin DE	69
				Jerome S. Rubin, Philadelphia PA	70
				Michael P. Yannell, Lafayette NJ	72
			N44999	Michael P. Yannell, Lafayette NJ	76/84
				Christopher F. Maier, Hope NJ	3.86
			N446CM	Christopher F. Maier, Hope NJ	7.86/96
88-15041•	SNJ-5	**Bu51938**		USNAM, NAS Pensacola FL	
				USS Yorktown Museum, Charlston SC: loan	93
88-15055•	AT-6D Mk. III	**41-33948**		(to RNFAA as EX976): shipped to India	4.44
				shipped to UK, no RN service: stored	46/56
				(to FA Portuguesa as 1657)	3.56
				Fleet Air Arm Museum, RNAS Yeovilton	82/96
				(displ. as "RNFAA EX976")	
88-15069•	AT-6D Mk.III	**41-33962**		(to RAF as EX989): shipped direct to S.Africa	1.44
				(to SAAF as 7530)	
				(to FA Portuguesa as 7700)	
				(to Mozambique PLAF as ......)	
				abandoned Maputo, Mozambique	.74/89
				recov. by Brian Zeederberg/Ian Popplewell, Syferfontein, Johannesburg	.89
				South African Airways Technical Training School	89
			ZS-WLQ	SAA Technical Training, Johannesburg	8.3.90/91
				(noted stored SAA maintenance base Jan Smuts 11.91)	
88-15095•	SNJ-5	**Bu51952**	N5198V	Harry W. Mitchell, Fort Worth TX	63/66
				Eastern Aviation Ltd, Piscataway NJ	69
			N15HB	Dabob Inc, Bernardsville NJ	72/77
				Donald R. Contant, Santee SC/Summerton SC	84/86

				T. Randy Hatchell, Timmonsville SC	6.88/96
				(flies as "14799/TA-799")	
88-15111•	SNJ-5	**Bu51968**	**N3263G**	Paul Pribble, Maywood CA	63/68
	SNJ-5B				
				USNAM, NAS Pensacola FL	.68/90
				USS Yorktown Museum, Charleston SC: displ.	89
				North West Arkansas World War Two Museum,	
				Siloam Springs AR	94/96
88-15114•	SNJ-5	**Bu51971**	**N3267G**	Robert J. Richardson, Hollywood CA	63/64
				John E. Ellison, Clovis NM	66
				William F. Toler, Opelousas LA	69/70
				Thomas W. Henley, Emelle AL	.73/77
				Alan F. Henley, Emelle AL	7.84/95
88-15118•	AT-6D	**41-33966**		(to RAF as EX993)	
	Mk.III			(to SAAF as 7527): shipped direct to S.Africa	2.44/46
				(ret. to RAF as EX993): shipped to UK, arr.	10.46
				(to Belgian AF as H14)	13.5.47/59
			F-BJBG	Air France, Cormeilles	21.5.59/65
				dam. Pontoise, France	21.11.61
				struck-off reg.	7.65
				Air France Technical School, Vilgenis	
				Professional School of Montmirault/LEP,	
				Cerny La Ville, Essonne: inst. airframe	87/89
88-15143•	AT-6D	**42-44709**		(to Spanish AF as C.6-45): sold at auction	1.84
			N4996P	Combat Aircraft Inc, Elkhart IN	5.84
				Douglas W. Goss, Topeka KS	12.84/85
			N4292C	Douglas W. Goss, Topeka KS	2.85/95
88-15156	AT-6D	**42-44722**		Autry Vocational Tech Centre, Enid OK	84
				(ex USAF inst. airframe, Sheppard AFB OK)	
			N3660V	Oklahoma State University	12.89
				Richard D. Tabery, San Mateo CA	90/92
				Vernon McCallister/SLV Crop Care Inc,	
				Del Norte CO	6.92/95
88-15162•	SNJ-5	**Bu51974**	**N3264G**	John F. Hamblin, Upland CA	63
				George L. Leslie, Las Vegas NV	.63/64
				Jerry D. King, Seaside CA	66/69
				William G. Palank, Fair Oaks CA	70/72
				Darren L. Wall, Floresville TX	76/77
				James E. Engleman, Vanderpool TX	86/96
88-15167•	SNJ-5	**Bu51979**	N6551D	Angelo J. Russo, West Islip NY	63/70
			N51979	Jerry D. King, Sand City CA	76/77
				(mod. with SBD engine/cowl/3 bladed prop.)	
				John Martin, Wasco CA (race #79)	79/86
				Gary Howard (race #79 "Tigger II")	87
				Donald T. Bayley, Petaluma CA	7.91/96
88-15173•	SNJ-5	**Bu51985**	N9454Z	Curtis J. Johnston, Las Vegas NV	63/73
			N64L	James U. Lemke, Delmar CA	76
				B & S Enterprises, Sacramento CA	.77/78
			N64EA	B & S Enterprises, Sacramento CA	1.78
			N154CF	rereg.	7.83
				Dennis W. Forestone, Los Alamitos CA	84
				All-Coast Forest Products,	
				Chino CA	86/93
				Craig M. Nelson, Orlas Island WA	.93/96
88-15187•	SNJ-5	**Bu51999**		(to Spanish AF as C.6-171/Code 793-121)	
			N29678	Jerald A. Baker, Donna TX	4.82
				Albert R. Baird, Harlingen TX	84/86
				Ricardo T. Baird, Tonawanda NY	2.89/96
88-15194•	SNJ-5	**Bu52006**	N7995C	James J. Dickson, Riverside CA	63/64
				Clifford G. Shirpser, North Hollywood CA	66/69

			N52006	Clifford G. Shirpser, North Hollywood CA	70/95
				(flies as "USAF 52006/Rescue")	
88-15205•	SNJ-5	**Bu52017**	N3260G	Joe B. Hill, Freemont CA	63/64
				Dudley A. Main, Georgetown SC/San Diego CA	66/72
			N543LB	Speedway Volkswagen, Indianapolis IN	76
				Lowell Blossom, Zionsville IN	.77
				Ed Buerckholtz, Chesterfield MO	84/92
				Albert I. Stix, St Louis MO	5.92/95
88-15208•	SNJ-5	**Bu52020**	**N8211E**	George T. Bishop, Marathon FL	63/64
				Carl Launderville, Rolling Hills CA	66/84
				sale rep., Inglewood CA: USCR	86/92
				USNAM, NAS Pensacola FL	90/94
				USS Lexington Museum, Corpus Christie TX:	
				loan, displ. on board carrier	93/96
88-15212•	AT-6D	**42-44728**		(to FA Mexicana as 812)	
			N7054N	Texas Turbo Jet Inc, Dallas TX	1.89
				John S. Lohmar, St. Charles MO	92
				sale rep., USCR	95
88-15235•	SNJ-5	**Bu52022**	**N3187G**	Will F. Sovereign, Bay City MI	63/70
				V. S. Sloan, Greer SC	84
				John H. Shell, Morganton NC	86/96
88-15239•	SNJ-5	**Bu52026**	N8159H	Coastal Aviation Corp, Alexandria VA: USCR	63/69
				(to Spanish AF as C.6-130)	
			N29941	Combat Aircraft Inc, Elkhart IN	19.4.82
				David Fain, Glencoe IL	11.83/84
			N144L	David Fain, Glencoe IL	1.84
			N29941	David Fain, Aspen CO/Denver CO	86/96
88-15244•	SNJ-5	Bu52031	**N3666F**	C. W. Holder, Hickory NC	63/69
				Air Repair Inc, Fabens TX/Lewisville TX	70/76
				George J. Ceshker, Azle TX	12.76/96
88-15304•	AT-6D	41-34374		(to USN as Bu43639)	
	SNJ-5		N3669F	Lake Air Corp, Michigan City IN	63/64
				Jerome B. Libby, Pontiac MI	66
			N8151	Jerome B. Libby, Lake Orion MI	69/77
				Robert C. Hagan, Sterling Heights MI	84/86
				Byrne Aviation, Bloomfield Hills MI	1.92/96
88-15307	AT-6D	41-34377		(to USN as Bu43642)	
	SNJ-5		N3653F	Samuel E. McIntosh Inc, Miami FL	63/69
				(to Spanish AF as C.6-161, Code 421-07)	
			D-FDDD	ntu: Hans Dittes, Mannheim, West Germany	11.81
			N2960T	John T. Evans, Maintal, WG	12.4.82/84
				dam., forced landing Dillenburg WG	22.5.83
				sold to France: struck-off USCR	5.84
			F-AZDM	Association Air Memorial	.84
				crashed, dest., Coulommiers, France	11.6.84
88-15308	AT-6D	41-34378		(to USN as Bu43643)	
	SNJ-5			(to FA Portuguesa as ....)	
			N1049A	Arthur D. Medore/Banaire, Hemet CA	6.79/86
				Craig S. Compton/Avag Inc, Richvale CA	8.89/95
				crashed, dest., Richvale CA	3.11.95
88-15312•	AT-6D	**41-34382**		(to USN as Bu43647)	
	SNJ-5B			disposal ex NAS Litchfield Park AZ	24.7.57
			N3274G	Growers Aerial Service, Imperial CA	63/69
				(last FAA annual inspection 7.59)	
				James A. Mott, Long Beach CA	76/89
				(race #42 *Mis-Chief*")	
				Michael Falls, Melbourne VIC	.89/90
				(shipped, assembled Toowoomba QLD .89)	

c/n	Type	Serial	Reg.	History	Date
			VH-OVO	Michael Falls/Shortstop Jet Charter, Melbourne-Essendon VIC	1.2.90/96
88-15333•	AT-6D Mk. III	**41-34016**		(to RAF as EZ143)	
				(to SAAF as 7570): shipped direct to S.Africa	3.44
				SAAF Museum	.75/92
				Atlas Aircraft Co Apprentice School, Johannesburg-Jan Smuts Airport: loan	79
				Atlas Aircraft Co, Bonaero Park: loan	92
88-15335•	AT-6D Mk. III	**41-34018**		(to RAF as EZ145)	
				(to SAAF as 7572): shipped direct to S.Africa	3.44
				SAAF Museum, Swartkop AB	94
			ZU-AKX	Stuart D. Davidson, Port Elizabeth	26.4.94
				Seaview Aerobatics	
			N7572	W. Scott Henry, Wilsonville OR	8.94/96
				(shipped to USA ex South Africa 8.94)	
88-15336•	AT-6D Mk. III	**41-34019**		(to RAF as EZ146)	
				(to SAAF as 7573): shipped direct to S.Africa	3.44
				displ. town square, Dunnottar, South Africa	.93
88-15356•	AT-6D SNJ-5	**41-34154**		(to USN as ....)	
			N35CE (1	reg. 12.4.88	
				Gerald L. Walbrun, Neenah WI	92
			N3286	rereg.	1.93
				Carl Schmieder/Cee Enterprises, Phoenix AZ	8.93/95
			N25CE	Carl Schmieder, Phoenix AZ: rereg. res.	3.94
88-15363•	AT-6D Mk. III	**41-34046**		(to RAF as EZ173)	
				(to SAAF as 7544): shipped direct to S.Africa	3.44/93
			ZU-AGK	M. J. Bolton, Inanda	12.6.93
88-15368 •	AT-6D SNJ-5	**41-34402**		(to USN as Bu43667)	
			N3146G	rep. stored unconv. Chino CA area	65/75
				(under rest. Chino CA .75)	
				Dennis G. Buehn, Compton CA	
				Greg G. Burnett, Oklahoma City OK	84
			N43AF	E. Alan Fitz, Iowa Falls IA	5.89/96
8-15370 •	AT-6D SNJ-5C	**41-34404**		(to USN as Bu43669)	
				(to FA Brasileira as FAB T-6 1703)	.60
			PT-KRD	reg., conv. for agricultural ops.	.76
				Jose Angelo Simioni, Campo de Marte	83
8-15378•	AT-6D SNJ-5	**41-34412**		(to USN as Bu43677)	
			N7999C	Ross Flying Service, Imperial CA	63/69
				Harry R. Wright, Calipatria CA	76/84
				sale rep., Pinedale WY	86
				High Expectations Inc, Evanston WY	4.86/96
8-15384•	AT-6D SNJ-5	**41-34418**		(to USN as Bu43683)	
			N3147G	noted open storage, unconv., Prineville OR	7.75/77
			N2550	James S. & Neil M. Rose, Vancouver WA	84/96
8-15385	AT-6D SNJ-5C	41-34419		(to USN as Bu43684)	
				(to FA Brasileira as FAB T-6 1704)	.60
			PT-KSX	reg., conv. for agricultural ops.	.76
				Silvio Teani Comenho, Jacarepagua	83
				crashed: struck-off reg.	6.83
8-15390•	AT-6D SNJ-5	**41-34424**		(to USN as Bu43689)	
			N9811C	William J. Reedy, Pasadena CA	63/64
				Walter E. Ohlrich, Tulsa OK	66
			N502	Walter E. Ohlrich, Moore OK/Norfolk VA	69/96
8-15400•	AT-6D	**41-34166**	N96211	reg. res.	84/92
			N14166	Charles R. Hall, Ramona CA	9.92/96
				(long-term rest. Ramona, ff .92)	

88-15486•	AT-6D	**41-34252**	**N6982C**	J. H. Ashmore, Gardena CA	63/84
88-15580•	AT-6D	**41-34434**		(to USN as Bu43699)	
	SNJ-5		**N169D**	David B. Robinson, Miami FL	63/95
88-15608•	AT-6D	**41-34047**		(to RAF as EZ174)	
	Mk. III			(to SAAF as 7555): shipped direct to S.Africa	3.44/46
				(ret. to RAF as EZ174): shipped to UK, arr.	9.46
				(to Belgian AF as H6)	2.47/59
			F-BJBD	Air France, Cormeilles/Toussus	19.8.59/64
				Aero Club Air France	2.64/67
				Ets Godet	9.67
				struck-off reg.	.70
				M. Chassagnard	9.72
				(noted at Etampes, France .77)	
				Collection Aero Club Jean Bertin, Chavenay	
				Groupe Aerien Victor Tatin, Chavenay	90/96
				(under rest. Rouen, France 90)	
88-15610•	AT-6D	**41-34049**		(to RAF as EZ176)	
	Mk.III			(to SAAF as 7557): shipped direct to S.Africa	3.44/92
			ZU-AGD	Stuart D. Davidson, Port Elizabeth	25.5.93
88-15611•	AT-6D	**41-34050**		(to RAF as EZ177)	
	Mk.III			(to RNZAF as NZ1079): shipped direct to NZ	12.44/78
				Paul B. Brice, Basye VA	.78
				(shipped NZ to Norfolk VA .78)	
			N111PB	Paul B. Brice, Bryce Mountain, Basye VA	12.78/88
				Gerald W. Morgan, Bedford TX	10.91/92
			N101NZ	Gerald W. Morgan, Roanoke TX/Anchorage AK	8.92/95
88-15665•	AT-6D	**41-34465**		(to USN as Bu43724)	
	SNJ-5B		N1045C	W. Florida Design Service, Punta Gorda FL	63
				Theodore M. Arnold, Punta Gorda FL	.63/64
				Kenneth T. Viall, Dryden NY	66/70
				Robert Gardner, Northampton MA	76
				Thomas J. Conlon, Massapequa Peak NY	.77
			N62724	Thomas J. Conlon, Massapequa Peak NY	2.79/84
				accident landing, Farmingdale NY	24.7.80
				Hughes Excavating Inc, Allendale IL	86
				Joe Kremp/Camion Corp, Washington IN	88/95
88-15666•	AT-6D	**41-34466**		(to USN as Bu43725)	
	SNJ-5B		N8085H	W. H. Sanders, Norfolk VA	63/64
				Beach Airways, Columbus OH	66
			N1666T	Gary W. Lund, Redwood Falls MN	.68/77
				John R. Sandberg, Minneapolis MN	80
				Leonard P. Stonich,	
				Shingle Springs CA/Brush Prairie WA	9.80/96
88-15673•	AT-6D	**41-34473**		(to USN as Bu43732)	
	SNJ-5B		N8214E	Frank A. Froehling, Coral Gables FL	63/66
				Cordero Orlando, Miami FL	69/72
				John Stamer, Louisville KY	76/77
			N214MB	Phyllis Stamer, Louisville KY/Morristown TN	7.78/84
				Victor A. Krause, St. Charles IL	11.87/96
88-15676	AT-6D	41-34476		(to USN as Bu43735)	
	SNJ-5B		N3437G	Bruce E. Jochim, Los Angeles CA	63
				Howard M. Pavlik, Los Angeles CA	.63/64
				Quentin Sondergaard, Panorama City CA	66
				Richard R. Tracy, Pasadena CA	69/70
				Burton W. Melcher, Cupertino CA	72
88-15677•	AT-6D	**41-34477**		(to USN as Bu43736)	
	SNJ-5B		**N3259G**	Robert L. Wood, Laredo TX	63
				Larry K. Payne, Safford AZ	.63/64
				Jay V. White, Rolla MO	66

				Spence J. Edwards, Northbrook IL	69/70
				Sydney R. Raike, Chicago IL	72
				W. C. Boldt & Co., Hammond IN	76/77
				Frank D. Ramuta, Joliet IL	83/84
				Casey Aviation Services, Willowbrook IL	86
				Frank L. Isbell/SNJ Aircraft Inc, Richmond VA	92
				Joseph N. Miller, Pocono Pines PA	8.92/96
88-15638•	AT-6D Mk. III	**41-34062**		(to RAF as EZ189)	
				(to SAAF as 7615): shipped direct to S.Africa	5.44/95
			N9272K	reg.	8.96
88-15698•	AT-6D Mk. III	**41-34067**		(to RAF as EZ194)	
				(to SAAF as 7601): shipped direct to S.Africa	4.44
				(to FA Portuguesa as ....)	
				abandoned Maputo, Mozambique	.74/89
				recov. by Brian Zeederberg/Ian Popplewell, Syferfontein, Johannesburg	.89
				South African Airways Technical Training School	89
			ZS-WLP	SAA Museum Society, Johannesburg	8.3.90/96
				(rest. Johannesburg, ff 14.4.90)	
88-15726•	AT-6D SNJ-5	**41-34506**		(to USN as Bu43745)	
			N1043C	Gregory R. Board, Tucson AZ	63/70
				Walter D. Malling, Tucson AZ	72
				Daniel J. Foley, Long Beach CA	80/88
				David E. Hooker, Huntington Beach CA	9.90/96
88-15737•	AT-6D SNJ-5	**41-34517**		(to USN as Bu43756)	
				(to Spanish AF as C.6-141, Code "421-53")	
			N29942	Combat Aircraft Inc, Elkhart IN	19.4.82
				Wholesale Builders Supply, Gaffney SC	84
				Paul E. Morgan, Gaffney SC	86
			N350HT	Herbert Thomas, Winston Salem NC	4.88/90
				Indiana Aircraft Sales, Indianapolis IN	92
				Matt Hagans, Indianapolis IN	92
				Paul Romine, Indianapolis IN	93
			N732WB	Warbird Operators Inc, Indianapolis IN: res.	12.93
			N350HT	Indiana Aircraft Sales, Indianapolis IN	6.95
88-15738•	AT-6D SNJ-5	**41-34518**		(to USN as Bu43757)	
			N437S	W. Martinmaas, Watertown SD	63
				Larry Vroman, Austin MN	.63/64
				Paul L. Taylor, Shakopee MN/Prior Lake MN	6.65/95
88-15744•	AT-6D Mk. III	**41-34073**		(to RAF as EZ200)	
				SOC RAF: sold to Coley scrapyard	2.50
				(to FA Portuguesa as ......)	
			N8539L	Arthur D. Medore/North American Aviation Inc, Hemet CA	10.80/86
				Carl F. Penner, Salt Lake City UT	12.86/96
88-15754•	AT-6D SNJ-5	**41-34524**		(to USN as Bu43763)	
			N7300C	Edward H. Swan, Pleasant Point CA	63/64
				Claude E. Morey, San Rafael CA	66/69
				Lee R. Donham, Santa Rosa CA	70/72
				Robert P. Mora, Grand Forks ND	76/77
				Vincent L. Murphy, San Diego CA	84/86
				Confederate Air Force, Midland TX	91/96
88-15757•	AT-6D SNJ-5	**41-34527**		(to USN as Bu43766)	
			N3242G	Robert C. Smith, Britt IA	63/64
				Leslie R. Stolle, Seabrook TX	66
				20th Century Fox Film Corp, Hollywood CA	68/71
				(conv. to Kate replica at Long Beach CA .68 for film"Tora Tora Tora"; open storage Long Beach CA 69/71, sold at auction 2.71)	
				Tallmantz Aviation Inc., Orange County CA	2.71/86
				John V. Rawson, Rocky Hill NJ	8.87/96

				(flies as Japanese Kate "AI-313")	
88-15762•	AT-6D	**41-34532**		(to USN as Bu43771)	
	SNJ-5		N8099H	Brockman Construction Co, Natoma CA	63
				Allen T. Ensor, Carmichael CA	.63/64
				Hersey Trucking Co, Camarillo CA	66/69
				Atwood Aviation, Salinas CA	72
			N612MD		
			N43771	Yankee Air Corps/	
				Yanks Air Museum, Chino CA	5.76/96
88-15766•	AT-6D	**41-34536**		(to USN as Bu43775)	
	SNJ-5		N5487V	Jack Sweetser, Knight Landing CA	63/70
			N43775	Pat A. Theige, Folsom CA	.77
				James C. Harris, Oklahoma City OK	84/86
				Raymond A. Houx, Ennis TX	4.87/96
88-15767•	AT-6D	**41-34537**		(to USN as Bu43776)	
	SNJ-5		**N82583**	George C. Borchin, Lewisville TX	76
				Harry S. Doan, New Smyrna Beach FL	84/92
				sold at Doan auction, New Smyrna Beach FL	31.10.92
				George C. Borchin, Lewisville TX	10.92
				Hal K. Litchfield, Kissimmee FL	10.92/93
				Warbird Rides & Adventures Inc, Orlando FL	2.93/96
88-15761•	AT-6D	**41-34531**		(to USN as Bu43770)	
	SNJ-5		**N830JD**	Lance Aircraft Supply, Dallas TX: candidate	3.10.94
				John A. Darznieks, Dallas TX	2.95
88-15770•	AT-6D	**41-34540**		(to USN as Bu43779)	
	SNJ-5		**N3645F**	Dover OHM Inc, Dover OH	63/64
				Roy Mitchell, Cincinnati OH	66/77
				Michael J. Devanney, Goshen OH	86/95
88-15774•	AT-6D	**41-34083**		(to RAF as EZ210)	
	Mk. III			(to SAAF as 7605): shipped direct to S.Africa	4.44/46
				(ret. to RAF as EZ210): shipped to UK, arr.	10.46
				(to Belgian AF as H19): BOC	4.47/61
				(to SAAF as 7731)	10.61
				SAAF Museum, Swartkop AB	94
88-15778•	AT-6D	**41-34087**		(to RAF as EZ214)	
	Mk. III			(to SAAF as 7578): shipped direct to S.Africa	4.44/46
				(ret. to RAF as EZ214): shipped to UK, arr.	9.46
				(to Begian AF as H16): BOC	4.3.47/59
			F-BJBH	Air France, Cormeilles	16.7.59/66
				struck-off reg.	2.66
				Air France Technical School, Vilgenis	90
				(inst. airframe)	
88-15799•	AT-6	**41-34102**		(to RAF as EZ229)	
				(to SAAF as 7592)	
			ZU-AOW	Harvard Club of South Africa: reg. res.	3.11.94
				Harvard Club of South Africa, Springs : reg.	8.8.95
				(note: SAAF quotes 7592 as EZ213)	
88-15821•	AT-6D	**41-34571**	**N87H**	Garrett Flying Service, Dallas TX	63
				C. M. Johnson, State Line CA	.63/64
				Glenn P. Kling, Chula Vista CA	66
				William R. Jewett, Yuma AZ	69
				Frederick G. Kohler, Los Angeles CA	70/77
				Andrew T. Gemellaro, Canoga Park CA	84/92
				Richard Siegfried/Gem Flyers Inc,	
				Downers Grove IL	4.93/96
88-15835•	AT-6D	**41-34585**		(to USN as Bu43791)	
	SNJ-5		**N7968C**	Kathlyn M. Cotton, Strongsville OH	63/64
				M. Leberman, Laceys Springs AL	66/77

				Jimmie Hunt, Fayetteville GA	84
				Harry M. Zerbey, Pottsville PA	5.84/96
88-15836•	AT-6D SNJ-5	**41-34586**		(to USN as Bu43792)	
			N9065Z	Andrew G. Mitchell, El Cajon CA	63/64
				Fred L. Parr, Redondo Beach CA	66
				Glenn L. Schroeder, Granada Hills CA	69/70
				Eric W. Shaeffer, Northridge CA	72
				Glenn L. Schroeder, Reseda CA	76/77
				Edmond J. Colbert, Calvin OK	84/86
				William C. Collins, Mansfield TX	12.87/96
88-15838•	AT-6D SNJ-5	**41-34588**		(to USN as Bu43794)	
				(to Spanish AF as C.6-153)	
			N39403	Combat Aircraft Inc, Elkhart IN	13.5.83
				Donald R. Polan, Dallas TX	84/87
				Greg Morse, Dallas-Addison TX	88/92
				(race #10 *Bad Ju-Ju*)	
				Cavanaugh Flight Centre, Dallas TX	92/93
				Scott A. Morse, Plano TX	3.93/96
88-15864•	AT-6D Mk. III	**41-34110**		(to RAF as EZ237)	
				(to SAAF as 7607): shipped direct to S.Africa	5.44
			ZU-ACU	Stuart D. Davidson, Port Elizabeth	.92
				sold to USA: struck-off reg.	22.11.93
			N554Q	James E. Beasley, Philadelphia PA	10.2.94/96
88-15870•	AT-6D Mk. III	**41-34116**		(to RAF as EZ243)	
				(to RNZAF as NZ1075): shipped direct to NZ	5.44/78
				Airferry International, Sydney NSW	.78
			ZK-ENI	Don G. Reidpath, Auckland	29.8.78/81
				Phil Hewitt, Auckland	78/81
				Hamish D. Brunton, Narromine NSW	6.81/82
				(del. to Australia 26.8.81): struck-off reg.	23.6.82
			VH-HVD	Hamish D. Brunton, Narromine NSW	21.6.82/89
				John Barnes/Fintonne Pty Ltd, Melbourne VIC	3.2.89/94
				D. Hamilton, Whorouly VIC	11.94/96
88-15871•	AT-6D Mk. III	**41-34117**		(to RAF as EZ244)	
				(to RNZAF as NZ1076): shipped direct to NZ	5.44/78
			ZK-ENB	Rex H. Brereton, Dunedin/Ohakea/Feilding	20.6.78/96
88-15872•	AT-6D Mk. III	**41-34118**		(to RAF as EZ245)	
				(to RNZAF as NZ1077): shipped direct to NZ	5.44/78
				(to RNZAF inst. airframe INST174)	
				sold as surplus by RNZAF	.64
				childrens playground Ashburton NZ	76
				Cliff Horrell, Ashburton NZ	78/96
				(displ. on pedestal at owner's house)	
88-15873•	AT-6D Mk.III	**41-34119**		(to RAF as EZ246)	
				(to RNZAF as NZ1078): shipped direct to NZ	5.44/78
			ZK-ENG	George A. Martin & D. J. Dailliess, Blenheim	10.7.78
				Harvard 78 Syndicate, Auckland-Ardmore	93/96
88-15878•	AT-6D	**41-34607**		(to FA Portuguesa as ....)	
			N8541B	Arthur D. Medore/North American Aviation Inc, Denville NJ/Hemet CA	10.80/86
				John P. Vick, Longmont CO	92/96
88-15897•	AT-6D SNJ-5	**41-34626**		(to USN as Bu43812)	
			N9824C	Marshall F. Knox, Gary IN	63/66
				Pat Hague, Chicago IL	67/69
				James D. Slaney, Dallas TX	72/77
				Aero Taxi Inc, Philadelphia PA	12.1.78
			N104FC	Frank Cannavo, Lester PA	1.78/86
			N180NB	Wayne S. Bullock, Warrington PA	7.91/93
				B & B Warbird Aviation, Wilmington DE	6.94
			N812BC	Bernard Cortese/B & B Warbird Aviation, Wilmington DE	12.94/96

c/n	Type	Serial	Reg	History	Date
88-15900•	AT-6D	**41-34629**		(to USN as Bu43815)	
	SNJ-5		**N3630F**	Frederick H. Mesmer, Babylon NY	63/64
				Harry Anapo, Katonah/Brewster NY	66/77
				Dickinson L. Morris, Wyckoff NJ	9.85/96
88-15902•	AT-6D	**41-34631**		(to USN as Bu43817)	
	SNJ-5		**N3687F**	Kent Gillingham, Ann Arbor MI	63/64
				Aloy S. Metty, Ann Arbour MI	66
				Gerald L. Walbrun, Chicago IL/Neenah WI	.66/92
				Michael J. Pangia, Washington DC	2.93/96
88-15903	AT-6D	**41-34632**		(to USN as Bu43818)	
	SNJ-5		**N6628C**	J. H. Overholser, Encino CA	63
				John Tayloe, Moorpark CA	.63/64
				Donald L. Colbenson, Boulder CO	66
				Air Repair Inc, Fabens TX	69
				Franklin D. Strickler, Grapevine TX	70/72
				Sandford M. Graves, Columbia MO	76/88
88-15920•	AT-6D	**41-34649**		(to USN as Bu43835)	
	SNJ-5		**N9060Z**	F. Penny Air Service, Los Angeles CA	63/64
				James F. Meagher, Rolling Hills Estate CA	66
				Keefe Corp, Pacific Palisades CA	69
				William Ross Enterprises, Chicago IL	70
				Austin J. Gibbons, Elgin IL	72/86
				SNJ-5 Inc, Bensenville/Rolling Meadows IL	1.88/96
88-15924•	AT-6D	**41-34653**		(to USN as Bu43839)	
	SNJ-5		**N3258G**	Faye M. Reynolds, Riverside CA	63/76
				Frederick A. Reynolds, Riverside CA	.77/88
				Ray Dieckman, Cincinatti OH/Chino CA	4.91/96
88-15925•	AT-6D	**41-34654**		(to USN as Bu43840)	
	SNJ-5		**N5598V**	Francis R. Fulton, Sharon Springs KS	63/64
				NYC Board of Education, Long Island City NY	3.65/96
88-..........•	AT-6D	....		(to USN as Bu43846)	
	SNJ-5		**N3326G**	Robert O. Butler, Paso Robles CA	63
				Lee L. Wilson, Hollister CA	66/69
				Meteorological Operations Inc, Hollister CA	70
				Aubrey R. King, Salinas CA	10.70/96
88-15943•	AT-6D	**41-34672**	**F-AZSC**	Amicale des Avions du Collection et de Sport, Yvetet	22.4.94
88-15950•	AT-6D	**42-84169**		(to RAF as EZ256)	
	Mk.III			(to SAAF as 7630): shipped direct to S.Africa	6.44/46
				(ret. to RAF as EZ256): shipped to UK, arr.	10.46
				(to Belgian AF as H21)	2.47
				Musee Royal de l'Armee, Brussels, Belgium	68/96
88-15963•	AT-6D	**42-84182**		(to RN FAA as EZ259)	
	Mk.III			(to SAAF as 7631): shipped direct to S.Africa	6.44
				(to RNFAA as EZ259) based S.Africa	1.45
				shipped to UK by 48: SOC	1.1.50
				Skylines Scrap Metal, Sandhurst	
				Dave Elvidge, Begbroke, Oxford: stored dism.	
				Lincolnshire Aviation Museum, Tattershall	83/85
				John & Maureen Woods, Bracknell: hulk	25.5.85
			G-BMJW	John Woods, Bracknell	11.85/91
				(dism. in garden 90: long term rest. project)	
				struck-off reg: no CofA	9.91
88-15992•	AT-6D	**42-84211**		(to Spanish AF as C.6-60, code 421-71)	
				sold at auction, Torrejon AB, Spain	9.7.83
				Lance Aircraft Supply, Dallas TX	84
				(stored dism. in Lance yard, Dallas 84)	

			N42897	Texas Turbo Jet Inc, Dallas TX: reg. res.	5.92
				Richard C. Slaney, Eugene OR	26.5.92/96
88-15997•	T-6D	**42-84216**		(to Republic of Korea AF as .....)	
				USAFM, Wright Patterson AFB, Dayton OH	.94
88-16022•	AT-6D	**42-84241**		(rebuilt as XAT-6E-NT, Ranger V-770-9)	
	XAT-6E		**NX74108**	(Cleveland race #61):	
				pilot Margaret McGrath, San Francisco CA	47
				Richard L. Peters/Western Museum of Flight,	
				Hawthorne CA: displ. while being rest.	90/93
88-16027•	AT-6D	**42-84246**		(to USN as Bu43855)	
	SNJ-5		**N3670F**	George E. Arthur, Springfield OH	63/66
				Iowa Tech Community College, Ottomwa IA	69/77
				Herbert M. Spector, Rock Island IL	86/93
				Paul H. Hulsey, Charleston SC	2.94/96
88-16047•	AT-6D	**42-84266**		(to USN as Bu43875)	
	SNJ-5		**N5199V**	Leo J. Demers, Madras OR	63/64
				Chuck Drake, Seattle WA	66
				Professional Planning Group, Seattle WA	69/70
				Aviation Unlimited, Renton WA	72
				West Pacific Electric, Grants Pass OR	76/77
				Marshal Wells (race # "Com'n Thru")	78
				Wilbert L. (Skeets) Mehrer, Portland OR	11.83/96
				(race #9 "Lickety Split")	
88-16049•	AT-6D	**42-84268**		(to USN as Bu43877)	
	SNJ-5			(to JMSDF as 6185)	
				Shimofusa NAS, Japan: displ.	90
88-16056•	AT-6D	**42-84275**		(to USN as Bu43884)	
	SNJ-5			(to Spanish AF as C.6-150)	
			N29937	Combat Aircraft Inc, Elkhart IN	19.4.82
				Lester D. Friend, San Diego CA	.82/84
				Bob Mitchell & David Bruce/	
				Pacific Western Aviation, Belgrade MT	86/92
				(race #4 "Dash One",later #55 "Slo Thunder")	
				Dave Baughman, Gilbert Becht, Norman Lewis/	
				Kentucky Aviation Museum, Louisville KY	2.93/96
88-16134•	AT-6D	**42-84353**		(to USN as Bu43902)	
	SNJ-5			Air Richmond Inc: USCR candidate	10.2.92
88-16138•	AT-6D	**42-84357**		(to USN as Bu43906)	
	SNJ-5		**N9060R**	Texas Aerosport	29.4.81
				Steven J. Crosby, Oklahoma City OK	84/86
				Caryl J. Ruterbories, Tilden NE	3.89/96
88-16143•	AT-6D	**42-84362**		(to RAF as EZ299)	
	Mk.III			(to RNZAF as NZ1082): shipped direct to NZ	8.44/78
				(to RNZAF inst. airframe INST175)	
				Engine Support Inc, Sebring FL	.78
				Trevor Bland & Ernie Thompson/Warbirds,	
				Auckland-Dairy Flat NZ: rest. project	.78
			ZK-TAF	ntu	
			ZK-ELN	Confederate Air Force (NZ Wing), Auckland	11.80/95
				struck-off reg.	27.3.91
			ZK-USN	Confederate Air Force (NZ Wing): reg. res.	94/96
				(rest. project 87/94; under rest. as SNJ-5	
				Auckland-North Shore 94/95: due to fly 2.95)	
88-16144•	AT-6C	**42-84363**		(to RAF as EZ300)	
	Mk.III			(to RNZAF as NZ1083): shipped direct to NZ	8.44/92
				(to RNZAF inst. airframe INST212)	
				Woodbourne AB: stored	78
				RNZAF Historic Flight: reserve aircraft	92/95
88-16181	AT-6D	**42-84400**		(to USN as Bu43919)	

	SNJ-5			Chesapeake Airways Corp: USCR candidate	3.4.89
88-16183•	AT-6D	**42-84402**		(to USN as Bu43921)	
	SNJ-5		**N3685F**	Robert E. Seff, Akron OH	63/64
				Don A. Cargill, Clawson MI	66
				W. M. Branch, Dallas TX	69/86
				Dan E. Ritter, Kennesaw GA	90
				Paul S. Cash, Morganton NC	3.91/96
88-16206•	AT-6D	**42-84425**		(to USN as Bu43924)	
	SNJ-5		N9814C	Ralph Gaetano, Las Vegas NV	63/66
				Howard Curtis, Hollywood CA	69/72
			N777AP	Charles T. Blaine, Phoenix AZ	76
				Jack Jordan, Phoenix AZ	.77
				Harold G. Watson, Tallahassee FL	84/86
				Joe Fagundes/La Grange Aero, La Grange GA	7.87/96
88-16210•	AT-6D	**42-84429**		(to USN as Bu43928)	
	SNJ-5			(to Spanish AF as C.6-174)	
			N39310	Combat Aircraft Inc, Elkhart IN	13.5.83
				Bahia Oaks Inc, Ocala FL	84
				Gerald V. Hutter, Baton Rouge LA	86
				Joe Hartung/Aerial Solutions, New Roads LA	87
			N817NP	Joe Hartung/Ventress LA (race #89)	6.87/90
				Ed Reed/Tee Six Inc, Casper WY	.90/96
88-16218•	AT-6D	**42-84437**		(to USN as Bu43936)	
	SNJ-5		N3641F	Marvin H. Wolff, Brentwood NY	63/64
				John W. Hardy, Kansas City MO	66/77
			N241F	Charles Harmon, Lockport NY	76/77
				sale rep., State College PA: USCR	84
				Dennis Marcotte, Tampa FL	86/88
				Bill Overcash	90
				Herb Thomas	.90/91
				Richard T. McNeil, North Wilkesboro NC	5.91/96
88-16220•	AT-6D	**42-84439**		(to USN as Bu43938)	
	SNJ-5		**N7980C**	Homer Gutchow Crop Dusting, Dos Palos CA	63/70
				Robert L. Strah, San Ramon CA	71/72
				Fred T. Brundrett, Chandler AZ	76/90
				Nancy Meade, Mesa AZ	5.92
				Stan C. Musick, Brownwood TX	10.92/96
88-16224•	AT-6D	**42-84443**		(to USN as Bu43942)	
	SNJ-5B			(to Spanish AF as C.6-134 "421-50")	
			N3931Z	Combat Aircraft Inc, Elkhart IN	13.5.83
				Richard D. Ervin, Indianapolis IN	84
				Ronald J. Kuhny, Hinsdale IL	3.85/96
				(flies as "USAF 14827/TA-827")	
88-16235•	AT-6D	**42-84454**		(to RAF as EZ310)	
	Mk.III			(to SAAF as 7625): shipped direct to S.Africa	6.44/46
				(ret. to RAF as EZ310): shipped to UK, arr.	9.46
				(to Belgian AF as H15)	2.47
				flown to South Africa ex Belgian Congo	c60
				(to SAAF as 7729)	1.61
				Fort Klapperkop Military Museum, Pretoria	
				South Africa: displ. as "SAAF 7729"	68/83
				SAA, Johannesburg-Jan Smuts: inst. airframe	
			ZS-WLT	ntu: SAA Museum Society, Johannesburg	.90/95
			ZS-WLR	South African Airways, Johannesburg	18.9.95
				(rebuilt Johannesburg-Jan Smuts 11.91/95)	
88-16300•	AT-6D	**42-84519**		(to USN as Bu43958)	
	SNJ-5		N6644C	Michael N. Wood, Whitemarsh PA	63/66
				Robert Gardner, Sunderland MA	69/70
				John M. Schleich, Galway NY	.77/86
				Aries Aviation & Development, Brookfield CT	12.87/88

			N3958	Aries Aviation & Development, Brookfield CT	2.88/96
88-16305•	AT-6D SNJ-5	**42-84524**		(to USN as Bu43963)	
			N600MF	Martin K. Fall, Indianapolis IN	30.3.94/96
				(completed long-term rest .94)	
88-16308•	AT-6D SNJ-5	**42-84527**		(to USN as Bu43966)	
			N7990C	Coastal Aviation Corp, Alexandria VA : USCR	63/69
				(to FA Chile as FAC285)	
			CC-DMI	Natiaonal Aeronautical Collection, Santiago	95
88-16310•	AT-6D SNJ-5	**42-84529**		(to USN as Bu43968)	
			N8212E	Underwood Bros Asphalt Paving,Princeton WV	63/64
				New Kent Airport, Quinton VA	66
				Edward L. Bankston, East Point GA	69/70
				Robert S. Henry, Atlanta GA	76/86
				Richard H. Maxwell, Grove City PA	4.87/96
88-16314•	AT-6D SNJ-5	**42-84533**		(to USN as Bu43972)	
			N7981C	Richard Stearns, Northbrook IL	63/66
				Paul C. Schorn, Miami/Pompano Beach FL	69/87
				(open storage, Kenosha WI 79/87)	
				Randy Miller, Grayslake IL	10.87/88
			N3972E	Randy Miller, Grayslake IL	8.88/96
88-16316•	AT-6D SNJ-5	**42-84535**		(to USN as Bu43974)	
			N7969C	Norman F. Brooks, San Diego CA	63/66
				Raymond E. Marsh, Canoga Park CA	69
				Richard T. Sykes, Toluca Lake CA	70/96
88-16324•	AT-6D Mk. III	**42-84543**		(to RAF as EZ329)	
				(to RNZAF as NZ1085): shipped direct to NZ	8.44/78
				Australian Aircraft Restoration Group/	
				Moorabbin Air Museum, Moorabbin VIC	.78
			ZK-ENM	Don G. Reidpath, Auckland: reg. for del.	10.78/80
				(del. to Sydney 12.5.79, arr. Essendon VIC 20.5.79)	
				Moorabbin Air Museum, Moorabbin VIC	6.79
			VH-SNJ	Bruce Andrews, Melbourne VIC	3.4.80/85
				Guido Zuccoli, Darwin NT/Toowoomba QLD	11.85/96
88-16325•	AT-6D Mk. III	**42-84544**		(to RAF as EZ330)	
				(to RNZAF as NZ1086): shipped direct to NZ	8.44/78
				(to RNZAF inst. airframe INST176)	
				Engine Support Inc, Sebring FL	.78
				d'E. Charles Darby, Auckland: stored	.78/95
				(INST176 noted stored Auckland-Dairy Flat 79)	
				fuse. to VH-AYO: see 88-13187	
88-16326•	AT-6D Mk. III	**42-84545**		(to RAF as EZ331)	
				(to RNZAF as NZ1087): shipped direct to NZ	8.44
				(to RNZAF inst. airframe INST213)	
				Woodbourne AB: stored	78
				RNZAF Museum, Wigram AB	84/96
				(displ. as "NZ948")	
88-16328•	AT-6D Mk. III	**42-84547**		(to RAF as EZ333)	
				(to RNZAF as NZ1089): shipped direct to NZ	8.44/78
				(to RNZAF inst. airframe INST177)	
				Taranaki Transport & Technology Museum,	
				New Plymouth NZ	.78/96
88-16336•	AT-6D Mk. III	**42-84555**		(to RNFAA as EZ341)	.44/56
				(to FA Portuguesa as 1662)	3.56
				Museo do Ar: stored Sintra AB, Portugal	78/90
				AJD Engineering Ltd,Sudbury	.90
				(arr. airfreight FAP C130 Stansted 27.7.90)	
			G-ELMH	Mark Hammond, Eye, Suffolk	22.7.92/96
				(rest. Crowfield, ff 26.3.94 "42-84555/EP-H")	
88-16388•	AT-6D	**42-84607**		(to USN as Bu43986)	

	SNJ-5		**N6436D**	Robert W. Oliver, Oklahoma City OK	63/64
				John Crisi, Shelton CT	66/69
				Renata M. Crisi, Wappingers Falls NY	72
				John D. Deardon, Princeton NJ	76/84
				Dan J. Caldarale, Vincentown NJ	9.84/96
88-16411•	AT-6D	**42-84630**		(to USN as Bu44009)	
	SNJ-5		N6639C	Lemmon Aircraft Co, Lemmon SD	63
				Burwell Flyers Inc, Burwell NE	.63/64
				Kensair Corp, Broomfield CO	66
				Justin W. Capps, Erie CO	69
				Marjorie L. Darr, Kansas City MO	70
			N30JF	James W. Flanagan, Independence MO	72
				West Pacific Electrical Inc, Grants Pass OR	76/77
				Wayne W. Cox, Del City OK	84
				Fighting Air Command Inc, Dallas TX	86
				Charles D. Foran, Dallas TX	88/96
88-16459•	AT-6D	**42-84678**		USAF sold as surplus	26.6.57
			N7095C	Walter Johnson, Minneapolis MN	63/64
				Josco Inc, Minneapolis MN	66
				Johan M. Larsen, Minneapolis MN	69/77
				Ronald M. Hankin, Palatine IL	84/86
				David Van Liere	88
				Paul M. Holman, Plymouth MI	11.88/96
88-16461•	AT-6D	**42-84680**		(to RCAF as 42-84680): BOC	12.5.51
	T-6D			ret. to USAF: SOC RCAF	26.10.53
			N7476C	Robert E. Sandham, Los Angeles CA	63/64
				Oakley D. Ostrander, Lemon Grove CA	66
				Robert P. Damberger, San Diego CA	69/72
				Robert B. Willson, Martinsburg PA	76
				J. L. Hammond, Fort Wayne IN	84/86
				James D. McCabe, Markle IN	12.87/95
88-16466•	AT-6D	**42-84685**		(to USN as Bu44014)	
	SNJ-5			(to FA Uruguay as .....)	
			N3642F	Frank T. Carroll, Rochester IN	63/64
				Thomas Streckert, Abbotsford WI	66/70
				Metternich Construction Co, Yachats OR	72
				Robert Morrow, Salem OR	76/77
				James D. Elkins, Salem OR	7.84/96
88-16469•	AT-6D	**42-84688**		(to USN as Bu44017)	
	SNJ-5			(to FA Colombiana as 777)	
			HK-2049P	H. E. Valez	.77/82
				Jose G. Pardo, Cali Colombia	92/96
88-16472•	AT-6D	**42-84691**		(to USN as Bu44020)	
	SNJ-5		N8096H	C. W. Ankerberg, St. Petersburg FL	63/72
			N14HB	David Anderson, Scotch Plains NJ	.77
				Haywood B. Bartlett, Pike Road AL	2.84/86
			N43WB	Haywood B. Bartlett, Pike Road AL	9.88/96
88-16484	AT-6D	42-84703		(to USN as Bu44032)	
	SNJ-5		N1042C	Gary B. Joslin, Conneaut OH	63/69
				John W. Reagan, Akron OH	70/72
88-16496•	AT-6D	**42-84715**		(to USN as Bu84825)	
	SNJ-5			(to Spanish AF as C.6-163, code 421-56)	
			N29944	Combat Aircraft Inc, Elkhart IN	19.4.82
				David E. Henry, Houston TX	84
				sold to Australia: struck-off USCR	13.3.90
				Nostalgair Ltd, Raglan NSW	.90
				Mike English, Bathurst NSW	90
			VH-XAN	P. Hanneman, Alloway Bank, Eglinton NSW	12.2.91/96
88-16497•	AT-6D	**42-84716**		(to USN as Bu84826)	

	SNJ-5		**N3272G**	Charles E. Smith. New Holstein WI	63
				Ankeny Flight Service, Ankeny IA	.63/64
				Alfred C. Pietsch, Minot ND	66
				Edward A. Klatka, Enid OK	69/70
				Gordon L. Grohs, Scottsdale AZ	72
				Herbert Taylor, Gallup NM	76/77
				John C. Hess, Brownsville TX	84/86
				Linda K. Finch & John Luther, San Antonio TX	11.86/96
				(race #26 USN 82", later race #20)	
88-16498•	AT-6D	**42-84717**		(to USN as Bu84827)	
	SNJ-5		**N7979C**	Aadu Karemaa, Fort Worth TX	63/72
				Wilbert L. Mehrer, Portland OR	76/96
88-16503•	AT-6D	**42-84722**		(to USN as Bu84832)	
	SNJ-5		N7982C	Richard E. Hyde, Woodside CA	63
				Edward A. Grens, Burlingame CA	.63/64
				Williams Flying Service, Tutwiler MS	66/76
			N2025T	reg.	8.89
			C-GKGE	General Air Care Ltd, Souris MAN	12.94/96
				op: Operation Fire Fly Aerial Combat, Souris	95
88-16504•	AT-6D	**42-84723**		(to RAF as EZ359)	
	Mk. III			(to RNZAF as NZ1090): shipped direct to NZ	7.44/78
				(to RNZAF inst. airframe INST178)	
				Engine Support Inc, Sebring FL	.78
				d'E. C. Darby, Auckland NZ	.78
				(INST178 noted stored Auckland-Dairy Flat 79)	
			VH-AUR	ntu: Hamish D. Brunton, Narromine NSW	30.4.82/84
				Hamish Brunton & Col Pay, Scone NSW	83/84
				(imported 5.83, stored dism. Scone NSW 84)	
				Frank Murray, Cessnock NSW	.84/96
				(under rest. to fly, Cessnock NSW 94/96)	
88-16505•	AT-6D	**42-84724**		(to RAF as EZ360)	
	Mk. III			(to RNZAF as NZ1091): shipped direct to NZ	7.44/78
			ZK-ENC	W. J. Derek Williams, Mount Maunganui	20.6.78/95
				(del. Wigram AB-Tauranga by Williams .78,	
				noted stored Dairy Flat 79)	
88-16506•	AT-6D	**42-84725**		(to RAF as EZ361)	
	Mk. III			(to RNZAF as NZ1092): shipped direct to NZ	7.44/78
			ZK-WAR	Trevor T. Bland & G. Stan Smith/Warbirds,	
				Auckland-Dairy Flat	1.9.78/81
				Trevor T. Bland & E. J. Schroeder, Ardmore	.81/93
				WAR Syndicate, Auckland-Ardmore	94/95
88-16570•	AT-6D	**42-84789**		(to USN as Bu84839)	
	SNJ-5		N3188G	Charles S. Stoll, Johannesburg CA	63/70
				David F. Samson, St. Augustine FL	84
				James J. Richardson, Tallahassee FL	86/89
				Wayne R. Witt, Wooddale IL	90
			N590WW	Wayne R. Witt, Wooddale IL	7.90/92
				Jerald Hanchey, Lafayette LA	4.95
88-16560•	AT-6D	**42-84779**	N7210C	Clayton J. Carriveau, Milwaukee WI	63/64
				Donald D. Douglas, Haines AK	66/70
			N7RK	Ronald F. Klemm, Fairbanks AK	76/78
			N7PK	ntu: Ronald F. Klemm, Fairbanks AK	6.78
			N7RK	Ronald F. Klemm, Fairbanks AK	12.88/96
88-16574•	AT-6D	**42-84793**		(to USN as Bu84843)	
	SNJ-5		**N3680F**	D. L. Price, Winston Salem NC	63/64
				Frank E. Bennett, Winston Salem NC	66
				Richard B. Minges, Fayetteville NC	69
				Edward O. Messick, San Antonio TX	70
				Lloyd P. Nolan, Mercedes TX	72/86
				Rudolph Perez, Valencia CA	6.91/96
88-16581•	AT-6D	**42-84800**		(to USN as Bu84850)	

	SNJ-5		**N7988C**	Kenneth R. Everson, Fillmore CA	63/70
				Terramar Inc, Cape Canaveral FL	76
				John W. Kehoe, Lakeland FL	6.83/96
88-16582•	AT-6D	**42-84801**		(to USN as Bu84851)	
	SNJ-5		N3452G	Joseph E. Kibler, Owings Mills MD	63/66
				Joseph M. Natoli, Lorton VA	69/70
				Samuel L. Huntington, Annapolis MD	72
			N11SH	Samuel L. Huntington, Annapolis MD	
				Raymond A. Rakers, Breese IL	76/77
				Scott O. Johnson, Clarendon Hills IL	8.82/96
88-16640•	AT-6D	**42-84859**	**N4748C**	Ferguson Flying Service, Pensacola FL	63/86
				Robert F. Wallin, Shell WY	92/93
				Hawkins & Powers Aviation, Greybull WY	10.93/96
88-16676•	AT-6D	**42-84895**		(to USN as Bu84865)	
	SNJ-5			(to JMSDF as ....)	
			N89014	Dennis G. Buehn/Warbirds West, Compton CA	10.77
				(recov. ex Japan, rest. Compton CA c78)	
				Brandon O'Brien CA	.79/84
				sale rep., Portland OR	84
				Confederate Air Force, Camarillo CA	86/96
88-16678•	AT-6D	**42-84897**		(to USN as Bu84867)	
	SNJ-5		**N6900C**	Alvin L. Horton, Tracy CA	63/70
				Michael Mockbee, Los Angeles CA	76
				Invader Aviation, Wilmington DE	84/86
				Danny Summers, Sugar City ID	7.89/96
88-16679	AT-6D	**42-84898**		(to USN as Bu84868)	
	SNJ-5		N3681F	Francis J. McCabe, Philadelphia PA	63/64
				William E. Davis, Philadelphia PA	66/70
				Robert J. Shaver, Linwood NJ	72
			N988E	Robert J. Shaver, Linwood NJ	76/77
				Tom Crevasse & Richard Sprague/	
				Simulated Automatic Weapons Inc, Live Oak FL	84/92
				crashed into sea, Stuart FL	15.6.85
88-16686•	AT-6D	**42-84905**		(to USN as Bu84875)	
	SNJ-5		**N3725G**	Marsh Aviation Co, Litchfield Park AZ	63/66
				20th Century Fox Film Corp, Hollywood CA	68/71
				(conv. to Kate replica at Long Beach CA .68 for film "Tora Tora Tora"; open storage Long Beach CA 69/71, sold at auction Long Beach 2.71)	
				Eugene Reid, Lakewood CA	2.71/72
				Eagle Aviation Inc, Tulsa OK	76
				Ronald Bryant, Springfield MO	.77
				Confederate Air Force, Harlingen/Midland TX	6.10.78/96
				(flies as Japanese Kate "AII-356")	
88-16712•	AT-6D	**42-84931**		(to RNFAA as EZ407)	.44/56
	Mk. III			(to FA Portuguesa as 1656)	3.56
				Fleet Air Arm Historic Flight, RNAS Yeovilton	83/94
				(stored RNAS Lee-On-Solent .83/94,"RN EZ407")	
				sold at auction	26.11.94
88-16714•	AT-6D	**42-84933**		(to RCAF as 42-84933): BOC	12.5.51
				ret. to USAF Tinker AFB OK: SOC RCAF	7.10.52
			N9103R	C. H. Shaw, Alexandria KY	63/69
				Barry Pruss, Dillsboro IN	70
				Robert L. Kimball, Ebensburg PA	11.70/82
			N420RK	Robert L. Kimball, Ebensburg PA	3.82/96
88-16756•	AT-6D	**42-84975**		(to USN as Bu84895)	
	SNJ-5		N3189G	Ralph F. Glasgow, Austin TX: USCR	63/70
				(to FA Mexicana as 718)	
			N7055C	Texas Turbo Jet Inc, Dallas TX	1.89

				(del. ex Mexico, stored McAllen TX .89)	
				Gary L. Petersen, Lincoln NE	.89/93
				(rest. Crete NE 90/91, ff .91)	
				Heritage Aircraft Sales, Indianapolis IN	9.93/96
88-16771•	AT-6D	**42-84990**		(to USN as Bu84910)	
	SNJ-5		**N3674F**	John P. Graff, Canyonwood PA	63
				Atlantic Aviation Service, Philadelphia PA	.63/64
				City of New York Board of Education,	
				Long Island City NY	66/96
88-16778•	AT-6D	**42-84997**		(to USN as Bu84917)	
	SNJ-5		N3668F	Bernard R. Froehlich, Cincinatti OH	63/66
				Emmit E. Risner, Monroeville OH	69/72
				Air Classics Inc, Lewisville TX	76/77
			N2023	Stutsman Aircraft Inc, Elkhart IN	.78
				Charles E. Waters, Elk Grove Village IL	84
				William R. Rose, Barrington IL	9.84/96
88-16784•	AT-6D	**42-85003**		(to USN as Bu84923)	
	SNJ-5			(to Spanish AF as .....)	
			N3931R	Combat Aircraft Inc, Elkhart IN	13.5.83
				Julius D. Clemmons, Ocala FL	11.83/96
88-16786	AT-6D	42-85005		(to USN as Bu84925)	
	SNJ-5		N3151G	Farmers Cropdusters, Bakersfield CA	63/64
				Alan L. Holden, Las Vegas NV	66
				Ivan O. Rasmussen, Englewood CO	69/72
				James K. McGuire, Wichita KS	81/83
			N91047	James K. McGuire, Wichita KS	4.83/86
				crashed Fairview OK (McGuire k.)	11.11.84
88-16790•	AT-6D	**42-85009**		(to USN as Bu84929)	
	SNJ-5		**N8521K**	reg. res.	12.80/92
88-16791	AT-6D	42-85010		(to USN as Bu84930)	
	SNJ-5		N3665F	M. A. Miller, Floyds Knob IN	63/70
				Don Rhynalds, Bealeton VA	76/77
				sale rep., Pepper Lake OH	86
				Sellersburg Aviation Museum, Sellersburg IN	88
				struck-off USCR	2.90
88-16849•	AT-6D	**42-85068**	N10595	R. B. Dillard, Sweetwater TX	63
				Sweetwater Dusting Co, Sweetwater TX	.63/64
				Harrington Flying Service, Abbeville LA	66
				Horst K. Heiles, St. Louis MO	69
				George Banjak, Wester Groves MO	70/72
				Smithville Dusting Service, Smithville GA	84/86
				struck-off USCR	2.3.88
			LN-LCN	ntu	
			LN-LCS	ntu	
			LN-AMY	Space Promotions Air Service, Fornebu	13.5.88
				op: Warbirds of Norway	93/95
				op: Old Flying Machine Co, Duxford UK: del.	4.93/96
88-16857•	AT-6D	**42-85076**		(to USN as Bu84936)	
	SNJ-5		N3667F	Samuel E. McIntosh Inc, Miami FL: USCR	63/69
				(to Spanish AF as ....)	
			N29912	Combat Aircraft Inc, Elkhart IN	20.5.82
			N67RB	Raymond H. Bachman, Minooka IL	9.83/84
			N64KP	Kevin Larosa Enterprises, Canoga Park CA	1.86/96
88-16873	AT-6D	42-85092		(to USN as Bu84952)	
	SNJ-5		N10605	Beverly Fritch, Detroit MI	63/66
				Joseph Cintula, Brunswick OH	69/70
				Gary Boucher, Natchitoches LA	76
				Frank Nelson, Vicksburg MS	.77
				A. P. Snyder, Houston TX	84
				crashed Houston-Cyprus Airport TX	21.4.84

88-16923•	AT-6D	**42-85142**	**N7211C**	Jack W. Madsen, Provo UT	63/66
				Earnest H. Olsen, Rebecca GA	69
				Lee Groff, Philadelphia PA	70
				Gordon L. Grohs, Scottsdale AZ	72
				Jack B. Watson, Fayetteville NC	84/86
				Richard B. Watson, Goleta CA	5.86/96
88-16973•	AT-6D	**42-85192**		(to USN as Bu84962)	
	SNJ-5			USMC Museum, MCAS Quantico VA	85/94
88-16974•	AT-6D	**42-85193**		(to USN as Bu84963)	
	SNJ-5			(to JMSDF as 6164)	
				Ozuki NAS, Japan: displ.	90
88-16979•	AT-6D	**42-85198**		(to USN as Bu84968)	
	SNJ-5		N9051Z	Richard B. Ferguson, Chula Vista CA	63/64
				Byron R. Sacquot, National City CA	66/70
				Kenneth E. Stout, Goddland KS	72
			N65BL	Ben Lowell, Boulder CO	76/77
			N17E	John P. Rahart, Saratoga WY	84
			N23ZH	John P. Rahart, Saratoga WY	11.85/86
				Miles G. Biggs, Covington LA	5.88/95
88-16980•	AT-6D	**42-85199**		(to USN as Bu84969)	
	SNJ-5		N1040C	Raymond L. Wilson, Cutbank MT	63/66
				Stanley J. Gnesa, Modesto CA	69/77
				John T. Flanagan, Chowchilla CA	84
				Clancy H. Flanagan, Chowchilla CA	1.85/90
			N6TF	Tom & Clancy H. Flanagan, Chowchilla CA	1.90/96
88-16990•	AT-6D	**42-85209**		(to USN as Bu84979)	
	SNJ-5		**N7296C**	Aerial Applicators Inc, Salt Lake City UT	63/72
				sale rep. USCR	76/77
				Robert S. Haun, Westminster CO	84/86
				Samuel B. Saxton, Allentown PA	9.88/96
88-16992•	AT-6D	**42-85211**		(to USN as Bu84981)	
	SNJ-5		**N85169**	Southwest Aerospace Manufacturing Corp, Mesa AZ	11.80
				Harold D. Rowe, Las Vegas NV	10.84/96
88-16994	AT-6D	**42-85213**		(to USN as Bu84983)	
	SNJ-5		N6434D		
			XB-FOS	Juan M. V. Ramirez, Mexico City	77/93
88-17002•	AT-6D	**42-85221**		(to USN as Bu84991)	
	SNJ-5		N5197V	Coastal Aviation Corp, Alexandria VA: USCR	66/69
				(to Spanish AF as ....)	
			N29940	Combat Aircraft Inc, Elkhart IN	20.5.82
				Thomas C. Webster, Detroit MI	84/86
				Yankee Air Museum, Willow Grove MI	88
				Polish Flyers Inc, Belleville MI	2.91/96
88-17004•	AT-6D	**42-85223**		(to RAF as EZ449)	
	Mk. III			(to RNZAF as NZ1096): shipped direct to NZ	11.44/78
			ZK-END	W. S. Bell & Rod D. Dahlberg, Mt. Maunganui	20.6.78/96
88-17010•	AT-6D	**42-85229**		(to RAF as EZ455)	
	Mk. III			(to RNZAF as NZ1098): shipped direct to NZ	11.44/78
				Airferry International, Sydney NSW	.78
			ZK-ENJ	Don G. Reidpath, Auckland	14.9.78
				K. R. Brooking, Waitakere/Tauranga	87/96
88-17011•	AT-6D	**42-85230**		(to RAF as EZ456)	
	Mk. III			(to RNZAF as NZ1099): shipped direct to NZ	11.44/78
				Airferry International, Sydney NSW	.78
			ZK-ENK	Don G. Reidpath, Auckland	14.9.78
				d'E. Charles Darby & Jim Pavatt, Auckland	87/95

				(rest. project 87, flying by 92 as "NZ1099")	
88-17025•	AT-6D	**42-85244**		(to IDFAF as .....)	
			4X-ARC	Marom Ltd, Herzlia	7.62/88
				IDFAF Museum, Hatzerim AB	.88/90
				(displ. as IDFAF "1125")	
88-17026•	AT-6D	**42-85245**	N6600C	R. A. Grunert, San Francisco CA	63
				Floyd E. Wood, San Jose CA	.63/72
				Charles McFarland, Gig Harbour WA	76/77
			N77LT	Herbert Mohr, Lynnwood WA	1.79/96
88-17076•	AT-6D SNJ-5	**42-85295**		(to USN as Bu84995)	
			N9813C	Albert G. Owen, Monroeville PA	63/66
				Russell Richards, Portage PA	69/70
				George W. Wrenn, Greensville TN	76
				Charles E. Lewis, Albuquerque NM later Leadville CO	9.81/95
88-17079	AT-6D SNJ-5 Biplane	**42-85298**		(to USN as Bu84998)	
			N6435D	Robert C. Stroop, Selma AL	63/70
				(conv. by Stroop to experimental biplane cropduster using another SNJ-5 mainplane)	
				J. F. Carter, Monroeville AL: ag ops.	
88-17082•	AT-6D SNJ-5	**42-85301**		(to USN as Bu85001)	
			N3689F	Frank B. Williams, Port Arthur TX	63/64
				Fornof Motor Co, Houma LA	66
				SNJ Corp, Cleveland OH	69/70
				Dennis K. Simpson, Anderson IN	76/77
				Don Tally/Magnificent Two Inc, Longview TX	3.84/96
88-17085•	AT-6D SNJ-5	**42-85304**		(to USN as Bu85004)	
			N6437D	C. D. Rivenbark, Dallas TX	63/77
				Elman H. Sandell, Dallas TX	84/86
				sale rep., Wilmington DE	92
				Joe Dee, Sheridan WY	1.94/96
88-17088•	AT-6D SNJ-5B	**42-85307**		(to USN as Bu85007)	
				NAS Litchfield Park AZ, for disposal: del.	19.7.57
			N6638C	San Tan Dusters, Chandler AZ	63/70
				(open storage, dism. unconv. orig. USN sc., Prineville OR 75/77)	
			N957ED	Eric A. Danfelt, Bellevue WA	2.91/96
				(long-term rest., ff Renton WA 14.10.92)	
88-17089•	AT-6D SNJ-5	**42-85308**		(to USN as Bu85008)	
			N7997C	J. E. Smith, Bull Head City AZ	63/64
				David M. White, Studio City CA	66
				Billy W. Merriner, San Diego CA	69/70
				Johnson National Bank, Prairie Village KS	72
			N777HL	Donald L. Fowler, Fort Worth TX	76/86
				Andres U. Katz, Dallas TX	5.86/96
88-17103•	AT-6D SNJ-5	**42-85322**		(to USN as Bu85022)	
				disposal ex NAS Pensacola FL: $385	15.12.58
			N3632F	Homer H. Terry, Knoxville TN	63
				Champion Distribution Corp, Georgetown TX	.63/70
				Perry J. Wilson, Grand Prairie TX	72
				C. Aubrey Hair & J. R. Almond/ Warbird Traders Inc, McKinney TX	11.87/93
				(last flew .68, stored in hangar 68/86; rest., ff .88 as "85022")	
				reg. pending, Plattville AL	95
88-17109•	AT-6D SNJ-5	**42-85328**		(to USN as Bu85028)	
			N3273G	Marvin Axelrod, Alliance OH	63
				A. E. Smith, Alliance OH	.63/64
				William I. France, Alliance OH	66
			N3771M	Willey Optical Corp, Melbourne FL	69/72

				George S. Morris, Dunedin FL	76/86
			N595SH	ntu: Russell A. Turner, Panama City FL	11.87
			N3771M	Russell A. Turner, Panama City FL	8.87/96
88-17125•	AT-6D	**42-85344**		(to FA Brasileira as 1633)	.54
				(to FA Paraguaya as 0101)	.60
			N3173L	World Wide Aeronautical Industries, Moorpark CA	19.9.91/92
				James D. Morgan, Aumsville OR	9.93/96
				(USCR quotes id. as "413279")	
88-17155•	AT-6D	**42-85374**		(to Spanish AF as C.6-12): sold at auction	1.84
			N49961	Combat Aircraft Inc, Elkhart IN	5.84/86
				sale rep., Irving TX	92/96
88-17181•	AT-6D	**42-85400**	N6075C	Malcolm Neal, Torrance CA	63/64
				John W. Gray, Tarzana CA	66
				George C. Madsen, Sylmar CA	69/70
			N65555	George C. Madsen, Sylmar CA	72/77
				Fred G. Kohler, Truckee CA/Scottsdale AZ	8.80/96
88-17189•	AT-6D	**42-85408**	**N6979C**	Marvin D. Hamrick, San Pablo CA	63/66
				Robert L. Wills, Twin Falls ID	69
				Oakland Air Force Inc, Oakland CA	70/72
				California Warbirds Inc, San Jose CA	76/96
88-17197•	AT-6D	**42-85416**		(to USN as Bu85036)	
	SNJ-5B		**N9805C**	Ben W. Widtfeldt, Phoenix AZ	63/70
				Roy D. Miller, Monterey CA	72
				Jack Flaherty, Hollister CA	76
				Robert F. Byrne, Bloomfield Hills MI	.77/88
				David Voglund, Radcliff KY	11.90/96
88-17199	AT-6D	42-85418		(to USN as Bu85038)	
	SNJ-5C			(to FA Brasileira as FAB T-16 1706)	.60
			PT-KRC	reg., conv. for agricultural ops.	.76
				(noted Sao Paulo, in service, advertising sc. 6.82)	
				Carlos Alberto Edo Palma, Jundiai	83
88-17200	AT-6D	42-85419		(to USN as Bu85039)	
	SNJ-5		N3163G	Eugene L. Treasrau, San Rafael CA	63/64
				Curtiss S. Turner, Kapaa Kauai HI	66
				John H. Weiser, Honolulu HI	69/72
88-17208•	AT-6D	**42-85427**		(to USN as Bu85047)	
	SNJ-5		N3640F	J. R. Carter, Felda FL	63/70
				A. Castillo, Homestead FL	76/77
			N242AT	ntu: Walter L. Goodrich, Oceanside CA	9.84
			N246AT	W. Ray Goodrich, Oceanside CA	10.84/90
			N4LH	Linda H. Goodrich, Oceanside CA	1.90/92
				Bruce L. Moore, Canaan NH	7.92/95
88-17237•	AT-6D	**42-85456**	**N9649C**	Joe H. Garrett, Travis AFB CA	63/64
				Herbert C. Harrison, Shreveport LA	66
				Walter H. Hackett, Niles OH	69/70
				Tim D. Ehlies, Miami FL	12.70/96
88-17274•	AT-6D	**42-85493**		(to USN as Bu85053)	
	SNJ-5		N8210E	Robert H. Myers, Columbiana OH	63/69
				Gorden Newell/New Air Service, Utica NY	72/76
			N777WS	William M. Stern, Alton IL	3.78/84
				Mustang Aviation, Fairfield NJ	84/86
				Henry Moretti, Cranston RI	88/96
88-17277	AT-6D	42-85496		(to USN as Bu85056)	
	SNJ-5		N447C	H. Clay Lacy, Wichita KS/Van Nuys CA	63/70
			N164CL	H. Clay Lacy, Boise ID	76/84

8-17284•	AT-6D	**42-85503**		(to USN as Bu85063)	
	SNJ-5		**N1047C**	Carl A. Shipman, Holly Hill SC	63/64
				Franklin Machine Co, Franklin NC	66/72
				Grant L. Zickgraf, Franklin NC	76/84
				Stone Mountain Aviation Mus., Clarkston GA	4.84/95
				Western North Carolina Air Museum,	
				Hendersonville NC	96
8-17287•	AT-6D	**42-85506**		(to USN as Bu85066)	
	SNJ-5		N7967C	Charles W. Pacey, Paxton IL	63/64
				Simon Rettberg & Garrison Inc, Champagne IL	66/69
			N666MC	Mark Clark/Courtesy Aircraft, Rockford IL	70/72
				William E. Henry, Ball Ground GA	76/77
			N7967C		
			N2676P	rereg.	2.82
				Courtesy Aircraft Inc, Rockford IL	84/96
8-17301	AT-6D	42-85520		(to USN as Bu85080)	
	SNJ-5		N1046C	Conrad K. Warren, Deer Lodge MT	63/64
				Wayne J. Rogers, Bradley OK	66
				Don C. Barrett, Dallas/Valley View TX	69/77
				(race #10)	
				Kale B. Webster, Odessa TX	84
8-17307•	AT-6D	**42-85526**		(to USN as Bu85086)	
	SNJ-5		**N12377**	W. H. Booth, Lambert MS	66
				Metropolitan Aerial Surveys, Fort Worth TX	69/70
				Robert J. Richardson, Burbank/Valencia CA	8.76/96
8-17308•	AT-6D	**42-85527**		(to USN as Bu85087)	
	SNJ-5		N3257G	Joe L. Phillips, San Bernadino CA	63/64
				Robert H. Garlow, Bakersfield CA	66
				Richard E. Lowney, San Jose CA	69/72
			N25SS	Duane Potts, Marengo IA	75/77
				John P. Silberman, Tampa FL	84/88
				Campbell Barnett, Mount Airy NC	7.89/96
8-17311•	AT-6D	**42-85530**		(to USN as Bu85090)	
	SNJ-5		N9050Z	Broward Improvement Corp, Hollywood FL	63
				Will C. Garrett, Dallas TX	.63/64
				William C. Childers, Temple TX	66
			N15090	William P. Edwards, Big Spring TX	69/76
				Wilson C. Edwards, Big Spring TX	84/96
				(flies as "USAF TA-090")	
8-17331•	AT-6D	**42-85550**		(to RCAF as 42-85550): BOC	12.5.51/54
				ret. to USAF, Tucson AZ: SOC RCAF	19.2.54
			N7471C	Max Potter, Stanfield AZ	63/64
				Mike Des Marais, Phoenix AZ	66
				William L. Robart, Phoenix AZ	69/72
				Weldon Ropp/Wellys Aircraft Sales,	
				Delray Beach FL	.72/88
				Roger D. Henderson, El Sobrante CA	9.91/96
8-17354•	AT-6D	**42-85573**		(to SAAF as ....)	
			ZU-ASF	J. H. Marx	6.4.95
8-17380•	AT-6D	**42-85599**		(to RCAF as 42-85599): BOC	18.5.51/54
				ret. to USAF, Tucson AZ: SOC RCAF	24.2.54
			N7421C	Ray Karrells, Port Washington WI	63/72
				Gerald A. Swayze, Mesquite TX	76
				James D. Slaney, Danville CA	84
				William Gossman, Louisville KY	86
				Edward J. Modes, Burbank CA	9.86/96
8-17400•	AT-6D	**42-85619**		(to USN as Bu90587)	
	SNJ-5		**N8213E**	Paul Ritter, Midland MI	63/70
				Robert Falicki, Sparta MI	76/77
				Sebring B. Simpson, Plaquemine LA	3.84/96

88-17412•	AT-6D SNJ-5	**42-85631**		(to USN as Bu90599)	
			N3726G	Western State Aviation, Gunnison CO	63/86
			N105DG	David H. Groak/Gamma Holdings Inc, Garland & Rockwall TX	2.89/96
88-17421•	AT-6D SNJ-5	**42-85640**		(to USN as Bu90608)	
			N3197G	John McGregor, Los Angeles CA	63/66
				Timothy C. Anderson, Hollywood CA	69/72
				Restoration Squadron, Los Angeles CA	84/86
				Robert M. Briggs, Sacramento CA	4.90/96
88-17425•	AT-6D SNJ-5	**42-85644**		(to USN as Bu90612)	
			N3261G	John C. Hooper, Metairie LA	63/66
				John F. Trainor, Ardmore PA	69/72
				Keener S. White, Pembroke MA	76/77
				Clark Motor Co, State College PA	84
				Carmen J. Scoppa, Little River SC	86/91
				Robert L. Chisholm, Memphis TN	3.91/96
88-17433•	AT-6D SNJ-5B	**42-85652**		(to USN as Bu90620)	
			N5486V	Glenn A. Johnson, Sacramento CA	63/66
				James A. Odell, Sepulveda CA	69/77
				Gerald A. Swayze, Mesquite TX	4.82/96
				(rebuild from components, ff .86)	
88-17477•	AT-6D	**42-85696**	**N2864D**	Sherman Chavoor, Sacramento CA	63/64
				Robert R. Miles, Sacramento CA	66
				Ben M. Harrison, Seattle WA	69/77
				William D. Lamberton, Mercer Island WA	84/86
				John R. Meyer, Seattle WA	88/96
88-17478•	AT-6D	**42-85697**		(to Spanish AF as AE.6-178, C.6-178)	
			N29947	Combat Aircraft Inc, Elkhart IN	20.5.82
				K & K Aircraft Inc, Bridgewater VA	84/86
				Joseph Natoli, Lorton VA	90
				Walter A. Newton, Lenoir NC	92
				Jim A. Cavanaugh/Cavanaugh Flight Museum, Dallas-Addison TX	93/96
88-17532•	AT-6D	**42-85751**	**N7214C**	Howard Clerf, Kittitas WA	63
				James A. McGillen, Kent WA	.63/64
				Reinhold I. Heinz, Auburn WA	66
				David E. Cooley, Seattle WA	69/70
				Robert P. Chandler, Santa Cruz CA	72
				Don Harris, Fremont CA	76/77
				J & J Aviation, Uvalde TX	84/86
				Connie N. Fleckenstein, Nacogdoches TX	2.87/96
88-17551•	AT-6D SNJ-5	**42-85770**		(to USN as Bu90623)	
				(to JMSDF as ......)	
			N89013	Dennis G. Buehn/Warbirds West, Compton CA	10.77/79
				(recov. ex Japan, rest. as "USN/90623")	
				James E. Beasley, Philadelphia PA (race #23)	10.79/96
88-17552•	AT-6D SNJ-5	**42-85771**		(to USN as Bu90624)	
			N3620F	Wings of Dade County, Miami FL	63/66
				Air Sales Inc, Miami FL	69
				Hector J. Deschnes, Dania FL	70
				Dan R. McNamara/Shamrock Aviation	72
				Dennis R. Hynes, Union Lake MI	72
			N13AA	Mechanical Systems, Silkeston MO	75/77
				Noel T. Hops, San Ramon CA	84
				Aero Nostalgia Inc, Stockton CA	.85
				George Markey, Camden NSW	.85/86
				sold to Australia: struck-off USCR	5.11.85
			VH-USN	George Markey/Solon Pty Ltd/ Australite Engines, Sydney NSW	17.1.86/93
				Michael Redmond, Brisbane QLD	8.93/96

88-17561•	AT-6D	**42-85780**		(to USN as Bu90633)	
	SNJ-5B		**N3644F**	David D. McInnis, Miami FL	63
				James E. Hodges, Okeechobee FL	.63/64
				William E. Webeser, Wantagh NY	66
				Casimir P. Trelka, Libertyville IL	69/77
				William J. Hardy, Tucson CA	86
				Lan Dale Co, Reno NV	1.87/96
88-17562•	AT-6D	**42-85781**		(to USN as Bu90634)	
	SNJ-5			(to Spanish AF as C.6-176, Code 793-117)	
			N29965	Combat Aircraft Inc, Elkhart IN	6.82
				Stanley E. Shapiro, Orange NJ	84
				Suzy Q Aviation, Orange NJ	86
				William G. Dodds & Stan Shapiro/	
				WW II Enterprises/Danaire Corp, Freehold NJ	86/96
88-17568•	AT-6D	**42-85787**		(to USN as Bu90640)	
	SNJ-5		**N3275G**	Growers Aerial Service, Imperial CA	63/69
				Floyd M. Wardlow, Las Vegas NV	70
				sale rep., USCR	9.72/96
88-17575•	AT-6D	**42-85794**		(to FA Mexicana as 781)	
			N70543	Texas Turbo Jet Inc, Dallas TX	1.89
			N991GM	McNeely Charter Service, Earle AR	6.90
				Gene McNeely/T-6 Inc, Earle AR	9.90/96
				(race #90 *Undecided*)	
88-17643•	AT-6D	**42-85862**		(to USN as Bu90645)	
	SNJ-5			Lance Aircraft Supply Inc, Dallas TX	.88
				Chesapeake Airways Corp: USCR candidate	3.4.89
88-17647•	AT-6D	**42-85866**		(to USN as Bu90649)	
	SNJ-5		N7976C	Richard B. Almour, Nogales AZ	63
				West Memphis Aviation Service, Memphis AR	.63/64
				Mayer Aviation, Dumas AR	66
				Gerald A. Swayze, Mesquite TX	69/70
				Kent W. Jones, Dallas TX	72
				I. N. Burchinall Jr, Paris TX	76/77
				Ron Ruble, Salem OR	84/86
			N101RF	Scott Ready/Exec Aviation Inc, Cincinatti OH	3.87/93
				Kipnis Inc, Chicago IL	11.94/96
88-17652•	AT-6D	**42-85871**		(to USN as Bu90654)	
	SNJ-5C		**N6438D**	Robert G. Jenkins, Atlanta GA	63/63
				David M. Forrest, Atlanta GA	.63/66
				A. T. George, Conyers GA	.66
				20th Century Fox Film Corp, Hollywood CA	68/71
				(conv. to Kate replica at Long Beach CA .68	
				for film"Tora Tora Tora"; open storage	
				Long Beach CA 69/71, sold at auction 2.71)	
				Challenge Publications, Van Nuys CA	2.71/84
				American Aeronautical Foundation Museum,	
				Van Nuys CA	84
				Confederate Air Force, Harlingen TX	.84
				Jay M. Horecky, Houston TX	86
				Douglas A. Peoples, Don Argall & Ron Grasso,	
				Collierville TN	88/96
				(flies as Japanese Kate "EII-301")	
88-17653•	AT-6D	**42-85872**		(to USN as Bu90655)	
	SNJ-5		**N30306**	Richard A. Benner, North Pole AK	1.95
88-17659•	AT-6D	**42-85878**		(to USN as Bu90661)	
	SNJ-5C		N5591A	Kentucky Air Transport, Louisville KY	63/66
			N1114	Kentucky Air Transport, Louisville KY	66
				Gordon Newell, Chadwicks NY	69
			N621BC	Joseph L. (Bud) Cashen, Woodland Hills CA	12.85/96
				(USCR quotes id. N621BC as "90654JC",	
				flies as "90654/BC-21": see two above)	

88-17660•	AT-6D SNJ-5C	**42-85879**		(to USN as Bu90662) (to Argentine Navy/Armada as 0462/2-A-304, later re-serialled 0462/4-G-78) Aero Club Coronal Suarez,Buenos Aires: displ. Museo de la Aviacion Naval Argentina, Espora NAS, Bahia Blanca, Argentina: arr. (static rest., displ. as "4-G-78")	 .58/70 80/90 11.90/92
88-17661•	AT-6D SNJ-5B	**42-85880**	 N3633F **VH-USS**	(to USN as Bu90663) Jack Toll, Golden CO George C. Nesbitt, Littleton CO Ray G. Smith, Denver CO Parcel Oil Co, Aberdeen SC Phillip D. Bostwick, Bethesda DC Richard H. Ferrell, New Iberia LA sold to Australia: struck-off USCR Colin M. Rodgers, Sydney NSW: arr by ship Colin M. Rodgers, Sydney NSW	 63/64 66 69 70/72 76/84 86 16.5.89 7.89 7.2.91/96
88-17662•	AT-6D SNJ-5B	**42-85881**	 **N3682F**	(to USN as Bu90664) Walter H. Hackett, Niles OH Gerald A. Swayze, Mesquite TX Ralph C. Parker, Wichita Falls TX	 66/67 69/88 10.87/96
88-17667•	AT-6D SNJ-5	**42-85886**	 **N9801C**	(to USN as Bu90669) Visco Flying Service, Imperial CA Robert E. Deford, Phoenix AZ Ernest Bishop, Los Angeles CA Carl E. Schwenker, Daytona Beach FL Robert Mazure, Washington NJ (USCR quotes id. "90-669": see next entry)	 63/70 72 76/77 84/86 3.87/96
88-17667•	AT-6D SNJ-5	**42-85886**	 F-AZBL F-WZBM **F-AZBL**	(to USN as Bu90669) reg. res. Aero Retro, St. Rambert-d'Albon (flew as "09905/56S.4") Aero Retro, St. Rambert-d'Albon (conv. to Zero lookalike , c/n SAM2-669) Aero Retro, St. Rambert-d'Albon (flies as "90669/TA-669": see entry above)	 7.79 8.80/87 6.87 89/93
88-17668•	AT-6D SNJ-5	**42-85887**	 **N8215E**	(to USN as Bu90670) New London Airport, New London PA Clayton Russell, Newark DE Eugene F. Bredlow, Fort Wayne IN Thomas A. Faulkner, Oultewah TN	 63 .63/64 66/70 9.74/96
88-17670•	AT-6D SNJ-5	**42-85889**	 **N6643C**	(to USN as Bu90672) Francis Fulton, Sharon Springs KS Richard D. Janitell/Pikes Peak Aviation, Fountain & Colorado Springs CO	 63/70 8.71/96
88-17676 •	AT-6D SNJ-5 SNJ-5C SNJ-7C	**42-85895**	 N4134A N830X **G-BRVG**	(to USN as Bu90678) NAS Litchfield Park AZ: wfu, open storage Ming Ayer Inc, Linden NJ: ex USN surplus Licalzi Air Service, Bridgeton NJ Richard C. Dupont, Middletown DE Frederick G. Krape, Wilmington DE Joe Dee, Lake Junaluska NC Russ Webb, Williamson GA Early Birds Ltd, Staverton (arr. dism. North Weald 1.90) Intrepid Aviation, North Weald	 11.54/56 8.56 62 13.7.62/74 12.6.74/84 86/88 89/90 24.1.90 .91/96
88-17678•	AT-6D SNJ-5	**42-85897**	 N6972C	(to USN as Bu90680) Edward J. Mitchell, San Carlos CA Darold W. Jolliff, Modesto CA	 63/66 69/77

				James K. Fox/Warbirds West, Compton CA	84/92
				(race #72 90680/*Terrible Texan*)	
				crashed on takeoff, Compton CA	.89
				(rebuilt Compton, using ex FA Uruguaya T6G)	
				Tom L.Jack/Jack Aircraft Sales, Franklin PA	2.92/96
88-17699•	AT-6D	**42-85918**	**N7096C**	Charles O. Diefendorf, Collidge AZ	63/70
				reappeared USCR	7.90
				reg. pending, Santa Paula CA	92/96
88-17716 •	AT-6D	**42-85935**	4X-ARB	Avitor Ltd, Tel Aviv	.63/72
88-17759•	AT-6D	**42-85978**		(to USN as Bu90691)	
	SNJ-5		**N3203G**	Norman E. Stanley, El Centro CA	63/66
				Floyd Wardlow, Las Vegas NV	69
				Robert F. Dodson, Reno NV	70/72
				Rodney E. Barnes, Oconomowoc WI	84/93
				Dwane A. Shank, Greensburg KS	6.93/96
88-17767•	AT-6D	**42-85986**		(to USN as Bu90699)	
	SNJ-5		**N26862**	Joseph Natol, Nokesville VA	12.81
				Daniel P. Dameo/Danair Corp, Bridgewater NJ	84/96
88-17780•	AT-6D	**42-85999**		(to USN as Bu90712)	
	SNJ-5		N7130C	Robert van Wimwegan, Phoenix AZ	63
				Kenneth C. Holaday, Tempe AZ	.63/64
				Richard T. Gregory, Phoenix AZ	66
				20th Century Fox Film Corp, Hollywood CA	68/71
				(conv. to Kate replica at Long Beach CA .68	
				for film *Tora Tora Tora*; open storage	
				Long Beach CA 69/71, sold at auction 2.71)	
				Johan M. Larsen, Minneapolis MN	2.71/77
				Ingemar E. Holm, Bloomington MN	7.78/96
				Minnesota Air & Space Mus., Minneapolis MN	88
				(displ. as Japanese Kate)	
88-17834•	AT-6D	**42-86053**		(to RCAF as 42-86053): BOC	12.5.51
				ret. to USAF: SOC RCAF	10.11.53
			N7417C	William R. Gibbs, Wilmington DE	63/64
			N117R	Stephen J. Roberts, Newark DE	66
				Peter D. Von Raits, New York NY	69/70
				Stephen J. Roberts, Newark DE	72/86
				Richard T. Neil, Newark DE	4.91/96
88-17849•	AT-6D	**42-86068**		(to Spanish AF as AE.6-27, C.6-27)	
				sold at auction, Spain	9.84
			N4086T	Aircraft Cylinder & Turbine Inc: candidate	20.10.94
				reg.	2.95
				John H. Muszala, Corona CA	6.95
88-17873•	AT-6D	**42-86092**		(to USN as Bu90725)	
	SNJ-5		**N3246G**	E. L. Honeywell, Fort Worth TX	63/64
				Aero Nutz Inc, Monroe LA	66
				Raymond K. Elias, Portland TX	69
				Confederate Air Force, Harlingen/Midland TX	11.1.73/96
88-17880•	AT-6D	**42-86099**		(to USN as Bu90732)	
	SNJ-5			(to FA Haiti as 86099)	1.49/54
				crashed Haiti	8.54
			N22140	Chuck Hall Aviation, Ramona CA: candidate	12.12.89
88-17883•	AT-6D	**42-86102**		(to USN as Bu90735)	
	SNJ-5		N7295C	Lester C. Tupper, Redondo Beach CA	63
				Hendrik Otzen, Glendale CA	.63/70
			N1HZ	Hendrik Otzen, Granada Hills CA	76/77
			C-GPIN	Helair Enterprises, Surrey BC	6.81/83
				dam. Oliver BC (repaired)	31.7.83
			N11HP	Courtesy Aircraft Inc, Rockford IL	9.86
				Currie B. Spiver/Cubco Inc, Greenville SC	88
				Gene Popma, Naperville IL	90

				Jim R. Porter/American Warbirds Collections, Chicago IL	9.88/96
88-17923•	AT-6D	**42-86142**		USAAC: BOC 10.44 SOC	8.54
				(to Spanish AF as C.6-30): sold at auction	1.84
			N4996M	Ray Stutsman/Combat Aircraft Inc, Elkhart IN	5.84
				David L. Tinker, Canton MI	6.84/96
88-17955•	AT-6D	**42-86174**		(to USN as Bu90747)	
	SNJ-5C		N3651F		
			F-AZRB	J. Bastet, La Ferte-Alais	13.5.94
88-17960•	AT-6D	**42-86179**		(to USN as Bu90752)	
	SNJ-5C		N3268G	Eugene O. Frank, Caldwell ID	63/84
				(noted derelict, Caldwell ID 7.75)	
				Peter M. Jones, Cleveland MS	86
			N964JD	Jack DeBoer/Warbird Corp of Kansas Inc, Wichita KS (race #64)	7.87/96
88-17981•	AT-6D	**42-86200**		(to USN as Bu90773)	
	SNJ-5		**N3617F**	Jack Blalock, Houston TX	63/64
				ABC Liquor Stores Inc, Carbondale IL	66
				R. C. Kirkpatrick, Guilford CT	69
				Kirks Marine Enterprises, Dover DE	70/72
				Milton Leshe, Flanders NJ	76/77
				Charles D. Clapper, Delray Beach FL	1.84/96
88-18022•	AT-6D	**42-86241**	N7215C	Keele Birdsall, Bridgeton NJ	63/64
				Spraymasters Co, Bridgeton NJ	66
				Suffolk Flight Associates, Huntington NY	69/70
				Donald H. Oberlander, College Park GA	72
				Richard Ryerson, Middletown NY	76/77
			N817TX	David R. Smith, San Antonio TX	7.81/88
				Michael J. McCormick, Bay City TX	1.92/96
88-18065•	AT-6D	**42-86284**		(to USN as Bu90787)	
	SNJ-5		N5498V	Coastal Aviation Corp, Alexandria VA: USCR	63/69
				(to FA Portuguesa as .....)	
				US reg. candidate:	5.83
			N45000	Combat Aircraft Inc, Elkhart IN	11.83
				Thomas J. Sarvay, New Castle IN	84
				Donald R. Quigley, Dewitt MI/Ft Meyers FL	86/96
88-18067•	AT-6D	**42-86286**		(to USN as Bu90789)	
	SNJ-5		N3366G	Neil D. Martin, Colver PA	63
				Arnold R. Tefft, Westlake OH	66
				Wellsville Aviation Club, Wellsville NY	69
			N41BT	Wellsville Aviation Club, Wellsville NY	76
				Michael L. Scanlan, Huntington Beach CA	.77/78
			N789NA	Michael L. Scanlan, Huntington Beach CA	8.78
			N41BT	Tired Iron Racing Team, Casper WY	80/87
				dam. ground collision, Casper WY	14.5.80
				Good War Birds Inc, Casper WY	3.87/96
				(race #77 "*Wildcatter*")	
88-18068•	AT-6D	**42-86287**		(to USN as Bu90790)	
	SNJ-5		**N3375G**	Ed Maloney/The Air Museum, Claremont CA later Ontario CA, Chino CA	63/96
88-18072•	AT-6D	**42-86291**		(to USN as Bu90794)	
	SNJ-5		N7998C	Civil Air Patrol (NH Wing), Manchester NH	63/64
				Robert Gardner, Sunderland MA	66/70
				Lawrence J. Donnerberg, Sandpoint ID	76/86
				David Lehman, Athol ID	88
				sold to South Africa: struck-off USCR	23.9.88
			ZS-WFD	D. deVos, Wonderboom	3.3.89

8-18078•	AT-6D	**42-86297**		(to USN as Bu90800)	
	SNJ-5B		N4749C	Kenneth C. Larkey, Memphis TN	63/64
				A. H. Starks, Miami FL	66
				Barry Harper, Houma LA	69
				Johnson Farms Inc, Agency IA	72
			N66JL	Charles Riley, Kansas City MO	76/77
				Joe J. Foretich, Baton Rouge LA	84/86
			N810JF	Foretich-Zimmer Construction Co,	
				Baton Rouge LA	5.86/88
				Steven D. Afeman, Baton Rouge LA	9.90/96
8-18109•	AT-6D	**42-86328**	**N7420C**	Ray Karrells, Port Washington WI	63/72
				Millard C. Marvin, Winchester CA: readded	30.3.93
				Kathleen Keller, Fellbach, Germany	7.93/96
8-18155	AT-6D	42-86374		(to RCAF as 42-86374): BOC	12.5.51
				ret. to USAF: SOC RCAF	10.10.53
			N7216C	Boyd E. Quate, Holland VA: USCR	63/69
			HP-330	P. Jansun/Aeroquimca SA	.62
				wfu: struck-off reg.	9.71
8-18171•	AT-6D	**42-86390**		(to USN as Bu90823)	
	SNJ-5		**N6432D**	William H. Wisner, Dallas TX	63/70
				Gerhard C. Rettberg, Champaign IL	76/77
				Melbourne J. Wilson, Cedar Rapids IA	84
				Magnum Aero Corp, Prescott AZ	86
				Bob Martin, Prescott AZ (race #52)	88
				Robert A. Elliott, Prescott AZ	4.88/96
8-18174	AT-6D	42-86393		(to USN as Bu90826)	
	SNJ-5		N7987C	Jesse H. Williams, Salina KS	63
				Marion M. Richards, Wichita KS	.63/64
				Pearl River Aviation, Picayune MS	66
				George Lazik, Ann Arbor MI	69/70
				crashed on takeoff, Ann Arbor MI	29.6.69
8-18185•	AT-6D	**42-86404**		(to USN as Bu90837)	
	SNJ-5		**N3724G**	Dewey Whatley, Tulare CA	63/64
				John H. Bell, Northridge CA	66
				Chaytor D. Mason, Pomona CA	3.68/96
8-18189•	AT-6D	**42-86408**		(to USN as Bu90841)	
	SNJ-5		N9057Z	G. Lincoln Air Service, Frazier Park CA	63/70
				(to Spanish AF as ....)	
			N3145J	J. O. Keever: reg. res.	28.10.91
				Richard Slaney, Eugene OR	92/96
8-18195•	AT-6D	**42-86414**		(to USN as Bu90847)	
	SNJ-5		N7978C		
			XB-GEM	Hector R. Salazar, Torreon, Mexico	77/96
8-18228•	AT-6D	**42-86447**		(to FA Peru as ......)	
				(to FA Uruguaya as 366)	
				Enrique Abeledo, Uruguay	92/96
				(rest. project: Colonia, Uruguay)	
8-18266•	AT-6D	**42-86485**		(to FA Brasileira as FAB 1517)	
				Museu Aerospacial, Compo dos Afoncos, Rio	79/96
8-18284•	AT-6D	**42-86503**		(to USN as Bu90866)	
	SNJ-5		N3650F	Henry W. Davison, Linthicum Heights MD	63/69
				Richard W. Kanoe, Catonsville MD	70
				Gene A. Johnson, Clinton MD	72
			N90866	Charlie Hammonds Flying Service, Houma LA	75/77
			N100GD	Grady C. Dixon, Yukon OK	1.7.78/84
				West R. Sanders, Bedford TX	86
				Bruce Redding & Dennis G. Buehn, Reno NV	86
				USMC Museum, MCAS Quantico VA: del.	.86/94
				(displ. as "90866/12")	
				USMC Museum, MCAS El Toro CA	93/96

88-18286•	AT-6D	**42-86505**		(to USN as Bu90868)	
	SNJ-5			(to JMSDF as 6205)	
			N9013A	Rick Clemens/Cactus Airforce, Sunland CA	81/89
				Karen M. Grimm/ Cactus Airforce,	
				Lakeview Terrace CA & Carson City NV	84/92
				Christopher L. Fahey, Layton UT	10.93/95
88-18300•	AT-6D	**42-86519**		(to USN as Bu90882)	
	SNJ-5		**N3148G**	sale rep., Long Beach CA: USCR	84
				Lionel J. Caeton, Dos Palos CA	86/96
121-41572	AT-6D	44-80850	N64577	Des Moines Technical School, Des Moines IA	63/84
121-41580 •	AT-6D	**44-80858**		(to Spanish AF as C.6-24, AE6-24)	
				sold by EdA auction, Torrejon AB, Spain	9.7.83
			N107FG	Frank M. Glover, Mount Pleasant TX	7.87/95
				(flies as "USN 90107")	
121-41623	AT-6D	44-80901		(to USN as Bu90907)	
	SNJ-5		N3673F	Stephen J. Roberts, Newark DE	63/64
				Alexis I. Dupont, Wilmington DE	66/69
				Aidair Museum, Wilmington DE	70
				Colonial Flying Corps Museum Inc,	
				Toughkenamon PA	72/92
			N9DA	Donald Anklin, Skaneateles NY	7.93
				crashed Skaneatles NY	15.10.93
121-41633 •	AT-6D	44-80911		(to USN as Bu90917)	
	SNJ-5			(to JMSDF as 201-6193, 90917): shipped	6.57
				Kanai-Shoji Co, Kanagawaken: as scrap	1.7.76
			N2266Z	Dennis Buehn, Long Beach CA: reg. candidate	5.78
			N1038A	Dennis G. Buehn/Warbirds West, Compton CA	5.79/80
				(recov. ex scrapyard Japan 5.78, shipped to CA,	
				rest. Compton: CofA 19.12.79 "Marines/90917")	
				Howard L. Gribble & John Colver, Lomita CA	1.80/86
				John A. Collver, Lomita CA	3.87/96
121-41634 •	AT-6D	**44-80912**		(to USN as Bu90918)	
	SNJ-5		N8158H	Floyd D. Doland, Pasadena CA	63/64
				Dave A. Williams, Pomona CA	66
				Donald J. Phillippi, Long Beach CA	69/72
				Dennis G. Buehn, Long Beach CA	76
			N96RM	Russell B. Mayberry, Woodland Hills CA	.77
			N26BT	Blue Thrailkill, Granada Hills CA	8.79/96
121-41642 •	AT-6D	**44-80920**		(to USN as Bu90926)	
	SNJ-5			(to JMSDF as 201-6210)	
			N2266W	Dennis G. Buehn/Warbirds West, Compton CA	5.78
				(recov. ex scrapyard Japan 5.78, shipped to CA)	
				Jeffrey T. Perkins, Richmond VA	84/88
				John G. Dankos, Ashland VA	.88/96
121-41732 •	AT-6D	**44-81010**		(to USN as Bu90946)	
	SNJ-5			John A. Darznieks/Lance Aircraft Supply,	
				Dallas TX	.84/90
			N125JD	John A. Darznieks, Dallas TX	1.90/96
				(racer rebuilt from parts .84/90,	
				race #21 *Mystical Power*)	
121-41736 •	AT-6D	**44-81014**		(to USN as Bu90950)	
	SNJ-5		N3239G	John M. Wallace, Nashville TN/Hurst TX	63/66
				20th Century Fox Film Corp, Hollywood CA	.68/71
				(conv. to Kate replica at Long Beach CA .68 for	
				film *Tora Tora Tora*; open storage Long Beach	
				CA 69/71, sold at auction Long Beach 2.71)	
				Gerald D. Weeks, Memphis TN	2.71/72

				Confederate Air Force, Harlingen TX	28.1.72/88
			N1689C	Clyde F. Barton, Angleton/Clute TX	11.89/92
				Wally Fisk/Amjet Aircraft Corp, St Paul MN	8.93/96
				(flies as Japanese Kate "AI-301")	
21-	AT-6D	**44-81016**		(to USN as Bu90952)	
1738 •	SNJ-5		**N3204G**	Wilbur E. Brewer, Bowman ND	63/69
				Harold W. Patton, Denver CO	70/72
				James E. Sullivan, Tarzana CA	76/77
				Charles E. Beck, Los Angles CA	84/86
				Joseph L. Chizmadia, Santa Monica CA	9.88/96
21-	AT-6D	**44-81020**		(to USN as Bu90956)	
1742 •	SNJ-5		**N3631F**	Martin L. Hallman, Vicksburg MS	63/64
				Harry B. Marioneaux, Shreveport LA	69/72
				Brull Interstate Aircraft Co., Higginsville MO	76/77
				Service Insurance Agency Inc, Rockford IL	84
				Walter R. Braun, Chicago IL	86
				Rudy Blakey Inc, Perry FL	8.86/96
21-	AT-6D	44-81035		(to FA Brasileira as FAB T-6D 1639)	.54
1757			PT-KUX	reg.	.76
				Luiz Raphael Vieiva Souta Costa, Rio	83
21-	AT-6D	**44-81103**		(to USN as Bu90974)	
1825 •	SNJ-5		N9818C	Coastal Aviation Corp, Alexandria VA: USCR	63/70
				(to Ejercito del Aire as C.6-124)	
				Escuela Superior de Ingenieros Aeronauticos,	
				Cuatra Vientos AB, Spain	82/88
21-	AT-6D	**44-81111**		(to USN as Bu90982)	
1833 •	SNJ-5			(to Ejercito del Aire as C.6-155)	
				Museo del Aire, Cuatra Vientos AB, Spain	85/96
21-	AT-6D	**44-81113**		(to USN as Bu90984)	
1835 •	SNJ-5		**N8223E**	Wallace F. Watson, Madison WI	63
				Grant E. Webster, Waunakee WI	.63/70
				Raymond Karrels, Port Washington WI	76/77
				Al Letcher, Mojave CA	77
				Haywood B. Bartlett, Pike Road AL	11.82/96
21-	AT-6D	**44-81118**		(to USN as Bu90989)	
1840 •	SNJ-5		**N9804C**	Frank Cannavo, Philadelphia PA	63/64
				Kenneth W. Wagner, Pennington NJ	66/69
				Robert Tobacco, Colts Neck NJ	70
				Verne J. & James W. Goodwin, Rutland VT	72/86
				Peter C. Pritchard, Amherst NH	1.86/96
21-	AT-6D	**44-81120**		(to USN as Bu90991)	
1842 •	SNJ-5		N8203E	J. F. Carter, Frisco City AL	63/64
				I. N. Burchinall Jnr, Honey Grove TX	66/70
			N73SL	Ben Lowell, Boulder CO	76/77
				Organik Inc, Houston TX	84
				Patrick O'Neil, Wichita Falls TX	86/88
				Scott E. Rozzell, Houston TX	1.91/96
21-	AT-6D	**44-81124**		(to USN as Bu90995)	
1846 •	SNJ-5B		N8201E	Jessie Bristow, Miami FL	63/64
				Calvin R. Weier, Boca Raton FL	66/86
			N12KY	Classic Aviation International, Rosharon TX	12.89/92
				op: Anita DeVillegas, Ocala FL	90/93
				Anita DeVillegas, Bellevue FL	4.94/96
21-	AT-6D	**44-81148**	**N10602**	Victor S. Baker, Los Angeles CA	63/64
1870 •				Robert W. O'Hara, San Fernando CA	66/72
				Earl R. Benedict, Fairfield CA	76/77
				Harold D. Rowe, Las Vegas NV	84
				Aaron Berkowitz, Phoenix AZ	86/88
				Navaro E. Nichols, Pleasant City OH	2.91/96

121-	AT-6D	**44-81210**		(to USN as Bu90996)	
41932 •	SNJ-5		N4230G	Ned R. Darr, Great Bend KS	63
				Wayne S. Nyland, Boulder CO	.63/64
				Jack M. Demoss, Independence MO	66/69
			N21JD	Jack M. Demoss, Independence MO	70/72
				Larry Cogan, Melbourne FL	76/77
				John C. Hunt, Thatcher AZ	84/86
				Vern L. Raburn, Atherton CA/Scottsdale AZ	11.86/96
121-	AT-6D	**44-81219**		(to USN as Bu91005)	
41941 •	SNJ-5C		N7806B	Roland J. Harrington, Abbeville LA	63
				T. F. Longcrier, Little Rock AR	.63/64
				Green Bay Aviation, Green Bay WI	66
				Robert Miller, Leland IL	67
				Courtesy Aircraft Ltd, Loves Park IL	69
				Eugene Glenn, Mesa AZ	
			N141SP	Susanne D. Parish, Hickory Corners MI	76/77
			N333SU	Susanne D. Parish/Kalamazoo Aviation History Museum, Kalamazoo MI	4.77/96
121-	AT-6D	**44-81222**		(to USN as Bu91008)	
41944 •	SNJ-5		N3202G	Jesse W. Young, Brawley CA	63/70
			N144KM(1	Kirk R. McKee, Sacramento CA	.77
				Gordon R. Kibby, Fremont CA	77/82
				(trucked to Fremont 23.4.77, rest: ff 23.6.84)	
			N9048P	Gordon R. Kibby: reg. res.	82
			N29GK	Gordon R. Kibby, Fremont /Pleasanton CA	11.82/96
121-	AT-6D	**44-81235**		(to USN as Bu91021)	
41957 •	SNJ-5		**N6971C**	Western State Aviation, Gunnison CO	63/77
				Lorren M. Kalish, Phoenix AZ	3.81/96
				(flies as "09873")	
121-	AT-6D	**44-81240**		(to USN as Bu91026)	
41962 •	SNJ-5		N45383	reg. candidate	11.83/86
				John J. Maney, Santa Rosa CA: reg.	2.89
			N914DM	John J. Maney, Windsor CA/Portland OR	3.89/96
121-	AT-6D	**44-81252**	**N1974M**	Ralph M. Farish, Jacksonville FL	63
41974 •				Jack Adams Aircraft Sales, Wells MS	.63/64
				reappeared USCR	10.95
121-	AT-6D	**44-81314**		(to USN as Bu91040)	
42036 •	SNJ-5B			Aircraft Engineering Inc, Charlotte NC	6.58
				(to Spanish AF as .....)	.58
			N29943	Combat Aircraft Inc, Elkhart IN	19.4.82
				Harold Mays/MMB Inc, Thomson GA	4.83/87
				William L. Macleod, San Diego CA	3.87
			N1944D	William L. Macleod, San Diego CA	8.87/95
121-	AT-6D	**44-81318**		(to USN as Bu91044)	
42040 •	SNJ-5B			dism. open storage, unconv. orig. USN sc., Prineville OR	7.75
			N31443	Classic Aviation Inc: reg. res.	11.91/92
				Classic Aviation International Inc, Arcola TX	28.6.94/96
121-	AT-6D	44-81319		(to USN as Bu91045)	
42041			N319DR	David W. Reynolds, Newnan GA	3.87/93
			N66TE	ntu: Todd Eberhard, Fulton GA	1.94
			N319TE	Todd Eberhard, New York NY	6.94
				crashed on beach nr. Vero Beach FL	21.4.95
121-	AT-6D	**44-81323**		(to USN as Bu91049)	
42045 •	SNJ-5B		**N3265G**	reg. candidate: foreign import	6.7.77
				Raymond A. Houx, Oklahoma City OK	84
				Walter C. Hubert, Belleville IL	86
				Thomas C. Hutchins, Advance NC	90/93
				Historical Warbirds & Antiques, Advance NC	11.93/96

121-42047 •	AT-6D SNJ-5	**44-81325**		(to USN as Bu91051)	
			N9817C	Coastal Aviation Corp, Alexandria VA	66/69
				(to Spanish AF as ....)	
				Aviation Industries Inc	28.7.81
			N2686D	David O. Dodd, Roanoke/Denton TX	12.81/92
				Minor A. & Julia Smith, Placitas NM	26.7.94/96
121-42068 •	AT-6D SNJ-5	**44-81346**		(to USN as Bu91072)	
			N6637C	Louis F. Heckelberg, Bartlesville OK	.59/92
				Roush Air Inc, Livonia MI	6.94/96
121-42070 •	AT-6D SNJ-5	**44-81348**		(to USN as Bu91074)	
				(to Spanish AF as .....)	
			N39313	Combat Aircraft Inc, Elkhart IN	13.5.83
				Robert A. Brown, Luthersville GA	84
				Ted A. Ryder, Medford OR	86/87
				Air Combat Museum, Springfield IL	4.90/96
121-42098 •	AT-6D SNJ-5	**44-81376**		(to USN as Bu91082)	
			N9823C	Howard W. McKewen, Granada Hills CA	63/64
				Joseph Hyde, Santa Barbara CA	66/70
				Lee W. Schaller, Sausalito CA	76/84
				exported: struck-off USCR	11.77
			N9823C	Paul R. Beck, Sausalito CA/Gold Hill OR	10.84/96
				(flies as "23380/208")	
121-42104 •	AT-6D SNJ-5	**44-81382**		(to USN as Bu91088)	
				(to Spanish AF as C.6-132)	
			N29930	Combat Aircraft Inc, Elkhart IN	20.5.82
				James P. Ball, Holt MO	84
				Douglas A. Clarke, Glendale CA	8.85/96
				(flies as "US Army 91088/X-104/1088")	
121-42105	AT-6D SNJ-5	44-81383		(to USN as Bu91089)	
			N3194G	M. W. Norman, Gardena CA	63/64
				Jack R. Lilly, Santa Fe Springs CA	66
				Clifford W. Putman, Westminster CA	69/72
				crashed, aerobatics, Kingman KS	31.7.72
121-42110 •	AT-6D SNJ-5	**44-81388**		(to USN as Bu91094)	
			N8218E	J. P. Tonnar, Glen Allan MS	63/64
				W. H. Booth, Lambert MS	66
				Thomas Otis, Arlington TX	69/70
				Thomas Horne, Fort Worth TX	76/77
				Steven L. Miles, Carmel Valley CA	84/86
				David C. Hall, Branford CT	5.87/96
121-42134	AT-6D	44-81412	N5634V	Hawaii Public Trade School, Honolulu HI	63/71
				(inst. airframe, Honolulu Airport 66/71)	
121-42175 •	AT-6D	**44-81453**	**N4983N**	C. B. Branan, Oklahoma City OK	63/64
				Joseph McGranahan, Hamilton OH	66
				Frederick W. Edison, Kalamazoo MI	68/70
				VFR Aero Inc, Kalamazoo MI	72/77
				Terry R. Jones, Baton Rouge LA	84/88
				Jeff P. Neff, Seattle WA	3.89/96
121-42190 •	AT-6D	**44-81468**	**N6984C**	Joseph Martinez, Los Angeles CA	63/64
				George E. Younghans, Las Vegas NV	66/77
				Chuck Krueger/Mustang Enterprises, Blairstown NJ	84/88
				Hartzell Propeller Inc, Piqua OH	4.92/96
				(flies as "SNJ-5 USN 481468")	
121-42202 •	AT-6D	**44-81480**	**N6980C**	Tyrell W. Smith, Los Alamitos CA	63
				Darrel A. Doran, San Mateo CA	.63/64
				Stephen C. Wilmans, Oceanside CA	66
				Ross F. Cronk, Santa Ana CA	69/72

				P. M. Dusters Inc, Chico CA	76/86
				Addison Pemberton, San Diego-Gillespie CA	90
				John Herlihy, Mount Shasta CA	2.92/96
121-42215 •	AT-6D	**44-81493**		(to RCAF as 44-81493): BOC	12.5.51
				ret. to USAF: SOC RCAF	26.10.53
			N7230C	Floyd Lukins, Pecos TX	63/64
				(last FAA annual inspection 10.58)	
				Aaron B. Cantrell, Andrews TX	66/70
				Jeanette T. Bryant, Jacksonville FL	72
				Richard J. Bowers, Rockford IL	76/77
				Joe B. McShane, Monahans TX	6.80/85
			N36JM	Joe B. McShane, Midland TX	1.85
			N36	Joe B. McShane, Monahans TX	6.85/96
121-42216 •	AT-6D	**44-81494**		(to RCAF as 44-81494): BOC	12.5.51
				ret. to USAF, Tucson AZ: SOC RCAF	24.2.54
			N7448C	Joseph. W. Quinn, Los Angeles CA	63/77
				Charles F. Nichols, Chino CA	12.83/84
			N63RB	Roland S. Bond/Sky Ranch Aviation, Jean NV	9.85/88
				K & R Investments, Sandy Valley NV	92
				Michael E. Jauregui & Bill Cotter, Newhall CA	9.92/96
121-42239 •	AT-6D	**44-81517**	N6496D	Mid Continent Aerial Sprayers, Hayti MO	66
				Horst K. Heiles, St Louis MO	69
				George Banjak, Webster Groves MO	70/77
				Donald H. Chapton, Kimberly ID	84
				Gary Wolverton, Twin Falls ID	86
			N45GK	Gary Kohs, Birmingham MI	5.89/96
121-42285 •	AT-6D	**44-81563**	**N7231G**	James E. Hicks, Crystal Lake IL	63
				John J. Brabant, Oak Lawn IL	.63/72
				B & F Aircraft Supply, Oak Lawn IL	76/86
				Eric G. Anderson, Oregon IL	1.90/95
				(USCR quotes "4881563", later "42-81563")	
121-42286 •	AT-6D	**44-81564**		(to FA Brasiliera as FAB T-6D 1643)	.54
			PT-TRB	reg.	79
				Luiz Raphael Vieiva Souta Costa, Rio	83
				Antonio Braga, Rio de Janiero	90
				Museu Aeroespacial, Campo dos Afonsos, Rio	94/96
121-42318 •	AT-6F SNJ-6	**44-81596**		(to USN as Bu......)	
			N211A	James W. Wallace, Robertsdale AL	63/64
				Gerald A. Swayze, Mesquite TX	66/69
				Windward Aviation, Enid OK	72/83
				Robert E. Deford, Prescott AZ	1.87/96
121-42356 •	AT-6F SNJ-6	**44-81634**		(to USN as Bu........)	
				(to FA Brasileira as 1631)	
				Monte Zema, Colville WA	.94/95
			N390TB	reg.	7.95
121-42368 •	AT-6F SNJ-6	**44-81646**		(to USN as Bu........)	
			N4485	Arthur D. Medore/Banaire, Hemet CA	23.10.86
				Greg W. Klassen, Bakersfield CA	5.92/96
				(see next entry)	
121-42368 •	AT-6	**44-81646**		(to FA Portuguesa as ....)	
			N8540P	Arthur D. Medore/North American Aviation Inc, Denville NJ/Hemet CA	10.80/84
				Gerry Miles (race #51 "Yaba-Daba-Doo")	90/91
				Classic Air Parts, Ontario CA	2.7.93/95
				(USCR quotes id. 42-81646-1: see entry above)	
121-42370 •	AT-6F	**44-81648**	**N9687N**	Arthur D. Medore/Banaire, Hemet CA	13.6.86/96

21-2372 •	AT-6F	**44-81650**		(to USN as Bu.......)	
	SNJ-6		**N4486**	Arthur D. Medore/Banaire, Hemet CA	23.10.86
				John J. Gostomski, Omaha NE	91/94
				Christopher Gruys, Santa Fe NM	11.94/96
21-2378 •	AT-6F	**44-81656**	**N7461C**	Horseshoe Lake Repair, Duluth MN	63/64
				Hubert M. Lewis, Shelby MI	66/72
				Sun Master Awnings, Mishawaka IN	76/77
				Thomas C. Vickerman, Columbus OH	84/88
				QRD Equipment Corp, Long Island City NY	92
				Mike R. Mayte, Ventura CA/Ashland OR	9.93/96
21-2384	AT-6F	44-81662	N87979	reg. candidate	9.77
				Shouling M. Barnes, Lancaster CA	84/86
				struck-off USCR	1.90
21-2409 •	AT-6F	**44-81687**	N68787	San Bernardino Junior College CA	63/64
				Victoria Air Maintenance, Victoria BC	
			N36JS	John A. Schwamm, Anchorage AK	15.1.86
			N164US	Phil Cooper, Reese Dill & Russ Noftsker/	
				T64 US Inc, Bedford MA	1.87/96
21-2412	AT-6F	44-81690	F-BJBT	Soc. Air France, Cormeilles	20.4.59/63
				CEDEA, Cormeilles	3.7.63/65
			OO-JBT	COGEA Nouvelle, Ostende	20.8.65/66
				J. Thiel, Wevelgem; later Monchengladbach	10.66/70
				C. Honcoop, Veen, Netherlands	7.70
				wfu, struck-off reg.	8.70
				to scrap yard, Bergen op Zoom, Netherlands	.71
				broken-up in scrapyard, Amsterdam	.80
21-2415 •	AT-6F	**44-81693**	N7418C	David B Roebuck, Cincinatti OH	63/64
				Carel I. Cadot, Columbus OH	66/70
			N85593	Howard J. Crowe, Toledo OH	76
				Courtesy Aircraft Inc, Rockford IL	.77
				Don M. Robinson, Los Fresno TX	84
				Linda Finch, San Antonio TX	86
				John D. Luther, San Antonio TX	11.87/96
				(flies as "USAAF 593")	
21-2438	AT-6F	44-81716	OO-ABD	Automotive Industries Inc NV, Moorsele	31.5.61
				sold to France, struck-off reg.	5.6.61
			N9752F	Henry L. Knight, Evreux Eure, France	5.6.61/70
				(del. & flew with false reg. "N9852F")	
				impounded, smuggling, Barcelona, Spain	8.64
				open storage, derelict, Barcelona-Muntadas	70/77
				(note: USCR quotes incorrect id. KF716)	
21-2452	AT-6F	44-81730	F-BJBU	Soc. Air France, Cormeilles	20.4.59/63
				CEDEA, Cormeilles	18.6.63/65
			OO-JBU	COGEA Nouvelle, Ostende	8.65/66
				J. Thiel, Wevelgem; later Monchengladbach	10.66/70
				C. Honcoop, Veen, Netherlands	7.70
				wfu, struck-off reg.	8.70
				to scrapyard, Bergen op Zoom, Netherlands	.71
				broken-up in scrapyard, Amsterdam	.80
21-2475 •	AT-6F	**44-81753**	**N2834D**	Rudolph W. Hazuka, Wilmington CA	63/86
				John C. Dimmer, Tacoma WA	11.90/95
21-2479 •	AT-6F	**44-81757**	**N6601C**	Eugene F. Rothlin, Fortuna CA	63/64
				Joseph M. Toledo, Arcata CA	66
				Charles Kluver, Rosebury OR	69/72
				Chan Stokes, Rosenburg OR	76
				Jefferson Flight Group, Grants Pass OR	.77
				James Garemore, Ocala FL	84/92
				Gerald S. Deaton, Toledo OH	8.93/95
				(flies as "52008/S-106")	
21-	AT-6F	44-81758	F-BJBP	Soc. Air France, Cormeilles	20.4.59/63

42480				CEDEA, Cormeilles	3.7.63/65
			OO-JBP	COGEA Nouvelle, Ostende	18.8.65/66
				J. Thiel, Wevelgem; later Monchengladbach	15.2.66/70
				C. Honcoop, Veen, Netherlands	7.70
				struck-off reg.	8.70
				stored garage, Aalburg Netherlands	.71/80
121-42490	AT-6F	44-81768	N445C	Stephen J. Linsenmeyer/Luft Inc, Monroe MI	63/69
				Robert V. Chirhart, Ann Arbor MI	70/84
121-42497	AT-6F	44-81775	F-BJBS	Soc. Air France, Cormeilles	20.4.59/63
				CEDEA, Cormeilles	3.7.63/65
			OO-JBS	COGEA Nouvelle, Ostende	10.8.65/66
				J. Thiel, Wevelgem; later Monchengladbach	10.66/70
				C. Honcoop, Veen, Netherlands	7.70
				wfu, struck-off reg.	8.70
				to scrap yard, Bergen op Zoom, Netherlands	.71
				broken-up in scrapyard, Amsterdam	.80
121-42500 •	AT-6F	**44-81778**	D-IDEM	Helmut Weekamp, Dusseldorf	1.58
			D-FDEM	Helmut Weekamp, Dusseldorf	7.58/64
				J. Hossl, Strasskirchen	.71/72
			PH-HAR	ntu: Fraco NV	17.9.76
			D-FDEM	J. Sauermann/Nordseeflug GmbH, Munchen	77
				wfu Leutkirch: struck-off reg.	1.80
				Flugausstellung in Hermeskeil Museum	.82/92
121-42518 •	AT-6F	**44-81796**		(to Royal Thai AF as .....)	
				R. Thai AF Museum, Don Muang AB, Bangkok	80/96
				(displ. as RTAF "CD758/85")	
121-42525 •	AT-6F	**44-81803**	N7809B	State of LA Delgado Trades & Tech. Institute,	
				New Orleans-Lakefront Airport LA	9.60/96
				(noted derelict, Delgado Institute 83)	
121-42541 •	AT-6F	**44-81819**	N7446C	Tallmantz/Movieland of the Air,	
				Orange County CA	62/68
				(at Oakland CA 9.62 as Zero lookalike)	
				Charles Gilbert, Rolling Hills CA	76/77
				Ronald W. Blondel, River Bend AZ	84
			N88RT (1	ntu: Rose Tillman Inc, Northbrook IL	6.85
			N7446C	Apex Associates Inc, Canby OR	86
				Bruce Redding & Dennis G. Buehn, Reno NV	86
				struck-off USCR	12.86
				USAFM, Dyess AFB TX: del.	.86/96
121-42548 •	AT-6F	**44-81826**	**N10434**	Charles F. Darnes, Miami FL	63/64
				Aviation High School, Long Island City NY	3.65/96
121-42555 •	AT-6F	**44-81833**	N7441C	James R. Stewart, Reseda CA	63/64
				Gerald J. Widmayer, Scappoose OR	66
				Frank L. Geelan, Aloha OR	69/72
			XB-EOD	Sergi V. Valencia, Mexico City	93
121-42563 •	AT-6F	**44-81841**	N10590	L. I. Payne, Tulsa OK	63/64
				Paul R. Bond, Tulsa OK	66/72
				Philip Bond, Irving TX	76/77
				John MacGuire, Fort Hancock TX	84/87
			N578JB	War Eagles Air Museum,	
				Santa Teresa NM	4.87/96
121-42579 •	AT-6F	**44-81857**	**N81854**	MARC, Chino CA	5.72/95
121-42583 •	AT-6F	**44-81861**	N124Q	Otto Enderton, Le Roy NY	63
				W. E. Howell Associates Inc, Lexington MA	.63/70
			N4503B	rereg.	11.83
				Collings Foundation, Wentworth NH	2.86/96

				(flies as "USAF 19818/44-81861/TA-624")	
121-42592 •	AT-6F	**44-81870**	**N4708C**	L. B. Schlemeyer, Odessa TX	63/64
				H. C. Palmer, Harrisburg AR	66
				Robert L. Younkin, Fayetteville AR	69/84
				David O. Dodd, Roanoke TX	86
				sale rep., Fort Worth TX: USCR	92/95
				(USCR quotes id. as "F48-1870")	
121-42606 •	AT-6F	**44-81884**	**N7460C**	Charles B. Dulgerian, Monroe NY	63/77
				sale rep., Teterboro NJ: USCR	84/96
121-42611 •	AT-6F	**44-81889**	N7465C	Simpier Motors, Everett WA	63/70
			N999JP	Aero Enterprises Inc, Seattle WA	76/77
				James E. Landry, Seattle WA	84
				Robert A. Barnick, San Jose CA	86
				Gerald Gabe, San Jose CA	3.87/96
				(flies as "USAF 81889/TA-889")	
121-42615 •	AT-6F	**44-81893**	N7363C	James E. Hall, Dallas TX	63/70
			N7463C	William M. Branch, Dallas TX	63/64
				Kent W. Jones, Dallas TX	66
				C. Fred Saunders, El Paso TX	4.67/70
			N706F	C. Fred Saunders, El Paso TX	70/93
121-42632 •	AT-6F	**44-81910**		USAFM, Randolph AFB TX	88/96
				(displ. as "USAF 84560")	
121-42642 •	AT-6F	**44-81920**		Kelly AFB TX: sold as surplus	.56
			N10490	J. S. Staedtler Inc, Hackensack NJ	63/72
				Raymond J. Urmston, Kinnelon NJ	76/96
121-42670 •	AT-6F	**44-81948**		(to USN as Bu111957)	
	SNJ-6		N9802C	Peter T. Johnson, Annette AK	63/64
				Arnold F. Jameson, Everett WA	66
				Donald S. Slipper, Bethell WA	69/70
			N4RC	Triple S. Co, Bingen WA	76
				Robert F. Jones, Federal Way WA	8.79/96
				(race #8 *Rent-A-Dent*, later #8 *All Star*, #8 "Phoenix")	
121-42679 •	AT-6F	**44-81957**		(to USN as Bu111966)	
	SNJ-6		N9828C	Amalio N. Polidor, Mundelein IL	63/77
				Gary Flanders & Mike Bogue, Menlo Park CA	86/92
				(stored Stockton CA, pending rest. 89/91	
				Dick Brooks Inc, Spartanburg SC	1.93/94
			N890DB	Dick Brooks Inc, Spartanburg SC	8.94/96
121-42687 •	AT-6F	**44-81965**		(to USN as Bu111974)	
			N3169G(2	Lendelle J. Kinder, Pacoima CA	69/70
				Gordon D. Brown, Glendale CA	86/87
				Carter B. Clark, Edwards AFB CA	7.91/96
121-42698 •	AT-6F	**44-81976**	**N7464C**	Clyde Wolf, Denver/Commerce City CO	66/86
				Kenneth J. Burnham, Fort Collins CO	6.89/96
121-42709 •	AT-6F	**44-81987**		(to USN as Bu112007)	
			N5485V	Louis J. Bianchi, Chicago IL	63/64
				James L. Peavy, Newnan GA	66
				Jerry H. Dean, Thomaston GA	69/72
				V. S. Sloan, Thomaston GA/Greer SC	76/84
				William K. Johnson, Fayetteville NC	7.88/95
21-2714 •	AT-6F	**44-81992**		(to USN as Bu112011)	
	SNJ-6		N7422C	Bert C. Fuller, South Gate CA	63/64
			N373N	Pete Hansen Co, Carson City NV	66
				Aero Union Corp, Chico CA	69/72
				Robert B. Spencer, Galena OH	7.75/96
21-	AT-6F	**44-82003**		(to USN as Bu111987)	

42725 •	SNJ-6		**N9825C**	Charles H. Mosman, Dallas TX	63/64
	SNJ-6B			Philip W. Stumm, Pasadena TX	66
				Harrington Flying Service, Abbeville LA	69/72
				Mid West Aviation Enterprises, Champaign IL	76
				Rudy Frasca/Frasca Air Museum,	
				Champaign IL	6.82/96
121-	AT-6F	**44-82027**	**N7475C**	Edward I. Newman, Aurora CO	63/66
42749 •				Robert J. Richardson, Burbank CA	69/77
				crashed near California City CA	18.7.81
				Dennis G. Buehn, Long Beach CA	84
				Marvin Quaid, Thomas Woolcock &	
				Frank Schultz, Monterey CA	12.84/96
				(flies as "82027")	
121-	AT-6F	**44-82028**	TF-FSA	reg.	4.47
42750 •	Bacon			Babb Co, New York NY	.53
	Super T-6			sold , struck-off reg.	10.53
			N66J	Erle L. Bacon Corp, Santa Monica CA	57/70
				(prototype Bacon Super T-6 trigear conv.,	
				ff Santa Monica CA 4.57)	
				William J. Reedy, South Pasadena CA	71/84
				William E. Leasure, Northridge CA	5.84/96
				(open storage, Whiteman Air Park CA 78/95)	
121-	AT-6F	**44-82046**	N9686N	Arthur D. Medore/Banaire, Hemet CA	13.6.86
42768				Sierra Warbirds Corp, Carnelian Bay CA	92
				struck-off USCR	11.92
121-	AT-6F	**44-82048**		(to USN as Bu......)	
42770 •	SNJ-6		**N4488**	Arthur D. Medore/Banaire, Hemet CA	10.86/96
121-	AT-6F	**44-82054**	**VT-AXS**	Maharaja Jam Sahib of Nawangar, Jamnagar	2.46
42776 •				Maharaja of Jaipur, Jaipur	22.3.49/79
121-	AT-6F	**44-82069**		(to USN as Bu112023)	
42791 •	SNJ-6		**N5500V**	Marion A. Scudder, Phoenix AZ	63/64
				Charles O. Diefendorf, Casa Grande AZ	66/72
				Edward A. Ray, Westlake Village CA	76
				James Cuseo (race #98)	83
				Robert V. Thompson, Orange CA	1.85/96
				dam. forced landing, Seal Beach CA (repaired)	28.8.86
121-	AT-6F	**44-82080**		(to USN as Bu112034)	
42802 •	SNJ-6		N3254G	C. F. Kirkendall, Seattle WA	63/64
				Hugh F. Glassburn, Bothell WA	66/72
				Robert Heale, Warden WA	76
			N41WD	Howard F. Jurgensen, Elma WA	5.80
			N2129	Billy G. Hartman, Stafford VA	7.80
				Howard Jurgensen, Elma WA	85
				Richard C. Clinton, Fair Oaks CA	1.86/96
121-	AT-6F	**44-82093**		(to USN as Bu112047)	
42815 •	SNJ-6		**N1122U**	Charlotte Aircraft Corp, Charlotte NC	63/69
				Hawkins & Powers Aviation, Greybull WY	89
				(noted stored unconv., Greybull WY 8.89)	
121-	AT-6F	**44-82095**		(to USN as Bu112049)	
42817 •	SNJ-6		**N9809C**	Hatton J. Martin, Hollister CA	63/69
				Jerry G. Brassfield, San Jose CA	70
				Spectrum Air Inc, Novato CA	72
				Middletown Enterprises, Richmond CA	76/86
				Quarry Products Inc, Richmond CA	92
				Kenneth D. Spiva, Cave Junction OR	11.92/96
121-	AT-6F	**44-82101**		(to USN as Bu112055)	
42823 •	SNJ-6		**N8217E**	Curtiss Morrison, Pontiac IL	63
				Ronald J. Cihon, New Philadelphia OH	.63/64

c/n	Type	Serial	Reg	Owner	Date
				Philip A. Auth, Bloomington IL	66
				William H. Mundhenk, West Alexandria OH	10.68/96
121-	AT-6F	**44-82114**		(to USN as Bu112068)	
42836 •	SNJ-6			NAS Atsugi, Japan: gate guard	88
				("USN 112068" port side, JMSDF sc. starboard side)	
121-	AT-6F	**44-82116**		(to USN as Bu112070)	
42838 •	SNJ-6		N8205E	Joe P. Brown Dusting Service, Immokalee FL	63/64
				E. D. Treadwell, Arcadia FL	66/70
			N68JS	Joe Speidel, Wheeling WV	74/76
			N311WW	ntu: Warbirds of the World, Dunnellon FL	11.80
			N68JS	Warbirds of the World, Dunnellon FL	11.80/84
				Warbirds World Interests Inc, Dunnellon FL	86
				Joe E. Scogna, Yardley PA	11.90/96
121-	AT-6F	**44-82117**		(to USN as Bu112071)	
42839 •	SNJ-6		**N3646F**	Harland Stubing, Newcomb NY	63/70
				Jim Malone, Oklahoma City OK	76
				Phillip R. Stallings, Keller TX	86
				Buck Brothers, Joliet IL	7.91/96
121-	AT-6F	**44-82132**	N1109V	Everett F. Sieckmann, Ithaca NY	63/69
42854 •				Joe Watts, Wallace ID	70
			N101BW	William M. Walters, Portland OR	71/72
				Jerry Rubin, Southampton PA	76/77
				Dean S. Edmonds, Weston MA	4.77/96
121-	AT-6F	**44-82135**		(to USN as Bu112079)	
42857 •	SNJ-6		**N1044C**	Louis C. McKinney, Titusville PA	63/64
				Harold J. Holt, Bossier City LA	66/69
				Lucian J. Frejlach, La Grange IL	70/72
				James H. Bohlander, Marengo IL	76
				Richard W. Willard, Durango CO	9.80/96
121-	AT-6F	**44-82149**		(to USN as Bu112093)	
42871 •	SNJ-6			Lance Aircraft Supply Inc, Dallas TX	.88
				Chesapeake Airways Corp: USCR candidate	3.4.89
121-	AT-6F	**44-82220**		(to USN as Bu112110)	
42942 •	SNJ-6		N3614F	Carolina Aircraft Sales	59
				Harry Frank, Statten Island NY	.59/63
				Donald L. Spereni, Statten Island NY	.63/66
			N299SF	Donald L. Spereni/Sperry Film Process Inc,	
				Staten Island NY	69/95
				struck-off USCR	.71
				(stored 72/93: planned rest. to fly .93)	
				Donald L. Spereni, Miami FL: readded	1.95
121-	AT-6F	**44-82224**		(to USN as Bu112114)	
42946 •	SNJ-6		N2855G	Donald J. Rule, Glendale CA	63/69
				Harvey R. McAllister, Reseda CA	70
			N58740	Crawford Deems, Leesburg FL	76
				C. H. Ratliff	85
				minor dam. takeoff, Tico FL (repaired)	3.85
				Jack B. Scoggins, Valdosta GA	88
				Ben Scott	90
				Michael J. Kobb, Boston MA/Conroe TX	10.91/96
121-	AT-6F	**44-82232**		(to USN as Bu112121)	
42954 •	SNJ-6		N2856G	Robert W. O'Hara, San Fernando CA	63
				Lesley L. Crowder, Sunland CA: readded	4.77/81
			N61JD	Lesley L. Crowder, Sunland CA	5.81
				USNAM, NAS Pensacola FL	91/96
				(displ. as "USN 112121")	
121-	AT-6F	**44-82234**		(to USN as Bu112123)	
42956 •	SNJ-6		**N7984C**	Richard Leaver, St. John IN	63/64
				Edwin H. Staehling, Ann Arbor MI	66/72
				John J. Staehling, Woodstock IL/Plano TX	3.79/96

121-42957 •	AT-6F SNJ-6	**44-82235**		(to USN as Bu112124)	
			N2857G	James W. Snody, Van Nuys CA	63/64
				Robert S. Herrera, Los Angeles CA	66/70
				Thomas H. Jones, San Ramon CA	76
121-42963 •	AT-6F SNJ-6	**44-82241**		(to USN as Bu112130)	
			N2860G	Gosta T. Nilson, Los Angeles CA	63/66
				Dale O. Luff Co, Burbank CA	69/72
				Merrell Gossman, Van Nuys CA	.77/82
				(visited UK, via Reykjavik 5.7.82/21.7.82)	
				crashed El Toro MCAS CA	27.4.85
				Andrew T. Gemellaro, Canoga Park CA	88/92
				(rebuilt 85/88, ff .88)	
				struck-off USCR	4.93
121-42964 •	AT-6F SNJ-6	**44-82242**		(to USN as Bu112131)	
			N2858G	Robert B. Gunderson, Sylmar CA	63/72
			N73RR	Ralph Rina, Huntingdon Beach CA	76/86
				(race #73 "Miss Everything")	
				Kathy Luke, Cordova TX	6.88
				Morton Aviation, Shrewsbury NJ	92
				(race #59 "*Blue Bayou*")	
				G. Scott Dill, Germantown TN	6.94/96
121-42981 •	AT-6F SNJ-6	**44-82259**		(to USN as Bu112148)	
			N3639F	F. W. Hughes, Fairhope AL	63/66
				John E. Dorr, Merigold MS	69/70
				Robert W. Speed, Monroe LA	76
				William R. Albers, Fairfax VA	9.77/96
121-42990 •	AT-6F SNJ-6	**44-82268**		(to USN as Bu112157)	
			N2861G	Ronald W. Exley, Los Angeles CA	63/64
				Richard T. Sykes, Los Angeles CA	66
				Raymond E. Marsh, Los Angeles CA	69/72
				Donald W. Bontz, Los Angeles CA/Minden NE	8.75/96
121-42994 •	AT-6F SNJ-6	**44-82272**		(to USN as Bu112161)	
			N2862G	George M. Knight, Los Angeles CA	63/64
				Jack M. Cupp, Saugus CA	66/70
				Roland T. Golan, Los Angeles CA	72/76
				USNAM, NAS Pensacola FL	90/94
				USNAM, NAS Whiting Field FL	93/96
121-43000 •	AT-6F SNJ-6	**44-82278**		(to USN as Bu112167)	
				Delbert Williams, Wasco CA (rest. project)	91/93
121-43001 •	AT-6F SNJ-6	**44-82279**		(to USN as Bu112168)	
			N2863G	Claude C. Morgan, San Fernando CA	63/64
				Donald R. Anderson, Van Nuys CA	66/69
				Charles G. Rei, Los Angeles CA	70/72
				Raymond G. Sparks, Woodland Hills CA	9.84/96
121-43002 •	AT-6F SNJ-6	**44-82280**		(to USN as Bu112169)	
			N2864G	Edmund Menke, Chicago IL	63
				Controlled Receivables Inc, Chicago IL	.63/64
				Robert J. Gardner, Sunderland MA	66
				Tan Air Industries Corp, North Granby CT	69
				Max Coates, Fayetteville NC	70
				Windward Aviation, Enid OK	72
				William G. Palank, Fair Oaks CA	2.75/96
121-43022	AT-6F	**44-82300**	**N2867D**	State of California Corrections Department, Tracy CA	10.57/96
121-43036 •	AT-6F SNJ-6	**44-82314**		(to USN as Bu112178)	
			N9820C	Erie Aviation, Erie PA	63/64
				Wesley Y. Bragg, Ft Lee NJ/Virginia Beach VA	66/76

				Confederate Air Force, Harlingen/Midland TX	86/96
121-43038 •	AT-6F SNJ-6	**44-82316**		(to USN as Bu112180)	
			N9831C	Spokane School District, Spokane WA	63/72
				Aero Enterprises Inc, Seattle WA	76
			N916DC	Dirk Cella, Ponte Verde FL	5.81
				Jim B. Clevenger, Black Mountain NC	3.86/95
			N916DC	Jim B. Clevenger, Marion NC	.88/96
121-43045 •	AT-6F SNJ-6	**44-82323**		(to USN as Bu112187)	
				(to FA Brasileira as FAB T6 1712)	.60
			PT-KVE	reg.	.76
				Armando Vianna Egreja, Penapolis	83
121-43055 •	AT-6F SNJ-6	**44-82333**		(to USN as Bu112247)	
			N7983C	James A. Sellers, Yakima WA	63/64
				Ralph D. Reed, Salt Lake City UT	66
				Ian Marnoch, Sunland CA	69/70
				Melvin L. Kissinger, Los Angeles CA	72
				Norman E. Goyer, Apple Valley CA	76
				Randolph E. Wilson, Dallas TX	8.84/96
121-43065 •	AT-6F SNJ-6	**44-82343**		(to USN as Bu112257)	
				Lance Aircraft Supply Inc, Dallas TX	.88
				Chesapeake Airways Corp: USCR candidate	3.4.89
121-43077 •	AT-6F SNJ-6	**44-82355**		(to USN as Bu112269)	
			N7975C	Columbia Airmotive, Troutdale OR	63/66
				George Pulse, Pendleton OR	69/70
			N269CB	A. C. Sears, Aurora OR	72/76
				Donald Rogers/SNJ Inc, Anchorage AK	88/89
				Robert J. Lessman, Sacramento CA: del.	.89/96
121-43104 •	AT-6F SNJ-6	**44-82382**		(to USN as Bu112201)	
				(to FA Boliviana as FAB 366)	
			N6617X	Robert L. Ferguson, Wellesley MA	10.90/92
				Edward Delrosso, Matawan NJ	4.93/96
121-43107 •	AT-6F SNJ-6	**44-82385**		(to USN as Bu112204)	
			N6515C	Dorel Graves, Indianapolis IN	63
				David Carnochan, Cincinatti OH/Fort Wayne IN	7.63/96
121-43111 •	AT-6F SNJ-6	**44-82389**		(to USN as Bu112208)	
			N7970C	P. J. Brown, Seattle WA	63/70
				reg. pending: struck-off USCR	8.91
121-43116 •	AT-6F SNJ-6	**44-82394**		(to USN as Bu112213)	
			N7298C	Charles E. Schalebaum, Ridgewood NJ	63
				Aaron Cornwell, Paterson NJ	.63/64
				Donald R. Contant, Morris Plains NJ	66
			N9161	Robert M. Harkey, Indianapolis IN	69/76
			N969RH	Robert M. Harkey, Indianapolis IN	9.77
				John R. Boothe. Aberdeen NC	92
				Robert W. Alexander, Caldwell ID	93/96
121-43123 •	AT-6F SNJ-6	**44-82401**		(to USN as Bu112220)	
			N7977C	Melvin G. Craig, Dyer IN	63
				David J. Evanseck, Gary IN	.63/64
				James F. Gaff, Grosse Pointe Farm MI	66/69
			N21BA	Robert V. Arnold, Rochester MI	70/72
				Kelly Chevrolet Cadillac, Butler PA	76
				Jeff J. Williams, Aurora IL	3.92/96
121-43130 •	AT-6F SNJ-6	**44-82408**		(to USN as Bu112227)	
			N9800C	Moore Aviation/TBM Inc, Tulare CA	63/82
				(noted Sequoia CA 8.76, 9.82)	
				Jerry Borchin, Kernersville NC	9.87/96
121-43140 •	AT-6F SNJ-6	**44-82418**		(to USN as Bu112237)	
			N7985C	Donald L. McCrae, Durham CA	63/64

				Chico Aerial Applicators, Chico CA	66
				Joseph J. Thesing, Nevada City CA	69
				Jerry C. Marracola, Sparks NV	72/76
				Al Goss/AG Flying Service, Woodland CA	83/94
			N75AG	Albert F. Goss, Woodland CA	2.94/96
				(race #75 "Warlock")	
121-	AT-6F	**44-82420**		(to USN as Bu112239)	
43142 •	SNJ-6		**N6442D**	Harry Porter, Chattanooga TN	63/66
				John L. Leavis, Hollywood FL	69
				Lanie S. Will, Opa Locka FL	70/76
				struck-off USCR	.77
				Robert T. Button, Stevensville MD	2.82/96
121-	AT-6F	**44-82433**		(to USN as Bu112301)	
43155 •	SNJ-6		**N9806C**	Milton L. Hamilton, Wichita KS	63/64
				J. R. Sirmons, Atoka OK	66/70
				Trissell Flying Service, Clarksville TX	72/86
				Texas Air Museum, Rio Hondo TX	6.87/96
121-	AT-6F	**44-82448**		(to USN as Bu112314)	
43170 •	SNJ-6		**N4135A**	Ernie Beckman, Battle Creek MI	63/64
				Kenneth A. Dalessandro, Cincinatti OH	66/69
				Edward E. Biehl, Cincinatti OH	70
				Robby R. Jones, Minter City MS	72
				Ag Air Inc, Los Fresnos TX	1.79/96
121-	AT-6F	**44-82450**		(to USN as Bu112316)	
43172	SNJ-6		**N6298C**	SNJ-6 & Co, Harlingen TX	63/70
				Confederate Air Force, Harlingen TX	75/76
121-	AT-6F	**44-82456**		(to USN as Bu112322)	
43178 •	SNJ-6		**N2118X**	Mitchell J. Zahler, Stillwater MN	6.95
121-	AT-6F	**44-82457**		(to USN as Bu112323)	
43179 •	SNJ-6		**N611F**	Clinton A. Woodward, Los Angeles CA	63
				Richard M. Fairchild, Maricopa CA	.63/64
				Robert J. Lehmann, Bakersfield CA	66/72
				Colene Giglio, Long Beach CA	76
				Repatria Inc, Reno NV	92
				(race #86 *Bad Company*)	
				John C. Moore, Paso Robles CA	92/96
121-	AT-6F	**44-82464**		(to USN as Bu112330)	
43186 •	SNJ-6		N186D	Jack C. Strother, Gastonburg AL	63/77
				(stored on farm .58/82 ex NAS Pensacola)	
				N. Floyd McGowin, Chapman AL	11.82/83
				(by road AL to Kalamazoo MI 7.82 for rest., ff .83 as "112330/47LF")	
			N47LF	N. Floyd McGowin, Chapman AL	1.83/96
121-	AT-6F	**44-82470**		(to USN as Bu112336)	
43192 •	SNJ-6		**N7976A**	Harry L. Whipple, Silex MO	63/72
				Richard S. Bostick, Kannapolis NC	84
				C. A. Porter, Concord NC: readded	4.93
				Vintage Aero Inc, Wilmington DE	5.96
121-	AT-6F	**44-82482**		(to USN as Bu112348)	
43204 •	SNJ-6		**N3238G**	reg.	9.59
				Lawrence Johnson, Villa Park IL	63/64
				Paul H. Jones, Lombard IL	66
				Iowa Community College, Council Bluffs IA: instructional airframe	69/77
				Rick & Steven Smith, Lincoln NE	.77/88
				(rest. Lincoln NE 77/89, ff .89 as "112348")	
				Terry D. Adams, Libertyville IL	6.88/96
121-	AT-6F	44-82487	N7466C	Evelie A. Perez, Tamiami Airport FL	63/84

c/n	Model	Serial	Reg.	Owner / History	Date
43209					
121-43211 •	AT-6F	**44-82489**	**N7462C**	Madison Flying Club, Tallulah LA	63/72
				Merle B. Gustafson, Tallulah LA	76/84
				Stephen M. Gustafson, Tallulah LA	2.83/95
121-43313 •	AT-6F	**44-82591**		(to USN as Bu112350)	
	SNJ-6			Lance Aircraft Supply Inc, Dallas TX	.88
	SNJ-6B			Chesapeake Airways Corp: USCR candidate	3.4.89
			N8052A	B. Bymgamer: reg. candidate	92
168-1 •	T-6G	**49-2897**	**N7197C**	Vo Boat Sales, Clarion PA	63/66
				Douglas W. Goss, Brookville PA/Aurora CO	69/76
				Fred Cummings, Crowley TX	86
				Edward D. Huber, Greeley CO	1.90/96
				Combat Air Museum, Topeka KS: loan	94
168-2 •	T-6G	**49-2898**	**N3715G**	Joseph V. Emmert, Flint MI	63/64
	AT-6G			Russ Moore Inc, Fort Wayne IN	66
				Thomas A. Watson, Fort Worth TX	69
				William H. Sole, Midland TX	72/76
				Carl Payne, Katy TX	.77
				Richard P. James, Fennimore WI	10.84/96
168-5	T-6G	49-2901		(to French AF/l'Armee de l'Air as 92901)	
				Amicale Jean-Baptiste Salis, La Ferte-Alais	75/85
				(dism., derelict La Ferte-Alais "WQ" 75/85)	
				minor remains by	91
168-12 •	T-6G	**49-2908**		(rebuilt from AT-6B 41-17246)	
				Davis Monthan AFB AZ: displ. at gate	66
				Pima County Air Museum, Tucson AZ	80/96
168-14 •	T-6G	**49-2910**	**N2813G**	Norward R. Hanson, Bloomington IN	63/64
				Donald L. Shacklette, Louisville KY	9.66/96
168-16 •	T-6G	**49-2912**		(to Spanish AF as C.6-182, Code 793-120)	
			N29936	Combat Aircraft Inc, Elkhart IN	20.5.82
				Michael A. McIntyre, Aptos CA	.82/90
				dam. landing Truckee CA (repaired)	.86
			N299CM	ntu: Michael A. McIntyre, Aptos CA	4.90
				(rebuilt Watsonville CA .90 as "92912")	
			N29936	Michael A. McIntyre, Aptos CA	.90/93
			N299CM	Michael A. McIntyre, Watsonville CA	9.93/96
168-19 •	T-6G	**49-2915**	N7813C	Bud Marquis, Marysville CA	63
				Darrin Halcomb, Las Vegas NV	.63/64
				James R. Rollans, Las Vegas NV	66/72
			N66JB	J. K. Biegger, Las Vegas NV	76/77
				Aaron Berkowitz, Phoenix AZ	86
				W. J. Burdis, Pittsburgh PA	90
				Daniel Baun, Elser Metro PA	.90
				Sierra Aviation, Boardman OH	92
				Steven D. Harrison, Rolla MO	8.92/96
168-24 •	T-6G	**49-2920**	**N55720**	Dennis G. Buehn, Compton CA: candidate	1.80
				Paul D. White, Sitka AK	86
				D. Mike O'Hearn, Alta Loma CA	9.89/96
168-32	T-6G	49-2928	N2886G	Rudy Malaspina, Seattle WA	63/69
				H & W Spraying Inc, Midland TX	76
				crashed during airshow, Beatrice NE	26.9.76
168-40 •	T-6G	**49-2936**	**N3717G**	Robert F. McKelvey, Detroit MI	63/66
				Gunther W. Balz, Kalamazoo MI	67/69
				Richard N. Hendrickson, Buffalo Grove IL	11.69/96
168-47 •	T-6G	**49-2943**	**N6253C**	Cloud Modification Service, Minot ND	63/69
				Maurice D. Birkholz, Minot MD	76/77
				Louis P. Thieblemont, Carslie PA	86

				Hal S. Darley, Griffin GA	9.87/96
168-50 •	T-6G	**49-2946**	**C-GBPL**	D. Currie & Associates, Toronto ONT	8.80
				Dennis J. Bradley/Canadian Warplane Heritage, Hamilton ONT	82/92
				(flies as "48884/TA-884")	
168-51 •	T-6G	**49-2947**	**N6183C**	Donald Aircraft Corp, Tucson AZ	63/64
				W. M. Branch, Dallas TX	66/86
				Hank Ketchum & Bob Martin, Dallas TX	88
				K & M Aircraft Corp, Carrollton TX	2.89/96
168-53 •	T-6G	**49-2949**		(rebuilt as T-6G from SNJ-5 Bu90765)	
			N5494V	Chico Aerial Applicators, Chico CA	66
				Roger D. Teuscher, Redding CA	.63/64
				Joseph H. Thesing, Nevada City CA	69
			N641NR	Nevada Rock & Sand Co, Las Vegas NV	72
			N4QU	Jeffery R. Michael, Lexington NC	76/96
168-54 •	T-6G	**49-2950**	N9045Z	S. E. Grafe, McAlester OK	63/66
				Kent W. Jones, Dallas TX	69
			N96143	Lloyd Freeman, Atlanta GA	76
				Adrian Blackmon, Atlanta GA	.77
				J. Vernon Ricks, Greenwood MS	1.80/96
168-61 •	T-6G	**49-2957**	**N2806G**	John F. Gregory, Birmingham MI	63
				William R. Judy, Berkley MI	.63/64
				Cloud Modification Service Inc, Minot ND	66/69
				C. H. Harvey, Berkeley CA	76/77
				Skarda Flying Service, Hazen AR	6.83/96
				(flies as "SNJ-3 Bu6773")	
168-66 •	T-6G	**49-2962**	N9676C	George M. Creamer, Salisbury MA	63
				Air Service Caravan Co, New Bedford MA	.63/64
			N12CC	C. G. Cox, Birmingham AL	72/77
				Southern Museum of Flight, Birmingham AL	8.83/96
168-69	T-6G	49-2965	N2885G	D. E. Dinkins, Porterville CA	63/66
				Jack D. Amis, Hopkinsville KY	69
				Arthur H. Bowles, Hopkinsville KY	72
168-78 •	T-6G	**49-2974**	**N9670C**	Ernst F. Bergmann, Stockton CA	63/64
				Stanley Kurzet, Covina CA	66
				Robert F. MacFarlane, Arcadia CA	69
				Louis E. Antonacci, Hampshire IL	76/77
				John F. Sucich, Chicago IL	12.84/96
168-81 •	T-6G	**49-2977**		(to Spanish AF as .....)	
			N29963	Combat Aircraft Inc, Elkhart IN	25.5.82
				Marion F. Gregory, Kenosha WI	4.85/86
			N117MG	Marion F. Gregory, Kenosha WI	1.87/88
			N29963	Marion F. Gregory, Kenosha WI	88/96
				(flies as "85077/PA-4")	
168-87 •	T-6G	**49-2983**		(to French AF/l'Armee de l'Air as 92983)	
				(to Morocco AF as Y61501)	
				recov. ex Tunisia: noted Etampes, France	10.92/93
168-89 •	T-6G	**49-2985**		Gerald L. Walbrun, Nennah WI	90/93
			N35CE (2	Gerald L. Walbrun, Ocala FL	2.93/96
168-91 •	T-6G	**49-2987**		(to Spanish AF as E.16-...)	
				reg. candidate	12.81
				N2757G	reg. 8.82
				Carl Schmieder, Phoenix AZ	5.84/96
				(flies as 2987/A-S)	
168-92 •	T-6G	**49-2988**	N7657C	Miles L. Burr, Seattle WA	63/69

				D. J. Weinberger, Kent WA	72
				Thomas P. Kelly, Peoria IL	76/77
			N584DD	David D. Smith, Seattle WA	3.82/88
				John D. McCoy, Villa Park CA	2.89
			N584M	John D. McCoy, Villa Park CA/Park City UT	6.89/96
				(flies as USAF 93584/LTA-584)	
168-94	•	T-6G	**49-2990**	N9035Z	Livingston Flying Service, Howell MI	63/64
					A. L. Mazen, Ferndale MI	66
					W. M. Branch, Dallas TX	69/72
					Leroy A. Smith, Wichita Falls TX	76/77
					Texas Flyers Inc	84
					Glen E. Johnson, Fort Worth TX	86/93
				C-GTEX	Dan Springer/Aviation Maintenance Ltd, Bar River ONT	25.5.93/96
				N9035Z	Bengt L. Kuller, Rockford IL	4.95
					(flies as USAAC 132961/X-512)	
168-100	•	T-6G	**49-2996**	**N2879G**	Hubert Koehler, Amarillo TX	63/72
					Edward O. Messick, San Antonio TX	76/77
					Mac MacGregor	82/84
					Wichita Leasing Co, Wichita Falls TX	86
					Tom Petcoff & Don Kohler, Lakeland FL	90
					Bruce A. Grassfield, Aspen CO	92/93
					Robert B. Burwell, West Chicago IL	5.94/95
					(flies as USAF 92-996/TA-996)	
168-102	•	T-6G	**49-2998**		(to FA Hondurena as 211)	
					B & G Aero, King City CA: candidate	12.82
					(del. Tegucigalpa AB, Honduras to USA .83)	
				N27810	Aerolind Inc, Sarasota FL	6.83
				N128WK	Greg & Larry W. Klassen, Bakersfield CA	6.85/87
					William A. Speer, La Mesa CA	92
					Robert Pingston, Brighton MI	9.93/96
168-105	•	T-6G	**49-3001**	**N9067Z**	Dales Aviation, Yuma AZ	63/64
					Border Aviation, Yuma AZ	66/69
					Charles T. Blain, Phoenix AZ	72
					Claiton R. Jordan, Phoenix AZ	3.76/96
168-107	•	T-6G	**49-3003**		(to Spanish AF as C.6-186, Code 421-70)	
				N39311	Combat Aircraft Inc, Elkhart IN	13.5.83
					Russell Cook/Warbirds of Dayton, Dayton OH	3.84/96
168-109	•	T-6G	**49-3005**	N9892C	Mario Villarreal, El Paso TX	63/69
					Roger A. Stout, El Paso TX	72
				N6FD	James C. Bennet, Chestertown MD	76/81
					Warbird Leasing Inc, White Marsh MD	86
					struck-off USCR	1.89
				N4313Z	Robert L. Youkin, Fayetteville AR	2.92/96
168-119	•	T-6G	**49-3015**		Kulis ANGB, Anchorage AK	93/94
					(displ. as "34555/TA ANG")	
168-134	•	T-6G	**49-3030**	**N9871C**	Texan Flying Club, Hinsdale IL	63
					E. L. Stringfellow, Leeds AL	.63/64
					Richard L. Markgraf, Joliet IL	66/72
					George D. Koren, Atlanta GA	76/77
					Zack B. Hinton, Cordova TN	92
					Gary F. Leggette, Atlanta GA	5.92/96
168-138	•	T-6G	**49-3034**		(to Spanish AF as C.6-187, "744-187")	
				N29939	Combat Aircraft Inc, Elkhart IN	19.4.82
					Wiley Sanders Truck Lines, Troy AL	9.83/96
168-141	•	T-6G	**49-3037**		(to Spanish AF as E.16-193)	
					L. Cazades	82
				F-AZCQ	L. Cazades/Assoc. pour Preserver Avions Historiques, Frontenas	26.8.83/90
					J. F. Chalumeau, Lons-Le Saunier	93/96

168-142 •	T-6G	**49-3038**		(to Spanish AF as ....)	
			N5451M	Dodson Aviation Inc, Ottawa KS	6.6.84
			N66TY	Pernicka Corp, Fort Collins CO	4.85
				Jeppco Limited, Aurora CO	86
				Glenn R. Jones, Aurora CO	8.88/96
168-152 •	T-6G	**49-3048**	N9890C	Arthur E. Hopkins, Anaheim CA	63/64
				Henry B. Faulkner, Brookline MA	66
				Charles S. Faulkner, Stoddard NH	69/72
				James D. Scully, Jenkintown PA	76
				J. Peter Vandersluis, Fitzwilliam NH	.76/78
			N51987	J. Peter Vandersluis, New Fairfield CT	3.78/93
				Mark L. Chamlis/Ace Flying School, Tallahassie FL	8.94/96
				(flies as "USAF 51-987/TA-987")	
168-160	T-6G	49-3056		(to Spanish AF as AE.6-188)	
				(open storage, Museo del Aire compound, Cuatro Vientos AB, Spain 83/89)	83/89
168-161 •	T-6G	**49-3057**	**N5296V**	Antellope Valley Aero Survey, Lancaster CA	63/66
				Roger Q. Beckstead, Vernal UT	69
				Atlantic Aero Inc, Greensboro NC	76/77
				William A. Davis, Rowland NC	86
				Robert L. Phillips, Wilkesboro NC	3.86/96
168-170 •	T-6G	**49-3066**		(to Spanish AF as .....)	
			N49388	Combat Aircraft Inc, Elkhart IN	5.4.84
				John C. Hooper, Harvey LA	86/88
				Michael T. Hooper, Harvey LA	3.91/96
168-175 •	T-6G	**49-3071**		(to Spanish AF as C.6-195, E.16-195, "422-77")	
			N2996Q	Combat Aircraft Inc, Elkhart IN	25.5.82
				Billy & Scott S. Burch, Winter Garden FL	86/88
				S. Victor Henry, Woodland MS	3.89/96
168-176	T-6G	**49-3072**	N2807G	Hoyette S. Hudson, Orlando FL	63/64
				Troy W. Dodd, Chicago IL	66
				Jaime Cervantes, Rockford IL	68/69
				Joseph Natoli, Nokesville VA	76/77
			G-BHTH	Jim Keen/Keenair Services Ltd, Speke	20.5.80/86
				(shipped US-Liverpool 4.80, assembled Speke .80, flew as "USN SNJ-7 2807/V-103")	
				Bryn R. Rossiter, Wellesbourne Mountford	10.86/87
				A. Reynard, Booker	30.4.87/91
				forced ldg, dam., Standrake	19.5.91
				dam. wheels-up landing, Southampton	30.12.91
				John J. Woodhouse, Thruxton	92/95
				landing accident Andover	13.3.95
168-185 •	T-6G	**49-3081**	**N7771C**	G. H. McGee, Raymondville TX	63/66
				Trissell Flying Service, Clarksville TX	69/77
				crashed Jasper TX	12.10.69
				John I. Watson, Blackwood NJ	86
				Red Carpet Helicopters, New Smyrna Beach FL	92
				Warbird Rides & Adventures, Orlando FL	6.92/96
168-189	T-6G	**49-3085**		(to Spanish AF as C.6-175 "421-45")	
			N29935	Combat Aircraft Inc, Elkhart IN	20.5.82
				R. L. Knisely/Radial Runners Inc, Silver Lake MN	1.85/96
168-190 •	T-6G	**49-3086**	**N5270V**	James H. Kibler, Baltimore MD	66/72
				Matthew H. Kibler, Baltimore MD	3.72/96
168-191 •	T-6G	**49-3087**	**N3173G**	Gerald M. Wanvick, Duluth MN	63/64
				Dorr H. Burns, Grand Junction CO	66

				Cloud Modification Service Inc, Minot ND	69
				Maynard Lund, Ritzville WA	76/86
				Michael J. McMahon, Melville NY	4.89/96
168-201 •	T-6G	**49-3097**	N5189V	James A. Rhodes, Seattle WA	63/69
			N3HG	L. B. Johnson, East Wenatchee WA	76/77
				Ardmore Aviation, Ardmore OK	86
				Edward L. Stringfellow, Cropwell AL	7.88/95
168-204 •	T-6G	**49-3100**	**N6625C**	Hubert Koehler, Amarillo TX	63
				Tradewind Airport Corp, Amarillo TX	.63/64
				Marion H. Wright, Fort Worth TX	66
				Gordon Travis, Fort Worth TX	69
				Robert L. Walker, Tulsa OK	72
				Danny R. Dunagan, Atlanta GA	76/77
				Bert L. Zeller, New Bern NC/Meridian MS	7.86/96
168-241 •	T-6G	**49-3137**	**N101GB**	Lasalle Elect, Galesburg IL	76/77
				Bob Barnes	80
				Darrell C. Stout, High Point NC	86/90
				William H. Overcash, Mocksville NC	3.90/96
168-242	T-6G	49-3138	N3748G	Bill Bowler, Tucson AZ	63/64
				Edward J. Casper, San Jose CA	66
				Huntley Motor Co, Charlotte NC	69
				James L. Chipukaizer, Soio OH	72
				Robert Fleagane, Cadiz OH	76/77
168-243 •	T-6G	**49-3139**	N2805G	Harold J. Bartizal, North Riverside IL	63/69
				Robert J. Mejdrich, La Grange IL	72/92
				Ronald R. Garner, Concord OH	1.95
168-245 •	T-6G	**49-3141**	N3749G	Jack E. Muston, Durand MI	63/64
				Thomas I. Wood, Kalamazoo MI	66/69
			N157DC	Donald Cassidy, Martinsville IN	72/77
				Cholly C. Howard, Houston TX	86
				David W. Manire, Crofton KY	92
				JA Air Centre, Chicago-DuPage IL	4.95
168-248 •	T-6G	**49-3144**		(rebuilt from AT-6D c/n 88-12383)	
			N55897	Walter E. Best, Seattle WA	63/64
				Cloud Modification Service Inc, Minot ND	66/69
				Charles Feken, Bloomington IL	76/77
				Midwest Aviation Museum, Danville IL	12.77/96
				(rest. Danville .86/90, ff .90 "93144/TA-144)	
168-249 •	T-6G	**49-3145**	**N9628C**	Cloud Modification Service, Minot ND	63/73
				Gregs Crop Care Co, Wilbur WA	76
				Topflight Aviation Inc, Imperial NE	.77
				crashed, Bowling Green OH	22.6.80
				Donald J. Anklin, Mooresville NC: USCR	86/96
168-255 •	T-6G	**49-3151**	N3140G	Ernest C. Jones, Cambridge City IN	63/66
				Robert E. Gordon, Tulsa OK	69
				William E. Harrison, Tulsa OK	72
			N151AT	John C. Williams, Tampa FL	76/77
				S. W. Muse, Weslaco TX	2.83/96
168-256 •	T-6G	**49-3152**	**N3158G**	A. D. Wells, Hayward CA	63/69
				Dennis W. Childers, Broken Arrow OK	86
				Richard L. Churchill, Boring OR/Mesa AZ	88/96
168-257 •	T-6G	**49-3153**		(rebuilt as T-6G from AT-6D 42-85848)	
			N5557V	Denver Public School District, Denver CO	63/64
				Chuck Easton, Greeley CO	76/77
				World Jet Inc, Fort Lauderdale FL	84/86
				Pat Poole, Evergreen AL	88
				sale rep., USCR	92/95
168-259 •	T-6G	**49-3155**	N2836G	Thunderbird Transport Co, Omaha NE	63/64

				Denver Diesel Inc, Commerce City CO	66
				William F. Gunn, Fort Worth TX	69/72
			N94155	Robert L. Wick, Worthington OH/Arlington TX	8.73/95
				Flying Tiger Museum, Paris TX: loan, displ.	87
168-262 •	T-6G	**49-3158**	N5187V	I. Dowverge, Rogue River OR	63/69
			N444RB	John Johnson, Rexburg ID	72/77
				Ted E. Contri, Reno NV	6.79/91
			N6HC	Ted E. Contri, Yuba City CA	2.91/96
168-263 •	T-6G	**49-3159**		(to Spanish AF as .....)	
			N43AW	reg. candidate	6.84/92
168-264 •	T-6G	**49-3160**		(rebuilt from AT-6C 41-33695: redel. 1.2.51)	
				Davis Monthan AFB AZ for disposal: SOC	9.57
			N6128C	Fisher Bros Furniture, San Fernando CA	63/64
				Stanley Aviation, Aurora CO	66/69
				Airtrek Inc, Aspen CO	72
				John Becker, Dallas TX	76/77
				Jack Goulding, Lubbock TX	86
				Anita deVillegas, Houston TX	88/90
			N5ZS	Birmingham Executive Aero, Birmingham AL	7.90
				Evan H. Zeiger/Hezca Inc, Pell City AL	3.92/96
168-268 •	T-6G	**49-3164**	**N5184V**	Frederick K. Baker, Media PA	63/69
				Board of Education Services, Westbury NY	7.70/96
168-275 •	T-6G	**49-3171**	N9043Z	Charles H. Van Dorsten, Battle Creek MI	63/66
				Edwin H. Staehling, Ann Arbor MI	69
				George M. Staehling, Woodstock IL	76/77
			N36913	Louis E. Antonacci, Hampshire IL	2.86/88
				William Melamed, Los Angeles CA	3.88
			N171WM	William Melamed, Los Angeles CA	7.88
			N36913	Edward H. Shipley, Malvern PA	92/96
				Laurie A. Shipley, Malvern PA	2.95
168-276 •	T-6G	**49-3172**	**N3172G**	Larry M. Smith, Elkhorn NE	63/64
				Cloud Modification Service Inc, Minot ND	66/69
				Arthur S. Kuchan, Hudson IL	76/87
				Kevin L. Batterton, Morton IL	7.87/96
168-281 •	T-6G	**49-3177**	**N3753G**	Ellen Kurath, Ypsilanti MI	66/69
				Emerson J. Davies, Davisburg MI	8.78/96
168-283 •	T-6G	**49-3179**	**N5289V**	Darrell D. Mallard, Shelley ID	63/66
				Cloud Modification Service Inc, Minot ND	69
				Charles Feken, Bloomington IL	76/77
				Jim Compton/Compton & Assoc., Griffin GA	86/88
				Aero Dynamics Inc, Wilmington DE	1.88/96
168-290 •	T-6G	**49-3186**		(T-6G rebuilt from AT-6C 41-32862)	
			N2893G	Lonnie D. Clark, Brownfield TX	63/66
				Clarks Aerial Service, Brownsville TX	69
				Sharon A. Sharp, Southfield MI	72
			N1751	Steven Seghetti, Vacaville CA	76/81
			VH-HAJ	Col Pay/Pays Air Service, Scone NSW	19.9.84/96
168-293 •	T-6G	**49-3189**	**N3142G**	Richard Casey, Marion OH	63
				Li Calzi Air Service, Bridgeton NJ	.63/66
				Board of Education Services, Verona NY	69/96
168-294 •	T-6G	**49-3190**	**N8399H**	Aero Enterprises Inc, Elkhart IN	63/64
				Cloud Modification Service, Minot ND	66/69
				Woods Aviation, East Prairie MO	76/77
				Gordon E. Swenson, Rake IA	11.79/96
168-295 •	T-6G	**49-3191**		(to Austrian AF as 4C-TE)	
	LT-6G			Heeresgeschichtliches Museum, Vienna	79/88

168-302 •	T-6G AT-6G	**49-3198**	**N5188V**	George Mustin, Menlo Park CA	63
				Warren L. Woods, San Jose CA	.63/72
				Walter R. Patten, Sacramento CA	76/89
				(open storage Sacramento-Executive 79/89)	
				Scott Main/Air Share Inc, Palo Alto CA	7.89/96
				(del. Palo Alto 7.89, rest. ff .91 "USAF 32421")	
168-306	T-6G	49-3202		(to FA Brasileira as FAB T-6G 1658)	.58
			PT-KVF	reg.	.76
				Luiz Rinaldo da Motta Rizental, Nova Igaucu	83
168-311 •	T-6G	**49-3207**	**N3100G**	Donald R. Brust, Covina CA	63/64
				James C. Jones, Covina CA	66
				Keith L. Hilton, Oceanside CA	69/77
				Arthur D. Medore/Banaire Inc, Hemet CA	1.80/95
168-312 •	T-6G	**49-3208**	**N7664C**	Clayton J. Carriveau, Milwaukee WI	6.62/95
168-313 •	T-6G	**49-3209**		(to FA Haiti as 3209)	3.57/82
				wfu, sold by FAH to US buyer	3.82
			N3240N	Nostalgia Aircraft Inc, Miami FL	8.82
				Nostalgic Aircraft Service, Miami FL	86
				Jim Carlin, Delray Beach FL	88
			G-DDMV	Paul J. & Elizabeth A. Morgan, Sywell	30.4.90/96
168-314 •	T-6G	**49-3210**	**N8335H**	R. J. Lidell, Tulelake CA	63
				Donald E. Murphy, Houston TX/Nelson CA	7.63/96
168-315 •	T-6G	**49-3211**	**N9893C**	Tallmantz Aviation, Orange County CA	63/64
				(displ. Movieland of the Air,	
				Orange County CA 63/68)	
				Rosen Novak Auto Co, Omaha NE	66
				Aircraft & Component Equipment Suppliers,	
				Arcadia CA	69
				Philip F. Waterman, Reno/Las Vegas NV	76/88
				Hans P. Christensen, Pahrump NV	11.88/95
168-319	T-6G	49-3215		(to Spanish AF as AE.6-173)	
			N29938	Combat Aircraft Inc, Elkhart IN	19.4.82
				crashed near Muskegon MI	1.8.83
				Thomas P. Balch, Edmore MI	86
				struck-off USCR	25.3.91
168-325 •	T-6G	**49-3221**	N7816C	Jesse Parer, Mountlake Terrace WA	63/69
			N302V		71
			N990JP	James Milliken, Narbeth PA	76
			N17498	Dennis G. Buehn, Long Beach CA	6.78
				(rest., using airframe recov. ex schoolyard	
				Japan c78, as "USAF 93221/TA-221")	
				Charles R. Hall, Ramona CA	86/91
				Cinema Air Inc, Houston TX/Carlsbad CA	2.91/96
168-326 •	T-6G	**49-3222**	N9042Z	Donald Aircraft Corp, Tucson AZ	63/64
				Les Weingarten, Albuquerque NM	66/69
				James G. Vagim, Porterville CA	72
				William J. Leff, Dayton OH	76/86
			N22NA	William J. Leff, Bloomington IL	5.90/96
168-329 •	T-6G	**49-3225**	N8039L	Courtesy Aircraft Inc, Rockford IL	7.2.89
				sold to Canada, struck-off USCR	5.11.91
168-336 •	T-6G AT-6G	**49-3232**		(T-6G rebuilt from AT-6C 42-32927)	12.50
				(to Spanish AF as C.6-66, E16-66,"793-16")	11.57
			N4993A	Combat Aircraft Inc, Elkhart IN	5.84
			N62RH	Robert Holloway, Jonesboro AR	9.85
				Robby R. Jones, Minter City MS	86
			N2449	Seth Ward, Little Rock AR	6.86
				Ray Kinney, Gainesville TX	12.89/95
				landing accident, Beaumont TX	21.5.95

168-340 •	T-6G	**49-3236**	**N3141G**	Robert B. Joyce, Roselle IL	63/69
				Melvin G. Craig, Crown Point IN	72
			N9MC	Melvin G. Craig, Crown Point IN	76/92
			N8FD	Frank A. Bosner, South Holland IL	12.93/96
168-345 •	T-6G	**49-3241**	**N8203H**	Estelle E. Bourland, Gardena CA	63/64
				Robert J. Torbet, Costa Mesa CA	66
				Bill Miller, Anaheim CA	69/77
				Richard J. Sinnott, Fort Pierce FL	86
				Patrick A. Harrison, Houston TX	92
				David K. & Robert Wall, Ocala FL/Denton TX	8.92/95
168-346 •	T-6G	**49-3242**	N9037Z	John C. Earley, Norman OK	63/69
				James H. Wilson, Dallas TX	72
			N51944	William D. Platero, Clifton NJ	76
				Donald Contant, Santee SC	.77
				Haig A. Avakian, Downstown NJ	86/88
				John I. Watson, Blackwood NJ	92
				Deborah Watson Longstreet, Mays Landing NJ	92/93
				Vintage War Birds Inc, Louisville KY	5.95
168-347 •	T-6G	**49-3243**	**N7613C**	George H. Stell, Phoenix AZ	63/64
				Frank Sylvestri, San Francisco/Millbrae CA	66/77
				Mark A. Moodie, Moreno Valley CA	3.84/95
168-349 •	T-6G	**49-3245**		(to Spanish AF as C.6-181)	
			N28955	Joseph Natol, Nokesville VA	2.82
				Ronald G. Fountain, Houston TX	84/86
				Trent Latshaw/Latshaw Drilling & Exploration, Houston TX	90/93
168-358 •	T-6G	**49-3254**	N6889C	Anthony Bernard, Inglewood CA	63/64
				Pauline J. Lincoln, Van Nuys CA	66
				Eonair Inc, Bakersfield CA	69
				Donald T. Bayley, Springfield VA	72
				Joe Rankin, San Francisco CA	76
				Foreign Automotive Inc, Santa Rosa CA	.77/86
			N53SB	Stephen Bolander/SWB Leasing Co, Libertyville IL	5.91/92
				Air Bear Corp, Waukegan IL	12.91/96
168-360 •	T-6G	**49-3256**	**N7487C**	Clover Park School District, Tacoma WA	63/69
				Everett Community College, Everett WA	76
				James Milliken, Narberth PA	.77
				Owls Head Transportation Museum ME	2.85/96
168-363 •	T-6G	**49-3259**	**N3168G**	Karl Von Brawner, Tampa FL	63
				Perry Boswell, Stuart FL	.63/64
				Peter H. Stewart, Sun City FL	66
				Herbert C. Weiss, Spokie IL	69/72
				David Fain, Skokie IL	76/77
				Rodney E. Barnes, Oconomowoc WI	12.83/96
168-370 •	T-6G	**49-3266**	N9604C	Charlotte J. Underwood, Phoenix AZ	63/69
				James H. Nunn, Ontario CA	72
				Elmer F. Ward, Santa Ana CA	76
				Richard Foote, Andover CT	.77
				Bruce D. McCauley, Keene NH	86
				George M. Krieger, Pound Ridge NY/ Dumfries Marine Corp, Dover DE	4.88/90
			N51KT	George M. Krieger/Dumfries Marine Corp DE (flies as "USAAF 284602")	5.90/96
168-383 •	T-6G	**49-3279**	**N7704C**	Stanley Aviation Corp, Denver CO	63
				Olympic Corp, Denver CO	.63/66
				Sacol Inc, Hurricane UT	69/72
				Chris Nelson, Wheatridge CO	76

				Al Trovinger Ford Inc, Mobile AL	.77
				John R. Cansler, Winston-Salem NC	86/93
				accident landing West Jefferson NC (repaired)	8.10.88
				Historical Warbird & Antique Aircraft, Advance NC	10.93/96
168-388 •	T-6G	**49-3284**	**N8204H**	Robert A. Gandy, Malibu CA	63/64
				Mustang Pilots Club, Beverly Hills CA	66/77
				Joseph J. Davis, Visalia CA	81/86
				Kenneth H. Dwelle, Auburn CA	8.89/96
				(race #7 *Yankee Air Pirate*)	
168-395 •	T-6G	**49-3291**		(to Spanish AF as C.6-196)	
			N29933	Combat Aircraft Inc, Elkhart IN	20.5.82
				Skytypers Inc, Los Alamitos CA	12.83/96
168-396 •	T-6G	**49-3292**	N9644C	Vincent L. Kreyer, Rochester NY	63/64
				Erwin L. Murray, Emporium PA	66
				Lebanon Valley Aero Club, Fredericksburg PA	69/72
				sale rep.	76/77
				Dorr H. Burns, Grand Junction CO	86/88
			N426DB	Dorr H. Burns, Grand Junction CO	10.88/93
				Jack W. Snodgrass, Dover DE	4.93/96
168-401 •	T-6G	**49-3297**	**N9627C**	Cloud Modification Service, Minot ND	63/72
				Charles Feken, Bloomington IL	76/77
				Confederate Air Force, Harlingen/Midland TX	12.4.82/96
168-404 •	T-6G	**49-3300**	**N3171G**	Martin L. Hallman, Vicksburg MS	63/64
				Frederick J. Hawkins, Mineral Wells TX	66
				Sandor Branozeisz, Red Hook NY	69/72
				Charles M. Dedrick, Vergennes VT	76/77
				Geoffrey L. Schussler, Eugene OR	86
				Hampton Air Inc, Griffin GA	4.86/96
168-406 •	T-6G	**49-3302**	N9609C	Russell B. Mayberry, Northridge CA	63/64
				Oakland Air Force Inc, Oakland CA	66/69
				Eric R. Christensen, Mills WY	72
				Stuart M. Schwartz, Southfield MI	76/78
			N666SS	Stuart M. Schwartz, Southfield MI	8.78
				Joe Kasparoff, Montebello CA	86/92
				Stuart C. Eberhardt, Danville CA	2.94/95
			N116SE	rereg. res: Stuart C. Eberhardt, Danville CA	3.95
168-407 •	T-6G	**49-3303**	**N5259V**	Ivan Tors Film Inc, Hollywood CA	63/66
				Ronald G. Ellis, Miami FL	69/76
				Outlaw Aircraft Sales Inc, Clarksville TN	.77
				Frederick T. Keister, Federick MD	7.78/96
168-409 •	T-6G	**49-3305**		(to Spanish AF as E.16-...)	
			N332CA	Combat Aircraft Inc, Elkhart IN	26.11.85
				Richard W. Hansen, Batavia IL	2.86/96
168-410 •	T-6G	**49-3306**	N5278V	Frank M. Coray, Hermosa Beach CA	63
				Aerocrete Concretes Inc, Los Angeles CA	.63/64
				Richard A. Mast, Santa Monica CA	66
			N7000S	sale rep.	76/86
				Richard Brakey, Hobbs NM	92
				Michael R. Bryan, Hobbs NM	2.95
168-411 •	T-6G	**49-3307**	N3159G	Daryl D. Sichel, Santa Rosa CA	63/66
			N3307	Edward J. Mitchell, Hollister CA	69/77
				Curtis J. Earl, Deer Valley AZ	86/96
168-414 •	T-6G	**49-3310**	**N7679C**	Ben Whitney Trading Co, Calexico CA	63/69
				Richard S. Fields, Fullerton CA: readded	3.90/95
				(rest. Chino CA 90/91)	
168-415 •	T-6G	**49-3311**		(to Spanish AF as C.6-167)	
			N3931Y	Combat Aircraft Inc, Elkhart IN	13.5.83

				Louis T. Spanberger, Plymouth MI	86/87
				Weeks Air Museum, Tamiami FL	2.89/96
				minor dam., Tamiami by Hurricane Andrew	24.8.92
168-417 •	T-6G	**49-3313**	**N7050C**	Combat Aircraft Inc, Elkhart IN	11.88
				reg. res.	92
168-424 •	T-6G	**49-3320**		(to Spanish AF as C.6-67, E.16-67, "793-21")	
				sold at auction, Spain	1.84
			N4996H	Combat Aircraft Inc, Elkhart IN	5.84
				John Strickland & Bill Smith/	
				Warbird Leasing Inc, White Marsh MD	11.85/96
168-430 •	T-6G	**49-3326**		(to Spanish AF as E.16-69)	
				sold at auction, Torrejon AB, Spain	9.7.83
			N100XK	Richard M. Runyan, Springdale OH	21.3.84/86
				Charles E. Murray, Crescent Springs KY	92/93
				Robert Stevenson, Geneva IL	5.94/96
168-431 •	T-6G	**49-3327**		(to Spanish AF as E.16-82): sold at auction	9.84
			N2205G	George F. Byard, Rosamond CA/Dayton NV	12.89/96
168-434 •	T-6G	**49-3330**		(to Spanish AF as C.6-85, E.16-85)	
				sold at auction, Spain	1.84
			N5115D	Combat Aircraft Inc, Elkhart IN	5.84
				Robert E. Bryan, Stone Mountain GA	86
				Forbes H. Mathews, Hampton/Fayetteville GA	92/94
				Robert A. Brown, Marietta GA	.94/95
				WRA Corp, Wilmington DE	3.95
168-440 •	T-6G	**49-3336**		(to Spanish AF as E.16-79, Code 793-20)	
				sold at auction, Spain	1.84
			N4993G	Combat Aircraft Inc, Elkhart IN	5.84
				Theodore Pechel, Brielle NJ	9.84/85
			N25KP	Theodore Pechel, Brielle NJ	10.85/96
168-443 •	T-6G	**50-1279**		(T-6G rebuilt from AT-6C 41-32950)	
				USAFM, Wright Patterson AFB, Dayton OH	58/90
				(displ. as AT-6A "USAAC 41279/304")	
168-448 •	T-6G	**50-1284**		(to FA Boliviana as 369)	
				D. G. Garcia	
				Aero Nostalgia Inc, Stockton CA: not del.	12.84
				George Markey, Camden NSW: not del.	12.84
				(sale cancelled due Bolivian military coup)	
			N1284	Robert H. Hawk, Westfield IN	9.7.90/96
				(USCR quotes id. "12463")	
168-451 •	T-6G	**49-3337**		(to Spanish AF as E.16-86)	
				Patrimoine Aeronautique Nat.,	
				Luxembourg-Findel: del. 14.10.83	10.83/85
				(stored Findel .83/89)	
			LX-PAD	Luxembourg Assoc. for Vintage Aircraft	21.8.89/94
			N22182	Michael A. Smyser, Galena OH	25.5.94/96
				(del. Luxembourg to USA, via Glasgow 6.6.94)	
			N73337	Michael A. Smyser, Galena OH	9.95
168-456	T-6G	49-3342		(to Spanish AF as E.16-71/Code 793-8)	
				Patrimoine Aeronautique Nat., Luxembourg	.83
			I-TSEI	Mario Ferrari/Ass. Amatori di Aerei d'Epoca,	
				Treviso	6.8.86/90
				crashed Salgareda, Italy (Ferrari k.)	9.8.90
168-461	T-6G	**49-3347**		(to Spanish AF as C.6-75)	
			N5449N	reg. candidate	8.84
168-463 •	T-6G	**49-3349**		(to Spanish AF as .....)	
			N5830Z	Dodson Aviation Inc, Ottawa KS	19.11.84

			N6G	Ray Gentile, Youngstown OH	6.85/86
				Ray Gentile & Al Reno/Quivira Flyers Inc, Olathe KS	9.86/96
				Combat Air Museum, Topeka KS: loan	91
168-464 •	T-6G	**49-3350**		(to Spanish AF as E.16-120): sold at auction	1.84
			N4993X	Combat Aircraft Inc, Elkhart IN	5.84
			N49RR	Edward M. Robinson, Sanger TX	7.85/88
				David R. Webb, Dallas TX	3.89/95
168-466 •	T-6G	**49-3352**		(to Spanish AF as C.6-92, E.16-92, "793-21")	
				sold by auction, Spain	1.84
			N49939	Combat Aircraft Inc, Elkhart IN	5.84
				Robert S. Remiro, Many Farms AZ	86
				Vaughn Olson	90
				Peter C. Hunt, Marietta GA/San Diego CA	12.91/95
168-470 •	T-6G	**49-3356**		(to Spanish AF as E.16-108)	
				sold by auction, Torrejon AB, Spain	9.7.83
			N5443X	reg.	9.84
				McNeely Charter Service, Earle AR	92
			N992GM	McNeely Charter Service, Earle AR	1.93
			N94SC	Stephen A. Clegg, Daytona Beach FL	6.93/96
168-471 •	T-6G	**49-3357**		(T-6G rebuilt from AT-6C 42-43899)	
				(to Spanish AF as E.16-109)	
				sold by auction, Spain	9.84
				John Muszala, Chino CA	
				Michael Hay: rest. Chino CA	90
			N6593D	Aircraft Cylinder & Turbine, Newport Beach CA	2.91/96
168-472 •	T-6G	**49-3358**		(to Spanish AF as E.16-94)	
				sold by EdA auction, Torrejon AB, Spain	9.7.83
			N4785E	Texas Turbo Jet Inc	3.3.84
				George D. Bass, Griffin GA	86
			N106RM	Ronald J. Maggard, Independence MO	4.87/92
				Dan Linkous, Mooresville NC: del.	21.3.92
			N116NA	Dan Linkous/Air Nostalgia Ltd, Mooresville NC	5.92
			C-GTXN	Dan & Annie Springer/Aviation Maintenance Ltd, Bar River ONT	1.3.93/94
			N8201V	Bengt L. Kuller, Rockford IL	4.95
				(flies as "168472/TA-472")	
168-473 •	T-6G	**49-3359**		(to Spanish AF as E.16-95)	
			N5830R	Dodson Aviation Inc, Ottawa KS	19.11.84
				Joseph M. Natoli, Nokesville VA	86
				Karl Stoltzfus/K & K Aircraft Inc, Bridgewater VA	10.86/96
168-477	T-6G	49-3363		(to Spanish AF as .....)	
				Patrimoine Aeronautique Nat., Luxembourg-Findel	
			N5451X	Dodson Aviation Inc, Ottawa KS	6.6.84
				Joseph M. Natoli, Nokesville VA	86
			N233TM	Thomas Migel, St. Cloud FL	2.87/88
			N44CT	Robert C. Tullius & Brian Fuerstenau/ Group 44 Inc, Winchester VA	7.90/93
				crashed, dest. Berryville VA	20.7.93
168-479 •	T-6G	**49-3365**		(to Spanish AF as E.16-98, Code 793-4)	
			N5830X	Dodson Aviation, Ottawa KS	11.84/85
			N496DK	Donald W. Keller, Prairie View IL	2.85/87
			N365TA	N. S. Gustin Co, Chicago IL	2.87
				Donald W. Keller, Barrington IL	88/96
168-481 •	T-6G	**49-3367**		(to Spanish AF as C.6-100)	
				sold by EdA auction, Spain	1.84
			N4994U	ntu	.84
			N4995C	Combat Aircraft Inc, Elkhart IN	5.84/86

				John Krueger, Redlands CA	5.88/96
168-482 •	T-6G	**49-3368**		(to Spanish AF as E.16-111)	
				sold by EdA auction, Spain	9.84
			N43FT	reg. res.	3.86
			N799MU	USAFM, Wright Patterson AFB, Dayton OH	10.88/96
168-490 •	T-6G	**49-3376**		(to Spanish AF as C.6-84, E.16-84)	
				sold by auction, Torrejon AB, Spain	9.7.83
			N49NA	John A. Darznieks, Dallas TX	10.1.85
				Appalachian Aircraft Inc, Front Royal VA	12.85/86
				L. Chris Christensen, Front Royal VA	88/91
				Fred Mesmer/White Knuckles Inc,	
				West Islip NY	.91/94
				Richard E. Zisa, Lantana FL	8.94/96
168-494 •	T-6G	49-3380		(to FA Brasileira as FAB T-16 1672)	
			PT-KQX	reg.	.76
				Aristedes de Araujo Leite, Nova Iguaca	83
				W. A. Weiss: struck off Brazilian reg.	30.6.93
			N40280	Classic Aviation International, Belleview FL	12.93
				Airplane Services Inc, Greenwood MS	6.94/96
168-496 •	T-6G	**49-3382**		(to Spanish AF as E.16-114)	
			N5451E	Dodson Aviation Inc, Ottawa KS	6.6.84
				Aubrey J. Vidrine, Broussard LA	86
				Frank C. Nelson, Vicksburg MS	11.86/96
168-498 •	T-6G	**49-3384**	N2816G	Albert Boughey, Upland CA	63/66
			N6900G	Adrian S. Kale, Lemars IA	4.74/96
168-500	T-6G	49-3386	N2889G	Thomas L. Moore, El Cerrito CA	63
				Crandal MacKey, Palo Alto CA	.63/69
				Darrel A. Doman, Sunnyvale CA	72
			N74DW	Elmer Reynolds, Whittier CA	76/77
168-502	T-6G	50-1288	N7765C	Peter J. Thurston, San Diego CA	63/64
				Roy Corella, San Gabriel CA	66/69
				Metal Units Inc, Riverside CA	72
				Richard S. Drury, Woodland Hills CA	76/81
				James W. Furlong, Northridge CA	86
				Francis W. Elliot, Tarzana CA	91/93
				(race #73 *Jutta*)	
				Jim Price, Thousand Oaks CA	93
				crashed dest., Green Valley CA (Elliot k.)	11.10.93
168-503 •	T-6G	**50-1289**		(to French AF/l'Armee de l'Air as 01289)	
				Amicale Jean-Baptiste Salis, La Ferte-Alais	79/89
				(rep. under rest. LFA 89, "01289/WV")	
				Yugoslavian National Aviation Museum,	
				Belgrade: displ. as "TT-152"	90
168-505 •	T-6G	**50-1291**	N3518G	Jack E. Gerst, San Jose CA	63/64
				Frank E. Wilson, West Mifflin PA	66/69
				Michael Schloss, New York NY	2.80
			N79MP	ntu: Michael Schloss, New York NY	5.80
			N3518G	Michael Schloss, New York NY	.80/96
				(flies as "USAF 50-291/TA-291")	
168-514 •	T-6G	**49-3390**	**N9492Z**	San Mateo Junior College, San Mateo CA	63/66
				Peralta Junior College, Oakland CA	69/72
				John R. Booth, Whitehall MT	8.77/96
168-515 •	T-6G	**49-3391**	**N2878G**	Dodd C. Boyd, Dallas TX	63/64
				Arthur Wilson, Flying W Ranch, Medford NJ	66
				Stewart Nicolson, Mount Holly NJ later	
				New Milford CT	8.67/96

168-516 •	T-6G	**49-3392**	N3746G	Robert S. Tapley, Grayling MI	63/64
				Cloud Modification Service Inc, Minot ND	66/69
				Commander Aviation Corp, Bismark ND	76/77
			N104DC	Frank Cannavo, Lester PA	6.78
				William M. Simmons, Avery Island LA	10.85/95
168-517 •	T-6G	**49-3393**	**N7767C**	Samuel J. Mallen, Malibu CA	63/64
				Haig Sakajian, Los Angles CA	66/69
				Nick N. Mehterian, Los Angeles CA	72
				T. G. Saltonstall, Pacific Palisades CA	76
				Sherman Aircraft Sales, West Palm Beach FL	86/87
	Super T-6			(rest. with R1820 as "Super T-6")	
				John Kordenbrock/3 Plus 6 Inc, Cincinatti OH	2.87/96
168-525 •	T-6G	**49-3401**		(to Spanish AF as E.16-115)	
				sold at auction, Spain	1.84
			N4995P	Combat Alrcraft Inc, Elkhart IN	5.84
				Frederic P. Cumblad, St Charles IL	86
				George D. Bass/T. S. Bass Inc, Griffin GA	88/93
				Carrier Aviation, High Point NC	9.94/96
168-526 •	T-6G	**49-3402**		(T-6G rebuilt from AT-6C 42-3890)	
			N9882C	Walker H. Harris, Denver CO	63/69
				reregistered.	2.84
			N85JR	John Roark, Fort Lupton CO (race #85)	1.85
				Planes of Fame East, Minneapolis-Flying Cloud MN	86/96
168-528 •	T-6G	**49-3404**		(T-6G rebuilt ex AT-6C 42-44081)	
			N9883C	Robert K. Mason, Anchorage AK	63/64
				Henry B. Best, Theinsville WI	66/77
				Carl Best, Dallas TX	88/96
				(rest. project, Plano TX 92/96)	
168-529 •	T-6G	**49-3405**	**N7618C**	Robert Henkel, Hamilton OH	63/64
				Jack D. Taylor, Ann Arbor MI	66/69
				Sheldon Prudhomme, Dayton OH	76/77
				Hibbard Aviation, Oakland CA	86
				Scott R. Groh, Louisville KY/Palm Beach FL	2.92/95
				(flies as "72342/TA-342")	
168-548 •	T-6G	**49-3424**		(to R Hellenic AF as 49-3424)	
				R Hellenic AF Museum, Tatoi AB	94/95
				(rest., displ. as "RHAF 49-3424")	
168-554 •	T-6G	**49-3430**		(to Spanish AF as E.16-103)	
				sold at auction, Spain	1.84
			N45CT	Thomas M. Jackson, Van Nuys CA	8.85
				John R. Morello, Mason OH	9.85/96
168-556 •	T-6G	**49-3432**		(to French AF as 93432)	
			F-AZGS	Les Ailes de France: reg. res.	.89
				Ass. des Amateurs d'Aeronefs de Collection/ Les Ailes de France, Luneville	11.6.90/93
168-571 •	T-6G	**49-3437**		(to Spanish AF as E.16-116)	
				sold by auction, Torrejon AB, Spain	9.7.83
			N8084G	Courtesy Aircraft, Rockford IL	15.9.89
				Scott A. Morse/Morse Aviation, Plano TX	9.92/96
168-583 •	T-6G	**49-3449**		(to Spanish AF as C.6-197, E.16-197)	
			N29931	Combat Aircraft Inc, Elkhart IN	20.5.82
				BOA Ltd, Chicago IL	86
				Classic Air Parts, Miami FL	7.91/96
				(race #51"*Yaba Daba Doo*)	
168-587 •	T-6G	**49-3453**		(to French AF as 93453)	
				(to Spanish AF as E.16-106)	
				Patrimoine Aeronautique Nat., Luxembourg-Findel: del.	14.10.83

				(stored unconv. Findel 83/87)	
			LX-PAE	Luxembourg Assoc. for Vintage Aircraft	2.9.87
168-622 •	T-6G	**50-1308**	**N2760A**	George A. Buchanan, Reno NV	63/72
				(last FAA annual inspection 9.58)	
				Robert Tobacco, Colts Neck NJ	76
				Victor Schilleci, Metairie LA	6.85/96
168-636 •	T-6G	**49-3492**	**N2897G**	Valley Leasing Co, San Jose CA	63
				Paul R. Macy, Tulelake CA	66/84
				Nick Macy/Six Cat Racing Inc, Tulelake CA	86/96
				(race #6 *Six-Cat*)	
168-644 •	T-6G	**49-3500**		(to Greek AF as 93500)	
				Hellenic War Museum, Athens	79/88
				(displ. as "32803")	
168-653 •	T-6G	**49-3509**	**N7057**	Aerospace Dynamics Corp, Chicago IL	72
				Richard S. Vogler, Appleton WI	76/77
				reregistered.	6.85
				Harry E. Tope, Mount Pleasant MI	86/92
				Diane E. Tope, Mount Pleasant MI: USCR	10.92/96
168-673 •	T-6G	**49-3529**	N9894C	Dunbar Murphy & Co, Palm Beach FL	63
				Robert D. Paul, Rawlins WY	.63/64
			N717UP	James M. Dinnen, Des Moines IA	66
				James G. Haller, Cheyenne WY	69
				Piper Aircraft Corp, Vero Beach FL	72
				Carl Fromhagen Aviation, Clearwater FL	5.76/96
168-680 •	T-6G	**49-3536**	**N165P**	Paul L. Taylor, Shakopee/Prior Lake MN	12.61/96
168-682 •	T-6G	**49-3269**		(to Spanish AF as C.6-170)	
			N3931U	Combat Aircraft Inc, Elkhart IN	13.5.83
				Willard S. Poss, Houston TX	86
			N61MH	Mike Horn, Little Rock AR	7.87/88
				MGH Enterprises Inc, Wilmington DE	88/92
				Northaire Inc, Wilmington DE	5.92/96
168-683	T-6G	49-3270	**N3166G**	Wilbur Brewer, Bowman ND	63/64
				Lemmon Aircraft Co, Lemmon SD	66/69
				David K. Ross, Texas City TX	72
				E. E. Burke, Galveston TX	.77
				Gary D. Hudson/Conservair Inc, Conroe TX	86/94
				dest. in hangar fire, Conroe TX	12.6.94
168-685 •	T-6G	**49-3272**	**N3167G**	Travel Associates Inc, Leominster MA	63/66
				Robert J. Gardner, Sunderland MA	69
				Alden E. Robinson, Accord NY	72
				Albert Costa, Newton MA/Nashua NH	76/95
168-687 •	T-6G	**49-3274**	**N7689C**	Grafton Insurance Agency, Grafton WI	63/72
				Cliff Hersey/Hersey Trucking, Camarillo CA	4.74/95
182-1 •	T-6G	**51-14314**		(to French AF/l'Armee de l'Air as 114314)	
			F-BOEN	Institute Aeronautique Amaury de la Grange,	
				Merville: reg. res.	6.74/85
				(inst. airframe Merville 77, "114314")	
				Metz-Frescaty AB, France: displ.	85/90
				(displ. as "114314/VM")	
182-5 •	T-6G	**51-14318**		(to FA Portuguesa as .....) GG	
			N1384Z	Arthur D. Medore/North American Aviation/	
				Banaire, Hemet CA	5.1.82/95
182-17 •	T-6G	**51-14330**		(to R Thai AF as AT-6G-185)	
				Civil Aviation Training Centre, Bongkok	95

182-20 •	T-6G	**51-14333**		(to French AF/l'Armee de l'Air as 114333)	
				offered for disposal by French AF	11.2.76
			N5599L	Steve Martin, Delhi LA	18.3.80/86
				Andrew J. Keenan, Gautier MS	1.87/95
182-29 •	T-6G	**51-14342**		(to French AF/l'Armee de l'Air as 114342)	
				(to FA Portuguesa as 1715)	
			G-BIHS	Aces High Ltd, Duxford	7.11.80/83
				sold to USA, struck-off reg.	17.5.83
			N4434M	June Mourad, Old Rebel Field, Mercedes TX	11.8.83/95
182-30 •	T-6G	**51-14343**		(to French AF/l'Armee de l'Air as 114343)	
				(to FA Portuguesa as ....)	
			N8048E	Arthur D. Medore/Banaire, Hemet CA	8.79
				Lee Maples, Vichy/Rolla MO	86/95
				(rest. 86/89, ff .89: rep. last flew .58)	
182-38 •	T-6G	**51-14351**		(to French AF/l'Armee de l'Air as 114351)	
				Musee de l'Air et Espace, Paris	90/92
				(stored Villacoublay, "114351/56")	
182-54 •	T-6G	**51-14367**		(to French AF/l'Armee de l'Air as 114367)	
			F-BVQD	Amicale J-B Salis, La Ferte-Alais: reg. res.	11.78
			F-AZBK	J-B Salis/Salis Aviation, La Ferte-Alais	9.81/87
			F-WZBK	Amicale Jean-Baptiste Salis, La Ferte-Alais	6.87
				(conv. to Zero lookalike .87 for film	
				Empire of the Sun, c/n "SAM2-367")	
			F-AZBK	Amicale J-B Salis, La Ferte-Alais	89/93
				P. Zmiro, Pontivy	
			F-AZHD	Salis Aviation, La Ferte-Alais: reg. res.	.90
				(NA-68 replica; c/n "SA-30")	
				J. Bastet/Salis Aviation, La Ferte-Alais	2.12.92/93
				(flying as Aeronavale F6F lookalike 93/95)	
182-61 •	T-6G	**51-14374**		(to French AF/l'Armee de l'Air as 114374)	
				Amicale Jean-Baptiste Salis, La Ferte-Alais	75/90
				(stored dism. La Ferte-Alais "DD" 75/90)	
182-74 •	T-6G	**51-14387**		(to French AF/l'Armee de l'Air as 114387)	
				Air France Technical School, Vilgenis	
				Centre d'instruction de Vilgenis	86
				D. Chable, Etampes: reg. res.	.86
			F-AZEF	D. Chable, Etampes	2.6.88/93
182-75 •	T-6G	**51-14388**		(to French AF/l'Armee de l'Air as 114388)	
				(to R Morrocco AF as ....)	
				D. Chable, Etampes, France	92
				(recov. ex Tunisia)	
182-78	T-6G	51-14391		(to French AF/l'Armee de l'Air as 114391)	
				Institut Amaury de la Grange, Merville	70/79
				(noted stored Merville 77, "114391/DL")	
182-81 •	T-6G	**51-14394**		Davis Monthan AFB AZ: del. for storage	12.53/56
				(to French AF/l'Armee de l'Air as 114394)	12.56/76
				offered for disposal by French AF	11.2.76
			N31RH	Steve Martin, Delhi LA: candidate, stored	3.79/86
				Larry Leaf, Williston FL: rest. project	88
				Andrew J. Michalak, Arnold MD: rest.	7.88/89
			N394NA	Andrew J. Michalak, Arnold MD	2.89/95
				(rest. Edgewater FL .88/89, ff 27.7.89 as	
				"MD ANG 14394")	
182-88	T-6G	51-14401		(to l'Armee de l'Air as 114401 "F-ULDI")	
				Air France Technical School, Vilgenis	
				Institut Amaury de la Grange, Merville	70/85
				(noted stored, Merville 77, "14401/D1")	
				Centre d'instruction de Vilgenis	86
182-116 •	T-6G	**51-14429**		(to l'Armee de l'Air as 114429): SOC	.65

				offered for disposal by French AF	11.2.76
				sold to US owner: stored until	.79
			N896WW	reg. candidate	8.79
				Leslie R. Coffman, West Monroe LA	86
				Ben A. Cunningham, Jackson MS	1.88/95
182-142 •	T-6G	**51-14456**		(to Spanish AF as E.16-191)	
				L. Cazades/APAH, Belleville: reg. res.	26.8.83
			F-AZCV	L. Cazades/Association pour Preserver	
				Les Avions Historiques Le Maupas, Frontenas	2.84/87
				Group Alcyons Lons, le Saulnier	10.88
				(rep. stored Lons-le Saulnier, pending rest. 89)	
				J. Grenotier/APAH, Belleville	90
				J. F. Chalumeau, Lons-Le Saulnier	93
182-155 •	T-6G	**51-14469**		(T-6G rebuilt ex AT-6C 41-32197)	
				(to Italian AF as MM54099)	
				noted on fire dump, Decimomannu AB Sardinia	85
				Old Flying Machine Company, Duxford UK	.87
				(hulk recov. ex Decimomannu AB, "RR-56":	
				airfreighted to UK, arr. RAF Lyneham 1.7.87)	
				Imperial War Museum, Duxford: arr.	.87/88
				Medway Aircraft Pres. Society, Rochester	.88
				(rest. Rochester using MM53692 for spares)	
				Historic Flying Audley End: rest. project	90
			G-BRBC	Anthony P. Murphy, Chigwell	4.9.92/96
182-209 •	T-6G	**51-14522**		(to French AF/l'Armee de l'Air as 114522)	
				Cognac AB, France: displ.	69
				Musee de l'Air et l'Espace, Paris-Le Bourget	10.77/94
				(displ. as "114915/RM")	
182-213 •	T-6G	**51-14526**		(T-6G rebuilt ex T-6 41-32473)	
				(to French AF/l'Armee de l'Air as 114526)	
				(noted Staverton UK: stripped hulk 1.83)	
				Sandy Topen, Bushey	85
				Aircraft Restoration Co, Duxford	9.89
			G-BRWB	Aircraft Restorations Ltd, Duxford	28.3.90/94
				rebuild Duxford 90/92,	
				op: British Aerial Museum, Duxford	94
				sold to Germany: struck off reg.	19.12.94
			G-BRWB	Monafield Ltd, Audley End	28.2.95
182-229 •	T-6G	**51-14542**		(to JASDF as 72-0178)	
				Nyutaburu AB, Japan: displ.	90
182-241 •	T-6G	**51-14554**		(to R Thai AF as ....)	
				R Thai AF Museum, Bangkok-Don Muang AB	96
182-244 •	T-6G	**51-14557**		(to R Thai AF as ....)	
				RTAF Tango Squadron, Chiang Mei	93/96
				(under rest. to fly, Bangkok-Don Muang 95)	
182-281	T-6G	51-14594		(to French AF/l'Armee de l'Air as 114594)	
				Amicale Jean-Baptiste Salis, La Ferte-Alais	77/79
				(stored dism., derelict La Ferte Alais 77/79)	
182-317 •	T-6G	**51-14630**		(to R Thai AF as 51-14630)	
				RTAF Tango Squadron, Chiang Mei	93/96
				(rest., flies as "RTAF 1-14630/2302")	
182-334 •	T-6G	**51-14647**		(to R. Thai AF as 51-14647)	
				RTAF Tango Squadron, Chiang Mei	93/96
				(under rest. to fly, Bangkok-Don Muang AB 95)	
182-349 •	T-6G	**51-14662**		(to R. Thai AF as 51-14662)	
				RTAF "Tango One" Display Team: rest.	93

c/n	Type	Serial	Reg.	History	Date
182-353 •	T-6G	**51-14666**		(to R. Thai AF as 51-14666)	
				RTAF Museum, Bangkok-Don Muang AB	80/95
				(displ. as "RTAF 1222")	
182-355	T-6G	51-14668		(to French AF/l'Armee de l'Air as 114668)	
				noted derelict Etamps France,"114668/RC"	.77
182-361 •	T-6G	**51-14674**		(to French AF/l'Armee de l'Air as 114674)	
				Air France Technical School, Vilgenis	70
				(inst. airframe)	
				Messrs. Decamps, Leroy, Ramadier &	
				Wadsworth, Chavenay: reg. res.	82/89
			F-AZEZ	S. Leroy & Partner, Chateau-La Borde	23.6.89/90
				(rest. Chavenay, flew as "14674" 90)	
				Y. Decamps, Cannes	93/96
182-371	T-6G	51-14684		(to French AF/l'Armee de l'Air as 114684)	
				Amicale Jean-Baptiste Salis, La Ferte-Alais	79
182-375 •	T-6G	**51-14688**		(to French AF/l'Armee de l'Air as 114688)	
				Amicale Jean-Baptiste Salis, La Ferte-Alais	79
				Escadrille de Souvenir, Etampes	82/87
				Amberieu AB, France: displ. as "14688/RC"	90
182-381 •	T-6G	**51-14694**		(to French AF/l'Armee de l'Air as 114694)	
			N7865	Robert E. Deford, Prescott AZ	86
				Andres U. Katz & Tad Foran, Dallas TX	6.87/95
				(stored in crate until 88, under rest. .88)	
182-383 •	T-6G	**51-14696**		(to French AF/l'Armee de l'Air as 114696)	
			F-BMJO	reg. res.	
				(parts used to rebuild 182-736/F-AZAS)	
				Air Classik, Berlin, Germany	79
				Berlin-Tegel Airport: displ. as "Y-34"	
				Vienna-Schwechat Airport: displ. as "Y-34"	89/94
				Franz List, Vienna: removed ex displ.	.94/96
182-387 •	T-6G	**51-14700**		(to French AF/l'Armee de l'Air as 114700)	
				Amicale Jean-Baptiste Salis, La Ferte-Alais	75/90
				(stored dism., derelict La Ferte Alais 75/90)	
				Aces High Ltd, North Weald UK	93
182-394 •	T-6G	**51-14707**		(to French AF/l'Armee de l'Air as 114707)	
				Amicale Jean-Baptiste Salis, La Ferte-Alais	75/90
				(stored derelict La Ferte-Alais 75/90 "14707/KN")	
182-405 •	T-6G	**51-14718**		(to French AF/l'Armee de l'Air as 114718)	
				Amicale Jean-Baptiste Salis, La Ferte-Alais	75/90
				(stored dism., derelict La Ferte Alais "DC" 75/90)	
182-407 •	T-6G	**51-14720**		(to French AF/l'Armee de l'Air as 114720)	
				(to Morrocco AF as Y61305)	
				D. Chable, Etampes, France	92
				(recov. ex Tunisia)	
182-413 •	T-6G	**51-14726**		(to French AF/l'Armee de l'Air as 114726)	
				offered for disposal by French AF	11.2.76
			N92761	reg.	1.77
				Roy H. Douglas, Delhi LA	86/92
				Don J. Judy, Bartow WV	3.94/96
82-421 •	T-6G	**51-14734**		(to French AF/l'Armee de l'Air as 114734)	.56
				offered for disposal by French AF	11.2.76
			N9705N	Lance P. Toland, Milner GA	11.86
				Alicia L. Gummo, Valdosta GA	92
				William Elkins, Aiken SC	93/94
				Aviation Heritage Inc, Wilmington DE	9.93/96
82-427 •	T-6G	**51-14740**		(to French AF/l'Armee de l'Air as 114740)	
				Amicale Jean-Baptiste Salis, La Ferte-Alais	75/90

				(stored dism., derelict La Ferte Alais 75/90)	
182-448 •	T-6G	**51-14761**		(to French AF/l'Armee de l'Air as 114761)	
				offered for disposal by French AF	11.2.76
			N9739T	R. Jones: reg. candidate	24.10.86
				Lance P. Toland, Milner GA	24.10.86
				Clara F. Pyle, Seminole FL	9.87/96
182-457	T-6G	51-14770		(to French AF/l'Armee de l'Air as 114770)	
				(to Biafran AF as .....)	.67
				not del.: impounded at wharf, Lisbon	6.67/69
				(noted at Tires aerodrome, Portugal 8.69,	
				noted Tires 10.69 in camouflage sc.)	
				open storage, derelict, Cascais, Portugal	84
182-477	T-6G	51-14790		(to French AF/l'Armee de l'Air as 114790)	
				J. Decoop/Escadrille de Souvenir: reg. res.	10.78
			F-AZAY	J. Decoop, La Ferte Alais/Mulhouse	11.79
				Amicale Jean-Baptiste Salis, La Ferte-Alais	85
				(flew as "USAF BA-132")	
				crashed Longuyon, France	9.6.85
182-478 •	T-6G	**51-14791**		(to French AF/l'Armee de l'Air as 114791)	
				offered for disposal by French AF	11.2.76
			N8044H	William Steve Martin, Delhi LA	8.79/86
				Mark L. Henley, Birmingham AL	8.88/96
182-	T-6G	51-14793		(to .... as G1-N14)	
				D. Heredia	
				F. Wright: US reg. candidate	5.8.88
182-481•	T-6G	**51-14794**		(to French AF/l'Armee de l'Air as 14794)	
				(to Biafran AF as .....)	.67
				not del: impounded at wharf, Lisbon, Portugal	6.67/69
				(noted Lisbon-Tires, camouflage sc.,10.69)	
				(noted Cascais, Portugal 84)	
				Museo do Air, Sintra AB, Portugal: dism.	
182-486 •	T-6G	**51-14799**		(to French AF/l'Armee de l'Air as 14799)	
				offered for disposal by French AF	11.2.76
			N92778	reg.	.77
				Charles R. Davis, Lake Providence LA	86
				John Crisi, North Eastham MA	5.91/96
182-487	T-6G	51-14800		(to French AF/l'Armee de l'Air as 14800)	
				(to Biafran AF as .....)	.67
				not del: impounded at wharf, Lisbon	6.67/69
				(noted Tires aerodrome, Portugal 8.69,	
				at Tires 10.69 assembled, still in FrAF sc.)	
				noted open storage "21", Cascais, Portugal	84
182-498	T-6G	51-14811		(to French AF/l'Armee de l'Air as 114811)	
				Amicale Jean-Baptiste Salis, La Ferte-Alais	75/90
				(dism., derelict La Ferte-Alais "14811/13" 75/90)	
182-514 •	T-6G	**51-14827**		(to French AF/l'Armee de l'Air as 114827)	
				offered for disposal by French AF	11.2.76
			N92796	reg.	1.77
				Larry D. Brown, Sayre PA	86
				William C. Kyle & Herbert N. Thomas,	
				Winston-Salem NC	2.88/95
182-526 •	T-6G	**51-14839**		(to French AF/l'Armee de l'Air as 114839)	
				Amicale Jean-Baptiste Salis, La Ferte-Alais	75/90
				(stored dism., derelict La Ferte-Alais	
				"114839/13/KQ" 75/90)	
182-529 •	T-6G	**51-14842**		(to French AF/l'Armee de l'Air as 114842)	

			N8FU	R. Jones: reg. candidate	8.10.86
				Greg Speed, Monroe LA	92
				William S. Martin, Delhi LA	5.94/96
82-535 •	T-6G	**51-14848**		(to French AF/l'Armee de l'Air as 114848)	
			F-BOEO	Institute Aeronautique Amaury de la Grange,	
				Merville: reg. res.	6.74/79
				(noted as inst. airframe, Merville 77)	
				Amicale Jean-Baptiste Salis: reg. res.	7.82
			F-AZBQ	Amicale Jean-Baptiste Salis, La Ferte-Alais	20.8.84/93
				(flies as "115237/QH")	
82-536 •	T-6G	**51-14849**		(to French AF/l'Armee de l'Air as 114849)	
				offered for disposal by French AF	11.2.76
			N9701Z	R. Jones: reg. candidate	12.9.86
				Lance P. Toland, Milner GA	11.86/96
82-558	T-6G	51-14871		(to French AF/l'Armee de l'Air as 114871)	
				noted derelict Etampes France, "114871/H"	.77
				Amicale Jean-Baptiste Salis, La Ferte-Alais	79
82-560	T-6G	51-14873		(to French AF/l'Armee de l'Air as 114873)	
				(to Biafran AF as .....)	.67
				not del: impounded at wharf, Lisbon	6.67/69
				Amicale Jean-Baptiste Salis, La Ferte-Alais	79
82-585 •	T-6G	**51-14898**		(to French AF/l'Armee de l'Air as 114898)	
			F-BMJQ	Institute Aeronautique Amaury de la Grange,	
				Merville: reg. res.	6.74/79
				(noted stored Merville, "114898/KW" .77)	
			F-AZIB	M. Berthelot, Anderville: reg. res.	.92/95
				M. Berthelot, Beau Vais: reg.	4.4.95
82-591 •	T-6G	**51-14904**		(to French AF/l'Armee de l'Air as 114904)	
				(to Spanish AF as E.16-198, Code 912-43)	
			EC-DUM	Club de Deporte Aereos SA, Sabadell	2.7.84/88
				Carlos Torralbo/Fundacion Infante de Orleans,	
				Cuatro Vientos AB Madrid	90/96
82-600 •	T-6G	**51-14913**		(to JMSDF as ....)	
			N257DB	Dennis G. Buehn, Reno NV	20.5.86
				Thomas A. Dodson & Jason Hoyle, Tulsa OK	7.88/96
				(flies as "USAF 93137/TA-137")	
82-602	T-6G	51-14915		(to French AF/l'Armee de l'Air as 114915)	
				Amicale Jean-Baptiste Salis, La Ferte-Alais	79
82-603 •	T-6G	51-14916		(to FA Hondurena as 208)	
			N27817	Gordon Plaskett/B & G Aero, King City CA	12.82
				(del. Tegucigalpa AB, Honduras to CA .83)	
				Jerry Rector, Big Cabin OK	86
				Jack M. Lowrey, Chino CA	92
				J. Ken Morley, Winlock WA	4.93/96
82-646 •	T-6G	**51-14959**		(to French AF/l'Armee de l'Air as 114959)	
				(to Biafran AF as .....)	.67
				not del: impounded at wharf, Lisbon	6.67/69
				noted stored Cascais, Portugal, "KK"	84
82-648	T-6G	51-14961	N4940E	Robert F. Middleton, Lansing IL	63
				Richard O. Burns, Hinsdale IL	.63/64
			N1190	Richard O. Burns, Hinsdale IL	66/77
82-657 •	T-6G	**51-14970**		(to Spanish AF as ......)	
			N25WT	John I. Watson, Blackwood NJ	11.82/96
82-666	T-6G	51-14979		(to French AF/l'Armee de l'Air as 114979)	
				Amicale Jean-Baptiste Salis, La Ferte-Alais	75/79
				(stored dism., derelict La Ferte Alais "Q" 75/79)	

182-678 •	T-6G	**51-14991**		(to French AF/l'Armee de l'Air as 114991)	
				(to Biafran AF as .....)	.67
				not del: impounded at wharf, Lisbon	6.67/69
				(noted Tires aerodrome, Portugal, camouflage sc. 10.69)	
				noted stored Cascais, Portugal	84
182-694 •	T-6G	**51-15007**		(to French AF/l'Armee de l'Air as 115007)	
				(to FA Portuguesa as 1681)	
				(to Mozambique PLAF as 1681)	
				abandoned Maputo, Mozambique	.74/89
				recov. by Brian Zeederberg/Ian Popplewell,	
				Syferfontein, Johannesburg: arr. dism.	3.89
				Aerofab, Thruxton: arr. dism.	12.89
			G-BSBD	Andrew Edie/Aerofab, Thruxton	5.3.90/92
				John J. Woodhouse, Thruxton	91
				sold: struck-off reg.	6.5.94
182-704	T-6G	51-15017		(to French AF/l'Armee de l'Air as 115017)	
				Amicale Jean-Baptiste Salis, La Ferte-Alais	75/90
				(dism. derelict La Ferte-Alais "115017/RD" 75/90)	
182-720 •	T-6G	**51-15033**		(to French AF/l'Armee de l'Air as 115033)	
				Robs Lamplough, Duxford UK: stored	74
			G-BDZZ	Robs Lamplough, Duxford	15.6.76
				Israeli Air Force Museum, Haifa AB	.76/84
				del. UK to Israel, struck-off reg.	20.12.76
				(displ. Haifa AB as "10" 84)	
				Israeli Air Force Museum, Hazerim AB	87/96
				(displ. as "001", maintained airworthy)	
182-729 •	T-6G	**51-15042**		(to French AF/l'Armee de l'Air as 115042)	
				(to FA Portuguesa as 1707)	
			G-BGHU	Gladaircraft Co Ltd, Biggin Hill	22.1.79/82
				(del. to Biggin Hill 6.5.79)	
				Philip S. Warner, Wellesbourne Mountford	11.81/86
				(at airshow Middle Wallop 7.88 "USAF 115042")	
				Christopher E. Bellhouse, Shoreham	12.86/96
182-733 •	T-6G	**51-15046**		(to French AF/l'Armee de l'Air as 15046)	
				(to Biafran AF as ....)	.67
				not del: impounded at wharf, Lisbon	6.67/69
				(noted dism. Tires aerodrome, Portugal 6.69)	
				noted stored Cascais, Portugal	84
182-735 •	T-6G	**51-15048**		(to French AF/l'Armee de l'Air as 115048)	
				(to FA Portugesa as .....)	
			N8513Z	Jerry E. Meadors, Indianapolis IN	11.80
				crashed Indianapolis-Eagle Creek Airpark IN	7.7.81
				(rebuilt 81/83 Compton CA "USAF 115048")	
			N42JM	Jerry E. Meadors, Indianapolis IN	5.81/96
				(race #48 *Slo Yeller*)	
182-736 •	T-6G	**51-15049**		(to French AF/l'Armee de l'Air as 115049)	
			F-BMJP	reg. res.	
				(composite rebuild with 182-383)	
			F-AZAS	Amicale Jean-Baptiste Salis: reg. res.	3.78/87
				Amicale Jean-Baptiste Salis, La Ferte Alais	8.80
			F-WZBN	J. Bastet, La Ferte-Alais	6.87
				(conv. to Zero replica .87, c/n SAM2-049)	
			F-AZAS	J. Bastet/Amicale J-B Salis, La Ferte-Alais	90/96
				rep. badly dam. by fire on ground, France	.93
182-747	T-6G	51-15060		(to French AF/l'Armee de l'Air as 115060)	
				Amicale Jean-Baptiste Salis, La Ferte-Alais	79
182-750 •	T-6G	**51-15063**		(to French AF/l'Armee de l'Air as 115063)	
				(to FA Portuguesa as 1710)	
			G-SURF	Euroworld International Ltd, Biggin Hill	28.3.79/80

				sold to USA, struck-off reg.	16.4.80
			N8048J	Arthur D. Medore/Banaire, Hemet CA	9.79
				Jimmy L. Gist/ Texas Red Ltd,	
				Grapevine TX	81/86
				(race #68 *Texas Red*)	
				Lone Star Flight Museum, Houston-Hobby TX	.86/88
				John Luther, San Antonio TX	5.88/96
				(race #99 *Texas Red*)	
182-769	T-6G	51-15082		(to French AF/l'Armee de l'Air as 115082)	
				Amicale Jean-Baptiste Salis, La Ferte-Alais	79
182-770 •	T-6G	**51-15083**		(to French AF/l'Armee de l'Air as 115083)	
				(to Biafran AF as .....)	.67
				not del: impounded at wharf, Lisbon Portugal	6.67/69
				(noted at Tires aerodrome, Portugal 6.69)	
				noted stored Cascais, Portugal	84
182-789 •	T-6G	**51-15102**		(to French AF/l'Armee de l'Air as 115102)	
				Ailes Anciennes, Tolouse-Blagnac	11.80/90
				(recov. ex Salis, La Ferte-Alais 11.11.80,	
				Musee d'Automobiles de Normandie,	
				Chateau de Cleres: displ.	87
				rest. to fly Laberge, France 90)	
182-792 •	T-6G	**51-15105**	N4297A	Harold J. Eagen, Springfield VA	63/64
				Geoffrey C. Greisz, Flint MI	66/72
			N66WP	William Pryor, Keego Harbour MI	76/77
				Joseph M. Natoli, Nokesville VA: rest. project	91/92
182-800 •	T-6G	**51-15113**		(to French AF/l'Armee de l'Air as 115113)	
			F-BNAU	Y. Collin, Troyes	4.7.67/68
				A. Butel, Toulouse	.68/73
				J. Decoop, La Ferte-Alais	.73/79
			F-AZAU	J. Decoop/Escadrille du Souvenir, Etampes	11.79/90
				J. P. Chivot, La Ferte-Alais	93
188-90 •	T-6G	**51-15227**		(to Italian AF as MM53664/Code RM-9)	2.52
				recov. ex Italy: shipped to Southampton. arr.	21.11.81
				(stored unconv. Woolston: "RM.9" .81/82,	
				arr. dism. Sandown IoW for rest. 10.82;	
			G-BKRA	Terry S. Warren, Sandown	19.8.83/84
				Andrew Edie Aviation Ltd, Shoreham	13.6.84/85
				(at airshows Duxford 9.85 "USN 51-15227",	
				Middle Wallop 7.88)	
				Pulsegrove Ltd, Shoreham	10.85/87
				Malcolm D. Faiers, Nympsfield	10.8.87/88
				Andrew D. M. Edie/Aerofab, Shoreham	91/93
195-1 •	T-6G	**51-17354**		(to ROKAF as 117354)	
				Korean War Museum, Seoul, South Korea	74/91
				(displ. as ROKAF "117354/TA-354")	
195-2 •	T-6G	**51-17355**		(to FA Portuguesa as .....)	
			N4269P	Arthur D. Medore/North American Aviation Inc,	
				Denville NJ/Hemet CA	24.3.81/86
				Andrew T. Gemellaro, Canoga Park CA	92
				William L. Hane, Mesa AZ	9.94
195-6 •	T-6G	**51-17359**		(to FA Portuguesa as .....)	
			N1385K	Arthur D. Medore/North American Aviation Inc,	
				Denville NJ/Hemet CA	5.1.82/95
195-10 •	T-6G	**51-17363**		(to FA Portuguesa as .....)	
			N1385H	Arthur D. Medore/North American Aviation/	
				Banaire, Hemet CA	5.1.82/95
197-3 •	T-6G	**52-8199**		(to FA Portuguesa as .....)	
			N1385B	Arthur D. Medore/North American Aviation/	
				Banaire, Hemet CA	5.1.82/95

197-15 •	T-6G	**52-8211**	N2821G	T. C. Ritchie, Seattle WA	63
				Charles R. Hall, Seattle WA	.63/64
				Peter R. Stanwick, Everett WA	66
				Donald E. Anderson, Snohomish WA	69/70
			N711AP	Omni Aviation Managers, Van Nuys CA	75/77
				Greg Aloia, Redmond WA	86
			N432RT	Ronald L. Thompson, Fullerton CA	1.88/92
197-20 •	T-6G	**52-8216**		(to French AF/l'Armee de l'Air as 28216)	
				(to Spanish AF as E.16-201)	.65
			EC-DUN	Club de Deporte Aereos SA, Sabadell	2.7.84/88
				Carlos Torralbo/Fundacion Infante de Orleans,	
				Cuatro Vientos AB, Madrid	90/93
				(flies in red sc. as "E.16-201" 91)	
197-22 •	T-6G	**52-8218**		(T-6G rebuilt ex AT-6D 42-81274)	8.52
			N5632V	Walter H. Dillingham, Honolulu HI	63/72
				John H. Weiser, Honolulu HI	76/77
				Conrad F. Yelvington, Daytona Beach FL	86/88
				Neal T. Schaefer/SSS Inc, Cincinatti OH	90/94
				Steve Hay, Syracuse IN	.94/95
				Eliot G. Cross, Fort Meade FL	2.95
197-35	T-6G	52-8231		(to French AF as 28231)	
				noted derelict, Etampes France "2-8231"	.77
				Amicale Jean-Baptiste Salis, La Ferte-Alais	79
197-40 •	T-6G	**52-8236**		(to FA Portuguesa as .....)	
			N4269R	Arthur D. Medore/North American Aviation/	
				Banaire, Hemet CA	5.1.82/86
				Jack Thunder, Broomfield CO	11.86/95
197-42 •	T-6G	**52-8238**		(rebuilt from AT-6A 42-85377)	
			N555Q	Dante Saracenti, Huntington NY	63/64
				Patrick Connell, New York NY	66/77
				(flew as "92900/TA-900")	
				Yankee Flyers Museum, Willow Run MI	3.84/95
				Yankee Air Museum, Willow Run MI: displ.	89/93
197-54 •	T-6G	**53-4558**		(to FA Portuguesa as .....)	
			N4269Q	Arthur D. Medore/North American Aviation/	
				Banaire, Hemet CA	5.1.82/86
				Claude W. Yew, Fairfax VA: rest. project	10.87/95
197-64 •	T-6G	**53-4568**		(to Spanish AF as E.16-200)	.56/82
			N153NA	Combat Aircraft Inc, Elkhart IN	26.11.85
				Fort Wayne Air Service, Fort Wayne IN: del.	5.86
				James J. Shuttleworth, Huntington IN	10.86/95
				(rest., ff 7.88 as "534568/TA-568")	
197-68	T-6G	53-4572		(to French AF as 34572)	
				Amicale Jean-Baptiste Salis, La Ferte-Alais	75/85
				(dism. derelict La Ferte Alais "534572/KA" 75/85)	
197-73 •	T-6G	**53-4577**	**N2831D**	Haig Sakajian, Los Angeles CA	63/64
				Joseph G. Sorokin, Sherman Oaks CA	66
				Stanley S. Landers, Sherman Oaks CA	69
				Creston W. Armiger, Cologne NJ	70/72
				John Brinkerhoff, Torrance CA	76/77
				Connie Bowlin & Associates, Griffin GA	3.84/95
197-75 •	T-6G	**53-4579**		(to French AF/l'Armee de l'Air as 34579)	
				Amicale Jean-Baptiste Salis, La Ferte-Alais	75/85
				(dism., derelict La Ferte-Alais "579/DJ" 75/85)	
				D. Chable, Etampes: stored	90
				(rep. under rest. La Ferte-Alais 10.92)	

c/n	Type	Serial	Reg	History	Date
197-88 •	T-6G	**53-4592**		(to French AF/l'Armee de l'Air as 34592)	
				Amicale Jean-Baptiste Salis, La Ferte-Alais	75/88
				(stored dism.,in woods La Ferte Alais	
				Philip Warner, Evesham:	
				(recov. ex open storage La Ferte-Alaias .88)	
			G-BTKI	Philip S.Warner, Evesham Worcs	17.4.91/96
				(rest. to fly, Tewkesbury 90/96)	
197-89	T-6G	53-4593		(to French AF/l'Armee de l'Air as 34593)	
				Amicale Jean-Baptiste Salis, La Ferte-Alais	75/79
				(stored dism. derelict, La Ferte-Alais 75/79)	
197-90	T-6G	53-4594		(to French AF/l'Armee de l'Air as 34594)	
				Amicale Jean-Baptiste Salis, La Ferte-Alais	75
				(stored dism. derelict, La Ferte-Alais 75)	
197-97 •	T-6G	53-4601		(to French AF/l'Armee de l'Air as 34601)	
				(to FA Portuguesa as .....)	
			N4269E	Arthur D. Medore/North American Aviation/	
				Banaire, Hemet CA	24.3.81
				Kenneth N. Clute, Wheat Ridge CO	86
				James D. Morgan, Aumsville OR	6.92/96
197-106 •	T-6G	**53-4610**		(to French AF/l'Armee de l'Air as 34610)	
				(to FA Portuguesa as .....)	
			N4269X	Arthur D. Medore/North American Aviation/	
				Banaire, Hemet CA	24.3.81
				Gerald L. Giroux, Plantation FL	7.81/95
197-107	T-6G	53-4611		(to French AF/l'Armee de l'Air as 34611)	
				Amicale Jean-Baptiste Salis, La Ferte-Alais	79
				(noted stored as 534611 79)	
CCF4-1 •	Mk. 4	**RCAF20210**		prototype Mk.4: ff Fort William ONT	24.10.51
				RCAF BOC 2.11.51: SOC	12.2.64
			CF-PTP	National Research Council, Ottawa ONT	.64/83
			C-FPTP	National Research Council, Ottawa ONT	86/95
CCF4-4 •	Mk. 4	**RCAF20213**		BOC 24.11.51: SOC	5.7.65
			CF-UUU	Sam Mazara, Toronto ONT	68/72
				Canadian Warplane Heritage, Hamilton ONT	74/93
CCF4-7 •	Mk. 4	**RCAF20216**		BOC 21.12.51: SOC	31.5.65
			N7552U	Rodney E. Barnes, Oconomowoc WI	76/90
				James A. Michaels, Oconomowoc WI	7.90/96
CCF4-8 •	Mk. 4	**RCAF20217**		BOC 21.12.51: SOC	8.8.66
			CF-VCM	J. F. Midgett, Buffalo Narrows SASK	68
				Raymond M. Ruelling, Hay River NWT	69/72
				Harry C. Sorenson, Yellowknife NWT	75/83
				C. Stiles, Edmonton ALTA	88/91
			N47217	Victor R. Stottlemyer, Wauwatosa WI	8.91/96
CCF4-9 •	Mk. 4	**RCAF20218**		BOC 21.12.51: SOC	29.1.65
			N4288C	Albert E. Fournier, Toledo OH	69/70
				Arlie P. Kelley, Euclid OH	76/77
				Daniel L. Petersen, Lincoln NE	86
				Gordon B. Richardson, Caldwell TX	89
			N91AM	Gordon B. Richardson, Caldwell TX	12.89/90
				Gene Woerner, Reid Hillview CA	90
				Eigleberry Ltd, Medford OR	92
				Barrie Snowden, San Ramon CA	.92/96
CCF4-13 •	Mk. 4	**RCAF20222**		BOC 11.1.52 : SOC	23.6.65
				(in compound dism. unconv., Mesa AZ 78)	
			C-FMKA	Norm Beckham, Woodstock ONT	88/89
CCF4-16 •	Mk. 4	**RCAF20225**		BOC 24.1.52 : SOC	25.3.68
			N15796	20th Century Fox Film Corp, Hollywood CA	69/70
				(conv. to Zero lookalike at Long Beach CA .68 for	

				Tora Tora Tora; open storage Long Beach CA 69/71, sold at auction Long Beach 2.71)	
				Tallmantz Aviation, Orange County CA	2.71/86
				F. Gene Fisher/Mid Atlantic Air Museum, Boiling Springs PA	92
				Chris Perry/Zeke Inc, Hampshire IL	8.92/96
				(flies as Japanese Zero "3-183")	
CCF4-19 •	Mk. 4	**RCAF20228**		BOC 22.1.52 : SOC	13.8.63
			N24GB	George H. Baker, New Smyrna Beach FL	3.5.85/95
				(rebuilt as Wirraway lookalike, R1340 .85)	
CCF4-20 •	Mk. 4	**RCAF20229**		BOC 22.1.52 : SOC	3.6.66
			CF-UVN		
			N1264	20th Century Fox Film Corp, Hollywood CA	.68/71
				(conv. to Kate lookalike at Long Beach CA .68 for film"*Tora Tora Tora*"; open storage Long Beach CA 69/71, sold at auction Long Beach 2.71)	
				reg. pending	72
				rereg.	8.86
				Caroline G. Harms, Jetmore KS	6.89/95
				(flies as Japanese Kate "AI-315")	
CCF4-23	Mk. 4	RCAF20232		BOC 5.2.52 : SOC	18.8.67
			N2048	20th Century Fox Film Corp, Hollywood CA	.67/71
				(noted Long Beach CA 9.67 "N2048/RCAF20232")	
				(conv. to Zero lookalike at Long Beach CA .68 for film "*Tora Tora Tora*"; open storage Long Beach CA 69/71, sold at auction Long Beach 2.71)	
				Bruce A. Dillon, Kalamazoo MI	2.71/72
				Confederate Air Force, Harlingen/Midland TX	7.5.74/94
				(flew as Zero "AI-116", later "V-128")	
				dest. by hangar fire, Conroe TX	12.6.94
CCF4-27 •	Mk. 4	**RCAF20236**		BOC 5.2.52 : SOC	21.2.66
			CF-GUY	John M. Carefoot, Brantford ONT	68
				Ross P. Watt, Bracebridge ONT	69/91
			C-FGUY	Hannu Halminen, Oshawa ONT: del.	5.91/95
CCF4-31	Mk. 4	RCAF20240		BOC 18.2.52 : SOC	23.6.65
			N20240	Earnest L. Farnsworth, Paonia CO	70/72
				James Peterson, Homosassa Springs FL	77
CCF4-33 •	Mk. 4	**RCAF20242**		BOC 29.2.52 : SOC	30.7.67
			CF-WPK	F. Swan & B. Muncaster, Sault Ste Marie ONT	68
				O. Piper & W. Armstrong,Sault Ste Marie ONT	69/72
			C-FWPK	James H. Vernon, Oakville ONT	75
				op: Canadian Warplane Heritage, Hamilton ONT	79
				Kent N. Beckham & R. A. Hewitt/Canadian Harvard Aircraft Association, Woodstock ONT	78/94
CCF4-34	Mk. 4	RCAF20243		BOC 29.2.52 : SOC	26.6.67
			CF-VYF	Arthur Knutson, Elbow SASK	68/79
			C-FVYF	Wayne N. Watson, Edmonton ALTA	81/83
CCF4-35	Mk. 4	RCAF20244		BOC 5.3.52 : SOC	15.8.67
			CF-WPM	Norman Lange, Rosser MAN	72/79
			C-FWPM	B. M. Pendrak & J. E. Anderson, Hondo ALTA	81/83
CCF4-38 •	Mk. 4	**RCAF20247**		BOC 5.3.52 : SOC	28.2.66
			CF-UZO		
			N1811B	Phillip H. Banks, Whittier CA	69/70
				(stored unrest., Chino CA 64/78)	
				Bill Melamed, Santa Monica CA: readded reg.	6.89/91
				(rest. Chino, ff .89 as "RCAF20247")	
				Lone Star Flight Museum, Galveston TX	10.91/95
CCF4-39 •	Mk. 4	**RCAF20248**		BOC 5.3.52 : SOC	21.7.67

			N1465	John C. Alden, Auburn NE/Los Angeles CA	.67/96
CF4-42 •	Mk. 4	**RCAF20251**		BOC 5.3.52 : SOC	21.2.67
			CF-VFK	Raynard R. Weaver, Ladner BC	68/70
			N10908	C. E. Slinger, Phoenix AZ	72/77
				Dunbar Spring & Wheel Inc, Phoenix AZ	86
				Jeff M. & Scott Nelson, Scottsdale AZ	4.86/96
CF4-46 •	Mk. 4	**RCAF20255**		BOC 14.3.52 : SOC	18.7.67
			CF-WPS	Pierre L. Klein & J. E. Tonglet, Montreal QUE	68/70
			C-FWPS	Armand Bourdeau, Cornwall ONT	72/83
				F. Guindon, Bear River NS	90
			N305GS	Greg N. Shelton, Nowata OK	10.90/96
CF4-47 •	Mk. 4	**RCAF20256**		BOC 14.3.52	
				accident Moose Jaw SASK 14.1.57: SOC	22.12.60
			N64820	ntu	
			N1387N	Richard A. Benner, Wasilla/Anchorage AK	3.82/88
				William H. Wisner, Gardland TX	10.89/96
				(flies as "ANG 44501")	
CF4-48 •	Mk. 4	**RCAF20257**		BOC 14.3.52 : SOC	23.6.65
				(in compound dism. unconv., Mesa AZ 78)	
			N98474	Dennis G. Buehn, Long Beach CA	17.8.81
				Dale Clarke, Dennis Firestone, &	
				Allan Wojciak, Chino CA	84/86
	NA-50 repl.			(rebuilt as NA-50 repl., ff Chino 31.10.85)	
				Liberty Aero Corp, Gardena CA	86
				J. Pete Vandersluis, Fitzwilliam NH	88/94
				John H. Shell, Morganton NC	9.94/96
CF4-50	Mk. 4	RCAF20259		BOC 25.3.52 : SOC	11.4.67
			CF-VTZ	Benjamin R. Janz, Steinbach MAN	68/70
				Ruston Mobile Homes Ltd, Burlington ONT	72
CF4-52 •	Mk. 4	**RCAF20261**		BOC 25.3.52 : SOC	25.9.67
			CF-WWO	Elmer A. Mutcher, Port Moody BC	68/70
				Donald Mercer, North Surrey BC	72/75
				Steen G. Larsen, Squamish BC	78/79
			C-FWWO	Eva & Walter Lannon, Delta Air Park BC	.81/93
CF4-53 •	Mk. 4	**RCAF20262**		BOC 25.3.52 : SOC	29.4.65
			CF-SWW	Frederick G. Wetherall, Calgary ALTA	68/75
				Armada Builders Ltd, Calgary ALTA	78/83
CF4-55 •	Mk. 4	**RCAF20264**		BOC 3.4.52 : SOC	22.9.67
			CF-WLO	Victor E. McMann, Ladner BC	.67/90
				Keith McMann, Delta Airpark BC	90/95
CF4-58	Mk. 4	RCAF20267		BOC 3.4.52 : SOC	29.6.67
			CF-XJC	Robert Elliott, Moose Jaw SASK	68/70
			N6TS	Thomas Short, Phoenix AZ	73/77
			C-GRLR	Shirley Air Services, Edmonton ALTA	11.81/82
				John C. Lunan & partners, Edmonton ALTA	822/83
				dest. midair collision with CF-UZH, Oliver BC	30.7.83
CF4-64	Mk. 4	RCAF20273		BOC 25.4.52 : SOC	27.10.64
			CF-RUJ	F. G. Wetherall, Calgary ALTA	66
				Henry Jaeger, North Battleford SASK	68/75
			C-FRUJ	Armada Builders Ltd, Calgary ALTA	78/83
CF4-66 •	Mk. 4	**RCAF20275**		BOC 25.4.52 : SOC	11.8.67
			CF-WLA	Frederick A. Durant, South Burnaby BC	68/75
				sale rep., Vente Signalee ALTA	78/82
				George S. Robertson, Langley BC	92/93
CF4-67	Mk. 4	**RCAF20276**		BOC 6.4.52 : SOC	30.9.64
			CF-RUD	DY Drill Ltd, Clgary ALTA	65/66
				Oliver G. Knopp, Sarnia ONT	68/70
			N4569	rereg.	

CCF4-74 •	Mk. 4	**RCAF20283**		BOC 9.5.52 : SOC	21.8.67
			CF-SNJ	P. D. Stenner & T. V. Stockhill, Victoria BC	68
				Flying Fireman Ltd, Sidney BC	69/72
			N14429	Clifford Baker, Eudora AR	77
				Joe Mabee, Midland TX	1.79/95
CCF4-75 •	Mk. 4	**RCAF20284**		BOC 9.5.52 : SOC	30.8.67
			CF-WWK	Wayne Collins, Winnipeg MAN	68
				G. Thompson, Saskatoon SASK	69
			N711SS	Merryl D. Schulke, Orlando FL	70/72
				Fred Webster/Harvard Corp, Hartford CT	1.74/96
CCF4-77	Mk. 4	**RCAF20286**		BOC 9.5.52 : SOC	22.1.68
			N13631	Robert B. Metcalf, Manhattan Beach CA	69/72
				(race #88 "*Super Slug*")	
				Robert Philips, Phoenix AZ	77
				sold to UK, struck-off USCR	5.82
			G-BKCK	Eric T. Webster, Bahrein	8.3.83
				struck-off reg: "not imported"	6.1.87
			N13631	Sonja C. Webster, Pomona CA	8.1.87
				(arr. crated North Weald UK 10.87, assembled 11.87, repainted as "RAF P5865/LE-W")	
			G-BKCK	Eric T. Webster, North Weald	17.9.90
				E. Webster & Anthony Haig-Thomas, N Weald	91/95
CCF4-83 •	Mk. 4	**RCAF20292**		BOC 9.5.52 : SOC	18.8.67
			N2047	20th Century Fox Film Corp, Hollywood CA	.67/71
				(noted Long Beach CA 9.67 "N2047/RCAF20292")	
				(conv. to Kate lookalike at Long Beach CA .68 for film "*Tora Tora Tora*"; open storage Long Beach CA 69/71, sold at auction Long Beach 2.71)	
				William E. Barnes, Lancaster CA	2.71/72
				Gifford Hamilton, Van Nuys CA	73
				John J. Stokes, San Marcos TX	77
				Confederate Air Force, Harlingen/Midland TX	23.3.79/96
				(flies as Japanese Kate "¶-110", later "310")	
CCF4-85 •	Mk. 4	**RCAF20294**		BOC 9.5.52 : SOC	9.11.64
			CF-RUQ	John Bootsma, Drayton Valley ALTA	66/70
				Maurice R. McCullagh, Drayton Valley ALTA	72/79
				John P. Bootsma, Drayton Valley ALTA	81/82
				Maurice R. McCullagh, Drayton Valley ALTA	.82/83
			N294CH	M. McCullagh	13.7.87
				Combat Air Museum, Topeka-Forbes Field KS	8.87/95
CCF4-88 •	Mk. 4	**RCAF20297**		BOC 14.5.52 : SOC	22.2.66
			CF-UJI	Lloyd M. Ruelling, Meadow Lake SASK	68/70
				Crown Distributors Ltd, Ponoka ALTA	72
			N777BT	US Bureau of Customs: reg. candidate	29.11.79
				T. Geouge, Miami OK	12.79
				A. Clark Sutherland, Ardmore OK	86/92
				William M. Reed, Denver CO	.92/93
				Robert A. Estock, Denver CO	6.94/96
CCF4-89 •	Mk. 4	**RCAF20298**		BOC 14.5.52 : SOC	22.2.66
			CF-UAT	Anthony Deloume, Cobble Hill BC	68
				V. Garside & S. Auer, Wellington BC	69/72
				G. E. Potter, Sasaktoon SASK	75
				Tyrone Josdal, Moose Jaw SASK	78/79
				Alan L. MacIntosh, Tisdale SASK	81/93
CCF4-93	Mk. 4	RCAF20302		BOC 15.5.52 : SOC	23.6.65
				(in compound dism. unconv., Mesa AZ 78)	
CCF4-97 •	Mk. 4	**RCAF20306**		BOC 15.5.52 : SOC	1.2.65
			N13595	John F. Gregory, Birmingham MI	66
				M. W. Fairbrother, Star Prairie WI	69/72

				Confederate Air Force, Harlingen/Midland TX	76/96
				(flies as "RCAF 595")	
CCF4-98 •	Mk. 4	**RCAF20307**		BOC 15.5.52 : SOC	23.6.65
				(in compound dism. unconv., Mesa AZ 78)	
				rest. project in garage, Portland OR	81
				F. Bert Davis, Leduc ALTA	.81
			CF-FBD	F. Bert Davis/Nostalgic Flights Ltd, Wetaskiwin ALTA	12.84/96
				(stored .81/92, rest. 92/93,)	
CCF4-100•	Mk. 4	**RCAF20309**		BOC 23.5.52 : SOC	23.6.65
			CF-UZP		
				(rep. stored in hangar Chino CA 66/88)	
			C-FROB	Bob Banman/E. D. Ventures Ltd, Steinbach MAN & Santa Paula CA	30.3.89/93
				(rest. Chino CA .89 as "RCAF20309")	
CCF4-104	Mk. 4	RCAF20313		BOC 10.6.52 : SOC	25.3.68
			N15795	20th Century Fox Film Corp, Hollywood CA	.68/71
				(conv. to Zero lookalike at Long Beach CA .68 for *Tora Tora Tora*; open storage Long Beach CA 69/71, sold at auction Long Beach 2.71)	
				Calvin Y. Sing, Stoneham MA	72
				Roland Harrington, Abbeville LA	77
				Confederate Air Force, Harlingen TX	11.9.81/86
				(flew as Japanese Zero "AI-117")	
				struck-off USCR	22.11.91
CCF4-109•	Mk. 4	**RCAF20318**		BOC 10.6.52 : SOC	21.10.64
			CF-RQC	Skyway Air Services, Langley BC	66
				Victor W. Garside, Wellington BC	68
				Henry Conrad, Wellington BC	69
				Edwin Goertz, Calgary ALTA	70
				Robert C. Wilkinson, Calgary ALTA	72
				R. J. Douglas, Edmonton ALTA	75/79
			C-FRQC	John E. Bachynski, Edmonton ALTA	81/83
			N161FE	Fighter Enterprises, Fort Lauderdale FL	12.3.87/92
				Mk. IV Aviation, Miami FL	.92
			N59TS	Aero Toystore Inc, Fort Lauderdale FL	8.94
				S. R. Levitz, Grand Prairie TX	3.95
CCF4-110•	Mk. 4	RCAF20319		BOC 10.6.52 : SOC	7.9.67
			CF-WWM	Booker Cornea, Drinkwater SASK	68/72
			N44110	reg.	.73
				Aircraft & Equip. Components, Arcadia CA	77
				(noted derelict Mojave CA 8.76/78, still in ex RCAF yellow sc., as CF-WWM)	
				(flying, RAF camouflage, Santa Paula CA 79)	
				Harley W. Payton, Banning CA	86
				Lawrence D. Leclair, Vacaville CA	11.91/96
				(rest. project 92)	
CCF4-112•	Mk. 4	**RCAF20321**		BOC 10.6.52 : SOC	21.2.66
			CF-UFZ	Albert Beach, Burns Lake BC	68/70
				Anthony J. W. Swain, Vancouver BC	72/96
CCF4-114	Mk. 4	RCAF20323		BOC 10.6.52 : SOC	23.6.65
				(in compound dism. unconv., Mesa AZ 78)	
CCF4-115•	Mk. 4	**RCAF20324**		BOC 10.6.52 : SOC	29.1.65
			N4289C	Carl B. Schmidt, Toledo OH	69/70
				Stephen F. Gripper, San Francisco CA	76/86
				Parker O'MalleyAeroplane Co, Ghent NY	7.91/96
CCF4-116	Mk. 4	**RCAF20325**		BOC 19.6.52: SOC	2.8.67
			CF-RFS	Ray's Flying Service Ltd, Saskatoon SASK	8.67/79
				Skywest International Air Ltd, Regina SASK	81/83
				E. Joe McGoldrick, Edmonton ALTA	92/93

CCF4-117•	Mk. 4	**RCAF20326**		BOC 10.6.52 : SOC	25.3.68
			N15799	20th Century Fox Film Corp, Hollywood CA (conv. to Zero lookalike at Long Beach CA .68 for film *Tora Tora Tora*; open storage Long Beach CA 69/71, sold at auction Long Beach 2.71)	.68/71
				Gerald D. Weeks, Memphis TN	2.71/72
				Confederate Air Force, Harlingen/Midland TX (flies as Japanese Zero "AI-113")	29.1.72/96
CCF4-119•	Mk. 4	**RCAF20328**		BOC 10.6.52 : SOC (in compound dism. unconv., Mesa AZ 78)	23.6.65
			N304GS	Gregory N. Shelton, Nowata OK	88/96
CCF4-123•	Mk. 4	**RCAF20332**		BOC 19.6.52 : SOC	4.3.65
			CF-RZP	Lynn Garrison, Calgary ALTA	66
				Evans Air Services, Stettler ALTA	68
				Sandford Pearce Ltd, Vancouver BC	69/72
			C-FRZP	Robert C. Wilkinson, Calgary ALTA	75/83
			N91264	Courtesy Aircraft Inc, Rockford IL	15.9.87
				William B. McHenry, Muskegon MI	88/96
CCF4-124•	Mk. 4	**RCAF20333**		BOC 19.6.52 : SOC	21.7.67
			N1466	H. A. Matteri, Santa Rosa CA	69/72
				Lee R. Donham, Santa Rosa CA (race #66)	2.84/96
CCF4-125	Mk. 4	RCAF20334		BOC 22.7.52 : SOC	4.1.67
			CF-VIR	Harry E. Whereatt, Assinoboia SASK	68/83
CCF4-128•	Mk. 4	**RCAF20337**		BOC 22.7.52 : SOC	30.8.67
			CF-UVQ	Jack L. Ellard, Victoria BC	68/69
				David A. Butler, Victoria BC	70/75
				Starkraft Aviation, Richmond BC	78/79
			C-FUVQ	Shirley J. Granley, St Albert ALTA	81/83
				Tom Rogers, White Rock BC	88/90
				sold to France, struck-off reg.	12.90
			F-AZIG	G. Guiton: reg. res.	.90
				A. Guitton, Etampes	12.91/93
CCF4-132•	Mk. 4	**RCAF20341**		BOC 22.7.52 : SOC	4.3.65
			CF-RZQ	Achim Dalaker, Weston ONT	66
				Harold Krautzun, Toronto ONT	68/72
				Paul A. Williams & Son, Toronto ONT	75
				op: Canadian Warplane Heritage, Hamilton ONT	74/79
				Logwood Leasing Ltd, Aldergrove BC	78/79
				Walter Davidson Corp, Aldergrove BC	81/83
			N452CA	Courtesy Aircraft Inc, Rockford IL	12.85/86
				Avery's Antique Airplanes Inc, Morganton NC	88/96
CCF4-133	Mk. 4	RCAF20342		BOC 22.7.52 : SOC (in compound dism. unconv., Mesa AZ 78)	23.6.65
CCF4-136•	Mk. 4	**RCAF20345**		BOC 22.7.52 : SOC (in compound dism. unconv., Mesa AZ 78; arr. dism. unconv, Chino CA: "RCAF 345" .79)	23.6.65
				Rob Coussens, Tarzana CA:	88/96
CCF4-143•	Mk. 4	**RCAF20352**		BOC 23.7.52 : SOC (in compound dism. unconv., Mesa AZ 78)	13.6.65
			C-GBQB	Jacques Lacombe/Les Placements JSGP Inc, Laval QUE: rest. project	3.87/96
CCF4-144•	Mk. 4	**RCAF20353**		BOC 23.7.52 : SOC	16.10.67
			CF-WWQ	Lorne Alger, Lake Valley SASK	68/70
				Stephen J. Roberts, London ONT	72/75
			N86056	Stephen J. Roberts, Newark DE	2.78
				sale rep., Langhorne PA	86
			N4329J	Gerald L. Walbrun, Neenah WI	5.90/96

CCF4-145 •	Mk. 4	**RCAF20354**		BOC 23.7.52 : SOC	29.4.65
			CF-SPC	Gavin Boyle, Toronto ONMT	66
				Cam-Roy Ltd, Gormley ONT	68/70
				Fred Larsen, Goderich ONT	72/75
			C-FSPC	John's Beetle Repairs, Richmond BC	78/79
				John Mrazek, Richmond BC	81/83
CCF4-148	Mk. 4	RCAF20357		BOC 23.7.52 : SOC	17.11.64
			CF-RUU	Rainier Development Corp, Calgary ALTA	66/72
				Steve Toczyski, Summerstown ONT	75
CCF4-153•	Mk. 4	**RCAF20362**		BOC 19.8.52 : SOC	25.3.68
			N15798	20th Century Fox Film Corp, Hollywood CA	.68/71
				(conv. to Zero lookalike. at Long Beach CA .68 for movie *Tora Tora Tora*; open storage Long Beach CA 69/71, sold at auction Long Beach 2.71)	
				reg. pending	72
				Richard E. Foote/Professional Aircraft Sales Co, New Smyrna Beach FL	85/86
				op: Anthony Hutton/The Harvard Team, North Weald UK	.89/92
				(arr. dism. North Weald 2.89, flying 3.89 as Zero "AI-110")	
				John P. Silberman, Tampa FL	92
				op: Old Flying Machine Company, Duxford UK	.91/92
				Classic Flying Machines Ltd, King City CA	10.92/95
			ZK-ZRO	Alpine Fighter Collection, Wanaka NZ: res.	93/96
CCF4-156•	Mk. 4	**RCAF20365**		BOC 19.8.52 : SOC	31.5.65
			N7553U	Robert D. Staehling, Dubois ID	76/77
				Roger A. Christgau, Edina MN	5.79/95
CCF4-157•	Mk. 4	**RCAF20366**		BOC 19.8.52 : SOC	29.3.66
			N16240	Aircraft Sales & Rentals, Coolidge AZ	66
				Gilbert H. Moyer, Coolidge AZ	69/95
CCF4-158•	Mk. 4	**RCAF20367**		BOC 19.8.52 : SOC	20.5.66
			CF-URH	Kenneth MacGray, Kitchener ONT	68
			N9097	20th Century Fox Film Corp, Hollywood CA	.68/71
				(conv. to Zero lookalike. at Long Beach CA .68 for film *Tora Tora Tora*; open storage Long Beach CA 69/71, sold at auction Long Beach 2.71)	
				Gerald D. Weeks, Memphis TN	2.71/72
				Confederate Air Force, Harlingen/Midland TX	29.1.72/96
				(flies as Japanese Zero "AI-112")	
CCF4-161•	Mk. 4	**RCAF20370**		BOC 19.8.52 : SOC	10.10.65
				Penhold AB, Red Deer ALTA: gate guard	76/92
CCF4-164•	Mk. 4	**RCAF20373**		BOC 19.8.52 : SOC	28.8.61
			CF-NSN	Skyway Air Services, Langley BC	.65/69
				Conair Aviation Ltd, Abbotsford BC	.69/80
			C-FNSN	Conair Aviation Ltd, Abbotsford BC	80/95
CCF4-165•	Mk. 4	**RCAF20374**		BOC 19.8.52 : SOC	19.9.61
			CF-KCX	M. Gaudet & J. Stinson, Powell River BC	65
				David Swithin, Nanaimo BC	66
				crashed Nanaimo BC: abandoned in situ	21.8.66
				Canadian Military Aviation Museum, Vancouver BC (static rest.)	82/83
CCF4-167	Mk. 4	RCAF20376		BOC 19.8.52 : SOC	13.10.64
			CF-RUL	Bruce Durfee, Lethbridge ALTA	66/72
			C-FRUL	Armada Builders Ltd, Calgary ALTA	75/83
CCF4-168•	Mk. 4	RCAF20377		BOC 19.8.52 : SOC	17.5.67
			CF-WGA	Donald Currie Associates Ltd, Toronto ONT	70/75
			C-FWGA	Jacques Lacombe, Laval QUE	78/88
				Claude Michaud/Aero Taxi, St Hubert QUE	88/93

CCF4-169	Mk. 4	RCAF20378		BOC 19.8.52 : SOC (in compound dism. unconv., Mesa AZ 78)	23.6.65
CCF4-171•	Mk. 4	RCAF20380	**N7757**	BOC 19.8.52 : SOC 20th Century Fox Film Corp, Hollywood CA (conv. to Zero lookalike at Long Beach CA .68 for film *Tora Tora Tora*; open storage Long Beach CA 69/71, sold at auction Long Beach 2.71) Challenge Publications, Van Nuys CA American Aeronautical Foundation, Van Nuys CA (flies as "U3-757", later "3-183","77-57")	12.10.67 .68/71 2.71/77 84/96
CCF4-172•	Mk. 4	RCAF20381	CF-NUQ C-FNUQ N514JK **N514FS**	BOC 19.8.52 : SOC Superior Airways, Fort William ONT J. A. Rodney & A. L. Teasdale, Ottawa ONT Paul McIlwain, Peterborough ONT Hugh Jervis-Read, Edmonton ALTA Ivor Oberholtzer, Banff ALTA Cornelis J. (Neil) Hardon, Phoenix AZ Pistachio Aviation, Las Cruces NM Frank Borman/Pistachio Aviation, Las Cruces NM	5.10.61 65/66 68 69/72 .72/79 81/83 11.86/90 2.91 6.91/96
CCF4-173	Mk. 4	RCAF20382	CF-VIJ	BOC 19.8.52 : SOC Don M. McTaggart, Kinderley SASK Armada Builders Ltd, Calgary ALTA	24.11.66 67/75 78/83
CCF4-175•	Mk. 4	**RCAF20384**	CF-UNL C-FUNL **N175JR** **F-AZGB**	BOC 19.8.52 : SOC Rainier Development Corp, Calgary ALTA Denis C. Hosking, Cochrane ALTA Jack A. Rose, Spangle WA John C. Giovanni, Rockford IL sold to France, struck-off USCR J. B. Berger, Etampes (flies as "521475")	5.5.66 68/75 81/83 10.9.85/87 8.87 14.3.88 11.88/93
CCF4-176•	Mk. 4	**RCAF20385**	**N7520U**	BOC 5.9.52 : SOC Philip Schwenk, Murdock MN John H. Bell, Northridge CA dam. in ground accident, Van Nuys CA Larry & Greg Klassen, Shafter CA (rebuilt Shafter CA , ff 4.93 as CCF4-176/*Canadian Mist*)	13.4.65 72 77/88 .88 .88/95
CCF4-178•	Mk. 4	**RCAF20387**	**CF-GBV**	BOC 5.9.52 RCAF Historical Collection, Rockcliffe ONT National Museum of Science & Technology, Ottawa ONT Canadian National Aeronautical Collection, Rockcliffe ONT National Aviation Museum, Rockcliffe ONT	 66 .73/83 79/82 9.82/96
CCF4-179•	Mk. 4	RCAF20388	N7521U **N2WS**	BOC 5.9.52 : SOC Schwenk Aircraft Co, Murdock MN Ramsten Construction Inc, Muncie IN	13.4.65 72 11.72/96
CCF4-181	Mk. 4	RCAF20390		BOC 5.9.52 : SOC (in compound dism. unconv., Mesa AZ 78)	23.6.65
CCF4-189•	Mk. 4	**RCAF20398**	**CF-UAB**	BOC 5.9.52 : SOC Rainier Development Corp, Calgary ALTA James Bradley, Rutland BC Quentin E. Washtock, North Bend BC Charles J. Money, Calgary ALTA	27.10.65 68/72 .72 75/82 .82/95
CCF4-191•	Mk. 4	**RCAF20400**	CF-SRJ	BOC 5.9.52 : SOC James H. Swartz, Vauxhall ALTA	29.3.66 68/83

			N600LM	James E. Smith, Fortine MT	22.9.87/96
CCF4-192•	Mk. 4	**RCAF20401**		BOC 2.10.52 : SOC	27.7.66
			CF-UZG	A. R. Cockburn, Victoria BC	68/72
				Jerry C. Janes, Vancouver BC	75/84
			N5101W	Courtesy Aircraft Inc, Rockford IL	31.5.84
				National Vehicle Testing & Leasing Inc, Niagara Falls NY	86
				Vincent P. Mancini, Salt Lake City UT	89/93
				Andrew Lewis/Daystar Aviation, Flowery Branch GA	11.93/96
CCF4-193•	Mk. 4	**RCAF20402**		BOC 2.10.52: crashed Moose Jaw SASK	31.5.62
				Harry Whereatt, Assiniboia SASK: wreck	.62/90
				Frank Thompson, Readlyn SASK (static rest. project)	92/95
CCF4-194•	Mk. 4	**RCAF20403**		BOC 2.10.52 : SOC	23.6.65
				disposal ex Moose Jaw AB SASK: sold to USA (in compound dism. unconv., Mesa AZ 78)	.65
			N90448	Courtesy Aircraft Inc, Rockford IL	25.3.87
				Alan Brast, Livermore CA	88/89
				G. Lloyd Owens, North Weald UK	8.89
			G-BRLV	G. Lloyd Owens, North Weald (flown CA-New Smyrna Beach FL 8.89, shipped to UK: arr. North Weald 9.89; flew as "9354/LTA-54/*Night Train*)	14.9.89/91
				Bar-Belle Aviation, London	92/96
CCF4-195	Mk. 4	RCAF20404		BOC 2.10.52 : SOC	22.12.66
			CF-VFG	Robert W. Haslam, Ladner BC	68/75
				Farmair Ltd, Okotoks ALTA	78/83
CCF4-196	Mk. 4	RCAF20405		BOC 2.10.52 : SOC (in compound dism. unconv., Mesa AZ 78)	23.6.65
CCF4-199•	Mk. 4	**RCAF20408**		BOC 2.10.52 : SOC	25.3.68
			N15797	20th Century Fox Film Corp, Hollywood CA (conv. to Zero lookalike at Long Beach CA .68 for film *Tora Tora Tora*; open storage Long Beach CA 69/71, sold at auction Long Beach 2.71)	.68/71
				Confederate Air Force, Harlingen/Midland TX (flies as Japanese Zero "AI-114")	29.1.72/96
CCF4-200	Mk. 4	RCAF20409		BOC 2.10.52 : SOC (in compound dism. unconv., Mesa AZ 78)	23.6.65
CCF4-201•	Mk. 4	**RCAF20410**		BOC 2.10.52 : SOC	3.3.65
			CF-RZO	Larry F. Hamer, Calgary ALTA	66/68
				J. Strang, Fort Mitchell KY	69/72
			N6865	Connie Edwards, Big Spring TX	76/93
CCF4-203•	Mk. 4	**RCAF20412**		BOC 9.10.52 : SOC	27.10.66
			CF-VMG	Sidney H. Bonser, Oakville ONT	68/75
			C-FVMG	Sidney H. Bonser, Lake Forrest IL	75/83
				op: Canadian Warplane Heritage, Hamilton ONT	79/92
CCF4-204•	Mk. 4	**RCAF20413**		BOC 9.10.52 : SOC	13.4.65
			N7518U	Hubert Boussard/Harvard Corp, Minneapolis MN, Oakdale MN & Hartford CT	11.70/95
CCF4-206•	Mk. 4	**RCAF20415**		BOC 9.10.52 : SOC	15.8.66
			C-FVCJ	Michael S. Hutchins, Oakville ONT	78/91
				op: Canadian Warplane Heritage, Hamilton ONT	79/95
CCF4-210•	Mk. 4	**RCAF20419**		BOC 9.10.52 : crashed Penhold AB: SOC	8.11.62
				Canadian Museum of Flight & Transportation, Surrey BC: composite rest. project	90/92
CCF4-211•	Mk. 4	**RCAF20420**		BOC 9.10.52 : SOC	23.6.65

				(in compound dism. unconv., Mesa AZ 78)	
			N1046Y	reg.	5.79
				Norman P. Friedrich, East Wenatchee WA	86
				Vlado Lenoch, LaGrange IL	88
				Jay B. Stokley, Opelika AL	5.88/95
				(flies as "USAF 20420/TA-420")	
CCF4-212•	Mk. 4	**RCAF20421**		BOC 9.10.52 : SOC	27.10.65
			CF-UAD	Rainier Development Corp, Calgary ALTA	68/72
				Dalton C. Deedrick & partners, Lacombe ALTA	75/83
				struck-off reg.	2.87
			N421QB	R. A. (Bud) Grunert, San Jose CA	3.87/88
				Carol J. Hunt, Anchorage AK	6.89/95
CCF4-213	Mk. 4	RCAF20422		BOC 9.10.52 : SOC	15.10.64
			CF-RZW	Tom Ladobruk, Steinback MAN	66/70
				L. R. Benvenuto, London ONT	72/83
CCF4-214•	Mk. 4	**RCAF20423**		BOC 9.10.52 : SOC	13.4.65
			N7522U	Donald W. Brunnell, Azusa CA	76/77
				Clayton S. Johnson, Van Nuys CA	86
				Richard Clinton, Fair Oaks CA	92/93
				James R. Booth, Memphis TN	5.94/95
CCF4-215•	Mk. 4	**RCAF20424**		BOC 9.10.52 : SOC	23.8.67
			CF-WPN	Peter D. Ritchie, Saskatoon SASK	68
			N7754	20th Century Fox Film Corp, Hollywood CA	.68/71
				(conv. to Zero looalike. at Long Beach CA .68 for film *Tora Tora Tora*; open storage Long Beach CA 69/71, sold at auction Long Beach 2.71)	
				reg. pending	72
				I. N. Burchinall Jnr, Paris TX	78
				op: Flying Tigers Museum, Kissimmee FL	78
				James Mathews, Winter Park FL	81
				Confederate Air Force, Harlingen TX	84
				Jane & Jane Inc, Boring OR	86
				Jack McWhorter, Prosser WA	86/88
				Lone Star Flight Museum, Galveston TX	.88/92
				Wings & Wheels Inc, Houston TX	2.93/96
				(flies as Zero "A9-147", later "V1-07")	
CCF4-216•	Mk. 4	RCAF20425		BOC 9.10.52 : SOC	31.7.67
			N20425	Travis Morris, Van Nuys CA	69/70
				accident landing Riverside-Flabob CA	2.73
				George W. Naphas, Pitman NJ	8.75/95
CCF4-217	Mk. 4	RCAF20426		BOC 9.10.52 : SOC	9.8.66
			CF-UZH	E. Joe McGoldrick, Edmonton ALTA	68
				Adrian Hobart, Edmonton ALTA	69/72
			C-FUZH	E. Joe McGoldrick, Edmonton ALTA	75/94
				crashed, midair collision C-GRLR, Oliver BC	30.7.83
CCF4-219•	Mk. 4	**RCAF20428**		BOC 30.10.52 : SOC	31.5.65
			N7554U	Edwin H. Staehling, Ann Arbor MI	72
				Jonathon J. Staehling, Woodstock IL/Plano TX	3.72/96
CCF4-222•	Mk. 4	**RCAF20431**		BOC 27.11.52 : SOC	12.7.66
			CF-UZW	R. L. Drake, Calgary ALTA	68
				Charles J. Money, Calgary ALTA	69/70
				John Spotton Co Ltd, Mississauga ONT	72/75
				op: Canadian Warplane Heritage, Hamilton ONT	73/79
				Collingwood Air Services, Collingwood ONT	78/79
				Bailey Aviation Service, Calgary ALTA	81/91
CCF4-223•	Mk. 4	**RCAF20432**		BOC 28.11.52, crashed RCAF Penhold ALTA	29.2.56
				RCAF Penhold: inst. airframe	23.3.56
			C-FHWU	Reynolds Aviation Museum, Wetaskiwin ALTA	29.3.90
				Gord Saylor	92

				Hannu Halminen, Oshawa ONT	6.92/96
				(trucked to Oshawa .92, rest. ff 28.7.93)	
CCF4-227•	Mk. 4	**RCAF20436**		BOC 28.11.52 : SOC	7.9.67
			CF-WWI	Percy Ellard, Caron SASK	68/70
				Robert C. Wilkinson, Calgary ALTA	72/83
			N436WL	William E. Lamon, Eugene OR	12.88/96
CCF4-228	Mk. 4	RCAF20437		BOC 28.11.52 : SOC	23.6.65
				(in compound dism. unconv., Mesa AZ 78)	
CCF4-230•	Mk. 4	**RCAF20439**		BOC 28.11.52: SOC	26.6.67
			N1254	Robert L. Jones, Scottsdale AZ	69
				James M. McLaren, Corvallis OR	70/72
				Robert E. Clopton, Windsor CA	77/93
				John J. Maney, Portland OR	11.93/95
CCF4-231•	Mk. 4	**RCAF20440**		BOC 28.11.52 : SOC	6.7.66
			CF-VTT	Hugh McPhail & Norman Miller,	
				North Battleford SASK	68/70
				Rocky Mountain Flying Club, Kimberley BC	72/75
			C-FVTT	Patricia E. Schrauwen, Armstrong BC	78/96
CCF4-233	Mk. 4	RCAF20442		BOC 28.11.52 : SOC	23.6.65
				(in compound dism. unconv., Mesa AZ 78)	
			C-GNJM	McClain Flight Services, Strathmore ALTA	8.83
				struck-off reg.	11.84
CCF4-234	Mk. 4	RCAF20443		BOC 28.11.52 : SOC	26.8.63
				to RCAF inst. airframe 657B, London AB	11.8.59
				displ. on pole, Smiths Falls ONT as "443"	86
CCF4-237•	Mk. 4	**RCAF20446**		BOC 28.11.52 : SOC	13.4.65
			N7519U	Schwenk Aircraft Co, Murdock MN	72
				readded USCR	11.87
				David K. Schmitz, Spooner WI	2.88/95
CCF4-240•	Mk. 4	**RCAF20449**		BOC 17.12.52 : SOC	23.6.65
				(in compound dism. unconv., Mesa AZ 78)	
			N155RH	Robert S. Haun, Westminster CO	18.4.85/95
CCF4-241•	Mk. 4	**RCAF20450**		BOC 17.12.52 : SOC	18.5.67
			N4447	20th Century Fox Film Corp, Hollywood CA	.68/71
				(conv. to Zero lookalike at Long Beach CA .68 for film *Tora Tora Tora*; open storage Long Beach CA 69/71, sold at auction Long Beach 2.71)	
				Gerald D. Weeks, Memphis TN	2.71/72
				Confederate Air Force, Harlingen/Midland TX	15.7.72/95
				(flies as Japanese Zero "AI-111")	
CCF4-242•	Mk. 4	**RCAF20451**		BOC 17.12.52 : SOC	23.6.65
				(in compound dism. unconv., Mesa AZ 78)	
				Rick Shanholtzer, McKinney TX: stored dism.	93
				Hannu Halminen, Oshawa ONT	7.93/94
				(arr. dism. Oshawa .93, rest. ff Oshawa 7.94)	
			CF-ROA	Hannu Halminen/Roaero Ltd, Oshawa ONT	7.7.94/95
CCF4-246•	Mk. 4	**RCAF20455**		BOC 17.12.52 : SOC	23.6.65
				(in compound dism. unconv., Mesa AZ 78)	
			N45918	Dennis G. Buehn, Long Beach CA	2.78
			N51943	ntu	3.78
			N45918	James W. Merrill, Long Beach CA	86/96
CCF4-250•	Mk. 4	**RCAF20459**		BOC 17.12.52 : SOC	23.6.65
				(in compound dism. unconv., Mesa AZ 78)	
			N98541	Dennis G. Buehn, Long Beach CA	17.8.81
				John A. Bassett, Fremont CA	83
			N459JB	John A. Bassett, Fremont CA	3.85/86
			N459JP	James L. Powers, San Jose CA	2.89/96

CCF4-252•	Mk. 4	**RCAF20461**		BOC 27.12.52 : SOC	25.5.67
			N17400	George H. Sanders, Higley AZ	69/77
				(noted Mesa AZ 10.72 "Luftwaffe AA+400")	
			N44NM	Phil L. Harris, Overland Park KS	8.86
			N884TC	Thomas C. Clayton, Overland Park KS	5.88/96
CCF4-254	Mk. 4	RCAF20463		BOC 27.12.52 : SOC	27.10.65
			CF-UAE	Rainier Development Corp, Calgary ALTA	68/70
			C-FUAE	Long Valley Aviation Ltd, Lacombe ALTA	72/83
CCF4-255	Mk. 4	RCAF20464		BOC 27.12.52 : SOC	27.7.66
			CF-WXY	George Nelson, Dinsmore SASK	68/79
				sale rep., Vente Signalee ALTA	78/83
CCF4-256	Mk. 4	RCAF20465		BOC 27.12.52 : SOC	30.11.67
			C-GURP	reg.	12.72
				struck-off reg.	2.76
				Lawrence W. Mantie	.78/83
				(recov. derelict ex farm, SASK: ferried to Vancouver for rest. .78)	
			C-GURP	Lawrence W. Mantie, Vancouver BC	7.79/85
				crashed, dest. Powell River BC (Mantie k.)	22.8.85
CCF4-261•	Mk. 4	**RCAF20470**		BOC 5.2.53 : SOC	23.6.65
				(in compound dism. unconv., Mesa AZ 78)	
			N53VC		
			N202LD	Larry E. Denton, Walla Walla WA	12.82/86
				(flying as NA-50 lookalike by 90)	
				Jack A. Rose, Spangle WA	90/94
				Kent Carlomagno, San Rafael CA	10.94/96
CCF4-262•	Mk. 4	**RCAF20471**		BOC 14.1.53: SOC	18.1.66
				Calgary Air & Space Museum, Calgary ALTA	1.66/94
CCF4-264•	Mk. 4	**RCAF20473**		BOC 14.1.53 : SOC	2.2.68
			N296W	20th Century Fox Film Corp, Hollywood CA	.68/71
				(conv. to Zero lookalike at Long Beach CA .68 for movie "Tora Tora Tora"; open storage Long Beach CA 69/71, sold at auction Long Beach 2.71)	
				Challenge Warbirds, Van Nuys CA	2.71/73
				William Childers, Temple TX	77
				EAA Aviation Foundation, Oshkosh WI	.83/92
			N60DJ	Douglas R. Jackson/J & R Investments Inc, Wichita KS	7.92/96
				(flies as Japanese Zero "AI-101")	
CCF4-265•	Mk. 4	**RCAF20474**		BOC 14.1.53 : SOC	9.8.66
			CF-UZI		
			N3666		
			CF-XEX	Fred G. Wetherall, Calgary ALTA	68
			N4048	Rex J. Kelsch, Mott ND	70
			C-FXEX	Pedagair Corp Ltd, Calgary ALTA	75/79
				Armada Builders Ltd, Calgary ALTA	81/83
				Arcot Aviation Ltd, Airdie ALTA	95
CCF4-266	Mk. 4	RCAF20475		BOC 14.1.53 : SOC	12.10.67
			C-GYYO	Marjorie Duncan, Saskatoon SASK	.78/83
CCF4-267•	Mk. 4	**RCAF20476**		BOC 14.1.53 : SOC	20.9.61
			CF-MWN	Douglas M. Nelson, Calgary ALTA	65/70
			N86057	Stephen J. Roberts, Newark DE	11.77
			C-FMWN	John C. Chase, Delta BC	.81/83
				Michael R. Langford, Vancouver BC	88/94
CCF4-270•	Mk. 4	**RCAF20479**		BOC 14.1.53 : SOC	18.7.67
			N1467	Dwight R. Sissell, Tempe AZ/Whittier CA	69/70
				Jacques Trudeau, Buckley WA	77
				Cliff Branch, Compton CA	80/83

				(rebuilt c80 Compton CA as lookalike NA A-27)	
				Sherman Aircraft Sales,	
				West Palm Beach FL	86/96
CCF4-288•	T-6J	**51-17106**		(to Italian AF as MM53785)	
				(Codes SL.16, later SC.62)	
				Castreete Scrapyard, Italy	
			I-TSIX	Mario Ferrari, Salgareda: rest.	89
				Luciano Sorlini, Montegaldella: rest. to fly	.91/96
CCF4-363•	T-6J	**51-17181**		(to Italian AF as MM53816)	
			N1363W	reg. res.	11.81
				Frank G. Compton, Torrance CA	86/95
				(rebuilt with geared R1340-61, 3 bladed prop)	
CCF4-384•	T-6J	**51-17202**		(to Italian AF as MM......)	
			HB-RAJ	F. Acris, Ecuvillens	3.8.94
CCF4-387•	T-6J	**51-17205**	C-FCLJ	Robert H. Jens, Vancouver BC	1.84
			C-GJCJ	Jerry C. Janes, Vancouver WA	7.85
				sold to USA, struck-off reg.	11.87
			N52494	W. F. Berry, Modesto CA	8.3.88
				Donald F. Monaco, Modesto CA	89/95
CCF4-400•	T-6J	**51-17218**		(to Italian AF/AMI as MM53835) "SC.74"	
				Castreete Scrapyard, Italy	
				Velentino Corsi Furniture Store: displ.	87
CCF4-407•	T-6J	**51-17225**		(to Italian AF/AMI as MM53844) "SL.30"	
				Castreete Scrapyard, Italy	87
			N587CB	Charles & Douglas Cartledge, Brecksville OH	12.5.87/95
				(rest. 87/90, ff 90 as "RCAF 407")	
CCF4-408•	T-6J	**51-17226**		(to FA Congolaise as AT-845)	
				noted dism. derelict, Kinshasa-N'dolo	10.93
CCF4-425•	T-6J	**52-8504**		(to Luftwaffe as AA+638)	
				(to FA Portuguesa as 1727): del.	3.7.64
				(to Mozambique PLAF as 1727)	
				abandoned Maputo, Mozambique	.74/89
				recov. by Brian Zeederberg & Ian Popplewell,	
				Syferfontein, Johannesburg: arr. dism.	3.89
				South African Airways Technical Training School	5.89
			ZS-WLU	South African Airways,	
				Johannesburg-Jan Smuts: inst. airframe	.90/92
				(noted SAA maintenance base Jan Smuts 11.91, painted as "Super B")	
CCF4-442•	T-6J	**52-8521**		(to Luftwaffe as AA+652)	
				(to FA Portuguesa as 1730)	
				(to Mozambique PLAF as 1730)	
				abandoned Maputo, Mozambique	.74/89
				recov. by Brian Zeederberg & Ian Popplewell,	
				Syferfontein, Johannesburg: arr. dism.	4.89
			G-BSBE	Andrew Edie/Aerofab, Thruxton: arr. dism.	12.89
				Pulsgrove Ltd, Thruxton	91
			G-TVIJ	Robert W. Davies, Ashford Kent	12.93/94
				(flies as "USAF 28521/TA-521")	
CCF4-448•	T-6J	**52-8527**		(to Luftwaffe as AA+658)	
				(to FA Portuguesa as 1731): del.	3.7.64
				(to Mozambique PLAF as 1731)	
				abandoned Maputo, Mozambique	.74/89
				recov. by Brian Zeederberg & Ian Popplewell,	
				Syferfontein, Johannesburg: arr. dism.	3.89
				South African Airways Technical Training School: arr. dism.	15.5.89
			ZS-WLR	South African Airways,	
				Johannesburg-Jan Smuts: inst. airframe	.90/92

				(noted at SAA maintenance base, Jan Smuts 11.91, painted in SAA colour scheme)	
CCF4-451•	T-6J	**52-8530**		(to Luftwaffe as AA+660)	
				(to FA Portuguesa as 1751): del.	17.7.64
				(to Mozambique PLAF as 1751)	
				abandoned Maputo, Mozambique	.74/89
				recov. by Brian Zeederberg & Ian Popplewell, Syferfontein, Johannesburg: arr. dism.	4.89
				South African Airways Technical Training School: arr. dism.	12.5.89
			ZS-WLS	South African Airways, Johannesburg-Jan Smuts: inst. airframe	.90/92
				(noted at SAA maintenance base, Jan Smuts 11.91)	
CCF4-464•	T-6J	**52-8543**		(to Luftwaffe as AA+068, later BF+068)	
				(To FA Portuguesa as 1766)	
				Ota AB: inst. airframe: del.	30.7.75/90
				Museo do Ar	12.11.90
				AJD Engineering, Sudbury UK	.91
				(airfreighted to Stansted by FAP C-130 27.7.91)	
			G-BUKY	Peter F. Monk & A. C. Savage, Maidstone	13.7.92/93
				(rest. West Malling, ff .93 as "52-8543")	
CCF4-465•	T-6J	**52-8544**		(to Luftwaffe as AA+615)	
			D-FABU	Federal Republic of Germany, Bonn	21.8.63/64
				struck-off reg.	.71
				Luftwaffen Museum, Uetersen AB	.73/92
CCF4-483•	T-6J	**52-8562**		(to Luftwaffe as AA+053, BF+053)	
				(to FA Portuguesa as 1753): del.	.66
				(to Mozambique PLAF as 1753)	
				abandoned Maputo, Mozambique	.74/89
				recov. by Brian Zeederberg & Ian Popplewell, Syferfontein, Johannesburg: arr. dism.	3.89
			G-BSBG	Andrew Edie/Aerofab, Thruxton: arr. dism.	12.89
				Pulsgrove Ltd, Thruxton	91
				(rest. Thruxton, ff. 7.91 as "RCAF20310")	
				John J. Woodhouse, Andover	92/93
				Toby St. John, Liverpool	94/95
CCF4-486•	T-6J	**52-8565**		(to Luftwaffe as AA+079, BF+079)	
				(to FA Portuguesa as 1774)	
				Museu do Ar, Montijo AB, Portugal	79/89
				Museu do Ar, Sintra AB	95
				(flies as "FAP 1774")	
CCF4-491•	T-6J	**52-8570**		(to Luftwaffe as AA+696, AA+622)	
				Luftwaffen Museum, Uetersen AB	79
				Norwegian AF Museum, Gardermoen AB	83/92
				(displ. as "RNoAF M-BS")	
CCF4-498•	T-6J	**52-8577**		(to Luftwaffe as AA+065, BF+065)	
				(to FA Portuguesa as 1762)	
				(to Mozambique PLAF as 3101)	
				abandoned Maputo, Mozambique	.74/89
				recov. by Brian Zeederberg & Ian Popplewell, Syferfontein, Johannesburg: arr. dism.	3.89
				Mark Kuster, Oribi, South Africa	.89
CCF4-499•	T-6J	**52-8578**		(to Luftwaffe as AA+624)	
			D-FABE	Federal Republic of Germany, Bonn	11.63/72
				R. Strossenreuther, Rosenthal-Field	
				K. H. Brader, Wilhelmshaven	76/77
				KBB Flugdienst Josef Koch KG, Augsburg	86
				Fliegendes Museum Augsburg, Augsburg	92
CCF4-509•	T-6J	**52-8588**		(to Luftwaffe as AA+633)	

			D-FACI	ntu: Federal Republic of Germany, Bonn	
				derelict, Dusseldorf-Munchengladbach	88
CCF4-511•	T-6J	**52-8590**		(to Luftwaffe as AA+058, BF+058)	
				(to FA Portuguesa as 1736)	
				(to Mozambique PLAF as 1736)	
				abandoned Maputo, Mozambique	.74/89
				recov. by Brian Zeederberg & Ian Popplewell,	
				Syferfontein, Johannesburg: arr. dism.	3.89
			G-BSBF	Andrew Edie/Aerofab, Thruxton: arr. dism.	12.89
				Pulsgrove Ltd, Thruxton	91
				sold to USA: struck-off U.K. reg.	6.5.94
				Harry M. Zerbey, Pottsville PA	94
CCF4-514	T-6J	52-8593		(to Luftwaffe as AA+603)	
			D-FABO	Federal Republic of Germany, Bonn	30.7.63/72
				R. Strossenreuther, Speichersdorf	76/77
				crashed Rosenthal-Field, Speichersdorf	8.8.88
CCF4-517•	T-6J	**52-8596**		(to Luftwaffe as AA+078, BF+078)	
				(to FA Portuguesa as 1769)	
				Museu do Ar, Montijo AB, Portugal	79/89
				Museu do Ar, Sintra AB	95
CCF4-520•	T-6J	**52-8599**		(to Luftwaffe as BF+059)	
				(to FA Portuguesa as 1754)	
				(to Mozambique PLAF as 1754)	
				abandoned Maputo, Mozambique	.74/89
				recov. by Brian Zeederberg & Ian Popplewell,	
				Syferfontein, Johannesburg: arr. dism.	3.89
				to syndicate, Nelspruit, South Africa	8.89
CCF4-529•	T-6J	**52-8608**		(to Luftwaffe as BF+064)	
				(to FA Portuguesa as 1740)	
				(to Mozambique PLAF as 1740)	
				A. Watson, Syferfontein, South Africa	.90
			ZU-ARZ	B. D. Beard, Johannesburg-Rand	24.3.95
				(ff Rand 7.4.95 as "USAF 28608 Night Train")	
				(shipped ex Durban to Canada 5.5.95)	
			C-FWBS	B. D. Beard, Langley BC	28.9.95
CCF4-537	T-6J	53-4618		(to Luftwaffe as AA+628)	
			D-FABI	Federal Republic of Germany, Bonn	10.63/64
			N73688	ntu	
			F-BRGA	Institute Aeronautique Amaury de la Grange,	
				Merville: reg. res.	7.73/77
				(noted as inst. airframe, Merville 77)	
				Salis Aviation, La Ferte Alais	.82
			F-AZFC	Paul Franceschi/Escadrille Mercure,	
				Le Castellet	15.3.88/93
				(rest., flew as "Aeronavale 25/54.S")	
				crashed, dest. Le Castellet	21.1.93
CCF4-538•	T-6J	**53-4619**		(to Luftwaffe as AA+050; BF+050)	
				(to FA Portuguesa as 1747)	.66
			G-BGPB	Robs Lamplough & Alistair G. Walker, Duxford	4.4.79/86
				(del. via Cherbourg to Southampton 15.6.79,	
				flew as "RCAF 20385")	
				G. Owens, North Weald	87/89
				crashed into ditch landing, Gransden	15.6.89
				Aircraft Restoration Co, Duxford	15.9.89/95
				(rebuild Duxford)	
				Propshop Ltd, Duxford	12.9.95
CCF4-539•	T-6J	**53-4620**		(to Luftwaffe as AA+637)	
				(to FA Portuguesa as 1755)	
				(to Mozambique PLAF as 1755)	
				abandoned Maputo, Mozambique	.74/89
				recov. by Brian Zeederberg & Ian Popplewell,	
				Syferfontein, Johannesburg	.89

			ZS-XXX	ntu	
			ZS-XYZ	del. Syferfontein ex Maputo, arr.	18.2.90
			ZS-WLL	Harvard Syndicate, Johannesburg-Rand	19.4.90
CCF4-543•	T-6J	**53-4624**		(to Luftwaffe as AA+690)	
				(to FA Portuguesa as 1748)	
				(to Mozambique PLAF as 1748)	
				abandoned Maputo, Mozambique	.74/89
				recov. by Brian Zeederberg & Ian Popplewell,	
				Syferfontein, Johannesburg: arr. dism.	3.89
				John Sayers, Lanseria, South Africa	5.89
			ZS-WSE	John Sayers, Lanseria	3.1.91
CCF4-548•	T-6J	**53-4629**		(to Luftwaffe as AA+055, later BF+055)	
				(to FA Portuguesa as 1741)	
				(to Mozambique PLAF as 1741)	
				abandoned Maputo, Mozambique	.74/89
				recov. by Brian Zeederberg & Ian Popplewell,	
				Syferfontein, Johannesburg	.89
			G-BSBC	Andrew Edie/Aerofab, Thruxton: arr. dism.	12.89
				John J. Woodhouse, Thruxton	91
			G-HRVD	M. Slater, Wellesbourne Mountford	8.12.92/93
CCF4-550•	T-6J	**53-4631**		(to Luftwaffe as AA+635)	
			D-FABA	Federal Republic of Germany, Bonn	10.7.63/72
			N73687	ntu	
			F-BRGB	ntu: J. Blondel, Amiens	7.73
			F-AZAT	J. Blondel, Beauvais	12.79/96
CCF4-555•	T-6J	**53-4636**		(to Luftwaffe as AA+689)	
				(to FA Portuguesa as 1788)	
				(to Mozambique PLAF as 1788)	
				abandoned Maputo, Mozambique	.74/89
				recov. by Brian Zeederberg & Ian Popplewell,	
				Syferfontein, Johannesburg: arr. dism.	4.89
			G-BSBB	Andrew Edie/Aerofab, Thruxton: arr. dism.	12.89
				John J. Woodhouse, Thruxton	91
				sold to USA: struck-off reg.	6.5.94
				Harry M. Zerbey, Pottsville PA	94
- •	T-6		**F-AZHE**	Salis Aviation, La Ferte-Alais: reg. res.	.90
				(NA-68 lookalike; id. quoted as "SA-31")	
				Amicale J-B Salis, La Ferte-Alais	7.5.93/95
				(flying as Aeronavale F6F lookalike 93/95)	
				(at airshow LFA 6.95 as Hellcat)	
- •	T-6		**F-AZJS**	Salis Aviation, La Ferte-Alais: reg. res.	.92/93
CCF4- •	Mk. 4	-		(to Italian AF as MM53846/Code RM-22)	
	T-6J		**G-BIWX**	Robs Lamplough, Duxford	29.4.81
				Guy Black/Aero Vintage Ltd	22.3.83
				Anthony E. Hutton, North Weald	30.6.83/94
				(flies as "RAF FT239")	
CCF4- •	T-6J	-		(to Italian AF as MM53802)	
				Robs Lamplough, Duxford: imported UK	16.7.81
			G-BJMS	Stephen Grey, Booker	5.10.81
				sold to France, struck-off reg.	4.3.82
			F-AZCM	Jacques David, Lons-le-Saulnier	3.3.82/89
				J. F. Chalumeau, Lons-Le Saulnier	90
				P. Lombard, Lons-Le Saunier	93
CCF4- •	T-6J	-		(to Italian AF as MM53795/Code SC.66)	
				Robs Lamplough, Duxford UK: imported	.81
			G-BJST	Vic Norman & Michael Lawrence, Coventry	12.81/92
				(under rest. Kemble 85, rebuild as Zero repl.	
				for film *Empire of the Sun* 87)	
				no CofA: struck-off reg.	26.7.94

Continued on Page 459

Fresh in the U.K. The Fighter Collection's Lockheed P38 NX3145X was unadorned even by paint, apart from the anti-dazzle panel on the nose when first shown on a beautiful day at Boscombe Down in 1992. A tiny registration can just be discerned below the tailplane. **James Kightly.**

Though only a static restoration, the job Champlin Fighter Museum made of the Kawanishi N1K1J Shinden-Kai George (c/n 5341) for the National Air & Space Museum, was superb, and goes some way to redressing the lack of restored Japanese aircraft on display. **Alan Gruening**

One of the most incredible recovery efforts was the extracation of P38F 41-17630 from inside the Greenland icecap, as narrated in W.W. and the book "The Lost Squadron". Progress has been more than satisfactory on its restoration since. **Wayne McPherson Gomes.**

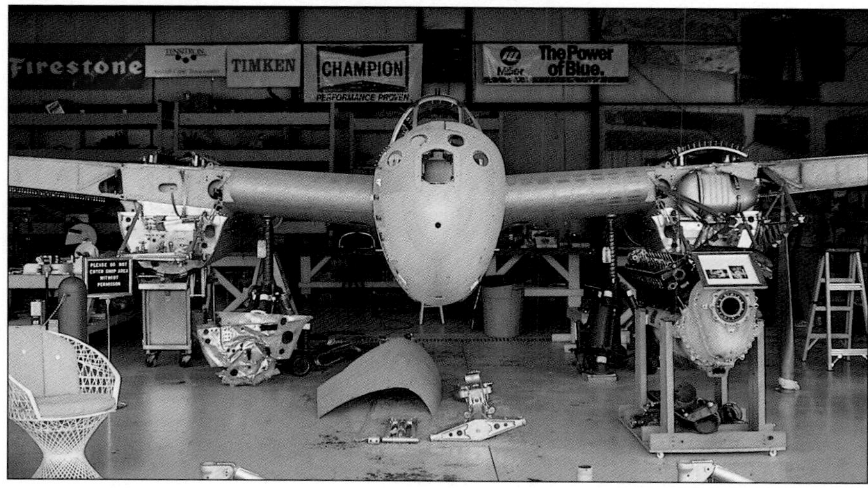

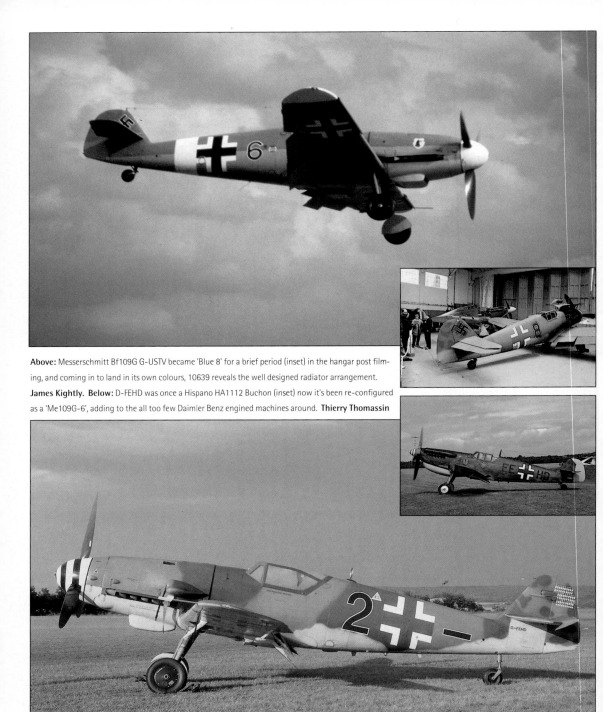

Above: Messerschmitt Bf109G G-USTV became 'Blue 8' for a brief period (inset) in the hangar post filming, and coming in to land in its own colours, 10639 reveals the well designed radiator arrangement. **James Kightly. Below:** D-FEHD was once a Hispano HA1112 Buchon (inset) now it's been re-configured as a 'Me109G-6', adding to the all too few Daimler Benz engined machines around. **Thierry Thomassin**

Planes of Fame P51A N4235Y wears German balkenkrutz and swastika over sand and spinnach British colours. In August '81, it returned to the air after years of static display. **Thierry Thomassin.**

The Kibbutz where some dreams started. Not often seen these days, a relatively complete airframe awaiting restoration. Ex-IDFAF '41' 44-72028 is now G-LYNE in Teeside, U.K. **Robs Lamplough**.

Mustang F-AZFI at Flying Legends, was was once G-PSID with Warbirds of Great Britain. It is refreshing to see the variety of authentic schemes now appearing on modern Mustangs. **Jim Winchester.**

Wearing an intreaguing low-viz U.S. scheme, North American T6 N7888G was seen at Tico, Florida, in 1984. **Dick Phillips**.

North American T6 C6-165 with an injunction for potential purchasers not to try climbing on it at Santander Airport July, '89. **Thierry Thomassin.**

North American Harvards are now becoming avaliable from South Africa, one of the last users of the type in quantity. Mk.III 7569 (ex-EZ312) displays its W.W.II colours. **Dave Becker.**

Above: Israel has been the source of several Spitfires - EN145 is seen as part of the I.A.F.D.F. Museum, while an unknown example sits in a revetment. **Gary Brown Collection & Simon Watson.** **Below:** SM832 - clipped wing Mk.XIV in the colours of Ginger Lacy and a new asset to the Fighter Collection. Stephen Grey is seen in the cockpit **(Mark Ansell)**, the engine is shown in some detail. **(Barry McKee)**

Race No.1 has always had pole position. Vought F4 U1A Corsair N31518 modefied with a R4360 'corncob' held top position at Reno for Jim Maloney and The Planes of Fame. **William T Larkins.**

One of the incredibly large batch of ex-Egyptian Yak 11's stored at La Ferte Alais, Allen Haage's OO-YAK, though Belgian registered is a regular visitor to its one-time home. **Thierry Thomassin.**

The 're-opening' of the Yak-3 production line is one of the most obvious recent successes of the warbird industry. Yak-3UA NX494DJ (construction number 0470103) owned by the Museum of Flying, Santa Monica, is the third built, and was photographed at Reno in 1994. **Thierry Thomassin.**

Hispano Ha200 N606HA at Paso Robles was imported into the U.S. by Nathanial Kalt as part of a large batch and was seen when oewned by Bill Russell of Russair Ltd. **Gary Robert Brown.**

Undoubtedly one of the hottest machines on any civil register, a considerable number of F104 Starfighters have been used for various purposes bearing civilian I.D. Lockheed F104 N104JR was to fly again on Armistice day 1987 for Combat Jets Flying Museum before joining the E.A.A. Aviation Foundation with the rest of the collection. **Thierry Thomassin.**

The T-33 is one of the most popular jet warbirds, a long production run and a variety of uses making it more than just an attractive trainer. Taken at Titusville, Randall Hames' N556RH (58-0665) wears the bright colours of the U.S.A.F. *Thunderbirds* aerobatic team; one of several jet warbirds in aerobatic team colours. **Erich Gandet.**

One of the most significant jet fighter families, the last decade has seen an explosion in the number of MiGs appearing in the west. MiG-15 UTI NX304SB is parked with other MiG-15 and MiG-17's at American Classics Ltd in 1994. **Thierry Thomassin.**

Despite the prevelance of MiGs worldwide, Britain has only just seen the acquisition of an airworthy MiG-15, while the MiG-21 (the example here offered in Christie's Auction by Aces High) is yet to display in the U.K. **James Kightly.**

One of three ex-Turkish Air Force North American F100C Super Sabres stored at Mojave in 1990 by Flight Systems Inc., this machine awaits conversion to drone or target tug status, like most other active 'Huns'. None have become show mounts as yet despite the wide range of colourful schemes avaliable and the popularity of the type, both with crew and enthusiasts. **Thierry Thomassin.**

 CONTINUED FROM PAGE 450

CCF4-	•	Mk. 4 T-6J	-		(to Italian AF as MM.........) sold as scrap	
				I-RYGA	Franco Actis, Turin (rest. .89/91, ff 15.5.91)	89/93
-		T-6	-	**N1041C**	Wayne Thomas, Plant City FL (id. quoted as "NAA 5638")	63/84
-		T-6	-	**N1050C**	Frank A. Froehling, Miami FL struck-off USCR (id. quoted as "NAA 7980")	63/69 6.91
CCF4-	•	T-6H Mk. 4	-		(to Italian AF as MM53833)	
				N1363R	reg. res. Dennis G. Buehn, Reno NV William Waterton, Melbourne VIC (flew as "VH-USB/*Lady Southern Cross*") struck-off USCR	11.81 86 .85/86 12.2.90
				VH-USR	Bill Waterton/C. Tracey & Co, Gisborne VIC (flies as "USAF 93555/LTA-555") (VH-USR id. quoted as "93555", but CCF Mk.IV)	26.4.90/96
-	•	T-6G	-		(to Italian AF as MM53655)	
				N1364J	reg. res. Robert W. Heckman, Ramona CA Charles Bivenour, Scottsdale AZ (flies as "115208/TA-208")	11.81 86 88/96
-	•	AT-6D	-		(to Italian AF as MM53418)	
				N1364N (2	reg. res. Earl C. Atkins, McAllen TX John Strickland & Bill Smith/Warbirds Leasing Inc, White Marsh MD Bruce L. Moore, Canaan NH (at airshow Kenosha WI 7.88 "53418/TA-418", Geneseo NY 8.91 "53418")	11.81 84/86 88/93 7.94/96
-		T-6			(to Spanish AF as .....)	
				N2055G	George Byaroil (under rest. Chino CA 89/90)	89/90
-	•	AT-6G	-		(to SAAF as 7721) shipped to Chile for airshow South African Armscor: civil disposal in Chile	94 .94 .94
				N26PW	John P. Vick, Longmont CO Medical Diagnostic Imaging Inc, St Louis MO	13.7.94 6.95
				N7721Z	reg. (id. quoted as "SA-068")	10.95
-	•	AT-6G	-		(to SAAF as 7726) shipped to Chile for airshow South African Armscor: civil disposal in Chile	94 .94 .94
				N26WR	John P. Vick, Longmont CO (id. quoted as "SA-079")	13.7.94/95
-	•	AT-6G	-		(to SAAF as 7703) shipped to Chile for airshow South African Armscor: civil disposal in Chile	94 .94 .94
				N26YP	John P. Vick, Longmont CO Centennial L L C, Denver CO (id. quoted as "SA-060")	13.7.94 2.95
-	•	T-6G	**49-.....**		(to Spanish AF as .....)	
				N27409	Combat Aircraft Inc, Elkhart IN Ord Equipment Corp,New York NY (USCR quotes id. as "49-3829")	20.5.82 2.86/96

-	•	T-6	-		(to SAAF as 7040)	
					(to FA Paraguaya as 0102)	6.79
					World Wide Aeronautical Industries CA	9.2.91
					(purchased at auction, Asuncion, Paraguay 9.2.91, shipped, arr. dism. Santa Paula CA 9.91)	
				N3171A	World Wide Aeronautical Industries, Moorpark CA	19.9.91/92
					James Morgan, Aumsville OR	94
					Robert H. Poynton & Dave Saunders/ Western Warbirds, Perth-Jandakot WA	4.94
					(shipped ex USA, arr. dism. Jandakot 15.6.94)	
					(id. quoted as 7040)	
-	•	T-6	-		(to SAAF as 7083)	
					(to FA Paraguaya as 0104)	6.79
					World Wide Aeronautical Industries CA	9.2.91
					(purchased at auction, Asuncion, Paraguay 9.2.91, shipped, arr. dism. Santa Paula CA 9.91)	
				N3173N	World Wide Aeronautical Industries, Moorpark CA	19.9.91/92
					James E. Kaylor, Ocala FL	1.93
					(noted stored Leeward Air Ranch FL 11.93)	
					(id. quoted as 7083)	
-	•	T-6	-		(to FA Paraguaya as 0107, to 0122)	
					World Wide Aeronautical Industries CA	9.2.91
					(purchased at auction, Asuncion, Paraguay 9.2.91, shipped, arr. dism. Santa Paula CA 9.91)	
				N3171H	World Wide Aeronautical Industries, Moorpark CA	19.9.91/92
					James Morgan, Aumsville OR	94
					Robert H. Poynton & Dave Saunders/ Western Warbirds, Perth-Jandakot WA	4.94/95
					(shipped ex USA, arr. dism. Jandakot 15.6.94)	
				VH-YPY	Peter Yates, Perth WA: rest. project	13.10.95
					(id. quoted as 412223)	
-	•	T-6	-		(to FA Paraguaya as 0108)	
					World Wide Aeronautical Industries CA	9.2.91
					(purchased at auction, Asuncion, Paraguay 9.2.91, shipped, arr. dism. Santa Paula CA 9.91)	
				N3171K	World Wide Aeronautical Industries, Moorpark CA	19.9.91/92
					James Morgan, Aumsville OR	94
					Robert H. Poynton & Dave Saunders/ Western Warbirds, Perth-Jandakot WA	4.94
					(shipped ex USA, arr. dism. Jandakot 15.6.94)	
					Guido Zuccoli, Darwin NT	.94
					Robert Lee-Guard, Hervey Bay QLD	.94
				VH-TOA	Norleigh Aviation, Hervey Bay QLD	16.6.95
					(trucked Jandakot-Darwin, arr. 1.9.94 for rest., due to fly .95 as "RNZAF NZ1014")	
					take-off accident, Toowoomba QLD	20.1.96
					(id. quoted as 412227)	
-	•	T-6	-		(to SAAF as 7500)	
					(to FA Paraguaya as 0109)	6.79
					World Wide Aeronautical Industries CA	9.2.91
					(purchased at auction, Asuncion, Paraguay 9.2.91, shipped, arr. dism. Santa Paula CA 9.91)	
				N3171N	World Wide Aeronautical Industries, Moorpark CA	19.9.91/92
					James Morgan, Aumsville OR	94
					Robert H. Poynton & Dave Saunders/ Western Warbirds, Perth-Jandakot WA	4.94
					(shipped ex USA, arr. dism. Jandakot 15.6.94)	
				VH-DGP	David F. Gibson, Perth WA	8.8.94
					(id. quoted as 7500)	

-	•	T-6	-		(to SAAF as 7320)	
					(to FA Paraguaya as 0116)	6.79
					World Wide Aeronautical Industries CA	9.2.91
					(purchased at auction, Asuncion, Paraguay 9.2.91,	
					shipped, arr. dism. Santa Paula CA 9.91)	
				N3171P	World Wide Aeronautical Industries,	
					Moorpark CA	19.9.91/92
					James D. Morgan, Aumsville OR	9.93/96
					(id. quoted as 7320)	
-	•	T-6	-		(to SAAF as 7229, 7700)	
					(to FA Paraguaya as 0119)	6.79
					World Wide Aeronautical Industries CA	9.2.91
					(purchased at auction, Asuncion, Paraguay 9.2.91,	
					shipped, arr. dism. Santa Paula CA 9.91)	
				N3171R	World Wide Aeronautical Industries,	
					Moorpark CA	19.9.91/92
					James D. Morgan, Aumsville OR	4.93/95
					(id. quoted as 7229)	
-	•	T-6	-		(to SAAF as 7324)	
					(to FA Paraguaya as 0123)	
					World Wide Aeronautical Industries CA	9.2.91
					(purchased at auction, Asuncion, Paraguay 9.2.91,	
					shipped, arr. dism. Santa Paula CA 9.91)	
				N3172H	World Wide Aeronautical Industries,	
					Moorpark CA	19.9.91/92
					James D. Morgan, Aumsville OR	9.93/95
					(id. quoted as 7234)	
-	•	T-6	-		(to SAAF as 7699)	
					(to FA Paraguaya as 0124)	
					World Wide Aeronautical Industries CA	9.2.91
					(purchased at auction, Asuncion, Paraguay 9.2.91,	
					shipped, arr. dism. Santa Paula CA 9.91)	
					World Wide Aeronautical Industries,	
					Moorpark CA: US reg. candidate	19.9.91
					(noted under rest. Leeward Air Ranch FL 11.93)	
					(id. quoted as 7699)	
-	•	T-6	-		(to FA Paraguaya as 0143)	
					World Wide Aeronautical Industries CA	9.2.91
					(purchased at auction, Asuncion, Paraguay 9.2.91,	
					shipped, arr. dism. Santa Paula CA 9.91)	
				N3172J	World Wide Aeronautical Industries,	
					Moorpark CA	19.9.91/92
					James D. Morgan, Aumsville OR	4.93/96
					(id. quoted as 417250)	
-	•	T-6	-		(to FA Paraguaya as 0147)	
					World Wide Aeronautical Industries CA	9.2.91
					(purchased at auction, Asuncion, Paraguay 9.2.91,	
					shipped, arr. dism. Santa Paula CA 9.91)	
				N3172M	World Wide Aeronautical Industries,	
					Moorpark CA	19.9.91/92
					James Morgan, Aumsville OR	94
					Robert H. Poynton & Dave Saunders/	
					Western Warbirds, Perth-Jandakot WA	4.94
					(shipped ex USA, arr. dism. Jandakot 15.6.94)	
					(id. quoted as 417233)	
-	•	AT-6G	-		(to SAAF as 7694)	
					(to FA Paraguaya as ....)	
					Luis & Henry Urgoiti, Santa Monica CA:	
					sold at auction, Asuncion Paraguay	9.2.91
				N522LU	Enrique G. Urgoiti, Santa Monica CA	8.7.91/95
					(del. Asuncion to Van Nuys CA 10.91-12.91)	
					(at Van Nuys CA 12.93 "USAF CF-57")	
					(id. quoted as 7694)	

c/n		Type	Mil. ID	Reg.	History	Date
-	•	SNJ-3	-		(to FA Paraguaya as ....)	
					Jay Wisler, Kissimmee FL	c89
					(stored at Weeks Air Museum storage facility, Tamiami FL)	
					Jerry H. Trachtman, Merritt Island FL	6.90/93
					(rest. Kissimmee FL 90/93, due to fly .93)	
				N625JT	Jerry H. Trachtman, Merritt Island FL	93
-	•	AT-6G	-		(to SAAF as 7725)	94
					shipped to Chile for airshow	.94
					South African Armscor: civil disposal in Chile	.94
				N725SD	Steve E. Dean/Phoenix Associates, Gilmer TX	27.6.94/95
					(id. quoted as "SA-070")	
-	•	AT-6G	-		(to SAAF as ....): disposal	94
				N826G	Parker Aviation Enterprises, Warren VT	5.94
					Gordon Rapp, Kensington CT	1.95
					(id. quoted as "SA-075")	
-	•	AT-6G	-		(to SAAF as ....): disposal	94
				N836G	Parker Aviation Enterprises, Warren VT	5.94
					Peco Foods Inc, Gordo AL	12.94/95
					(id. quoted as "SA-076")	
-	•	T-6G	-		(to SAAF as 7690)	
					(to FA Paraguaya as ....)	
				N97FP	Frank's Aircraft Sales, Fort Worth TX	10.7.91/95
					(id. quoted as 7690)	
-	•	AT-6G	-		(to SAAF as 7695)	
					(to FA Paraguaya as ....)	
				N98FP	Frank's Aircraft Sales, Fort Worth TX	10.7.91/92
					Louis E. Edmonson, Tierra Verde FL	92
					Randy York FL	93
					William M. Reed, Denver CO	4.94/95
					(id. quoted as 7695)	
-	•	AT-6	-	**N3174B**	reg.	10.91
					(id. quoted as "15526", NA/Schmieder AT-6)	
CCF4-		Mk 4	**RCAF20....**	**N3544**	Forrest Bennett, Milwaukee MI	77
					J. W. Duff Aircraft Co, Denver CO	6.82/95
					(id. quoted as "42", type CCF Harvard 4)	
-	•	T-6 *Wildfire racer*	-	**N3941Y**	Charles Beck/Racing Aircraft Configuration, Los Angeles CA	9.83/95
					(mod. racer, new design wing/tail, P&W R2800, rebuild completed Van Nuys CA .84, ff Mojave CA .84, then stored Mojave 84/88)	
-	•	AT-6	-	**N50MQ**	Daniel M. McCue, Somerworth NH	7.86/90
					(rebuilt New Smyrna Beach FL as lookalike NA-50, fitted P&W R1340-61. ff .86)	
					Larry C. Hardin/F1 Systems Inc, Bandon OR	5.90/95
					(id. quoted as "NA50-01M")	
-	•	T-6	-	**N50RT**	Ray Thompson & William Russell, Houston TX	91/95
					(composite rebuild, parts from various T-6 models: A62M-22 Zero lookalike)	
					(flies as Japanese Zero "02-888")	
-	•	T-6	-		Whiteford Antique Air	
					Classic Air Parts Inc: reg. candidate	24.11.93
				N545GW	Gary A. Whiteford, Chino CA	12.4.94
					(USCR quotes id. 42-17575)	
-	•	T-6H	-		(to Italian AF as MM54135)	

					for sale by auction, Bari AB: poor condition	25.9.86
					US reg. candidate	9.86
				N604R	Joe Hartung, New Roads LA	7.4.88/96
-	•	T-6		N7033C	Michael Schaefer, Riverdale IL	63/69
					reg. pending: USCR	72
					Eric S. Clifford, Paris TX	1.84/96
					(flies as "42-44570/EC/TA-777/Big Foot")	
					(USCR quotes id. 88-94276)	
-	•	T-6			(to FA Mexicana as 782)	
				N7054R	Texas Turbojet Inc, Dallas TX	1.89
					Matthew J. Bennett, Keymar MD	12.90/96
					(USCR quotes id. 88-112429)	
-	•	T-6			(to FA Mexicana as 808)	
				N7055K	Texas Turbo Jet Inc, Dallas TX	1.89
					Sky Tech Aero Inc, Little Rock AR	92
					Pat Robinson, Greenfield IN	.92
					Hossier Microfilm Inc, Washington IN	11.92/96
					(flies as "US Marines SNJ-4 43709")	
					(USCR quotes id. 50-709E)	
-	•	T-6	-	N7078C	Roderick M. MacKenzie, Edmonds WA	63/64
					Northwest Pacific Packing Co, Seattle WA	66
					Howard E. Bothell, Auburn WA	69/72
					Clifton Peterson, San Rafael CA	86
					Christopher O. Prevost, Sonoma CA	2.91/96
					(USCR quotes id. "55-53150")	
-	•	T-6H	-		(to Italian AF as MM54136)	
					for sale by auction, Bari AB: poor condition	25.9.86
					reg. candidate	9.86
				N8021R	Texas Turbo Jet Inc, Dallas TX	5.4.89
					Kenneth W. Stowe, Little Rock AR	92/94
					Jay Brentlinger, Lac du Flambeau WI	.94/96
-	•	T-6G	-		(to FA Portuguesa as .....)	
				N8048N	Arthur D. Medore/Banair, Hemet CA	8.79
					sale rep., Mechanicville VA	86/96
					(USCR quotes id. 51-15182)	
-	•	AT-6	-		(to FA Uruguay as 336)	
					E. J. D. Heredia, Acton CA	
				N8160Y	Frank L. Wright, Valencia CA	6.2.89/96
					(USCR quotes id. "336")	
-	•	AT-6D SNJ-5			(to FA Portuguesa as .....)	
				N8539G	Arthur D. Medore, Hemet CA	4.11.80/92
					(USCR quotes id. 88-19133)	
-	•	T-6G	-	N8540P	Arthur D. Medore, Hemet CA	10.80
					Classic Air Parts, Ontario CA	7.93/95
					(USCR quotes id. 42-81646)	
-	•	T-6G	-	N8540U	Arthur D. Medore, Hemet CA	10.80/95
					(USCR quotes id. "55-14454-1")	
-	•	Mk.II	-		(to RCAF as ......)	
				N986G	Gerald L. Giroux, Plantation FL	10.83/95
					(USCR quotes id. "AJN9868")	
-	•	T-6	-		USAFM, McClellan AFB CA: arr.	.94
					(displ. as "USAF 15124/TA-124")	
-	•	T-6	-		(to FA Mexicana as ....)	
					Gene Nunn, Amarillo TX: rest. project	92
-		AT-6	-		(to FA Brasileira as ......)	
				PT-KSW	reg., conv. for agricultural ops.	.76

-	T-6	-		(to FA Brasileira as ......)	
			PT-KSY	reg., conv. for agricultural ops.	.76
-	T-6	-		(to FA Brasileira as ......)	
			PT-KSZ	reg., conv. for agricultural ops.	.76
-	T-6	-		(to FA Brasileira as ......)	
			PT-KTB	reg., conv. for agricultural ops.	.76
-	T-6	-		(to FA Brasileira as ......)	
			PT-KTF	reg., conv. for agricultural ops.	.76
-	T-6	-		(to FA Brasileira as ......)	
			PT-KTG	reg., conv. for agricultural ops.	.76
				struck-off reg.	.87
				(id. quoted as "5686": not a FAB serial)	
-	T-6	-		(to FA Brasileira as ......)	
			PT-KZY	noted derelict, FAB camouflage sc.,	
				Lencois Paulista, Sao Paulo State, Brazil	12.80
-	T-6G	-	SX-AEA	Andreas Potamianos, Pireaus	
				CofA expired, struck off reg.	.86
•	AT-6G	-	**SX-AEB**	Andreas Potamianos, Pireaus	
				CofA expired, struck-off reg.	.86
				Nick Petritsis & Danny Roussinos, Athens	90/93
-	AT-6	-	**YS-172P**	H. J. Kowalzeyk	77
- •	AT-6	-	**YS-183P**	H. J. Kowalzeyk	77
				arr. USA on flight from El Salvador	17.8.79
- •	AT-6D	-		(to SAAF as ....)	
				(to FA Gabonais as .....)	
			ZS-WLV	South African Airways,	
				Johannesburg-Jan Smuts: inst. airframe	.90
- •	T-6G	-		(to SAAF as 7727)	
			ZU-AGC	S. D. Davidson, Port Elizabeth	24.5.93
				(arr. airfreight Antwerp, Belgium 31.8.94)	
			N4109C	Seaview Princess Inc, Whippany NJ	9.94/95
				(arr. Antwerp civil sc. "ZU-AGC/7727")	
				(id. quoted as "SA-078-7715: USCR "SA-078")	
- •	AT-6G	-		(to SAAF as 7082)	
			ZU-AOP	Harvard Club of South Africa	.94
- •	AT-6G	-		(to SAAF as 7152)	
			ZU-AOS	Harvard Club of South Africa	.94
- •	AT-6G	-		(to SAAF as 7643)	
			ZU-AOX	Harvard Club of South Africa	.94
- •	AT-6			(to Argentine Navy/Armada as ......)	
				Punta Indio NAS, Argentina: displ.	92
				(displ. as "Armada EAN-001")	
- •	AT-6			(to Argentine Navy/Armada as ......)	
				Escuala Naval Militar, Argentina	92
				(poor condition, displ. as "Armada EAN-002")	
88-	AT-6D	-		(to FA Brasileira as FAB 1320)	.45
				Museu Aerospacial, Compo dos Afoncos AB,	
				Rio de Janeiro, Brazil	79/81
88-	AT-6D	-		(to FA Brasileira as FAB 1339)	.45

				Museu de Armas e Veiculos Motorizados Antigos, Bebeduoro, Brazil	79/90
119-	•	AT-6D	-	(to FA Brasileira as FAB T-61LS-1390)	.46
				(assembled by Construcoes Aeronauticas S.A. at Lagoa Santa, Brasil .46)	
				Museu Aeronautica da Fundacau, Sao Paulo	79/90
119-	•	AT-6D	-	(to FA Brasileira as FAB T-61LS-1517)	.50
				(assembled by Construcoes Aeronauticas S.A. at Lagoa Santa, Brasil .50)	
				displ. Brasilia, Brazil	90
119-	•	AT-6D	-	(to FA Brasileira as FAB T-61LS-1559)	.50
				(assembled by Construcoes Aeronauticas S.A. at Lagoa Santa, Brasil .50)	
				Museu Aerospacial, Campo dos Afoncos AB, Rio de Janeiro	79/90
				(c/n quoted as "008/05")	
119-	•	AT-6D	-	(to FA Brasileira as FAB T-61LS-1575)	.50
				(assembled by Construcoes Aeronauticas S.A. at Lagoa Santa, Brasil .50)	
				Museu de Armas e Veiculos Motorizados Antigos, Bebeduoro, Brazil	79/90
-	•	SNJ-6	-	(to FA Brasileira as FAB 1718)	
				Pirassununga AB, Brazil: displ	90
-	•	AT-6G	-	(to FA Chile as 264)	
				Los Condores AB: gate guard	92
-	•	AT-6G	-	(to FA Chile as 285)	
				Museo Aeronautico, Los Cerillos AB Chile	79/92
-	•	AT-6	-	(to FA Colombiana as FAC 720)	
				Madrid-Barroblanca AB, Colmbia: gate guard	90
-	•	AT-6	-	(to FA Colombiana as FAC 772)	
				Museo Aeronautico, Bogota-El Dorado	79/95
-	•	AT-6	-	(to FA Colombiana as FAC 791)	
				Luis F. Pinto AB, Colmbia: gate guard	90
-	•	AT-6	-	(to FA Colombiana as FAC 798)	
				Cali AB, Colombia: gate guard	90
-	•	AT-6A	-	(to FA Ecuatoriana as 20310)	
				Museo Aereo de FA Ecuatoriana, Quito AB	79/93
				(displ. as "FAE 20310/TB-310")	
-	•	AT-6	-	(to FA Ecuatoriana as 43233)	
				Museo Aero de FAE, Quito	79
-	•	AT-6	-	(to FA Ecuatoriana as 53233)	
				Museo Aero de FAE, Quito	79
-	•	SNJ-6	-	(to Aeronavale as ......)	
				Lorient-Lann Bihoue AB, France: displ.	90
				(displ. as "981/2S-81")	
-	•	AT-16 Mk. IIb	-	(to R Netherlands East Indies AF as B-416)	.48
				(arr. by ship Tandjong Priok .48, ex RCAF)	
				(to AURI/Indonesian AF as B-416)	
				Armed Forces Museum, Jakarta	79/93
-	•	AT-16 Mk. IIb	-	(to R Netherlands East Indies AF as B-424)	.48
				(arr. by ship Tandjong Priok .48, ex RCAF)	
				(to AURI/Indonesian AF as B-424)	
				Padang City Museum, Padang, Indonesia	90

-	•	AT-16 Mk. IIb	-	(to AURI/Indonesian AF as B-427) Indonesian Air Force Museum, Adisutjipto AB, Yogyakarta	 85/93
-	•	AT-16 Mk. IIb	-	(to AURI/Indonesian AF as B-440) Indonesian Air Force Academy, Yogyakarta	 88/90
-	•	AT-16 Mk. IIb	-	(to AURI/Indonesian AF as B-442) Indonesian Air Force Academy, Yogyakarta	 88/90
-	•	AT-16 Mk. IIb	-	(to AURI/Indonesian AF as B-448) Indonesian Air Force Museum, Adisutjipto AB, Yogyakarta	 85/93
-	•	AT-6D	-	(to IDFAF as 08) Tel Nof AB, Israel: displ. Israeli Air Force Museum, Hazerim AB (static displ. as "08") (id. quoted as 77-4613/41-534: but 77-4613 is 41-654)	 87 90
-	•	AT-6A	-	(to IDFAF as 10) Haifa AB, Israel: displ. (id. quoted as 78-6169/41-16061 : but 78-6169 is Bu6932)	 87/90
-	•	AT-6D	-	(to IDFAF as 14) Israeli Air Force Museum, Hazerim AB, Israel (static displ. as "14", blue/sand camouflage)	 90
-	•	AT-6D	-	(to IDFAF as 24) Israeli Air Force Museum, Hazerim AB, Israel (static displ. as "24")	 90
-	•	AT-6D	-	(to IDFAF as 25) Israeli Air Force Museum, Hazerim AB, Israel (displ. as "25", maintained airworthy)	 90
-	•	AT-6D	-	(to IDFAF as 39) Israeli Air Force Museum, Hazerim AB, Israel	 90
-	•	AT-6D	-	(to IDFAF as 48) Tel Nof AB, Israel: displ.	 87/90
-	•	AT-6D	-	(to IDFAF as 54) Israeli Air Force Museum, Hazerim AB, Israel (static displ. as "54")	 90
-	•	AT-6D	-	(to IDFAF as 92) Israeli Air Force Museum, Hazerim AB, Israel	 90
-	•	AT-6D	-	(to IDFAF as 102) Israeli Air Force Museum, Hazerim AB, Israel (static displ. as "102")	 90
-	•	AT-6C/D	-	(to Italian AF as MM53432) recov. ex Italy, shipped to UK, arr. (stored unconv. Woolston UK: "RM.11" 81/82) John Eagles, Staverton: rest. Staverton (carried ficticious reg "EI-ASI" during rest!) trucked ex Staverton	 21.11.81 .82/85 .85
-	•	T-6G	-	(to Italian AF as MM53652) recov. ex Italy, shipped to UK, arr. stored unconv. Woolston UK Peter Croser, Mt Eliza VIC (rest. project) Robert H. Poynton/Panama Jack's Aircraft	 21.11.81 81/82 86/93

				Service, Perth-Jandakot WA (rest. project)	.93/94	
				(orig. markings : "T-6G MM53652")		
-	•	T-6G	-	(to Italian AF as MM53657)		
				Castrete Scrapyard, Italy	81/89	
-	•	T-6	-	(to Italian AF as MM53670)		
				Castello di Annone: displ.	90	
-	•	T-6	-	(to Italian AF as MM53679)		
				Scuola Specialisti, Capua, Italy	90	
-	•	T-6H	-	(to Italian AF as MM53692)		
				on fire dump Decimomannu AB, Sardinia	83/85	
				Old Flying Machine Co, Duxford UK	.87/88	
				(arr. airfreight RAF Lyneham 19.1.88)		
				Medway Aircraft Pres. Society, Rochester	.88	
				(spares for MM54099 rest., Rochester .88)		
CCF4-	•	T-6J	-	(to Italian AF as MM53796/Code SC.52)		
				Robs Lamplough, Duxford UK: imported	.81	
				(under rest. Kemble 85)		
		T-6H	-	(to Italian AF as MM53806)		
				for sale by auction, Bari AB: poor condition	22.9.86	
				USCR reg. candidate	9.86	
-	•	T-6H	-	(to Italian AF as MM53818)		
				gate guard, Viterbo	.82	
-	•	T-6H	-	(to Italian AF as MM53820)		
				displ. in gardens, Italy	85/95	
				acquired by Italian restoration group	5.95	
-	•	T-6H	-	(to Italian AF as MM53822)		
				Raccolta Della Base di Rivolto, Rivolto AB	88	
-	•	Mk.4	-	(to Italian AF as MM53823): "SC70"		T-6J
				Nido della Aquile Air Museum, Padua	80/83	
				(static rest. at Padua .83)		
				Museo Dell'Aria, Castello di San Pelagio	83/88	
-	•	T-6H	-	(to Italian AF as MM53825)		
				displ. Guidonia	83	
-	•	T-6H	-	(to Italian AF as MM53828)	.54	Mk. 4
				AMI Experimental Flying Unit	93	
				(rest. Algheron AB .91/93, due to fly .93)		
-	•	T-6H	-	(to Italian AF as MM53835)		Mk. 4
				displ. Cascino, Italy	83	
-	•	T-6D	-	(to Italian AF as MM53864)		
				Camp Darby, Italy: displ.	83	
-	•	T-6G	-	(to Italian AF as MM54097/Code RR-67)		
				Museo Storico Dell Aeronautica,		
				Vigna di Valle AB, Rome	79/88	
-	•	T-6G	-	(to Italian AF as MM54098/Code SL-37)		
				displ. Grazzanise, Italy	83/92	
-	•	T-6H	-	(to Italian AF as MM54099/Code RR-56)		
				on fire dump Decimomannu AB, Sardinia	83/85	
				Old Flying Machine Co, Duxford UK	.87/88	
				(arr. airfreight RAF Lyneham .87, arr. dism.		
				Duxford 31.10.87; rest. Rochester 88)		
-	•	T-6G	-	(to Italian AF as MM54106)		
				displ. Novara-Cameri, Italy "53-27"	.79/83	

				Raccolta Della Base de Cameri, Cameri AB	88
-	•	T-6G	-	(to Italian AF as MM54114) Museo Nazionale Della Scienza e Della Technica, Milan	79/88
-	•	T-6H	-	(to Italian AF as MM54143) Raccolta Della Base di Gallarate, Gallarate AB	85/88
-	•	T-6H	-	(to Italian AF as MM54144) Assoc. pour la Sauvegarde des Avions Anciens, Orion, France	90
-	•	T-6H	-	(to Italian AF as MM54146) Museo Della Guerra, Italy: displ.	88
-	•	T-6H	-	(to Italian AF as MM54149) Castel del Rio, Italy: displ.	83
-	•	T-6H	-	(to Italian AF as MM54292/Code SC.79 Conegliano D'Otranto, Italy: displ.	87
-	•	Mk. 4 T-6J	-	(to Italian AF as MM.......) Tom Campau, Plymouth MI	91/93
-	•	T-6G	-	(rebuilt ex AT-6 41-32197) (to Italian AF as MM.......) rest. project, Essex UK	92
182-	•	T-6G	-	(to JMSDF as 52-0002) Ashiya AB, Japan: displ.	90
182-	•	T-6G	-	(to JMSDF as 52-0011) Shizuhama AB, Japan: displ.	90
182-	•	T-6G	-	(to JMSDF as 52-0022, 72-0022) Iruma AB, Japan: displ. as "72-0022"	90
182-	•	T-6G	-	(to JMSDF as 52-0074) Hamamatsu AB, Japan: displ.	90
182-	•	T-6G	-	(to JMSDF as 52-0075) JASDF Officer School, Nara-shi, Japan: displ.	90
182-	•	T-6G	-	(to JMSDF as 52-0080) Matsushima AB, Japan: displ.	90
182-	•	T-6G	-	(to JMSDF as 52-0082) Komatsu AB, Japan: displ.	90
182-	•	T-6G	-	(to JMSDF as 52-0099) Tokorozawa Aviation Museum, Kokukoen Park, Tokyo	94
182-	•	T-6G	-	(to JMSDF as 52-0100) Gifu AB, Japan: displ.	90
182-	•	T-6G	-	(to JMSDF as 52-0118) Kyushu Gakuin University, Japan: displ.	87
182-	•	T-6G	-	(to JMSDF as 52-0128) Kumagaya Air Force Technical School Collection, Kumagaya, Japan: displ.	90
182-	•	T-6G	-	(to JMSDF as 72-0132) Naka Nihon Koku Senmon Gakko College, Seki-Shi, Japan: displ.	90

-	•	SNJ-5	-	(to JMSDF as 6192) Kyushu Gakuin University, Japan: displ.	 87
-	•	AT-6	-	(to FA Mexicana as EAN-757) Colegio del Aire, Zapopan AB, Jalisco: displ.	 90
-	•	AT-6	-	(to FA Mexicana as 005, later EAN-795) El Cipres AB, Ensenada: displ.	 81/90
-	•	T-6	-	Royal Air Maroc Engineering School, Casablanca-Anfa, Morrocco inst. airframe: "RAM-1"	 94
-	•	T-6	-	Royal Air Maroc Engineering School, Casablanca-Anfa, Morrocco inst. airframe: "RAM-2"	 94
-	•	T-6G	-	(to Pakistan AF as T4200) Pakistan Air Force Museum, Peshawa AB	 79/90
-	•	AT-6G	-	(to Philippine AF as .....) Philippine AF Museum, Nichols Field AB renamed Villamor AB, Manila (displ. as "150162/662")	 75/91
-	•	T-6 Mk.II	-	(to RAF as EX...) (to SAAF as ....) (to FA Portuguesa as 1512) Museo do Ar: stored derelict, Sintra AB	 .69 88/89
-	•	Mk. II	-	(to RAF as EX...) (to SAAF as ....) (to FA Portuguesa as 1527) Museo do Ar, Alverca AB, Portugal: stored	 .69 88/89
-	•	AT-6 Mk. II	-	(to RAF as EX...) (to SAAF as ....) (to FA Portuguesa as 1546) Museo do Ar, Alverca AB, Portugal: stored Museo do Ar, Sintra AB, Portugal: displ.	 .69 88/89 95
-	•	T-6J	-	(to FA Portuguesa as 1705) wings arr. Johannesburg-Rand ex Beira (wings stored at Aero Services hangar Rand)	 11.94
-	•	T-6J	-	(to FA Portuguesa as 1737) Museo do Ar, Alverca AB, Portugal: stored	 88/89
-	•	T-6G/J	-	(to FA Portuguesa as 1769) Museu do Ar, Montijo AB, Portugal (flies as FAP 1769)	 85/90
-	•	T-6G/J	-	(to FA Portuguesa as 1774) Museu do Ar, Montijo AB, Portugal (flies as FAP 1774)	 85/90
CCF4-...	•	Mk. 4M	-	(to FA Portuguesa as 1780) (to Mozambique PLAF as 1780) abandoned Maputo, Mozambique recov. by Brian Zeederberg/Ian Popplewell, Syferfontein, Johannesburg: arr. dism. arr. dism., Thruxton UK	 .74/89 3.89 12.89
-	•	AT-6G	-	(to SAAF as 7722) shipped to Chile for airshow South African Armscor: civil disposal in Chile	94 .94 .94
-	•	T-6G	-	(to Spanish AF as E.16-63) Patrimoine Aeronautique Nat., Luxembourg-Findel: del.	 14.10.83

- •	T-6G	-	(to Spanish AF as E.16-97) Museo del Aire, Cuatro Vientos AB	88
- •	T-6G	-	(to Spanish AF as E.16-110) Patrimoine Aeronautique Nat., Luxembourg-Findel: del.	14.10.83
- •	T-6G	-	(to Spanish AF as E.16-114) Patrimoine Aeronautique Nat., Luxembourg-Findel: del.	14.10.83
- •	AT-6D	-	(to Spanish AF as C.16-159) Museo del Aire, Cuatro Vientos AB	88
- •	T-6G	-	(to Spanish AF as E.16-168) Lance Aircraft Supply, Dallas TX (stored dism. in their Dallas yard 84)	84
-	T-6	-	(to Swiss AF as U-323) Swiss Air Force Museum, Dubendorf AB	75
-	T-6	-	(to Swiss AF as U-328) Swiss Air Force Museum, Dubendorf AB	75/85
- •	AT-6D	-	(to Syrian AF as 44) Syrian War Museum, Damascus: displ.	88/91
- •	T-6G	-	(to Turkish AF as 7504) Turk Hava Muzesi, Istanbul-Ataturk AB (displ. as "04")	87
- •	T-6	-	(to FA Venezolana as 2175) Maracay, Venezuala: displ. on roundabout	95
- •	T-6	-	(to FA Venezolana as 2506) Sucre AB, Venezuala: displ.	95

159-6 •	T-28A JT-28A	**49-1494**		USAFM, Wright-Patterson AFB, Dayton OH	65/95
159-7 •	T-28A	**49-1495**	N9019V	George J. Rivera, San Jose CA	1.79
			N2800A	George J. Rivera, San Jose CA	6.79
				Glenn A.Ware, Costa Mesa CA/Carson City NV	84/93
				Howard Jurgensen, Euphrata WA	5.93/94
				Tony N. Grout, Spanaway WA	5.94/95
159-8 •	T-28A ET-28A JT-28A T-28D	**49-1496**		retired to Davis-Monthan AFB AZ: storage	9.62/65
				North American Aviation, Columbus OH	6.65/66
				(rebuild to T-28D by NAA completed 7.66)	
				(to R Thai AF as 91496)	.66
				(to R Lao AF as 3407)	
				open storage, Thong Hi Hin AB, Xiengkhong, Laos: derelict	75/88
				Col Pay syndicate, Scone NSW	.88
				(recov. from Xiengkhong, Laos: trucked overland to Bangkok, shipped to Australia 12.88)	
				Sanders Aircraft Services, Chino CA	3.88/89
				Brian & Shellie Kenney, Chino CA	5.89
			N1496K	Brian P. Kenney, Myrtle Point OR	5.90
			N2496	Brian P. Kenney, Myrtle Point OR/Irvine CA	6.90/96
				(rest. Chino CA, flies as "USAF 49496/AD")	
159-15	T-28A	**49-1503**	**N7668C**	Larry S. Martin, San Fernando CA	63/64
				Lyon Laboratories, Royal Oak MI	66/70
				sale rep., USCR	78/95
159-25 •	T-28A	**49-1513**	**N9879C**	Thomas C. Owens, Dallas TX	63
				Don C. Barrett, Dallas TX	.63/64
				(to FA Dominicana as 280_)	
			HI-315	reg.	.77
			N300AF	George Baker/International Jet Transport Inc, Daytona Beach FL	84/87
				Teresa E. Wisdom, Mansfield OH	8.87/96
159-26	T-28A	49-1514	N9669C	E. G. Husband, Hollywood CA	63/70
				Institute of Atmospheric Sciences, Rapid City SD (hail suppression ops.)	70/78
159-27 •	T-28A	**49-1515**	**N7708C**	Joseph M. Nagy, South Pasedena CA	63/70
				sale rep., USCR	1.72/96
159-28 •	T-28A	**49-1516**	N7665C	Mark Hurd Aerial Surveys, Minneapolis MN	63/66
			N510MH	Mark Hurd Aerial Surveys, Minneapolis MN	
				Meteorology Research Inc, Altadena CA	69
				Institute of Atmospheric Sciences, Rapid City SD (weather research ops.)	3.70/96
159-31 •	T-28A T-28D	**49-1519**	**N8098H**	Max L. Biegert, Phoenix AZ	63
				Aircraft Specialties Inc, Mesa AZ	.63/64
				Lou Kaufman, Mesa AZ	66
				Sylvia J. Guthrie, Los Angeles CA	69/70
				(to R Lao AF as 3408)	
				open storage, Thong Hi Hin AB, Xiengkhong, Laos: derelict	75/88
				Col Pay syndicate, Scone NSW	.88
				(recov. from Xiengkhong, Laos: trucked overland to Bangkok, shipped to Australia 12.88)	
				John Weymouth/Heli-Muster, Victoria River Downs Station, Katherine NT	.89/91
			VH-AVC	John Weymouth/Heli-Muster, Katherine NT	22.5.91/96
				(rest. Darwin NT, ff .91: race #571)	
159-32 •	T-28A	**49-1520**	C-GTDG	Skywest Airways Inc, Regina SASK	3.86

			N7038U	Kenneth F. McLaughlin, Nashua NH	8.88/96
159-37 •	T-28A	**49-1525**	**N76912**	Daniel Jackson, Seymour TX	78
				James E. Kaylor, New Port Richey FL	84/86
				Ernest F. Durbano/Durbano Metals, Malad ID	87/90
				Peter H. Baier & John M. O'Connor/T-28 Inc, Northbrook IL	92/93
				767070 Ontario Limited, Niagara ONT	3.95
159-46 •	T-28A	**49-1534**	**N2814G**	Earl Dodge, Anchorage Ak	63/64
				Larry R. Matson, Anchorage AK	66
				cr. Big Bar Creek BC, during del. from AK	7.8.69
				Michael E. Coutches, Hayward CA	1.69/96
159-47 •	T-28A	**49-1535**	N9687C	Photography Unlimited, El Paso TX	63/64
				K. E. Pickles, San Jose CA/Richland WA	1.66/85
			N91535	K. E. Austin, Richland WA	10.85/96
159-51 •	T-28A Nomad	**49-1539**	N3519G	(rebuilt by NAA as NA-260 Nomad)	
				Puckett Aerial Surveys Inc, Concordia KS	63/64
				Aerial Sales Survey Co, Tucson AZ	66
				Gloria Burchinall, Brookston TX	69/76
				Albert Shirkey, Tulsa OK	78
				Paul H. Poberezny/EAA, Oshkosh WI	.81/84
			N1F	Paul H. Poberezny/EAA, Oshkosh WI	8.84/92
				William E. Harrison, Tulsa OK	92
				Red Stevenson, Bixby OK	95
159-52 •	T-28A	**49-1540**	N3708G	Byron A. Susan, Grand Prairie TX	63
	T-28D			(to FA Nicaragua as 217)	70/77
			N99395	David C. Tallichet/MARC, Chino CA	25.3.77/86
				(dep. Managua on del. to USA 26.3.77)	
				Ross & Marsha Diehl, Reno NV/Chino CA	11.86/95
159-55	T-28A	49-1543		op. USAF 606th SOS Laos & Cambodia	60s
	AT-28D			(to FA Dominicana as .....)	
			HI-283	W. Willard	.77
				rep. sold to St. Thomas USVI	21.7.77
159-56 •	T-28A	**49-1544**		(to FA Mexicana as T28-917)	
			N6FY	E. J. D. Heredia, Acton CA	12.88
				Gregory Flying Service, Tynan TX	89/93
				Frank R. Arrufat, St Louis MO	12.93/95
159-57 •	T-28A	**49-1545**	N6514C	Donald V. Lykins, Los Alamitos CA	63/64
	T-28D			Harry V. Fugguitt Sr, La Puente CA	66/70
				(to FA Ecuatoriana as 49-1545)	
				Museo Aereo de FA Ecuatoriana, Quito AB	77/96
159-59 •	T-28A	**49-1547**	N200AF	Ronald T. Stone/Northeast Excavation Co, Sandusky OH	81/94
			N228AF	Northeast Excavation Co, Sandusky OH	2.94
				Marshall Air Service, Chesterton IN	12.94/95
159-66	T-28A	49-1554	N2891G	George F. Kreitzburg, Salem OR	63/64
				Lincoln City Livestock Co, Roswell NM	66/70
	AT-28D			(to Philippine AF as AT-28D 49-1554)	
				(to Philippine Army as AT-28D 49-1554)	
159-73 •	T-28A	**49-1561**		op: Air America, Udorn AB, Thailand	71/74
	AT-28D			Thai-Am Co, Udorn AB, Thailand	3.10.74
				(op. R Lao AF as 49-1561)	74
				(to Philippine AF as 49-1561)	9.11.74
				(not used, open storage dism. USAF sc., Villamor AB, Manila 80/90)	
				H. Ken Hawkins/Business Air Charter, Newnan GA	.88
				F. W. (Bill) Pike, Cessnock NSW	.89/94

c/n	Type	Serial	Reg.	Owner/History	Date
				(shipped Australia 5.90, stored dism. Cessnock)	
				John Wakefield, Attunga NSW: stored dism.	.94/96
159-77 •	T-28A	**49-1565**	**N7663C**	Munsey E. Crost, Allenhurst & Neptune NJ	63/88
				Billy L. Gibson/Gibson Air Academy, Farmingdale NJ	5.90/95
159-78 •	T-28A	**49-1566**	**N3232G**	John H. Batte, Vineburg CA	6.78/95
159-86 •	T-28A	**49-1574**	N80696	noted Chino CA as "N80696/91574"	80
			N3742R	reg. candidate	3.80
			N28TE	Thomas Wright, Eden Prairie MN	8.80
			N80696	Roger A. Christgau, Edina MN	4.81/95
159-91 •	T-28A	**49-1579**		(to FA Mexicana as T28-980)	
			N7055N	Texas Turbo Jet Inc, Dallas TX	1.89
				Tom Lake, Boise ID	10.89/95
159-92 •	T-28A	**49-1580**		Aerocrafters: reg. candidate	30.3.93
159-96 •	T-28A Nomad AT-28D	**49-1584**	N8391H	California Airmotive, Van Nuys CA	58
				(conv. to NA.260 Nomad by California Airmotive)	
				Grimes Manufacturing Co, Urbania OH	63/64
				John M. Mount, McLean VA	66/69
				(to R Thai AF as ....)	
				(to R Lao AF as 3410)	
				open storage, Thong Hi Hin AB, Xiengkhong, Laos: derelict	75/88
				Col Pay syndicate, Scone NSW	.88
				(recov. from Xiengkhong, Laos: trucked overland to Bangkok, shipped to Australia 12.88)	
				Jack McDonald, Melbourne/Caboolture QLD	89/91
				Bruce Andrews, Melbourne VIC	.91/92
				(arr. dism. Caboolture QLD for rest. 9.2.91)	
			VH-BJF	ntu: Don M. Kendell, Wagga NSW	.92/93
				(arr. dism. Albury NSW ex Caboolture 11.92, rest., ff Albury .93 as "49-1584/410")	
			VH-CIA	Don M. Kendell, Wagga NSW (race #410)	22.9.93/96
159-104•	T-28A	**49-1592**		(to FA Mexicana as T28-916)	
			N7055M	Texas Turbo Jet Inc, Dallas TX	1.89
				Rudy Blakey Inc, Perry FL	4.89/95
159-108•	T-28A	**49-1596**	N800DM	Dean Martin/Warplanes Inc, Burlington VT	6.77/78
				Jimmie R. McMillan, Breckenridge TX	.79
			N1557A	Donald J. Anklin, Mooresville NC	1.80/81
				Peter G. Knox, Mooresville NC	84
				Richard D. Ervin, Indianapolis IN	12.84/96
				(USCR quotes id. "1300DM")	
159-123•	T-28A	**49-1611**		USAFM, Lackland AFB TX	79/94
159-125	T-28A	49-1613	N7641C	Kenneth Burmeister, Seattle WA	63/64
				Joseph M. Natoli, Lorton VA	66
				crashed Hagerstown MD	7.4.66
				Michael Hyrasyn, Hillside NJ	69
				sale rep., USCR	78/95
159-126•	T-28A	**49-1614**	**N3233G**	sale rep., Winlock WA	84
				Ronald A. Bobarge, Edmonds WA	87
				Mitchell Zahler, Stillwater MN	88
				Roger A. Christgau, Edina MN	11.88/90
			N628AR	Roger A. Christgau, Edina MN	3.90/96
159-128•	T-28A	**49-1616**	N2882G	Del Thoman, San Raphael CA	63/64
				Omeddon Inc, Indianapolis IN	66/70
				sold abroad : off USCR by	72
			N400AF	Seagull Enterprises Inc, Daytona Beach FL	11.80
				Deakins Carroll Insurance, Port Salerno FL	84/86
				John L. Moore, Sarasota FL	87/88

				ISRMS Inc, Land-o-Lakes FL	11.91/96
159-130 •	T-28A	**49-1618**		(to FA Mexicana as T28-910)	
			N7054L	Texas Turbo Jet Inc, Dallas TX	1.89/96
159-131•	T-28A	**49-1619**	N7491C	William E. Padden, Pasadena CA	63/64
				Richard B. Hoegh, Los Angeles CA	66/72
				Richard Holland, Fountain Valley CA	78
				August Doppes, Fort Lauderdale FL	83
			N113CA	August Doppes/Colorado Aircraft Brokers, Ft Lauderdale FL	1.84
				Dolphin Aviation Inc, Sarasota FL	86
			N128AF	Walter M. Mayer, Beaumont TX	4.87
				Ernest F. Durbano, Ogden UT	2.88/96
159-132•	T-28A	**49-1620**	**N23ES**	D. & J. Rhodes: reg. candidate	31.5.90
				Earl Schafer, Waco TX	9.90/92
				Texas Air Adventures, Waco TX	2.95
159-138•	T-28A	**49-1626**	**N9624C**	Edward T. Maloney, Claremont CA	64/70
				Helena Votech, Helena MT: inst. airframe	
				Sydney A. Torgerson, Kalispell MT	9.85/92
				(wfu, open storage Kalispell Municiple MT 91)	
				Philip O. Petrik, Sidney MT	11.92/96
159-139	T-28A	49-1627	N2837G	William Nielson, Edmonds WA	63
				S. B. J. Clark, Seattle WA	.63/64
				Wayne A. Joslin, Redmond WA	66/70
	AT-28D			(to R Lao AF as AT-28D 49-1627)	
159-142•	T-28A	**49-1630**		Davis Monthan AFB AZ: sold as surplus	24.5.78
	GT-28A			Rick R. Clemens, Sunland CA: del. ex DMAFB	19.7.78
			N28NA	Rick Clemens/Cactus Air Force, Sunland CA	11.84/89
				(rest. Sun Valley CA 78/88, ff 12.88)	
				Jeff Kertes/Cactus Air Force, Carson City NV	90/96
159-144•	T-28A	**49-1632**		Davis Monthan AFB AZ: sold as surplus	24.5.78
	GT-28A			George J. Rivera, San Jose CA: ex DMAFB	19.7.78
			N9022A	George J. Rivera, San Jose CA	1.79
				Bernard G. Combos, Simi Valley CA	84/86
				Robert E. Albee, Northridge CA	87/88
				Rick R. Clemens/Cactus Air Force Inc, Carson City NV	89/96
159-146•	T-28A	**49-1634**	N9878C	Ben A. Franklin, San Francisco CA	63/64
				George J. Rivera, Sunnyvale CA	66/70
	AT-28D			(to FA Zaire as AT-28D FG-634)	
			N99160	William Nelson, El Paso TX	12.77/78
				(del. via Biggin Hill UK, arr. 16.12.77; dep. for USA 7.9.79)	
				Mike Bogue, Oakland CA	81
				Wiley Sanders Truck Lines Inc, Troy AL	10.83/96
159-150•	T-28A	**49-1638**	**N2868G**	Floyd R. Kingston, Zephyr Hills FL	63/64
				Robert F. Burt, Fort Myers FL	66
				Desert Aerial Photographic Co Corp, Independence MO	69
				sale rep., USCR	78/95
159-155•	T-28A	**49-1643**	N9674C	Norman B. Dennis Jr, Brookneal VA	66/72
			N28RE (1	Robert Eggmann, Belleville IL	78/84
			N81643	Edward A. Buerckholtz, Chesterfield MO	8.85/95
159-156	T-28A	49-1644	N9872C	Daco Rubber Inc, Van Nuys CA	63/72
				Air Training Inc, Knoxville TN	3.77/81
			N700H	Air Training Inc, Knoxville TN	3.81/84
				cr. dest. Louden County TN	23.6.84

159-157•	T-28A	**49-1645**	N2851G	Thomas R. Preston, Knoxville TN	63
				MACO Sales Financial Corp, Palos Park IL	.63/64
				(to FA Nicaragua as 218)	
			N99394	MARC, Chino CA	3.77/85
				(dep. Managua on del. to USA 26.3.77)	
				USAFM, March AFB CA: loan	85
				Robert W. Nightingale, Ontario CA	86/88
				Art Medore/Banaire Enterprises, Hemet CA	89/93
				sale rep., Fallon NV	95
159-158•	T-28A	**49-1646**		(to FA Dominicana as ....)	
			HI-276	reg.	.77
			N70743	Associated Aircraft, Newton Falls OH	78
				Heritage Aircraft Museum, Fayetteville GA	84
				Richard P. Mouhut, Lantana FL	84/88
				James L. Griffin, Tulsa OK	91/93
				G A K Aircraft, Austin TX	4.94/96
159-159•	T-28A	**49-1647**	**N9859C**	Larry Hamilton, San Anselmo CA	63
				Robert O. Butler, Paso Robles CA	.63/64
				Edward G. Peters, Shafter CA	66
				(to FA Ecuatoriana as 0-91647)	
				Museo Aereo de FA Ecuatoriana, Quito AB	77/96
159-166•	T-28A	**49-1654**	**N5251V**	Ben Wenberg, Houghton MI	63/64
				Kemp Pontiac Cadillac Inc, Newington CT	66
				Metropolitan Air Services Inc, New York NY	69/70
				Charles Smith, Knoxville TN	74
				Anthony Guirreri, Atlanta GA	78
				Richard I. Williams, Aurora CO	84
				David K. Burnap Advertising Inc, Dayton OH	11.84/96
159-168•	T-28A	**49-1656**	**N28SV**	H. J. Schroeder, Danville IL: reg. candidate	8.89/91
				Henry J. (Butch) Schroeder, Danville IL	1.91/93
				Terry Sheddan: rest. project	.93
				Raymond N. Thomas, Decatur IL	5.95
159-174	T-28A	**49-1662**	**N9630C**	Richard A. Harter, Corona CA	63
				Emmett J. Woodard, Van Nuys CA	.63/64
				Rusk Aviation Inc, Kankakee IL	66/70
				sale rep., USCR	78/95
159-175•	T-28A AT-28D	**49-1663**		USAFM, Hurlburt Field FL	78/94
				(displ. as "USAF 41863")	
159-177•	T-28A AT-28D	**49-1665**		(to FA Dominicana as ....)	
			HI-282	W. Willard	.77
				sold to St. Thomas USVI	21.7.77
			N64785	Donald Anklin, Davidson NC	7.77/78
				Robert W. Urbine/Aviation Insurance Unlimited, Greensboro NC	81/86
				Daniel D. Blackwell, Pittsburgh PA: del.	9.86/89
			N665DB	Daniel D. Blackwell, Pittsburgh PA	9.89/91
			N665PB	Randal E. & Barbara Patrick, Gaithersburg MD	12.91/93
				Robert C. Tullius, Winchester VA	2.95
59-181	T-28A	49-1669	N9867C	John V. McHugh Jr, Bloomfield NJ	63/70
				Benjamin J. Demonstranti, Juno FL	9.73/85
				crashed dest., Lantana FL	24.11.85
59-182•	T-28A	**49-1670**		(to FA Mexicana as ....)	
			N8156Y	Texas Turbo Jet Inc, Dallas TX	4.89/96
59-185	T-28A	49-1673	N9611C	Border Aviation Inc, Yuma AZ	66
				Donald R. Alderson, Van Nuys CA	69/72
				William Blakemore, Midland TX	78
				Confederate Air Force, Harlingen TX	7.7.82/84
				Carsan Charters, Lovington NM	86/87
				Jack Gaulding/Confederate Air Force	87
				crashed NM (Gaulding k.)	9.5.87

159-188•	T-28A	**49-1676**	N2896G	Robert Marts, Somers Point NJ	63/70
				George J. Rivera, Santa Clara CA	78
			N6851D	Rick R. Clemens/Cactus Air Force, Sunland CA later Carson City NV	4.78/96
159-191•	T-28A	**49-1679**		USAFM, Reese AFB TX	88/94
159-194•	T-28A	**49-1682**		USAFM, Laughlin AFB TX	88/94
159-195•	T-28A	**49-1683**		(to FA Mexicana as T28-975)	
			N7062K	David Bieber/Paladin Aircraft, San Diego CA	12.88/96
159-199	T-28A	49-1687	N7686C	Helvin Flying Service, San Antonio TX	63
				Richard M. Vartanian, Pasadena CA	.63/64
				Graham Elliot Associates Inc, Dallas TX	66/70
159-201•	T-28A	**49-1689**		USAFM, Vance AFB OK	88/94
159-202	T-28A	49-1690		(to R Saudi AF as 49-1690)	
				noted open storage, Jeddah	81
159-205•	T-28A	**49-1693**		(to FA Mexicana as 49-1693)	
				Tijuana AB: displ. on pole as "FAM 49-1693"	82/91
159-206•	T-28A	**49-1694**	**N7497C**	United Aerial Survey Inc, Tulare CA	63/66
				Rays Aircraft Service, Porterville CA	69/72
				Rolland Kruckow, Minneapolis MN	78
				Todd C. Fruen, Scottsdale AZ	84/93
				American Fighter Aces Museum, Mesa AZ	1.94/95
159-207•	T-28A	**49-1695**		USAFM, Randolph AFB TX	88/96
				(displ. as "USAF 17882")	
159-212•	T-28A	**49-1700**	**N3659G**	Robert E. Reynolds, Blue Point NY	63/66
				Margaret J. Yates, Mt Holly NJ	69
				Gordon J. Newell, New Hartford NY	70/72
			N28JS	Sun Master Awnings Inc, Mishawaka IN	3.77/78
			N28AM	Arthur E. Muth, Darien CT	11.78/84
				Yankee Flyers Museum Inc, Fraser MI	86/87
				Harry S. Purnell, Birmingham AL	88
				Dennis T. Hallman, Lake Wylie SC	92
				Sabre Society of NC, Hickory NC: displ.	93/94
				Walter A. Newton, Lenoir NC	2.95
159-213	T-28A	49-1701	N9665C	Furniture Wholesalers Inc, Pompano Beach FL	66/72
159-215•	T-28A	**49-1703**	N7642C	Daniel J. Donahoe, San Francisco CA	63/64
				Art Holst, Eugene OR	66
				Lewis P. Hanke, Sunnyside WA	69/70
			N28100	Richard J. Dieter, South Bend IN	.73/90
				Michael Florence, Lawrence MA	.90/91
				David H. Worthington, Cincinatti OH	92
				David Baughman, Louisville KY	10.93/95
159-218•	T-28A	49-1706	**N5951V**	Darrel G. Dikeman, Syracuse KS	63/70
				sale rep., USCR	78/95
159-225•	T-28A	**49-1713**		(to R Saudi AF as 49-1713)	
				for proposed RSAF Museum, Riyadh	79
				(noted derelict in compound, Riyadh Airport 81)	
				Saudi AF Academy Collection, Riyadh	90
159-228	T-28A	49-1716	N5247V	Leslie H. Fleming, Ponce PR	63
				Sunny South Aircraft Svce, Ft. Lauderdale FL	.63/64
				Hifly Photos, Wichita KS	66/70
	AT-28D			(to R Lao AF as AT-28D 91716)	

159-231•	T-28A	**49-1719**	**N7245C**	Robert R. Pitcairn, Bryn Athyn PA	63/72
				George J. Rivera, Santa Clara CA	78
				Rick R. Clemens/Cactus Air Force, Sun Valley CA	8.88/96
159-233	T-28A	49-1721	N182U	Hamilton Aviation Co Inc, Tucson AZ	c58
	T-28R-2			(converted to Hamilton T-28R-2 c/n 9)	c58
	Nomair			Electronics Corp of America, Cambridge MA	63/64
				North America Maritime Corp, Cambridge MA	66/72
				crashed landing, Martinez GA	2.7.83
159-236•	T-28A	**49-1724**	N2884G	Munsey E. Crost, Allenhurst NJ	63/64
				G. C. Dewey Corp, New York NY: USCR	66/70
	AT-28D			(to R Lao AF as AT-28D 91724)	69/73
				open storage, Thong Hi Hin AB, Xiengkhong, Laos: derelict	75/88
				Col Pay syndicate, Scone NSW	.88
				(recov. from Xiengkhong, Laos: trucked overland to Bangkok, shipped to Australia 12.88)	
				Stephen Death, Albury NSW	89/92
			VH-MEO	Stephen Death/Hazair Agricultural Services, Albury NSW	29.5.92/96
				(rest. Albury NSW, ff 30.5.92 as "0-91724")	
159-239•	T-28A	49-1727	**N9862C**	Joseph H. Thesing, Sylmar CA	63/64
				Chain Lightning Aircraft Sales, Burbank CA	66/70
				Merle H. Maine, Ontario OR	3.78/95
159-243	T-28A	49-1731	N9858C	Vernon D. Jarvis, Decatur IL	63/64
				Crescent Airways Inc, West Hollywood CA	66/70
159-250•	T-28A	49-1738	**N7692C**	Grafton Insurance Agency, Grafton WI	63/64
				Victory Air Museum, Mundelein IL: displ.	68/74
				I. N. Burchinall Jnr, Paris TX	75
				Daniel B. Jackson, Seymour TX	4.75/95
159-252	T-28A	49-1740	N9096Z	Francis R. Fulton, Sharon Springs KS	63/69
159-254•	T-28A	**49-1742**	N9442Z	C. P. Dill, Borger TX	69/70
	T-28D			Michael Eisenstadt, Las Angeles CA	78
			N668WB	Wallace Burlingame & Assoc., Van Nuys CA	4.80
				(stored dism. Van Nuys CA by Omni Aviation: rebuilt Van Nuys .82, ferried to Charlotte NC .82 for rest. as T-28D "USAF 91742")	
			N1742R	WW2 Rebuilders, Charlotte NC	8.82
				Ronald G. Roth Co, Scottsdale AZ	83/88
				Bill Rheinschild	90
				Wayne Brooks, Huntington Beach CA	11.91/95
71-2	T-28A	50-0196	N9688C	Robert L. Hill, Naples FL: USCR	63/69
				(to FA Haiti as 53): del.	9.64/80
			N514FR (1	Summit Aviation, Middletown DE	2.84/87
				Air Armco Inc, Middletown DE	88
				struck-off USCR	1.90
71-7 •	T-28A	**50-0201**	**N9102Z**	H. W. Bruce, Dallas TX	66/72
				Marcia Kenyon, Eaton CO	78
				James C. Harris, Oklahoma City OK	3.84/88
				Joseph L. Little, Cleveland TN	3.89/95
71-8 •	T-28A	**50-0202**	**N9104Z**	(conv.to Hamilton T-28R-1 Nomair)	
	T-28R-1			(to Brazilian Navy as N-703)	
	Nomair			(To FA Brasileira as 0862)	
				Museu Aeroespacial, Campo dos Afoncos, Rio	78/95
				(displ. as Marinha 50202/N-703)	
71-15	T-28A	50-0209		USAF/Inter-American Air Forces Academy,	
	GT-28A			Howard AFB, Panama Canal Zone (as "G-2")	74
71-22 •	T-28A	**50-0216**	**N9120Z**	Hardwick Aire, El Monte CA	66/69

				sale rep., USCR	78/95
171-27 •	T-28A	**50-0221**	N3336G	Robert W. Trow, Fort Lauderdale FL Jack H. Mantz, Sarasota FL Art S. Kuchan, Hudson IL Sonic Corporation, Wilmington DE	63 .63/70 84/88 89
			N221LH	Laurence C. Hofmeister, Milford MI	2.89/95
171-31 •	T-28A	**50-0225**	**N9698B**	Rick R. Clemens/Cactus Air Force, Sun Valley CA, later Carson City NV	 84/95
171-40 •	T-28A	**50-0234**		(to FA Hondurena as E.A.M.215)	
			N234NA	Courtesy Aircraft Inc, Rockford IL (dism. at Comeyagua AB, Honduras 9.85, shipped to USA 10.85: ten total) Jim E. Uhley, Clawson MI Yankee Flyers Museum, Willow Run MI	9.85/88 89 4.92/95
171-50 •	T-28A AT-28D	**50-0244**		(to FA Zaire as AT-28D FG-244) impounded by Customs, Ostend Airport, Belgium: arr. crated ex Africa: stored sold, Ostend Belgium	 82/93 .93
171-52 •	T-28A	**50-0246**	**N9092Z**	Fred Andrea, New Richmond WI sale rep., USCR	63/64 78/95
171-78 •	T-28A	**50-0272**		(to FA Hondurena as E.A.M.212)	
			N272NA	Courtesy Aircraft Inc, Rockford IL (dism. at Comeyagua AB, Honduras 9.85, shipped to USA 10.85: ten total) Walter M. Mayer, Beaumont TX Rick Hegenberger & Associates, Westport CT Steven E. Smith, Tulsa OK	9.85/86 87 .87/93 6.93/95
171-89 •	T-28A AT-28D	**50-0283**	N7666C	William J. Furlick, Caldwell NJ Simsbury Flying Service Inc, Simsbury CT (to R Lao AF as AT-28D ....) open storage, Thong Hi Hin AB, Xiengkhong, Laos: derelict Col Pay syndicate, Scone NSW (recov. from Xiengkhong, Laos: trucked overland to Bangkok, shipped to Australia 12.88) Randal W. McFarlane, Brisbane QLD	63 .63/69 75/88 .88 12.88/90
			VH-XVT	Randal W. McFarlane, Brisbane QLD (ff Bankstown 31.11.90, as "SVNAF 38372") John V. Weymouth/Heli-Muster, Darwin NT dam. forced landing, RAAF Williamtown NSW (CAA quote id. as 50-0273, flies with fuselage data block "AT-28D-10 50273")	7.12.90/93 .93/95 12.94
171-90 •	T-28A	**50-0284**	**N9692C**	Robert A. Mitchem, Broomfield CO Aero Enterprises Inc, La Porte IN Orville K. Anstaett, Garden City KS Harry Noe, Houston TX	63 .63/64 66/72 5.75/95
171-96 •	T-28A	**50-0290**	**N9640C**	Harry S. Thomas, North Ogden TX Bruce & Gunn Inc, Addison TX Paul S. Array, Delray Beach FL Earl J. Schafer, Waco TX John K. Bagley, Rexburg ID	63/64 66/78 84/88 92 3.94/95
171-105•	T-28A T-28R Nomair	**50-0299**	N9095Z	(to Brazilian Navy as .....) (To FA Brasileira as 0863) Museu Aeroespacial, Campo dos Afoncos, Rio	
			N9095Z	Mid Atlantic Air Museum, Reading PA	5.90/95
171-106•	T-28A	**50-0300**	N3292G	Eagle Squadron Inc, Sidney MT Stanley J. Sweetack, Fond Du Lac WI	63/66 69

			N213PC	Joseph F. Dulvick, Lake Orion MI	77
			N28JD	Joseph F. Dulvick, Lake Orion MI	4.77
				Conrad Hagle, Kennesaw GA	84
				Centre Equities Corp, Atlanta GA	86/87
				Consolidated Aviation Ent., Burlington VT	88
				Robert DelValle/ISRMS Inc, Land-o-Lakes FL	1.91/95
171-110	T-28A	50-0304	N7667C	Charles A. Ohanlon, San Jose CA	63
				W. E. Howell Associates Inc, Lexington MA	.63/66
			N151P	Stephen J. Roberts, Newark DE	69/78
174-17 •	T-28A	**51-3479**	CF-IWJ	Leonard Kelly, Peterborough ONT	65/66
			N499KB	Aero Enterprises Inc, Fresno CA	69
				Marilyn F. Baker, Artois CA	70
				Nation Flight Service, Santa Rosa CA	72
			N699	rereg.	.73
				K. R. Williamson, State College PA	77/78
				Richard L. Woodruff, Birmingham AL	10.83/95
174-43 •	T-28A Fennec	**51-3505**		(to l'Armee de l'Air as Fennec No.47)	
				(to Moroccan AF as ....)	
			N9873A	Jeff Hawke & David C. Tallichet/	
				Euroworld California, Long Beach CA	5.78
				(to FA Nicaragua/Sandanista as FAS162)	80/87
				Victoria Aircraft Maintenance BC: recov.	6.87
			C-FNAF	Charles J. Money, Calgary ALTA	11.7.88/95
				(rest. Victoria BC, flies as "RCN 131228"	
			N436BK	reg.	7.95
				(C-FNAF/N436BK id. quoted as "436"; owner quotes Fennec 51-362: not conv. to Fennec)	
174-51 •	T-28A	**51-3513**		(to l'Armee de l'Air as Fennec No.51)	Fennec
				(to Moroccan AF as ....)	
			N9868A	Jeff Hawke & David C. Tallichet/	
				Euroworld California, Long Beach CA	5.78
				(stored at Fort Lauderdale Executive 79/81)	
				Visionaire International Inc, Miami FL	80/83
				MARC, Chino CA	3.83/87
				Floyd R. Murphy, Walnut CA	88/91
				Frank J. Hoover, Upland CA	3.92/96
74-63 •	T-28A Fennec	**51-3525**		(to l'Armee de l'Air as Fennec No.46)	
				(to Moroccan AF as 51-3525)	
				Royal Air Maroc Engineering School,	
				Casablanca-Anfa Airport	94
74-66	T-28A Fennec	51-3528		(to l'Armee de l'Air as Fennec No.52)	
			CN-AEK	(to Moroccan AF as 51-3528)	
			HR-231A	(to FA Hondurena as FAH 231)	.78
				rep. impounded USA ; not del.	.78
				(stored FLL-Exec. FL 79/81 as HR-231)	
				Euroworld Inc, Miami FL	.79
				Specialty Restaurants Co/MARC, Chino CA	2.10.79
			N8523B	Euroworld Inc : reg. reserved	6.80
				Jeff Hawke & David C. Tallichet/	
				Visionaire International Inc, Miami FL	12.80/84
				Ron Maggard, Independence MO	
			N128RM	Ron Maggard, Independence MO	7.85/88
				struck-off USCR	11.88
74-67 •	T-28A Fennec	**51-3529**		(to l'Armee de l'Air as Fennec No.44)	
				(to Moroccan AF as ....)	
				David C. Tallichet/MARC, Chino CA	93
				Quonset Air Museum, Quonset Point RI	93/96
				(displ. orig. sc. "Morroccan 51-3529/No.44")	
74-68 •	T-28A Fennec	**51-3530**		(to l'Armee de l'Air as Fennec No.49)	
			CN-AEH	(to Moroccan AF as ....)	
			HR-230A	(to FA Hondurena as FAH 230)	.78
				rep. impounded USA; not del.	.78

				(stored FLL-Exec. FL 79/81 as HR-230A)	
				Euroworld Inc, Miami FL	.79
				Specialty Restaurants Co/MARC, Chino CA	2.10.79
			N8523A	Euroworld Inc: reg. res.	6.80
				Jeff Hawke & David C. Tallichet/	
				Visionaire International Inc, Miami FL	12.80/84
				David C. Tallichet/MARC, Chino CA	86/93
				Clyde E. Barton, Herrington TX	9.94/96
				(trucked to Herrington TX ex KS, rest. to fly)	
174-72 •	T-28A	**51-3534**		(to R Thai AF as AT-28D 0-13534)	
	AT-28D			Chiang Rai AB: gate guard	84
				Thai AF Air Classics Association, Chiang Mei	.84/96
				(recov. ex gate guard .84, rest. by Tango 1 Team	
				flies as "RTAF 0-13534/5306")	
174-86 •	T-28A	**51-3548**		(to R Thai AF as 0-13548)	
				RTAF Tango Squadron: rest., flying	95
174-90 •	T-28A	**51-3552**	N5205V	W. H. Ostenberg, Morrison CO	63
			N254JB	Baugh & Mouchet Inc, Charlotte NC	.63/66
				Valley Aerial Services Inc, Bakersfield CA	69/70
				sale rep., Bakersfield CA	78/96
174-91 •	T-28A	**51-3553**		(to l'Armee de l'Air as Fennec No. 100)	
	Fennec		N14101	Waco-Pacific Inc, Van Nuys CA	.68
				Winter Wolff & Co, New York NY	69/72
				Stephen Folkman, Philadelphia PA	78
			N991CA	Courtesy Aircraft Inc, Rockford IL	1.80/84
			C-GJCJ	Jerry C. Janes, Vancouver BC	8.84
			N5832X	William G. Bennett, Las Vegas	6.85/86
				Enstrom West Corp, Palos Verdes CA	87/92
				sale rep., Tustin CA	95
174-92 •	T-28A	**51-3554**		(to l'Armee de l'Air as Fennec No. 48)	
	Fennec			(to Moroccan AF as 13554/CNA-EW)	
			N54613	Jeff Hawk & David C. Tallichet/	
				Euroworld California Inc, Long Beach CA	3.78/79
				u/c collapse during del., Dinard, France	18.7.78
				(del. via Blackbushe 18.8.78/3.7.79)	
				(to FA Nicaragua/Sandanista as 165)	80/87
				Victoria Aircraft Maintenance, BC: recov.	6.87
			C-FSAN	322052 BC Ltd, Sidney BC	5.10.88
				Victoria Air Maintenance, Victoria BC	89/90
				(rest. Victoria BC .88 as "FA Nicaragua 165")	
				T. W. (Bill) Bailey, Victoria BC	90/92
			N203CB	Charles L. Byrd, Lauderhill FL	7.92/96
				(C-FSAN & N203CB id. quoted as "485")	
174-95 •	T-28A	**51-3557**		(to l'Armee de l'Air as Fennec No.43)	
	Fennec		CN-AEE	(to Moroccan AF as ....)	
			HR-229A	(to FA Hondurena as FAH 229)	.78
				rep. impounded USA ; not del.	.78
				(stored FLL-Exec. FL 79/80 as HR-229)	
				Euroworld Inc, Miami FL	.79
				Specialty Restaurants Co/MARC, Chino CA	2.10.79
			N85228	Euroworld Inc : reg. res.	6.80
				MARC, Chino CA	12.80
				Jeff Hawke & David C. Tallichet/	
				Visionaire International Inc, Miami FL	3.83/87
				Robert W. Nightingale, Ontario CA	88/96
174-100•	T-28A	**51-3562**		(to FA Mexicana as T28-929)	
			N5206V	reg. pending	78/88
			N128DR	Jack L. Rhoades, Columbus IN	13.3.91/95
				(USCR quotes N5206V as "51-3562",	
				N128DR as "929": also rep. ex FAM T28-946)	

74-103•	T-28A	**51-3565**		(to l'Armee de l'Air as Fennec No. 56)	
	Fennec		CN-AEN	(to Moroccan AF as ....)	
			HR-232A	(to FA Hondurena as FAH 232)	.78
				rep. impounded USA ; not del.	.78
				Euroworld Inc, Miami FL	.79
				Specialty Restaurants Co/MARC, Chino CA	2.10.79
			N8522Z	Euroworld Inc: reg. res.	6.80
				MARC, Chino CA	12.80/88
74-108•	T-28A	**51-3570**		(to l'Armee de l'Air as Fennec No. 98)	
	Fennec		N14103	Waco-Pacific Inc, Van Nuys CA	.68
				Winter Wolff & Co, New York NY	69/70
				Quality Components Inc, Los Angeles CA	72
				(to FA Haiti as 1241): del.	10.73/78
			N14103	Lan-Dale Co, Reno NV	3.78
				Warbirds Inc, Queens NY	84/87
				Robert W. Urbine, High Point NC	88/92
				LTA Insurance Brokers, Greensboro NC	92
				Cannon Aircraft Sales, Greensboro NC	11.93/96
74-111•	T-28A	**51-3573**		(to l'Armee de l'Air as Fennec No. 82)	
	Fennec		**N14119**	Waco-Pacific Inc, Van Nuys CA	.68
				Winter Wolff & Co, New York NY	69/72
				LaSalle Electronics, Galesburg IL	78
				Harold Mays/MMB Inc, Thomson GA	12.81/95
74-112•	T-28A	**51-3574**		(to FA Argentina as E-608)	
				Museo Nacional de Aeronautica,	
				Aeroparque Airport, Buenos Aires	68/96
74-126•	T-28A	**51-3588**		(to R Lao AF as AT-28D 3405)	
	AT-28D			open storage, Thong Hi Hin AB, Xiengkhong,	
				Laos: derelict	75/88
				Col Pay syndicate, Scone NSW	.88
				(recov. from Xiengkhong, Laos: trucked	
				overland to Bangkok, shipped to Australia 12.88)	
			VH-WPA	ntu: F. W. Pike, Sydney NSW	89/93
			VH-PFM	F. W. (Bill) Pike, Cessnock NSW	30.9.93/94
				(rest. Sydney-Bankstown NSW 90/94,	
				ff 6.7.94 as "49543/TO")	
				William J. R. Hamilton, Sydney NSW	2.94/96
				(note: aircraft arr. painted as RLAF13388,	
				but NAA plate shows 51-3588)	
74-128•	T-28A	**51-3590**		(to l'Armee de l'Air as Fennec No.54)	
	Fennec			(to Moroccan AF as ....)	
			N9863A	Euroworld California Inc, Long Beach CA 5.78	
				Visionaire International Inc, Miami FL	78/80
				(to FA Nicaragua/Sandanista as 163)	80/87
				Victoria Aircraft Maintenance BC: recov.	6.87
			C-FXRD	Randy B. Diaper, Calgary ALTA	11.7.88/96
			N521DF	reg.	8.95
				(id. quoted as "521")	
74-150•	T-28A	**51-3612**		(to US Army as 51-3612)	
				US Army Aviation Museum, Fort Rucker AL	82/88
				USAFM, Robins AFB GA	94
74-154	T-28A	51-3616	N1384T		
	T-28D		**N28TW**	844 Squadron Inc, Boulder CO	9.82/83
				crashed into mountain, Winter Park CO	12.2.83
74-155•	T-28A	**51-3617**		(to R Thai AF as AT-28D 0-13617)	
	AT-28D			Thai AF Air Classics Association, Chiang Mei	90/96
				(recov. ex gate guard, rest. by Tango 1 Team	
				flies as "RTAF 0-13617/22103")	
74-158•	T-28A	**51-3620**		(to l'Armee de l'Air as Fennec No. 60)	
	Fennec		N14104	Waco-Pacific Inc, Van Nuys CA	.68
				Winter Wolff & Co, New York NY	69/70

				Quality Components Inc, Los Angeles CA	72
				(to FA Haiti as 1244): del.	10.73/78
			N14104	Lan-Dale Co, Reno NV	3.78
				(del. Tucson AZ 5.78 as "FAH 1244")	
				Gary Flanders, Oakland CA	81
				Lee W. Schaller, New Athens IL	7.81/96
174-164•	T-28A Fennec	**51-3626**		(to l'Armee de l'Air as Fennec No. 96)	
			N14121	Waco-Pacific Inc, Van Nuys CA	.68
				Winter Wolff & Co, New York NY	69/70
				Quality Components Inc, Los Angeles CA	72
				(to FA Haiti as 1238): del.	10.73/78
			N14121	Lan-Dale Co, Reno NV	3.78
				(del. Tucson AZ 5.78 as "FAH 1238")	
				Les Crowder & Rick Shanholtzer	83
				Alan Preston, Dallas TX	84
				sale rep., Dallas TX	84/86
			C-GJMT(1	Dan Springer/Aviation Maintenance Ltd, Sault Ste Marie QUE	5.87/88
			N5015L	Courtesy Aircraft Inc, Rockford IL	1.88
				Bill Rheinschild, Van Nuys CA	91/92
				(raced at Reno NV 9.91, race #44 "Stumpy")	
				Museum of Flying, Santa Monica CA	2.93/96
				(USCR quotes N5015L id. as T-28D "557")	
174-165•	T-28A Fennec	51-3627		(to l'Armee de l'Air as Fennec No.64)	
			CN-AEY	(to Moroccan AF as ....)	
			HR-233A	(to FA Hondurena as FAH 233)	.78
				rep. dam. in FAH service	21.7.78
				(stored FLL-Exec. FL 79/80 as HR-233)	
				Euroworld Inc, Miami FL	.79
				Specialty Restaurants Co/MARC, Chino CA	2.10.79
			N8539A	Euroworld Inc, Miami FL : reg. res.	6.80
				MARC, Chino CA	12.80/88
				WW2 Rebuilders Inc, Mooresville NC	.82
				William F. Smith, Mooresville NC	84/88
				R. A. "Bob" Mathews, Dunnelon FL	90
				ISRMS Inc, Land-o-Lakes FL	92
				Quick Air Inc, Wilmington DE	2.94/96
174-168•	T-28A Fennec	**51-3630**		(to l'Armee de l'Air as Fennec No. 73)	
			N14105	Waco-Pacific Inc, Van Nuys CA	.68
				Winter Wolff & Co, New York NY	69/72
				crashed, Lakeside TX	7.1.77
			N289RD (1	Kal-Aero Inc, Kalamazoo MI	8.78
			N500JG	Kal-Aero Inc, Kalamazoo MI	5.79/88
				Maurice R. Hovious, Vicksburg MI	4.90/96
174-185•	T-28A Fennec	**51-3647**		(to l'Armee de l'Air as Fennec No. 29)	
				(to Argentine Navy as ......)	.66
			N992CA	Courtesy Aircraft Inc, Rockford IL	4.83/84
			C-GLPM	Jacques Lacombe, Lavale QUE	7.84/88
			N28FE	Courtesy Aircraft Inc, Rockford IL	5.7.89
				Joseph F. Ware, Camarillo CA	.89/92
				Park Aveneue Group, Miami FL	95/96
174-197	T-28A	51-3659	N3319G	Thomas P. Mathews, Monterey CA	63
				Walter R. Wright, San Francisco CA	.63/64
				Paul Robert, Rawlins WY	66
				Bertz Aviation, Cadiz OH	69/70
	AT-28D			(to Philippine AF as AT-28D 51-3659)	
174-201•	T-28A Fennec	**51-3663**		(to l'Armee de l'Air as Fennec No. 68)	
			N14106	Waco-Pacific Inc, Van Nuys CA	.68
				Winter Wolff & Co, New York NY	69/72
			N2800W	Tulsa Piper Inc, Tulsa OK	78
				David L. Clinton, Leucadia CA	82/87
				(rest. 82/87 as T-28F)	

			N280DC	Darton International Inc, Leucadia CA & Reno NV	6.87/96
174-202•	T-28A Fennec	**51-3664**		(to l'Armee de l'Air as Fennec No. 93)	
			N14107	Waco-Pacific Inc, Van Nuys CA	.68
				Winter Wolff & Co, New York NY	69
				(to Chinese Nationalist AF as T-2833)	
				Chung Cheng Museum, Taipei Airport, Taiwan	90/92
174-216•	T-28A Fennec	**51-3678**		(to l'Armee de l'Air as Fennec No. 118)	
			N14122	Waco-Pacific Inc, Van Nuys CA	.68
				Winter Wolff & Co, New York NY	69/72
				John P. Silberman, Key West FL	78/84
				James A. Atkinson, Newport WA	1.87/92
174-219•	T-28A AT-28D	**51-3681**		(to FA Hondurena as AT-28D E.A.M.226)	
			N81NA	Courtesy Aircraft Inc, Rockford IL	9.85/87
				(dism. at Comeyagua AB, Honduras 9.85, shipped to USA 10.85: ten total)	
			C-GXUO	Bill Bailey/Bailey Aviation Service, Calgary ALTA & Sun City AZ	8.88/93
174-222•	T-28A Nomad II	**51-3684**	N260P	Pacific Airmotive Corp, Burbank CA	63/64
				(conv. by PacAero as last of four civil Nomads, the only Nomad Mk.II: c/n 615)	
				Sidney J. Freedman, Buffalo NY	66/69
				Ray Karrels, Port Washington WI	70
				dam. landing: struck-off USCR	.71
				George J. Rivera, Irving TX	2.76/78
			N2800G(2	George J. Rivera, Santa Clara CA/Irving TX	1.78/96
174-228•	T-28A Fennec	**51-3690**		(to l'Armee de l'Air as Fennec No. 42)	
				(to Moroccan AF as 51-3690)	65
			N54612	Jeff Hawke & David C. Tallichet/ Euroworld California Inc, Long Beach CA	3.78
				Visionair International Inc, Miami FL	78/80
				(del. to USA via Blackbushe UK 15.8.78/23.6.79)	
				(to FA Nicaragua/Sandanista as ....)	80/87
				Victoria Aircraft Maintenance BC: recov.	6.87
			C-GMWN	Michael R. Langford, Vancouver BC	27.9.89/94
				(rest. Victoria BC as "51-3690/Fennec No.42")	
174-231•	T-28A Fennec	**51-3693**		(to l'Armee de l'Air as Fennec No. 90)	
			N14124	Waco-Pacific Inc, Van Nuys CA	.68
				Winter Wolff & Co, New York NY	69/72
				Dennis M. Sherman, West Palm Beach FL	78
				Joseph F. Keenan, Sunnyvale CA	7.83/96
174-238•	T-28A AT-28D	**51-3700**		(to R Lao AF as AT-28D 3406)	
				open storage, Thong Hi Hin AB, Xiengkhong, Laos: derelict	75/88
				Col Pay/Noel Vinson syndicate, Scone NSW	.88
				(recov. from Xiengkhong, Laos: trucked overland to Bangkok, shipped to Australia 12.88)	
				Noel Vinson, Sydney-Bankstown NSW: stored	.88/95
				Ian Cust, Geelong VIC: trucked ex Bankstown	4.95
174-243•	T-28A	**51-3705**		(to US Army as 13705)	
			N74193	Palo Alto Unified School District, Palo Alto CA	78
			N3705D	Stephen R. Scott, Foster City CA	5.78/83
			N83705	Stephen R. Scott, Foster City CA	1.83/96
174-245•	T-28A	**51-3707**		(to FA Mexicana as T28-934)	
			N8156G	Texas Turbo Jet Inc, Dallas TX	3.3.89/96
174-260•	T-28A AT-28D	**51-3722**		(to R Thai AF as AT-28D 51-3722)	.65/75
				(to Philippine AF as AT-28D 51-3722)	.76
				(parts used in rebuild of 51-3728 at Manila .88)	
				Ian H. Kenny, Brisbane QLD	.90/96
				(rest. to fly, Brisbane-Archerfield QLD 93/96)	

174-263•	T-28A	**51-3725**		(to NASA Langley AFB as NASA 223)	.59
			N502NA	NASA Langley Research Centre, Hampton VA	70/80
			N302NA	Maryland Aviation Historical Society Inc	2.80
				Maryland Avn. Hist. Society, Annapolis MD	84/86
				William G. Bennett, Las Vegas NV	.86/88
				Silver State Aviation, Las Vegas NV	92
				Robert Powelson/Trojan Aerospace Ltd, Wilmington DE	8.93/95
174-278•	T-28A AT-28D	**51-3740**		(to R Thai AF as AT-28D 13740)	
				Don Muang AB, Bangkok: displ.	94/95
174-280•	T-28A Fennec	**51-3742**		(to l'Armee de l'Air as Fennec No. 104)	
			N14141	Waco-Pacific Inc, Van Nuys CA	.68
				Winter Wolff & Co, New York NY	69/72
				sale rep.	78
				Ray Karrels, Port Washington WI	84/88
				Caroline Karrels, Port Washington WI	4.90/95
174-289•	T-28A Nomad Fennec	**51-3751**	N78Z	North American Aviation, Los Angeles CA	
				(rebuilt as civil NA-260 Nomad)	
				Pacific Airmotive Corp, Burbank CA	59
				(rebuilt as second prototype Fennec No. 02)	
				(to l'Armee de l'Air as Fennec No. 147)	
			N14108	Waco-Pacific Inc, Van Nuys CA	.68
				Winter Wolff & Co, New York NY	69/70
				Quality Components Inc, Los Angeles CA	72
				(to FA Haiti as 1245)	10.73/78
			N14108	Lan-Dale Co, Reno NV	3.78
				(noted Tucson AZ as "FAH 1245" 10.78)	
				Harold L. Abrams, Tucson AZ	1.84/95
174-294•	T-28A Fennec	**51-3756**		(to l'Armee de l'Air as Fennec No. 103)	
			N14142	Waco-Pacific Inc, Van Nuys CA	.68
				Winter Wolff & Co, New York NY	69/72
				Grafton Insurance Agency, Grafton WI	78/88
				William M. Claybaugh, West Bend WI	12.89/95
174-304•	T-28A T-28D	**51-3766**	**N766NA**	William B. Sullivan/Wide Band Systems, Verona & Franklin NJ	8.12.89/95
				(rest. Phillipsburg PA 87/92 as T-28D)	
174-320	T-28A AT-28D	51-3782		(to Philippine AF as AT-28D 51-3782)	
			RP-R280	Jose Mari Roa, Manila	.88
				struck-off reg.	.93
				(note: composite rebuild with PAF 51-3722)	
174-323	T-28A Fennec	51-3785		(to l'Armee de l'Air as Fennec No. 111)	
			N14143	Waco Pacific Inc, Van Nuys CA	.68
				Winter Wolff & Co, New York NY	69/70
				(to FA Haiti as 12...)	10.73
174-324	T-28A YAT-28E	51-3786		conv. to second YAT-28E prototype: ff	15.2.63
				Merle H. Maine, Ontario OR	
			N2800E	George J. Rivera, Santa Clara CA	1.78
174-326•	T-28A YAT-28E	**51-3788**		conv. third YAT-28E turboprop prototype	64
				Merle H. Maine, Ontario OR	
				Pima County Air Museum, Tucson AZ	5.71/74
174-344•	T-28A Fennec	**51-7491**		(to l'Armee de l'Air as Fennec No.121)	
				Musee de l'Air et d'Espace, Le Bourget	84/88
174-346•	T-28A AT-28D	**51-7493**		(to R Lao AF as AT-28D 14793)	
				open storage, Thong Hi Hin AB, Xiengkhong, Laos: derelict	75/88
				Col Pay syndicate, Scone NSW	.88

c/n	Type	Serial	Reg	History	Date
				(recov. from Xiengkhong, Laos: trucked overland to Bangkok, shipped to Australia 12.88)	
				Steve Death, Albury NSW : spares source	.89/91
				Don Brown, Kongwack VIC : rest. project	91/94
174-353•	T-28A AT-28D	**51-7500**		(to Philippine AF as AT-28D 51-7500)	
				Philippine AF Museum, Fernando AB, Lipa City	68/78
174-362•	T-28A AT-28D	**51-7509**		(to Philippine AF as AT-28D 51-7509)	
				(to R Lao AF as 3402)	
				open storage, Thong Hi Hin AB, Xiengkhong, Laos: derelict	75/88
				Col Pay syndicate, Scone NSW	.88
				(recov. from Xiengkhong, Laos: trucked overland to Bangkok, shipped to Australia 12.88)	
				Gordon F. Glynn, Sydney NSW: stored	91/95
				(stored dism. Camden NSW 95)	
174-364	T-28A Fennec	51-7511		(to l'Armee de l'Air as Fennec No. 120)	
			N14110	Waco-Pacific Inc, Van Nuys CA	.68
				Winter Wolff & Co, New York NY	69/70
				Quality Components Inc, Los Angeles CA	72
				(to FA Haiti as 1240): del.	10.73/78
			N14110	Lan-Dale Co, Reno NV	3.78/84
				(del. Tucson AZ 5.78 as "1240")	
				crashed, dest., Rialto CA	15.3.84
174-374•	T-28A AT-28D	**51-7521**		(to R Lao AF as AT-28D 3403)	
				open storage, Thong Hi Hin AB, Xiengkhong, Laos: derelict	75/88
				Col Pay syndicate, Scone NSW	.88
				(recov. from Xiengkhong, Laos: trucked overland to Bangkok, shipped to Australia 12.88)	
				Guido Zuccoli, Darwin NT	.89/92
				Arthur A. Schmidt, Darwin NT	92/93
			VH-DUK	Arthur A. Schmidt, Alice Springs NT	5.8.93/95
				(rest. Darwin, ff .93 as "USN 7521")	
174-383	T-28A Fennec	51-7530		(to l'Armee de l'Air as Fennec No. 115)	
			N14111	Waco-Pacific Inc, Van Nuys CA	.68
				Winter Wolff & Co, New York NY	69
				off USCR by 72; rest. to USCR	11.78
174-386•	T-28A Fennec	**51-7533**		(to l'Armee de l'Air as Fennec No. 116)	
			N14144	Waco-Pacific Inc, Van Nuys CA	.68
				Winter Wolff & Co, New York NY	69/70
				Quality Components Inc, Los Angeles CA	72
				(to FA Haiti as 1237): del.	10.73/78
			N14144	Lan-Dale Co, Reno NV	3.78
				(del. Tucson AZ 5.78 as "FAH 1237")	
				H. A. Giffen, Phoenix AZ	9.84/88
				Ronald E. Evans, Highland CA	11.88/95
174-389•	T-28A AT-28D	**51-7536**		(to FA Nicaragua as AT-28D ....)	
			N99393	David C. Tallichet/ MARC, Chino CA	4.77/95
				(USCR quotes id. "389")	
174-395•	T-28A Fennec	**51-7542**		(to l'Armee de l'Air as Fennec No. 124)	
			N14112	Waco-Pacific Inc, Van Nuys CA	.68
				Winter Wolff & Co, New York NY	69/70
				Quality Components Inc, Los Angeles CA	72
				(to FA Haiti as 1242): del.	10.73/78
			N14112	Lan-Dale Co, Reno NV	3.78
				(del. Tucson AZ 5.78 as "FAH 1242")	
				Wiley Sanders Truck Lines, Troy AL	12.82/96
174-398•	T-28A Fennec	**51-7545**		(to l'Armee de l'Air as Fennec No. 119)	
			N14113	Waco-Pacific Inc, Van Nuys CA	.68
				Winter Wolff & Co, New York NY	69/70
				(to FA Haiti as 1236): del.	10.73/78

			N14113	Lan-Dale Co, Reno NV	3.78
				(del. Tucson AZ 5.78 as "FAH 1236")	
				Jacob S. Kamborian, Nashua NH	11.78/95
				(USCR quotes id. "81-1")	
174-411•	T-28A	**51-7558**		George J. Rivera, San Jose: del. ex DMAFB	27.9.78
			N90198	George J. Rivera, San Jose CA	1.79/86
				King City Aviation Inc, King City CA	87/88
				Bishop P. King, Pacific Grove CA	89/92
				Mark T. Vieira, Turlock CA	7.92/95
174-429•	T-28A AT-28D	**51-7576**		(to R Lao AF as AT-28D 3401)	
				open storage, Thong Hi Hin AB, Xiengkhong, Laos: derelict	75/88
				Col Pay syndicate, Scone NSW	.88
				(recov. from Xiengkhong, Laos: trucked overland to Bangkok, shipped to Australia 12.88)	
				Guido Zuccoli, Darwin NT	.89/94
				(rest. to fly, Darwin NT 91/94)	
			VH-ZUC	Guido Zuccoli, Darwin NT	2.11.94/95
				(ff Darwin 6.11.94 as "USAF TL-576", race #576 *Just Dreamin*)	
174-435•	T-28A	**51-7582**		(to FA Mexicana as ....)	
			N8156L	Texas Turbo Jet Inc, Dallas TX	4.89/95
174-441•	T-28A	**51-7588**		(to FA Mexicana as T28-946)	
			N129DR	Jack L. Rhoades, Columbus IN	3.91
				Richard A. Benner, Wasilla AK	92
				Jeffrey W. Brooks, Fairbanks AK	8.93/95
				(USCR quotes 946: also rep. as FAM T28-929)	
174-459•	T-28A Fennec	**51-7606**		(to l'Armee de l'Air as Fennec No. 136)	
				(to Argentine Navy as ....)	.66
			N9103F	Westair International USA Inc, Monument CO	7.87/88
				(adv. for sale by Jim Cullen/Westair .88: dism.)	
				Phil Godlewski	90
				(rest. to fly Cape May NJ 90)	
				Richard D. Janitell, Colorado Springs CO	3.91/95
174-471•	T-28A Fennec	**51-7618**		(to l'Armee de l'Air as Fennec No. 128)	
			N14114	Waco-Pacific Inc, Van Nuys CA	.68
				Winter Wolff & Co, New York NY	69/72
				Dellis W. Dodson, Tustin CA	78/88
				William Ross Enterprises, Incline Village NV	91/93
				Howard F. Jurgensen, Euphrata WA	8.93/95
174-485•	T-28A Fennec	**51-7632**		(to l'Armee de l'Air as Fennec No. 1)	.59
			CN-AEP	(to Moroccan AF as ....)	
			HR-226A	(to FA Hondurena as E.A.M.226)	.78/85
			N632NA	Courtesy Aircraft Inc, Rockford IL	9.85/86
				(dism. at Comeyagua AB, Honduras 9.85, shipped to USA 10.85: ten total)	
				William S. Sullivan, Verona NJ	87/88
				David Sowerby/DMS Management, Manchester NH & Sanford ME	89/93
				John P. Shoffner, Emerald Isle NC	1.94/95
174-508•	T-28A Fennec	**51-7655**		(to l'Armee de l'Air as Fennec No. 141)	.59
				(to Argentine Navy as ....)	7.66
				William S. Scully, Marina del Rey CA	90
			N141BS	William S. Scully, Marina del Rey CA	4.91/94
				Stroeh Corporate Ventures, Incline Village NV	11.94/95
174-522•	T-28A Fennec	**51-7669**		(to l'Armee de l'Air as Fennec No. 2)	
			N9860A	Euroworld California Inc, Long Beach CA	84
				MARC, Chino CA	4.84/95

174-534•	T-28A	**51-7681**		Aerocrafters: reg. candidate	30.3.93
174-544•	T-28A	**51-7691**	**N3313G**	William Fitchen, Capistrano Beach CA	63/64
				Lycoming Division of Avco, Stratford CT	66
				Delbert L. Aurey, Southport CT	69/72
				Wolcott Air Service, Wolcott CT	78
				David Schlingman, Kansas City MO/Tampa FL	79/95
				EAA Air Museum, Lakeland FL: displ.	93/96
174-545•	T-28A Fennec	51-7692		(to l'Armee de l'Air as Fennec No. 142)	
				displ. on roof Villeneuve, France	
			F-AZFV	Amicale des Ailes Tremontoises, Tremons	11.88/96
				(rest. Dijon-Longevic, ff 16.11.88)	
174-548•	T-28A	51-7695	**N8089H**	Avia Union, Santa Ana CA	63/64
				C. O. Hammerwold, Long Beach CA	66
				Richard S. Tobey, Newport Beach CA	69/70
				Steve Tognoli, Oakland CA	78
				Alan Preston/Fighting Air Command Inc, Dallas TX	8.84/86
				Ken F. & Shane McLaughlin, Nashua NH	1.87/96
174-553•	T-28A Nomad	**51-7700**	N8088H	Daniel Ninburg, Anaheim CA	63/66
				(rebuilt by NAA as NA-260 Nomad)	
				Waco-Pacific Inc, Van Nuys CA	69
				Richard M. Vartanian, Arcadia CA	70/72
			N100JE	Kal-Aero Inc, Kalamazoo MI	78/84
				Kalamazoo Aviation History Museum, Kalamazoo MI	86/93
174-554•	T-28A	**51-7701**		Aerocrafters: reg. candidate	30.3.93
174-583	T-28A Fennec	51-7730		(to l'Armee de l'Air as Fennec No. 4)	
				(to Moroccan AF as 517730)	
			N9857A	Jeff Hawke & David C. Tallichet/ Euroworld California Inc, Long Beach CA	5.78
				(del. via Blackbushe 14.8.78/25.6.79)	
				Visionair International, Miami FL: USCR	78/80
				(rep. to FA Nicaragua as .....)	
174-602•	T-28A Fennec	**51-7749**		(to l'Armee de l'Air as Fennec No. 135)	
				Dijon AB, France : displ.	87/88
			F-AZHR	Amicale les Ailes Tremontaises, Tremons	20.3.92/96
174-613•	T-28A	**51-7760**		(to Philippine AF as 7760)	
				San Fernando AB, Lipa Town: gate guard	82/96
174-635	T-28A Fennec	51-7782		(to l'Armee de l'Air as Fennec No. 113)	
				(to Argentine Navy as ......)	.66
			N993CA	Courtesy Aircraft Inc, Rockford IL	4.83/87
				B. Z. Corp, Santa Clara CA	88
				John Castelluci, Los Angeles CA	89/91
				crashed nr. Hollister CA	8.7.91
174-642•	T-28A	51-7789	N3320G	Ray Karrels, Port Washington WI	63/72
				North American Aerial, Richmond VA	78
			N28EG	Gene Glenn/North American Aerial, Mesa AZ	84/91
				Richard D. Ervin, Indianapolis IN	8.91/93
			N28RE (2	Richard D. Ervin, Indianapolis IN	2.93/96
174-645•	T-28A	**51-7792**		surplus sale ex Davis Monthan AFB AZ	.59
			N8166H	Cherokee Corp, Bedford OH	63/64
			N96329	Grafton Insurance Agency Inc, Grafton WI	5.77
				John Arbet Co, Chicago IL	5.77/78
				Byrne Aviation Co, Bloomfield Hills MI	82/83
				James E. Neundorfer, Houston TX	84
				Byrne Aviation Co, Bloomfield Hills MI	86/87
				John C. Hooper, Harvey LA	88
			N28GW	George W. Westmoreland, Rogers AR	12.89/92
				James A. O'Neal, Tulsa OK	5.93/95

				dam. (gear-siezed in up position) landing, Oshkosh WI	30.7.95
174-652•	T-28A Fennec	**51-7799**		(to l'Armee de l'Air as Fennec No. 26)	
				(to Argentine Navy as ....)	.66
				(prob. to FA Uraguay as ......)	
			N91020	Westair International USA Inc, Monument CO	7.87
				Richard D. Janitell, Colorado Springs CO	88/92
				Philip J. Godlewski, New Castle DE	5.91/96
174-654	T-28A	51-7801	N3201G	GHS Aircraft Group, Phoenix AZ	63/64
				Richard S. Tubey, Newport Beach CA	66
174-656•	T-28A	**51-7803**	N8087H	American Aerial Surveys Inc, San Antonio TX	63/70
				John A. Ortseifen, Chicago IL: survey ops.	8.71/96
174-687•	T-28A Fennec	**51-7834**		(to l'Armee de l'Air as Fennec No. 25)	
				(to Argentine Navy as .....)	.66
			N994CA	Courtesy Aircraft Inc, Rockford IL	4.83/88
				Fraser Sales Inc, Lee MA	.92/96
174-688•	T-28A	**51-7835**		(to l'Armee de l'Air as Fennec No. 24)	
			N14145	Waco-Pacific Inc, Van Nuys CA	.68
				Winter Wolff & Co, New York NY	69/72
				Tom Austin, Greenville TN	78
				dam. forced landing, Dedham MA	28.8.80
				Kal Aero Inc, Kalamazoo MI	84/92
189-2 •	T-28A	**52-1187**		(to R Thai AF as ....)	
				(recov. dism. ex Thailand .88)	
			N8009G	Courtesy Aircraft Inc, Rockford IL	8.3.89
				Jeff Balkema, Kalamazoo MI	90/92
				Marion Recovery Inc, Kalamazoo MI	92
				T T M Inc, Oklahoma City OK	11.94/96
189-41 •	T-28A Fennec	**52-1226**		(to l'Armee de l'Air as Fennec No. 23)	
			CN-AEC	(to Moroccan AF as ....)	
			HR-228A	(to FA Hondurena as FAH 228)	
				rep. impounded USA; not del.	.78
				(stored FLL-Exec. FL 79/81 as HR-228A)	
				Euroworld California Inc, Miami FL	.79
				Specialty Restaurants Co/MARC, Chino CA	2.10.79
			N8522X	Euroworld Inc, Miami FL : reg. res.	1.81
				David C. Tallichet/MARC, Chino CA	81/93
				Liberal Air Museum, Liberal KS: loan	93
189-53 •	T-28A Fennec	**52-1238**		(to l'Armee de l'Air as Fennec No. 15)	
				(to Argentine Navy as ......)	.66
			N995CA	Courtesy Aircraft Inc, Rockford IL	4.83/86
				Enrique R. Vazquez, San Fernando CA	87/88
			N238V	J. E. Pistons Inc, Huntington Beach CA	1.92/96
200-3 •	T-28B	**Bu137640**	**N2206G**	World Wide Aeronautical Industries Inc, Moorpark CA	12.89
				George L. Gayler, Thermal CA	8.90/96
200-6	T-28B	Bu137643	N80473	reg. candidate	8.79
200-8 •	T-28B	**Bu137645**	N132Z	US Forestry Service, Albuquerque NM	66/72
				Davis-Monthan AFB AZ: del. for storage	5.5.76/81
			N70482	Smith & Smith International Ltd	8.93
				Richard L. Standage, Simi Valley CA	3.95
200-15 •	T-28B	**Bu137652**	**N652AS**	Airplane Sales International, Beverly Hills CA	7.86/87
				Mona Benson, Suisun CA	88/92
				William H. Steen, Charlotte NC	3.93/96
200-18 •	T-28B	**Bu137655**	**N261FM**	Flight Management Inc, Tulsa OK	20.6.94/96

200-20 •	T-28B	**Bu137657**		Pima Air Museum, Tucson AZ: arr. ex DMAFB	17.1.82
			N3250D	reg. res.	10.82
				Courtesy Aircraft Inc, Rockford IL	8.85/87
				(remained stored Pima County Air Museum 86)	
				Ronald O'Beirne, Angola IN/Port St Lucie FL	9.87/96
200-24 •	T-28B	**Bu137661**		(to R Thai AF as AT-28D 0-37661)	
	AT-28D			R Thai AF Museum, Don Muang AB, Bangkok	.88/96
200-25 •	T-28B	**Bu137662**	N662WW	World Wide Aeronautical Industries Inc,	
				Moorpark CA	12.89/92
				(open storage unconv., Mesa AZ 92)	
				Robert T. Cottrill, New London NH	11.92/93
			N662BC	Robert T. Cottrill, New London NH	3.93
			N662WW	Robert T. Cottrill, New London NH	18.5.94/96
200-26 •	T-28B	**Bu137663**	**N137NA**	Airplane Sales International, Beverly Hills CA	10.85
	QT-28B			Steve Wilmans/King City Aviation,	
	T-28B			King City CA	86/88
				John F. Strehl, Sonoma CA & Minden NV	.90/96
200-31 •	T-28B	**Bu137668**		(to US Army as 37668)	
				retired to Davis Monthan AFB AZ	86/89
				(ret. to US Army as 37668)	.89
				Pima Air Museum, Tucson AZ	92
			N228KM	T-34 Inc, Seattle WA	6.95
200-32 •	T-28B	**Bu137669**	N669RR	Al Redick, Reno NV	1.86
				Les S. Salz, Reno NV	10.86/90
			N137LS	Les S. Salz, Reno NV	1.90/96
200-34 •	T-28B	**Bu137671**		(to R Thai AF as 0-37671)	
				R Thai AF Classics Association, Chiang Mai	91/92
				(rest., flies as "0-37671")	
200-36 •	T-28B	**Bu137673**		(to R Thai AF as 0-37673)	
	AT-28D			(recov. dism. ex Thailand .88)	
			N80401	Courtesy Aircraft Inc, Rockford IL	16.2.89/96
				(id. assumed: USCR quotes "53-7673")	
200-41 •	T-28B	**Bu137678**		Tom Reilly Vintage Aircraft, Kissimmee FL	93/94
				(recov. dam. ex junkyard: rest. project)	
200-51 •	T-28B	**Bu137688**		Pima Air Museum, Tucson AZ: stored	93
200-55 •	T-28B	**Bu137692**	N1184N	Time Aviation, Tucson AZ: ex DMAFB	24.8.81
				Arlie P. Kelly, Willowick OH	84/86
				Courtesy Aircraft Inc, Rockford IL	87
			N237JB	Harlow R. James, Fennimore WI	6.89/96
200-59 •	T-28B	**Bu137696**		Pima Air Museum, Tucson AZ: arr. ex DMAFB	17.1.82
			N27556	Lynn C. Hunt, Santa Rosa CA	7.82
			N428B	Lynn C. Hunt, Santa Rosa CA	3.83/96
200-60 •	T-28B	**Bu137697**		(to R Lao AF as 54-137697)	
	AT-28D			open storage, Thong Hi Hin AB, Xiengkhong,	
				Laos: derelict	75/88
				Col Pay syndicate, Scone NSW	.88
				(recov. from Xiengkhong, Laos: trucked	
				overland to Bangkok, shipped to Australia 12.88)	
				(stored dism., Nowra NAS NSW .89)	
				shipped from Australia to USA	
				Herbert R. Baker, Milwaukee WI: under rest.	91/96
200-61 •	T-28B	**Bu137698**		(to Philippines AF as 54-137698)	
	AT-28D			(not used, open storage dism., USAF sc.,	
				Villamor AB, Manila 80/88)	
			N2067A	H. Ken Hawkins/Fighter Imports, Portland OR	3.8.89/92
				sale rep., Yorba Linda CA	95

200-63 •	T-28B	**Bu137700**		(to Philippines AF as 54-137700)	
	AT-28D			(not used, open storage dism., USAF sc.,	
				Villamor AB, Manila 80/88)	
			N20681	H. Ken Hawkins/Fighter Imports, Portland OR	3.8.89/96
200-65 •	T-28B	**Bu137702**		(to US Army as 137702): based Edwards AFB	80
				USAFM: Edwards AFB CA	88/93
				(displ. as "US Army 137702")	
200-69 •	T-28B	**Bu137706**		(to SVNAF as ....)	
			N4698S	Dennis M. Sherman, West Palm Beach FL	4.84
				Donald Clemmons, Ocala FL	86/89
				Flying Legends Inc, Saulte Ste Marie MI	6.90/96
200-74 •	T-28B	**Bu137711**		(to R Thai AF as 0-37711)	
				R Thai AF Tango Squadron, Chiang Mai	93
				(rest., flies as "RTAF 0-37711/23105")	
200-75 •	T-28B	**Bu137712**	**N262FM**	Flight Management Inc, Tulsa OK	20.6.94/96
200-79 •	T-28B	**Bu137716**		(to Philippines AF as 54-137716)	
	AT-28D			(not used, open storage dism., USAF sc.,	
				Villamor AB, Manila 80/88)	
			N2060V	H. Ken Hawkins/Business Air Charter,	
				Portland OR	3.8.89
			N514FR(2	Air Armco Inc, Middletown DE	3.90/92
				Tom Neal, Prescott AZ	6.93/96
200-86 •	T-28B	**Bu137723**	N47797	State of Alaska Division of Forestry AK	8.84
			N215SF	State of Alaska, Anchorage AK	1.85/92
				Cub Enterprises	94
				Bob Stickel/Bob's Flying Service,	
				Knights Landing CA	6.10.94/96
200-89 •	T-28B	**Bu137726**		USAFM, Davis-Monthan AFB AZ	92/93
				(displ. on Davis-Monthan "Celebrity Row")	
			N128MD	M. D. Aire Co, Encino CA	1.10.93/96
200-97 •	T-28B	**Bu137734**		(to Philippines AF as 54-137734)	
	AT-28D			(not used, open storage dism., USAF sc.,	
				Villamor AB, Manila 80/88)	
			N20677	H. Ken Hawkins/Fighter Imports, Portland OR	3.8.89/92
				sale rep., Knoxville TN	95
				(stored dism. unconv., Chino CA)	
200-99	T-28B	Bu137736	N28TP	Ted R. Pieper, Aurora CO	7.6.89
				John L. Breit, Englewood CO	91/95
				broke-up in flight, crashed Calhan CO	9.7.95
200-104 •	T-28B	**Bu137741**		(to Philippines AF as 54-137741)	
	AT-28D			(not used, open storage dism., USAF sc.,	
				Villamor AB, Manila 80/88)	
			N2052H	H. Ken Hawkins/Fighter Imports, Portland OR	3.8.89/92
				Jim Worley/Worley Aviation, Dover DE	8.94/96
200-106 •	T-28B	**Bu137743**	**N5439X**	Courtesy Aircraft Inc, Rockford IL	8.84
				Karl Stoltzfus/Rockingham Aviation Inc,	
				Bridgewater VA	10.84/96
200-108 •	T-28B	**Bu137745**	**N9038L**	David C. Tallichet/MARC, Chino CA	3.87/88
				William R. Montague, Oakland CA	
				sale rep., Oakland CA	92/96
200-110 •	T-28B	**Bu137747**		(to US Army as 37747)	
				US Army Aviation Museum, Ft Rucker AL: del.	3.86/89
				(ret. to US Army as 37747)	.89
				(rest. Ft Rucker, ff 24.3.89: based Pope AFB NC)	

				US Army Aviation Museum, Fort Rucker AL	94/96
200-112 •	T-28B	**Bu137749**		(to US Army as 137749): retired DMAFB	87/89
				USAFM, Hill AFB UT	.89/93
				(displ. as "137749/ZD003")	
200-113 •	T-28B	**Bu137750**		BOC USN 28.5.54: retired to DMAFB	.78
			N578HT	Red Stevenson, Jenks OK	9.86
				Ronald J. Lee, Long Beach CA	9.86
			N750RL	Ronald J. Lee, Long Beach CA	12.86/88
			N300PT	Robert A. Vermeulen, Franklin MI	9.90/92
				Norman J. Miller & Bob Page, Southfield MI	93
			N280CM	Norman J. Miller & Thomas Murchie, San Jose CA	6.93/96
200-115 •	T-28B	**Bu137752**	**N752WW**	World Wide Aeronautical Industries Inc, Moorpark CA	12.89/96
200-122 •	T-28B	**Bu137759**	N49914	reg.	5.84/88
				(del. Topeka KS ex Davis Monthan AFB AZ .84)	
			N759T	Combat Air Museum, Topeka-Forbes Field KS	5.89/96
200-123 •	T-28B	**Bu137760**	**N128KA**	Allan B. Krosner, Santa Ana CA	2.90/95
				(wfu USN .78, rest., ff 5.90)	
200-127 •	T-28B	**Bu137764**	**N2207Y**	C. Glen Hyde, Roanoke TX	3.10.89
				Dennis A. Smith, Salem OR	
				John R. Murphy, Chesterfield MO	2.92/96
200-128 •	T-28B	**Bu137765**		San Diego Aerospace Museum CA	88/91
			N3178U	San Diego Aerospace Museum CA	23.10.91
				Jim Price Aircraft Inc, Memphis TN	11.91/96
200-136 •	T-28B AT-28D	**Bu137773**		(to R Thai AF as 54-37773)	
				(to R Lao AF as 3411)	
				open storage, Thong Hi Hin AB, Xiengkhong, Laos: derelict	75/88
				Col Pay syndicate, Scone NSW	.88
				(recov. from Xiengkhong, Laos: trucked overland to Bangkok, shipped to Australia 12.88)	
				Gregory Lovett, Melbourne VIC	.89/90
				(rest project, Melbourne-Essendon VIC)	
				John P. Morgan, Glenview IL: under rest.	91
			N128TB	Tim Brutsche/Central Michigan Crematory, Battle Creek MI	10.93
				John P. Morgan, Glenview IL	3.94/96
			N5291Y	John P. Morgan: rereg. res.	3.94
200-138 •	T-28B	**Bu137775**	**N28CT**	Lan Dale Co, Reno NV	5.89/96
200-140 •	T-28B	**Bu137777**	**N377WW**	World Wide Aeronautical Industries Inc, Moorpark CA	12.89
				Lew Mahieu Leasing Inc, State Line NV	7.90/96
200-145 •	T-28B	**Bu137782**	**N9039Z**	David C. Tallichet/MARC, Chino CA	3.87/88
				(open storage, unconv., Chandler AZ 88/89)	
				William R. Montague, Oakland CA	
				sale rep., Oakland CA	92/96
200-150 •	T-28B	**Bu137787**	**N787AS**	Airplane Sales International, Beverly Hills CA	7.86/88
				Del Fogg, Reno NV	91
				sale rep., Ione CA	92/96
200-152 •	T-28B	**Bu137789**	**N52424**	B. W. Orbiss, Inglewood CA	5.84
				Peter A. Triolo, Garden City KS	86/87
				Robert J. Beranger, Rochester NH	12.87/96
200-153 •	T-28B	**Bu137790**	N4779N	State of Alaska Division of Forestry AK	3.84
			N104SF	State of Alaska, Anchorage AK	1.85/88
				struck-off USCR	8.88

				USNAM, NAS Pensacola FL: readded	2.94
				Lee Griffin & Charles Jurgens, North Pole AK	10.94/96
200-156 •	T-28B	**Bu137793**	**N815SH**	John C. Harrison, Sacramento CA	8.85/96
200-159 •	T-28B	**Bu137796**		(to USAF as 47796)	
				NAS Anacostia DC: displ. on pole	88
200-162 •	T-28B	**Bu137799**		(to R Lao AF as 54-137799, later 3412)	.70
	AT-28D			open storage, Thong Hi Hin AB, Xiengkhong, Laos: derelict	75/88
				Col Pay syndicate, Scone NSW	.88
				(recov. from Xiengkhong, Laos: trucked overland to Bangkok, shipped to Australia 12.88)	
				Guido Zuccoli, Darwin NT	89
				Dennis Sanders/Sanders Aircraft, Chino CA	
			N28YF	Neil Weaver, Ben Scott, Ronald J. Kitchen/ Yesterdays Flyers, Carson City NV	3.3.92/96
				(rest. Carson City, ff 13.2.93 as "0-37799")	
200-164 •	T-28B	**Bu137801**	**N57973**	Aero Nostagia, Portland OR	11.84
				Vincent L. Murphy, Portland OR	86/88
				Walter E. Strow, Brookings OR	4.88
				Charles W. McCoy, Brookings OR	1.90/96
200-166 •	T-28B	**Bu137803**	**N68803**	Northwest Warbirds Inc, Twin Falls ID	1.87
				Raymond J. St. Germain, Pearland TX	.87
				Western Wings Aircraft Sales Co, Oakland OR	88
				John J. Mason, Washington DC	89
				Bengt L. Kuller, Rockford IL	92/93
				T W Inc, Ashland KY	2.93/96
200-171 •	T-28B	**Bu137808**	**N303NA**	Maryland Aviation Hist. Soc., Annapolis MD	9.86/88
				Michael E. Keenum/Air Classics Air Museum, DuPage IL	89/96
200-174 •	T-28B	**Bu138103**	**N130AS**	Airplane Sales International, Beverly Hills CA	7.86/87
				Mona Benson, Suisun CA	88/92
				Duncan R. Miller, Suisun CA	6.94/96
200-181 •	T-28	**Bu138110**		(to Philippines AF as 54-138110)	
	AT-28D			(not used, open storage dism., USAF sc., Villamor AB, Manila 80/88)	
			N2054K	H. Ken Hawkins/Fighter Imports, Portland OR	3.8.89/96
200-188 •	T-28B	**Bu138117**	**N88AW**	GWB Inc, Canby OR	9.85/88
				Chris Peatridge, Saugus MA	88
				Arthur Grabowski, Manchester NH	89
				Peter Sideris, Jupiter FL/Colts Neck NJ	12.91/95
200-190 •	T-28B	**Bu138119**	**N119DB**	Dennis G. Buehn, Reno NV	8.86
				Alvin R. Eatinger, Belmont CA/Ashland OR	87/93
				Paragon Ranch Inc, Broomfield CO	11.94/95
200-193 •	T-28B	**Bu138122**		(tfd. to USAF as 138122)	
			N28RF	Richard C. Fernalld, Anchorage AK/Yelm WA	11.85/96
200-196 •	T-28B	**Bu138125**	N653Z	Maryland Aviation Hist. Soc., Annapolis MD	10.91/92
			N28FM	Frank Lowry & Russ Newman/ Flight Management Inc, Tulsa OK	6.93/95
				(arr. dism. for rest., Tulsa OK .93/94)	
200-200 •	T-28B	**Bu138129**	**N32257**	World Aircraft Museum Inc, Calhoun GA	10.82/88
				William Jones, Tucson AZ	91/93
				R. Neal Melton, Luttrell TN	94/95
200-201 •	T-28B	**Bu138130**	N944RJ	Robby R. Jones, Minter City MS	1.87
				D. R. Webber	1.87

				Airplane Services Inc, Greenwood MS	5.89
			N228JS	ntu: John Strickland, White Marsh MD	7.90
			N944RJ	John Strickland/Maryland Warbird Museum, White Marsh MD	7.90/95
200-206 •	T-28B AT-28D	**Bu138135**		USAF, Udorn AB, Thailand	
				(to Philippines AF as 53-138135)	
				(not used, open storage dism., USAF sc., Villamor AB, Manila 80/88)	
			N2061W	H. Ken Hawkins/Business Air Charter, Portland OR	3.8.89
				Conrad H. Hagle, Portland OR	10.91/96
				(long-term rest. project at owner's house)	
200-207 •	T-28B	**Bu138136**		William E. Strickler, Rolla MO	.87/88
			N7044W	William E. Strickler, Rolla MO	11.88/90
			N27WS	William E. (Wes) Strickler, Rolla MO	6.90/93
				(dam. on ground MO by floods .93: rest. 94)	
			N28XP	William E. Strickler, Rolla MO	4.94/96
200-211 •	T-28B	**Bu138140**	**N504GH**	C. Glen Hyde, Dallas TX	4.86
				David M. Forrest, Dunwoody GA	87
				Randall O. Porter, Woodstock GA	88
				Tan Air Ltd, Manchester NH	5.91/96
200-212 •	T-28B	**Bu138141**	**N263FM**	Flight Management Inc, Tulsa OK	20.6.94/96
200-213	T-28B	**Bu138142**	**N54912**	reg. res.	9.84/92
200-215 •	T-28B	**Bu138144**		NAS Whiting Field, Milton FL	88/96
				(displ. as "USN 138701")	
200-220 •	T-28B	**Bu138149**	N391NA	Maryland Aviation Hist. Soc., Annapolis MD	2.86/87
				struck-off USCR	8.88
				People's Liberation Army Air Force Museum, Datangshan, China	90/96
				(displ. as "USN 138149/216")	
200-221 •	T-28B	**Bu138150**	**N138WW**	World Wide Aeronautical Industries Inc, Moorpark CA	12.89/96
200-229 •	T-28B	**Bu138158**	**N138RR**	Classics In American Aviation, Reno NV	7.86/88
				Cecil H. Harp, Canby OR	92
				John Herlihy, Mount Shasta CA	95
200-235 •	T-28B	**Bu138164**	**N9060F**	Charles A. Osborn/Blue Sky Aviation, Louisville KY & Sellersburg IN	7.87/96
200-242 •	T-28B	**Bu138171**	N8064H	B & B Enterprises. Cartersville GA	17.4.89
				Bill Walker & Associates, St. Simmons Is. GA	.89/90
				Byron H. Alperstein, Santa Monica CA	5.90
			N171BA	Byron H. Alperstein, Santa Monica CA	10.90/92
				Anton Ostermeier, Gardena CA	.92/93
200-243 •	T-28B	**Bu138172**	**N82AW**	Apex Associates Inc, Canby OR	1.86
				Neale C. Ducharme, Phoenix AZ	87/89
				Jeff Clyman, New York NY	.89
				QRD Equipment Corp, Long Island City NY	3.89/96
]200-244 •	T-28B	**Bu138173**		(to R Thai AF as 0-38173)	
				Ta Khli AB, Thailand: displ.	90
200-246 •	T-28B	**Bu138175**	**N28EP**	Eric C. Paul, Charlotte NC/Grapevine TX	11.88/96
				(noted Davis Monthan AFB AZ 6.88: stripped)	
200-249 •	T-28B	**Bu138178**	**N28TY**	Lan-Dale Co, Reno NV	1.85
				Roger R. Babb, Saranac MI	2.86/96
200-250 •	T-28B	**Bu138179**		Time Aviation, Tucson AZ: ex DMAFB	31.3.82
			N3905H	Dennis G. Buehn, Long Beach CA	4.83/84

				William E. Harrison, Tulsa OK (race #33)	84
				GWB Inc, Canby OR	86/87
			OE-ESA	Siegfried Angerer, Innsbruck	1.88
				Paul Doblinger, Innsbruck	.89/91
				Dieter Mateschitz, Salzburg	.93
200-252 •	T-28B AT-28D	**Bu138181**		(to Philippines AF as 53-138181) (not used, open storage dism., USAF sc., Villamor AB, Manila 80/88)	
			N2063T	H. Ken Hawkins/Business Air Charter, Portland OR	3.8.89/92
				sale rep, West Bend WI	95
200-255 •	T-28B	**Bu138184**	**N251NA**	Maryland Aviation Hist. Soc., Annapolis MD	11.88/96
200-258 •	T-28B	**Bu138187**	**N187GH**	C. Glen Hyde, Roanoke TX	12.90
				Dreamships Inc, Roanoke TX	2.1.91/96
200-262 •	T-28B	**Bu138191**	N54913	reg. reserved	9.84/87
			N107NA	Maryland Aviation Hist. Soc., Annapolis MD	5.88
				Robert C. Hansen, Delavan WI	12.89/96
200-263 •	T-28B AT-28D	**Bu138192**		(to Philippines AF as 53-138192) (not used, open storage dism., USAF sc., Villamor AB, Manila 80/88)	
			N2065F	H. Ken Hawkins/Fighter Imports, Portland OR	3.8.89/96
200-265 •	T-28B	**Bu138194**	**N194RR**	Leeward Aeronautical Sales, Ocala FL	6.86
				Leeward Racing Inc, Ocala FL	11.86
				William Stealey/Microprose Software Inc, Hunt Valley MD	4.87/95
200-273 •	T-28B	**Bu138202**		(to R Thai AF as 0-38202)	
				State of Alaska: ex Davis Montha AFB AZ (not flown, stripped for parts)	.86
				USNAM, NAS Pensacola FL	93
			N887N	USNAM, NAS Pensacola FL	11.93
				Lee Griffin & Charlie Jurgen, North Pole AK (rest. project, purchased as stripped hulk)	94/95
200-274 •	T-28B	**Bu138203**	N131Z	US Forestry Service, Albuquerque NM	66/72
				Davis Monthan AFB AZ: del. for storage	6.5.76
			N950N	US Narcotics Force,Tucson AZ: ex DMAFB	27.12.78
				Sunair Inc	
				Westair International Inc, Monument CO	7.82
				Dapro Rubber Inc, Van Nuys CA	2.83
			N372C	Dapro Rubber Inc, Van Nuys/Broken Arrow OK	9.83/95
200-277 •	T-28B	**Bu138206**	**N5493G**	reg. res.	9.84/92
200-280 •	T-28B	**Bu138209**	**N209WW**	World Wide Aeronautical Industries Inc, Moorpark CA	12.89/92
				(noted stored, Wilmot Metals, Tucson AZ 11.91)	
				Frank Sigona/Sigtronics Corp, Covina CA	3.94/95
200-281 •	T-28B	**Bu138210**		(to US Army as 138210): wfu, stored DMAFB	87/89
				(ret. to US Army as 138210)	.89
				Pima Air Museum, Tucson AZ: stored	92/93
			N262A	reg. res.	7.95
200-284 •	T-28B	**Bu138213**	**N312AS**	Airplane Sales International, Beverly Hills CA	7.86/88
				sale rep., Ione CA	92/95
200-286 •	T-28B	**Bu138215**	**N7044L**	Lenair Corp, Hubbard OR	11.88
				Curly Brehm Leasing, Devine TX	89/90
				Tiger Aviation Enterprises, Wilmington DE	5.90
				Lloyd Owens, North Weald UK	.90/91
				(stored Torrance CA 90/91)	

				Frank Sigona/Sigtronics Corp, Covina CA	4.91/95
200-287 •	T-28B	**Bu138216**	**N285MS**	Michael W. Stevenson Ltd, Pasadena MD	10.85/95
				Herb Robinson, Cambridge MD	94/95
200-289 •	T-28B	**Bu138218**	N283JR	Coke V. Stuart, Valdosta GA	7.85/87
			N283V	H. Rapone/Nav-Air Ltd, Fort Salonga NY	8.87/91
			N1283	Nav-Air Ltd, Fort Salonga NY	8.91/95
200-291 •	T-28B	**Bu138220**		Armoflex Inc, Santa Maria CA	
			N220NA	Dannie Nault, Muskogee OK	3.86/95
200-292 •	T-28B	**Bu138221**	**N221MS**	Michael W. Stevenson Ltd, Pasadena MD	8.85/88
				Dave Zeller, Meridian MS	88
				Richard B. Woodward, Charlotte SC	92
				Ram Air Inc, Alpena MI	12.93/95
200-294 •	T-28B	**Bu138223**		USNAM, NAS Pensacola FL	90
			N5109Y	USNAM, NAS Pensacola FL	10.92/93
			N679SC	ntu: Steve Carter, Oklahoma City OK	3.93
			N5109Y	Steve T. Carter, Eagle Point OR	3.93/95
200-295 •	T-28B	**Bu138224**		USNAM, NAS Pensacola FL	85
			N628B	L. K. Parker, Orland GA	5.86/87
				M. Chuck Leshe, Chandler AZ	88/89
				Gregory Weber, Redmond WA	1.90/95
200-302 •	T-28B	**Bu138231**		Davis Monthan AFB AZ: retired	11.2.79/93
			C-FTTZ	Victoria Air Maintenance, Sidney BC	9.9.93/94
			N28CU	The Williams Group, Seattle-Boeing Field WA	12.94/95
200-303 •	T-28B AT-28D	**Bu138232**		(to R Thai AF as 55-138232)	
				(to R Lao AF as 38232, later 3416)	
				open storage, Thong Hi Hin AB, Xiengkhong, Laos: derelict	75/88
				Col Pay syndicate, Scone NSW	.88
				(recov. from Xiengkhong, Laos: trucked overland to Bangkok, shipped to Australia 12.88)	
				John Rayner, Melbourne VIC	.88/91
				Ian Sylvester, Darwin NT	11.91/94
				(stored dism. Melbourne-Essendon .88/91, trucked to Darwin 11.91 for rest.)	
			VH-DPT	Ian Sylvester/Trojan Air-Tech, Darwin NT	14.1.93/95
				(ff Darwin 26.1.93 as "USN 138232/DP232")	
200-309 •	T-28B	**Bu138238**	N238WW	World Wide Aeronautical Industries Inc, Moorpark CA	12.89/92
				Robert B. Watts, Eagle Point OR	.92/94
				(trucked to Torrance CA .92 for rest. ex Davis Monthan AFB AZ)	
			N313WB	Robert B. Watts, Torrance CA	3.1.94/95
200-310 •	T-28B	**Bu138239**	N239GH	C. Glenn Hyde, Roanoke TX	5.89
			N726A	James I. Arbogast, Hamilton OH	7.90/95
200-311 •	T-28B	**Bu138240**	**N240WW**	World Wide Aeronautical Industries Inc, Moorpark CA	12.89/95
200-312 •	T-28B AT-28D	**Bu138241**		(to Philippines AF as 55-138241)	
				(not used, open storage dism., USAF sc., Villamor AB, Manila 80/88)	
			N2067K	H. Ken Hawkins/Fighter Imports, Portland OR	3.8.89/92
				sale rep., Fort Worth TX	95
200-313 •	T-28B	**Bu138242**		Anthony J. d'Alessandris, Reno NV	
			N242J	Lan-Dale Co, Reno NV	1.86/87
				Sam J. Brunetto/Brunetto Enterprises Inc, Dover DE & Coolidge AZ	9.87/95
200-316 •	T-28B	**Bu138245**	**N65491**	Randall Porter, Cartersville GA	11.90/92

				David M. Mills, Moline IL	7.92/95
200-318 •	T-28B	**Bu138247**	N54911	reg.	12.84
				John MacGuire, El Paso TX	4.85/87
			N572JB	War Eagles Air Museum, Santa Teresa NM	4.87/95
200-330 •	T-28B	**Bu138259**	N86AW	Apex Associates Inc, Canby OR	2.86
				Ken D. Kuhlman, Huntington Beach CA	87/89
				Kim Rolph-Smith, Brisbane QLD	.89/90
			VH-SHT	Kim Rolph-Smith, Brisbane QLD	28.6.90/95
200-334 •	T-28B	**Bu138263**		Lester Industries, San Antonio TX: ex DMAFB	31.3.80
				(to FA Hondurena as E.A.M.231): del.	.80/85
			N63NA	Courtesy Aircraft Inc, Rockford IL	9.85/86
				(dism. at Comeyagua AB, Honduras 9.85, shipped to USA 10.85: ten total)	
				Duane Knotts, Alexandria IN	12.87/95
200-336 •	T-28B	**Bu138265**	N7139J	Western Wings Aircraft Sales, Oakland OR	30.4.90/92
				Trojans Ltd, Wilmington DE	11.93/95
			N555PF	Trojans Ltd, Wilmington DE	1.95
200-337 •	T-28B	**Bu138266**	**N391W**	Westair International USA Inc, Monument CO	7.86
				Loran Development Corp, Manuh CT	87/92
				William E. Harrison, Tulsa OK	94
				Thomas L. Barrow, Huntsville AL	4.95
200-342 •	T-28B	**Bu138271**		USNAM, Pensacola NAS FL	88/96
				USS Lexington Museum, Corpus Christi TX: loan, displ. on board carrier	93/94
200-343 •	T-28B	**Bu138272**		Davis Monthan AFB AZ: del. for storage	9.11.76/93
			C-FPTR (2	Tom Rogers/415150 BC Ltd, White Rock BC	10.9.93
200-346 •	T-28B	**Bu138275**	N75AF	Doris E. Elkins, Bend OR	11.86
			N28DE	Armoflex Inc, Bend OR	12.86
				Doris E. Elkins, Bend OR	87/90
				Janet L. Allen, Klamath Falls OR	92/96
200-349 •	T-28B	**Bu138278**	N138NA	Arthur W. McDonnell, Mojave CA	10.85
				Ron Amiran, Portland OR/Encino CA	10.85/87
				(shipped to Australia, assembled Tyabb VIC 2.88)	
			VH-NAW	Judy Pay/Mt Gallipoli Pty Ltd, Melbourne VIC	24.5.88/96
200-351 •	T-28B	**Bu138280**	N4781P	State of Alaska Division of Forestry AK	8.84
			N218SF	State of Alaska, Anchorage AK	1.85/92
				Roger Brooks, Fairbanks AK	7.94/96
200-353 •	T-28B	**Bu138282**		stored, stripped hulk, Ocotillo Wells CA	93/94
200-357 •	T-28B	**Bu138286**	N5492X	Maryland Aviation Hist. Soc., Annapolis MD	6.85
			N351NA	Maryland Aviation Hist. Soc., Annapolis MD	7.85/88
				Courtesy Aircraft Inc, Rockford IL	12.91/96
200-358 •	T-28B AT-28D	**Bu138287**		(to Philippines AF as 53-138287)	
				(not used, open storage dism., USAF sc., Villamor AB, Manila 80/88)	
			N2065S	H. Ken Hawkins/Fighter Imports, Portland OR	3.8.89
			N28NB	Niel R. Anderson, Fort Worth TX	7.91/96
200-360 •	T-28B	**Bu138289**	N80701	B & B Enterprises, Cartersville GA	17.4.89
				John K. Bachmann, Oldwick NJ	.89
			N828B	John K. Bachmann, Fort Lauderdale FL	9.89/92
				Wally Fisk/Amjet Aircraft Corp, St Paul MN	8.93/96
200-362 •	T-28B	**Bu138291**	**N8574**	Northwest Warbirds Inc, Twin Falls ID	10.86
				Peter A. Triolo, Garden City KS	1.87

				Buddy Bryan/Utilco, Tifton GA	87/88
				Gary L. Hornbarrier & Hank Wade/	
				Carrier Aviation Inc, High Point NC	11.89/96
200-363 •	T-28B	**Bu138292**	**N28FL**	Lincoln A. Dexter, Fort Myers FL	10.85/87
				Austin J. Gibbons, Elgin IL	12.87/96
200-365 •	T-28B	**Bu138294**	**N5440F**	Courtesy Aircraft Inc, Rockford IL	8.84
				Southern Cal. Aviation Inc, Newport Beach CA	86/88
				David Moore/Dasan Farms Inc, Grimes CA	12.90/96
200-370 •	T-28B	**Bu138299**	**N54936**	reg. res.	9.84/92
200-372 •	T-28B	**Bu138301**	**N264FM**	Flight Management Inc, Tulsa OK	20.6.94
				T-34 Inc, Seattle WA	6.95
200-373 •	T-28B	**Bu138302**		(to R Thai AF as 38302)	
				Lopburi AB, Thailand: gate guard	95
200-374 •	T-28B	**Bu138303**	**N9671N**	Arthur W. McDonnell, Mojave CA	10.85/87
				Myles S. Douglas, Orlando FL	.87/88
				Estrella Flying Club, Paso Robles CA	92
				H. A. Cooper, Westlake Village CA	92/93
				struck-off USCR	3.11.94
200-377 •	T-28B	**Bu138306**	**N306WW**	World Wide Aeronautical Industries Inc,	
				Moorpark CA	12.89/92
				(open storage unconv., Mesa AZ 92)	
				Tim Brutsche/Central Michigan Crematory,	
				Battle Creek MI	2.94/95
200-379 •	T-28B	**Bu138308**	**N284MS**	M. W. Stevenson Ltd, Pasadena MD	10.85/88
				Larry Leaf/Williston Aircraft Associates,	
				Williston FL	5.89/90
				Museum of Flying, Santa Monica CA	90/93
				Eagles Nest of the Ozarks Inc, Springfield MO	8.94/95
200-381 •	T-28B	**Bu138310**	N393W	Westair International USA Inc, Monument CO	7.86
				Forrest B. Fenn, Santa Fe NM	87/90
				Apache Aviation, Dijon, France: del. ex USA	25.7.90/93
				Lafayette Classic Air, Wilmington DE : USCR	92
			F-AZIF	C. Jacquard/Lafayette Aviation, Dijon-Darois	20.9.93
				dismantled 2/96 shipped to USA	
200-382 •	T-28B	**Bu138311**	N4781E	State of Alaska Division of Forestry AK	3.84
			N214SF	State of Alaska, Anchorage AK	1.85/95
200-384 •	T-28B	**Bu138313**	**N128TD**	Lan-Dale Co, Reno NV	12.85/95
200-385 •	T-28B	**Bu138314**	**N392W**	Westair International USA Inc, Monument CO	7.86
				Mystic Marketing Co, Mystic CT	87/88
				Mauro J. Agnelneri, Indianapolis IN	9.88/95
200-385 •	T-28B	**Bu138317**		(to Philippines AF as AT-28D 55-138317)	
	AT-28D			(not used, open storage dism., USAF sc.,	
				Villamor AB, Manila 80/88)	
			N20551	H. Ken Hawkins/Fighter Imports, Portland OR	3.8.89/92
				Trojan Phlyers, Fort Worth TX	4.95
			N28NE	Trojan Phlyers: rereg. res.	4.95
200-390 •	T-28B	**Bu138319**	**N93AW**	APEXX Co Inc, Canby OR	6.86
	DT-28B			Duncan R. Miller, Suisun CA	87/95
200-391	T-28B	Bu138320		(to R Thai AF as AT-28D 55-138320)	
	AT-28D			(to R Lao AF as 0-138320)	
				open storage, Thong Hi Hin AB, Xiengkhong,	
				Laos: derelict	75/88
				Col Pay syndicate, Scone NSW	.88
				(recov. from Xiengkhong, Laos: trucked	
				overland to Bangkok, shipped to Australia 12.88)	

				Ray Delaney & Geoff Milne, Melbourne VIC	89/90
				John Rayner & Jack McDonald, Essendon VIC	91/92
				(rest. Essendon, ff 16.4.92 as "RLAF 0-138320")	
			VH-LAO	John G. Rayner, Melbourne VIC	12.3.92/95
				fcd. landing, dam., Wangaratta VIC (repaired)	13.6.92
				(race #7) crashed dest., Launceston TAS	20.2.95
200-392 •	T-28B	**Bu138321**	N52897	Armoflex Inc, Santa Maria CA	6.84
			N28AF	Armoflex Inc, Santa Maria CA	11.84/86
				Edward J. Elkins, Bend OR	87/88
				Ernest F. Durbano, Ogden UT	91/92
				Michael S. Mitchell, Klamath Falls OR	92
				Janet L. Allen, Klamath Falls OR	5.94/96
200-396 •	T-28B	**Bu138325**		(to Philippines AF as AT-28D 53-138325)	
	AT-28D			(not used, open storage dism., USAF sc.,	
				Villamor AB, Manila 80/88)	
			N2061Q	H. Ken Hawkins/Fighter Imports Inc,	
				Portland OR	3.8.89/92
				Gerald L. Giroux, Williamson GA	.92/96
200-397 •	T-28B	**Bu138326**		USNAM, NAS Pensacola FL: displ.	90/94
200-398 •	T-28B	**Bu138327**		(to US Army as 138327)	73
				USAFM, McClellan AFB CA	88/93
				(displ. as "US Army 138327")	
200-400 •	T-28B	**Bu138329**	**N5440W**	Courtesy Aircraft Inc, Rockford IL	8.84
				Cunningham Aviation Inc, Lawton OK	86
				Colonel Aircraft Sales Inc, Oklahoma City OK	9.86/96
200-401 •	T-28B	**Bu138330**	N54419	ntu:	
			N4781K	Courtesy Aircraft Sales Inc, Rockford IL	7.84
				State of Alaska Division of Forestry	8.84
			N217SF	State of Alaska, Anchorage AK	1.85/96
200-402 •	T-28B	**Bu138331**		(to R Lao AF as AT-28D 0-38331)	
	AT-28D		N5442X	Courtesy Aircraft Inc, Rockford IL	8.84
			N8331R	John M. Ware, Atlanta GA	2.85/96
200-405 •	T-28B	**Bu138334**		(tfd. to USAF as 138334)	
			N394W	Westair International USA Inc, Monument CO	6.86
				Mystic Marketing Co Inc, Mystic CT	87/88
				Evergreen Heritage Collection, Marana AZ	2.89/96
200-410 •	T-28B	**Bu138339**	N8065E	B & B Enterprises, Cartersville GA	17.4.89
				Bill Walker & Associates, St. Simmons Is. GA	.89
			N28XT	Ralph Glasser, Springfield IL	9.89/96
200-411 •	T-28B	**Bu138340**	**N5524L**	reg. res.	10.84
				J. A. Carter, Alameda CA	3.87/88
				Gary Anderson, Vacaville-Nut Tree CA	.88
				Howard S. Roberts, Grants Pass OR	1.92/6 .
200-412 •	T-28B	**Bu138341**	N47801	State of Alaska Division of Forestry AK	8.84
			N105SF	State of Alaska, Anchorage AK	10.84/96
200-414 •	T-28B	**Bu138343**		Lester Industries,San Antonio TX: ex DMAFB	31.3.80
				(to FA Hondurena as E.A.M.229): del.	.80/85
			N343NA	Courtesy Aircraft Inc, Rockford IL	9.85
				(dism. at Comeyagua AB, Honduras 9.85,	
				shipped to USA 10.85: ten total)	
			C-FRZQ	Walter Davidson Corp, Fort Langley BC	3.86
			N343NA	Courtesy Aircraft Inc, Rockford IL	12.87
				John Mitchell, Norwalk CT	7.88/96
200-418 •	T-28B	**Bu138347**	**N83AW**	Apex Associates Inc, Canby OR	2.86
				Robert E. Buschmann, Costa Mesa CA	87/88

				Boyce Thelen/TCC Aviation, Roseville CA	2.90/96
200-420 •	T-28B	**Bu138349**	**N4614**	reg. res.	9.86/92
				Merrill B. Thruston, Alameda CA	88/93
				(USCR quotes "52-9263", owner Bu138349)	
200-422 •	T-28B AT-28D	**Bu138351**		(to R Lao AF as AT-28D 0-38351)	
				(to Philippine AF as 53-138351)	
				(not used, open storage dism., USAF sc., Villamor AB, Manila 80/88)	
			N20580	H. Ken Hawkins/Fighter Imports, Portland OR	3.8.89/92
				sold to Canada, struck-off USCR	3.95
			C-FPAB	P. Brossard, Beloiel QUE	16.6.95
200-423 •	T-28B AT-28D	**Bu138352**		(to R Lao AF as AT-28D 0-38352)	
				(to Philippine AF as 53-138352)	
				(not used, open storage dism., USAF sc., Villamor AB, Manila 80/88)	
			N20523	H. Ken Hawkins/Fighter Imports, Portland OR	3.8.89/92
				sold to Canada, struck-off USCR	3.95
200-424 •	T-28B	**Bu138353**		displ. on pole, Milton FL	91
				(displ. as "136000/E-701")	
200-425 •	T-28B	**Bu138354**	**N1328B**	Ralph E. Davis, Fort Lauderdale FL	14.6.89/96
200-427 •	T-28B	**Bu138356**	**N91AW**	Apex Associates, Canby OR	1.86
				APEXX Co Inc, Canby OR	6.86
				Symbolic Warriors Inc, Weston MA	88
				John P. Morgan/Pride Aircraft, Rockford IL	8.89/90
				John P. Morgan/Symbolic Warriors Inc, Glenview IL	92/96
200-428 •	T-28B	**Bu138357**	**N114DH**	Harry S. Doan/Doan Helicopter Inc, Daytona Beach FL	7.87/88
				Robert L. Dixon, Winston-Salem NC	10.88/96
200-435 •	T-28B AT-28D	**Bu138364**		(to USAF as AT-28D 38364)	
				(to SVNAF as 38364)	
			N4698P	Dennis M. Sherman, West Palm Beach FL	4.84/86
				Michael D. Hynek, Rhinelander WI	1.87/96
200-436 •	T-28B	**Bu138365**	**N365FL**	Flying Legends Inc, Wilmington DE	10.92/96
200-437 •	T-28B	**Bu138366**		(to Philippines AF as 55-138366)	
				(not used, open storage dism., USAF sc., Villamor AB, Manila 80/88)	
			N2053C	H. Ken Hawkins/Fighter Imports, Portland OR	3.8.89
				Duane S. Doyle, Castro Valley CA	11.90/96
218-1 •	RT-28B	-	**JA3096**	Mitsubishi Industries	.54
				(to JASDF as 63-0581)	4.56/81
				dam. in accident	.63
				JASDF Technical School, Kumagaya Hamamatsu AB, Japan: displ. as "63-0581"	90/96
219-3 •	T-28B	**Bu140004**	N52475	Mike Burks, Carriere MS	10.92
			C-GTTI	Pacific Beach Investments Ltd, Victoria BC	19.1.93
219-4 •	T-28B AT-28D	**Bu140005**		(to Philippines AF as AT-28D 55-140005)	
				(not used, open storage dism., USAF sc., Villamor AB, Manila 80/88)	
			N20517	H. Ken Hawkins/Fighter Imports, Portland OR	3.8.89/92
				Bryan Air Inc, Richmond Hill GA	2.94/96
219-6	T-28B	Bu140007	**N5443E**	Courtesy Aircraft Inc, Rockford IL	8.84
				Randall Porter, Woodstock GA	86/87
				struck-off USCR	4.88
219-8 •	T-28B	**Bu140009**	**N300JH**	John V. Holden, Houston TX	11.85/86

				Menton Aircraft Inc, Bandera TX	87
				Gary L. Hornbarrier/Carrier Aviation Inc, High Point NC	88/90
				Ed & Connie Bowlin, Griffin GA	91
				Aero Dynamics Inc, Wilmington DE	92
				James D. Compton, Griffin GA	93
				op: Clay Klabo, Ocala FL	.93/94
				Fat Cat Flying Inc, Wilmington DE	6.93/96
219-11 •	T-28B	**Bu140012**	**N283MS**	M. W. Stevenson Ltd, Pasadena MD	10.85/88
				Bryan Bumgarner, Marana AZ	92
				(stored unconv., Avra Valley AZ 93)	
				William E. Harrison, Tulsa OK	8.93/96
219-14 •	T-28B	**Bu140015**	N5827T	reg. res.	10.84/87
			N108NA	Maryland Aviation Hist. Soc., Annapolis MD	6.88/96
219-15 •	T-28B	**Bu140016**		(to SVNAF as ....)	
			N46984	Dennis M. Sherman, West Palm Beach FL	4.84
				Stewart Dawson, McKinney TX	2.85/96
219-17 •	T-28B	**Bu140018**		(to US Army as 140018): retired DMAFB	87/89
				(ret. to US Army as 140018)	.89
				USAFM, Lowry AFB CO: ex DMAFB	.90
				USAFM, Pima Air Museum AZ	93
219-19 •	T-28B	**Bu140020**		Wes Strickler, Rolla MO	.88
			N8046D	Robert H. Nottke, Carson City NV	11.5.89
				Cermac Corp, Houston TX	12.89/96
219-24 •	T-28B	**Bu140025**		Lester Industries,San Antonio TX: ex DMAFB	31.3.80
				(to FA Hondurena as E.A.M.233): del.	.80/85
			N125NA	Courtesy Aircraft Inc, Rockford IL	9.85/86
				(dism. at Comeyagua AB, Honduras 9.85, shipped to USA 10.85: ten total)	
			C-FJVW	J. Johnston, Edmonton ALTA	1.87
				Don Crowe/Nahanni Helicopters, Victoria BC	89/91
				crashed Lindell BC	20.8.90
				sold to US: struck-off reg.	8.91
			N228AC	Stallion Aircraft Inc, Bensenville IL	10.91/96
219-27 •	T-28B	**Bu140028**		Pima Air Museum, Tucson AZ	92
219-28 •	T-28B	**Bu140029**	**N54916**	reg. res.	9.84/92
219-29 •	T-28B	**Bu140030**		Anthony J. d'Alessandris, Reno NV	
			N130TD	Lan-Dale Co, Reno NV	1.86/87
				Victor Schilleci, Metairie LA	3.88/96
219-30 •	T-28B	**Bu140031**		Lester Industries,San Antonio TX: ex DMAFB	31.3.80
				(to FA Hondurena as E.A.M.232): del.	.80/85
			N31NA	Courtesy Aircraft Inc, Rockford IL	9.85/86
				(dism. at Comeyagua AB, Honduras 9.85, shipped to USA 10.85: ten total)	
			C-FMGI	R. A. Yri, Surrey BC	1.87
			N31NA	David Kensler, Union Lake MI	6.12.89/91
				A & T Recovery Inc, Berwyn IL	92
				Robert H. Stevenson, Batavia IL	93
				Ten Air Aircraft Corp, Minneapolis MN	2.95
219-34 •	T-28B	**Bu140035**	N281MS	M. W. Stevenson Ltd, Pasadena MD	10.85/86
				Christopher O. Miller, Carson City NV	5.89/93
			N281CM	Christopher O. Miller, Carson City NV	4.93/96
219-40 •	T-28B	**Bu140041**	N9995H		
			N28BP	Robert J. Pond/Planes of Fame East, Minneapolis-Flying Cloud MN	21.5.90/96

219-42 •	T-28B	**Bu140043**	**N265FM**	Flight Management Inc, Tulsa OK	20.6.94/96
219-43 •	T-28B AT-28D	**Bu140044**		(to R Lao AF as AT-28D 0-40044)	
				(to Philippines AF as 54-140044)	
				(not used, open storage dism., USAF sc., Villamor AB, Manila 80/88)	
			N2052D	H. Ken Hawkins/Fighter Imports, Portland OR	3.8.89/92
				sale rep., Carter MT	95
219-45 •	T-28B	**Bu140046**		USNAM, NAS Corpus Christi TX	91/96
219-46 •	T-28B	**Bu140047**	**N5443U**	Courtesy Aircraft Inc, Rockford IL	8.84
				Southern Cal. Aviation Inc, Newport Beach CA	86/88
				Arthur W. McDonnell, Mojave CA	6.9.88/89
				Robert F. Yancey, Klamath Falls OR	92
				Patty Wagstaff Airshows Inc, Anchorage AK	11.93/96
219-47 •	T-28B	**Bu140048**		(to US Army as 140048)	
				USAFM: Wright-Patterson AFB, Dayton OH	88
				USAFM, Edwards AFB CA	89
219-48 •	T-28B	**Bu140049**	N87AW	Apex Associates, Canby OR	1.86
				APEXX Co Inc, Canby OR	6.86
				David M. Forrest, Dunwoody GA	12.86/87
			N228DF	David M. Forrest, Dunwoody/Marietta GA	2.87/96
219-49 •	T-28B	**Bu140050**	**N89AW**	Apex Associates, Canby OR	1.86
				APEXX Co Inc, Canby OR	6.86
				Classic Aviation International, Rosharon TX	87/88
				Anita deVillegas, Bellevue FL	87
				Tom Warmus, Franklin MN/Lighthouse Pt FL	.87/90
				sale rep., Southfield MI	92
				Nancy K. Dailey, Lighthouse Point FL	5.95
226-1 •	T-28C	**Bu140053**	N51841	County City Defense, Laurel MS: ex DMAFB	19.1.78/87
			N111TN	Tom Neal/California Coast University, Burbank CA	4.88/91
			N28TN (2	California Coast University, Santa Ana CA	7.91/96
226-4 •	T-28C	**Bu140056**		USNAM, NAS Corpus Christi TX	82/94
226-8 •	T-28C	**Bu140060**	N28LD	Brian Bumgarner, Marana AZ: reg. res.	92
			N28UH	Pride Aircraft Inc, Rockford IL	8.94
				Lud Corrao/Corrao Inc, Reno NV	19.8.94/96
				(USCR quotes N28UH id. as "C-008")	
226-9 •	T-28C	**Bu140061**	**N9036B**	reg. res.	2.87
226-10 •	T-28C	**Bu140062**	N9719G	Jet Dynamic Co	3.85
				Jones Flying Service, Minter City MS	4.85/86
			N128RH	Eagle Aviation Inc, Jonesboro AR	5.86
			N9719G	David K. Brady, Cartersville GA	3.87/96
226-11 •	T-28C	**Bu140063**		Bradley Air Museum, Windsor Locks CT : del.	16.1.78/81
				New England Air Museum, Windsor Locks CT	81/88
			N31431	reg. res.	5.11.91
				John B. Carlton, Charleston WV	9.92/96
226-12 •	T-28C	**Bu140064**	**N55534**	reg. res.	9.84/88
				Fred E. Weisbrod Aircraft Museum, Pueblo CO	88/93
226-16 •	T-28C	**Bu140068**	**N621JT**	James R. Tobul/Smith & Smith Aircraft	25.11.91
				James R. Tobul, Bamberg SC	2.92/95
226-19 •	T-28C	**Bu140071**	**N28ZZ**	C. Glen Hyde, Roanoke TX: reg. candidate	5.4.89
				C.E. Brehm Aircraft Sales, Devine TX	5.89
				Patrick F. Taylor/Taylor Energy Co, New Orleans LA	.89/93
				Combat Aircraft Inc, Elkhart IN	11.93/95

226-24 •	T-28C	**Bu140076**	N176RR	Classics in American Aviation Inc, Reno NV	11.85/87
				Robert M. Lanyon, Renfrew BC Canada	10.87/93
			N176RD	Richard A. Davis, Miami FL	4.95
226-31 •	T-28C	**Bu140454**		NAS South Weymouth MA: fire practice	
				USS Massachusetts Memorial, Fall River MA	86/88
				(rest., displ. as "USN 137765")	
226-33 •	T-28C	**Bu140456**		(to SVNAF as AT-28D 140456)	
	AT-28D			(to Philippines AF as 54-140456)	
				(not used, open storage dism., USAF sc.,	
				Villamor AB, Manila 80/88)	
			N2065J	H. Ken Hawkins/Fighter Imports, Portland OR	3.8.89/95
226-34 •	T-28C	**Bu140457**		(to R Lao AF as AT-28D 0-40457)	72
	AT-28D			(to SVNAF as 140457)	
				(to Philippines AF as 54-140457)	
				(not used, open storage dism., USAF sc.,	
				Villamor AB, Manila 80/88)	
			N2065R	H. Ken Hawkins/Fighter Imports, Portland OR	3.8.89/92
				MBSP Enterprises Inc, Wilmington DE	8.94/95
226-35	T-28C	Bu140458	N256X	no further information	
226-38 •	T-28C	**Bu140461**	N9025T	Georgia Historical Aviation Museum,	
				Stone Mountain GA	11.78/87
				(del. ex Davis Monthan AFB AZ 22.11.78)	
				Ghost Aircraft Rest. Inc, Stone Mountain GA	8.87/88
			N404DK	Duane Kalember/Ghost Aircraft Restoration Inc,	
				Stone Mountain GA	10.88/95
226-41 •	T-28C	**Bu140464**	**N2800J**	reg. candidate	6.79
				Weber Mary & Pinrod Inc, Baton Rouge LA	84/87
				Barry Landy/Mustang Aviation, Fairfield NJ	88/89
				Stuart M. Lamb, Amesbury MA	10.89/95
226-50 •	T-28C	**Bu140473**	**N31425**	Michael D. Vadeboncoeur, Danville IL	10.91/95
226-52 •	T-28C	**Bu140475**	**N9025Y**	Georgia Historical Aviation Museum,	
				Stone Mountain GA : del. ex DMAFB	11.78/92
				reg. pending, Birmingham AL	95
226-57 •	T-28C	**Bu140480**	**N2800N**	George J. Rivera, Pensacola FL	84
				sale rep., Auburn CA	86/95
226-58 •	T-28C	**Bu140481**		Pima Air Museum, Tucson AZ: arr. ex DMAFB	10.3.77/93
226-65 •	T-28C	**Bu140488**	**N28CX**	Smith & Smith Aircraft International Ltd	1.91
				Eric C. Paul, Charlotte NC	5.91/95
226-66 •	T-28C	**Bu140489**	**N9019L**	Civil Defence Council, Waynesboro MS	.78/88
				(del. ex Davis Mothan AFB AZ 9.11.78)	
				Wayne Rescue Unit, Waynesboro MS	9.91/95
226-68 •	T-28C	**Bu140491**		B. Bumgarter, Marana AZ: reg. candidate	15.12.92
226-69 •	T-28C	**Bu140492**		IN Museum of Military History,Indianapolis IN	88/90
			N4168H	Courtesy Aircraft Inc, Rockford IL	3.91/92
			C-GTTF	Helair Enterprises Ltd, Delta BC	29.6.92/93
226-78 •	T-28C	**Bu140501**	N9749N	Mystic Marketing Co Inc, Mystic CT	1.87
				William W. Whorley, Greensboro GA	7.88
			N900BW	William W. Whorley, Greensboro GA	12.88/96
226-86 •	T-28C	**Bu140509**	**N280BJ**	AMCEP Inc, Tucson AZ	9.91
				John Noble, Upper Lake CA	92
				Aircraft Cylinder & Turbine, Sun Valley CA	5.94/96

226-88 •	T-28C	**Bu140511**		USNAM, NAS Pensacola FL: displ.	80/84
			N140NA	Airplane Sales International, Beverly Hills CA	10.85
				King City Aviation Inc, King City CA	.85/86
				Alvin P. Grant, Fountain Valley CA	11.86/89
			N140AG	Alvin P. Grant, Fountain Valley CA	9.89/96
226-91 •	T-28C	**Bu140514**	**N2141D**	Dennis G. Buehn, Long Beach CA	3.83
				Frank G. Crompton, Torrance CA	84
				Byron M. Tarnutzer, Costa Mesa CA	86/87
				Ray D. Fulwiler, Green Bay WI	88/93
				William K. Manly, Santa Rosa CA	5.93/96
226-93 •	T-28C	**Bu140516**		(to Republic of Congo AF as FA-516)	
				(to FA Zaire as FG-516)	.72
			N99141	Euroworld Ltd	2.77
				William Nelson, El Paso TX	12.77/78
				(del. via Biggin Hill UK 16.12.77/17.4.78)	
			N99153 (3	Raymond F. Mabrey/R. J. Enterprises,	
				Robstown TX, later McAllen TX	80/87
				William R. Montague, Oakland CA	6.88/96
				(note: id. confused with 226-153: que se)	
226-96 •	T-28C	**Bu140519**	**N9019N**	County Civil Defense, Jackson MS: ex DMAFB	9.11.78
				Civil Defense Council, Waynesboro MS	84/88
				Laurel Flying Service, Laurel MS	92
				Double Eagle Aviation, Haskell OK	95
226-97 •	T-28C	**Bu140520**	**N678MC**	Michael V. Crawford, Colorado Springs CO	22.6.93/96
226-98 •	T-28C	**Bu140521**		USNAM, NAS Pensacola FL	80/84
226-100 •	T-28C	**Bu140523**	**N470**	B & D Restoration Inc	5.6.90
				James L. Maroney, Fargo ND	92
				James L. Griffin, Tulsa OK	7.93/96
226-101 •	T-28C	**Bu140524**		sold as scrap ex NAS Corpus Christi TX	
				Ken Hilderbrant/Warrior Aviation,	
				Burlington CO (rest. to fly)	86
226-102	T-28C	Bu140525	C-GTTE	Ed MacPherson/Helair Enterprises, Delta BC	5.12.91/93
				crashed Delta Air Park BC	17.6.93
226-103 •	T-28C	**Bu140526**	N7160B	Dave Butler: reg. candidate	24.5.90
			N526D	Brian G. Cole, Tucson AZ	11.91/96
226-105 •	T-28C	**Bu140528**	**N71546**	Trojan Aircraft Inc, Matthews MD	2.90
				Koenig Farms Inc, Yuma CO	92
				Mike Horn/Northaire Inc, Wilmington DE	10.93/96
226-108 •	T-28C	**Bu140531**		Indiana Museum of Military History,	
				Indianapolis IN	87
			N91550	Courtesy Aircraft Inc, Rockford IL	11.87/88
			N944SD	Stuart W. Dingman, Belleville MI	2.89/96
226-110 •	T-28C	**Bu140533**		(to Philippine AF as AT-28D 40533)	
	AT-28D			Philippine AF Museum, Villamor AB, Manila	89/93
				(displ. as "54-0533")	
226-113 •	T-28C	**Bu140536**	**N3142B**	Grand Rapids Bible & Music School	17.10.91
				William T. Ingram, Catlin IL	3.92/96
226-114 •	T-28C	**Bu140537**	N7164Z	B & D Restoration Inc: reg. candidate	15.6.90
				Steve J. Masket, Los Angeles CA	9.90
			N537Z	Steve J. Masket, Los Angeles CA	10.90/93
				M. S. Air Inc, Reno NV	12.94/96
226-116 •	T-28C	**Bu140539**	N4993Y	Confederate Air Force, Harlingen TX	10.78/84
				(del. ex Davis Monthan AFB AZ 18.12.78)	
			N28TN (1	Tom Neale/California Coast University,	
				Santa Ana CA	5.85/88

			N166ER	Cinema Air Inc, Houston TX/Carlsbad CA	5.90/96
226-119 •	T-28C	**Bu140542**	**N5321X**	Courtesy Aircraft Inc, Rockford IL	1.88
				sale rep., San Jose CA	92/96
226-120 •	T-28C	**Bu140543**	**N80269**	Harry Doan/Doan Helicopters, Daytona Beach	26.6.89
				Dave Maruna/Maruna Airplane Co, Akron OH	2.90/91
				Anthony Jurak, Dorval QUE	7.91
				Dave Maruna/Maruna Airplane Co, Akron OH	91/92
				Pegasus Investments Inc, West Palm Beach FL	1.94/96
226-124 •	T-28C	**Bu140547**	N2800Q	reg. candidate	6.79
				Tifton Contractors Inc, Tifton GA	84
				H. C. Dodson Farms Inc, Tifton GA	86
				Bardolph Limited, New York NY	86/90
				op: Scandinavian Historic Flight	.86/91
				(arr. UK for airshows 23.6.86, based Norway)	
				J. Sporrer, Toulous Blagnac, France	.91
				struck-off USCR	22.10.91
			F-AZHN	J. Sporrer/Sport Air, Tolous Blagnac	2.4.92/94
226-125 •	T-28C	**Bu140548**		USNAM, NAS Pensacola FL	80/84
			N548NA	Airplane Sales International, Beverly Hills CA	10.85
				Steve Wilmans/King City Aviation, King City CA	9.86/96
226-126 •	T-28C AT-28D	**Bu140549**		(to SVNAF as AT-28D 140549)	
			N34BJ	Aircraft Cylinder & Turbine, Charlotte NC	29.1.91
				Telesite Corp, Healdsburg CA	2.92/96
226-127 •	T-28C	**Bu140550**	**N990DB**	J. Maxwell	20.1.94
				Dick Brooks, Greer SC	3.94/96
226-128 •	T-28C	**Bu140551**	**N9748Y**	Westair International USA Inc, Monument CO	11.86
				John H. Batto & Glenn Lyman, Vineburg CA	2.87/96
226-130 •	T-28C	**Bu140553**		USAFM: Robins AFB GA	87/89
226-134 •	T-28C	**Bu140557**		USMC Museum, MCAS Quantico VA	88/96
226-140 •	T-28C	**Bu140563**	N563GH	C. Glenn Hyde, Roanoke TX	24.4.89
				John Gasho, Phoenix AZ	89
			ZK-JGS	John I. Greenstreet, Auckland	11.89/90
				Trojan 63 Syndicate, Auckland-Ardmore	91/96
226-141 •	T-28C	**Bu140564**		Dennis Hallman, Lake Wylie SC	.92
				Harold O. Norton: reg. candidate	16.3.94
			N40980	Smith & Smith Aircraft International Ltd	30.6.94
				Harold O. Norton, Winston-Salem NC	12.94/96
226-143 •	T-28C	**Bu140566**	**N556EB**	Emil F. Blomberg, Reno NV	12.85/86
				Sonoma Valley Aircraft Limited, Sonoma CA	87
				Robert D. Marshall, San Rafael CA	88/92
				Sonoma Valley Aircraft Inc, Vineburg CA	5.95
226-147 •	T-28C	**Bu140570**		Davis Monthan AFB AZ: retired for storage	5.78
				Pima County Air Museum, Tucson AZ	88
			C-FNAA	Larry M. Lysiuk, Delhi ONT	18.6.93
226-151 •	T-28C	**Bu140574**	**N7066J**	Donald R. Weber, Baker LA	10.93/96
226-152 •	T-28C	**Bu140575**		Pima County Air Museum, Tucson AZ	86/88
			N575FL	Flying Legends Inc, Wilmington DE	10.92/96
226-153 •	T-28C	**Bu140576**		(to FA Zaire as FG-576)	
			N99153 (2	Euroworld Ltd	
				William Nelson, El Paso TX	78
			N289RD (2	Ronald L. Doney, North Attleboro MA	6.79/84

				Alan Clark/Fighting Air Command/ Flytex Inc, Dallas TX	.84/87
				Kenneth W. Stowe & Bill Whorley, North Little Rock AR	.87/89
				Bill Melamed, Chino CA	90/91
				Joseph M. Rieger, Snohomish WA	10.91/96
				(note: id. confused with 226-93: que se)	
226-155 •	T-28C	**Bu140578**	**N8039S**	C. Glen Hyde, Roanoke TX	15.2.89
				Bert J. Zwaagstra, Mesquite NM	.89/92
				Noah Curtiss Kimball, Sterling CO	12.92/96
226-158 •	T-28C	**Bu140581**	**N581JS**	JM Classics in Aviation Inc	1.91
				John Strickland/Maryland Warbird Museum, White Marsh MD	2.91/96
226-163 •	T-28C	**Bu140586**	N2800R	reg. candidate	6.79
				George J. Rivera, Pensacola FL	84
				sale rep., Mojave CA	86/87
				Courtesy Aircraft Inc, Rockford IL	88/91
			N128CT	Jerry C. Janes & Associates, Rockford IL	6.91/96
226-166 •	T-28C	**Bu140589**	G-USAF	Barry Walker, Sheffield	28.6.82
				(stored dism. Marlow UK 82/89, arr. dism. Booker .89 for rest.)	
				Tom Rogers, Boundary Bay BC	.90/92
				(shipped to Canada ex Felixstowe Docks UK 23.1.91)	
			C-FPTR (1	Tom Rogers/415150 BC Ltd, White Rock BC	23.3.92/93
			N280CR	Richard W. Boehlke, Gig Harbour WA	28.4.93/96
226-170	T-28C	Bu140593	N9022Y	County Civil Defense, Jefferson City MO	11.78
				(del. ex Davis Monthan AFB AZ 17.11.78)	
				Civil Defense Council, Greenwood MO	84
				Southwest Aviation Inc, Fairacres NM	86
				Ronald S. Miller, Woodland Hills CA	87
				crashed on takeoff, Van Nuys CA	1.1.87
				Courtesy Aircraft Inc, Rockford IL	88
200-179 •	T-28C	**Bu140602**	N3948B	James P. MacIvor, Miami FL	2.84
			N602JM	James P. MacIvor, Miami FL	4.84/96
200-184 •	T-28C	**Bu140607**	**N70447**	Harry S. Doan/Doan Helicopters, Daytona Beach/New Smyrna Beach FL	11.88/92
				sold Doan auction, New Smyrna Beach FL	30.10.92
				Arthur C. Worley/Worley Aviation, Dover DE	12.92/96
200-187 •	T-28C	**Bu140610**	**N8084V**	C. Glenn Hyde, Roanoke TX	9.2.89
				Lee Maples/Baron Aviation Services, Vichy MO	3.89/96
200-188 •	T-28C	**Bu140611**		Chesapeak College; reg. candidate	14.9.92
200-202 •	T-28C	**Bu140625**	**N30625**	R. John Germain, Houston TX	30.5.90/96
226-214 •	T-28C	**Bu140637**	N65647	Bert J. Zwaagstra, Mesquite NM	12.90
			N28BZ	Bert J. Zwaagstra, Mesquite NM	7.91/96
226-216	T-28C	Bu140639	**N775CH**	Avtec Leasing & Sales Inc, Titusville FL	8.86/88
				crashed, dest., Tico FL	10.3.89
226-222 •	T-28C	**Bu140645**	**N9016R**	reg.	11.78
				Delhi Richland Parish Civil Defense, Delhi LA	84/86
				Steve Martin, Delhi LA	6.86/96
226-224 •	T-28C	**Bu140647**	**N757K**	Ken Stowe/Trojan Aircraft Inc,Wilmington DE	30.9.94/96
				(stored dism. pending rest. to fly 95)	
226-226 •	T-28C	**Bu140649**		USAFM: Robins AFB GA	87
			N649JS	John Strickland/Maryland Warbird Museum, White Marsh MD	15.4.91/92

				Exec Aviation Inc, Cincinatti OH	1.95
226-227 •	T-28C	**Bu140650**	**N51928**	County City Defense, Laurel MS : ex DMAFB	28.2.78/87
				Robby R. Jones, Minter City MS	88/92
				Aguilas Inc, Climax Springs MO	4.93/95
				Marion Gregory, Climax Springs MO	.95
226-229 •	T-28C	**Bu140652**	N652T	Lan-Dale Co, Reno NV	10.85/87
			N28LC	Lud J. Corrao, Reno NV	8.88/96
226-230 •	T-28C	**Bu140653**	N10260	reg.	4.79
				Warbirds Inc, Miami FL	84
				Vincent Tirado, Miami FL	86
				Donald F. Bellek, Zephyr Cove NV	3.86/87
			N653DB	Donald F. Bellek, Zephyr Cove NV	4.87/96
226-234 •	T-28C	**Bu140654**	**N75947**	Jeff J. Bumgarner, Tucson AZ	9.91/92
				Martin A. Steiner & Evan Wolfe, Auburn CA	2.94/95
226-235 •	T-28C	**Bu140658**	**N5094J**	Courtesy Aircraft Inc, Rockford IL	11.87/88
				Ray D. Fulwiler/Fulwiler Air Inc, Green Bay WI	3.90/96
226-236 •	T-28C	**Bu140659**	**N75ES**	Pate Museum of Transportation, Fort Worth TX: displ.	88/94
226-238 •	T-28C	**Bu140661**	**N661NA**	Airplane Sales International, Beverly Hills CA	10.85
	T-28D			King City Aviation Inc, King City CA	88/92
				Herbert R. Baker, Milwaukee WI	93/96
226-239 •	T-28C	**Bu140662**	**N22134**	F. R. Parker: reg. candidate	27.12.89
				reg.	3.90
				Gary L. Fritzler, Denver CO	11.90/96
226-243 •	T-28C	**Bu140666**	**N9022N**	County Civil Defense, Jefferson City MO	11.78
				(del. ex Davis Monthan AFB AZ 17.11.78)	
				Civil Defense Council, Greenwood MO	84
				Lone Star Flight Museum, Houston TX	86/88
				Louis E. Fischer, Kissimmee FL	89
				Sherman Aircraft Sales,West Palm Beach FL	5.89
				Joel C. Hilgenberg, New Orleans LA	5.90/96
252-2 •	T-28C	**Bu146239**		IN Museum of Military History,Indianapolis IN	88/90
			N4168E	Courtesy Aircraft Inc, Rockford IL	26.2.91
				Howard & Scott Ross, Glencoe IL	92/93
				Kipnis Inc, Dover DE & Chicago IL	3.92/96
252-3 •	T-28C	**Bu146240**	N240CJ	Gerald A. Smith, Long Beach CA	7.86/87
				Coke V. Stuart, Valdosta GA	88/89
				Jeffrey S. Gorman, Mansfield OH	6.89/91
			N240CG	Jeffrey S. Gorman, Mansfield OH	7.91/96
252-5 •	T-28C	**Bu146242**	**N1188C**	Louis Fricke/Fast Corporation, Wilmington DE	7.86/96
252-9 •	T-28C	**Bu146246**	**N2800M**	reg. candidate	6.79
				M.A. Inc, Oshkosh WI	2.81/96
252-12 •	T-28C	**Bu146249**		Richard G. Sugden, Wilson WY	89/90
				(civil rest. Victoria BC 89/90)	
			N6535K	Richard G. Sugden, Wilson WY	11.90
			N28CV	Richard G. Sugden, Jackson WY	1.91/96
252-13 •	T-28C	**Bu146250**		World Aircraft Museum, Calhoun GA	88
252-16 •	T-28C	**Bu146253**	N912KK	Southern California Avn., Corona del Mar CA	1.86
				Daniel W. Lawson, Las Vegas NV	8.87/92
			N311LK	Daniel W. Lawson, Las Vegas NV	2.92/96

252-17 •	T-28C	**Bu146254**	N910KK	Southern California Avn, Corona del Mar CA	1.86/87
				John F. Hulls & Pete Pemrick, St Cloud MN	.87
			N254PJ	John F. Hulls, St Cloud MN	7.88
				Greg Brinkman/Seahorse Aviation, Rye NY	92/93
				Robert E. Livingston, Fort Lauderdale FL	2.95
252-18 •	T-28C	**Bu146255**		(to FA Zaire as FG-255)	
			N49308	reg. pending	12.77/78
				(del. via Biggin Hill UK 16.12.77/17.4.78)	
			N39408(2	Sunmaster Awnings Inc, Mishawaka IN	4.79/87
			C-GJMT(2	Dan Springer/Aviation Maintenance Ltd,	
				Sault Ste Marie ONT	1.88/93
			N255JM	Jacob Mast, Byron Centre MI	5.4.93/96
252-20 •	T-28C	**Bu146257**		USAFM, Robbins AFB GA	88
				Randall Porter/Air Acres Air Museum,	
				Cartersville GA (rest. project)	93/96
252-23 •	T-28C	**Bu146260**	**N260AN**	Aero Nostalgia Inc, Stockton CA	8.86
				Cecil H. Harp, Canby OR	87
				Richard S. Drury, Goleta CA/Anchorage AK	88/93
				Warbirds Inc, Las Vegas NV	4.95
252-24 •	T-28C	**Bu146261**	**N728C**	Seth & Jo Dempsey/Hooked On Trojans,	
				Sebastopol CA	3.91/96
252-25 •	T-28C	**Bu146262**	**N7160C**	Dave Butler: reg. candidate	24.5.90
				Dennis A. Smith, Salem OR	6.90/96
252-29 •	T-28C	**Bu146266**		(to FA Zaire as AT-28D ....)	
	AT-28D		**N99163**	William Nelson, El Paso TX	78
				(del. via Biggin Hill UK 23.1.78/20.6.78)	
				William E. Harrison, Tulsa OK	4.78/96
252-33	T-28C	Bu146270	N9746Z	Westair International USA Inc, Monument CO	11.86
				Mystic Marketing Co Inc, Mystic CT	87
				Wayne A. Sutton, Brooks GA	87/88
				(still stored Davis Monthan AFB AZ 12.87)	
			N128PS	Wayne A. Sutton, Brooks GA	5.88/90
				T Bird Inc, Hollywood CA	2.91
			N842GP	ntu: T Bird Inc, Reno NV	3.91
			N128PS	Pierre Dague, St. Rambert d'Albon, France	.91
				crashed St. Rambert d'Albon (Pierre Dague k.)	8.9.91
252-36 •	T-28C	**Bu146273**	N14NW	Northwest Warbirds Inc, Twin Falls ID	2.87
			N46273	Gary M. Boutz, San Jose CA & Reno NV	4.87/96
252-42 •	T-28C	**Bu146279**	C-FPUG	Falls Aviation Ltd, Welland ONT	3.6.94
252-44 •	T-28C	**Bu146281**	N2215D	B & D Restoration: reg. candidate	19.1.90
			reg.	3.90	
				Gene S. Nunn, Elkhart KS/Amarillo TX	92/93
				Robert B. Atac, Aurora IL	8.94/96
252-46 •	T-28C	**Bu146283**	N1184T	Time Aviation, Tucson AZ: ex DMAFB	24.8.81
				Roland S. Bond, Jean NV	84
				Robby R. Jones, Minter City MS	86
				Ellis Stuart/Airplane Services Inc, Benoit MS	87
				Richard C. Slaney, Eugene OR	88
				William A. Schiro, Okemos MI	7.90/96
252-49 •	T-28C	**Bu146286**	N146GB	Gerald S. Beck, Wahpeton ND	12.85/88
				Gregory A. Fieber, St Paul MN	8.89/90
			N146GF	Gregory A. Fieber, St Paul MN	2.90/96
52-50 •	T-28C	**Bu146287**	N2304K	LeTourneau College, Longview TX	8.78
				Peter G. Knox/City Blue Print, Allentown PA	3.84/96
52-51 •	T-28C	**Bu146289**		(to Republic of Congo AF as FA-289)	.64

		AT-28C AT-28D		N99153 (1	(to FA Zaire as FG-289) Euroworld Ltd/B-17 Ltd, London UK cr. during del. flight, Limoges, France (fuse. & parts trucked to UK, stored East Ham.) Norfolk & Suffolk Aviation Museum, Flixton UK (displ. as "FG-289", later "USN 146289/2W")	.72 2.77/81 14.12.77 5.81/96
-	•	T-28A T-28R-2 Nomair	-	N28DS	Hamilton Aircraft, Tucson AZ (conv. to Hamilton Nomair c/n 10) Dwight Reimer, Shafter CA (flew as USN "150099/DR206") J. Bruce Wallace, Grants Pass OR	 78/83 2.86/96
-	•	T-28A AT-28D	-	N367NA	(to FA Hondurena as E.A.M.213) Courtesy Aircraft Inc, Rockford IL (dism. at Comeyagua AB, Honduras 9.85, shipped to USA 10.85: ten total) David Huff, Schuylkill Haven PA (USCR quotes id. "367")	 9.85/87 9.87/96
-		T-28D	-	N39408(1	William Nelson, El Paso TX (USCR quotes id. "H750")	78
-	•	T-28A	-	N8156U	(to FA Mexicana as ....) Texas Turbo Jet Inc, Dallas TX (USCR quotes id. "49-1960")	 3.3.89/96
-	•	AT-28D	-	N99412	(to FA Zaire as ....) MARC, Chino CA (USCR quotes id. "122")	 4.77/96
-	•	T-28D	-	N99414	(to FA Zaire as ....) MARC, Chino CA (del. to USA via Biggin Hill/Stornoway 4.78) (USCR quotes id. "222")	 4.77/96
-	•	T-28A	-		(to FA Mexicana as T28-936) Military College, Mexico City: displ.	 82/91
-	•	T-28A	-		(to FA Mexicana as T28-944) stored dism. Seymour IN reg. candidate USCR	 90 4.9.90
-	•	T-28A	-		(to FA Mexicana as T28-957) stored dism. Santa Rosa Air Centre CA (poor condition, with two other FAM T-28s)	 90
-	•	T-28A	-		(to FA Mexicana as T28-963) Harry S. Doan, New Smyrna Beach FL: dism. offered for sale, rest. project, Doan auction	 92 30.10.92
-	•	T-28A	-		(to FA Mexicana as T28-966) La Paz AB, Mexico: displ.	 82/91
-	•	T-28A	-		(to FA Mexicana as T28-974) La Paz AB, Mexico: displ.	 82/91
-	•	T-28A Fennec	-		(to Argentine Navy as ....) displ. on pole, Punta Indio AB, Argentina (displ. as "1-A-251")	 91
-	•	T-28A Fennec	-		(to Argentine Navy as 3-A-331) noted stored dism., Tucson AZ	 87/90
-	•	T-28A Fennec	-		(to Argentine Navy as 3-A-332) noted stored dism., Tucson AZ	 87/90

2-	B-25	**40-2168**		Gen. Hap Arnold's RB-25 VIP transport	43/44
837 •	RB-25		N75831	Charles R. Bates, Chatanooga TN	22.1.47
				Bankers Life & Casualty Co, Chicago IL	4.11.48
				Hughes Tool Co, Houston TX	28.6.51/62
				Hughes/Acme Aircraft Co, Lomita CA	.62/64
			XB-GOG	reg.	.62
			N2825B	JRT Aero Service, Wichita Falls TX	19.1.67/71
				John P. Silberman, Savannah GA	25.8.71/74
				SST Aviation Museum, Kissimmee FL	8.10.74/79
				Mustang Productions Inc	.75
				Samuel Pool, Lake Wales FL	.77
				Dewey Miller, Mobile AL	28.8.77/83
				(del. Kissimmee FL to Mobile AL 12.12.78,	
				rest. as *Proud Mary*)	
				Alan Clarke/Fighting Air Command,	
				Dallas TX (flew as 02168/*The General*)	.83/87
				TBF Inc, Tenafly NY	11.89/96
				(flies as "*Miss Hap*")	
2-	B-25B	**40-2347**		Ed Maloney/The Air Museum, Ontario CA	66/67
016 •				(fuse. recov. ex movie studio by Maloney c66)	
				(fuse. displ. Ontario CA "T-702/Lemon Queen" 67)	
				Admiral Nimitz Found., Fredericksburg TX	
				Carl Scholl/Aero Trader, Chino CA	88/96
				(fuse. stored Ocotillo Wells CA 88/94)	
2-	B-25C	**41-12442**		(499th BS/*Feather Merchant*)	
077 •				hulk recov. ex airstrip Tadji, PNG	.74/90
				(displ. Tadji, fitted tail section from	
				41-30074 *Tin Liz* recov. ex Dagua)	
2-	B-25C	**41-13251**	NL75635	Charles E. Mathews Co, Miami FL	49
886 •				(to FA Dominicana as 2502)	7.49
			N3968C	Hughes Tool Co, Culver City CA	54/72
				Antelope Valley Air Museum, Lancaster CA	.74/81
				Milestones of Flight Museum, Lancaster CA	87/95
				(stored dism., Lancaster-Fox Field 74/94)	
				rep: Weeks Air Museum, Tamiami FL	92/94
2-	B-25C	**41-13285**		ditched Lake Greenwood SC: "Skunkie"	6.6.44
920 •				(recov. from lake .85: static rest. 85/93)	
				SC State Museum, Columbia SC: displ.	.92/93
7-	B-25D	**41-29784**	NL5078N		
949 •	TB-25D		N5078N	Timken Roller Bearing Co, Canton OH	54
			N122B	Timken Roller Bearing Co, Canton OH	.54/64
				Fred Clausen, Minneapolis MN	66
				Westernair of Albuquerque, Albuquerque NM	69/70
				Lucille N. Ekmpton, Mesa AZ	72
			N2DD	Richard DuPont, Greenville DE	78
			N2XD	Patriots Point Naval & Maritime Museum,	
				Charleston SC	.81/94
				(del. Summit DE to Columbia SC 29.4.81,	
				displ. on USS Yorktown, as *Furtile Turtle*)	
7-	B-25D	**41-30163**		(38 BG/*Butch*: 345th BG)	
328 •				crashed Port Moresby PNG	8.43
				National Museum, Port Moresby PNG	79/88
7-	B-25D	**41-30222**		(380 BG/*Hawg-mouth*)	
387 •				forced landed 75m E of Tennant Creek NT	25.1.45
				(recov. by Darwin Aviation Historical Society	
				Darwin NT 6.74: towed out of desert)	
				East Point Artilliary Museum, Darwin NT	74/76
				Darwin Aviation Museum, Darwin NT	.76/95
				(rest., displ. as *Hawg-mouth*)	

87-8957 •	B-25D Mk. II	**41-30792**		(to RAF as FR193: 320 (Dutch) Sqn): BOC	23.4.44/47
				(to MLD as A-17, M-6, B-6, 2-6): BOC	7.47/54
				Deelen Technical School, Netherlands	.55/59
				National War & Resistance Museum, Overloon, Netherlands	.59/93
				(displ. as "2-6", later "FR193/NO-L")	
94-12762 •	B-25C	**42-32354**		used as movie studio prop	
				Jack Hardwick, El Monte CA	
				(stored dism. in yard, El Monte CA)	
				Carl Scholl/Aero Trader, Chino CA	88
				(rest. to fly Ocotillo Wells & Chino CA 88/90)	
93-12587	B-25C	42-32479	XA-PAD	Juan C. M. Rodrigez: still on Register	93
				(no evidence that this still exists)	
100-23634 •	B-25D Mk. II	**43-3308**		(to RCAF as KL156): BOC 5.1.45: SOC	22.11.61
			N8011	Bellomy Aviation, Miami FL	64
			HP-428	Aerovias Internacional Alianza	.66
			CP-915	Transportes Aeros Benianos, La Paz	4.70
				Sudamericana, La Paz	
				J.S.Angueza, La Paz	
				(noted La Paz, "Bolivian Airways" 12.72, wfu La Paz, derelict by 76)	
				Roy M. Stafford, Jacksonville FL	.87
				(shipped to USA, rest. Chino CA as PBJ-1D .87)	
				USMC Museum, Quantico VA	.87/96
				(disp. as "USN PBJ-1D" in grey sc.)	
100-23644 •	B-25D Mk. II	**43-3318**		(to RCAF as KL161): BOC 19.1.45: SOC	12.2.62
			CF-OGQ	Joe E. Goldney, Vancouver BC	2.62
				(noted Vancouver 4.64, RCAF sc.)	
			N88972	San Juan Agencies Inc, Seattle WA	.67
				North Star Aviation Corp, Fairbanks AK	69
				Colco Aviation Inc, Fairbanks AK	6.69/72
				(wfu Fairbanks AK, ex fire bomber 77/81)	
				Noel Merrill Wien, Anchorage AK/Kent WA	.83/87
				Robert J. Pond, Plymouth MN: op. TFC	10.87/95
				The Fighter Collection, Duxford UK: del.	7.11.87/95
				(flies as KL161/VO-B/*Grumpy*)	
100-23700 •	B-25D RB-25D	**43-3374**		stored Davis-Monthan AFB AZ	50/57
				USAFM, Wright-Patterson AFB, Dayton OH	.57/90
				(rest. as B-25B by NAA; del. to USAFM 4.58)	
				(displ. as Gen. Jimmy Doolittle's "02344")	
100-23960 •	B-25D Mk. II	**43-3634**		(to RCAF as KL148): BOC 18.10.44: SOC	18.6.62
			CF-NWV	Hicks & Lawrence Ltd, St Thomas ONT	6.63
			N3774	Glenn H. Lamont, Detroit MI	66/87
				Yankee Air Force Museum, Willow Run MI	.87/95
				(flies as *Yankee Warrior*)	
108-24356 •	B-25J VB-25J	**43-4030**		Gen. Dwight D. Eisenhower's VIP transport	5.43/44
			N3339G	Eldorado Corp, Dallas TX	63
				Joseph C. Frazier, El Paso TX	64/70
				The Air Museum, Chino CA	78
				USAFM, March AFB CA	84/85
				(displ. as 34030 *Blonde Bomber*)	
				USAFM, Ellsworth AFB SD	87/94
				(displ. as "34030")	
98-21107 •	B-25H	**43-4106**		Charles E. Mathews Co, Miami FL	49
				(to FA Dominicana as 2501)	7.49
			N5548N	Bendix Aviation Corp, Detroit MI	54
				Bendix Corp, Towson MD	61/69
				Richard D. Lambert, Plainfield IL	72/78
				(wfu, open storage on farm, Plainfield IL 70/81)	

				Heritage In Flight Museum, Springfield IL	72
				Louis A. Fulgaro & Walter Wild/	
				Weary Warriors Squadron, Rockford IL	.80/95
				(del. ex farm, Plainfield 17.10.81,	
				rest. Rockford IL with 75mm cannon nose,	
				ff 19.5.92 Rockford as 34380/*Barbie III*)	
98- 21109 •	B-25H	**43-4108**	**N58HA**	US Historical Aircraft Preservation Museum,	
				Anchorage AK: reg. res.	3.85
98- 21121 •	B-25H	**43-4120**		(to Chinese AF as 120)	
				Chinese Peoples Revolution Museum,	
				Peking/Beijing	65/90
				(id. unconf., in storage by 90)	
8- 21330 •	B-25H	**43-4329**		(to Chinese AF as 329)	
				Chinese Peoples Revolution Museum,	
				Peking/Beijing	65/90
				(id. unconf., in storage by 90)	
8- 1337	B-25H	43-4336	N67998	Grand Central Aircraft Co, Glendale CA	9.11.50/54
			N96GC	Grand Central Aircraft Co, Glendale CA	59
				Bert Wheeler, Fort Worth TX	63
				Aero Industries, Addison TX	66/72
				Ben Kerr, Dallas TX	c72
				I. N. Burchinall Jr, Paris TX	.73
				Charles V. Moody, Tampa FL	.74
				struck mountain, Dawsonville GA	3.6.75
8- 1433 •	B-25H	**43-4432**	N90399	Barbara Hutton, New York NY	
			N10V	Porifio Rubirosa, Washington DC	54
				Mechanical Products Inc, Jackson MI	54
				Husky Oil Co, Cody WY	58
				Long Island Airways, New York NY	63/66
				Filmways Inc, Hollywood CA	68/72
				(flew in film *Catch 22*: as*Berlin Express*)	
				Sherman Cooper, Merced CA	.72
				EAA Aviation Foundation, Oshkosh WI	8.72/95
				(flies as 34030/*City of Burlington*)	
8- 1514 •	B-25H	**43-4513**		ran off strip landing, Talasea, New Britain	3.9.44
				still in situ, derelict, on undercarriage	84
8- 1644	B-25H TB-25H	43-4643	N1203	Paul Mantz, Glendale CA	19.2.46/61
				(purchased ex War Assets Corp, Seacy Field OK)	
				"The Bug Smasher"	
				Tallmantz Aviation, Santa Ana CA	.61/72
				(flew in film *Catch 22* 68/69)	
				Vicki Meller, Burbank CA	.78
				crashed Colombia,	c78
8- 1900 •	B-25H TB-25H RB-25H	43-4899		State Teachers College, Dickinson ND	
				SAX Aviation Co, Dickinson ND	7.5.50
				Theodore X. Fabian, East Orange NJ	17.3.52
			N66572	William L. Rausch, Hackensack NJ	18.3.52
				Rausch Aviation, Teterboro NJ	17.7.52/55
			N1582V	Rausch Aviation, Teterboro NJ	14.1.55
			N37L	Le Franc Corp, San Francisco CA	12.8.55/59
				(exec. conversion: tip tanks, airstair,	
				Jato units; fitted mod. wings ex N5865V)	
				Oakland Airmotive Co, Oakland CA	3.6.59
				Carrier Services Corp, Flint MI	16.9.59/63
				Grimes Manufacturing Co, Urbana OH	7.5.63/64
				Air International, Columbus OH	24.9.64/70
				Golden Isles Aviation Inc, St Simons Is. GA	7.7.70/72
				dam., forced landing ,	
				St. Simons Island, Brunswick GA	4.12.70
				Glynn County Sheriff GA: seized	12.70
				John Hanson, Manistee MI	14.3.77/80
				(trucked dism. GA-Manistee for planned mus.)	

				Kalamazoo Aviation History Museum MI	2.2.80/96
				(static rest. Kalamazoo, displ. as "USAAF 4899")	
98-22000 •	B-25H	**43-4999**		Jack P. Hardwick, El Monte CA	50
				(to FA Dominicana as 2503): del.	.50
				Babb Co Inc, Newark NJ	7.52
			N3970C	Babb Co Inc, Newark NJ	27.1.53/54
				(advertised for sale in full military config., including guns 6.53)	
				(aban., derelict,West Trenton NJ 58/69)	
				Bradley Air Museum, Windsor Locks CT	4.70/84
				(dism. West Trenton, trucked Windsor Locks: static rest. as 34999/*Dog Daize*)	
				badly dam. by tornado at museum	3.10.79
				(stored dam., dism. at museum site 79/86)	
				New England Air Museum, Windsor Locks CT	86/94
				(rest. 86/93, displ. as 34999/*Dog Daize*)	
108-34725 •	B-25J TB-25N	**43-27712**		displ. main gate, Davis Monthan AFB AZ	65/69
				USAFM, Pima County Museum, Tucson AZ	10.69/93
				(displ. as "0-32712/BD-712")	
108-34881 •	B-25J TB-25N	**43-27868**	N9077Z	Dothan Aviation Corp, Dothan AL	63/72
				Charles Skipper, Boerne TX	78
				Confederate Air Force, Harlingen TX	19.9.79
			N25YR	Confederate AF, Harlingen/Midland TX	8.81/95
				(flies as "327868/*Yellow Rose*/AW")	
108-35072 •	B-25J TB-25N	**43-28059**	N9857C	Blue Mountain Air Service, La Grande OR	59
				Earl Dodge, Anchorage AK	63/70
				Edgar Thorsrud, Missoula MT	78
			C-GTIM		
			N26795	Kermit A. Weeks, New Tamiami FL	11.81/84
			N1943J	Weeks Air Museum, Tamiami FL	3.84/94
				(rest. to fly, Chino CA 86/94)	
108-35109 •	B-25J	**43-28096**		(to FA Venozolanas as FAV 5-B-40)	.48
				Museo Aeronautico FAV, Maracay AB	79/96
				(also rep. ex 44-30369)	
108-35117 •	B-25J TB-25N	43-28204	N9856C	Blue Mountain Air Service, La Grande OR	59
				Idaho Aircraft Inc, Boise ID (tanker)	63
				Dennis G. Smilanich, Boise ID	63/66
				Filmways Inc, Hollywood CA	68/72
				(flew in film *Catch 22* 68/69)	
				Ted Itano Chino CA	.72/96
				(flies as 3-28204/*Pacific Princess*)	
108-35235 •	B-25J TB-25N	43-28222	N5256V	Zack C. Monroe, Burbank CA	63
				Les Bowman, Los Angeles CA	64/70
				(derelict, engineless, Grass Valley CA 78)	
				Ralph M. Ponte, Grass Valley CA	78/80
				USAFM, Beale AFB CA: del.	8.80/93
				(displ. as 328222)	
108-35262 •	B-25J TB-25N	**43-35972**	**N9552Z**	Dothan Aviation, Dothan AL	63/72
				John J. Stokes, San Marcos TX	78
				Confederate Air Force, Harlingen TX later Midland TX	13.1.82/96
				(long-term rest. Mesa AZ 85/95)	
108-35364 •	B-25J TB-25N	**43-36074**	**N9079Z**	Donaire Inc, Phoenix AZ (tanker #32)	63/64
				Hubert H. Clements, Indiantown FL	66
				Clements & Howe Aviation, Indiantown FL	69/72
				SST Aviation Museum, Kissimmee FL	73/82
				(displ. as "430734")	
				Bob Bolin, Patrick O'Neil & Jack Myer/ BOM Corp, Wichita Falls TX	.82/90

				(rest. Kissimmee, ff 3.86 430734/Panchito)	
				dam. landing Wichita Falls TX (repaired)	18.9.88
				Richard F. Korff, Lewiston NY	91/92
				(note: USCR changed id. from 43-36074 to 44-30734 in 72: see N9080Z)	
08-2013 •	B-25J TB-25N	**44-28738**	**N3441G**	United Aerial Applicators Inc, Papillion NE	64/66
				Midwest Seafoods Inc, Denver CO	69/70
				(derelict, unconv., Omaha NE "BD-738" 73)	
				USAFM, Offutt AFB NE	.75/94
				(displ. with sectioned fuselage)	
08-2040 •	B-25J TB-25N VB-25N	**44-28765**	**N9443Z**	Dothan Aviation Corp, Dothan AL	63/72
				Heritage of Flight Museum,Springfield IL	c78
				(displ. as *Piece of Cake*)	
				Carl Scholl/Aero Trader, Chino CA	c80/94
				(stored dism., Ocotillo Wells CA 88/94)	
08-2109 •	B-25J TB-25N	**44-28834**	**N9865C**	E. D. Weiner, Los Angeles CA (tanker #30)	63
				Hollywood Air Inc, Miami FL	64
				Peter Coward, Opa Locka FL	70/72
				James Hazlitt, Galveston TX	78
				Carl Scholl/Historical Aircraft Preservation Group, Borrego Springs CA	84/86
				Gerald S. Beck, Wahpeton ND	87/88
				USAFM, Grand Forks AFB ND	89/94
				(displ. as 327899)	
08-2141 •	B-25J	**44-28866**	N5277V	Wenatchee Air Service Inc, Wenatchee WA	63/64
			CF-OND (2	Wenairco of Canada Ltd, Vancouver BC	65/66
				Northwestern Air Lease, St Albert ALTA	70/78
				(tanker #90)	
				G & M Aircraft Ltd, St Albert ALTA (#90)	81
				Northwestern Air Lease, Edmonton ALTA	90/93
			N225AJ	BHA Leasing Inc, Carmel MD	5.11.93/96
08-2150 •	B-25J TB-25N	**44-28875**		displ. Servicemens Centre, San Angelo TX	65
				USAFM, Goodfellow AFB, San Angelo TX	88/94
08-2200 •	B-25J TB-25N	**44-28925**	**N7687C**	Parsons Air Park, Carpinteria CA: ex USAF	.58/64
				Aerial Applicators Inc, Salt Lake City UT	66
				Trans West Air Service, Salt Lake City UT	68
				Tallmantz Aviation Inc, Orange County CA	.68/70
				(flew in movie Catch 22: *Tokyo Express*)	
				Veterans Cemetery, Pittsburg PA	.71/84
				(displ. on pole as 428925/*Daisy Jean*)	
				Valiant Air Command, Titusville FL	.84
				Harry S. Doan, Daytona Beach FL	.84/92
				(trucked to Florida for rebuild 10.84; stored dism., Kissimmee FL 84/90)	
				offered dism. at Doan auction: rest project	30.10.92
				Cavanaugh Flight Mus., Dallas-Addison TX	10.92/96
				(trucked to Chino CA .93 for rest., ff 6.95 as *How 'Boot That!*)	
08-2207 •	B-25J TB-25N	**44-28932**	**N3476G**	Earl Dodge, Anchorage AK	63/64
				Robert P. Schlaefli, Port Orchard WA	66/84
				Collings Foundation, Stowe MA	11.85/96
				(flew as 428932/7A/*Hoosier Honey*)	
08-2213 •	B-25J TB-25N	**44-28938**	**N7946C**	Wenatchee Air Service Inc, Wenatchee WA	63/64
				Red Dodge Aviation Inc, Anchorage AK	69/72
				(tanker #4)	
				Yolanda Rodriguez, Tucson AZ	78
				James D. Ricketts/Aero Nostalgia Inc, Stockton CA	82/94
				World Jet Inc, Fort Lauderdale FL	15.7.94
				Flight Management Inc, Tulsa OK	29.9.94/96
				(flies as 428938/9C/*Dream Lover*)	

c/n	Type	Serial	Reg	History	Date
108-32220	B-25J VB-25J	44-28945		(Gen. Hap Arnold's personal aircraft)	
			N3184G	Edwards Petroleum Co, Fort Worth TX	
				Wilson C. Edwards, San Angelo TX	63
				Bendix Corp, Baltimore MD: del.	5.10.63/68
				Santiago Perez/Double A Leasing, Miami FL	3.68/70
			CP-970	Transaereos Beni, La Paz, Bolivia	.72
				crashed	7.6.76
108-32297 •	B-25J	**44-29022**		(to NEIAF/KNIL as N5-233; later M-433)	
				(to AURI/Indonesian AF as M-433)	
				Indonesian Air Force Academy Collection, Jawa Tengah, Yogyakarta	87/91
108-32307 •	B-25J	**44-29032**		(to NEIAF/KNIL as N5-239; later M-439)	
				(to AURI/Indonesian AF as M-439)	
				Indonesian Air Force Museum, Yogyakarta	.78/93
108-32310 •	B-25J	**44-29035**	N3516G	(to FA Venezuala as ....)	
				El Libertador AB, Venezuala : open storage	80/92
				Steven A. Detch, Alpharetta GA: crated	.92
			N61821	Steven Detch/Military Aircraft Restoration Corp, Alpharetta GA	22.1.93
108-69 32396 •	B-25J TB-25N	**44-29121**	**N86427**	Compass Aviation, San Francisco CA	63/
				(flew as "02344": Doolittle raid 25th anniversary, NAS Alameda CA 10.67)	
				American Air Museum Society, Oakland CA	70/72
				Lee Schaller, Las Vegas NV	78
				Visionair International Inc, Miami FL	6.78/85
				arr. Luton UK for movie "Hanover Street"	11.5.78
				(flew as 151724/*Brenda's Boys*, later 151451/Miami Clipper)	
				(abandoned Malaga, Spain .79/85: wing dam. during low flying for movie *Cuba*)	
				Museo del Aire, Cuatro Vientos AB, Madrid	87/93
				(displ. as Ejertico del Aire/41-30338)	
108-32402 •	B-25J TB-25N	**44-29127**	**N9899C**	Constantine Zaharoff, Arlington TX	64/70
				Anthony J. Martella, Grand Prairie TX	72
				I. N. Burchinall Jr, Paris TX	78/84
				Colvin Aircraft Inc, Big Cabin OK	9.84/95
108-32403 •	B-25J Mk. III	**44-29128**		(to RCAF as 5236): BOC 24.1.52: SOC	23.5.62
			N92872	Columbus L. Woods, Lewistown MT	.61
				Roy M. Egeland, Missoula MT	63/64
				Lebate Corp, Los Angeles CA	66/70
				Technical Museum, Mexico City	72/96
				(displ. on pole, Chapultepec Park, Mexico City)	
108-32474 •	B-25J	**44-29199**	**N9117Z**	A. B. Sellards/Abe's Aerial Service, Safford AZ	63/64
				Aircraft Specialties Inc, Mesa AZ (tanker #C35)	66/72
				(wfu open storage, Mesa AZ 69/76)	
				John J. Stokes, San Marcos TX	77
				Robert A. Lumbard, Diamond Bar CA	78
				Air Force of The Potomac/Yankee Air Mus.	79
				William P. Muszala, Rialto & Fontana CA	84
				Robert A. Lumbard, Fontana CA	4.84/96
				(flies as "429199/ *In The Mood*")	
108-32641 •	B-25J TB-25N	**44-29366**	**N9115Z**	Sonora Flying Service, Columbia CA	63/66
				Filmways Inc, Hollywood CA	68/72
				(flew in movie *Catch 22* 68/69)	
				MARC, Chino CA	.72/79
				Yesterdays Air Force, St. Petersburg FL (displ. as "*Toujours-au-Danger*")	77/78

				arr. Luton UK for film "*Hanover Street*"	16.5.78
				(flew as "151645/Marvellous Miriam")	
				Warbirds of GB Ltd, Blackbushe	.79/82
				RAF Museum, Hendon: arr. dism.	10.82/96
				(rest., displ. as "USAAF 34037")	
108-32740 •	B-25J TB-25N	**44-29465**	N3523G	Ernest Beckman, Battle Creek MI	63/70
				Glenn H. Lamont, Detroit MI	8.75/84
			N25GL	Glenn H. Lamont, Detroit MI	2.86/96
				(flies as 429465/*Guardian of Freedom*)	
108-32782 •	B-25J TB-25N VB-25N	**44-29507**		USAF disposal: to owner, Elkhart IN	27.7.59
				(civil conv. Michigan City IN .62:	
				cargo hold installed in bomb bay)	
			N3698G	Verco Tropical Fisheries, Columbus OH	63/64
				Robert R. Johnson, Fort Lauderdale FL	66
				Austin Williams, West Palm Beach FL	69/72
				sale rep.	78
				Donald R. Webber/Aerial Solutions Inc,	
				Baton Rouge LA (flew as "Cochise")	84/89
				Duke of Brabant Air Force, Netherlands	6.6.89
			N320SQ	Amho Corp, Wilmington DE	1.90/95
				(rest. Baton Rouge LA, ff 15.5.90,	
				del. Baton Rouge-Eindhoven 22/25.5.90)	
				op: Duke of Brabant Air Force, Eindhoven,	
				Netherlands	5.90/96
				(flies as "HD346/ND-V/*Lotys II*")	
108-32953	B-25J VB-25J	44-29678	N9958F	Babb Co Inc, Newark NJ	53/54
				adv. for sale flyaway unconv. Newark NJ	6.53
				Bob Bean Aircraft, Blythe CA	63/66
				Glen W. Dunn, Lawndale CA	69/70
			XB-DOF	displ. Mexico City	
				scrapped	.89
108-33083	B-25J TB-25N	44-29808	N5248V	Jasper Oil Tool Corp, Long Beach CA	3.1.58
				Les-Calco, Long Beach CA	15.1.58/62
				Los Angeles Board of Education CA	29.1.62
				LA Trade Tech. School, LAX: inst. airframe	62/76
				broken-up for scrap	.76
108-33087 •	B-25J TB-25N	**44-29812**	**N2854G**	off USCR by	63
				Paul Bunyan Amusement Park, Brainard MN	73/84
				(displ. as "BD-812")	
108-33110 •	B-25J TB-25N	**44-29835**	**N3676G**	Jerome A. Eddy, San Antonio TX	63/64
				Rowsey Development Inc, Kerrville TX	66
				Confederate Air Force, Harlingen TX	69/80
				(static displ. "Randy's Raiders")	
				USAFM, Lackland AFB TX	.80/96
				(trucked dism. to Lackland .80 for static rest.,	
				dedicated Lackland AFB 12.12.80)	
108-33114	B-25J TB-25N	44-29839	N7669C	United Aerial Applicators Inc, Pappilion NE	64/70
				sale rep., USCR (does this still exist?)	78/95
108-33144 •	B-25J	**44-29869**	N3160G	Lysdale Flying Service, St. Paul MN	60
				spray operator, Anoka WI	63/70
				(stored unconv. Anoka WI 63/70)	
				Dr. Kundel, Rice Lake WI	70/78
				(del. to Rice Lake WI c71, open storage)	
				Harvard Corp/CAF, Minneapolis MN	.78
				Confederate Air Force, Harlingen TX	13.8.79/91
				(del. Rice Lake to St. Paul-Fleming Field .79,	
				long term rest. to fly)	
			N27493	Confederate Air Force, Midland TX	6.91/96
				(rest. completed St. Paul-Fleming Field MN,	
				ff 16.4.93 as "327493/*Miss Mitchell*")	
108-	B-25J	**44-29887**	**N10564**	US Forestry Service CA (tanker #E91)	.59/61

c/n	Type	Serial	Reg	History	Date
33162 •	TB-25N			Parsons Air Park Inc, Carpinteria CA	63/64
				(tanker #E91)	
				Hemet Valley Flying Service, Hemet CA	65/68
				stored engineless, Hemet CA	65/68
				Tallmantz Avn, Santa Ana CA	.68/71
				(flew in movie "*Catch 22*" 68/69)	
				David Allen/Davu Aviation Inc, Sarasota FL	72/73
				Wings of Yesterday Museum, Santa Fe NM	75/78
				John Marshall/Warbirds of the World, Dunnellon FL	80/85
				(flew as *Little Brown Jugs*/6Y, later 429887/*Carol Jean*/6M)	
				NASM: stored Washington-Dulles Airport	.85/95
108-33214 •	B-25J TB-25N	**44-29939**	**N9456Z**	Tallmantz Aviation, Santa Ana CA	63/70
				(flew in movie "*Catch 22*" 68/69)	
				Donald Buchele, Columbia Station OH	3.71/78
				Gene Fisher, Harrisburg PA	.78/81
				Mid Atlantic Air Museum, Middletown PA	12.81/95
				(flies as "327638/*Briefing Time*/9D")	
108-33218 •	B-25J TB-25N	**44-29943**	N9444Z	Colco Aviation, Anchorage AK	63/70
				(derelict on fire dump, Fairbanks AK 76/79)	
				Richard A. Benner, Wasilla AK	86/87
				(hulk airlifted by helicopter ex Fairbanks .86)	
			N943	Hal Kading/Southwest Aviation Inc, Fairacres NM	8.87/95
				(rest. to fly, Wasalla AK)	
108-33285 •	B-25J TB-25K	**44-30010**	**N9641C**	H. H. Coffield, Rockdale TX	60
				Arrow Sales Co, Hollywood CA	63/70
				H. H. Coffield/Rockdale Flying Service TX	73/83
				sold at auction, Rockdale TX	15.10.83
				Gerald S. Beck/Tri-State Aviation, Wahpeton ND	10.83/94
				(del. Rockdale-Wahpeton .84, stored 84/94)	
108-33344 •	B-25J	**44-30069**		(to FA Brasileira as 5127)	
				Museu Aeroespacial, Campo dos Afoncos, Rio de Janeiro	79/90
108-33352 •	B-25J TB-25N	**44-30077**	**N2849G**	Avery Aviation, Greybull WY	63/66
				Filmways Inc, Hollywood CA	68/72
				(flew in movie "Catch 22": *Mouthy Mitchell*)	
				Richard A. Sawyer, Clarence IA	78
				(displ. Flying Tigers Air Museum, Kissimmee FL: "Mouthy Mitchell" 78)	
				Georgia Historical Aviation Museum, Stone Mountain GA	.81/84
				Tom Reilly Vintage Aircraft, Kissimmee FL	4.84/96
				(stored dism. Kissimmee, *Mouthy Mitchell*, under rest. to fly Kissimmee 93/94)	
108-33365 •	B-25J TB-25K	**44-30090**	**N9633C**	Rockdale Flying Service, Rockdale TX	60/83
				(stored unconv., Rockdale TX 60/83)	
				sold at auction, Rockdale TX	15.10.83
				Carl Scholl/Aero Trader, Chino CA	10.83/96
				(stored dism., Ocotillo Wells CA & Chino 84/90)	
108-33404 •	B-25J TB-25N	**44-30129**	**N7947C**	C. C. Wilson, San Diego CA	63
				Arthur Jones, Slidell LA	64
				Walter Soplata Collection, Newbury OH	65/83
				Steven A. Detch, Alpharetta GA	12.90/96
				(id. also quoted as 44-30121)	
108-33434	B-25J	44-30159	N9655C	Donaire Inc, Phoenix AZ	63/64
				Oklahoma Liquid Fertilizer Corp, El Reno OK	66
				Clements & Howe Aviation, Indiantown FL	69/72

c/n	Type	Serial	Regn	Owner / history	Date
108-33478 •	B-25J	**44-30203**		(to FA Venezolanas as 3898) El Libertador AB, Venezuala : open storage Steven A. Detch, Alpharetta GA: crated Lynn C. Hunt/Pacific Coast Air Museum, Santa Rosa CA: rest. project (id. also quoted as 44-30302)	 91/92 .92 93/96
108-33485 •	B-25J TB-25N	**44-30210**	**N9455Z**	disposal ex MASDC, Davis-Monthan AFB Paul Mantz Air Service, Santa Ana CA (tanker: based Caracas, Venezuela 61) Les Bowman, Long Beach CA (tanker #82) Daryl M. Jackson, Moses Lake WA David C. Tallichet/MARC, Chino CA (del. Luton UK for film *Hanover Street* 11.5.78: flew as "151863/*Big Bad Bonnie*") (stored Blackbushe & Dublin 78/81) Jeff Hawke/Mitchell Flight, Cranfield: del. (abandoned u/s Avignon, France 7.82/83) Warplane Flying Grp,Wellsbourne Mountford (dep. UK on ferry to Chino CA 1.8.86) USAFM, March AFB CA : loan (displ. as "30210/*Big Bad Bonnie*/8U") (open storage Chino CA "02344" 91/95)	31.12.59 61 64/70 72 7.75/93 5.81/83 .83 87/90
108-33518 •	B-25J TB-25N	**44-30243**	N9622C N17666	Clyde C. Werner, Elkhart IN Aero Enterprises Inc, Elkhart IN Jerry Christenson, Tacoma WA (open storage, Elkhart IN 67) Aero Dix, New Albany OH Earl T. Reinert/Victory Air Museum, Mundelein IL (displ. as *Tokyo Express*) Tom Reilly Vintage Aircraft, Kissimmee FL	63 64 66 69/72 .71/79 94
108-33529 •	B-25J Mk. III	**44-30254**	 CF-MWC **N41123**	(to RCAF as 5211): BOC 25.10.51: SOC Cascade Drilling Co, Calgary ALTA Northwestern Air Lease, Edmonton ALTA G & M Aircraft Ltd, St Albert ALTA (tanker #2, #337) Jeff Thomas/Vintage Wings, Seattle WA	7.11.61 65/66 70/78 81/95 6.95
108-33599 •	B-25J TB-25N	**44-30324**	CF-OND (1 **N3161G**	 Aviation Rental Service, St Paul MN Lynn L. Florey, New Brighton MN Archaeopteryx Corp, Minneapolis MN MARC, Chino CA	 66/69 12.69/70 72/78 5.81/95
108-33638 •	B-25J TB-25J	**44-30363**		USAFM, Offutt AFB NE (displ. as "0-43363/Desert Boom")	65/94
108-33653	B-25J	44-30378		Aircraft Industries Museum, Louisville KY	73
108-33674 •	B-25J	**44-30399**		(to NEIAF/KNIL as N5-258; later M-458) (to AURI/Indonesian AF as M-458) Armed Forces Museum, Jakarta	 79/96
108-33696 •	B-25J Mk. III	**44-30421**	 CF-OVN **N7674**	(to RCAF as 5272): BOC 20.8.53: SOC Robert Sturges, Troutdale OR sale rep., Burlington NC	16.2.62 69/78 84/92
108-33698 •	B-25J	**44-30423**	**N3675G**	Ed Maloney/The Air Museum, Ontario CA Planes of Fame, Chino CA (flies as "*Shangri-la Lil*", *Photo Fanny*)	65/72 73/96
108-33719 •	B-25J TB-25M	**44-30444**		General Mitchell Airport, Milwaukee WI (displ. as "0-30444/WISC ANG")	71/94
108-	B-25J	**44-30456**	N3512G	R. H. Hickish, Pico-Rivera CA	63/64

c/n	Type	Serial	Reg	Owner / history	Date
33731 •	TB-25N			Airstream Aviation, Carlsbad CA	66
				A. C. Ellis, Galveston TX	69/70
			C-GTTS	resident, Carman, MAN del.	17.4.73
				Air Spray Ltd, Edmonton ALTA	.81
			N43BA	William G. Arnot, Breckenridge TX	.82/94
				(flew as *Silver Lady*/BA)	
				Jack A. Erickson, Medford OR	30.8.94/96
108-33745	B-25J	44-30470	N3443G	Henry E. Huntington, Carmel CA	63/64
				Westair Co, Westminster CO	66
				Yankee Air Club Inc, Sunderland MA	69/70
				landing accident Turners Falls, Orange MA	8.9.70
108-33759	B-25J Mk. III	44-30484		(to RCAF as 5250): BOC 9.5.52: SOC	22.11.61
			N92882	Columbus L. Woods, Lewistown MT	.61
				H. D. Anderson & T.A. Tiegen, Bozeman MT	1.9.64
				derelict, impounded Port-au-Prince, Haiti	74/76
108-33768 •	B-25J TB-25J TB-25M	**44-30493**	**N9451Z**	National Metals Inc, Phoenix AZ	15.1.60
				Spring Aviation, Tucson AZ	24.8.60/67
				Tallmantz Aviation, Santa Ana CA	13.7.68
				Filmways Inc, Hollywood CA	11.9.68/71
				(flew in movie "Catch 22" 68/69: "Dumbo")	
				Tallmantz Aviation, Santa Ana CA	18.8.71/85
				Sherman Aircraft Sales, W. Palm Beach FL	.85
				USAFM, Malmstrom AFB MT	86/93
108-33810 •	B-25J TB-25N	**44-30535**	**N9462Z**	Dothan Aviation Corp, Dothan AL	63/72
				Edward George, Minster OH	78
				Kenneth R. Cunningham, Lawton OK	84
				Ada Aircraft Museum, Oklahoma City OK	6.84/95
				Mid-America Air Museum, Liberal KS: loan	.88/94
				(flies as 0535/Iron *Laiden Maiden*)	
108-33881 •	B-25J TB-25N	**44-30606**	N5249V		
			N201L	C. M. Jasper, Reno NV	
				Union Bank, Los Angeles CA	63/64
				Jack Davis, La Jolle CA	66/70
				Warbirds Inc, Hobbs NM	72/87
				Ted R. Melsheimer, Carson City NV	4.89/95
				(flies as "430606/Tootsie")	
108-33882 •	B-25J TB-25N	**44-30607**	**N9582Z**	Avery Aviation, Greybull WY	63/70
				sale rep., Jeanerette LA	78/95
108-33902 •	B-25J	**44-30627**		(to FA Venezolanas as ....)	
				open storage, El Libertador AB	80/92
				Venezolana de Motores Aeronauticas	
				Steven A. Detch, Alpharetta GA: crated	.92
			N45HA	Steven A. Detch, Alpharetta GA	12.92/96
108-33910 •	B-25J TB-25N	**44-30635**		USAFM, Chanute AFB, Rantoul IL	65/96
				(displ. as "02344"; later 2279/*Whiskey Pete*)	
108-33924 •	B-25J TB-25N	**44-30649**	**N9452Z**	Filmways Inc, Hollywood CA	.68/72
				(del. Orange County CA .68 in unconv. USAF scheme for use in film *Catch 22* .68)	
				USAFM, Wright-Patterson AFB, Dayton OH 74	
				USAFM, Tuskegee AL	86
				USAFM, Maxwell AFB AL	.87/94
				(displ. as "42-53373 & 44-34974/*Poopsie*", later "253373")	
108-33996	B-25J	44-30721	N5455V	noted with spray bars, Sacramento CA	
				(tanker #3)	7.58
				Robert B. Becker, Miami FL	63
				Servicios Americanos S.A., Miami FL	64

				Maravilla Inc, Miami FL	66/70
108-34008 •	B-25J	44-30733	**N9088Z**	Johnson Flying Service, Missoula MT	.58/66
				Edgar L. Thorsrud, Missoula MT	69/70
				(tanker #8Z)	
				cr. on river sandbar, near Fairbanks AK	27.6.69
				(stripped wreck still in situ 92)	
108-34009	B-25J	44-30734	N9080Z	Donaire Inc, Phoenix AZ: tanker	63/64
			XB-NAJ	(see 43-36074/N9079Z)	
108-34012	B-25J	44-30737	N9446Z	Richard B. Flint, Tucson AZ	63/64
				Donald Aircraft Corp, Tucson AZ	66
				Darryl Berg, Los Angeles & San Diego CA	69/72
				I. N. Burchinal Jnr, Paris TX	73/74
				Air Chicago Freight Lines, Chicago IL	18.7.74/75
				War Aero Inc, Chicago IL	1.4.75
				crashed Chicago-Midway Airport IL	6.8.76
108-34023 •	B-25J TB-25N	**44-30748**	N3447G		
			N8195H	Avery Aviation, Greybull WY	63/66
				Filmways Inc, Hollywood CA	68/72
				(flew in movie "*Catch 22*" 68/69)	
				Milan S. Pupich, Van Nuys CA	5.74/96
				(flies as "430748/*Heavenly Body*")	
108-34031 •	B-25J TB-25N	**44-30756**	**N9936Z**	Colco Aviation Inc, Anchorage AK	63/70
				(derelict & stripped, Fairbanks AK 76/79)	
				John C. Morgan, La Canada CA	84
				Southwest Aviation Inc, Fairacres NM	1.86/96
				(stored dism. Alaska 88, Ocotillo Wells CA 94)	
108-34036 •	B-25J	**44-30761**	**N3398G**	Ed Maloney/The Air Museum, Ontario CA	65/72
				Planes of Fame, Chino CA	78/92
				(flew as "Betty Grable")	
				Aero Trader, Chino CA	6.94/96
108-34047 •	B-25J	**44-30772**	**N9076Z**	Aero Insect Control Inc, Rio Grand NJ	63/64
				Nico Inc, Miami FL	66/70
				noted impounded at Ascuncion, Paraguay	3.72
				derelict, Ascuncion, Paraguay	83
108-34054	B-25J	44-30779		rep. displ. in park, Odessa TX	73
108-34076 •	B-25J TB-25N	**44-30801**	N3699G	Avery Aviation, Greybull WY	63/66
				Filmways Inc, Hollywood CA	.68/72
				(in movie *Catch 22* 68/69: *Vestal Virgin*)	
				Ed Schnepf/Challenge Publications, Van Nuys CA	.72/78
			N30801	Challenge Publications, Van Nuys CA	78/84
				American Aeronautical Foundation, Van Nuys/Camarillo CA	1.85/96
				(flies as 430801/*Executive Sweet*)	
108-34098 •	B-25J TB-25J VB-25J VB-25N	44-30823	**N1042B**	Ralph Richardson, Yakima WA	.58
				Earnest Lee & Arb Osen, Yakima WA	10.58
				Wenatchee Air Service Inc, Wenatchee WA	12.58/62
				Tallmantz Aviation, Santa Ana CA	17.5.62/85
				(used in movie *Catch 22* 68/69)	
				Sherman Aircraft Sales, West Palm Beach FL	.85/87
				Dean Martin/Consolidated Aviation Enterprises, Burlington VT	11.87/89
				Universal Aviation Corp, Dover DE	3.89/92
				op: Aces High Ltd, North Weald, UK: del.	9.4.88/92
				(flies as "430823/69/*Dolly*)	
				World Jet Inc, Fort Lauderdale FL	1.95
				(dep. UK 26.7.95 on del. to USA)	

108-34107 •	B-25J TB-25N	44-30832	**N3155G**	J. J. Rivituso, West Covina CA	63/64
				Joanne M. Mahr, San Clemente CA	66/72
				Carl Scholl, Borrego Springs CA	78
				Donald C. Davis, Casper WY	.80/86
				First National Bank, Evanston WY	87
				Southwest Aviation Inc, Fairacres NM	11.87
				(flew as *Bronco Bustin Bomber*/0832)	
				Jerry Tepper/Showplanes & Aircraft Co, Arvada CO (flies as "Can Do")	89/92
				Wally Fisk/Amjet Aircraft Corp, St. Paul-Anoka County MN	8.93/96
108-34129 •	B-25J JB-25J	44-30854		Doolittle Memorial, Valparaiso FL	72
				USAFM, Eglin AFB FL	79/94
				(displ. as Doolittle's "USAAC 02344")	
108-34136 •	B-25J TB-25J	**44-30861**	N9089Z	Aero American Corp, Cincinatti OH	61/63
				(del. to UK .61 as camera ship for films *The War Lover* & *633 Squadron*, flew as "RAF N908/*Moviemaker II*" .61/63)	
				Aero Associates Inc, Tucson AZ	64/69
				(abandoned Biggin Hill UK after filming .64/66)	
				Malcolm D. N. Fisher/ Historical Aircraft Preservation Society, Biggin Hill	.66/67
				Historic Aircraft Museum, Southend	7.67/83
				(arr. by road 7.67, displ. as "HD368/VO-A")	
				Jeff Hawke/Visionair International, London	10.5.83
			G-BKXW	ntu: Aces High Ltd, Duxford: arr. dism.	8.84/87
				(displ. as "HD368/VO-A")	
				Aces High Ltd, North Weald: arr. dism.	10.87/89
				(static displ. as 430861/*Bedsheet Bomber*)	
				The Fighter Collection,	.89/92
				(still stored, North Weald: last flown 64)	
108-34200 •	B-25J TB-25N	**44-30925**	N9494Z	National Metals Co, Phoenix AZ	.60
				John C. Estes, Beaumont TX	66
				Filmways Inc, Hollywood CA	.68/69
				(used in movie *Catch 22* 68/69)	
				Confederate Air Force, Harlingen TX	72
				John J. Stokes, San Marcos TX	78
				(flew as *Laiden Maiden*)	
				Visionair International Inc, Miami FL	.78/92
				arr. Luton UK for film *Hanover Street*	11.5.78
				(flew as "151632/*Gorgeous George-Ann*", later "*Thar She Blows*")	
				Warbirds of GB Ltd, Blackbushe	78/82
				(stored Blackbushe after filming .78/82, trucked to Wellesbourne Mountford 10.82, trucked to Coventry 9.85, open storage 9.85/94)	
				sold: trucked Coventry-Headcorn, Kent	3.94
			G-BWGR	Aces High Ltd., North Weald	18.8.95
108-34251 •	B-25J	**44-30976**	N8193H	Oscar S. Wyatt, Corpus Christi TX	63/66
				United Traffic Corp, Miami FL	69/70
				noted abandoned, Ascuncion, Paraguay	3.72
				derelict, Ascuncion, Paraguay	83
108-34254 •	B-25J TB-25N	**44-30979**		Ed Maloney/The Air Museum, Ontario CA later Chino CA	67/76
108-34263 •	B-25J	**44-30988**	**N5865V**	Oilfield Aviation Corp, Houston TX	54
				Robert Gure, Chicago IL	63
				Air Services Inc, Addison TX	64
				Aero Industries, Addison TX	66/69
				Robert A. Mathews, Jacksonville NC	71/72
				(stored derelict Fort Lauderdale FL 72/79)	
				Tom Reilly, Orlando FL	.78

				Craig Tims, Conifer CO & Roanoke TX	.81/88
				(rebuilt Kissimmee FL, ff 11.82 : reg. 8.83)	
				Confederate Air Force, Harlingen TX later	
				Midland TX	6.88/95
				(flies as *Big Ole Brew'n Little Ole You*)	
108-34271	B-25J TB-25N	44-30996	N9991Z	James J. Wright, Cleveland OH	63/64
				Freddy Van Dux, Chicago IL	66
			PI-C905	Aero Service Corp, Manila PI	
				dest. by cyclone, Virac Island airstrip PI	14.10.70
108-34279 •	B-25J TB-25N	44-31004	**N9463Z**	Dothan Aviation Corp, Dothan AL	63/72
				USS Alabama Battleship Memorial Park,	
				Mobile AL	74/94
				(displ. as "431004", later Doolittle's "02344")	
108-34307 •	B-25J TB-25N	**44-31032**	**N3174G**	Walston Aviation Inc, East Alton IL	66
				Filmways Inc, Hollywood CA	.68/72
				(used in film"Catch 22" 68/69)	
				MARC, Chino CA	.72/93
				USAFM, March AFB CA: loan	82/93
108-34379 •	B-25J	**44-31104**	**N39E**	General Electric Corp, Schenectady NY	54/58
				Irving Reingold, Hackensack NJ	63/70
				(noted derelict,Teterboro NJ 70)	
				Hawkeye Military Surplus, Pawling NY	.73
				(stored derelict, Pawling NY 74/83)	
				Harry S. Doan/Doan Helicopters Inc,	
				New Smyrna Beach FL: dism.	87/91
108-37196 •	B-25J	**44-31121**		Walter Soplata Collection, Newbury OH	85
				Steven A. Detch, Alpharetta GA: hulk	.90/92
108-37246 •	B-25J JTB-25J	**44-31171**	**N7614C**	Radio Corporation of America, Camden NJ	59/64
				Flying W Productions, Medford OR	66/69
				Euramericair Inc, Fort Lauderdale FL	70
				(del. Luton UK .70 for filming, then stored .70/71;	
				impounded Dublin, Prestwick, Shoreham 72/76)	
				Imperial War Museum, Duxford: arr. dism.	10.76/96
				(static rest. for American Air Museum	
				Duxford)	
108-37247 •	B-25J TB-25N	**44-31172**	**LV-GXH**	Enrique Denwert	19.6.61
				Empresa Provincial de Aviacion	
				static displ., Santiago del Estero Airport	76/83
108-37333 •	B-25J	**44-31258**		(to KLu as N5-264)	
				(to RAAF as N5-264: 18 (NEI) Sqn): del.	25.6.45
				(to KNLI as M-464: later to AURI as M-464)	
				Militaire Luchtvaart Museum, Soesterberg	.71/95
				(shipped Indonesia to Netherlands, arr. 12.5.71:	
				displ. as "RNAF M-464")	
108-37460 •	B-25J TB-25J	**44-31385**	**N3481G**	Grafton Insurance Inc, Grafton WI	63
				Northwest Development Corp, Kohler WI	64
				John C. Lowe, Riverside IL	66
				Jack L. Rhoades, Seymour IN	69/83
				dam. on ground by windstorm, Seymour IN	.69
				(open storage, Seymour IN 69/75,	
				rest. to fly by Rhoades .75, flying 76)	
				Air Classics Inc, St Charles MO	3.83/84
				Confederate Air Force, Harlingen TX later	
				Midland TX	10.85/95
				(flies as *Show Me*/1361)	
108-37474	B-25J Mk. III	44-31399		(to RCAF as 5234): BOC 15.1.52: SOC	26.4.62
			CF-NTV	ferried to Kamloops BC	c62
				derelict, unconverted, Kamloops BC	71
108-	B-25J	44-31493		(to RCAF as 5249): BOC 3.4.52: SOC	26.4.62

An anonymous looking Spitfire Mk.XVIII (G-BRAF, SM969) is one of the airframes recovered from India by Ormonde and Wensley Haydon-Baillie in the seventies. It flew again in 1985 and is seen here in mid-engine run at Biggin Hill under the watchful eye of owner Doug Arnold, standing by the port wingtip. **Gary Robert Brown.**

Having reverted from Dutch roundels to R.A.F. targets, Spitfire Mk.IX MK932 'Baby Bea' was to join two-seater ML407 in bearing 'OU' codes for 1994 and 1995. An unfortunate (and expensive) undercarriage problem and forced landing has since been repared with some help from the Royal Netherlands Air Force, and the only low-countries Spitfire is set for a full season in 1996. **Jim Winchester.**

The Shuttleworth Spitfire Mk.Vc AR501 G-AWII is a familiar sight, and it has as a result almost become taken for granted. Changed subtly over the years; the recent three stub exhausts have be re-replaced with the more familiar six stub units and the codes 'NN-D' were changed a few years ago to 'NN-A' when details of these codes came to light. AR501 was given a fifty year overhaul by original makers Westland. **Jim Winchester.**

It is often forgotten that the ever popular Folland Gnat was itself derived from the single seater Midge. Though not adopted in its country of origin, the Midge was a success as the Adjeet in India. **Thierry Thomassin** caught these ex-Indian Air Force Adjeets at Chino in 1989, awaiting restoration.

Ex-Swiss Hawker Hunter J4087 is seen here at North Weald, Essex, in the ownership of Aeromech International Resources Ltd. who have purchased the complete Swiss spares inventory for this ever more popular jet warbird. **N Brody**. See full page advertisement inside the back cover of this Directory

A classic design by any measure, the North American F-86 Sabre has been a long term stalwart of the jet warbird scene. Like many others representing the breed, NX4589H is an ex-Canadian built Canadair Mk.5 (RCAF23293) restored by Fort Wayne Air Service, and now owned by the Cavanaugh Flight Museum, Dallas, Texas, and bearing the Korean era markings of Major F.C. Blesse. **Cavanaugh Flight Museum.**

37568	Mk. III		CF-NTX	ferried to Kamloops BC	c62
				derelict, unconverted, Kamloops BC	71
108-	B-25J	**44-31504**		(to RCAF as 5218): BOC 21.11.51: SOC	16.2.62
37579 •	TB-25N		**N9753Z**	A. J. Warlick, Seattle WA	63
				Flair Inc, Kauai HI	66/70
				Technical Trade School, Honolulu Airport HI	71/74
				Pacific Aerospace Museum, Honolulu HI	77/93
				USAFM, Hickam AFB HI: loan	77/93
				(displ. as "USAAF 1504")	
108-	B-25J	**44-31508**	**N6578D**	Trans Calypso Inc, Miami FL	63/64
37583 •				Leon H. Patin, Miami FL	66
				Euramericair Inc, Fort Lauderdale FL	67/70
				(del. Bovington UK 15.12.67: camera ship for *Battle of Britain* film, Spain & UK 67/68)	
				Airspeed International Inc, Ft Lauderdale FL	72
				derelict Caldwell-Wright Field NJ	74/77
				Tom Reilly, Kissimmee FL	.78
				(ferried Caldwell to FL for rebuild 3.2.79)	
				B-25 Bomber Group Inc, Ocala FL	81/94
				Dan Powell, Fair Oaks Ranch, Boerne TX	6.9.94/96
				(flies as 431508/*Chapter XI*)	
108- 47448	B-25J	44-86694	N3525G	Dothan Aviation Corp, Dothan AL	63/72
108-	B-25J	**44-86697**		(to RCAF as 5239): BOC 24.1.52: SOC	23.5.62
47451 •	Mk. III		N92876	Columbus L. Woods, Lewistown MT	.61
				(to FA Venozolanas as ......)	
				El Libertador AB, Venezuala : open storage	91
				Steven A. Detch, Alpharetta GA: crated	.92
			N62163	William P. Lear/Tricon Aero Corp, Elwood Park NJ	17.2.93/96
				(rest. to fly Kissimmee FL 93: "Killer B")	
108-	B-25J	**44-86698**		(to RCAF as 5248): BOC 15.1.52: SOC	30.11.61
47452 •	Mk. III		CF-NWU	Eldon M. Armstrong, Toronto ONT	66
			N543VT	I. N. Burchinall Jr, Paris TX	69/72
				Daniel Jackson, Seymour TX	78
				SST Aviation Museum, Kissimmee FL: loan	78
			C-GUNO	G & M Aircraft Ltd, St Albert ALTA	5.83/96
				(tanker #3, #338)	
108-	B-25J	**44-86699**		(to RCAF as 5244): BOC	25.1.52
47453 •	Mk. III			Canadian National Aeronautical Collection, Rockcliffe AB ONT	.64/82
				National Aviation Museum, Rockcliffe ONT	9.82/91
				(displ. as "RAF 98 Sqn "D")	
108-	B-25J	44-86701	N7681C	Filmways Inc., Hollywood CA	.68/72
47455	TB-25N			(arr. Orange County CA 10.68 for *Catch 22* movie, unconv. USAF scheme)	
				David C. Tallichet/MARC, Chino CA	72/79
				(arr. Luton UK 11.5.78 for movie *Hanover Street*, flew as 151790/*Amazing Andrea*)	
				abandoned France after film work	.78
				Musee de l'Air, Paris-Le Bourget (stored)	.79/90
				dest. by museum hangar fire, Le Bourget	17.5.90
108-	B-25J	**44-86715**	**N3442G**	United Aerial Applicators Inc, Papillion NE	64/66
47469 •	TB-25N			Midwest Seafoods Inc, Denver CO	69/70
				(derelict unconv., South Omaha Airport NE 79)	
				Joseph L. Davis, Clovis CA	.79/84
				William R. Klaers, Apple Valley CA	11.86/95
				(stored dism. "BD-715", Ocotillo Wells CA 94)	
108-	B-25J	**44-86724**		(to RCAF as 5203): BOC 6.7.51: SOC	26.4.62

47478 •	Mk. III		**CF-NTU**	Avaco Service: ferried to Kamloops BC	.62
				(derelict, unconv., Kamloops BC 71)	
				CAFB Winnipeg MAN: displ. at gate	74/87
108-47479 •	B-25J Mk. III	44-86725		(assigned to RCAF as 5224: ntu)	28.11.51
				(to RCAF as 5243): BOC 25.1.52: SOC	12.11.63
				(to FA Venozolanas as 5880)	
				(to FA Boliviana as TAM541)	
				La Paz, Bolivia: displ. as gate guard	83
			N25NA	C. A. Bird: reg. res.	5.85
				Harry S. Doan/Doan Helicopters Inc, New Smyrna Beach FL: del. ex La Paz	.86/92
				forced landing in swamp, Cocoa Beach FL	2.4.87
				(rest. project New Smyrna Beach FL 88/92)	
				sold at Doan auction: partially rest.	30.10.92
				Stallion Aircraft Inc, Bensenville IL	7.93/95
				op: Jack Rogers/Air Classics Aviation Museum, duPage IL: rest., flying by	4.94
108-47480 •	B-25J Mk. III	44-86726		(to RCAF as 5237): BOC 24.1.52: SOC	19.2.62
			N92880	Columbus L. Woods, Lewistown MT	.61
			CF-NTP	Belmore H. Schultz/Belmore's Altamont Museum, Coutts ALTA	88
				Reynolds Air Museum, Wetaskiwin ALTA	92/95
				(displ. whole, unconv. as "RCAF 5237")	
108-47481 •	B-25J Mk. III	44-86727		(to RCAF as 5230): BOC 15.1.52: SOC	23.5.62
			N92875	Columbus L. Woods, Lewistown MT	.61/64
				South West Air Contractors, Deming NM	66
				Met. Operations Inc, Hollister CA	69/72
				Arthur W. McDonnell, Mojave CA	75
				USMC Museum, MCAS Quantico VA	76/79
				(flew as "328217")	
				USMC Museum, MCAS El Toro CA	.87/94
				(displ. as "USMC PBJ-1J")	
108-47482	B-25J Mk. III	44-86728		(to RCAF as 5247): BOC 15.1.52: SOC	26.4.62
			CF-NTW	ferried to Kamloops BC	c.62
				derelict, unconv., Kamloops BC	71
108-47488 •	B-25J	**44-86734**	N9090Z	Commercial Engineering & Construction Co, Falls Church VA	63/64
				Peninsula Piling Co, Williamsburg VA	66/70
				Douglas Hazel, Broad Run VA	78
				(wfu, open storage VA 64/79)	
				Dean Martin, East Middlesbury VT	4.79/80
				(trucked dism. to East Middlebury VT .79 for rest., ff 8.80)	
			N600DM	Dean Martin, East Middlesbury VT	5.80/84
			N333RW	Robert L. Waltrip/Air Service Inc, Houston TX	1.86/87
				Robert L. Waltrip/Lone Star Flight Museum, Houston, later Galveston TX	11.87/95
				(flies as "USN PBJ-1J 486734/Special Delivery")	
108-47501 •	B-25J TB-25N	**44-86747**	**N8163H**	Frontier Flying Service, Fairbanks AK	63/64
				RJD Corp, Fairbanks AK	66
				Donald Gilbertson, Fairbanks AK	69/72
				(tanker #7)	
				Noel M.Wien, Anchorage AK	78
				The Air Museum, Chino CA	.79/86
				Robert J. Pond/Planes of Fame East, Minneapolis-Flying Cloud MN	.86/95
				(flies as "287293/Mitch The Witch")	
108-47503 •	B-25J	**44-86749**	**N8194H**	H. M. Trussel, Houston TX	63/64
				Hugh E. Wandel, Longview TX	66/69
				open storage derelict, Ascuncion, Paraguay	72/83

c/n	Type	Serial	Reg	Owner / History	Date
108-47512 •	B-25J	**44-86758**	**N9643C**	Rockdale Flying Service, Rockdale TX	.59/76
				Vernon Thorpe & Walter Wootton/CAF	3.76
				E. W. Broyles & Lou Hilton/CAF	.77/80
				Three Point Aviation, Belton MO	78
				Confederate AF, Harlingen TX/Midland TX	5.11.80/96
				(rest. Rockdale TX 76/80, del. to Harlingen .80, rest. as USMC PBJ-1J *Devil Dog*, ff 7.81)	
108-47526 •	B-25J TB-25N	**44-86772**	**N9333Z**	David W. Brown, Miami FL	63/64
				(abandoned, Teodolina, Santa Fe Argentina 62)	
				Villa Canas Aero Club, Villa Canas: displ.	63
				(derelict Villa Canas airfield, Argentina 83)	
				Don Whittington/World Jet Inc, Fort Lauderdale Exec FL: stored dism.	92/96
108-47527 •	B-25J Mk. III	**44-86773**		(to RCAF as 5282): BOC 8.10.53: SOC	22.11.61
			N8010	Bellomy Aviation, Miami FL	64
			YV-E-IPU	reg.	7.65
			YV-19CP	rereg.	c.75
				crashed	11.8.77
				derelict at Caracas-Maiquetia	83
108-47531 •	B-25J TB-25N	**44-86777**	N9167Z	Fike Plumbing Inc, Phoenix AZ	63/66
				James E. Landon, Phoenix AZ	69
				Allan R. Crosby, Wauwatosa WI	70/73
				Crosby Enterprises Inc, Wauwatosa WI	78
				Richard T. Crosby, Wauwatosa WI	84/86
				(flew as "486777/BD-777")	
				Tom Reilly/Vintage Aircraft Inc, Kissimmee FL	87
				Ed Stringfellow/Mid South Lumber Co, Cropwell AL (flew as *Martha Jean*)	6.88/92
				Executive Aviation, Cincinatti OH	11.92/93
			N345BG	Executive Aviation, Cincinatti OH	3.93/96
108-47539 •	B-25J TB-25N	**44-86785**	**N5262V**	Charlie T. Jensen, Tonopah Air Service NV	c58/76
				(stored in hangar, Tonopah NV c58/76)	
				Mid Pacific International Inc, Eugene OR	78
				Gary Flanders, Oakland CA	82/83
				Wiley Sanders Truck Lines Inc, Troy AL	6.83/96
				(flies as 486785/*Georgia Mae*)	
108-47545 •	B-25J TB-25J	**44-86791**	N8196H	Ace Smelting Inc, Phoenix AZ	18.5.59
				Merrill & Richard Wien, Fairbanks AK	19.5.59/61
				Merric Inc, Fairbanks AK	8.6.61/62
				Frontier Flying Service, Fairbanks AK	19.5.62/63
				RJD Company, Fairbanks AK	3.2.63/67
				Aero Retardent, Fairbanks AK	4.4.67/77
				Pacific Alaska Airlines, Fairbanks AK	13.6.77/79
				Donald Gilbertson, Fairbanks AK	28.8.79/82
				Aero Heritage, Melbourne VIC	4.6.82/85
				(arr. Brisbane on del. from USA 20.12.83)	
			VH-XXV	Australian War Memorial, Canberra ACT	85/96
				(flew as "A47-31/KO-P", last flight 30.11.87, then long term storage Canberra)	
108-47551 •	B-25J TB-25J	**44-86797**	**N3438G**	William H. Wisner, Dallas TX	64
				Caribbean Enterprises Int., Gulfport MS	66
				Herbert G. Ransom, Brentwood CA	69/72
				Carl Scholl/Aero Trader, Chino CA	.73/84
				Richard Skadsheim	84
				Wiley Sanders Truck Lines Inc, Troy AL	.84/96
				(flew as *Samantha; Old Grey Mare*; later "USN 486797/WS")	
108-47574	B-25J Mk. III	44-86820		(to RCAF as 5204): BOC 6.7.51: SOC	23.5.62
			N92874	Columbus L. Woods, Lewistown MT	.61
			N232S	Quick Freeze Corp, St Thomas USVI	63/65

				Curtiss National Bank, Miami FL	66
			CP-808	F. Garcia, La Paz	4.67
				crashed at Itagua, Bolivia	19.4.67
				Servicios Aereos Bolivianos	
				Boliviana de Aviacon, La Paz	72/77
				crashed	21.11.77
108-47597 •	B-25J TB-25N	44-86843	**N3507G**	Major Air Corp, Tucson AZ (tanker #05C)	63/66
				Filmways Inc, Hollywood CA	.68/69
				(used in movie *Catch 22* 68/69)	
				USAFM, Grissom AFB IN	74/96
				(displ. as "486843/*Passionate Paulette*)	
108-47598	B-25J	44-86844	N3453G	Art Jones, Slidell LA	63/70
				derelict New Orleans-Lakefront AP LA	73/77
108-47620 •	B-25J	**44-86866**	**N9069Z**	Amazon Trading Co, Miami FL	63
				Donald E. Lynch, Miami FL	66/70
				(impounded Quito, Ecuador)	
				Museo Aero de FA Ecuatoriana, Quito AFB	78/93
				(displ. as "FAE B-N9069Z")	
108-47626 •	B-25J	**44-86872**	**N2888G**	Blue Mountain Air Service, La Grande OR	59
				Dennis G. Smilanich, Boise ID	64/70
				(derelict & stripped, Boise ID 83)	
				Aero Nostalgia Inc, Stockton CA (rest.)	87
				USAFM, Robins AFB GA	.87/94
				(displ. as 486872)	
108-47627	B-25J TB-25K	44-86873	N9639C		
			N87Z	California Aircraft Engine Co, San Lorenzo CA	63/66
				Midwest Seafoods Inc, Denver CO	69/70
				(open storage, Tamiami FL 80/82)	
				Marcelo R. Ortiz, Miami FL	3.81/82
				crashed,Long Island, Bahamas	2.8.82
108-47634 •	B-25J TB-25N	**44-86880**		USAFM, Reese AFB TX: displ. on pole	65/94
				(displ. as 44-6880)	
108-47645 •	B-25J	**44-86891**	N3337G	L. K. Roser, Phoenix AZ	63/64
				Aero Industries, Addison TX	66/69
				Jeanette T. Bryant, Jacksonville FL	70
				The Payne Company, Pecos TX	72
				J. K. West, Corpus Christi TX	c72
				John J. Stokes, San Marcos TX	.73
				Dwight Reimer, Shafter CA	78
				L. W. Richards, Chico CA	11.79
				USAFM, Castle AFB CA: del.	14.1.80/94
				(displ. as "02344", later *Lazy Daisy Mae*)	
108-47647 •	B-25J	**44-86893**	**N6123C**	A. B. Sellards/Abe's Aerial Service, Safford AZ	63/64
				Aircraft Specialties Inc, Mesa AZ	66/72
				(tanker #C34)	
				wfu, derelict Mesa AZ, by	69/76
				John J. Stokes, San Marcos TX	77
				Kansas City Warbirds Inc, Kansas City MO	9.77/95
				(flies as 486893/*Fairfax Ghost*)	
108-47662 •	B-25J	**45-8811**	N9621C	Air Traders Inc, Miami FL	63/64
				C. M. Stephenson, Miami FL	66/69
				Richard G. Lloyd, Miami FL	12.69/70
				Antonio Rodriguez, San Juan PR	72
				Seagull Enterprises, Christiansted USVI	78
				Doan Helicopter Inc, Daytona Beach FL	.80/91
				(ferried St Croix to Daytona Beach FL .80, rest., ff 2.82: flew camouflaged as "HD")	
				Apache Aviation, Dijon, France	5.91/92
				(del. via St.Johns-Lisbon 21.5.91)	

			F-AZID	Franklin Devaux/Lafayette Aviation/	
				Flying Legends, Dijon-Longvic	1.9.92/96
108-47686 •	B-25J TB-25J	**45-8835**	NX69345	Bendix Aviation Corp, Teterboro NJ	45/48
			N69345	Bendix Aviation Corp, Teterboro NJ	48/66
				Bendix Field Engineering Corp, Columbia MD	69/72
				E. H. Koons, Edmonton ALTA	8.72
			CF-DKU	Aurora Aviation Ltd, Edmonton ALTA	12.72/75
			C-FDKU	G & M Aircraft Ltd, St Albert ALTA	78/93
				(tanker #1, later #336)	
				Aero Trader Inc, Chino CA: del. for resale	9.93
				Jim Cargill, Minneapolis MN	.94
			N5672V	C & P Aviation Services, Wayzata MN	28.7.94/96
108-47733	B-25J	**45-8882**	N75754	Albert Trostel & Sons Co, Milwaukee WI	
			N32T	Albert Trostel & Sons Co, Milwaukee WI	54
				New Jersey Air Co, Teterboro NJ	64/70
				(open storage, derelict, Teterboro 70/74)	
				broken-up, Teterboro (for rebuild N34E)	.74
				Carl Scholl/Aero Trader, Chino CA	89
				(forward fuselage section only)	
108-47734 •	B-25J	**45-8883**	N75755	reg.	.47
				Northern Pump Co, Minneapolis MN	54
				Bendix Corp, Teterboro NJ	
				Perter Volid, Chicago IL	63/64
				crashed dam., Northbrook IL	16.8.65
				Jack Adams Aircraft Sales, Walls MS	66
				R. H. Wood, Laurel MD	69/70
				Wilbert Vault Service Inc, Laurel MD	72
			C-GCWA	ntu: Canadian Warplane Heritage, Sidney BC	.75
			C-GCWM	Canadian Warplane Heritage, Hamilton ONT	5.75/96
				(flies as HD372/VO-D)	
108-47735 •	B-25J TB-25N	**45-8884**	N3156G	Aviation Rental Service, St Paul MN	66
				Johan M. Larsen, Minneapolis MN	69/78
				Minnesota Aircraft Museum,	
				Minneapolis-Flying Cloud Airport MN	.72
				Jerry C. Janes, Vancouver BC	79/80
			C-GCWJ	Canadian Warplane Heritage, Sidney BC	8.80/85
				(flew as *Death Watch*; "*City of Edmonton*";	
				flew to Tahiti .82 for film *Endless Sea*)	
			N5833B	David Brady, Cartersville GA	26.8.85
				Randall Porter/Air Acres Air Museum,	
				Cartersville GA	.85/93
				(flew as 458884/*Georgia Girl*)	
				C & P Aviation Services, Wayzata MN	10.93/96
108-47738 •	B-25J TB-25N	**45-8887**	**N3680G**	H. H. Coffield, Rockdale TX	63/70
				Rockdale Flying Service, Rockdale TX	72
				I. N. Burchinall Jr, Paris TX	c75
				Frederick Bates, Austin TX	78
				(flew as "Ahm Available Too")	
				dam. landing, u/c collapsed, Vega TX	c78
				Mark Thompson	c80
				Carl Scholl/Historic Aircraft Preservation	
				Group/Aero Trader, Chino CA	6.80/95
				(trucked from TX: stored dism. Ocotillo Wells CA	
				Ahm Available Too 84/94)	
108-47740	B-25J	45-8889		Rockdale Flying Service, Rockdale TX	73/74
				(unconv., Rockdale "0-5889/BD-899 73/74)	
108-47749 •	B-25J TB-25N	45-8898		Rockdale Flying Service, Rockdale TX	60/83
				(open storage, unconv., Rockdale TX 60/83)	
				sold at auction, Rockdale TX	15.10.83
				Aero Trader, Chino CA	15.10.83
			N898BW	Vern Raburn/Binary Warriors Inc,	

				Weston MA	12.85/95
				(flies in RAF camouflage scheme)	
- •	B-25J	-		(to FA Boliviana as FAB 542)	
				Cochabamba AB, Bolivia: displ. on pylons	83/94
- •	B-25J	-		(to FA Brasileira as 5075)	
				Sao Paulo AFB, Brazil: displ.	67/75
- •	B-25J	-		(to FA Brasileira as 5097)	
	CB-25J			Museu de Armas e Vehiculos Motorizados	
				Antigos, Bebeduoro, Brazil	79/81
				Eduardo Andrea Matarazzo War Museum,	
				Bebeduoro, Brazil	83
- •	B-25J	-		(to FA Brasileira as 5133)	
				Air Force Academy Museum,	
				Pirassununga AB, Sao Paulo, Brazil	85
- •	B-25J	-		(to FA Uruguaya as G3-158)	6.50
				Museo Nacional de Aviacion, Montevideo	79/91
				(displ. as "160")	
- •	B-25J	-		(to FA Venozolanas as 4-B-40)	
				Teniente Vicente Landaeta Gil AB,	
				Barquisimeto, Venezuala: gate guard	91

North American Aviation/Commonwealth Aircraft Corporation & Cavalier Aircraft Corporation P-51/F-51 Mustang

3-3101•	XP-51	**41-038**		(allotted to RAF as AG348: not del.): ff	20.5.41
				NACA, Langley VA: BOC 27.12.41: SOC	14.12.42
				NASM, stored Park Ridge IL/Silver Hill MD	49/75
			N51NA	EAA Foundation, Hales Corner/Oshkosh WI	.75/96
				(rest. Fort Collins CO, ff .76;	
				retired to EAA Museum after last flight 1.8.82)	
7-5883 •	A-36A	**42-83665**	NX39502	Essex Wire Corp, (race #44; #2)	.46
				(race #15 "City of Lynchburg")	.47
				crashed during race, Cleveland OH	1.9.47
			N39502	Hanby Enterprises	
				Harry McCandless & Ben Widfelt	c50/52
				(open storage, Council Bluffs IA 49/52)	
				Walter H. Erickson, Minneapolis MN	c53
				(last FAA annual inspection 3.53)	
				Charles P. Doyle, Rosemount MN	63/70
				(rep. recov. ex trade school, Winona MN)	
				USAFM, Wright-Patterson AFB, Dayton OH	.71/96
				(static rest. by MN ANG .73;	
				displ. USAFM Dayton as "83665/BF/*Margie H*")	
7-5949 •	A-36A	**42-83731**		Jack P. Hardwick, El Monte CA (stored)	50/75
				Thomas L. Camp, Livermore CA : for rebuild	.75
			N50452	Dick Martin, Carlsbad CA	8.80
			N251A	Tom Friedkin/Cinema Air Inc, Carslbad CA	83/95
				Champlin Fighter Museum, Mesa AZ: loan	91/93
				Lone Star Flight Museum, Galveston TX: loan	94/96
				(flies as "42-83731/F")	
7-5956 •	A-36A	**42-83738**	**N4607V**	Sidney Smith, Sheridan IL & Bradenton FL	63/72
				(rep. ex storage, Jack Hardwick, El Monte CA)	
				Wings of Yesterday Air Museum, Santa Fe NM	75/79
				John R. Paul, Hamilton MT & Boise ID	6.80/95
				John Paul/Warhawk Air Museum, Caldwell ID	90/96
				(long-term rest. as P-51B, Oakland CA 85,	
				continuing at Boise-Caldwell ID)	

99-22109 •	P-51A	**43-6006**		forced landing Fairbanks-Anchorage AK	24.2.44
				wreck recov. by Waldon Spillers	10.77
			N51Z	Waldon D. Spillers, Versailles OH	2.78/96
				(rebuilt Versailleswith ex TNI-AU mainplane: ff 7.85 as "36006")	
99-22281 •	P-51A	**43-6178**		Harry McCandless & Ben Widfelt	c50/52
				(open storage, Council Bluffs IA 49/52)	
				Walter H. Erickson, Minneapolis MN	c53
			N8647E	Walter H. Erickson, Mineapolis MN	63/78
				Kermit A. Weeks, Tamiami FL	81/84
			N51KW	Kermit Weeks/Weeks Air Museum,Tamiami FL	12.84/95
				(stored Tamiami pending rest.)	
				rep. dam. Tamiami, by Hurricane Andrew	24.8.92
				(rest. to fly Salinas CA 94/96)	
99-22354 •	P-51A	**43-6251**		Cal Aero Technical Institute, Glendale CA	.46/53
				Ed Maloney/The Air Museum, Claremont CA	.53/65
				The Air Museum, Ontario/Chino CA	65/81
			N4235Y	Planes of Fame Museum, Chino CA	2.81/96
				(rest. Chino ex static displ., ff 19.8.81)	
99-22377 •	P-51A	**43-6274**	NX73630	racer	48
			N73630	Harry McCandless & Ben Widfelt	c50/52
				(open storage, Council Bluffs IA 49/52)	
				Walter H. Erickson, Minneapolis MN	c53/78
			N90358	Yanks Air Museum, Chino CA	.78/96
				(arr. Chino .78 as stripped hulk: rest. Chino rolled-out 12.93 as "USAAC 36274/AX-H")	
102-24539	P-51B	43-6351	N68738	crashed badly damaged, Hayward CA	.57
				broken up	.57
				(major parts into rebuild of N51PR: que se)	.81
103-26199 •	P-51C	**42-103645**		static displ., Billings MT; recov. by CAF	c65
				Confederate Air Force, Mercedes TX: stored	c65
			N9288	Confederate Air Force, Harlingen TX: rest.	73/85
			N215CA	Confederate Air Force, Harlingen/Midland TX	85/96
				(long-term CAF rest. project Omaha NE 73/80, St. Paul-Fleming Field MN 85/94)	
103-26385 •	P-51C	**42-103831**		Paul Mantz, Glendale CA	19.2.46
				(USAAF surplus ex Stillwater AFB OK 19.2.46)	
				NX1204 Paul Mantz, Los Angeles CA	.46
				(race #60 "Latin American"; later #46)	
			N1204	Tallmantz Aviation/Movieland of the Air Museum, Orange County CA	48/84
				Frank G. Tallman, Orange County CA	60/84
				Kermit A. Weeks/Weeks Air Museum, Tamiami FL: stored pending rest.	.85/95
				rep. dam. Tamiami, by Hurricane Andrew	24.8.92
				(rest. to fly, Salinas CA 94/96)	
103-26778 •	P-51C	**43-25147**		Holtz Technical School, Tel Aviv: hulk	60/75
			N51PR	Peter Regina, Van Nuys CA	3.81/86
				(composite rebuild Van Nuys CA, using P-51B mainplane & P-51D fuselage ex IDFAF 13: both recov. ex Israel; ff 11.6.81 as *Shangri-la*)	
				Joseph Kasparoff, Montebello CA	2.86/96
				(flies as "36913/*The Believer*/VF-T")	
				(id. also rep. as 43-25171)	
104-25789 •	P-51B	**43-24760**	NX28388	Jacqueline Cochran, Los Angeles CA	.46/48
				(race #13) : crashed	9.48
				rep. crashed Hayward CA	.59
				Michael Coutches, Hayward CA: parts	
				rep. stored, Indio CA	73

105-25931 •	XP-51G	**43-43335**		used as cockpit electronics trainer Reynolds Aluminium: as scrap (hulk recov. ex scrap dealer .75) John Morgan, La Canada CA (rest. project: using some P-51H parts)	 75 .75/96
109-26890 • **(c/n 11)**	P-51D EF-51D Cavalier II	**44-13257**	 N4222A **N51DL**	(to NACA as NACA 108): BOC 22.12.44: SOC Charles Snydor (sold surplus ex storage NAS Norfolk VA .57) Trans Florida Aviation, Sarasota FL Cavalier Aircraft Corp, Sarasota FL (conv. to Cavalier Mk.II, underwing hardpoints, ff 12.67, demonstrator in camouflage sc.) (military demo tour El Salvador 12.68) Lindsay Newspapers Inc, Sarasota FL David B. Lindsay/Lindair Inc, Sarasota FL	12.7.57 .57 .59/67 .67/69 70 72/96
109-26911 •	P-51D	**44-13278**		Yugoslavian Aviation Museum, Belgrade (stored, incomplete airframe)	84/92
109-27024 •	P-51D Cavalier T Mk. 2	**44-13571** 68-15796		Cavalier Aircraft Corp, Sarasota FL (to US Army as 68-15796) US Army Museum, Fort Rucker AL USAFM, Armament Museum, Eglin AFB FL (also rep. ex 44-13574: displ. as "413571")	67 .67 79/94
109-27924 •	P-51D	**44-14291**		crashed, forced landing on beach, Cap Ferrett near Bordeaux, France: abandoned Ailes Anciennes ile de France, Paris (excavated from beach Cap Ferrett 3.5.81) Musee de l'Air, Paris-Le Bourget (displ. unrest. as crash scene) (id. also rep. as 44-13954 CL-P/*Da Quake*)	 26.8.44 .81 84/96
109-28207 •	P-51D	**44-14574**		(479th FG/436th FS, Wattisham *Little Zippie*) ditched off Clacton Pier, Essex East Essex Aviation Museum, Clacton: recov. (corroded hulk displayed in 'crash scenario')	 13.1.45 16.8.87/93
109-28459	P-51D	**44-14826**	 N1740B **N551D** (3	Trottner Iron & Metal Co, San Antonio TX (destined RNZAF: still in original packing case) Dal-Air, Dallas-Love Field TX Aircraft Sales Ltd, Dallas TX (to FA Haiti as 14826, later 826): del. (to FA Dominicana): for disposal Cavalier Aircraft Corp, Sarasota FL Gordon Plaskett, King City CA Bruce Morehouse, San Antonio TX: fuse.only Bruce Morehouse, San Antonio TX: USCR (id. tfd. to CA-17 c/n 1364:) J Erickson OR	.49 .51 .51 51 10.7.51 c73 c73/74 c73 .78 78/84 96
109-28549	P-51D		 N1736B	Trottner Iron & Metal Co, San Antonio TX (destined RNZAF: still in original packing case) Dal-Air, Dallas-Love Field TX Aircraft Sales Ltd, Dallas TX (to FA Haiti as 14916, later 916): del. (to FA Dominicana): for disposal rep. to Cavalier Aircraft Corp, Sarasota FL rep. to Gordon Plaskett, King City CA	.49 .51 .51 51 4.51 c73 c73 c73
109-35934 •	P-51D	**44-15651**	 NX79111 **N79111**	sold surplus ex Walnut Ridge AFB AR Steve Beville & Bruce Raymond IL (race #77 "The Galloping Ghost") planned export to Israel: impounded Clifford D. Cummins, Riverside CA (stripped hulk rest. Chino CA c65, flew as "413366", race #69 *Miss Candace*) dam., forced landing Reno NV (rebuilt Long Beach CA .71)	.46 7.46/49 47/49 63/79 9.70

				Dave Zeuschel & Wiley Sanders, Van Nuys CA	.78/80
				crashed takeoff, Van Nuys CA (rebuilt .80)	4.9.80
				Wiley Sanders/Sanders Truck Lines,Troy AL	.80/81
				(race #69 *Jeannie*)	
				Bahia Oaks Inc, Ocala FL	.81/96
				(race #10 *Spectre* later #9 *Cloud Dancer*)	
109-35958	P-51D	**44-15655**		Trottner Iron & Metal Co, San Antonio TX	.49
				(dest. for RNZAF: still in orig. packing case 51)	
			N1738B	Dal-Air, Dallas-Love Field TX	.51
				Aircraft Sales Ltd, Dallas TX	51
				(to FA Haiti as 15655, later 655): del.	10.7.51
				(to FA Dominicana): for disposal	c73
				rep. Gordon Plaskett, King City CA	c73
				rep. Cavalier Aircraft Corp, Sarasota FL	c73/74
111-29080 •	P-51C	**44-10947**		Paul Mantz, Glendale CA	19.2.46
				(sold surplus ex Stillwater AFB OK 19.2.46)	
			NX1202	Paul Mantz, Los Angeles CA	9.8.46/50
				(race #46 "Excalibur"; later #60 *Houstonian*)	
			N1202	Charles F. Blair, New York NY	27.5.50/52
				("Stormy Petrel", later "*Excalibur III*" :	
				record NY-London flight 31.1.51,	
				return flight over North Pole to NY 29.5.51)	
				Smithsonian Institution/NASM, Silver Hill MD	29.5.52/93
				California Museum of Science & Industry,	
				Los Angeles CA: loan	88/93
111-29286	P-51K	**44-11153**		(to FA Salvadorena as FAS 409)	9.68
				(recov. ex Salvador by Jack Flaherty .74)	
			N34FF	Flaherty Factors Inc, Monterey CA	1.11.74
				Scott Smith, Orlando FL	
				William Clark/Clark Motor Co,	
				State College PA (race #3 *Dolly*)	79/85
			N51WE	Clark Motor Co, State College PA	9.85/88
				crashed near State College PA (Clark k.)	7.3.88
				(USCR quotes. id. 44-11153: also rep. to be	
				45-11559, FAS 409: que se)	
111-29940 •	P-51K	**44-11807**		USAFM, McEntire Field ANGB, Florence SC	73/92
				David C. Tallichet/MARC, Chino CA	
				Mark Clark/Courtesy Aircraft, Rockford IL	93/94
				(stored dism. Rockford IL 93, offered for sale)	
				Shauver Bros AZ	.94
			N30991	Wally Fisk/Amjet Services International,	
				Minneapolis MN: reg. candidate	22.2.94
				MDS Enterprises, Mesa AZ	3.94/96
111-30249 •	P-51K	**44-12116**	NX79161	Robert Swanson	.46
				(race #80 "Second Fiddle")	
				Thompson Products Museum, Cleveland OH	58
				Frederick Crawford Museum, Cleveland OH	79/88
				(displ. as NX79161/#80 *Second Fiddle*)	
111-30258 •	P-51K	**44-12125**		(to R Netherlands AF as H-307)	
				Delft Technical School, Delft, Netherlands	65
				Militaire Luchtvaart Museum, Soesterberg AB	68/95
111-30259 •	P-51K	**44-12126**	N9140H	(to IDFAF as ....)	50s
				rep. Israeli Air Force Museum	84
111-30273 •	P-51K	**44-12140**	NX66111(2		.46
			N66111(2	Al Hanes	63
				Charles E. Yost, Granada Hills CA	63
				Frank J. Moore, Los Angeles CA	.63/64
				Glenn Hussey, Carmichael CA	66/70
				crashed	7.7.68

				Aadu Karemaa, San Diego CA: rebuild	81/89
			N119AK	Aadu Karemaa, San Diego CA	10.89/92
			N119VF	Aadu Karemaa, San Diego CA	4.92/95
				(rest. San Diego, flies as "412119/A-VF")	
				(note: USCR quotes 111-30273, ie. 44-12140,	
				but owner quotes id. as 44-12119)	
111-30591 •	P-51K	**44-12458**		(to ROKAF as ....)	
				(captured by Chinese AF as 3003)	
				Peking Peoples Museum, Peking	65
				Beijing Aeronautical Institute, Beijing	88
				People's Liberation Army Air Force Museum,	
				Datangshan, China: displ. as "03"	90/96
111-36100 •	F-6K Cavalier	44-12817	N4963V		
			N85BW		
			N5151T	Trans Florida Aviation, Sarasota FL	63/64
				Bob Abrams (flew as "N5151")	65
				crashed racing, Las Vegas NV (Abrams k.)	.65
				Cavalier Aircraft Corp, Sarasota FL	66/70
				Lindsay Newspapers, Sarasota FL	72/80
				David B. Lindsay/Lindair Inc, Sarasota FL	7.80/96
				(rep. stored King City CA 85/87)	
111-36123 •	F-6K FP-51K	**44-12840**		Victory Air Museum, Mundelein IL: dism.	68/76
				Bill Conner	82/84
				(stored dism. Chino CA 84)	
				Joseph Kasparoff, Montebello CA	87/90
				(under rest., Chino CA 82/87)	
111-36135 •	P-51K F-6K	**44-12852**	NX66111	race #80 "Full House"	46
				crashed fcd. landing, Cleveland OH	.46
			N90613	Alfred W. Schwimmer/Intercontinental Airways,	
				Canastota NY	12.52/54
				(rebuilt by Jack Hardwick, El Monte CA .54	
				with dual controls: id. quoted as "ICA-5131")	
			N22B	B. L. Tractman/Aviation Corp of America	15.3.54
		Cavalier		(to FA Dominicana as FAD 1900)	26.4.54/84
				Brian O'Farrell/Johnson Aviation, Miami FL	19.5.84/89
			N21023	James E. Beasley, Philadelphia PA	7.89/95
				(trucked to Ft. Wayne IN for rest., ff .90	
				flies as "413318/C5-N/*Frenesi*")	
			N357FG	reg.	10.95/96
111-36292 •	P-51D	**44-13009**		(to RAAF as A68-687): BOC 21.7.45: SOC	22.12.47
				(to Indonesian AF/TNI-AU as ....)	
				Stephen Johnson/Vanpac Carriers, Oakland CA:	
				recov. ex Indonesia	.78
			N31RK	Richard E. Knowlton, Portland ME	85/96
				(rest. project: fuselage still marked "A68-687")	
111-36299 •	P-51D	**44-13016**		(to RAAF as A68-674): BOC 4.7.45: SOC	12.48
				Pearce Dunn/Warbirds Aviation Museum,	
				Mildura, VIC	.66/82
				(recov. ex farm Benalla VIC .66: stored dism.)	
				Vincent Thomas, Geoff Milne & Alan Lane,	
				Albury NSW: stored dism.	.82/84
			VH-CVA	Vincent Thomas, Albury NSW: reg. res.	82/87
				(shipped to Shafter CA .84, rest. 84/87)	
			N9002N	Steve Wilmans/King City Aviation	12.87
			N9200N	King City Aviation, King City CA	12.87/96
				(rest. King City CA 90/92, ff .92)	
111-36388 •	P-51D	**44-13105**		(to RAAF as A68-679): BOC 7.45: SOC	12.48
				Pearce Dunn/Warbirds Aviation Museum,	
				Mildura, VIC	.66/80
				(recov. from farm Benalla VIC .66,	
				static rest., displ. as "A68-679")	
				David Zeuschel, Van Nuys CA	c80
				(shipped to USA, rebuilt as mod. racer,	

				race #7 *Strega*; components rep. used in	
				P-51D static rest. Barksdale AFB LA)	
			N71FT	Bill Destefani, Shafter CA & Sisters OR	12.83/95
111-36389 •	P-51D	**44-13106**		(to RAAF as A68-648): BOC	6.45/50
				Royal Melbourne Institute of Technology	30.6.50/83
				Australian War Memorial, Canberra ACT	.83/94
				(static rest., RAAF Point Cook VIC 86/92)	
122-31076 •	P-51D	**44-63350**	N2870D	Clarence A. Head, Elgin IL	63/64
				Mark R. Foutch, Champaign IL	66/84
				Tom Kelly & John Dilley/Ft Wayne Air Services,	
				Fort Wayne IN	.84/86
				(rest. Ft Wayne IN 84/85 as TP-51D)	
			N51TK (2	Fort Wayne Air Services, Fort Wayne IN	5.86/88
				crashed on takeoff, Ft. Wayne IN	11.4.89
				International Aircraft Ltd, Hockessin DE	4.89/92
			N151RR	ntu: International Aircraft, Balliston Spa NY	10.89
			N51TK (2	International Aircraft Ltd, Hockessin DE	10.89/92
				Charles Greenhill, Mettawa IL	9.93/95
				crashed, forced landing, Round Lake IL	29.12.94
				(being rebuilt Wahpeton ND 96)	
122-31133 •	P-51D	**44-63407**		(to FA Guatamalteca as FAG 324)	
			N63407	Don C. Hull, Sugerland TX	.72
				Wilson C. Edwards, Big Spring TX	84/96
122-31207	P-51D Cavalier	44-63481		(to RCAF as 9553): BOC 7.6.47: SOC	27.12.57
			N6303T	James H. Defuria & Fred J. Ritts/	
				Intercontinental Airways, Canastota NY	11.56/60
				Aero Enterprises, Elkhart IN	10.5.60/61
				Century Mutual Insurance, Des Moines IA	18.3.61
				Aero Enterprises, Elkhart IN	12.7.61/62
				Bernard Little/Pinellas Aircraft Inc,	
				St. Petersburg FL	7.2.62
				The Brane Corp, Largo FL	25.4.62
				Bernard Little/Agels Inc, Tampa FL	23.8.63/64
				Richard K. Kestler/Pizza On Call Franchise Inc,	
				Columbus GA	15.2.64/72
				(race #13 *Miss Diet Rite* ,*Miss Gatorade Cola*)	
				(mod. to tall fin Cavalier by TFA 66/67)	
				crashed, minor damage, Atlanta GA	12.5.67
				crashed, dest., Griffin GA (Kestler k.)	3.6.72
122-31233	P-51D	**44-63507**		(to RCAF as 9554): BOC 7.6.47: SOC	20.9.60
			N6345T	James H. Defuria & Fred J. Ritts/	
				Intercontinental Airways, Canastota NY	25.2.57/60
				(stored unconv., Carberry MAN 57/61)	
				Aero Enterprises, Elkhart IN	10.5.60/63
				Harold R. Hacker, Noblesville IN	12.63/64
				crashed, minor dam., La Porte IN	22.2.64
				Aero Enterprises, La Porte IN	7.3.64
				Hammonton Investment Co, Hammonton NJ	1.9.64
				John Dilley, Elkhart IN	10.64/65
				Gardner Flyers Inc, Brownwood TX	16.9.65/72
				crashed, badly dam., Brownwood TX	c68
			N12073	ntu	
			N38FF	ntu: Marvin L. Gardner, Brownwood TX	
			N13410	Ray Stutsman, Elkhart IN	78/81
				(rebuilt, adopted id. 44-72483/N13410,	
				flew as "414303/SX-B/*Double Trouble two*")	
			N51EA	Don C. Davidson, Nashua NH (race #27)	4.82/90
				Max Vogelsang/Swiss Warbirds, Basle: del.	26.8.90/95
				(flies as 463684/SX-B/*Double Trouble two*)	
122 31233 (2)				(subsequently, id. & hulk of 44-63507)	
			N6345T	Marvin L. Gardner, Mercedes TX : hulk	4.85/90
				Pioneer Aero Service, Chino CA : hulk	90/92

				(rest. Chino CA 93/95 as TF-51D, ff 24.3.95 Chino as "414061/PE/*Little One III*")	
				Paul Peters, Willow Run MI	.94/95
			N973	Paul Peters, Willow Run MI: reg. res.	.94/95
122-31262	P-51D Cavalier Turbo Mustang III Piper PA-48 Enforcer	44-63536		(to FA d'L GN Nicaragua as GN 116)	.58/63
			N6167U	Will W. Martin/MACO Sales Financial Corp, Chicago IL	2.9.63
				T. J. Black Co, Atlanta GA	66
				Cavalier Aircraft Corp, Sarasota FL	2.68/73
				(rebuilt by Cavalier .68 with RR Dart 501 turboprop as prototype "Turbo Mustang III")	
PE1-1001			N201PE	Piper Aircraft, Lakeland FL: "PE1"	71/72
				(remanufactured by Piper with Lycoming T55 turboprop as single-seat Enforcer, ff 28.4.71)	
				(after test flying programme, stored Sarasota later Lakeland FL 72/83: rep stripped for parts)	72/83
				(USCR quotes id. 44-63775: dest. Hawaii 27.11.45)	
122-31268 •	P-51D	**44-63542**		sold surplus McClellan AFB CA	11.12.57
			N5450V	David L. (Homer) Rountree, Marysville CA	18.2.58/79
				(open storage, Marysville CA 58/81)	
				Ted E. Contri, Reno NV	.79
			N51HR	Ted E. Contri & Homer Rountree, Reno NV	6.82/91
				Contri Construction Co, Yuba City CA	1.91/95
				(race #99 "463542")	
122-31302 •	P-51D	44-63576	NX37492	Ron Freeman	
				(race #37 *Wraith*, later *Jay Dee*)	.46/49
				(stored dism. 50/70)	
			N37492	Edward G. Fisher, Kansas City KS	63/66
				John E. Dilley, Muncie IN	69/72
				Max I. Ramsay, Johnson KS: USCR	77/83
			N51DH	Consolidated Airways, Fort Wayne IN	2.81/84
				(rest. Chino CA 77/85)	
				Frank Strickler/Fox 51 Limited, Denton TX	1.85/86
				Louis Shaw, Dallas TX	86
				Evergreen Heritage Collection, Marana AZ	.86/96
122-31303 •	P-51D	**44-63577**		(to FA Uruguaya as FAU 265)	4.4.49
				Museo de Aeronautica, Montevideo, Uruguay	60/85
				(displ. as "FAU 285")	
				Dante Heredia, Montevideo	1.85
			N51TE	Tyrone Elias, Tulsa OK	2.85/94
				(long-term rest. to fly)	
			N151JT	John R. Turgyan, New Egypt NJ	7.94/96
122-31341 •	P-51D	**44-63615**		(to FA Uruguaya as FAU 270)	.50
				Carrasco AB, Montevideo, Uruguay: displ.	65/84
				Joseph Kasparoff, Montebello CA	.84/90
				(static rest. Van Nuys CA 86/87)	
				displ. Tuskegee Foundation, Tuskegee AL	89
				Ascher Ward, Sepulveda CA: adv. for sale	93
				ILOC Corp: US reg. candidate	2.5.94
				(note: id. also rep as 44-63613)	
122-31381 •	P-51D J 26	**44-63655**		(to R Swedish AF as Fv26152)	
				(to FA d'L GN Nicaragua as GN 84)	17.1.55
			N6153U	Will W. Martin/MACO Sales Financial Corp, Chicago IL	2.9.63
				dam. forced landing Nicaragua, on del. flight	1.5.65
			N5500S	Will W. Martin/Wings & Wheels Inc, Palos Park IL	1.85/96
				(also rep. that Fv26152 cr in Nicaragua on del)	
122-31389 •	P-51D	**44-63663**		Trans Florida Aviation, Sarasota FL	c58
				(to FA Guatemalteca as FAG 354)	.62
			N41749	Don Hull, Sugarland TX	8.72
				Wilson C. Edwards, Big Spring TX	78/96

c/n	Type	Identity	Regn	History	Date
122-31401 •	P-51D J 26	**44-63675**		(to R Swedish AF as Fv26152)	
				(to FA d'L GN Nicaragua as GN 91)	
				displ. Officers Mess , FAN Base	
				Will W. Martin/MACO Sales Financial Corp, Chicago IL	2.9.63
			N5452V (2	Dave Allender	73
				(rest., ff 11.9.73; race #19)	
				Roger A. Christgau, Edina MN	4.77/78
			N1751D	Roger A. Christgau, Edina MN	23.2.78/96
				(flew as 463675/E6-D/*Sierra Sue II*)	
				(flies "463675/Sierra Sue/Fv26152")	
122-31427 •	P-51D J 26 Cavalier	**44-63701**		(to R Swedish AF as Fv26015)	23.4.45/52
				(to FA Dominicana as FAD 1904)	12.52/84
				Brian O'Farrell/Johnson Aviation, Miami FL	19.5.84/87
				Vincent Tirado, Miami FL: rest.	87/91
			N51VT	Vincent Tirado, Miami FL	7.90/92
				Brian O'Farrell	96
122-31514 •	P-51D	**44-63788**	N6171C	Haber Aircraft Inc, Burbank CA	20.9.57
				E. D. Weiner, Los Angeles CA	30.11.57
			N335J (1	E. D. Weiner, Los Angeles CA	13.1.58
			N3350	E. D. Weiner, Los Angeles CA	24.2.58
				Jim Morton Co Inc, Cheyenne WY	4.9.58/59
				Robert A. Mitchem, Broomfield CO	16.3.59
				William D. Roosevelt, Englewood CO	6.11.59/67
				George A. Whipple, New York NY	11.67/68
			N166G	George A. Whipple, New York NY	10.68/72
				Bruce D. DeJager & Peter P. Hoffman, Minneapolis MN	14.8.72/73
				Bruce D. DeJager, Minneapolis MN	9.2.73
				A. R. Buckner, Albuquerque NM	13.8.73/74
				Westernair Of Albuquerque, Albuquerque NM	6.5.74
				Mike Smith, Johnson KS	14.6.74/75
				Mike Smith & Ronald K. Kendrick, Johnson KS	1.12.75/78
				Sylmar Aviation, Sylmar CA	.78/79
				Warbirds of GB Ltd, Blackbushe	2.79
				(arr. Blackbushe on del. ex USA 11.11.79)	
			G-PSID	Fairoaks Aviation Services	27.7.81/87
				The Fighter Collection, Duxford	1.87/88
			F-AZFI	Jean-Baptiste Salis Collection, La Ferte-Alais	2.88/93
				(flies as French AF "412471/Y-R7")	
122-31533 •	P-51D Cavalier	44-63807		(to FA Uruguaya as FAU 272)	4.12.50/60
				(to FA Boliviana as FAB 506)	19.3.60/77
				Arny Carnegie, Edmonton ALTA	12.77
			C-GXUO	Bill Bailey Aviation Service, Calgary ALTA	7.78/84
			N20MS	Ed L. Stringfellow/Mid South Lumber Company, Birmingham AL	6.85/96
122-31536 •	P-51D	44-63810		Norton AFB CA: displ. as "463810"	63
				Ed Maloney/The Air Museum, Ontario CA	65/72
				(rest. to fly Chino .72: adopted id. 45-11367)	
			N63810	Ed Maloney/The Air Museum, Buena Park CA	72
				Robin Collard, Merced CA/Weslaco TX	73/78
				(towed to Fullerton CA for rest. c73, flew as "463810/C-B6/Stump Jumper")	
				Jerry Hayes, Henderson CO	82/88
				dam. belly landing, Denver CO (repaired)	6.84
				Bernard H. Raouls, Zephyr Cove NV	.88/92
				Joseph K. Newsome, Cheraw SC	9.92/93
			N451BC	Joseph K. Newsome, Cheraw SC	8.93/96
				(flies as 463497/FT-I/*Angels Playmate*)	
122-31590 •	P-51D J 26	**44-63864**		(to R Swedish AF as Fv26158)	17.6.49
				(to IDFAF as 3506)	9.2.53/58
				Israeli Aircraft Industries, Tel Aviv	58

			N251L	William P. Lear/Lear Inc, Los Angeles CA	18.7.60
				William R. Pearce, Fullerton CA: USCR	12.62/70
				crashed Keflavik, Iceland during del. from	
				Israel to USA, via Paris	6.6.63
				(wreck rep. moved Iceland to USA .89)	
			N42805	Cham S. Grill, Central Point OR	5.91
				Kenneth A. Hake, Tipton KS	3.92/95
				(see 4X-AIM/SE-BKG at end of listing)	
122-31591 •	P-51D J 26	**44-63865**		(to R Swedish AF as Fv26018)	4.45/54
				(to FA d'L GN Nicaragua as GN 90)	17.1.55/63
			N6163U	Will W. Martin/MACO Sales Financial Corp,	
				Chicago IL	23.9.63
				PAAL Inc, East Point GA	66
				O. J. Kistler, Long Valley NJ	69/72
			N51JK	O. J. Kistler, Long Valley NJ (race #47)	73/96
122-31597 •	P-51D J 26	**44-63871**		(to R Swedish AF as Fv26039	
				(To IDFAF as ......)	
			N9772F	Robert D. Turner/Marom Air Services Ltd,	
				Tel Aviv, Israel	63/70
				(noted, minor damage, Cannes, France 9.65)	
				Musee de l'Air, Paris-Le Bourget	75/95
				(displ. as "466318/MO-C")	
				(USCR quotes id. 44-63821)	
122-31598	P-51D	44-63872		(to RCAF as 9552): BOC 10.7.47: SOC	27.12.57
			N6519D (1	James H. Defuria & Fred J. Ritts/	
				Intercontinental Airways, Canastota NY	11.56/60
				Aero Enterprises, Elkhart IN	10.5.60
				Gerald L. Walbrun, Chicago IL	28.12.60
				(N6518D/19D painted on incorrect airframes!)	
			N6518D (2	Gerald L. Walbrun, Chicago IL	3.4.61/66
				Robert R. Runte, Greendale WI	20.8.66/67
				David M. Halla, Minneapolis MN	2.10.67/68
				James Fugata/Air Carrier Inc, Aurora OR	12.68/69
				John Gale, Minneapolis MN	8.1.69
				May Air Inc, Boulder CO	19.4.69
				Courtesy Aircraft Ltd, Loves Park IL	4.4.69
				Tom J. Kuchinsky, Milwaukee WI (race #18)	17.7.69/70
				crashed, dest., Harlingen TX (Kuchinsky k.)	27.6.70
122-31615 •	P-51D	**44-63889**	N7710C	Harry E. Padley, Hamilton OH	63/64
				Harold Reavis, Fayetteville NC	66/69
				Dan Furtrell, Nashville TN	8.69
				W. R. Rodgers, Rolling Fork MS	70/72
			CF-FUZ	Gary D. McCann, Stratford ONT: del.	12.73/83
			C-FFUZ	Gary D. McCann, Stratford ONT	84/91
122-31619 •	P-51D	44-63893		(to RCAF as 9560): BOC 7.6.47: SOC	9.60
				stored unconv., Carberry MAN	57/60
				Aero Enterprises Inc, Elkhart IN	60/62
				RCAF Lincoln Park, ALTA : gate guard	.60/62
				Ed Fleming, Calgary ALTA : rebuilt	.63
			CF-PIO	Helmsworth Construction, Wetaskiwin ALTA	65/66
				Keir Air Transport, Edmonton ALTA	
			N3333E	David C. Tallichet/Specialty Restaurants Inc,	
				Long Beach CA	69/75
				David C.Tallichet/MARC, Chino CA	75/95
				USAFM, March AFB CA: loan	80/90
				(USCR quotes id. 122-51619)	
122-31718 •	P-51D J 26	**44-63992**		(to R Swedish AF as Fv26020)	
				(to IDFAF as 2353)	
				Flygvapenmuseum Malmen, Linkoping, Sweden	12.65/96
122-31731 •	P-51D	**44-64005**		(to RCAF as 9561): BOC 7.6.47: SOC	20.9.60
			N6339T	James H. Defuria & Fred J. Ritts/	
				Intercontinental Airways, Canastota NY	12.58/60
				(stored unconv., Carberry MAN 57/61)	

				Aero Enterprises, Elkhart IN	10.5.60/62
				(del. Carberry-Winnipeg-Elkhart .62)	
				Lewis C. Buell, Springfield OH	27.9.62/65
				Sherman Aircraft Sales, Baer Field IN	8.5.65
				G. S. Vincent, Winchester MA	30.7.65
				Robert Bleeg, Seattle WA	10.67/73
			N51WB (1	Wayne Brown, Port Gibson MS	.73
				Joe Arnold, Eudora/Mulberry AR	4.10.75
			N51CK	Charles S. Kemp, Jackson/Hazlehurst MS	20.7.78/96
				landing accident King City CA (rebuilt)	.81
				(flies as 464005/E9-Z/*Mary Mine*)	
122-	P-51D	**44-64122**		(to R Swedish AF as Fv26130)	
31848 •	J 26			(to FA d'L GN Nicaragua as GN 80)	17.1.55/63
		S 26	N6151U	Will W. Martin/MACO Sales Financial Corp,	
				Chicago IL	23.9.63
			N150U	John Lowe, Chicago IL	
				Gardner Flyers Inc, Brownwood TX	66
				Wilson C. Edwards, Big Spring TX	5.67/96
				(wfu, stored Big Spring TX 81/96)	
122-	P-51D	**44-72028**	N22B	reg.	.48
31887 •				(to IDFAF as 41)	18.7.48
				hulk recov. ex Palmahim kibbutz playground,	
				Israel by Robs Lamplough, Duxford UK: arr.	12.76
				Noel Robinson & David Laight, North Yorks	80/95
			G-LYNE	E. Noel Robinson & Partner	5.12.95/96
				(rest. project Tees-side Airport 80/93,	
				using mainplane IDFAF 43)	
122-	P-51D	**44-72035**	N5411V	Whiteman Enterprises, Pacoima CA	63/78
31894 •			HK-2812P	H. Escobar, Bogota Colombia	5.82/87
			HK-2812X		
			N5306M	reg ntu	12.88
			F-AZMU	Jacques Bourret/Aero Retro, St. Rambert	9.89/93
				(flies as 472035/*Jumpin' Jacques*)	
122-	P-51D	**44-72051**		(to R Swedish AF as Fv26026)	21.5.45/52
31910 •	J 26			(to FA Dominicana as FAD 1912)	10.52/84
Cavalier				Brian O'Farrell/Johnson Aviation, Miami FL	19.5.84/85
				John R. Sandberg, Minneapolis MN	.85
			N68JR	John R. Sandberg, Minneapolis MN	4.88/91
				(rest. Chino CA, ff 21.3.91 as #28 "Platinum Plus")	
				Janet S. Bjornstad, Scottsdale AZ (race #28)	10.91/95
				sold Minneapolis	1.96
122-	P-51D	**44-72059**		(to R Swedish AF as Fv26142)	
31918 •	J 26			(to FA d'L GN Nicaragua as GN......)	17.1.55/63
			N6150U	Will W. Martin/MACO Sales Financial Corp,	
				Chicago IL	2.9.63/66
				Aviacion Sanford, Gardena CA	.66
				(to FA Boliviana as FAB 513)	6.66
			N711WJ	World Jet Inc, Fort Lauderdale FL	1.95
			N951HB	reg.	9.95
122-	P-51D	**44-72086**		(to R Swedish AF as Fv26009): del.	21.4.46/52
31945 •	J 26			(to FA Dominicana as FAD 1936)	20.5.53/84
	Cavalier			Brian O'Farrell/Johnson Aviation, Miami FL	19.5.84
				(conv. to TF-51 dual controls by FAD .84)	
			N789DH	Brian O'Farrell/Johnson Aviation, Miami FL	4.86
				Joseph E. Scogna/Vintage Air, Yardley PA	.87/92
			N510JS	Joseph E. Scogna/Vintage Air, Yardley PA	7.94/95
				(flies as 415137/LH-R/*Baby Duck*)	
122-	P-51D	**44-72123**		(to R Swedish AF as Fv26092)	21.8.47/52
31982 •	J 26			(to FA Dominicana as FAD 1914)	31.10.52
				San Isidro AB, Dominican Rep: displ. on pole	.84/90

122-38604 •	P-51D	**44-72145**	N6169C		
			N311G	John C. Seidel, Sugar Grove IL	63/70
				Waldo (Clay) Klabo, Pleasanton CA	78/83
				(race #85 "Fat Cat")	
				Don Whittington, Fort Lauderdale FL	.84
				Peter McManus, Fort Lauderdale FL	.84
			N51PT	Peter McManus/Castlewood Realty, Miami FL	1.85/86
				Castlewood Airmotive, Baltimore MD	8.86/95
				flies as "472145/HO-M/*Petie 3rd*)	
122-38651 •	P-51D	**44-72192**	**N5460V**	James H. Bohlander, Roselle IL	63/64
				William S. Cochran III, Houston TX	66
				John V. Crocker, San Mateo CA	69/72
				California Warbirds, San Jose CA	6.78/95
				(flies as "414111/"Straw Boss 2/PE-X")	
122-38661 •	P-51D J 26	**44-72202** Cavalier		(to R Swedish AF as Fv26112): del.	13.6.47
				(to FA Dominicana as FAD 1917)	12.52/84
				Brian O'Farrell/Johnson Aviation, Miami FL	19.5.84/87
				SAAF Historic Flight, Lanseria AB	.87/93
				(arr. dism. Lanseria 19.11.87: planned long-term rest. to fly as "SAAF 325")	
				SAAF Museum, Swartkop AB: arr.	.93/94
122-38675 •	P-51D J 26	**44-72216**		(to R Swedish AF as Fv26116)	25.2.48
				(to IDFAF as 2343)	19.3.53
				Robs Lamplough/British Aerial Museum, Duxford UK: shipped	.76/81
				(recov. from Ein Gedi kibbutz, Israel .76)	
			G-BIXL	Robs Lamplough, Duxford/North Weald	3.7.81/96
				(rest. Duxford, later North Weald using mainplane ex 44-72770 recov. ex Dutch technical school: ff North Weald 5.5.87, flew as "472216/HO-L & HO-M" later "AJ-L for Memphis Belle film")	
122-38798 •	P-51D J 26	**44-72339** Cavalier		(to R Swedish AF as Fv26115)	13.6.47
				(to FA Dominicana as FAD 1918)	10.52/84
				Brian O'Farrell/Johnson Aviation, Miami FL	19.5.84
				Elmo Hahn, Muskegon MI	.84
			N51EH	Elmo Hahn/Hahn Inc, Muskegon MI	11.85/90
				(shipped ex FAD 9.84, ff Ft.Wayne IN 15.10.85)	
				James A. Cavanaugh, Dallas TX	.90/91
			N251JC	James A. Cavanaugh/Jani-King International Inc	
				Cavanaugh Flight Museum, Dallas-Addison TX	12.91/95
				(flies as "472339/WD-C")	
122-38823 •	P-51D J 26	**44-72364** Cavalier		(to R Swedish AF as Fv26061): del.	25.4.47
				(to FA Dominicana as FAD 1916)	12.52/84
				Brian O'Farrell/Johnson Aviation, Miami FL	19.5.84/87
				Brian O'Farrell, Miami, FL planned restoration	96
122-38859 •	P-51D	**44-72400**	NX69406	Woody Edmondson, Lynchburg VA	
				(race #42 "City of Lynchburg VA")	1.7.46
			NX13Y	Woody Edmondson, Lynchburg VA	5.12.46
				DiPonti Aviation, Minneapolis MN	21.12.46
				Anson Johnson, Miami FL (race #45)	21.7.47/59
				(attempt on piston airspeed record .52)	
			N502	Robert Bean, Danville IL	28.9.59
				John Juneau & George Nesmith, Opa Locka FL	5.62
				John Juneau, Opa Locka FL	11.62
				Robert D'Orsay, Opa Locka FL	c12.62
				Frank W. Lloyd, Miami FL	63/64
				Walter E. Ohlrich, Tulsa OK	2.65
			N913Y	Richard Vartanian, Pasedena CA	3.66/72
				Leonard Tanner, Granby CT	19.7.72
			N13Y	Bradley Air Museum, Windsor Locks CT	16.8.72/88
				(rest. Skaneateles NY 84)	

				New England Air Museum, Bradley CT	.88/90
				(stored, pending rest.)	
122 38860	P-51D	**44-72401**		surplus sale ex Walnut Ridge AFB AR	7.46
			NX65453	Earl Ortman/Ortman-Mighton Aviation Co,	
				Tulsa OK (race #2)	7.46
				M. W. (Lee) Fairbrother (race #21)	.47/49
				Jim Cook, Scottsbluff NE: cloud seeding ops.	55/56
	Cavalier		N71LN	Trans Florida Aviation, Sarasota FL	.62/64
				Cavalier Aircraft Corp, Sarasota FL	66/70
				Lindsay Newspapers Inc, Sarasota FL	72
				David B. Lindsay, King City CA (stored)	83/87
				struck-off USCR	10.83
				(NX65453 also rep. to Cuba: see 44-73978,	
				NX65453 also rep. as 44-73401)	
122-38897 •	P-51D J 26	**44-72438**		(to Swedish AF as Fv26131) del.	24.4.48
		Cavalier		(to FA Dominicana as FAD 1920)	12.52/84
				Brian O'Farrell/Johnson Aviation, Hialeah FL	19.5.84/87
				Selby R. Burch, Kissimmee FL	.87/95
				(stored dism. Kissimmee 87/91; rest. 94/96)	
			N7551T	Selby R. Burch, Kissimmee FL	9.95
122-38905	P-51D J 26	44-72446		(to Swedish AF as Fv26139)	
				(to FA d'L GN Nicaragua as GN 76)	17.1.55/63
			N6164U	Will W. Martin/MACO Sales Finance Corp,	
				Chicago IL	2.9.63
				impounded Mexico during ferry flight to USA	.63
				(open storage FA Mexicana AB, Mexico City 63/72;	
				released, trucked dism. to Chicago IL 9.72)	
			N12700	Will W. Martin, Palos Park IL	.72/81
				(rest. Chicago-Midway, flew as *El Gato Rapido*)	
				Don Knapp/DK Precision Inc, Ft Lauderdale FL	9.81/90
				crashed Dyess AFB, Abilene TX (Knapp k.)	23.6.90
				(USCR quotes id. 44-26139)	
122-38942 •	P-51D J 26	**44-72483**		(to Swedish AF as Fv26087): BOC	25.9.47
				(to FA d'L GN Nicaragua as GN 85)	17.1.55/63
			N6160U	Will W. Martin/MACO Sales Finance Corp,	
				Chicago IL	23.9.63
				(del. ex Nicaragua: id. quoted as 44-63769)	
				David M. Forrest, Avondale CA	.65/66
			N13410	David M. Forrest, Avondale CA: USCR	.66/69
				(flew as "413410/E2-C/Lou IV")	
				(to FA Salvadorena as FAS 411): del.	7.69/74
				Jack W. Flaherty/Flaherty Factors Inc,	
122-39198 •	P-51D	**44-72739**		Ascher Ward, Van Nuys CA	8.70
				(recov. ex open storage Universal Studios,	
				Hollywood CA 8.70)	
			N44727	Ascher Ward, Van Nuys CA	71/73
				Elmer F. Ward/Pioneer Aero Service,	
				Chino CA	8.75/95
				(flies as "414292/QP-A/"*Man O'War*	
122-39226 •	P-51D Cavalier	**44-72767**	**N6836C**	Walter Oaks, Ida Grove IA	63/64
				O. K. Airways Inc, Chicago IL	66
				Cavalier Aircraft Corp, Sarasota FL	69/70
				Lindsay Newspapers Inc, Sarasota FL	72/85
				David B. Lindsay, King City CA (stored)	84/87
				Pioneer Aero, Chino, CA, in store	92
122-39232 •	P-51D	**44-72773**		(to FA d'L GN Nicaragua as GN 120)	31.5.58/63
			N12066	Will W. Martin/MACO Sales Finance Corp,	
				Chicago IL	8.7.63
				I. N. Burchinall Jr, Honey Grove & Paris TX	66/84
				Robert L. Ferguson, Wellesley MA	85/86
				Charles Church (Spitfires) Ltd, Winchester	.86/87
				(del. by air, arr. UK 26.6.87)	

			G-SUSY	Charles Church (Spitfires) Ltd, Micheldever	23.7.87/91
				Paul J. Morgan, Sywell	1.5.90/95
				(flies as 47773/*Susy*)	
122-39236 •	P-51D Cavalier Mk. 2	**44-72777** **72-1537**		Trans Florida Aviation, Sarasota FL	28.8.59/67
				(to Indonesian AF/TNI-AU as F-344)	.67/78
				Stephen Johnson/Vanpac Carriers, Oakland CA: recov. ex Indonesia	.78
				Al Letcher, Mojave CA	16.7.79/81
			N8064V	Al Letcher, Mojave CA	4.81/84
				(trucked ex Oakland, rest. Mojave, ff 22.4.81)	
			N151D	Steve Seghetti, Vacaville CA	14.4.84/96
				(rest. Vacaville CA, ff 23.4.87)	
				dam. landing, Vacaville-Nut Tree Airport CA	.91
				(rebuilt, ff .94 as "472777/*Sparky*, race #68)	
122-39270 •	P-51D	**44-72811**		(to IDFAF as 13)	
				Holtz Technical School, Israel: reg. candidate	10.1.80
				Angelo Regina & Ascher Ward, Van Nuys CA	80/82
				(rest. Van Nuys .82 as TF-51D dual control, using ex CA ANG airframe recov. ex movie prop)	
			N268BD	Phil "Buck" Dear, Terry MS	83/85
				(rest. completed at Chino CA, ff .83 as "472218/WZ-I/Big Beautiful Doll")	
				Bob Byrne, Bloomfield MI	.87/88
			N215RC	Robert Converse, Sisters OR	.88
			N471R	R. Converse/Cascade Warbirds Co, Sisters OR	4.89/95
				(race #71 "472276/LH-I/*Huntress III*)	
				(USCR quotes id. 44-26060)	
122-39285 •	P-51D	**44-72826**		(to RCAF as 9563): BOC 7.6.47: SOC	20.9.60
			N6344T	James H. Defuria & Fred J. Ritts/ Intercontinental Airways, Canastota NY	25.2.57/60
				(stored unconv., Carberry MAN 57/62)	
				Aero Enterprises Inc, Elkhart IN	10.5.60/62
				(ferried Carberry-Winnipeg-Elkhart 7.62)	
				John Milton, Edwardsville IL	4.5.64/73
				Max & Danny Ramsay, Johnson KS	31.3.73/78
				Thomas J. Watson, Stowe VT	4.1.78/85
			C-FBAU(2	Dennis J. Bradley/Canadian Warplane Heritage, Hamilton ONT	3.85/91
			N51YS	Steve C. Collins, Dunwoody GA	4.11.91/96
				(flies as "472826/Old Boy/TJ-W")	
122-39299 •	P-51D	**44-72840**	N7718C (2	David B. Lindsay, King City CA (stored)	84/88
122-39303 •	P-51D Cavalier	**44-72844**		sold surplus McClellan AFB CA	17.2.58
			N5076K	Trans Florida Aviation, Sarasota FL	59
			N156C	Trans Florida Aviation, Sarasota FL	59
			N764C	Chamberlain Engineering Corp, Akron OH	63/66
				Edward C. Kellermeyer, Haileah FL	9.9.66
				Cavalier Aircraft Corp, Sarasota FL	8.5.68/69
			N7406	Lindsay Newspapers, Sarasota FL	10.69/83
				David B. Lindsay, King City CA (stored)	84/87
122-39361 •	P-51D	**44-72902**		(to RCAF as 9564): BOC 7.6.47: SOC	20.9.60
			N6343T	James H. Defuria & Fred J. Ritts/ Intercontinental Airways, Canastota NY	25.2.57/60
				(stored unconv., Carberry MAN 57/61)	
				Aero Enterprises Inc, Elkhart IN	10.5.60/64
				(ferried Carberry-Elkhart .61)	
			N335	E. D. Weiner, Long Beach CA (race #14)	17.4.64/73
				Violet M. Bonzer, Los Angeles CA	8.5.73/96
				EAA Museum, Hales Corner WI: loan, del.	.73/80
122-39366 •	P-51D	**44-72907** Cavalier		(to FA Guatamalteca as FAG 357)	.58
			N41748	Don Hull, Sugarland TX	8.72
				Wilson C. Edwards, Big Spring TX	78/96

122-39381 •	P-51D Cavalier	**44-72922**	N7718C (1	Robert H. Fee, San Antonio TX	17.2.58
			N18Y	Larry Sheerin, San Antonio TX	5.58
				Robin Eschauzier, Lackland AFB TX	11.58/61
			N6803T	Robin Eschauzier, Lackland AFB TX	3.2.61/62
				William D. Owens, Hondo TX	10.62/63
			N577WD	William D. Ownes, Hondo TX	28.1.63
				Space Systems Laboratory Inc, Melbourne FL	63/66
				David B. Lindsay/Trans Florida Aviation, Sarasota FL	24.3.67/71
				Lindsay Newspapers Inc, Sarasota FL	10.9.71/84
				(rep. stored King City CA 71/85)	
				Gordon W. Plaskett, King City CA	.84/85
				James Shuttleworth, Huntington IN	91/93
				John Dilley/Fort Wayne Air Service, Fort Wayne IN	.85/90
				rebuilt Ft. Wayne 91/93 as TF-51D)	
			N93TF	James Shuttleworth, Kenney TX	5.93/95
				(ff Ft.Wayne IN 6.6.93 as "922/W-LZ/*Scat VII*)	
122-39393 •	P-51D	**44-72934**		Merlin Aire Ltd	
			N513PA	Pioneer Aero Service, Chino CA	2.91
				Warbirds of GB Ltd, Biggin Hill UK	.91/92
				(rebuild Chino CA .91, flew as 472934/VF-T/*Shangrila*, shipped to UK; ff Biggin Hill 3.3.92)	
122-39395 •	P-51D	**44-72936**	**N7711C**	Arthur J. Stasney, Altadena CA	63/66
				(major rebuild, Van Nuys CA 68)	
				Solomon J. Pasey, Coatesville PA	6.69
				Flight Lease Inc, Columbus OH	70
				Warren G. Schulden, Elizabeth NJ	72/78
				crashed, Eufala AL	16.12.79
				Marvin L. Crouch, Encino CA (rebuild project)	3.83/96
122-39401 •	P-51D	**44-72942**	**N5427V**	Robert Fulton Co, Newtown CT	63/83
				Gordon W. Plaskett, King City CA	.83/85
				(rest. King City, ff .85 as 414151/*Petie 2nd*)	
				Anthony A. Buechler, Elm Grove WI	9.85/96
				(prev reported as. 44-74942)	
122-39407 •	P-51D	**44-72948**		USAFM, Charleston ANGB WV	57/94
				(displ. as WV ANG/*Wham Bam*")	
122-39448 •	P-51D	**44-72989**		USAFM, Volk Field ANGB WI	84/94
122-39449 •	P-51D	**44-72990**		(to RCAF as 9283): BOC 23.1.51: SOC	29.4.58
			N6322T	James H. Defuria & Fred J. Ritts/ Intercontinental Airways, Canastota NY	25.2.58/60
				Aero Enterprises, Elkhart IN	10.5.60/62
				Eastern Truck Rentals, Lowell MA	17.4.62/63
				James W. Vandeveer, Dallas TX	24.1.64/65
				John Peters, Norwood CO	5.5.65/66
				crashed, Grand Junction CO (rebuilt)	21.8.65
				Stanley W. Kurzet, Covina CA	2.2.66/67
				US Army, Edwards AFB CA: del.	27.4.67/78
				(chase plane, flew as "US Army 0-72990")	
				US Army Aviation Museum, Fort Rucker AL	7.2.78/96
				(displ. as "US Army 0-72990")	
122-39486 •	P-51D Cavalier	**44-73027**		(to RCAF as 9250): BOC 6.12.50: SOC	15.10.59
			N9146R	Trans Florida Aviation, Sarasota FL	20.5.59/60
				E. D. Weiner, Los Angeles CA	8.11.60/61
				Mario Villareal, El Paso TX	11.61
				El Paso Airmotive Inc, El Paso TX	7.12.61/65
				Southwest Air Rangers, El Paso TX	25.3.65
				Harold Barlow, Los Angeles CA	27.3.65/66
				Haynes McLellan & John Percival, Tracy CA	10.66/70

c/n	Type	Serial	Reg.	Owner / History	Date
				Roger Wolfe, Fallon NV (race #12)	11.70/72
			N5747	Robert E. Guildford/Mustang Pilots Club,	
				Beverley Hills CA	7.9.72/77
				dam. landing wheels-up, Mojave CA	10.74
				(arr. UK on visit 15.6.77, ret. USA 7.7.77)	
				crashed, wheels-up landing due in-flight fire,	
				Bakersfield Air Park, Bakersfield CA	9.10.77/78
				(rebuilt Chino, Philippine AF mainplane, ff .80)	
			N51MP	Mustang Pilots Club, Los Angeles CA	1.78/80
				crashed and dest., Lancaster CA	4.10.80
				William A. Speer, La Mesa CA (race #56)	7.91/93
				(rep. rebuild based on TNI-AU airframe)	
				sold to France: shipped ex Chino CA	2.93
			F-AZJM	Christophe Jacquart/Mustang Warbird Ltd/	
				Flying Legends Association, Dijon-Longvic	8.6.93/96
				(flies as *Temptation*)	
122-39488 •	P-51D	**44-73029**		(to FA d'L GN Nicaragua as GN 122)	31.5.58/63
			N7999A	Will W. Martin/MACO Sales Finance Corp,	
				Chicago IL	13.7.63
				James R. Almand, Grand Prairie TX	63/64
				Jerald L. Baker, Angleton TX	66
			N51JB	Jessie A. Baker, Houston TX (race #51)	6.69/78
				James E. Beasley, Philadelphia PA	10.79/96
				accident landing Chino CA (repaired)	7.84
				(flies as "473029/B7-E/*Bald Eagle*)	
122-39504 •	P-51D	**44-73053**		(to Indonesian AF/TNI-AU as F-3.....)	
				Fighter Rebuilders, Chino CA: under rest.	84
122-39538 •	P-51D	**44-73079**	N7716C	surplus sale ex McClellan AFB CA	2.58
				Joseph P. Dangelo, Campbell CA	63
			N576GF	Growers Frozen Foods, Salinas CA	.63/66
				Jerry G. Brassfield, San Jose CA	6.69/71
				Robert Love, Oakland CA	73
				Experimental Aircraft Assn., Franklin WI	78
				Robert J. Love, Oakland CA	82/85
				Russell R. Francis, San Francisco CA	87/88
			N151BL	Russell R. Francis, South Lake Tahoe CA	7.89/90
				Bill Dause, Wellington UT	4.91/96
122-39540 •	P-51D	**44-73081**	**N5074K**	Michael E. Coutches/	
				Museum of American Aircraft, Hayward CA	7.63/93
122-39557 •	P-51D	**44-73098**		(to Italian AF as MM4292): BOC 26.2.45: SOC	7.2.49
				to instructional airframe Rome-Ciampino	
				stored dism., Cappenelli, Italy "SM-64"	
				recov. by Robs Lamplough, Duxford UK	c80
				Paul Raymond/Whitehall Theatre of War	.82/85
			G-BMBA	Robs Lamplough, North Weald: at auction	5.6.85
				Aces High Ltd, Duxford	6.85
				sold to USA, struck-off reg.	2.8.85
				Steve Dill, Orlando FL (shipped ex UK)	.85
				Cougar Helicopters, Daytona Beach FL	87
				(under rest. to fly)	
122-39588 •	P-51D	44-73129		Tony Randozza, Oakland CA	.58
			N5480V	J. M. Jackson, Long Beach CA	63
				Thomas W. Winship, Corona Del Mar CA	.63/64
				Stan's Aircraft Sales, Fresno CA	66
				Frank A. Barrena, San Luis Obispo CA	69
				(to FA Haiti as FAH 15650): del.	7.69
				dam. mid-air collision another FAH P-51	c70
				(recov ex Haiti, stored dism. Miami FL 72)	
			N51SL	Dixon J. Smith, Seattle WA	72
				Rodney Barnes, Oconomowoc WI	78/86
				(rest. Chino CA 82/85)	
				Stuart Eberhardt, Danville CA (race #22)	7.86/94
			N151SE	Stuart Eberhardt, Danville CA (race #22)	9.94/95
				(flies as "473129/FF-129/Merlin's Magic")	

122-	P-51D	**44-73140**		(to RCAF as 9567): BOC 7.6.47: SOC	20.9.60
39599 •			N6337T	James H. Defuria & Fred J. Ritts/	
				Intercontinental Airways, Canastota NY	25.2.57/60
				(stored unconv., Carberry MAN 57/62)	
				Aero Enterprises, Elkhart IN	10.5.60/64
				(ferried Carberry-Winnipeg-Elkhart 7.62)	
				J. D. Kent, Des Moines IN	13.4.64/67
				N169MD(2 Dr. Burns M. Byram, Marengo IA (race #71)	8.11.67/78
			N51N	Charles Ventors/Aerodyne Sales, El Reno OK	10.78/82
			C-FBAU (1	Dennis J. Bradley, Burlington ONT	1.82/84
				crashed, burned, fcd. landing, Massey ONT	7.7.84
				(rep. id. tfd. to rest. project: airframe unknown):	
			C-GZQX	ntu: Fill-R-Up Ltd, Edmonton ALTA	7.85
				Trans America Helicopters, Edmonton ALTA	86
				Marvin L. Gardner, Mercedes TX	4.86
			N314BG	Gordon Plaskett/BG Aero, King City CA	9.86
				Brett Ward/Pioneer Aero Service, Chino CA	1.87/88
				(rebuild Chino CA: ff 25.7.88; del. to UK)	
				Warbirds of GB Ltd, Biggin Hill	.88/92
				(painted as 414151/HO-M/*Petie 2nd*)	
				Eastwind Inc, Wilmington DE	2.93/96
122-	P-51D	**44-73142**	N6173C	Michael T. Loening, Salmon ID	63/64
39601				Westair Co, Westminster CO	66
				Vernon S. Peterson, Valley View TX	68/78
			N51PW	Vernon S. Peterson, Valley View TX	4.78
			N51VP	Vernon S. Peterson, Valley View TX	
				Universal Life Church TX	83/84
				J. Bradford Enterprises, Prescott AZ	87/89
				crashed on takeoff, Denton TX (Peterson k.)	6.9.89
			N51BK	Bruce C. Morehouse, Jefferson TX	4.91/96
122-	P-51D	**44-73149**		(to RCAF as 9568): BOC 7.6.47: SOC	20.9.60
39608 •			N6340T	James H. Defuria & Fred J. Ritts/	
				Intercontinental Airways, Canastota NY	25.2.57/60
				(stored unconv., Carberry MAN 57/61)	
				Aero Enterprises, Elkhart IN	10.5.60/62
				(trucked dism. Carberry-Elkhart 6.62)	
				Ernest W. Beehler, West Covina CA	30.7.62/74
				Charles E. Beck & Edward J. Modes,	
				Burbank CA (race #7 *Candy Man*)	19.8.74/76
				Robert E. MacFarlane, Placerville CA	4.8.76/80
				The Fighter Collection, Duxford	5.80/86
				(del. via Reykjavik to Geneva 30.8.80,	
				arr. Biggin Hill 2.5.81 based UK since)	
			N51JJ	John V. Crocker, San Mateo CA	5.86/91
				leased: The Fighter Collection, Duxford	86/91
				accident Stapleford UK (repaired)	9.8.90
			G-BTCD	The Fighter Collection, Duxford	11.1.91/96
				(flies as 463221/G4-S/*Candyman*/*Moose*)	
122-	P-51D	**44-73163**		(to RCAF as 9285): BOC 8.2.51: SOC	29.4.58
39622 •			N6300T	James H. Defuria & Fred J. Ritts/	
				Intercontinental Airways, Canastota NY	5.2.57/60
				Aero Enterprises, Elkhart IN	10.5.60/61
				Suncoast Aviation, St. Petersburg FL	8.7.61
				Valair Aircraft Inc, Cincinatti OH	28.9.61/63
				Farnum Brown, Michigan City MI	4.3.64
				Robert A. Mitchem, Broomfield CO	12.3.64
				James D. Morton/Aero Enterprises,Elkhart IN	14.4.64
				D. K. Fesenmyer, Mount Pleasant MI	25.4.64
				Robert H. Pollock, Abbotstown PA	21.5.65/66
			N5151M	Herbert E. (Mickey) Rupp, Mansfield OH	17.11.66
			N5151R	Rupp Industries Inc, Mansfield OH	69
			N51MR	Rupp Industries Inc, Mansfield OH	72/74
				Edward O. Messick, San Antonio TX	2.3.74/79
				(flew as 473656/TX ANG/*Minute Man*)	
				Charles Knapp, Los Angeles CA	83/89

				crashed on takeoff, Santa Monica CA	2.9.89
				Jackson McGoon Aircraft, Los Angeles CA	89/95
				Randall Kempf: rebuild project	96
122-39655	P-51D	44-73196	N5449V	Fred H. Johnson, Summitville OH	63/64
				Walter H. Hackett, Smithville OH	66/70
				Charles Milam, Layfayette LA	78
				Don C. Davis/Tired Iron Racing Team, Casper WY (race #81 "Habu")	12.81/84
				crashed, dest. nr Aspen CO (Earl Ketchen k.)	15.7.84
122-39665 •	P-51D Cavalier 2000	**44-73206**	N7724C	sold surplus at McClellan AFB CA	.58
				Trans Florida Aviation, Sarasota FL	63/64
			N3751D	Henry B. Faulkner, Stoddard NH	66/70
			F-AZAG	Jean-Francios Lejeune, Faaa, Tahiti (shipped to Tahiti ex Chino CA .76)	.75/83
			N3751D	Jean-Francios Lejeune, Chino CA	4.83
				Clyde Logan Neill, Indian Wells CA (shipped Tahiti-CA deck cargo "Polynesia" .83, rest. Chino ff 2.84 "JF-L/Hurry Home Honey")	4.83
				Al Ashbourne, Chino CA	85
				Charles A. Osborn/ Blue Sky Aviation, Louisville KY & Sellersburg IN (flies as "413586/C5-T/*Hurry Home Honey*)	85/95
122-39669 •	P-51D Cavalier 2000	44-73210	N5461V	Flying W Inc, Medford NJ	63
				Rusk Aviation, Kankakee IL	.63/64
				Edward G. Fisher, Kansas City KS	66/69
				Gardner Flyers Inc, Brownwood TX	70/72
				Kenneth Bloomhower KS	73
				crashed, Valley Airpark CO (Bloomhower k.)	17.5.73
				Angelo & Peter Regina, Van Nuys CA (parts used in rebuild Van Nuys, based on IDFAF airframe recov. by Reginas ex kibbutz playground, Israel: arr. Long Beach CA 13.1.78: ff Van Nuys 30.1.80 as 473210/WD-B/*Widowmaker*)	78/80
			N1040N	Angelo Regina, Van Nuys CA	1.80/87
				Joseph Kasparoff, Van Nuys CA	88/92
			CF-IKE	Manitoba Ltd, The Pas MAN	11.7.95/96
122-39675	P-51D	**44-73216**		(to RCAF as 9569): BOC 7.6.47: SOC	12.6.58
			N6302T	James H. Defuria/Intercontinental Airways, Canastota NY	20.5.58/60
				Aero Enterprises, Elklhart IN	15.8.60/61
				Richard B. Dillard, Laredo TX	7.5.61/62
				crashed, Cape Girardeau MS	7.5.61
				Barrett Investment Co, San Antonio TX	4.5.62/64
				Stan E. Shaw, Saratoga CA	28.8.64/67
				Jack R. Urich, Hacienda Heights CA	1.3.67
				Joe H. Garrett, Tulsa OK	15.9.67/69
				Dan Futrell, Nashville TN	8.10.69/71
				crashed, dest., Hot Springs AR	24.3.71
				(rep. id. tfd. to P-51D rebuild, origin unknown): Rick Brickert, Manhattan Beach CA	81
			N3278D	Jerry D. Owens, Scottsdale AZ	9.82/87
				Wayne Meylan, Elkhorn NE	3.87
				crashed, dest., Manistee MI (Meylan k.)	26.6.87
				Meylan Enterprises Inc, Omaha NE	90/96
				still on USCR	96
122-39699	P-51D	44-73240	N7721C	D. R. Simpson, Hanford CA	63/64
			N469P	Douglas W. Wood, Fresno CA (race #7)	66
				Kent W. Jones, Dallas-Addison TX	69/70
				Roger W. Dennington, Atlanta GA	72
				crashed, dest.	8.4.73
122-39713 •	P-51D	**44-73254**		(to RCAF as 9571): BOC 7.6.47: SOC	20.9.60
			N6328T	James H. Defuria & Fred J. Ritts/ Intercontinental Airways, Canastota NY (stored unconv., Carberry MAN 57/61)	27.2.57/60

				Aero Enterprises Inc, Elkhart IN	10.5.60/61
				(ferried Carberry-Elkhart .61)	
				Clifford C. Pettit, Ligonier IN	3.10.61/70
				crashed Crumstown IN	31.5.63
				(rep. id. tfd. to rebuild, source unknown):	
				A. C. Lofgren, Battle Creek MI	6.6.72
				Donald R. Weber, Baton Rouge LA	15.8.74/96
				(rest., ff. 1.78)	
122-39719	P-51D Cavalier	**44-73260**	N5075K		
			N451D	Joseph E. Anzelon, Whitestone NY	63/64
				Howard Olsen, Midland TX	66
				Trans Florida Aviation, Sarasota FL	69
				Cavalier Aircraft Corp, Sarasota FL	8.69/70
				(to Indonesian AF/TNI-AU as F-360)	
				crashed Java	24.6.75
				rep. recov. by Stephen Johnson, Oakland CA	.79
122-39723 •	P-51D	**44-73264**	**N5428V**	Mathew P. Kibler, Luray VA	63
				Chas B. Schalebaum, Ridgewood NJ	.63/64
				John M. Sliker, Wadley GA	66
				William Ross Enterprises Inc, Chicago IL	69
				Confederate Air Force, Harlingen TX	70
				George F. Williams, Hobbs NM	72
				Confederate Air Force, Harlingen/Midland TX	3.11.77/96
				crashed Omaha NE (repaired)	17.6.81
				(flies as *Gunfighter II*/CY-U")	
122-39732 •	P-51D	**44-73273**		(to FA Salvadorena as FAS......)	7.69
			N34DD	reg. res.	76
			N200DD	Donald R. Anderson, Saugus CA	78
				John G. Deahl, Denver CO	5.80/81
				John G. Deahl Estate, Denver CO: USCR	84/95
			N210DD	ntu: Charles Mothon, Gallway NY	89
122-39734 •	P-51D	**44-73275**		sold surplus McClellan AFB CA	16.9.57
			N2868D	Richard E. Blakemore, Tonopah NV	63/64
			N119H	Vernon E. Thorpe, Oklahoma City OK	.66
				Paul D. Finefrock, Hobart OK	69
				Richard L. Wood, Houston & Refugio TX	6.69/72
				Jack W. Flaherty, Monterey CA (race #9)	73
				Wilson C. Edwards, Big Spring TX	78/83
				Foy Midkiff, Houston TX	84/85
				Alan S. Kelly, Middlebury CT	88
				Kelco Aircraft, Wilmington DE	89/90
				John Mills	91
				John Breit/Aviation Sales Inc, Englewood CO	3.92/95
122-39746 •	P-51D	**44-73287**		surplus ex McClellan AFB CA: $957	.58
			N5445V	William Kelbaugh, Chico CA	3.58/64
				William S. Cooper, Merced CA	.64/72
				James Francis, Medina OH	.74
				Courtesy Aircraft, Rockford IL	.77/78
				James S. Francis, Medina OH	24.1.78/80
			N51DF	James S. Francis, Medina OH	8.80
				Jack A. Rose, Spangle WA	6.82/87
				dam. landing, Reno-Cannon NV (repaired)	9.9.86
			N751JC	C & C Vintage Aircraft, Rockford IL	10.88
			N5445V	John J. Castrogiovanni, Rockford IL	.88
				Michael J. George/Air Combat Museum, Springfield IL	.89/96
				(flies as "473287/J-D7/*Worry Bird*)	
122-39779 •	P-51D Cavalier	**44-73320**	**N5463V**	Trans Florida Aviation, Sarasota FL	63/64
				Cavalier Aircraft Corp, Sarasota FL	66/70
				Lindsay Newspapers Inc, Sarasota FL: USCR	72/85
				David B. Lindsay, King City CA (stored)	78/88

c/n	Type	Serial	Reg	Owner / History	Date
122-39782 •	P-51D	**44-73323**	N6167C	Aero Service Inc, Nogales AZ	63/64
				Darryl G. Greenamyer, Van Nuys CA	66
				Michael A. Geren, Kansas City MO	69/70
			N4270P	Marvin L. Crouch, Encino CA	1.81
			N151MD	Marvin L. Crouch, Encino CA (rest. project)	4.81/95
122-39798 •	P-51D	**44-73339**		(to FA Costarricense as 2): del. ex TX ANG	16.1.55
				rep. crashed	19.1.55
				(to Indonesian AF/TNI-AU as F-3..)	
				Stephen Johnson/Vanpac Carriers, Oakland CA: recov. ex Indonesia	.79
				Ronald M. Runyan, Fairfield OH	82/84
				(rest. Chino CA 82/84: adopted id. 44-74008, ff Chino .84 as *Dallas Doll*)	
			N151MC	ntu: Ronald M. Runyan, Fairfield OH	2.84
			N51RR	Ronald M. Runyan, Fairfield OH: del.	12.84/95
				Robs Lamplough, North Weald UK	.89/91
				Intrepid Aviation, North Weald	.91/96
				(del. ex USA 14.2.91, flies as "474008/VF-R")	
122-39802 •	P-51D	**44-73343**	N5482V	Ben W. Hall, Seattle WA	63/67
				(race #2 *Seattle Miss*)	
				Chance Enterprises Inc, Half Moon Bay CA	69
				Michael T. Loening, Boise ID, (race #2)	6.69/72
				crashed, badly damaged Reno NV	9.71
				(rebuilt Chino CA 74)	
				Bruce Morehouse, San Antonio TX	83/87
				struck-off USCR	6.87
122-39806 •	P-51D	**44-73347**		(to RCAF as 9298): BOC	16.3.51
				Canadian War Museum, Ottawa ONT	9.8.61/64
				Canadian National Aeronautical Collection, Rockcliffe AB ONT (displ. as "9298/Y2-E")	.64/82
				National Aviation Museum, Rockcliffe ONT	9.82/93
122-39808 •	P-51D	**44-73349**		(to Swiss AF as J-2113): BOC 6.11.48: SOC	11.4.58
				Swiss Air Force Museum, Dubendorf AB	60/93
				Swiss Transport Museum, Lucerne: loan	77/90
122-39809 •	P-51D Cavalier	**44-73350**	N6176C	Donald F. Baldocchi, San Francisco CA	63/64
			YS-210P	Archie A. Baldocchi, Illopango, El Salvador	.65/69
				(to FA Salvadorena as FAS 402)	7.69/74
			N33FF	Jack W. Flaherty/Flaherty Factors Inc, Monterey CA	1.11.74
				Wilson C. Edwards, Big Spring TX	78/88
				Robert H. Nottke, Barrington Hills IL	.88/92
				Lee O. Maples, Vichy MO	2.95
122-39874 •	P-51D	**44-73415**		(to RCAF as 9289): BOC 8.2.51: SOC	14.8.59
			N6526D	James H. Defuria/Intercontinental Airways, Canastota NY	21.7.58/60
				R. Ferrer, Patchoque NY	21.3.60/66
				crashed, badly dam., Richmond VA	15.2.62
				Frederick W. Wild, Averne NY	6.1.66
				Airlease Inc, Chicago IL	10.1.66
				Frank Guzman, Massapequa PA	10.1.66/68
				Don Bateman, Las Vegas NV	9.3.68/69
				Michael E. Coutches, Hayward CA	17.6.69/74
				H. Matteri, State Line NV	15.1.74/75
				William Veatch, Olympia WA	1.9.75/77
				crashed on takeoff, Olympia WA	19.3.77
				William A. Speer, La Mesa CA	.80/94
				(rebuilt Chino CA, ff .88 race #45,#55 *Pegasus*; components also used for P-51D static rest. for RAF Museum: see end of listing)	
				sold at auction, San Diego-Montgomery Field	10.12.94
				Delbert Williams (race #55 *Voodoo Chile*)	96
122-39879 •	P-51D	**44-73420**		sold as surplus McClellan AFB CA	.58
			N7722C	Michael E. Coutches/American Aircraft	

				Sales Co, Hayward CA	17.2.58
				Ronald E. West/ West Foods Inc, Soquel CA	.58
				Richard B. McFarlane	21.7.58
				Donald G. Bell, Livermore CA	25.8.58/64
				Robert G. Bixler, San Jose CA	10.65/71
				Robert H. Phillips, Phoenix AZ	3.71/78
				Robb Satterfield, Aaron F. Giebel &	
				Dallas L. Smith, Harlingen TX	9.9.78/89
				Dallas L. Smith, Midland TX	90/92
				Brian Hore/Alpine Fighter Collection NZ	.93/94
				(shipped to NZ 12.93, assembled Wanaka)	
			ZK-PLI	Brian Hore & Tim Wallis/	
				Alpine Fighter Collection, Wanaka	28.3.94/96
				(flies as "473420/524/*Miss Torque*)	
122-39882 •	P-51D	**44-73423**	N5465V	Albert Boughey, Upland CA	63/64
				George Biss, Los Angeles CA	66/69
				Edward Bliss, San Diego CA	12.69/70
			N31248	Fred Sebby, Bullhead City AZ	80
			N51DJ	Fred Sebby, Bullhead City AZ	5.80
				Diane Dejacomo, Scottsdale AZ	.80/92
				(race #51, later #100 41073/*Sunshine*)	
				Classic Air Parts Inc, Ontario CA	3.94/96
				(USCR quotes id. 44-61449)	
122-39887	P-51D	44-73428		(to FA d'L GN Nicaragua as GN 118)	23.5.58/63
			N6324T (2	Will W. Martin/MACO Sales Finance Corp,	
				Chicago IL	8.7.63
			N12065	Edward I. Gilbert, Phoenix AZ	.63/64
				Marvin L. Gardner/Gardner Flyers Inc,	
				Brownwood TX	66
				crashed, dest.	18.11.67
				J. G. Ghormley, Fort Worth TX	70
122-39894 •	P-51D	**44-73435**		(to RCAF as 9290): BOC 8.2.51: SOC	1.11.60
			CF-MWN	James H. Defuria/Intercontinental Airways,	
				Canastota NY	12.58/60
			N6311T	Aero Enterprises, Elkhart IN	10.5.60/61
				Suncoast Aviation, St. Petersburg FL	10.61/62
				James G. Shaw, Columbia SC	27.2.62/63
				Angels Aviation, Zephyrhills CA	3.5.63
				Selby R. Burch, Wintergarden FL	3.5.63/69
				crashed Daytona Beach FL	6.7.68
				Marvin L. Gardner/Gardner Flyers,	
				Mercedes TX (hulk)	84
				Pioneer Aero, Chino CA	87/89
122-39895 •	P-51D	**44-73436**		(to RCAF as 9300): BOC 16.3.51: SOC	1.11.60
			N6313T	James H. Defuria/Intercontinental Airways,	
				Canastota NY	12.58/60
				Aero Enterprises, Elkhart IN	.60/62
				Ralph Rensink, Lewiston ID	10.1.62
				Walter D. Peterson, Manson WA	26.6.62/77
			N51TK (1	Tom Kelly & John Dilley/Consolidated Airways,	
				Fort Wayne IN (race #19 *Lou IV*)	17.8.77/86
			N51KD	Dean Cutinshall/American Horizons Inc,	
				Fort Wayne IN	3.86/92
				(race #91 413926/E2-S/*Cutters Capers*)	
				Wally Fisk/Amjet Aircraft Corp, St. Paul MN	8.93/96
122 39903 •	P-51D	**44-73444**		(to Italian AF as MM4323): BOC 22.3.45: SOC	10.9.50
				Italian Air Force Museum, Vigna di Valle AB	84/96
122-39913 •	P-51D Cavalier 2000	**44-73454**	N6172C	Ligonier Flying Service Inc, Ligonier IN	63
				Champion Developers Inc, Jacksonville FL	66
				crashed Jacksonville FL	14.5.67
			N2051D	Cavalier Aircraft Corp, Sarasota FL	68

				Rufus A. Applegarth, Plymouth Meeting PA	.68/72
				John J. Schafhausen, Spokane WA	5.72/73
				Richard Bach	.73
				crashed on landing, Midland TX	24.9.73
				Gordon Plaskett, King City CA	
				(rebuilt ex Cavalier config. to stock P-51D)	
				John Herlihy, Montara CA	76/84
				Richard A. Bjelland, Dairy OR	4.84/95
				(flies as "414911/P2-M/*This Is It*)	
122-39917 •	P-51D Cavalier Mustang II	**44-73458**		(to RCAF as 9294): BOC 16.3.51: SOC	14.8.59
			N6525D	James H. Defuria/Intercontinental Airways, Canastota NY	21.7.58
			N6347T	James H. Defuria, Canastota NY	60
			N554T	Ray A. Alexander, Memphis TN	63/64
				W. R. Rodgers, Rolling Fork MS	66/69
				(to FA Salvadorena as FAS 404)	.69/74
				(mod. to TF-51D by FAS, crashed in FAS service)	
			N36FF	Jack W. Flaherty/Flaherty Factors Inc, Monterey CA: wreck	28.10.74
				John Herlihy/C-Vu Airmotive, Half Moon Bay CA : wreck	12.3.75
			N4151D	Gordon W. Plaskett, King City CA	24.6.75/78
				(rebuilt Chino CA, using wing 44-74012/N6519D as TF-51D, ff 22.11.77 as "484662/TF-662")	
				Ben R. Bradley, Fort Lauderdale FL	81
				Basil C. Deuschle, Pompano Beach FL	.81/83
				Don Whittington/World Jet Inc, Fort Lauderdale FL	.83/85
				Lone Star Flight Museum, Houston TX	87/88
				Warbirds of GB Ltd.	88
				William L. Hane, Mesa AZ	10.91/96
				(flew as "484660/TF-660")	
				(displ. Champlin Fighter Museum, Mesa AZ)	
122-39922 •	P-51D	**44-73463**		(to RCAF as 9575): BOC 7.6.47: SOC	20.9.60
				James H. Defuria & Fred J. Ritts/ Intercontinental Airways, Canastota NY	27.2.57/60
				(stored unconv., Carberry MAN 57/61)	
				Aero Enterprises Inc, Elkhart IN	.60/62
				(stripped, trucked Carberry-Elkhart 6.62)	
				sold as scrap metal	
				Leonard Tanner, North Granby CT	
				(rep. recov. ex scrapyard, Decatur IL)	
				Duane Egli, Fabens TX	
				Richard Ransopher, Grapevine TX: rest.	77/82
				Richard Ransopher, Kernersville NC/Tampa FL	82/89
				(rest. project: fuse. section RCAF 9575, wings and other parts from N1335, N6175C, N5478V: project moved from TX to NC .85)	96
122-39942 •	P-51D Cavalier	**44-73483**	N351D	Graubart Aviation Inc, Valparaiso IN	63
				Jack Shaver/Maryland Airmotive MD	64
				Chance Enterprises Inc, Half Moon Bay CA	66
				crashed in swamp, major dam., AL	9.66
				Elaine Loening, San Francisco CA	69/70
				Waldon Spillers, Versailles OH (hulk only)	84
122-39953 •	P-51D	**44-73494**		(to Rep. of Korea AF as 205)	
				Yongdungpo AB, Seoul, South Korea: displ.	67/89
122-39977 •	P-51D	**44-73518**	N5483V	Edward G. Fisher, Kansas City KS	63/72
				Don Whittington, Fort Lauderdale FL	78/83
				(mod. racer #09 "Precious Metal")	
				EAA Aviation Foundation, Oshkosh WI	85
				Don Whittington/World Jet Inc, FLL FL	88/92
				(rebuilt as mod. racer, RR Griffon with contra-rotating props .88, #09 "Precious Metal")	
				accident, Reno NV (rebuilt)	17.9.88
				ditched in sea near Galveston TX (salvaged)	24.1.90

c/n	Type	Serial	Reg	Owner / History	Date
			N6WJ	World Jet Inc, Fort Lauderdale FL	6.94/96
				(rebuilt: Griffon contra-rotating props, race#38)	
				(USCR quotes N6WJ id. as "44-88")	
122-40002 •	P-51D	**44-73543**	N5458V	Trans Florida Aviation, Sarasota FL	.58
				(to Indonesian AF/TNI-AU as F-3......)	
				Stephen Johnson/Vanpac Carriers, Oakland CA:	
				recov. ex Indonesia	.78
				Chris Warrilow, Woburn Green, Bucks UK	.80/85
				(shipped to UK , arr 2.81: rest. project)	
			G-BLYW	Chris Warrilow, High Wycombe	3.6.85
				Don Knapp/D. K. Precision Inc,	
				Fort Lauderdale FL	3.6.85/86
			N800DK	D. K. Precision Inc, Fort Lauderdale FL	4.86/87
				Whittington Bros., Fort Lauderdale FL	88
				sale rep., Fort Lauderdale FL	90/92
			N51SB	Steve Bolander/SWB Leasing, Libertyville IL	7.92
				Steve Bolander/Air Bear Corp, Libertyville IL	4.94/96
				dam., struck parked Bonanza, Kenosha WI	20.5.95
				(flies as "M-SB/*Mary Bear*)	
122-40033	P-51D	**44-73574**	N5478V	Marvin L. Gardner, Mercedes TX	63
				Gardner Flyers Inc, Brownwood TX	.63/66
				Beth Allen Truck Rental Inc, Stowe PA	69/70
				Richard Ransopher, Kernersville NC	84/87
				under rebuild to fly	96
122-40043 •	P-51D Cavalier	**44-73584**	N5447V		
			N51Q	Trans Florida Aviation, Sarasota FL	63/64
				Cavalier Aircraft Corp, Sarasota FL	66/70
				Lindsay Newspapers Inc, Sarasota FL	72
				David B. Lindsay, King City CA (stored)	78/88
				struck-off USCR	10.83
122-40045	P-51D	44-73586	N5412V	Tri State Aviation Service, Huntington WV	63
				Thomas P. Luck, Lancaster PA	.63/66
				Garden State Aviation, Neptune NJ	69/74
				crashed, dest.	10.74
122-40196 •	P-51D Cavalier 750	**44-73656**	N5073K	sold as surplus McClellan AFB CA	.58
				Delta A & E Parts Inc, NC	2.58
				Michael E. Coutches/American Aircraft	
				Sales, Hayward CA	5.58
				Trans Florida Aviation, Sarasota FL	.58/63
				Stanley Dunbar Studios, Charlotte NC	.63
				Howard Olsen, Midland TX (race #1)	.63/66
				Duncan Airmotive Inc, Galveston TX	.68
				(to FA Salvadorena as FAS 406)	12.68/74
			N32FF	Jack W. Flaherty/Flaherty Factors Inc,	
				Monterey CA	1.11.74
				(adopted id. P-51K 44-12473 on return to USA)	
				Gordon W. Plaskett, King City CA	.75
				(rest. .76 as 414237/*Moonbeam McSwine*/HO-W)	
			N2151D	Gordon W. Plaskett, King City CA	76/81
				Chris Williams, Ellensburg WA	.81/87
				Vlado Lenoch, La Grange IL	4.88/96
122-40223 •	P-51D	**44-73683**		(to FA d'L GN Nicaragua as FAN GN119)	23.5.58/63
			N12064	Will W. Martin/MACO Sales Financial Corp,	
				Chicago IL	.63
				E. D. Weiner, Los Angeles CA	.63/64
				George W. Drucker Jr, Los Angeles CA	66
				George A. Brown, Canoga Park CA	69
				Meteorological Operations Inc, Hollister CA	69
				John S. Steinmetz, Londonerry NH	70/72
			N5551D	Tri-T Aviation, Griffin GA	78
				Heritage Aircraft Inc, Fayetteville GA	.80/90
				(flew as *Jumpin Jaques* 80)	

				(flies as "414251/WZ-I/*Contrary Mary*)	
				San Diego Aerospace Museum CA	92/94
				struck-off USCR: type Aero Classics P-51D	12.5.92
				(stored SDAM hangar, "414251/WZ-I/*ContraryMary*",	
				San Diego-Gillespie Field CA 3.93/94)	
122-40233 •	P-51D	**44-73693**		(to FA d'L GN Nicaragua as FAN GN116)	23.5.58/63
			N6357T	Will W. Martin/MACO Sales Financial Corp,	
				Chicago IL	9.63
				Ronald L. Bryant, Jacksonville Beach FL	66
				Alvin T. George, Atlanta GA	69
				(to FA Salvadorena as FAS 408)	7.69/74
			N35FF	Flaherty Factors Inc, Monterey CA	1.11.74
				(adopted id. 44-13253 on return to USA)	
				Wilson C. Edwards, Big Spring TX	78/87
				(race #45 *Risky Business*)	
				Richard L. Pack/Mustang 4 Inc, Chino CA	88/95
				op: Bill Rheinschild/Unlimited Air Racing Inc,	
				Van Nuys CA (race #45 *Risky Business*)	91/96
122-40244 •	P-51D	**44-73704**	**N6168C**	Plauche Electric Inc, Lake Charles LA	63/69
				Marvin L. Gardner/Gardner Flyers Inc,	
				Brownwood & Mercedes TX	70/92
				(race #25 *Thunderbird*)	
				Musco Inc, Dallas TX	2.94/96
122-40291 •	P-51D	**44-73751**	**N5444V**	Robert Mitchum, Broomfield CO	63/64
				Keith Larkin, Watsonville CA	66/69
				Ron Van Kretgan/PTI Inc, San Jose CA	8.69/96
122-40362	P-51D	44-73822	**N5484V**	Bernard Coski, Tacoma WA	63/64
				William Myers, Ballwin/St Charles MO	66/78
				Henry J. Schroeder, Danville IL	.81/91
				(id. tfd. to 44-84786/N51BS: que se)	
122-40372	P-51D	44-73832	N2873D		
			N117E	Edward I. Gilbert, Phoenix AZ	63/64
				Frank C. Sanders, Phoenix AZ	66
				David Webster, Glendo WY	69/72
				Scott Smith, Orlando FL	78
				crashed Ellisville MS	15.2.78
				Gary McCann FL: rest. project	83/85
				Clarke Aviation Corp, Daytona Beach FL	87/88
				(flew as "357th FG/Hurry Home Honey")	
				Bob Byrne Aviation, Bloomfield MI	89
				Harvey E. Hunewill/Hunewill Construction Co,	
				Wellington NV	89/95
				crashed at ranch, Wellington NV (Hunewill k.)	21.11.92
122-40383 •	P-51D	**44-73843**		(to RCAF as 9271): BOC 11.1.51: SOC	4.12.56
			N10601	Stinson Field Aircraft, San Antonio TX	10.56/57
				Lloyd P. Nolen/Mustang & Co, Mercedes TX	10.57/77
				Confederate Air Force, Harlingen/Midland TX	12.77/96
122-40389	P-51D	*44-73849*		(to RCAF as 9247): BOC 6.12.50: SOC	27.12.57
			N6516D	James H. Defuria & Fred J. Ritts/	
				Intercontinental Airways, Canastota NY	26.11.56
				Aero Enterprises Inc, Elkhart IN	10.5.60
			N335J (1	Ed Weiner, Los Angeles CA	10.60/62
			N835J	Aero Enterprises, Elkhart IN	21.6.62/63
				Joseph A. Truhill, Addison TX	2.11.64/65
				Jim Vandeveer, Dallas TX	1.10.65/71
				Gerald A. Swayze, Mesquite TX	13.1.71
				Robert Walker, Tulsa OK	11.71/73
			N51WH	William E. Harrison, Tulsa OK	19.4.73/74
			N51JL	Jack N. Levine, Livonia MI	10.74/84
				crashed dest., Ray MI (Levine k.)	17.11.84
122-40396 •	P-51D	**44-73856**	N5077K	Jim Jeffers, Stateline NV (race #83)	63
				Contractors Equipment Co, Salem OR	.63/64

				Fowler Aeronautical Services, Burbank CA	66
				Air Carriers Inc, Aurora OR	69
			N711UP	Gale Aero Corp, Minneapolis MN (race #0)	8.69/70
			N7TF	Cinema Air Inc, Houston TX/Carlsbad CA	76/95
				(flies as "473856/F/*Susie*)	
122-40397	P-51D	44-73857		(to RCAF as 9244): BOC 6.12.50: SOC	1.1.1.60
			N6315T	James H. Defuria/Intercontinental Airways, Canastota NY	30.12.58
				Aero Enterprises, Elkhart IN	10.60/61
			N651D	Richard G. Snyder, Tucson AZ	11.61/66
				(mod. wet-wing racer, #45 *Miss Phoebe II*)	
				Michael R. Cuddy, Klamath Falls OR	13.2.66/69
				Bill Kemp Pontiac & Cadillac, Dover DE	30.3.69/71
				Bill Kemp/Kemp Aircraft Corp, Potomac MD	5.4.71/75
				Don Plumb/Spitfire Inc, Windsor ONT	23.1.75
				John Boulton, Sanford FL	21.2.75
				crashed dest., Big Spring TX (Boulton k.)	15.10.75
122-40411	P-51D	**44-73871**		(to RCAF as 9245): BOC 6.12.50: SOC	2.5.56
				crated at Whiteman Air Park CA for Israel	.59
				(to IDFAF as ....)	.59
				Israeli Aircraft Industries	64
			N7098V	Pioneer Aero Service, Burbank CA	22.6.64/70
				Cavalier Aircraft, Sarasota FL	8.9.70/78
				Albert McKinley, Hillsboro OH	14.8.78
				Elmer Ward/Pioneer Aero Service, Chino CA	90/91
				(id rest. Chino CA as TF-51D, ff .91 as "473871/TF-871")	
				Warbirds of GB Ltd, Biggin Hill	.91/92
				(shipped to UK, ff Biggin Hill 19.3.92)	
				struck-off USCR	5.5.94
122-40417 •	P-51D	**44-73877**		(to RCAF as 9279): BOC 23.1.51: SOC	29.4.58
			N6320T (1	James H. Defuria & Fred J. Ritts/ Intercontinental Airways, Canastota NY	25.2.57/60
				Aero Enterprises, Elkhart IN	.60
			CF-PCZ	Neil McClain, Strathmore ALTA	.60/68
			N167F	Paul D. Finefrock, Hobart OK	29.4.68/70
				accident Euless TX (rebuilt)	1.9.69
				Paul D. Finefrock, Brownwood TX	10.70/80
				RLS 51 Ltd, CA	8.80/83
				Anders Saether/RLS 51 Ltd/ op Scandinavian Historic Flight, Oslo Norway	84/95
				(rest. Ft.Collins CO 80/84; del. Oslo 27.6.86)	
				(flies as "473877/*Old Crow*/BS-6")	
122-40442 •	P-51D Cavalier	44-73902		(to FA Guatelmateca as FAG 315)	16.12.54
			N38227	Don Hull, Sugarland TX	8.72
				Wilson C. Edwards, Big Spring TX	78/96
				(USCR quotes 44-77902, FAG 342 also quoted)	
122-40460 •	P-51D	**44-73920**		(to Chinese Nationalist AF as ....)	15.3.46
				(to Chinese AF as "03")	1.10.49
				Military Museum of the Chinese People's Revolution, Beijing: displ. as "03"	87/96
122-40512 •	P-51D	**44-73972**		USAFM, Fresno ANGB, Fresno CA	65/93
122-40513 •	P-51D	**44-73973**		(to RCAF as 9281): BOC 23.1.51: SOC	29.4.58
			N6325T (2	James H. Defuria & Fred J. Ritts/ Intercontinental Airway, Canastota NY	25.2.57/60
				Aero Enterprises, Elkhart IN	10.5.60/62
				Peter Rosi, Notre Dame IN	10.62/63
				Aero Enterprises, Elkhart IN	3.4.63/64
				Farnum Brown, Michigan City IN	4.3.64
				Joseph D. Wade, Houston TX	6.3.64/65

				A. E. Lee, Atlanta GA	10.65/66
				James W. Gentle, Birmingham AL	16.6.66/67
				Wendell K. Trogden, Fort Lauderdale FL	10.8.67/69
				(to FA Salvadorena as FAS......)	7.69/74
			N35DD	ntu: Jack W. Flaherty, Monterey CA	1.11.74
			N37FF	Flaherty Factors Inc, Monterey CA	6.3.75
				(adopted id. 44-10755 on return to USA)	
			N51JC	Jerry C. Janes, Vancouver BC	14.8.75/79
				(composite: ex FAS aircraft;	
				rebuilt Chelan WA 76/77, del. Vancouver 1.78)	
			C-GJCJ (1	Jerry C. Janes/Grabber Screw Products,	
				Vancouver BC	11.79/83
			N51JC	David G. Price, Los Angeles CA	11.83
			N151DP	David G. Price, Santa Monica CA	1.84/96
				(race #49 *Cottonmouth*)	
122-40519 •	P-51D	**44-73979**		(to RCAF as 9246): BOC 6.12.50: SOC	16.5.51
				accident, grounded in RCAF service	16.5.51
				conv. to Instructional Airframe A-612	10.5.55
				College Militaire Royale, St Jean QUE	.55
				RCAF St Jean QUE: gate guard	60
				Imperial War Museum, Duxford UK	6.72/89
				Imperial War Museum, Lambeth, London	.89/96
				(displ. as "472258/WZ-I/*Big Beautiful Doll*")	
122-40530 •	P-51D	**44-73990**		(to RCAF as 9282): BOC 23.1.51: SOC	14.5.59
			N8674E	James H. Defuria/Intercontinental Airways,	
				Canastota NY	27.2.59/60
				Aero Enterprises, Elkhart IN	18.6.60
				Kieran Aviation Sales, Birmingham AL	14.8.60/62
				Jack Adams Aircraft Sales, Walls MS	3.2.62
				T. E. Guillot/Jackson Dental, Jackson MS	5.62
				Robert Graf, Tarkio MO	13.8.62/65
				Leonard A.Tanner/Tan Air Industries Inc,	
				North Granby CT	19.1.65/70
			N51LT	Len Tanner, North Granby CT	72/73
			N2116 (2	ntu: John P. Silberman, Sherborn MA	8.4.73
				crashed, struck car landing, Yanceyville NC	6.9.73
			N51LT	Len Tanner, North Granby CT	18.3.75/79
				(rebuilt, using parts from A68-175/N64824)	
			N51TH	Tom W. Henley, Emelle AL	8.1.79/96
122-40548	P-51D	44-74008		(to RCAF as 9274): BOC 11.1.51: SOC	14.5.59
			N8676E	James H. Defuria/Intercontinental Airways,	
				Canastota NY	27.2.59/60
				M. N. Bostick, Waco TX	24.6.60/66
				Courtesy Aircraft, Loves Park IL	16.12.69
				Richard W. Foote/Automatic Business	
				Products Inc, Hartford CT (race #51, #71)	20.1.69/73
			N76AF	C. G. Kreuger/ North American Flyers,	
				Brookfield CT,	12.73/74
				John Crumlish, Southbury CT	74/75
				crashed, Marthas Vineyard CT (Crumlish k.)	8.6.75
			N151MC	Mark D. Clark, Rockford IL : wreck	7.78/83
				Ronald M. Runyan, Fairfield OH : minor parts	83
				(id. tfd. to 44-73339/N51RR: que se)	
122-40549 •	P-51D	44-74009		(to RCAF as 9275): BOC 11.1.51: SOC	17.9.57
			N6323T (1	James H. Defuria & Fred J. Ritts/	
				Intercontinental Airways, Canastota NY	25.2.57/60
			N988C	Aero Enterprises, Elkhart IN	1.5.60/61
				SuncoastAviation, St. Petersburg FL	8.7.61/62
				A. Fasken, Midland TX	29.9.62/63
				Houston Aircraft Sales, Houston TX	1.5.63/65
				William Fiore, Clairton PA	30.4.65/68
				Frank Cannavo Jr, Lester PA	3.2.68/69
				Robert J. Shaver, Brigantine & Linwood NJ	26.6.69/79
				Robert L. Ferguson, Wellesley MA	4.79/96
				(flies as *Ain't Misbehavin*/RL-F)	

122-40552 •	P-51D	**44-74012**		(to RCAF as 9243): BOC 6.12.50: SOC	17.8.59
			N6518D (1	James H. Defuria/Intercontinental Airways, Canastota NY	21.7.58/60
				Aero Enterprises, Elkhart IN	15.8.60/63
				(N6518D/19D painted on incorrect airframes!)	
			N6519D (2	Jerry McCutchin, Dallas TX	10.63/64
				Gordon Travis/River Oaks Aircraft & Engine Brokers, Fort Worth TX	9.12.64/66
				Robert R. Redding, Houston TX	13.6.66/68
				Leroy B. Penhall, Anaheim CA (race #81)	4.11.68/75
				crashed, forced landing, Hudson WI	4.8.74
				Gordon W. Plaskett, King City CA: wreck	30.9.75
			C-GPSI (1	Robert H. Jens/Executive Air Craft Ltd, Vancouver BC (rebuild: not completed)	27.9.76/84
			N6519D (2	Duane Williams, Kellogg ID: rebuild	2.84/87
				James E. Smith, Fortine MT	9.87/96
122-40742 •	P-51D	**44-74202**	**N5420V**	Michael E. Coutches, Hayward CA	12.66/83
				Mike Bogue, Oakland CA	84/87
				Michael E. Coutches, Hayward CA	90/96
122-40744	P-51D	44-74204	N5451V	Robert F. Deweese, Newport Beach CA	63/64
				David S. Salerno, Santa Ana CA	66/70
			N51U	David S. Salerno, Santa Ana CA	72
				George Enhorning/Wolcott Air Service, Wolcott CT	78/90
				(race #51 413691/*Passion Wagon*)	
				crashed, dest., Cape Cod MA (Enhorning k.)	29.9.90
				William A. Speer, La Mesa CA	25.3.93/94
				(rebuilt as race #56 *Deja Vu*)	
				crashed , Reno NV (Bill Speer k.)	12.9.94
122-40756 •	P-51D	**44-74216**		USAFM, USS Alabama Battleship Memorial, Mobile AL	74/94
				(displ. in camouflage, sharks mouth, as "13")	
122-40769 •	P-51D Cavalier	**44-74229**		(to Indonesian AF/TNI-AU as F-362)	
				Indonesian AF HQ, Jakarta: displ. on pole	90/93
122-40770 •	P-51D	**44-74230**	**N5466V**	Robert G. Bixler, San Jose CA	63/64
				C. L. Caprioglio, Fresno CA	66
				Frank R. Davis, Beaverton OR	69/70
				United States National Bank, Beaverton OR	72
				David Norland, Denver CO (race #76)	73/89
				James F. Norland, Wasilla AK	90/92
				David M. Norland, Denver CO	5.94/96
122-40802 •	P-51D	**44-74262**	**N515J**	C. H. Henderson: reg. candidate	7.92
				J. A. Milender, Fort Mojave AZ	11.92/96
122-40851 •	P-51D	**44-74311**		(to RCAF as 9577): BOC 7.6.47: SOC	27.12.57
				James H. Defuria & Fred J. Ritts/ Intercontinental Airways, Canastota NY	11.56/60
				Aero Enterprises, Elkhart IN: stored crated	.60/62
				Louis Hecklesberg, Bartlesville OK: stored	.62/84
			C-GPSI (2	Ritchie Rasmussen/Trans-Am Helicopters, Edmonton ALTA	2.85/91
				(rest., stored Edmonton ALTA)	
122-40931 •	P-51D Cavalier	**44-74391**		(to FA Guatelmateca as FAG 351)	
			N38229	Don Hull, Sugarland TX	8.72
				Wilson C. Edwards, Big Spring TX	78/96
122-40944 •	P-51D	**44-74404**		(to RCAF as 9276): BOC 11.1.51: SOC	27.12.57
			N4132A(1	James H. Defuria & Fred J. Ritts/ Intercontinental Airways, Canastota NY	11.56/60
				M. L. Alson/Aero Enterprises, Elkhart IN	60
				crashed landing, Elkhart IN	

				Gary Harris, Half Moon Bay CA: fuse. only	74/88
				William A. Spear, San Diego CA: rest. project	
				Gerald S. Beck/Tri-State Aviation, Wahpeton ND: rest. project	90
			N7129E	Robert J. Odegaard, Kindred ND	9.90/94
			N151RJ	Robert J. Odegaard, Kindred ND	9.9.94/96
				(rest. project Kindred 90/95, ff .95)	
122-40947 •	P-51D	**44-74407**		USAFM, Hector Field ANGB, Fargo ND	65/96
				(displ. on pole as "NDAK ANG 474407")	
122-40949 •	P-51D	**44-74409**		(to RCAF as 9235): BOC 6.12.50: SOC	30.12.58
			N6319T	James H. Defuria & Fred J. Ritts/ Intercontinental Airways, Canastota NY	12.58/60
				Aero Enterprises, Elkhart IN	20.10.60
				J. H. Cunningham, Lexington NC	14.7.61/62
				Dean J. Ortner, Wakeman OH	19.8.62/68
				Joe Bruce, Palm Springs CA	15.5.68
				Cavalier Aircraft Corp, Sarasota FL	3.6.68/69
				Clint R. Hackney, Friendswood TX	11.4.69/71
				Frank D. Strickler, Denton TX	2.11.71/77
			N4409	Frank D. Strickler, Grapevine TX	30.12.77
				Peter Bottome, Caracas, Venezuela	.81
			N555BM	Gordon W. Plaskett, King City CA	1.81/82
				(rest. King City CA 81/84 as *Barbara M 4th*)	
			YV-508CP	Peter Bottome, Caracas	.82/90
				Robert C. Tullius, Winchester VA: del.	12.90
			N555BM	Robert C. Tullius, Winchester VA	3.91
			N51RT	Robert Tullius/Group 44 Inc, Winchester VA	9.4.91/95
				(flies as "413317/VF-B/*Donald Duck*)	
122-40957 •	P-51D	**44-74417**		(to RCAF as 9586): BOC 2.11.50: SOC	1.11.60
			CF-MWB	James H. Defuria/Intercontinental Airways, Canastota NY	12.58/60
			N6327T	Aero Enterprises, Elkhart IN	10.5.60/63
				Garland R. Brown, Freeland MI/Ft.Wayne IN	16.2.63/87
				crashed Fort Wayne IN (repaired)	4.8.66
				Robert Byrne, Bloomfield Hills MI	.87/89
				Richard P. James, Fennimore WI	9.89/96
				(flies as "472197/FF-197/*Tabasco*)	
122-40963 •	P-51D	**44-74423**		(to RCAF as 9595): BOC 8.11.50: SOC	14.8.59
			N6517D	James H. Defuria/Intercontinental Airways, Canastota NY	21.7.58/59
				Madison Aviation Corp, Canastota NY	11.11.59
				Naylor Aviation Inc, Clinton MD	12.11.59
			N182XF	North American Maritime Corp,Cambridge MA	11.59/62
				Hamilton Aircraft Co, Tucson AZ	2.10.62
				Hillcrest Aviation Industries, Lewiston ID	1.11.62/64
				California Airmotive Corp, Burbank CA	1.5.64/70
				(op. by Clay Lacy, race #64)	
			N64CL	H. Clay Lacy, Van Nuys CA (race #64)	70/96
				(note: FAA changed id. to "10216" .67;	
122-40965 •	P-51D	**44-74425**		(to RCAF as 9591): BOC 8.11.50: SOC	29.4.58
			N6522D	James H. Defuria & Fred J. Ritts/ Intercontinental Airways, Canastota NY	25.2.57/59
				Madison Aviation Corp, Canastota NY	20.10.59
				Naylor Aviation, Clinton MD	10.59/63
				Frank J. Capone/Bonanza Inc, Broomall PA	3.1.63/64
				Eli Graubart/Graubart Aviation, Valparaiso IN	25.6.64
				Joseph W. Bohmeir/New London Airport, New London PA	27.7.64
				James Fugate, Oswego OR	30.9.64
				R. A. Hanson Co, Palouse WA	8.12.64/66
				Charles P. Harral/Superstition Air Service, Mesa-Falcon Field AZ	6.1.66/68
				Larry N. Mitchell, Hopkinsville KY	10.68/71
			N51HB	ntu: Harold F. Beal, Concord TN	18.6.71

C/n	Type	Identity	Reg.	History	Date
			N6522D	Jack W. Flaherty/Flaherty Factors Inc,	
				Monterey CA	1.9.71
				Harold F. Beal, Concord TN	72
				dam. landing, Knoxville TN	10.72
			N11T	John Herlihy, Half Moon Bay CA (race #8)	.73
				ground collision, Half Moon Bay CA	10.11.74
				Johnny Bolton Ford Inc, Maitland FL	3.9.75
				Pete Sherman Exotic Cars, Maitland FL	2.3.76/78
				Ben R. Bradley, Oakland Park FL	11.1.78
				Gordon W. Plaskett, King City CA	.81/82
				dam., forced landing, Piedmont OK	23.10.82
				Bob Amyx, Oklahoma City OK	83
				Robert Byrne, Bloomfield MI	84/85
				WW II Enterprises Inc, Scotch Plains NJ	87/88
				John Goltra, Scotch Plains NJ	89
				Bill Woods/Western Wings Aircraft Sales Co,	
				Oakland OR	.89
				Robert J. Pond/Planes of Fame East,	
				Minneapolis-Flying Cloud MN	90/92
				Bill Klaers/Klaers Aviation, Rialto CA	
				Western Aviation Maintenance Inc, Mesa AZ	.94/95
				op: Stichting Dutch Mustang Flight, Lelystad	4.94/96
				(shipped to Netherlands, arr. dism. Lelystad 6.4.94,	
				ff 8.4.94 in Holland as "474425/OC-G/*Damn Yankee*)	
122-40967 •	P-51D Cavalier	**44-74427**		(to RCAF as 9592): BOC 8.11.50: SOC	15.10.59
			N9148R	Trans Florida Aviation, Sarasota FL	20.5.59/62
			N2251D	Robert A. Hoover/North American Aviation,	
				El Segundo CA	19.3.62/67
				dam. accident, Myrtle Beach FL (repaired)	20.1.65
				North American Rockwell Corp, Los Angles CA	10.67/70
				badly dam., ground explosion, Oshkosh WI	9.8.70
				Steve Shulke & John B. Bolton, Maitland FL	.70/75
				(rebuilt Chattanooga TN, using components of	
				N130JT/44-74435, flew as *Doc's Doll*)	
				John J. Stokes, San Marcos TX	6.8.75/78
				John T. Baugh/Baugh Aviation, Nashville TN	10.1.78/89
				(flew as *Miss Coronado*/JT-B)	
				Paul C. Romine, Indianapolis IN	90/94
				Brian Hoffner/Kenair Inc, West Palm Beach FL	18.8.94/95
				(flies as "411622/G4-C/*Nooky Booky IV*)	
122-40970	P-51D	44-74430		(to RCAF as 9588): BOC 8.11.50: SOC	14.5.59
			N8673E	James H. Defuria/Intercontinental Airways,	
					Canastota NY
27.2.59/60				Aero Enterprises, Elkhart IN	18.6.60/61
				John Hibbard, Corcoran CA	3.3.61/62
				Gerald T. Smith, Bakersfield CA	13.4.62/63
				Ronald A. Hevle, Bakersfield CA	23.1.63/64
				Glenn Johnson Realty, Sacramento CA	16.9.64/65
				Leland F. Spalding, Sacramento CA	13.2.65
				Robert J. Love, San Jose CA	11.5.65
			YS-149P	Robert J. Love, El Salvador	.65/67
			TG-REI	Roberto & Enrique Ibarguen, Quezaltenango	.67/78
			N2265P	William Harrison & Terry Randall/	
				HarRan Aircraft Sales, Muskogee OK	5.78
			N52HA	Lynn Florey, Eden Prairie MN	5.6.78
				crashed Tuxtla Gutierrez, Mexico on del.	
				flight to USA (pilot Burns Byram k.)	5.6.78
122-40975 •	P-51D	**44-74435**		(to RCAF as 9221): BOC 15.11.50: SOC	29.4.58
				James H. Defuria & Fred J. Ritts/	
				Intercontinental Airways, Canastota NY	29.4.58
				Aero Enterprises, Elkhart IN	60
			CF-LOQ	Lynn Garrison, Calgary ALTA	26.9.61/63
				Gerald W. Wolton, Calgary ALTA	13.3.63/66
			N130JT	John W. Temple, Signal Mountain TN	26.4.66/70
				crashed, minor dam., Calgary ALTA (rebuilt)	29.4.66

				crashed, badly dam.	23.10.70
				(parts used in rebuild N2251D/44-74427 .70)	
				James J. Chernich, Lake Zurich IL	20.2.76/95
122-40981	P-51D Cavalier	44-74441		(to RCAF as 9593): BOC 8.11.50: SOC	15.10.59
			N9149R	Trans Florida Aviation, Sarasota FL	20.5.59/62
		2000		J. W. (Bill) Fornof/Fornof Motor Co, Houma LA	4.8.62/72
				G. R. Dunagan/Crawford & Co, Atlanta GA	14.3.72
				crashed, dest., Gainesville FL	30.12.72
122-40985 •	P-51D	**44-74445**		(to RCAF as 9594): BOC 8.11.50: SOC	4.12.56
			N4143A	Stinson Field Aircraft, San Antonio TX	10.56/57
				Truman E. Miley/Big Piney Aviation, Roy UT	3.5.57/59
			N4132A(2	M. L. Alson/Aero Enterprises Inc, Elkhart IN	1.10.59/61
				George E. Monea & Mario I. Corbi, Alliance OH	5.8.61/62
				Harold J. Shelton, Belle Fourche SD	28.3.62
				Grazing Inc, Alzada MT (cloud seeding mods)	9.5.62
				M. L. Alson/Aero Enterprises, Elkhart IN	10.62
				Richardson Construction Co, Sterling VA	2.11.62
				Harold L. Barkman, Indianapolis IN	15.1.63/67
				John E. Dilley, Auburn IN	11.67/69
				Bill H. Hubbs, Pecos TX (race #71)	5.5.69/95
122-40986 •	P-51D	**44-74446**		(to RCAF as 9223): BOC 15.11.50: SOC	1.11.60
				James H. Defuria/Intercontinental Airways, Canastota NY	30.12.58
				Aero Enterprises, Elkhart IN	.60
			CF-LOR	Milt Harradance, Calgary ALTA	.60/65
				Gary L. Oates, Weston ONT	.65/66
				Gary L. Oates & Mike Malagies, Toronto ONT	.68/69
				Froates Aviation, Toronto ONT	.69/70
				Howard A. Sloan	20.8.70
				John W. Temple & R. L. Robertson TN	6.11.70
			N1451D(2	John W. Temple, Signal Mountain TN	14.3.75
				John J. Stokes/Cen-Tex Aviation, San Marcos TX	13.11.75
				Cecil H. Harp, Lodi CA	12.1.76/78
				Michael Clarke, Phoenix AZ/Prescott AZ	26.3.78/92
				(flew as "Unruly Julie/MX-C")	
				dam. forced landing, AZ	9.87
				(rebuilt Chino CA 88/94, ff 4.4.94)	
				crashed, forced landing, near Chino CA	4.4.94
				William A. Speer, La Mesa CA: wreck	4.94
				Brian O'Farrell, Miami, Florida	95/96
122-40992 •	P-51D	**44-74452**		(to RCAF as 9225): BOC 15.11.50: SOC	29.4.58
				James H. Defuria & Fred J. Ritts/ Intercontinental Airways, Canastota NY	29.4.58/59
				(noted stored unconv., Canastota NY 7.59)	
				(to FA Guatelmateca as FAG 366)	3.62/72
			N74190	Don Hull, Sugarland TX	8.72/76
				Wilson C. Edwards, Big Spring TX	.76/96
				(USCR quotes incorrect id. 44-75452)	
122-40993 •	P-51D Cavalier	**44-74453**		(to RCAF as 9597): BOC 8.11.50: SOC	15.10.59
			N9150R	Trans Florida Aviation, Sarasota FL	20.5.59/60
			N1335	E. D. Weiner, Los Angles CA	29.7.60/61
				Margaret & Frank Woodside, Lubbock TX	10.61/62
				Aero Enterprises, Elkhart IN	12.3.62/63
				John M. Barker, Indianapolis IN	25.2.63/70
				crashed landing, Indianapolis IN (Barker k.)	17.3.63
				Bill Destafani, Shafter CA: wreck	81/84
				(rebuild Shafter, rep. using TNI-AU airframe, adopted id. 44-13903)	
			C-GJCJ (2	Jerry C. Janes, Vancouver BC	87/89
			N151JP	James R. Priebe, Findlay OH	88/92
				(flies as *Glamorous Jan*)	
			N251HR	Kipnis Inc, Dover DE	5.93/95
				(N151JP/N251HR id. quoted as "44-13903JP")	

122-	P-51D	**44-74458**		(to RCAF as 9226): BOC 15.11.50: SOC	15.10.59
40998 •	Cavalier		N9145R	Trans Florida Aviation, Sarasota FL	20.5.59/61
				Marine Maintenance Co, Galveston TX	10.1.61
				Lorraine P. Bodine, Texas City TX	28.2.61/62
				Aero Enterprises Inc, Elkhart IN	21.8.62
				crashed in cornfield, near Elkhart IN	9.3.63
				Dave Zeuschel & Mike Geren CA: wreck	
				Aerospace Modifications, Van Nuys CA	.70
				(rebuild Van Nuys CA to TP-51 config. 70)	
				John Marlin, Los Angeles CA	71
			N65206	John Marlin	.73/87
				(rebuild Compton CA 71/77, ff .77 as race #17	
				Green Machine")	
			N351DM	David Marco/Barnstormers Aviation,	
				Jacksonville FL	2.88/96
				(dism. Chino, trucked to Ft. Lauderdale FL .88,	
				rest. 88/91 as "415326/QP-H/*Sizzlin' Liz*)	
122-	P-51D	**44-74466**		(to RCAF as 9227): BOC 15.11.50: SOC	4.1.56
41006 •			**N10607**	Stinson Field Aircraft, San Antonio TX	26.10.56
				George D. Hanby, Evanston IL	27.2.57
				Thermal Belt Air Service, Tryon NC	12.5.57
				Northrop Carolina Inc, Ashville NC	3.8.57
				George D. Hanby, Philadephia PA	63/69
				John M. Sliker, Wadley GA	19.3.69/76
				(race #17 "*Escape*")	
				Madelaine H. Sliker, Wadley GA	24.3.76/84
				Wiley C. Sanders, Troy AL	85/92
				crashed Reno NV (rebuilt)	14.9.85
				(race #69 *Georgia Mae*)	
				Parmley Aviation Services, Council Bluffs IA	12.93/96
122-	P-51D	**44-74469**	N7723C	Trans Florida Aviation, Sarasota FL	.58/60
41009 •	Cavalier			(to FA Dominicana as FAD 1919)	.60/84
	Mk. 2			Brian O'Farrell/Johnson Aviation, Miami FL	19.5.84
				(recov. ex Dominican Republic to Miami .84)	
			N7723C	Jerry Miles/Fighterbirds West, Riverbend AZ	.86/90
				(rest. Chino CA, ff 13.9.87)	
				Classic Air Parts, Miami FL	92
				struck-off USCR	27.1.93
122-	P-51D	**44-74474**		(to RCAF as 9270): BOC 11.1.51: SOC	20.9.60
41014 •			N6341T	James H. DeFuria & Fred J. Ritts/	
				Intercontinental Airways, Canastota NY	11.56/60
				(stored unconv., Carberry MAN 57/61)	
				Aero Enterprises, Elkhart IN	10.5.60/62
				(ferried Carberry-Winnipeg-Elkhart 7.62)	
				Margaret Kahlow, Madisonville KY	27.8.62/65
				William L. Sullivan/Audubon Service Inc,	
				Henderson KY	12.6.65/70
				TAS Flight Services, Granville OH	29.7.70/71
				A. C. Lofgren, Hickory Corners MI	3.11.71/81
				Bob Byrne Aviation, Bloomfield Hills MI	.81/92
				Rousch Technologies Inc, Livonia MI	26.9.94/95
			N51RZ	Rousch Technologies Inc, Livonia MI: reg. res.	12.94
				(flies as "474774/*Rascal*)	
				(USCR quotes id. 44-74774)	
122-	P-51D	**44-74483**		(to RCAF as 9228): BOC 15.11.50: SOC	17.8.59
41023 •			N6523D	James H. Defuria/Intercontinental Airways,	
				Canastota NY	21.7.58
				minor damage, Basking Ridge NJ	4.2.60
				Robert J. Hartland/Dogwood Inc, Summit NJ	7.7.60/61
				Stencel Aero Engineering Corp, Ashville NC	17.2.61
				W. R. Lowdermilk, Greenville SC	25.9.62/64
				Airplanes Inc, Fort Worth TX	31.10.64
				John H. Herlihy, San Meteo CA	11.65/66

				George Perez, Daly City CA (race #8)	5.12.66/72
			N51GP	George Perez, Sonoma CA/Anchorage AK	77/96
122-41034 •	P-51D	**44-74494**		(to RCAF as 9237): BOC 6.12.50: SOC	1.11.60
			N6313T(1	ntu: James H. Defuria/Intercontinental Airways, Canastota NY	12.58/60
				(ferried to USA as N6313T but not reg.)	
			N6356T	Aero Enterprises, Elkhart IN	10.5.60/63
				Capital Steel, Baton Rouge LA	13.6.63/64
				Aero Enterprises, Elkart IN	20.3.64
				Benjamin B. Peck/Interocean Airways, Luxembourg & Munich WG	20.2.64/66
				(del. US to Luxembourg, arr. 28.7.64)	
				Charles Masefield, Shoreham UK	8.66/70
				(dep. Shoreham for Spain 15.1.69, for film *Patton*, painted as USAAF "643147")	
				Ed A. Jurist/Vintage Car Store, Nyack NY	15.3.70/72
				(shipped to USA 1.71, flew as "415271/OC-E")	
				Ed A. Jurist/Vintage Aircraft International, Brownwood TX	27.2.72/75
				MARC, Chino CA	3.75/79
				Wally McDonnell, Mojave CA	.79
				Bill Destefani, Bakersfield CA	.79/81
			N72FT	Bill Destefani, Shafter CA	1.81/87
				(race #72 "*Mangia Pane*/474494/LH-D")	
				Vintage Aircraft Inc, Mountain View CA	9.87/95
				(flies as "411661/*Iron Ass*)	
122-41037 •	P-51D	**44-74497**		(to RCAF as 9230): BOC 15.11.50: SOC	1.11.60
			N6320T(2	James H. Defuria/Intercontinental Airways, Canastota NY	30.12.58
				Aero Enterprises, Elkhart IN	60
				Ralph W. Rensink, Lewiston ID	10.1.62/66
				Kenneth W. Neal, Medford OR	26.3.66/70
				crashed Lancaster CA	2.8.69
				Glenn Cook, Seattle WA	26.1.70
				Mike Smith, Johnson KS	.70/72
				(trucked Seattle-Johnson KS, rebuilt: ff 3.71)	
				I. N. ("Junior") Burchinall, Paris TX	14.11.72
				Kent Jones, Dallas TX	3.1.73/75
				John Rutherford, Fort Worth TX	11.75/79
				Heritage Aircraft Inc, Fayetteville GA	7.79/95
				(flies as "415080/QI-B/*Vergeltungswaffe*")	
122-41042 •	P-51D	**44-74502**		(to RCAF as 9232): BOC 6.12.50: SOC	1.11.60
			CF-MWC	James H. Defuria/Intercontinetal Airways, Canastota NY	30.12.58
			N6321T	Aero Enterprises, Elkhart IN	60
				rep. seized en route to Cuba	.62
				Otha D. Aishman, Salina KS	20.7.62/64
				Edward Fisher Flying Service, Kansas City KS	2.7.64/73
				Leroy Penhall, Balboa CA (race #33)	21.8.73
				Military Aircraft International Inc, Miami FL	2.11.73
			N70QF	Ken Burnstine (race #34 "Miss Foxy Lady")	76
				M. D. Pruitt Furniture Co, Phoenix AZ	5.3.76
				Gary Levitz/Western Aircraft Leasing, Scottsdale AZ	4.6.76
			N51VC	John V. Crocker, Oakland CA, Ione CA	3.8.76/95
				(race #6 "*Sumthin Else*")	
				landing accident , Seattle WA	7.90
122-41045 •	P-51D	**44-74505**		(to RCAF as 9233): BOC 6.12.50: SOC	7.12.56
			N3990A	Stinson Field Aircraft, San Antonio TX	26.10.56
				Jack Adams Aircraft Sales, Memphis TN	.56/57
				Pat Moore, Hutchinson KS	15.11.57
			N68DR	David B. Robinson, Miami FL	6.1.58
				Allen McDonald, Miami Springs FL	20.11.58
				(to FA Rebelde (Cuba) as FAR401): del.	11.58
				(to FA Revolucionaria (Cuba) as .....)	
				Museum de la Revolucionaria, Playa Giron,	

				Havana: displ. as "FAR 401"	63/96
				(note: FAR-401 prev. rep. as 44-73978/N89E)	
122-41046 •	P-51D	**44-74506**		(to RCAF as 9231): BOC 6.12.50: SOC	1.12.60
			CF-MWM	James H. Defuria & Fred J. Ritts/	
				Intercontinental Airways, Canastota NY	30.12.58
			N6325T	ntu: Aero Enterprises, Elkhart IN	60
				(ferried to Elkhart as N6325T, but not reg.)	
			N6317T	Aero Enterprises, Elkhart IN	60
			N335J (3	Ed Weiner, Los Angeles CA (race #14, #49)	24.3.63/73
				Violet M. Bonzer, Los Angeles CA	8.5.73/79
				loan: EAA Museum, Hales Corner WI : del.	.73/79
				Max R. Hoffman, Fort Collins CO	.79
				Wolcott Air Services, Wolcott CT	80
				Gary Norton/Norton Aero, Athol ID	82/90
				Sierra Aviation, Boardman OH	92
				(flies as "474832/GA-N")	
				struck-off USCR	5.93
			F-AZJJ	Rene Bouverat/Ste. Air B Aviation, Chamberg, France	12.8.93/96
122-41076 •	P-51D	**44-74536**	N5452V (1	Donald G. Singleton, Van Nuys CA (race #19)	63/64
				David S. Allender, San Aario CA	66
			N991RC	Robert N. Cleaves	69
				Keefe Corp, Pacific Palisades CA	6.69
			N991R	Howie Keefe/Keefe Corp, Van Nuys CA	70/78
				(race #11 *Miss America*)	
				Ron & Janette Smythe, Everett WA	.83/84
				RGS Incorporated, Edmonds WA	85/88
				Hanover Aero Inc, Nashua NH	6.89/92
				Brent N. Hisey, Oklahoma City OK	9.93/96
122-41083	P-51D	**44-74543**		(to RCAF as 9252): BOC 6.12.50: SOC	17.9.57
				James H. Defuria & Fred J. Ritts/	
				Intercontinental Airways, Canastota NY	25.2.57
				(ferried to Canastota NY .57, open storage)	
				Ray O. Denman, Brewerton NY: as scrap	28.6.61/65
				Richard M. Vartanian, Pasadena CA	30.6.65
				(trucked from Canastota 6.74, stored dism.	
				Brewerton & Johnstown NY 80/82)	
			N4543	Richard M. Vartanian, Los Angeles CA	78/95
				(rep. used in rebuild Chicago IL .90, adopting id.	
				44-63655/N5500S)	
122-41122 •	P-51D	**44-74582**		(to RCAF as 9253): BOC 6.12.50: SOC	19.8.59
			N6524D	James H. Defuria/Intercontinental Airways,	
				Canastota NY	21.7.58
			N6329T	Aero Enterprises, Elkhart IN	11.60/61
				A. G. Ainsworth/A-Mack Co, Luling TX	10.61/63
				Landon Cullum, Wichita Falls TX	14.3.63/84
				John C. Hooper, Harvey LA	.84/87
				Robert Byrne, Bloomfield Hills MI	88/90
			N51JT	ntu: Joseph H. Thibodeau, Denver CO	2.91
			N6329T	Joseph H. Thibodeau, Denver CO	1.91/96
122-41140	P-51D	44-74600		Trottner Iron & Metal Co, San Antonio TX	.49
			N1739B	Dal-Air, Dallas-Love Field TX	.51
				(to FA Haiti as 74600, later 600): del.	4.51
				(to FA Dominicana): for disposal	c73
				rep. to Cavalier Aircraft Corp, Sarasota FL	c73
				rep. to Gordon Plaskett, King City CA	c73
				Robert J. Bleeg, Mercer Island WA	85
			N512ED	Robert J. Bleeg, Mercer Island WA	6.87/89
				(rest., ff 7.10.87 as "474600/E2-D")	
				Robert J. Pond, Plymouth MN	5.90/95
				crashed near Flying Cloud MN	18.6.90
122-41142 •	P-51D	**44-74602**		(to RCAF as 9255): BOC 6.12.50: SOC	1.11.60
			N6318T	James H. Defuria/Intercontinental Airways,	

				Canastota NY	30.12.58
				Aero Enterprises, Elkhart IN	19.8.61
				Robert E. King, South Bend IN	11.61/63
				Aero Enterprises, Elkhart IN	27.3.63
			N35N	C. E. Crosby, Bellingham WA	20.5.63/67
				(race #3 *Mr Choppers*)	
			N3580	Jack C. Hovey/Hovey Machine Products,	
				Walnut Creek CA, later Oakland CA	10.7.67/95
				Jack C. Hovey/Hovey Machine Products, Ione, CA	96
				(race #2 "HM-P")	
122-41167 •	P-51D	**44-74627**		(to Philippines AF as 73373)	
				Basa AB Philippines: displ.	77/96
				(displ. as 3733/001/*Shark of Zimbales*)	
122-41234	P-51D Cavalier 2000	44-74694		sold surplus at McClellan AFB CA	15.8.58
			N7720C	Marshall H. Ratliffe, Battle Creek MI	63
				Samuel T. Whatley, Mt Clemens MI	.63/64
			N16S	Louis H. Long, Aberdeen SD	66
			N6851D	Jerry Tyler, Ellenton FL	
				Cavalier Aircraft Corp, Sarasota FL	
				(del. to Italy via Shannon 8.12.68)	
			I-BILL	Ditta Billi & Co, Florence	5.69/77
				Ormond Haydon-Baillie, Duxford, UK	6.77
				cr. Mainz-Finthen, Germany(Haydon-Baillie k)	3.7.77
122-41279 •	P-51D Cavalier	**44-74739**		(to RCAF as 9297): BOC 16.3.51: SOC	14.5.59
			N8672E	James H. Defuria/Intercontinental Airways,	
				Canastota NY	27.2.59/60
				Aero Enterprises, Elkhart IN	18.6.60/61
				Midwest Airways, Cincinatti OH	10.5.61/62
				(Cavalier conv. by Trans Florida Aviation 4.62)	
			N151Q	Aerial Services Inc, London OH	10.62/63
				Valair Aircraft, Cincinatti OH	23.5.63
				E. R. Cantrell/Angels Aviation, Zephyrhills FL	30.5.63/64
				Space Systems Laboratory Inc, Melbourne FL	3.7.64/67
				Trans Florida Aviation Inc, Sarasota FL	28.3.67
				Cavalier Aircraft Corp, Sarasota FL	4.8.67/71
				(remanufactured as Cavalier .71)	
			N51RH	Robert A. Hoover/North American Rockwell	
				Corp, El Segundo CA	8.5.71
				Robert A. Hoover/Rockwell International,	
				El Segundo CA	74/85
				dam., wing fire, Marysville OH (repaired)	8.9.84
				Robert A. Hoover, Los Angeles CA	8.86/95
122-41296	P-51D	44-74756	N5443V	Elmo C. Johnson, Hunsville AL	63/64
			N2112	J. J. Tururek Manufacturing Co, Chicago IL	66
				William D. Ross, Chicago IL	67
				Leasing Consultants Inc, Forest Hills NY	69/70
			N69QF	Ken Burnstine	73/76
				(race #33 "Miss Suzy Q")	
				crashed, dest., Mojave CA (Burnstine k)	16.6.76
122-41353 •	P-51D	**44-74813**		(to RCAF as 9261): BOC 10.1.51: SOC	17.8.59
			N6301T	James H. Defuria/Intercontinental Airways,	
				Canastota NY	21.7.58
				rep. crashed and dest., Canastota NY	27.6.60
				Aero Enterprises, Elkhart IN	30.8.60
				D.C. Mullery, Chicago IL	11.62/66
				Richard D. Burns, Hinsdale IL	28.9.66/87
				John D. Rodgers, Rockford IL	.87/89
				Richard D. Burns, Hinsdale IL	90/92
				Jack D. Rodgers, Rockford IL	6.93/95
				op: Air Classics Aircraft Museum, DuPage IL	95
				(flies as "*Cripes a' Mighty IV*")	
122-41367 •	P-51D Cavalier	**44-74827** **72-1541**		Trans Florida Aviation, Sarasota FL (stored)	58/66
				Cavalier Aircraft Corp, Sarasota FL	66

				(to Indonesian AF/TNI-AU as F-367)	.68/76
				(stored Bandung AB, Indonesia 76/85)	
				RNZAF Museum, Wigram AB NZ	.85/95
				(displ. as "RNZAF NZ2410")	
122-41369 •	P-51D	**44-74829**		(to RCAF as 9265): BOC 10.1.51: SOC	14.5.59
				N8675EJames H. Defuria/Intercontinental Airways, Canastota NY	27.2.59/60
				(stored Winnipeg MAN, ferried to USA .59)	
				Aero Enterprises, Elkhart IN	18.6.60
			N169MD(1	Dr. Burns M. Byram, Marengo IA	18.8.60/66
				crashed, night fcd. ldg. near Des Moines IA: Byram unhurt, passenger bailed out	6.4.67
			N769MD	John E. Dilley, Muncie IN	11.1.68/73
				Max I. Ramsay, Johnson KS	10.1.73/78
				(noted stored dism., Chino CA 77; used in rebuild of 45-11558/N6175C at Chino .79)	
				Fort Wayne Air Service/Consolidated Airways, Fort Wayne IN	81/84
				(rebuilt Ft.Wayne 81/84 as composite, using ex TNI-AU P51D: ff 13.11.84)	
				Tim Wallis/Alpine Helicopters, Wanaka NZ	.84
			ZK-TAF	Tim Wallis/Alpine Deer Group, Wanaka	27.5.86/89
				(shipped to NZ, ff 23.1.85; flies as "NZ2415")	
				NZ Historic Aircraft Trust, Ardmore	89/96
122-41372	P-51D	**44-74832**		(to RCAF as 9269): BOC 10.1.51: SOC	1.11.60
			CF-MWT	James H. Defuria/Intercontinental Airways, Canastota NY	30.12.58
			N6310T (1	James H. Defuria, Canastota NY	60
				Aero Enterprises, Elkhart IN	10.5.60
				Clyde C. Werner, Elkhart IN	17.6.61/68
				Courtesy Aircraft, Loves Park IL	5.6.68
				William J. Allen, Greensboro NC	13.9.68/69
				Tifton Air Services, Tifton GA	7.6.69/71
				Max R. Hoffman, Fort Collins CO	4.3.71/78
				Gerald Konig/Konig Spraying Svce, Yuma CO	10.76/78
				Max R. Hoffman, Fort Collins CO	1.2.78/79
				Ward Wilkins, Linden IN	80
				Gary Norton/Norton Aero, Athol ID	81
				(displ. Henley Aerodrome & Museum of Transportation, Athol ID)	
				dest. in hangar fire, Athol ID	8.81
				Micky Rupp, Port Salerno FL: wreck	83/85
				(id. tfd. to 45-11453/N551MR)	
122-41376 •	P-51D	**44-74836**		(to RCAF as 9260): BOC 10.1.51: SOC	4.12.56
			N3991A	Stinson Field Aircraft, San Antonio TX	26.10.56
				Jack Adams Aircraft Sales, Memphis TN	30.5.57/58
			N69X	James E. Hall, Abilene TX	1.4.58/63
				crashed, Dallas-Love Field TX	1.1.59
				wreck to junkyard, Dallas	c60/c80
				Walter Soplata Collection, Newbury OH: hulk	79/86
				Brian O'Farrell/Johnson Aviation, Miami FL	86/96
122-41390	P-51D	44-74850	N6726C	James E. Hodges, Fort Lauderdale FL	63/64
			N2116 (1	John M. Sliker, Wadley ID	66
				John P. Silberman, New York NY	69/70
				Westernair of Albuquerque, Albuquerque NM	71/72
			CF-USA	Don Plumb/Spitfire Inc, Windsor ONT	10.72/75
				crashed, near Big Spring TX (Plumb k.)	16.10.75
122-41399 •	P-51D	**44-74859**		(to RCAF as 9257): BOC 10.1.51: SOC	17.11.51
				crashed Carlton Place ONT	9.11.51
				rep. to Israel with other dam. RCAF P-51Ds (to IDAFAF as 39) : unconf.	
				Sterling Aircraft Supply	64
			N7097V	Pioneer Aero Service, Burbank CA	2.12.64

c/n	Type	Serial	Reg	History	Date
				Pioneer Aero Service, Chino CA: stored	78/90
				(rest. Chino CA 88/90 as TF-51D "473871")	
				Warbirds of GB Ltd, Biggin Hill/	
				(USCR quotes id. 44-74839)	
122-41405 •	P-51D	**44-74865**		(to RCAF as 9258): BOC 10.1.51: SOC	14.5.59
			N8677E	James H. Defuria/Intercontinental Airways, Canastota NY	27.2.59
				(stored Winnipeg MAN, ferried to USA .59)	
				Aero Enterprises, Elkhart IN	18.6.60/61
				Walter H. Erickson, Minneapolis MN	11.4.61/65
				crashed on take-off, Minneapolis MN (rebuilt)	.61
				Don H. Novas, Blackfoot ID	5.5.65/96
122-41418 •	P-51D	**44-74878**		(to RCAF as 9259): BOC 10.1.51: SOC	17.9.57
			N6306T	James H. Defuria & Fred J. Ritts/ Intercontinental Airways, Canastota NY	25.2.57/60
				Aero Enterprises, Elkhart IN	10.5.60/61
				Suncoast Aviation, St. Peterserburg FL	8.7.61
				Florida Airmotive Sales, Ft. Lauderdale FL	14.11.61
				Sherman Aircraft Sales, Fort Wayne IN	7.7.62/64
				Howard Olsen Development Co, Midland TX	3.8.64/65
				Huntley Aviation Service, Leland MS	7.1.65/69
				Gardner Flyers Inc, Brownfield TX	7.1.69
				Tom Wood Aircraft Co, Kalamazoo MI	6.3.69
				Tom Wood Pontiac, Indianapolis IN	10.71/96
122-41448 •	P-51D Cavalier	**44-74908**		(to RCAF as 9273): BOC 11.1.51: SOC	14.5.59
				crashed landing, Winnipeg MAN (stored)	17.6.56
			N1070Z	James H. Defuria/Intercontinental Airways, Canastota NY	27.2.59
				(RCAF surplus: engineless airframe,Winnipeg; open storage Winnipeg 59/62)	
				Aero Enterprises, Elkhart IN	13.5.59/62
				Charles P. Doyle, Minneapolis MN	15.3.62
				(rebuilt Winnipeg, del. by Doyle 18.7.63)	
			N965D	Charles P. Doyle, Apple Valley MN	69/78
			N151BP	Robert J. Pond/Planes of Fame East, Spring Park MN (flies as "USAAF E2-S")	6.80/96
122-41450 •	P-51D Cavalier	**44-74910**		sold surplus at McClellan AFB CA	17.8.59
				Cavalier Aircraft Corp, Sarasota FL	
				(to Indonesian AF/TNI-AU as F-351)	
				Stephen Johnson/Vanpac Carriers, Oakland CA: recov. ex Indonesia	.78
			N51SJ	Stephen J. Johnson, Oakland CA	4.81/86
				Yankee Air Corps, Chino CA	.87/88
			N74920	Yankee Air Corps/ Yanks Air Museum, Chino CA	2.88/95
				(rest. as "474910/J-JA/*Miss Judy*")	
122-41463 •	P-51D	**44-74923**	N5438V	J. J. Wolohan, Livingston CA	63/64
				Walter M. Fountain/Hawke Dusters, Modesto CA	66/69
				(to FA Salvadorena as FAS 410)	7.69
				(adopted id. 44-11353 on return to USA)	
			N132	Donald R. Anderson, Saugus CA	.76
			N100DD	Donald R. Anderson, Saugus CA	78
				(rebuilt by Dave Clinton & Don Anderson 74/81)	
				John R. Sandberg, Robstown TX	.81/84
				(race #28/*Tipsy Too*)	
				crashed Reno NV (repaired)	9.83
			N345	Gary R. Levitz, Dallas TX	10.84/94
				(race #38 *Miss Ashley*)	
			N6395	Shelly R. Levitz, Phoenix AZ	4.94/95
				Sodenal Group, Berne, Switzerland	.96
				(crated Kissimmee FL 3.95,)	
122-41476 •	P-51D	**44-74936**		USAFM, Wright-Patterson AFB, Dayton OH	.58/90
				(displ. as *Shimmy IV*, later *Sharpshooter*)	

122-41479 •	P-51D	**44-74939**		NASM, Washington DC	65/96
122-41490 •	P-51D	**44-74950**	N5464V		
			N511D	Melvyn Paisley, Great Falls MT	63
				Mustang Pilots Club Inc, Van Nuys CA	.63/72
				crashed, dest. near Lancaster CA	25.8.71
				(id. transferred to CA-18 c/n 1500: que se)	
			N20JS	John P. Silberman, Key West & Tampa FL	76/84
			N7496W	Selby R. Burch, Winter Garden FL	11.84/93
				Dick Thurman, Louisville KY	.93/94
				(flies as "USAF 200")	
				Vintage War Birds Inc, Louisville KY	5.95
			N51DT	Dick Thurman/Vintage War Birds Inc, Louisville KY	10.95
122-41502 •	P-51D	**44-74962**		(to Indonesian AF/TNI-AU as F-3......)	
				Stephen Johnson/Vanpac Carriers, Oakland CA: recov. ex Indonesia	.78
				Consolidated Airways, Fort Wayne IN	12.3.80
			N51DK	Consolidated Airways, Fort Wayne IN	11.80/84
				Fort Wayne Air Service, Fort Wayne IN	1.84/96
122-41516 •	P-51D Cavalier	**44-74976**		(to Indonesian AF/TNI-AU as F-311)	8.59/78
				Stephen Johnson/Vanpac Carriers, Oakland CA: recov. ex Indonesia	.78
				Ralph W. Johnson, Oakland CA	.79/81
			N98582	Ralph W. Johnson, Oakland CA	13.8.81/85
				(rest. Chino CA , ff .83)	
				Jeffrey R. Michael, Lexington NC	3.86/96
				(flies as 474976/*Obsession*)	
122-41517 •	P-51D	**44-74977**	**N5448V**	Earl Dodge, Anchorage AK	63/66
				Michael E. Coutches/ Museum of American Aircraft, Hayward CA	69/93
				(stolen Tonopah NV 5.5.84: found Merced CA 9.84)	
				Christopher Gruys, Sante Fe NM	5.94/96
122-41518	P-51D	44-74978		(to FA Costarricense as 4): del.	16.1.55
			N6169U	Will W. Martin/MACO Sales Financial Corp, Chicago IL	31.3.64
				Richard M. Vartanian, Pasadena CA	66/70
			N74978	Richard M. Vartanian, Arcadia/Shafter CA	72/88
				Arthur W. McDonnell, Mojave CA	26.2.88
				dest. in hangar fire, Shafter CA	7.88
122-41536 •	P-51D	**44-74996**	**N5410V**	Prevost F. Smith Parachute Co, Santee CA	63/69
				Donald E. Walker, Orinda CA	70
				Michael E. Coutches, Hayward CA	78
				Bill Destefani, Bakersfield CA	81/83
				(rebuilt Shafter CA 81/82 as mod. racer, #4/*Dago Red*)	
				Frank Taylor Racing Inc, Bakersfield CA	.83/85
				Alan Preston, Dallas TX	87/88
				Sherman Aircraft Sales, West Palm Beach FL	88
				David G. Price/ Liberty Aero Corp/ American Golf Development, Santa Monica CA	.88/95
				(race #4)	
122-41547 •	P-51D Cavalier	**44-75007**	N5462V	Trans Florida Inc, Sarasota FL	63/64
			N3451D	Trans Florida Aviation, Sarasota FL	66
				(conv. to "Cavalier Executive" model)	
				Tempress Research Co Corp, Sunnyvale CA	69
				Jerry G. Brassfield/Pacific Military Air Museum, San Jose CA (race #96)	70/73
				Paul H. Poberezny/EAA, Oshkosh WI	3.77/95

				minor dam., mid-air collision, Tallahassie FL (flies as 4475007/*Paul IV*)	24.3.81
122-41549 •	P-51D	44-75009	N5474V	David L. Rountree, Anderson CA	66/69
				Homer Rountree, Anderson CA	70/78
				Ted E. Contri, Reno NV	84/87
			N51TC (2	Ted E. Contri, Yuba City CA (rest., ff 4.85, flies as *Rosalie*)	3.87/95
122-41564 •	P-51D	**44-75024**		(to Indonesian AF/TNI-AU as F-3......)	
				John MacGuire, El Paso/Fort Hancock TX	84/89
			N4261U	John MacGuire: reg. candidate (cockpit displ. Minnesota ANGB Museum 93)	7.6.91
			N96JM	War Eagles Air Museum, Santa Teresa NM	5.94/96
124-44246 •	P-51D	**44-84390**	**N2869D**	Charles A. Lyford , Belleview WA (race #8/"*Bardahl Special*")	63/72
				Life Science Church, San Diego CA	78
				Charles Hall, San Diego CA (race #3)	81
				Bruce Ellis, San Diego CA	82
				Douglas D. Driscoll, American Falls ID (race #3 "484390", later race #27)	2.83/96
124-44345 •	P-51D	**44-84489**		(to RAAF as A68-750): BOC 6.8.45: SOC (allotted target use, RAAF Williamtown NSW .51)	1.4.52
				American Aeronautics Corp., Burbank CA	2.53
				Peter N. Anderson, Sydney NSW	.87/94
			VH-AMG	Peter N. Anderson, Sydney NSW: reg. res. (fuselage stored CA, planned rest. project)	20.6.94/96
124-44471 •	P-51D	**44-84615**		(to IDFAF as ......)	
			N7099V	Pioneer Aero Service, Burbank CA	66
				Larry R. Strimple, Mansfield OH	69/70
			N9LR	Larry R. Strimple, Mansfield OH	
			N55JL	Jimmy Leeward/Bahia Oaks Inc, Ocala FL (race #9 "*Cloud Dancer*")	.74/95
124-44490 •	P-51D	**44-84634**		(to FA d'L GN Nicaragua as GN96)	
			N6165U	Will W. Martin/MACO Sales Financial Corp, Chicago IL	2.9.63
				Thomas J. Kuckinsky, Menomonee Falls WI	66/69
				Aviation Business Services Inc	70
				Air Sales Inc, Fort Lauderdale FL	72
				Max I. Ramsay, Johnson KS	78
			N51JV	Associated Enterprises Inc, Painesville OH	.79
				Firebird Enterprises OH	83/89
				Ohio Associated Enterprises, Painesville OH	90
				Edward H. Shipley, Malvern PA	91/92
			N51ES	Edward H. Shipley, Malvern PA (rest. Chino CA 92/93, ff 7.93 as 472218/WZ-I/*Big Beautiful Doll*") (note: USCR quotes id. 44-85634, id. also rep. as 44-63634: que se)	2.92/95
124-44514 •	P-51D TF-51D Cavalier	**44-84658**		(to FA d'L GN Nicaragua as GN99)	20.2.58
			N851D (1	Trans Florida Aviation, Sarasota FL	63/64
				Cavalier Aircraft Corp, Sarasota FL	66/69
				(to Indonesian AF/TNI-AU as F-361)	c68
				Stephen Johnson/Vanpac Carriers, Oakland CA: recov. ex Indonesia	.78
				John MacGuire, El Paso TX (rebuilt as TF-51D, Fort Collins CO .83/85)	79/84
			N51TF	John MacGuire, Fort Hancock TX: del.	1.85/88
				John MacGuire/War Eagles Air Museum, Santa Teresa NM (flies as "484658/*The Friendly Ghost*)	89/95
124-44516	P-51D TF-51D	44-84660		(to FA Guatemalteca as FAG 345)	10.57/72
			N38228	Don Hull, Sugarland TX	8.72/73

	Cavalier			Wilson C. Edwards, Big Spring TX	76
				crashed landing, Big Spring TX	21.8.76
124-44525 •	P-51D TF-51D	**44-84669**		(to Rep. of Korea AF as 201)	
				Taegue AB, South Korea: displ.	64/72
				Korean War Museum, Seoul (displ. as "ROKAF 51-8424")	88/93
124-44601 •	P-51D TF-51D Cavalier	**44-84745**	N5439V	Cline Cantarini, Lancaster CA	63/64
				Stanley M. Kurzet, Covina CA	66/69
				Lindsay Newspapers, Sarasota FL (dism.)	72/82
			N851D (2	David B. Lindsay/Lindair Inc, Sarasota FL	6.82
				Gordon W. Plaskett, King City CA (rebuilt King City & Chino CA 83/84 as TF-51D, using TF-51D fuse. ex FA Salvadorena, flew as "484662/TF-662")	84
				Bob Amyx, Oklahoma City OK	.84/85
				Bob Byrne Aviation, Bloomfield MI	87
				Doug Schultz & Lee Lauderback Stallion 51Corp, Kissimmee FL (flies as 484745/*Crazy Horse*)	4.87/96
124-44609 •	P-51D	**44-84753**	N5436V	Robert L. Rodman, Fullerton CA	63/64
				Les Grant, Santa Barbara CA	66/73
			N51TC (1	Ted E. Contri/Contri Construction, Reno NV	24.6.78/86
			N51BE	ntu: Ted E. Contri, North Highland CA	11.86
			N251BP	Planes of Fame East, Plymouth MN	2.87/96
124-44642 •	P-51D F-6D	**44-84786**		sold surplus at McClellan AFB CA	25.11.49
				rep frustrated export to IDFAF: to scrapyard	
				Michael E. Coutches, Hayward CA: stored	c52/61
				Bill Myers, St Louis MO: stored dism.	.61/81
				Henry J. "Butch" Schroeder, Danville IL	.81
			N51BS	Midwest Aviation Museum, Danville IL (rest. Danville IL 83/93, ff 17.6.93 as F-6D "484786/5M-K/*Lil Margaret*")	1.83/96
124-44706 •	P-51D Cavalier	**44-84850**		(to Indonesian AF/TNI-AU as F-3.....)	
				Stephen Johnson/Vanpac Carriers, Oakland CA: recov. ex Indonesia	.78
			N87JB	John MacGuire, El Paso TX (rest., flew as 484850/*Ghost Rider*)	1.82/88
				John MacGuire/War Eagles Air Museum, Santa Teresa NM	88/94
				Picacho Aviation	.94
				Frank Borman, Las Cruces NM	10.8.94/96
			N15FS	Frank Borman, Las Cruces NM (flies as "484850/*Su Su*)	8.95
124-44716 •	P-51D	**44-84860**		(to Indonesian AF/TNI-AU as F-3......)	
				Stephen Johnson/Vanpac Carriers, Oakland CA: recov. ex Indonesia	.78
			N55509	John MacGuire, El Paso & Ft Hancock TX	8.84/88
			N327DB	Darryl Bond/Aero Classics, Chino CA (rebuilt Chino CA as TF-51D: ff 19.5.89; composite: CAC mainplane, fuse. ex Enforcer programme: new id. "PAS82087") (flies as "484860/*Lady Jo*", race #52)	1.89/96
124-44720 •	P-51D ETF-51D	**44-84864**		(to NACA as NACA126): BOC 27.8.45: SOC (mod. by NACA to tall vertical fin)	12.7.57
			N4223A	Kibler Bros (sold surplus ex storage NAS Norfolk VA .57)	.57
				Sidney A. Franklin, Pacific Palisades CA	63
				Glenn Johnson Realty, Sacramento CA	.63/69
				Michael E. Coutches/American Aircraft Sales Co/ Museum of American Aircraft, Hayward CA	.69/95

				Wagons to Wings Museum, Morgan Hill CA:loan	79/96
124-44752 •	P-51D	**44-84896**	**N5416V**	Lake Air Corp, Michigan City IN	63
				James C. Keichline, Huntington Park CA	.63/70
				Kenneth M. Scholz, Playa del Ray CA	4.73/95
124-44756 •	P-51D ETF-51D	**44-84900**		(to NACA as NACA127): BOC 4.9.45: SOC	5.6.52
				USAFM, Greater Pittsburgh ANGB PA	73/94
				(displ. on pole as "48490/AJ-S")	
			N51YZ	reg. (rest. to fly, Chino)	7.95
				only Mustang ever to land on an aircraft carrier!	
124-44789 •	P-51D	**44-84933**		sold surplus McClellan AFB CA for $2160	20.9.57
			N2874D	Earl V. Dakin, Sacramento CA	20.9.57/58
				Douglas W. Brown/Mustang Aviation, Great Falls MT	11.58/62
				Kathleen C. Murphy, Great Falls MT: dism.	8.10.62/64
				Edward G. Fleming, Calgary ALTA	10.3.64
				(trucked Great Falls to Calgary, rebuilt)	
			CF-RUT	Edward G. Fleming, Calgary ALTA	4.8.65
				Donald F. McGillivray, Nanaimo BC	13.8.65/67
				Charles E. Roberts/Calg-Air Sales, Calgary	4.11.67
			N201F	Futrell Aircraft Sales, Hot Springs AR	12.67/69
				Alexander J. Edelman, Great Neck NY	69
				Suffolk Flight Associates, Huntington NY	6.69/72
				John J. Mark, Milwaukee WI	78/83
				John J. Mark/ MA Inc, Oshkosh WI	83/96
124-44808 •	P-51D	**44-84952**	N6495C		
			N210D	Art Holst, Eugene OR	63/64
				Contractor Equipment Co, Salem OR	66
				Joseph Hartney, Chino CA	78
				Steve Tognoli CA	83/85
				Northeast Aircraft Associates, Wilmington DE	8.86/96
124-44817 •	P-51D RB-51	**44-84961**		sold surplus McClellan AFB CA	2.58
		P-51D	**N7715C**	Capitol Airways/Air Sales, Nashville TN	2.58/64
				Charles F. Willis, Frank Lynott & Charles R. Hall, Seattle WA (race #5)	7.64/67
				Charles R. Hall, Seattle WA	.67/71
				(conv. .67 to mod. racer #5 *Miss RJ*)	
				Gunther W. Balz, Kalamazoo MI	7.71/73
				(further race mods: #5, *Roto-Finish*)	
				John M. Sliker, Wadley GA	10.73/74
				Ed Browning/Brownings Inc, Idaho Falls ID	2.74/79
				(rebuilt Van Nuys CA: mod. racer RB-51 with Griffon 54, contra-rotating props; ff 3.6.75: race #5 *Red Baron*)	
				(world piston record 499.018mph -14.8.79)	
				crashed, wrecked during race, Reno NV	16.9.79
				Richard Ransopher, Grapevine TX (wreck)	.80
				Steven J. Hinton/Fighter Rebuilders, Chino CA	9.85/96
				(id. tfd to rebuild of ex TNI-AU P-51D at Chino, ff Chino 9.85 as stock P-51D 413334/G4-U	
				(hulk of RB-51 to Terry & Bill Rogers, Sherman TX .89 : planned rebuild as Griffon RB-51 racer)	
124-44818 •	P-51D Cavalier	**44-84962**		(to ROKAF as ......)	
				(to Indonesian AF/TNI-AU as F-312)	
				Stephen Johnson/Vanpac Carriers, Oakland CA: recov. ex Indonesia	.78/79
			N9857P	Lee W. Schaller, Montville NJ/New Athens IL	13.8.81/95
				(rest. Chino CA, ff .83)	
124-48120	P-51D	45-11367	N2871D	American Aircraft Sales Co, Hayward CA	63
				Michael E. Coutches, Hayward CA	.63/64
				James L. Ventura, Goleta CA	66/67
				crashed during air race (Ventura k.)	3.9.67
				Ed Maloney/Air Museum, Ontario CA: wreck	70
			N4078K	reg. res.	

c/n	Type	Serial	Reg'n	History	Date
				(id. tfd. to 44-63810/N63810): que se	.72
124-48124	P-51D	45-11371		(to FA d'L GN Nicaragua as GN121)	31.5.58/63
			N12067	Will W. Martin/MACO Sales Financial Corp, Chicago IL	8.7.63
				Joe Binder, Fremont OH	63/70
			N1051S	George Sullivan/Mustangs Aviation, Miami FL	6.70/79
				Peter McManus, Fort Lauderdale FL	7.79/84
				Whittington Bros, Fort Lauderdale FL	.84
				Rick E. Sharpe, Rosharon TX	84
			N751CB	Connie Bowlin/Bowlin Enterprises, Griffin GA	5.85
			N1051S	Jimmie R. MacMillan/Breckenridge Air Museum, Breckenridge TX	10.85/87
				(rest. Breckenridge, ff 22.4.86 as "511371")	
				Myrick Aviation, Miami FL/ Flakair Inc, Fort Collins CO/Leavesden UK	1.87/94
				(del. USA to UK arr. Southend 22.6.87, based UK 87/94 as "511371/VF-S/*Sunny VIII*"; dism. Duxford 1.94: shipped to USA 1.94)	
			N51KF	George Krieger/US Army Air Corps Museum, Dover DE	3.94/95
				crashed at airshow, Malone NY (Krieger k.)	2.7.95
124-48134 •	P-51D Cavalier	**45-11381**	N5471V	Vulcan Engineering Co Inc, Little Rock AR	63/66
				Jack Huismann/Mustang Corp, Pewaukee WI	69/72
				Ed Browning/Brownings Inc, Roberts ID	78
				crashed near Casper WY	6.81
				Ritchie Rasmussen, Sherwood Park ALTA	83
				(rebuilt, ff .83 as race #66 "Flying Undertaker")	
			C-GRLR	Ritchie Rasmussen, Edmonton ALTA	9.83/84
				(later flew as "45-11381/*Flying Undertaker*")	
			N151MR	Herbert E. Rupp, Port Salerno FL	4.85
			N551CB	Connie Bowlin/Bowlin Enterprises, Griffin GA	9.85/90
				Gary Honbarrier/Carrier Aviation Inc, High Point NC	7.90/96
				(flies as "414888/B6-Y/*Glamorous Glen III*")	
124-48144 •	P-51D	**45-11391**	N6170C	Thomas A. Drummond, Ridgecrest CA	63/64
				Jeffrey D. Cannon, Los Angeles CA	66
				Arthur R. Tucker, Norwood NJ	69/70
			N5151N	Arthur R. Tucker, Norwood NJ	.70
			N51WT	John I. Watson, Blackwood NJ	78/92
				Fly Rock Inc, Warrenton VA	2.94/95
				(#00 "*Nervous Energy V*")	
124-48206 •	P-51D Cavalier	45-11453	N5479V	John A. Colling, Scottsdale AZ	63
				T. A. Underwood, Buckeye AZ	.63/64
				Sanford Aviation, Gardena CA	66
				(to FA Boliviana as FAB 511)	10.6.66
			C-GXUP	Arny Carnegie, Edmonton ALTA (dism.)	12.77
			N59038	George Roberts FL: reg. candidate	5.78
			N6310T(2		.78
				Whittington Bros, Ft. Lauderdale FL	
				(rest. Ft.Collins CO, ff 5.85: adopted id. 44-74832)	
			N551MR	Herbert E. (Mickey) Rupp, Port Salerno FL	6.85/96
				(flew as "414450/*Old Crow*", race #5)	
				landing asscident badly dam by fire Florida 2.96	
124-48211 •	P-51D	**45-11458**		(to RAAF as A68-801): BOC	9.45
			N4886V	American Aeronautics Corp, Burbank CA	23.2.53
				(to FA Boliviana as FAB 504)	c2.55
				Museo Aeronautico, Maracay AB, Venezuela	87/91
124-48224 •	P-51D	**45-11471**	N5481V		
			N332	David Maytag, Colorado Springs CO (race #9)	63/69
				David J. Zeuschel, Van Nuys CA	70/78
				James Barkley, AZ	79

				crashed, Borrego Springs CA (Barkley k.)	21.8.79
				Alan Preston Air Racing Team, Dallas TX	7.9.84/87
				(rest. using fus. of IDFAF 69 & wing of IDFAF 28 as mod. racer #84 *Stiletto*)	
				Sherman Aircraft Sales, West Palm Beach FL	.87/89
				Liberty Aero Corp, Santa Monica CA	11.89/96
	TF-51D			TF-51D conversion Square One Aviation, Chino, CA	95/96
124-48236	P-51D	45-11483		(to RAAF as A68-813): BOC 9.45: SOC	1.53
				American Aeronautics Corp, Burbank CA	23.2.53
			N4674V(1	American Aeronautics Corp, Burbank CA	17.8.54/56
				Dwight Gibson, Los Angeles CA : dism.	5.9.56/58
				Jack Wollom/Sterling Aircraft Supply Co, Hollywood CA : dism.	21.2.58/64
			N7096V	Pioneer Aero Service, Burbank CA	12.64/68
				Leo E. Pike, Bakersfield CA	20.3.68/70
				(id. tfd. to CA-18 c/n 1523: que se)	
				(also rep. to FA Boliviana as FAB-503 1.2.55)	
124-48242	P-51D Cavalier	45-11489	N5421V		
			N551D (2	(conv. to 2nd prototype Trans Florida Cavalier)	
				Stan Hoke/Stanley Dunbar Studios, Charlotte NC (race #99)	63/64
				crashed, dest., Lincoln VA	17.4.66
			N5421V	Ed Browning/Brownings Inc, Roberts ID	78
				(id. tfd. to CA-17 c/n 1364: que se)	
124-48260 •	P-51D	**45-11507**		(to RNZAF as NZ2417): shipped, arr. NZ	6.9.45/58
				(stored dism. Ardmore 45/52, assembled 4.52, wfu 11.8.55, stored Woodbourne AB 55/58)	
				Ron E. Fechney, Canterbury NZ	4.58
			ZK-CCG	Ron Fechney & Jack MacDonald, Aylesbury	31.8.64/74
				(rest. Christchurch, ff 29.11.64; later stored)	
				(flown to Christchurch 4.4.74 for shipping USA)	
			N921	John F. Schafhausen, Spokane WA	10.74/75
				Gene Stocker Chevrolet, State College PA	78/79
				Von Weeks Flugwerke Inc, Tamiami FL	.79/83
				Weeks Air Museum, Tamiami FL	1.83/96
				(flies as "413321/HO-P/*Cripes a Mighty 3rd*")	
				dam. Tamiami by Hurricane Andrew	24.8.92
				(rebuild Salinas CA 93/94)	
124-48266 •	P-51D	**45-11513**		(to RNZAF as NZ2423): shipped, arr. NZ	27.8.45/58
				(stored dism. Ardmore 45/52, assembled .52, not used, stored Rukuhia & Woodbourne 52/58)	
				W. Ruffell, Blenheim NZ	5.58/64
				John R. Smith, Gardeners Valley, Mapua NZ	.64/96
				(stored dism: wings torched off)	
124-48271 •	P-51D	**45-11518**		(to RNZAF as NZ2427): shipped, arr. NZ	27.8.45
				(stored dism. Ardmore 45/52, assembled .52, not used, stored Rukuhia & Woodbourne 52/58)	
				Peter Coleman, Blenheim NZ : stored dism.	5.58/90
				(stored dism., incomplete airframe)	
				Alpine Fighter Collection, Wanaka NZ	.90/96
				(rest. to fly,)	
124-48278 •	P-51D Cavalier	**45-11525**		(to Indonesian AF/TNI-AU as F-3....)	
				Stephen Johnson/Vanpac Carriers, Oakland CA: recov. ex Indonesia	.78
			N91JB	John MacGuire, El Paso & Ft Hancock TX	3.82/88
				War Eagles Air Museum, Santa Teresa NM	88/96
				(rest., flies as "511525/*Silver Ghost*)	
124-48293 •	P-51D	**45-11540**	N5162V	James W. Steverson, Littleton CO	63/64
				(rebuilt Chino & Van Nuys CA c74)	
				Dennis Schoenfelder, Santa Barbara CA	78
			N151W	Joe G. Mabee, Midland TX	83/92
				J. A. Michaels, Oconomowoc WI	5.93/96

				(flies as "4511540/*Queen B*")	
124-48299	P-51D	45-11546	N5470V		
			N518M	Northern Air Service, Grand Rapids MI	63/64
			N518MC	Don Shepherd, Houston TX	66
			N518M	Douglas L. Champlin, Enid OK	69
				Well Aircraft Inc, Hutchinson KS	8.69
			PI-C1046	Enrique Zobel, Manila Philippines	
			RP-C1046	Enrique Zobel, Manila Philippines	
			N51JW	John P. Wright, San Francisco CA	.71/82
				crashed, dest., Elko NV (Wright k.)	9.82
124-48306 •	P-51D	**45-11553**		sold surplus McClellan AFB CA	20.9.57
			N5414V		
			N713DW	Richard D. Weaver, Van Nuys CA	63/69
				(race #6, later #15)	
				Thomas A. Neal, Pasadena CA	70
			N22DC	Anthony J. D'Alessandris, Reno NV	72
			N51T (1	Anthony J. D'Alessandris, Reno NV	77
			N51TZ	Anthony J. D'Alessandris, Reno NV	6.77
			N5415V (2	Anthony J. D'Alessandris, Reno NV	11.77
				Richard Smith, Bradbury CA	.77/88
				(rebuilt using components 45-11571/N5415V)	
				RWR Development, Las Vegas NV	89
				Erin Rheinschild/Unlimited Air Racing Inc, Van Nuys CA	90/92
				(race #553 "511553/FF-553/*Miss Fit*)	
			N38JC	Avirex/NA-50 Inc, New York NY	6.93/96
				(rest. Rialto CA, ff 7.93 "511553/WZ-I/*Jacky C*")	
124-48311 •	P-51D Cavalier	**45-11558**	**N6175C**	Aerodynamics Inc, Pontiac MI	63/64
				James C. Gorman, Mansfield OH	66
				Herbert E. Rupp, Port Salerno FL	.66
				crashed, Georgia	.67
				(rebuilt using parts 44-74829 & 44-73822)	
				John E. Dilley, Auburn IN	69/72
				John Rutherford, Fort Worth TX	78/79
				Mark Clark/Courtesy Aircraft, Rockford IL	.82
				Joseph Kasparoff, Van Nuys CA	5.83/95
				(race #39 *The Healer*)	
				cr. takeoff, Van Nuys CA (repaired)	6.8.85
124-48312 •	P-51D Cavalier	**45-11559**	N5469V	Jim B. Tregoning, Bakersfield CA	63/64
				Burford Co International Corp, Maysville OK	66
			N6451D	Levitz Furniture Co, Dallas TX	69
				Volkmer Manufacturing Co, Dallas TX	6.69
				(to FA Salvadorena as FAS-401)	7.69
			N30FF	Jack W. Flaherty/Flaherty Factors Inc, Monterey CA	1.11.74
				(also rep. as 44-11153/FAS-409: que se)	
				Ward Wilkins, Linden IN	78
				Henry J. "Butch" Schroeder/Midwest Aviation Museum, Danville IL	82/95
				(flew as "5-11559/ *North American Maid*")	
				Warbird Operators Inc, Indianapolis IN	5.95
	TF-51D			under restoration to TF-51D configuration	96
124-48324 •	P-51D	**45-11571**	N5415V (1	Arni L. Sumarlidason, Nice France	63/64
				Marvin Parker, Shelton CT	66/69
				South Delta Aviation, Rolling Fork MS	8.69
				Jet America Inc, Wilmington DE	70
				Anthony J. D'Alessandris, Reno NV	4.71/77
				(race #15, rebuilt: adopted id. 45-11553)	
			N51T (2	Anthony J. D'Alessandris, Reno NV	7.77/92
124-48335 •	P-51D	**45-11582**	**N5441V**	sold surplus McClellan AFB CA	11.57
				Edward T. Maloney/The Air Museum,	

				Claremont CA, later Ontario CA & Chino CA	6.11.57/95
				(flew as 413334/G4-U/*Spam Can*,	
				later 414888/B6-Y/*Glamorous Glen III*,	
				later race #8 *Spirit of Phoenix*)	
				(tour of Japan: shipped ex Chino CA 3.95)	
124-48339	P-51D	45-11586		sold surplus McClellan AFB CA	1.57
			N5423V	Walter D. Oakes, Chicago IL	63/70
				Albert Shirkey, Tulsa OK	78
			N51HA		
			N13LF	Lynn L. Florey FL	83/85
				Harry E. Tope, Mount Pleasant MI	11.86
			N51HT	Harry E. Tope, Mount Pleasant MI	2.87/90
				(flew as *Death Rattler*)	
				crashed, dest., Ottawa ONT (Tope k.)	1.7.90
124-48373	P-51D	45-11620		sold surplus McClellan AFB CA	.57
			N2872D	Michael E. Coutches/American Aircraft Sales Co	
				Hayward CA	.57/64
				Kevin D. Derth, Novota CA	66
				William Penn Patrick/Holiday Magic Inc/	
				Spectrum Air Inc, San Rafael CA	.68/73
				crashed, dest., Lake County CA (Patrick k.)	9.6.73
124-48381 •	P-51D	**45-11628**	N5446V	Michael E. Coutches, Hayward CA	61
				Thomas P. Mathews, Monterey CA	63/64
			N151X	Walter E. Stewart, Monterey CA	66/72
				Jack W. Flaherty, Monterey CA (race #8)	73
				John T. Johnson, Rexburg ID	75/81
				William L. Hane, Portland OR/Mesa AZ	11.81/96
				disp: Champlin Fighter Museum, Mesa AZ:	83/93
				(flies as *Ho Hun*/CY-H)	
124-48386 •	P-51D	**45-11633**	**N5413V**	William G. Lacy/Lacy Steel Inc, Honolulu HI	63/95
				dam. ground accident, Honolulu HI	c72
				(rep. under rebuild)	
124-48389 •	P-51D	**45-11636**	N5467V	Tallmantz Aviation Inc, Glenview CA	63/64
				Rosen Novak Auto Co, Omaha NB	66
			N11636	John E. Dilley, Fort Wayne IN	68
				Michael W. Bertz, Cheyenne WY/Nashville TN	8.68/78
				Michael W. Bertz, Broomfield CO	78/96
				(flies as 511636/WD-KK/*Stang Evil*)	
126-37691 •	P-51H	**44-64265**		USAFM, Chanute AFB, Rantoul IL	65/94
				dismantled into store	95
126-37740 •	P-51H	**44-64314**	N1108H	William E. Hogan, Hamilton OH	63/64
				Michael E. Coutches, Hayward CA	66
				(rebuild: composite of parts ex scrap dealers	
				and wreck recov. ex crash site Utah c62)	
			N551H	Michael E. Coutches/American Aircraft Sales Co	
				Museum of American Aircraft, Hayward CA	68/96
				(race #51 "464551")	
126-37801 •	P-51H	**44-64375**		wreck salvaged from Alaska	
			N67149	Paul Shoemaker, Orting WA	78/90
				(long-term rest. project)	
				James R. Parks, Bend OR	5.90/96
126-37802 •	P-51H	**44-64376**		USAFM, Lackland AFB TX	65/96
				(displ. as 464376/HO-M)	
126-37841 •	P-51H	**44-64415**		(to NACA as NACA130): BOC 18.12.46: SOC	4.61
				(NACA Moffett Field CA: to USN as salvage .61)	
			N313H	William E. Hogan, Hamilton OH (race #3)	66/78
			N49WB	Bill & Don Whittington/World Jet Inc,	
				Fort Lauderdale FL (race #94, #08)	6.78/96
				accident Reno NV (rebuilt)	9.79
				(flies as "RAF KN987")	

COMMONWEALTH AIRCRAFT CORPORATION PTY MUSTANGS

1326 •	CA-17	**A68-1**		RAAF BOC 7.45 : ff Fishermans Bend VIC	5.46
	Mk. 20			used for Atomic tests, Emu Junction SA	10.53
				(abandoned in desert at Emu test site 53/67)	
				Stanley Booker/Stan Air Inc, Fresno CA	8.67
				(del. Emu to Adelaide-Parafield 31.10/1.11.67,	
				stored Parafield: Australian civil reg. frustrated)	
			VH-EMQ	ntu: Tony Schwerdt, Adelaide SA	.69
				dam. during shipping Adelaide to USA	6.69
			N7773	Stan Air Inc, Fresno CA	.70
				Ed Jurist/Vintage Aircraft Int'l, Nyack NJ	
				Randy Sohn	
				Gary Levitz, Dallas TX	
			N51WB (2	Bill & Don Whittington, Fort Lauderdale FL	.79/81
				(stored dism. since arr. USA; rest. Ft Collins CO	
				79/80, ff 11.80: adopted id. 44-15757)	
				Wiley C. Sanders Truck Lines, Troy AL	.81/96
				dam. fcd-landing, nr. Rockford IL (repaired)	4.84
				(race #38 "RAAF A68-1001")	
1364 •	CA-17	**A68-39**		RAAF BOC 12.45: SOC	12.53
	Mk. 20		VH-BOY	Fawcett Aviation/Illawarra Flying School,	
				Bankstown NSW (target-towing ops.)	10.59/78
				crashed on take-off Bankstown (rebuilt)	5.6.76
				Warbirds of GB Ltd, Blackbushe UK	.78
				Gordon W. Plaskett, King City CA	.79
				Flying Tiger Farms, Bakersfield CA	.81
			N551D (3	Bill Destefani, Bakersfield CA	83
				(rebuilt, adopted id. 45-11489; ff 5.10.83)	
				(later adopted new id. 44-14826/N551D)	
				Jack A. Erickson/Erickson Air Crane,	
				Medford OR (flies as "A68-39/BF-D")	11.83/95
1396 •	CA-17	**A68-71**		RAAF BOC 16.4.46: dam. landing Pearce WA	24.4.49
		Mk. 20		to RAAF "Inst. No. 14" at RAAF Pearce: SOC	10.52
				Midland Technical School Aeronautical Annexe,	
				Perth Airport WA: inst. airframe	10.52/72
				RAAF Association Aviation Museum, Perth	22.3.72/84
				(trucked ex Annexe 28.4.73: stored dism.)	
				Derek A. Macphail, Perth WA/UK	28.6.84/96
				(rest. to fly, Perth WA)	
1425 •	CA-18	**A68-100**		RAAF BOC 6.11.47: SOC	4.58
	Mk. 21			A. J. R. Oates, Sydney NSW	23.4.58
				Fawcett Aviation, Sydney-Bankstown NSW	.60/61
			VH-BOW	ntu: Fawcett Aviation, Bankstown NSW	25.8.61/67
				(mods. for high altitude survey, ff Bankstown	
				8.12.61, last flight 1.3.62: parked Bankstown)	
				Ed Fleming/Skyservice Aviation, Camden NSW	.67
				James Ausland, Seattle WA	20.11.67
				(shipped to Seattle, rebuilt 68/71:	
				adopted id. 44-14777/N51AB)	
			N51AB	James Ausland/Sports Air, Seattle WA	7.71
				Joe Arnold, Greenville MS	20.2.74
				Robby R. Jones, Minter City MS	25.8.75/89
				Norman Lewis/Lewis Aviation, Louisville KY	90/96
				(flew as 414777/J-RR/*Miss Escort*,	
				now 413500/HL-N/*Flying Dutchman*)	
1429 •	CA-18	**A68-104**		RAAF BOC 11.47: SOC	4.58
	Mk. 21			Taren Point Non-Ferrous Metals P/L, Sydney	23.9.60
				A. J. R. Oates, Sydney NSW	60
				Adastra Airways, Sydney-Mascot NSW	11.62/64
				(open storage Sydney-Mascot 62/64)	
				Tony Fisher, Jerilderie NSW: del. ex Mascot	2.8.64/70
				(based on farm, Jerilderie NSW .64/70)	
			VH-BOB	Robert L. Eastgate, Melbourne VIC	10.70/95
				(del. Jerilderie to Melbourne-Essendon 26.3.73,	

				rest. Essendon ff 26.2.76 as "A68-104")	
1430 •	CA-18	**A68-105** Mk. 21		RAAF BOC 21.11.47: SOC	23.4.58
				R. H. Grant Metals, Tocumwal NSW	4.58
				Peter Freason, Laverton VIC	8.60/64
				(displ. Fleetwings Garage, Laverton VIC 8.60/65)	
				Richard E. Hourigan, Melbourne VIC	11.64/95
				Moorabbin Air Museum, Melbourne VIC: displ.	11.64/74
				RAAF Museum, RAAF Point Cook VIC: loan	7.77/90
			VH-JUC	Richard E. Hourigan, Melbourne VIC: reg. res.	.90/94
				(trucked to Tyabb VIC 24.3.90, rest. to fly)	
				Dick Hourigan & Judy Pay, Tyabb VIC	94/96
1432 •	CA-18 Mk. 21	**A68-107**		RAAF BOC 12.47: SOC	5.58
			VH-AUB	A. J. R. Oates, Bankstown NSW	24.4.58/66
				Ewan McKay, "Rosedale" Station, Jericho QLD	4.66/74
				(wfu, stored "Rosedale" Station 66/74)	
				Col Pay, Scone NSW	75/95
				(rest. Scone NSW, ff .80 as "A68-107")	
1443 •	CA-18 Mk. 21	**A68-118**		RAAF BOC 10.5.48: SOC	4.58
				Wilmore Aviation Services, Moorabbin VIC	23.4.58
			VH-WAS	Joe R. Palmer/Wilmore Aviation Services	7.8.59/78
				(wfu Bankstown NSW 6.8.60, parked 60/73)	
				Camden Museum of Aviation NSW: loan, arr.	7.7.73/78
			VH-AGJ	Jeff Trappett, Morwell VIC	.78/96
				(trucked Camden to Morwell 2.1.79 for rest.,	
				ff Morwell 19.4.81 as "A68-118")	
1444	CA-18	A68-119 Mk. 21		RAAF BOC 11.6.48: SOC	23.4.58
				R. H. Grant Trading Co, Tocumwal NSW	4.58
				Ralph H. Capponi, Apollo Bay VIC	.64/67
				(flown on DCA permit as "A68-119")	
				Ed Fleming/Skyservice Aviation,Camden NSW	11.67/68
			N65119	ntu: Stanley Booker/Stan Air Inc, Fresno CA	.68
				Langdon Badger, Adelaide SA	.68
			VH-IVI	Langdon Badger Furnishings, Adelaide SA	20.6.69/70
				Raymond J. Whitbread, Sydney NSW	30.9.70/73
				crashed dest. Windsor NSW (Whitbread k.)	11.6.73
1462 •	CA-18 Mk. 23	**A68-137**		RAAF BOC 26.11.48: SOC	2.60
				Aeronautical Research Labs., Melbourne VIC	.60/70
				RAAF Museum, Point Cook VIC (ex fire dump)	74
			VH-PPV	ntu: Vic Perry, RAAF Base Townsville QLD	74/80
				RAAF Museum, RAAF Base Townsville QLD	80/96
				(rest. to taxy condition, displ. as "KH791/CV-P")	
1495 •	CA-18 Mk. 23	**A68-170**		RAAF BOC	2.50
				RAAF Stores Depot., Toowoomba, QLD: displ.	60/70
				RAAF Museum, RAAF Point Cook VIC	10.70/95
				(displ. as A68-170/*Duffy's Delight*)	
			VH-SVU	RAAF Museum, RAAF Point Cook VIC	28.8.95
				(rest. to fly, RAAF Point Cook 89/96)	
1500 •	CA-18 Mk. 23	**A68-175**		RAAF BOC 4.50: SOC	1.59
				Col Pay, Narromine NSW	60/65
				Ed Fleming/Skyservice Aviation,Camden NSW	.65/67
			CF-WWH	John C. Kehler, Plumb Coulee MAN	1.5.67/71
				(shipped to Vancouver, rebuilt Carman MAN:	
				conv. 4-seater, CF-100 canopy)	
			N64824	Frank Martucci, Roslyn Heights NY	18.5.71/73
			N5789	ntu: flew with this unauthorised reg.	
			N64824	Frank Gruzman, West Babylon NY	31.1.73
				John P. Silberman, Sherborn MA	8.11.73/75
				Arthur S. & Dan Vance, Santa Rosa CA	5.8.75/96
				(id. tfd. to composite rebuild rep. using	
				ex TNI-AU airframe & hulk ex Illinois junkyard:	
				rebuilt Shafter CA 75/82, ff 5.82;	
				flies as 413678/V-C5"/*Million Dollar Baby*)	

1512 •	CA-18	A68-187		RAAF BOC 10.50: SOC	4.58
	Mk. 22			A. J. R. Oates, Sydney NSW	23.4.58
				Adastra Airways Pty Ltd, Mascot NSW	.60/61
				Fawcett Aviation, Sydney-Bankstown NSW	.61/67
				(open storage Bankstown 61/67)	
				Chieftain Aviation Pty Ltd, Bankstown NSW	.67/69
				(advertising displ. on pole, Bankstown Airport)	
				Hockey Treloar, Sydney NSW	7.69/95
			VH-UFO	ntu: Hockey Treloar, Sydney NSW	3.73
				(rest. with RR Dart turboprop, Canberra ACT	
				76/77: not flown, conv. abandoned; stored	
				Toowoomba QLD 90/95, shipped to USA .95)	
			N919WJ	World Jet Inc, Fort Lauderdale FL	8.95
				Frank Borman, NM	
	TF-51D			rebuilt to TF-51D config with Square One Aviation	96
1517 •	CA-18	**A68-192**		RAAF BOC 8.3.51: SOC	4.58
	Mk. 22		VH-FCB	F. Chris Braund, Tamworth NSW	4.58/61
				Jack McDonald, Moorabbin VIC	.61/66
				Ed Fleming/Skyservice Aviation, Camden NSW	10.66/69
			PI-C651	George Scholey/Prontino Inc, Manila	27.2.69/75
				serious landing accident, Manila Airport	18.10.73
				(rebuild commenced Manila, using centre-section	
				and parts of ex Philippine AF P-51D 44-72917)	
				Ray Hanna & Mal Rose/Hong Kong Aeronautical	
				Engineering Co, Kai Tak Airport, Hong Kong	.75/85
				(rebuilt Kai Tak 76/85, ff 2.85 as "H-CV")	
			VR-HIU	D. E. Baker & Partners, Hong Kong	.81
			G-HAEC	The Old Flying Machine Company, Duxford	
				arr. Gatwick by airfreight	28.2.85/96
				(flew as "472917/*Ding Hao*", later	
				"588/*Missy Wong from Hong Kong*",	
				later "RAAF A68-192")	
1518	CA-18	A68-193		RAAF BOC 5.51: SOC	4.58
	Mk. 22			R. H. Grant Trading Co, Tocumwal NSW: scrap	.58/63
				Tony Fisher, Sydney NSW	.63/69
				(based on farm, Jerilderie NSW: del. .63/69)	
			VH-DBB	Don Bushe, Melbourne VIC	4.4.69/70
				crashed dest., airshow Bendigo VIC (Bushe k.)	15.2.70
1523 •	CA-18	**A68-198**		RAAF BOC 7.51: SOC	4.58
	Mk. 22			Fawcett Aviation, Sydney-Bankstown NSW	.61/68
				(open storage Bankstown 61/68)	
				Arnold J. Glass, Sydney NSW	66/68
				Ed Fleming/Skyservice Aviation, Camden NSW	.68
				Stanley Booker/Stan Air Inc, Fresno CA	.68
				(shipped to USA, noted at Bakersfield CA 11.68)	
			N65198	Joe Banducci & Elmer Rossi, Bakersfield CA	.68/70
			N4674V(2	Joe Banducci & Elmer Rossi, Bakersfield CA	.70/77
				(adopted id. 45-11483/A68-813/N4674V)	
				(race #86 *Ciuchetton*)	
			N607D	ntu:	76
			N86JB	Joe F. Banducci, Bakersfield CA (race #86)	10.77/82
			N286JB	Joe F. Banducci, Bakersfield CA	3.82
				Don Whittington, Fort Lauderdale FL	84
				Frank Strickler/Fox 51 Ltd, Denton TX	85/88
				Lewis Shaw/Fox 51 Ltd, Dallas TX	89/90
				(flew as "511483/FF-483")	
				Victor Haluska/Santa Monica Propeller CA	91
				Flying Eagles Inc, Wilmington DE	91
				Franklin Devaux/Apache Aviation, Dijon	5.91
				(shipped to France ex Chino CA .91)	
			F-AZIE	Lafayette Aviation/Flying Legend Association,	
				Dijon-Longvic	1.9.92/96
				(flew as 511483/*The Best Years of Our Lives*)	
				badly dam. in-flight fire, forced landing, Dijon	5.9.93
				(rebuilt .94 as 415622/AJ-T/*Short-Fuse Sallee*)	

c/n	Type	Serial	Registration	History	Date
				dismantled Dijon en route USA 18.1.96	
				Courtesy Aircraft, Rockford IL for buyer	96
1524 •	CA-18 Mk. 22	**A68-199**		RAAF BOC 7.51: SOC	4.58
				A. J. R. Oates, Bankstown NSW	.60
			VH-BOZ	Fawcett Aviation/Illawarra Flying School, Bankstown NSW (target-towing ops.)	11.60/79
			G-MUST	ntu: Warbirds of GB Ltd, Blackbushe	20.12.79
				HM Customs Australia: impounded	12.79/84
				RAAF Museum (stored dism., RAAF Stores Depots, Sydney & Dubbo NSW 79/92; trucked to RAAF Williamtown NSW 15.2.92)	.84/95
				Fighter World Museum, RAAF Williamtown NSW	94/96
- •	Cavalier T Mk. 2	**67-14865**		Cavalier Aircraft Corp, Sarasota FL	67
				(to FA Boliviana as FAB 522)	10.67
				rep. stored by FAB for planned museum	85
- •	Cavalier T Mk. 2	**67-14866**		Cavalier Aircraft Corp, Sarasota FL	67
				(to FA Boliviana as FAB 521)	19.1.68/77
			C-GXUR	Arny Carnegie, Edmonton ALTA	12.77
				Neil J. McClain/McClain Flight Service, Strathmore ALTA	11.78/91
			N20TF	Tom Friedkin/Cinema Air, Houston TX	10.91/96
- •	Cavalier Mk. 2	**67-22579**		Cavalier Aircraft Corp, Sarasota FL	67
				(to FA Boliviana as FAB 519)	10.67/77
			C-GXRG	Arny Carnegie, Edmonton ALTA	12.77
				Neil J. McClain/McClain Flight Service, Strathmore ALTA	11.78/84
			N52BH	Robert E. Hester, Bladenboro NC	9.85/92
			N251RM	Russell McDonald, Park City UT (flies as "722579/FF579")	4.92/96
- •	Cavalier	**67-22580** Mk. 2		Cavalier Aircraft Corp, Sarasota FL: built	24.11.67
				(to FA Boliviana as FAB 520)	19.1.68/77
			C-GXUQ	Arny Carnegie, Edmonton ALTA	12.77
				Neil J. McClain/McClain Flight Service, Strathmore ALTA	8.78/84
			N151RK	Richard F. Korff, Lockport NY	10.86/92
				Aero Classics Inc, Daytona Beach FL (flies as 422580/*Six Shooter*)	5.92/96
- •	Cavalier	**67-22581** Mk. 2		Cavalier Aircraft Corp, Sarasota FL: built	12.2.68
				(to FA Boliviana as FAB 523)	9.5.68/77
			C-GMUS	Arny Carnegie, Edmonton ALTA	12.77
				Ross F. Grady, Edmonton ALTA (del. ex Bolivia 8.78, flies as FAB 523/*Whats up Doc?*)	8.78/91
- •	Cavalier T Mk. 2	68-15795		Cavalier Aircraft Corp, Sarasota FL	67
				(to US Army as 68-15795)	.67
				RAF Museum : airfreighted to Mildenhall AFB (refurbished Upper Heyford AFB 76/77)	22.6.76
				RAF Museum Store, RAF Henlow: arr.	11.77/80
				USAFM: returned by RAFM as unsuitable	.80
				USAFM, Minnesota ANGB, Minneapolis MN (displ. as "USAF 45024")	82/96
PE2-1001	TF-51D Cavalier Enforcer			Cavalier Aircraft Corp, Sarasota FL (rebuilt by Cavalier with Lycoming T55 turboprop as 2 seater Enforcer prototype)	67/69
	Enforcer	Piper	N202PE	Piper Aircraft, Lakeland FL: "PE2" (completed by Piper, ff Lakeland FL 29.4.71)	71
				crashed, Vero Beach FL	12.7.71
48-8301001 •	PA-48 Enforcer		N481PE	Piper Aircraft, Lakeland FL: "EN1" (manufactured by Piper with Lycoming T55 turboprop, ff Lakeland FL 9.4.83)	83

				del. to Edwards AFB CA for USAF evaluation	.83/84
				del. to MASDC, Davis Monthan AFB AZ	8.84/86
				(dism. in crate, MASDC markings, Eglin AFB FL 87)	
				Davis Monthan AFB AZ: open storage	91
				USAFM, Wright Patterson AFB OH	93/96
48-8301002•	PA-48 Enforcer		N482PE	Piper Aircraft, Lakeland FL: "EN2"	7.83
				(manufactured by Piper with Lycoming T55 turboprop, ff Lakeland FL 8.7.83)	
				del. to Edwards AFB CA for USAF evaluation	.83/84
				del. to MASDC, Davis Monthan AFB AZ	8.84/89
				USAFM, Edwards AFB CA (stored dism.)	.90/96
- •	Cavalier Mk.2	-		Cavalier Aircraft Corp, Sarasota FL: built	23.10.68
				(to FA Salvadorena as FAS 405)	12.68
			N31FF	Jack W. Flaherty/Flaherty Factors Inc, Monterey CA	1.11.74
				(adopted id. 44-10753 on return to USA)	
				Wilson C. Edwards, Big Spring TX	78/96
- •	P-51D	-	**N51KJ**	Jerry D. Owens, Scottsdale AZ	8.82/95
				(USCR quotes id. 44-12962: not a P-51 serial)	
- •	P-51D	-	**N3139T**	Clyde J. Driskill, McPherson KS	12.91/95
				(USCR quotes id. "004", type "NA/Driskill P-51D")	
- •	P-51D	-	**N4451C**	Barone Bros Partnership, San Bernadino CA	12.91/95
				dam. landing George AFB, Victorville CA	28.10.94
				(USCR quotes id. "003", type "NA/Barone P-51D")	
- •	P-51D Vendetta	-	**N91JD**	John Dilley/Fort Wayne Air Service IN	8.87/88
				(mod. racer, Learjet mainplane &tail; race #19/*Vendetta*)	
			N91KD	Fort Wayne Air Service, Fort Wayne IN	6.88
				North American Dilley Inc, Fort Wayne IN	9.88
				Fort Wayne Air Service, Fort Wayne IN	3.89/90
				crashed: struck-off USCR	4.90
				(rep. rebuilt by FWAS as stock P-51D)	
				(USCR quotes type P-51R, id. "87-1001")	
- •	P-51D	-		Ed Field/Mustang Fighter Trust, Hong Kong	3.94/96
				(composite rest. project, shipped ex USA to Caboolture QLD for assembly, arr. 26.5.95)	
				(id. quoted as CA-18 c/n 1335/A68-110: which was rep broken for scrap, RAAF Tocumwal NSW .57)	
- •	P-51D	-		Eagle Squadron Association, San Diego CA	86/89
				(static rest. Chino CA based on ex TNI-AU airframe,with parts from 44-73415/N6526D)	
				RAF Museum, Hendon	.89/95
				(airfreighted to RAF Lyneham 13.2.89: displ. Hendon as 413573/B6-V/*Little Friend*)	
- •	P-51D	-		(to FA Guatemalteca as FAG 336)	3.56
				displ. Guatemala City	
				La Aurora AB, Guatemala: displ. as"FAG 360"	79/87
- •	P-51D	-		(to IDFAF as ....)	
				Israeli AF Museum, Hatzerim AB, Israel	91
				(displ. as "IDFAF 01")	
- •	P-51D	-		(to IDFAF as 28)	
				Robs Lamplough, Duxford/North Weald UK	.78/90
				(hulk recov. ex kibbutz playground, Saar, Israel: rest. RAF Watton .78/80 using wing ex IDFAF 41, under rest. to fly North Weald 87/90)	
				shipped USA	92

	Type		Reg	History	Date
- •	P-51D	-		(to IDFAF as 38)	
				IDFAF Museum, Haifa AB, Israel	84
				Israeli AF Museum, Hatzerim AB, Israel	87/91
				(displ. as "IDFAF 2338")	
- •	P-51D	-		(to IDFAF as ....)	
		(		Israeli AF Museum, Hatzerim AB, Israel	91
				displ. as "IDFAF 39")	
- •	P-51D	-		(to IDFAF as ....)	
				Israeli AF Museum, Hatzerim AB, Israel	91
				(composite rest: displ. as "IDFAF 008")	
- •	P-51D	-		(to Italian AF as MM.....)	
				(to IDFAF as 2338)	
				Israeli Air Force Museum, Herzlia: stored	78
				Israel Yitzhaki, Sde-Dov, Israel	3.78/84
				(rest. Herzlia 78/84, using parts ex USA:	
				adopted id. 44-63864: ff Herzlia 5.2.84)	
			4X-AIM	Israel Yitzhaki, Herzlia	2.84/86
			SE-BKG	Leif Jaraker/Novida AB/Flygexpo Vasteras,	
				Vasteras	24.4.87/94
				(del. from Israel via Frankfurt 12.86, arr. Malmo	
				Sweden 23.12.86; flew as "Fv26158/16K")	
				Duke of Brabant Air Force, Eindhoven,	
				Netherlands: loan, del.	9.94/96
				(flies as "R Neth. East Indies AF N3-615")	
- •	P-51D	-		(to IDFAF as 146)	
				hulk recov. ex kibbutz playground, Israel by	
				Robs Lamplough, Duxford UK: arr.	12.76/90
				loan: Rebel Air Museum, Great Saling UK	82/87
				(stored, North Weald 89)	
- •	P-51D	-		(to Swedish AF as Fv.....)	
	J 26			(to IDFAF as ....)	
				static rest. completed Camiel, Israel "2338"	.89
- •	P-51D	-		(to Indonesian AF/TNI-AU as F-303)	
				Halim AB, Jakarta, Indonesia: displ. on pole	75/93
- •	P-51D	-		(to Indonesian AF/TNI-AU as F-338)	
	Cavalier			Indonesian Air Force Museum, Yogyakarta	.78/93
- •	P-51D	-		(to Indonesian AF/TNI-AU as F-....)	
				Indonesian Air Force HQ, Jakarta	90/93
				(displ. on pole as "F-338")	
- •	P-51D	-		(to Indonesian AF/TNI-AU as F-347)	
				Armed Forces Museum, Jakarta, Indonesia	77/95
- •	P-51D	-		(to Indonesian AF/TNI-AU as F-354)	
				Museum Palagan, Jawa Tengah, Indonesia	90
- •	P-51D	-		(to Indonesian AF/TNI-AU as F-363)	
				rep. displ. Kalijati AB, Indonesia	87
- •	P-51D	-		(to Philippine AF as ......)	
				PAF Museum, Nichols/Villamor AB, Manila	79/91
- •	P-51D	-		USAFM, Barksdale AFB LA	87/96
				(composite static rest., displ. as "44-14570")	
- •	P-51D	-		USAFM, Robins AFB GA	93/94
				(composite static rest., displ. as "44-13704")	
- •	P-51B	-		(to Soviet AF as ......)	
				Central Museum of Armed Forces, Moscow	c50
				Zhukovsky Memorial Museum, Moscow	79/90

North American Aviation F-82 Twin Mustang

c/n	Type	Serial	Reg	History	Date
120-43743 •	XP-82 ZXF-82	**44-83887**		op by NACA: BOC 10.47 SOC Walter Soplata Collection, Newbury OH (incomplete airframe)	5.50 65/85
123-43748 •	F-82B	**44-65162**	 **N12102**	USAFM, Lackland AFB TX Confederate Air Force, Mercedes TX (ferried Lackland AFB to Mercedes TX .66) Confederate Air Force, Mercedes TX, later Harlingen TX, Midland TX landingaccident , Harlingen TX (rest. to fly,)	.56/65 .66/68 31.1.68/96 10.10.87
123-43754 •	F-82B	**44-65168**		(to NACA as NACA132): BOC 9.50: SOC USAFM, Wright-Patterson AFB, Dayton OH (displ. as 465168/PQ-168/*Betty-Jo*)	6.57 21.6.57/92
144-38142 •	F-82E EF-82E	**46-256**		(to NACA as NACA133): BOC 1.50: SOC Walter Soplata Collection, Newbury OH	3.54 65/85
144-38148 •	F-82E	**46-262**		USAFM, Lackland AFB TX (displ. as USAF "6262/FQ-262")	.56/96

Northrop P-61 Black Widow

c/n	Type	Serial	Reg	History	Date
964 •	P-61B	**42-39445**	 **N550NF**	forced landed, 7000ft up Cyclops Mountain, Sentani, Dutch New Guinea (Irian Jaya) recov. commenced by MAAM, abandoned Mid Atlantic Air Museum, Middletown PA recov. completed, shipped to Reading PA (planned rest. to fly)	10.1.45 .85 5.88/95 2.91
- •	P-61C	**43-8330**		NASM, Silver Hill MD	65/92
- •	P-61C	**43-8353**		Boy Scouts of America, Urbania OH Earl Reinert, Wheeling IL: not collected USAFM, Wright-Patterson AFB, Dayton OH (displ. as "239468/"Moonlight Serenade")	54/58 20.6.58/92
- •	P-61C	**-**		Beijing Aeronautical Institute, Beijing China (displ. as "7602", "25171")	87/93

Polikarpov I-16 Rata

c/n	Type	Serial	Reg	History	Date
- •	I-16	-		(to Chinese AF as 5806) People's Liberation Army Air Force Museum, Changping, China	90/94
- •	I-16	-		(to Soviet AF as .....) displ. complete in museum, St Petersburg	94
- •	I-16	-		new aircraft produced from wrecks Alpine Fighter Collection, Wanaka NZ	.95 .94/96
- •	I-16	-		Restoration in Russia Old Flying Machine Company, Duxford UK (rep. using parts recov. ex crash sites,	90/96
- •	I-16	-		The Fighter Collection, Duxford UK (under rest. Russia 95: using major structures recov. ex Russian crash sites & original unused components)	90/96
- •	I-16	-		The Fighter Collection, Duxford UK (hulk recov. ex peat bog crash site Russia)	90/96
- •	I-16	-		The Fighter Collection, Duxford UK (hulk recov. ex peat bog crash site Russia):	90/96

Polikarpov I-153 Chaika

		Type	Serial	Reg	History	Date
-	•	I-153	-		Musee de l'Air, Paris-Le Bourget	90/96
					(displ. as "9")	
-	•	I-153	-		Russian production run of three:	
					Alpine Fighter Collection, Wanaka NZ	.95
-	•	I-153	-		Stored in Russia awaiting restoration	
					The Fighter Collection, Duxford UK	.95

Reggiane Re2000 Series

		Type	Serial	Reg	History	Date
-	•	Re 2000	**Fv2340**		(to R Swedish AF as Fv.2340)	
		J20			Flygvapenmuseum Malmen, Malmslatt,Sweden	66/92
					(displ. as "10")	
-	•	Re 2000	**MM8287**		Museo Storico dell'Aeronautica Militaire	
					Italiana, Vigna di Valle AB	84/92
					Museo dell' Aeronautico Gianni Caproni,	
					Vizzola Ticino: loan (unrest. fuselage)	87/92
-	•	Re 2001	**MM8071**		ditched in sea off Sardinia	
					recov. complete at Cagliari docks, Sardinia	23.11.91
					Museo Storico dell'Aeronautica Militaire	
					Italiana, Vigna di Valle AB	.91/95
					(static rest. Guidonia AB 92/95)	
126	•	Re 2002	**MM....**		University of Bologne School of Engineering	
					Museo Storico: recov. derelict	
					(static rest. commenced by Caproni Museum,	
					taken over by Group Aviazone Reggiane .86)	
					Museo Storico dell'Aeronautica Militaire	
					Italiana, Vigna di Valle AB	12.92/93
-	•	Re 2002	**MM....**		(to Luftwaffe as DV+B1) used against partisans	
					rep. shot down by partisans, Limoges area	c44
					displ. on plinth, town square, Limoges France	60/82
					removed from display	.82
					(rep. as fuse. only, poor condition 90)	
-	•	Re 2005	**MM92352**		Museo Storico dell'Aeronautica Militaire	
					Italiana, Vigna di Valle AB	84/92
					Museo dell' Aeronautico Gianni Caproni,	
					Vizzola Ticino: loan (wreck)	87/92

Republic P-47 Thunderbolt

		Type	Serial	Reg	History	Date
-	•	P-47D	**42-8066**		William G. Chapman/PNG War Museum	.68/72
					(recov. ex swamp, Lake Iraguma, near	
					Port Moresby PNG by Robert Diemert .68)	
					Kokoda Track War Memorial Museum,	
					Port Moresby , PNG	.72
					d'E. C. Darby, Auckland NZ	.75
					Museum of Transport & Technology, Auckland 80/91	
					(static rest., displ. as "28068" later"428066")	
					RNZAF Museum, Wigram AB NZ	.91/95
					Robert Greinert/Historical Aircraft Restoration	
					Society, Sydney NSW	3.95
					(airfreighted to Sydney by RNZAF C-130,	
					stored dism. Sydney-Bankstown, pending rest.)	
-	•	P-47D	**42-8205**	NC75640	Texas Railroad & Equipment Co	49
		TP-47D			(to FA Boliviana as ....)	10.49
					(del. Clinton AFB OK to Washington DC 5.10.49,	
					then ferried to La Paz 10.49: never operational)	

				La Paz-El Alto AB: gate guard "FAB 007"	55/73
				Jim Cullen/Westair International Inc,	
				Monument CO: recov. ex La Paz	7.73
			N14519	Westair International, Monument CO	12.73
				Doug Champlin/Windward Aviation, Enid OK	2.76/79
				(rest. Carlsbad CA 76/81; ff .81)	
				Champlin Fighter Museum, Mesa AZ: del.	5.81/95
				(flies as *Big Stud*/88)	
- •	P-47D	**42-8320**		BOC USAAF 30.5.43; crashed Lake Kerr FL	12.8.43
				recov. from Lake Kerr by Jay Wisler FL	c84
				P-47 Heritage Commission, Evansville IN	87
				(static rest., displ. as "222250"/*Hoosier Spirit*")	
- •	P-47D	**42-19663**		(to FA Brasileira as P-47D 4120): BOC	28.10.44
				Guaratingueta AB: inst. airframe	14.1.60
				Guaratingueta AB: displ. on pole as "FAB D5"	80/90
- •	P-47D	**42-23278**		Hancock College of Aeronautics,	
				Santa Maria CA: inst. airframe	.47
				Bob Bean Aircraft, Blythe CA (stored Blythe)	.53/61
			N5087V	Republic Aviation Corp, Farmingdale NY	4.61/64
				(flown in UK and Europe .63)	
			N347D	USAFM, Wright-Patterson AFB, Dayton OH	11.64/92
- •	P-47G TP-47G	**42-25068**		Aero Industries Technical Institute,	
				Oakland Airport CA: inst. airframe	.46/52
				Jack P. Hardwick/Hardwick Aircraft Supply,	
				El Monte CA	.52/75
				(used by Flying Tiger Line as ground engine test rig	
				Oakland; stored Hardwick's yard, El Monte c55/75)	
				Eagle Aviation, Tulsa OK (rest. commenced)	.75
				Hurley Boehler/Sirrus Aviation, Tulsa OK	
				Ray Stutsman, Elkhart IN	7.12.79/81
			N42354	Ray Stutsman, Elkhart IN	5.81/82
			N47DG	Ray Stutsman, Elkhart IN	2.82/87
				(rest. Elkhart, ff 4.82 as 28476/*Little Demon*)	
				Lone Star Flight Museum,	
				Houston, later Galveston TX	5.87/96
- •	P-47G	**42-25234**		Grand Central Aircraft Co, Glendale CA	.44
				Cal-Aero Technical Institute, Glendale CA	50/55
				Ed Maloney/The Air Museum, Claremont CA	10.55
			N3395G	Ed Maloney/The Air Museum, Ontario CA	63/71
				(rest. Kirtland AFB NM .58/63; flew as	
				Roscoe's Retreat/MX-W",later"226387/NM-U)	
				crashed during airshow, NAS Point Mugu CA	23.10.71
				(rebuilt Chino CA, ff .76 as "28487/M-UN")	
				Planes of Fame Museum, Chino CA	.76/96
				(FAA quotes id. 42-25254)	
- •	P-47D	**42-26757**		(to FA Brasileira as P-47D 4107): BOC	28.10.44
				Rio-Santa Cruz AB: instructional airframe	14.6.60
				Rio-Santa Cruz AB: displ.	78/96
				(displ. as "4107", later "419660/C5")	
- •	P-47D	**42-26760**		(to FA Brasileira as P-47D 4109): BOC	28.10.44
				Curitiba AB: instructional airframe	14.1.60
				Museu de Aeronautica, Sao Paulo	17.6.69/96
- •	P-47D	**42-26762**		(to FA Brasileira as P-47D 4110): BOC	19.1.45
				Curitiba AB: inst. airframe	30.12.52
				Curitiba AB: displ.	89/90
93F- 12000 •	P-47D YP-47M	**42-27385**	NX4477N	Republic Aviation: retired, dismantled	46/47
				William P. Odom/Dallas Aero Service	7.47
				(race #42 *Reynolds Bombshell*)	

				Earl T. Reinert, Chicago IL	6.48/63
				(stored engineless, Oklahoma c50/63)	
				Earl T. Reinert/Victory Air Museum,	
				Mundelein IL (displ. as "MX-F")	.63/84
			N4477M	Yankee Air Corps, Chino CA	10.85/91
			N4464N	Yankee Air Corps, Chino CA	3.86/90
			N27385	Yanks Air Museum, Chino CA	10.90/96
				(rest. Chino 85/93, rolled-out 12.93 "227385")	
- •	P-47D	**44-20371**		(to l'Armee de l'Air as 420371)	
				Musee de l'Air: stored St Cyr, Paris	74
				Musee de l'Air et de l'Espace, Paris	75/96
				(displ. as AdlA "420371")	
- •	P-47D	**44-32691**		NASM, Silver Hill MD	65/90
				NASM, Washington DC	93/94
				(displ. as "432691/LH-E")	
				USAFM, Robins AFB GA: loan	12.93/94
- •	P-47D	**44-32809**		(to FA Venezolana as FAV 10B-36): del.	5.4.49
				Museo Aeronautico, Maracay AB	80/96
				(displ. as FAV "10B36")	
- •	P-47D	**44-32814**		(to FA Venezolana as FAV 8A-36): del.	5.4.49
				displ. Fort Tiuna, Caracas	82
				Escuela Superior de la Fuerza Aerea, Caracas	80/91
				(displ. as FAV "8A-36")	
399-53778 •	P-47D	**44-32817**	**N767WJ**	World Jet Inc, Fort Lauderdale FL	1.95
				Jack A. Erickson, Medford OR	5.95
- •	P-47D	**44-33712**		(to Turkish AF as TC-21)	
				Turk Hava Muzesi, Cumaovasi AB, Izmir	66
				Turkish Air Force Museum, Istanbul	82/88
549-C6765 •	P-47N	**44-88548**		(to FA Nicaragua as GN72): del.	16.6.54
			N6148U	Glenn Martin/MACO Sales Financial Corp,	
				Chicago IL	2.9.63/64
				forced landing on beach Mexico, on del. flight	26.9.64
				Confederate Air Force, Merecedes TX	.64
				(recov. from beach, stripped for parts)	
				Confederate Air Force, Albuquerque NM	87
				(fuselage only)	
539-C1537 •	P-47N	**44-89320**		Miguel Such Vocational School, San Juan PR	.54/67
				Muniz ANGB, Isla Verde PR: displ.	.67/70
				(displ. as "489320/PR ANG")	
			N345GP	Gabriel I. Penagarico/Thunderbolt Inc,	
				Santurce PR	.70/78
				(rest. San Juan, ff. 20.9.72, "489320/5A-Z")	
				dam., tipped on nose, Myrtle Beach AFB SC	10.6.77
				impounded by US Govt. due breach of sale	
				conditions	.77
				USAFM, Eglin AFB FL: displ. as "126"	11.78/96
- •	P-47N	**44-89348**		USAFM, Lackland AFB TX	.56/96
				(displ. as "489348/HV-A")	
- •	P-47N	**44-89425**		American Legion Post, Shortsville NY	68
				USAFM, Sampson AFB NY: gate guard	
				USAFM, Stewart AFB NY	10.69
				USAFM, Perrin AFB TX	71
				USAFM, Peterson AFB CO	5.71/96
				(displ. on pole as "489425/PE-425")	
- •	P-47N	**44-89436**		(to FA Guatemala): CIA operations	53/54
				(to FA Nicaragua as GN71): del.	16.6.54
				Dick Disney/Confederate Air Force TX	.62
			N478C	Lloyd P. Nolan/Thunderbolt & Co,	
				Mercedes TX: del. ex Managua	7.2.63/70

			N47TB	Confederate Air Force, Harlingen/Midland TX	.70/94
				crashed Vero Beach FL	29.4.71
				(rebuilt .76, flies as "UN-S")	
				Cavanaugh Flight Museum, Addison TX: loan	94
				(FAA quotes "453436", CAF quotes 44-53436, other sources quote 44-88436 & 45-53456!)	
- •	P-47N	**44-89444**		USAFM, Langley AFB VA	c56
				USAFM, Wright-Patterson AFB, Dayton OH	57/61
				USAFM, Greater Pittsburgh ANGB PA	71/78
				Cradle of Aviation Museum, Mitchell Field NY	6.78/95
				(trucked ex Pittsburgh 6.78, displ. as "489444/08/*Cheek Baby*")	
- •	P-47D	**44-89746**		(to Italian AF as MM4653)	1.3.51
				Pisa University Engineering School: del.	19.5.53/73
				Museo Storico Dell'Aeronautica Militare Italiana, Vigna di Valle AB	.73/88
				(static rest., displ. as "MM4653/51-19")	
- •	P-47D	**44-90205**		(to FA Mexicana as PZT 1012): del.	7.11.45
				FAM: *Fantasma*	
				Colegio del Aire: displ.	80/90
- •	P-47D	**44-90217**		(to FA Mexicana as PZT 1016): del.	7.11.45
				FAM: *Pancho Pistolas*	
				Museo de la FAM, Santa Lucia AB: displ.	78/94
- •	P-47D	**44-90368**		(to FA Venezolana as FAV490368/6): del.	28.10.47
				Steve Schulke, Orlando FL	.71
				(with 2 others: deal not completed)	
				J-B Salis Collection, La Ferte-Alais, France	84/87
				(noted stored unrest., La Ferte-Alais 84/85)	
				Charles A. Osborn, Louisville KY	.87
			N4747P	Charles A. Osborn/Blue Sky Aviation, Louisville KY & Sellersburg IN	6.91/95
				(rest., flew as 432773/4P-S/*Big Ass Bird II* - see cover)	
- •	P-47D	**44-90438**		(to Yugoslav AF as 13021)	2.52
				Yugoslav Aeronautical Museum, Belgrade	84
				Warbirds of GB Ltd,	.85
				John Whittington, Knoxville TN	.86/91
				(rest. to fly, Knoxville TN)	
399-55592 •	P-47D	**44-90447**		(to Yugoslav AF as ....)	
				rep. Yugoslavian Aviation Museum, Belgrade	
				(recov. derelict ex playground, Yugoslavia)	
				David Price, Bill Clark, Tiger Destefani/ Museum of Flying, Santa Monica CA	.89/93
				(rest. Shafter CA, ff 6.93 as "490447/LH-I")	
			N1345B	William P. Clark/Repatria Inc, Paso Robles CA & Museum of Flying, Santa Monica CA	12.4.93/96
				(USCR quotes id. 44-90447)	
				(note: rep. ex Yugoslavia as above by owner,	
399-55605 •	P-47D	**44-90460**		(to FA Brasileira as F-47 4175): BOC	30.10.53
				retired, stripped for spares: SOC	17.3.58
				Recife AB, Brazil: displ. as "226450/A1"	70/87
				Museu Aeroespacial, Campo dos Afoncos, Rio	.87/88
				(arr. dism. Chino CA ex Brazil 9.88: 4 total)	
				Airplane Sales International: reg. candidate	5.8.91
			N9246B	Airplane Sales International, Beverly Hills CA	9.95
399-55616 •	P-47D	**44-90471**		(to FA Peruana as 532, reserialled 114): BOC	12.52
				open storage Piura AB, Peru	63/69
			N47DA	Vintage Aircraft International Ltd, Nyack NY	7.69/75
				(arr. *SS Rosaldina*, Brownsville TX 5.9.69; assembled by CAF, Harlingen TX, ff 26.8.71)	

				David C. Tallichet/ MARG, Chino CA	4.75/95
				(stored Barstow-Daggett CA 75)	
				56th FG Restaurant, Farmingdale NY: del	4.83/87
				(displ. as "421175/"Zemke's Wolfpack/UN-Z")	
				National Warplane Museum, Geneseo NY: loan	4.87/90
				Air Heritage Inc, Beaver Falls PA: leased	91/93
				(rest. to fly commenced, Beaver Falls PA)	
				Midwest Aviation Museum Danville IL	.94/96
				(rest. to fly Danville IL .94/96)	
- •	P-47N	**44-95171**		NASM, Silver Hill MD: stored	71
				(fuselage & tailplane only)	
399-55641 •	P-47D	**45-49102**		(to FA Colombiana as FAC 861): del.	12.9.54
				Museo Aeronautico, Bogota-Catam AB,	72/96
				(displ. as "FAC 861")	
399-55669 •	P-47D	**45-49130**		(to FA Brasileira as F-47 4181): BOC	10.9.53
				Fortaleza AB: inst. airframe	6.6.57
				Fortaleza AB, Brazil: displ.	70/87
				Museu Aeroespacial, Campo dos Afoncos, Rio	88
				(arr. dism. Chino CA ex Brazil 9.88: 4 total)	
				Airplane Sales International: reg. candidate	5.8.91
			N9246W	Airplane Sales International, Beverly Hills CA	9.95
399-55690 •	P-47D	**45-49151**		(to FA Brasileira as F-47 4184): BOC	13.8.53
				Sao Jose dos Campos: inst. airframe	60
				Quaratingueta AB, Sao Paulo	67/72
				Museu Aeroespacial, Campo dos Afoncos, Rio	78/96
				(displ. as FAB "420339/D3";	
				rest. to fly 87/96)	
399-55706 •	P-47D	**45-49167**		(to FA Peruana as 540, reserialled 116): del.	16.3.53
				open storage, Piura AB, Peru	63/69
			N47DB	Vintage Aircraft International Ltd, Nyack NY	69/75
				(arr. *SS Rosaldina*, Brownsville TX 5.9.69;	
				assembled by CAF, Harlingen TX,	
				ff 2.12.71 as USAAF "226422/LH-E")	
				(raced at Reno as #13 by M. L. Gardner 9.74)	
				David C. Tallichet/MARC, Chino CA	4.75/81
				(stored Barstow-Daggett CA 75)	
				56th FG Restaurant, St Petersburg FL: displ.	
				dam. by storm St Petersburg, rebuilt Chino	.79
				USAFM, Wright-Patterson AFB, OH: del.	5.81/96
				(displ. as "432718")	
399-55720 •	P-47D	**45-49181**		(to FA Peruana as 539, reserialled 115): BOC	3.53
				open storage, Piura AB, Peru	63/69
			N47DC	Vintage Aircraft International Ltd, Nyack NY	7.69/75
				(arr. SS Rosaldina, Brownsville TX 5.9.69;	
				assembled by CAF, Harlingen TX,	
				ff 28.8.72 as USAAF "420473/FT-L")	
				MARC, Chino CA	4.75/77
				(stored Barstow-Daggett CA .75/77)	
				Lester Friend, Carlsbad CA	4.77
			N159LF	Lester Friend, Carlsbad CA	.78/79
				(flew as "549181/LD-F")	
				Preston Parish, Kalamazoo MI	26.7.79
			N444SU	Kalamazoo Aviation History	
				Museum, Kalamazoo MI	3.83/96
				(rest. Kalamazoo, ff .84 as "226418/HV-A")	
399-55731•	P-47D	**45-49192**		(to FA Peruana as 545, reserialled 119): BOC	3.53
				open storage, Piura AB, Peru	63/69
			N47DD (1	Vintage Aircraft International Ltd, Nyack NY	7.69/75
				(arr. *SS Rosaldina*, Brownsville TX 5.9.69;	
				assembled by CAF, Harlingen TX: ff .73	
				as USAAF "226641/*Grumpy*")	
				David C. Tallichet/ MARG, Chino CA	4.75/80
				(stored Barstow-Daggett CA 4.75/77)	

c/n	Model	Serial	Reg.	History	Date
				Yesterdays Air Force Kansas Wing,	
				Forbes Field, Topeka KS: del.	2.77/80
				Robin P. Collard, Del Rio TX	1.80
				crashed on take-off on del. flight, Tulsa OK	9.2.80
				(trucked to Del Rio TX .80)	
				Jon Ward, Saugus CA	6.80/82
				Stephen Grey, Duxford UK	.85
				(basis of static rebuild: N47DD(2 resurrected as	
				composite with parts of 45-49192: see below)	
				Imperial War Museum, Duxford UK: arr.	11.85/96
				static rest. Duxford for American Air Museum	
399-55744 •	P-47D	**45-49205**		(to FA Peruana as 547, reserialled 122): BOC	3.53
				open storage, Piura AB, Peru	63/69
			N47DE	Vintage Aircraft International Ltd,Nyack NY	7.69/75
				(arr. *SS Rosaldina*, Brownsville TX 5.9.69,	
				assembled by CAF, Harlingen TX: ff .73)	
				David C. Tallichet/ MARG, Chino CA	4.75/79
				(stored Barstow-Daggett CA .75/79)	
				Warbirds of GB Ltd, Blackbushe	5.79/85
				(arr. Blackbushe on del. ex Chino CA 11.11.79)	
			G-BLZW	Warbirds of GB Ltd, Blackbushe	15.7.85
				Stephen Grey, Duxford: del.	18.9.85
			N47DE	Planes of Fame East,	
				Minneapolis-Flying Cloud MN	17.12.85
				(crated Duxford, shipped to Chino CA, ff 6.86)	
			N47RP	Robert J. Pond, Eden Prairie MN	3.86/95
				(flies as 228473/*Big Chief*/HV-P)	
399-55758 •	P-47D	**45-49219**		(to FA de Chile as 750): del.	18.7.53
				FAC, retired	21.4.59
				FAC Museum, El Bosque AB, Santiago	87/92
				(displ. as "FAC 750")	
399-55834 •	P-47D	**45-49295**		(to Yugoslav AF as 13064)	
				Yugoslav Aeronautical Museum, Belgrade	85
				Warbirds of GB Ltd.	.85
				RAF Museum store, RAF Cardington: arr.	6.86/95
				(static rest. Fighter Collection Duxford 94/95	
				as "RAF KL216/RS-L"),	
				trucked to RAF Cosford 6.95 for displ.)	
				(id. prev. incorrectly rep. as 42-22936/13024)	
399-55885 •	P-47D	**45-49346**		(to FA Brasileira as F-47 4191): BOC	10.9.53/67
				displ. in park, Sao Paulo City, as "4191/C3"	68/72
				dam. by student riots, Sao Paulo	.69
				FAB Academy, Pirassununga AB: displ.	87
				(displ. as "4226762/C1", later "4194/C1")	
				Museu Aeroespacial, Campo dos Afoncos, Rio	88
				(arr. dism. Chino CA ex Brazil 9.88: 4 total)	
				Airplane Sales International Corp: candidate	12.6.90
			N3152D	Yanks Air Museum, Chino CA	13.8.91/96
				(rest. to fly, Chino CA 93/96)	
399-55924 •	P-47D	**45-49385**		(to FA Peruana as 549, reserialled 127): BOC	3.53
				open storage Piura AB, Peru	63/69
			N47DF	Vintage Aircraft International Ltd, Nyack NY	7.69/74
				(arr. *SS Rosaldina*, Brownsville TX 5.9.69;	
				assembled by CAF, Harlingen TX: ff .73)	
				(flew as "228790/GQ-E/Unadilla Killa")	
				Tom Friedkin, Palomar CA	74
				MARC, Chino CA	4.75/94
				(stored, Barstow-Dagget CA .75/80)	
				crashed on take-off, Barstow CA	3.7.80
				(rebuilt Tulsa OK, later Casper WY 80/86)	
				Liberal Air Museum, Liberal KS: loan	.86/90
				dam. forced landing near Flagstaff AZ, during	

c/n	Type	Serial	Reg	History	Date
				ferry flight Topeka-Chino (trucked to Chino, rebuild commenced 91/93)	10.90
				Klaers Aircraft Inc, Rialto CA (rest. Rialto 94/95, as "549385") (note: prev. rep. incorrectly as 44-49335)	.94/96
399-55945 •	P-47D	**45-49406**		(to FA Brasileira as F-47 4192): BOC	10.9.53
				Sao Jose dos Campos AB: inst. airframe	14.1.60
				Campo Grande AB: displ.	
				Natal AB: displ.	.86
				Museu Aeroespacial, Campo dos Afoncos, Rio (arr. dism. Chino CA c9.88, ex Brazil)	
			N7159Z	Victor Haluska/Santa Monica Propeller Inc, Santa Monica CA	7.90/92
				Wixair Inc, Janesville WI	5.93/95
399-55991 •	P-47D	**45-49452**		(to FA Peruana as 450): BOC	21.7.47
				Las Palmas AB, Lima: displ. as "FAP 450"	90
399-55997 •	P-47D	**45-49458**		(to FA Peruana as 451): BOC	21.7.47
				USAFM: donated by FAP (airfreighted via Howard AFB, Canal Zone 10.71)	.71/91
				Bradley Air Museum/New England Air Museum, Windsor Locks CT: loan (displ. as "420344", later "549458/54/*Norma*)	11.72/91
399-56048 •	P-47D	**45-49509**		(to FA de Chile as 760): del.	13.11.47
				rep. gate guard, FAC base, Chile	80/90
- •	P-47D	-		(incomplete fuselage P-47N ex trade school (id incorrectly quoted as "44-95471")	
				MARC, Chino CA (stored Barstow-Daggett CA 75/80)	75
				Wayne Williams (adv. for sale as project)	.80
				Robin Collard, Del Rio TX (composite rest., trucked to Tahoe NV .80: parts N47DD/45-49192, wing ex S.America)	.80
				Jon Ward, Saugus CA (rest. at Truckee CA & Agua Dulce CA 82/84)	6.80/82
				Jim Kirby, Tahoe NV (rest. 70% complete)	.84
			N47DD (2	Steven J. Hinton/Fighter Rebuilders Inc, Chino CA: leased to:	9.85/95
				The Fighter Collection, Duxford (rest. completed at Chino, ff. 8.85; shipped to UK, arr. Duxford 22.1.86) (flies as "226671/MX-X/*No Guts No Glory*")	.85/95
			G-THUN		
- •	P-47D	-		(to FA Cubana as ......)	
				displ. Havana, Cuba	76/88
- •	P-47D	-		(to FA Mexicana as .....)	
				rep. at Guadalajara, Mexico: derelict	87
- •	P-47	-		(to FA Nicaragua as GN.....)	
				rep. displ. Managua Airport, Nicaragua	
				rep. Roy M. Stafford, Jacksonville FL	c87
- •	P-47D	-		(to FA Venezolana as FAV 15B36)	
				displ. Venezuala: "15B36"	75
				rep. stored dism. El Libertador AB, Maracay	90
- •	P-47D	-		(to Yugoslav AF as 13056)	
				Yugoslavian Aviation Museum, Belgrade	84/92
- •	P-47D	-		(to Yugoslav AF as 13109)	
				Technical Museum, Zagreb, Yugoslavia	84/92
-	P-47N	-		Earl T. Reinert, Chicago IL (recov. ex Republic: uncompleted airframe)	

				Walter Soplata Collection, Newbury OH	85
				(fuselage and tailplane only)	
- •	P-47D	-		Beijing Aeronautical Institute, Beijing China	80/94
				(displ. as "7601")	
499-6808 •	P-47N	-		Beijing Aeronautical Institute, Beijing China	80/94
				(incomplete fuselage, stored)	

RYAN FR FIREBALL

- •	FR-1	**Bu39657**		Planes of Fame, Chino CA	72/89
				Fighter Jets Museum, Chino CA	89/93
-	FR-1	Bu39707		NASM, Washington DC	76
				San Diego Air & Space Museum CA (loaned)	76/78
				dest. by fire at San Diego Museum	22.7.78

SHORT SUNDERLAND

SB.2018 •	Mk. III	**JM715**	ZK-AMH	Tasman Empire Airways Ltd - TEAL,	
	(SH.32C)Mk. V			Auckland NZ *Auckland*	10.47/50
	Sandringham 4		VH-BRC	Barrier Reef Airways, Brisbane QLD	.50/53
				Beachcomber	
				Ansett Flying Boat Services, Sydney NSW	.53/74
				Beachcomber	
			N158C	Antilles Air Boats, St Thomas USVI	11.74
				Southern Cross	
			VP-LVE	Antilles Air Boats, St Thomas USVI	.75
			N158C	Antilles Air Boats, St Thomas USVI	78/81
				(del. San Juan PR to Calshot 10.80 - 2.2.81)	
				Science Museum, London	.82/94
				Southampton Hall of Aviation: loan	8.83/95
				(displ. as "VH-BRC/*Beachcomber*)	
SB.2022 •	Mk. III	**JM719**	G-AKCO	British Overseas Airways Corp - BOAC	18.3.48
(SH.57C)	Sandringham 7			*St. George*	
			VH-APG	Capt. P. G. Taylor, Sydney "Frigate Bird III"	14.10.54
			F-OBIP	Reseau Aerien Interinsulaire - RAI, Papeete	5.58/65
				(wfu Papeete, open storage 65/78)	
				Douglas Pearson Jnr	.75
				(recov., shipped to France by French Navy 7.78)	
				Musee de l'Air, Le Bourget: handed over	3.11.78/94
				dam. by storm at museum (repaired)	2.84
- •	GR Mk. III	**ML796**		(to Aeronavale as ML796/50-S-3)	51/60
				Robert Bertin : ex storage Brest	.65
				Maisden-La-Riviere, Hydrobase, Nantes	.66/69
				(in use as bar/night club)	
				moved to La Baule France : night club	.69/76
				Imperial War Museum, Duxford: displ.	.76/96
SH.974 •	Mk. III	ML814		(to RNZAF as NZ4108)	
(SH.55C)	MR. V		VH-BRF	Ansett Flying Boat Services, Rose Bay	.63/74
	Sandringham			"Islander"	
			N158J	Antilles Air Boats, St Thomas USVI	25.9.74/81
				"Excalibur VIII"	
				Edward Hulton, Calshot: del.	5.81
			G-BJHS	Edward Hulton/Sunderland Ltd, Chatham	11.9.81/92
				dam. by gales, Calshot (repaired)	16.10.87
			EI-BYI	ntu: Ryanair Ltd, Foynes "Spirit of Foynes"	8.89
				(del. Chatham-Shannon River, Killaloe 3.8.89)	
			G-BJHS	Kermit A. Weeks/Fantasy of Flight,	
				Polk City FL	10.92/93
				(dep. Calshot on del. to USA 20.7.93)	
			N814ML	Fantasy of Flight, Polk City FL	9.93/96

-	•	GR Mk. V	**ML824**		(to Aeronavale as ML824) del. 28.8.50 wfu	.60
					Peter F. M. Thomas/Sunderland Trust,	
					Pembroke Dock, Wales: del.	24.3.61/71
					RAF Museum, Hendon	3.71/95
					(displ. as "ML824/NS-Z")	
SH.1552	•	GR Mk. V	**SZ584**	G-AHJR	British Overseas Airways Corp - BOAC	16.7.46/48
		MR Mk. V			returned to RAF as SZ584	4.48
					(to RNZAF as NZ4115 "Q"): del.	9.53/66
					Museum of Transport & Technology,	
					Auckland NZ : arr. by road	25.2.67/96

TACHIKAWA KI-24

-	•	Ki-24	(to R Thai AF as ....)	.40
			R Thai AF Museum, Don Muang AB, Bangkok	70/91
-	•	Ki-24	(to R Thai AF as ....)	.40
			R Thai AF Museum, Don Muang AB, Bangkok	

TACHIKAWA KI-36 'IDA'

-	•	Ki-36	(to R Thai AF as ....)	.40
			R Thai AF Museum, Don Muang AB, Bangkok	70/95
-	•	Ki-36	People's Liberation Army Museum,	
			Da Tang Shan, Beijing, China	94
			(displ. as "3/102")	

TACHIKAWA KI-54 'HICKORY'

-	•	Ki-54	Japanese surrender aircraft, Labuan Borneo	10.9.45
			(shipped to RAAF Laverton VIC ex Borneo 4.46)	
			Australian War Memorial, Canberra ACT	.46
			(stored RAAF Fairbairn, Canberra ACT)	
			RAAF Fairbairn: fuselage in playground	65/80
			RAAF Museum, RAAF Point Cook VIC: fuse.	.80/95
-	•	Ki-54	Beijing Aeronautical Institute, China	91/93
			(fuselage only	

TUPOLEV TU-2

	•	Tu-2S	(to Chinese AF as 20465)	
			People's Liberation Army Air Force Museum,	
			Changping, China	90
			(still flying 81, then stored in cave Changping)	
			War Eagles Air Museum,	
			Santa Teresa NM: arr. dism.	12.8.91/96
			(assembled Santa Teresa .91, displ.)	
-	•	Tu-2S	(to Chinese AF as ....)	
			People's Liberation Army Air Force Museum,	
			Changping, China	90
			War Eagles Air Museum,	
			Santa Teresa NM: arr. dism., stored	12.8.91/96
-	•	Tu-2S	(to Chinese AF as ....)	
			Aero Trader, Chino CA	.88
			arr. dism. Chino, green/grey camouflage	.88
			Weeks Air Museum, Tamiami FL	.88/96
			(cockpit section displ. in museum .91/92)	
-	•	Tu-2S	(to Chinese AF as ....)	

			Aero Trader, Chino CA arr. dism. Chino, green/grey camouflage Weeks Air Museum, Tamiami FL	.88 .88 .88/96
1098751 •	Tu-2S		(to Chinese AF as ......) Beijing Aeronautical Insitute, Beijing, China	91
- •	Tu-2		(to Chinese AF as 44792) Military Museum of the Chinese People's Revolution, Beijing (displ. complete, under cover)	75/96
-	Tu-2		(to Chinese AF as 2130) Peking Peoples Museum, Peking	65
- •	Tu-2S		(to Chinese AF as 20582) People's Liberation Army Air Force Museum, Changping, China	90
- •	Tu-2S		(to Chinese AF as 0462) People's Liberation Army Air Force Museum, Changping, China	90/96
- •	Tu-2S		(to Chinese AF as 20608) People's Liberation Army Air Force Museum, Changping, China	90
- •	Tu-2S		(to Chinese AF as ....) People's Liberation Army Air Force Museum, Changping, China: displ. as "20"	90/96
- •	Tu-2S		(to Chinese AF as ..093) People's Liberation Army Air Force Museum, Changping, China	90
- •	Tu-2S		(to Chinese AF as 20661) People's Liberation Army Air Force Museum, Changping, China	90
- •	Tu-2S		(to Chinese AF as 20664) Aero Trader, Chino CA: reg. candidate	9.6.94
- •	Tu-2S		(to Chinese AF as 20668) Aero Trader, Chino CA: reg. candidate	9.6.94
- •	Tu-2		Museum of Aircraft & Astronautics, Krakow Poland: displ.	83/92
- •	Tu-2		Polish Army Aviation Museum, Warsaw	68/93
- •	Tu-2		Soviet AF Museum, Monino AB, Moscow	90/92
- •	Tu-2		Plovdiv Museum, Bulgaria: displ. as "251"	95

VICKERS SUPERMARINE SPITFIRE

6S. 30225 •	F Mk. 1a	**K9942**	RAF Cardiff: for exhibition use RAF Newark: displ. RAF Bicester: travelling exhibit RAF Museum, Hendon: arr. (displ. as "K9942/SD-V")	28.8.44 9.51 60/71 9.11.71/95
- •	F Mk. 1	**N3200**	Fortresse de Mimoyecques, France (recov. buried complete under sand on beach, Sangatte France .86)	.86/96
CBAF. 14 •	F Mk. IIa	**P7350**	RAF Colerne : stored John Dale & Sons Ltd: sold as scrap RAF Colerne Collection: displ.	24.7.44/47 .47 .47/67

			G-AWIJ	Spitfire Productions Ltd, Elstree	25.4.68
				(flew in movie *Battle of Britain* .68)	
				(returned to RAF as P7350)	10.68
				RAF Battle of Britain Memorial Flight	10.68/96
				dam. on takeoff, RAF Chivenor (repaired)	29.7.92
				(flies as "P7350/RN-S")	
- •	F Mk. IIa	**P7540**		crashed into Loch Doon, Ayrshire	25.10.41
				Dumfries & Galloway Aviation Museum, Tinwald Downs, later Polmont Prison	.82/96
				(recov. ex Loch Doon, static rest. project)	
CBAF. 492 •	F Mk. IIa	**P7973**		shipped to Melbourne VIC: display aircraft	7.45/50
				Australian War Memorial, Canberra ACT	3.50/96
				(displ. as "P7973/R-H")	
CBAF. 711 •	F Mk. IIb	**P8332**		RAF presentation aircraft "Soebang (N.E.I.)"	20.3.41
				(to RCAF as P8332): BOC	1.4.42
				displ. various RCAF bases	47/64
				RCAF Museum Collection, Rockcliffe AB ONT	6.12.64
				Canadian National Aeronautical Collection, Rockcliffe ONT	68/93
				National Museum of Science & Technology, Ottawa ONT: loan	83/86
				Canadian War Museum, Ottawa ONT: loan	90/96
				(displ. as "P8332/ZD-L")	
- •	F Mk. Ia	**P9306**		Museum of Science & Industry, Chicago IL	11.44/96
- •	F Mk. Ia	**P9374**		Musee de l'Air, Vannes, France	.80/96
				(wreck recov. from beach, Calais, France 9.80)	
6S/ 30613 •	F Mk. Ia	**P9444**		RAF: allotted for displ. use	28.8.49
				RAF Newark	.51
				Science Museum Store, Sydenham, London	16.12.54
				Science Museum, South Kensington, London	.63/96
6S/ 80914 •	F Mk. Ia	**R6915**		Imperial War Museum, Lambeth, London	26.8.46/96
6S/ 81254 •	F Mk. Ia	**X4590**		RAF Cardiff : for exhibition use	28.8.44
				RAF Air Historical Branch Collection	54
				RAF Bicester : travelling exhibit	60/72
				RAF Museum Store, RAF Henlow	74
				RAF Museum, RAF Cosford	.77/78
				RAF Museum, Hendon	.78/96
				(displ. as "X4590/PR-F")	
CBAF. 1061 •	LF Mk. Vb	**AB910**	G-AISU	Allen H. Wheeler (race #82)	10.46/55
				Vickers-Armstrongs Ltd, Weybridge	5.55/65
				(donated to RAF as AB910)	9.65
				RAF Battle of Britain Memorial Flight	15.9.65/96
				(flew in film *Battle of Britain* .68)	
				dam. landing, Duxford (repaired)	6.76
				badly dam. in ground collision with Harvard, Bex, Switzerland	21.8.78
				(rebuilt, redel. BBMF, RAF Coningsby 26.10.81, flies as "AB910/AE-H")	
- •	LF Mk. Va	**AD540**		Dumfries & Galloway Aviation Museum, Tinwald Downs, later Polmont Prison	94/96
				(recov. ex wartime crash site: static rest.)	
WASP/ 20/2 •	F Mk. 1a	**AR213**	G-AIST	Allen H. Wheeler, Booker	10.46/72
				(stored Old Warden 46/63)	
				RAF Abingdon: loan	.63/69
				(flown in film *Battle of Britain* .68)	
				Hon. Patrick Lindsay, Booker	.72/89
				Victor Gauntlett & Peter Livanos, Booker	4.89/95
				Blue Max Museum of Film Flying, Booker	96

c/n	Mark	Serial	Reg	History	Date
				(flies as "AR213/PR-D")	
WASP/ 20/223 •	LF Mk. Vc	**AR501**		Loughborough Technical College, Leics: del.	21.3.46/61
				Shuttleworth Collection, Old Warden	6.61/67
				(stored dism. Old Warden .61/67; arr. Henlow 29.12.67 for film *Battle of Britain*)	
			G-AWII	Spitfire Productions Ltd, Duxford	25.4.68
				Shuttleworth Trust, Old Warden	10.68/96
				(arr. Duxford 7.5.73 for rest., ff Duxford 27.6.75; flies as "AR501/NN-A")	
WASP/ 20/288 •	F Mk. Vc	**AR614**		RAF Padgate : displ.	49
				RAF West Kirby	52/58
				RAF Hednesford	1.58
				RAF Bridgenorth: gate guard	.58/63
				Air Museum of Calgary ALTA: shipped	.64/70
				(open storage in shipping crate Calgary .64/70)	
				Donald Campbell, Kapuskasing ONT	.70
			C-FDUY	Donald Campbell, Kapuskasing ONT	86/92
				(long-term rest. to fly not completed)	
				Old Flying Machine Company, Duxford UK	.92
				(shipped to UK .92, for rest. at Duxford)	
			G-BUWA	Ray G. Hanna/Old Flying Machine Co.	19.3.93/94
				Alpine Fighter Collection, Wanaka NZ	.94/96
				(rest. Audley End UK 94/96)	
- •	F Mk. V	**BL370**		crashed in marshland near Humber Estuary	.44
				Julian Mitchell & Stephen Arnold, Kidlington	88/96
				(recov. ex crash site, static rest.)	
CBAF. 1646 •	F Mk. Vb	**BL614**		RAF Credenhill : displ. as "AB871"	3.55/67
				(taxy scenes, film *Battle of Britain* .68)	
				RAF Wattisham : stored	69
				RAF Museum, RAF Colerne	75
				RAF Museum, RAF St Athan	8.75/82
				Manchester Air & Space Museum, Manchester	.82/85
				Museum of Science & Industry, Manchester	.85/95
				(displ. as "BL614/F-ZD": to Rochester .95 for rest.)	
CBAF. 1660 •	F Mk. Vb	**BL628**		(to RN FAA as BL628)	
				Peter Croser & Michael Aitchison, Melbourne VIC	.77/95
				(forward fuse. derelict on farm St Merryn, Cornwall: recov., shipped Australia .78: rest. project, Melbourne & Adelaide, using wings and parts ex UK scrapyards)	
				shipped to UK for rest.	.88/95
			G-BTTN	D. J. T. John/Aerofab Restorations, Thruxton	13.8.91
				returned to Australia 6.95: struck-off reg.	12.4.95
			VH-FVB	Peter Croser, Melbourne VIC	8.6.95/96
- •	F Mk. Vb	**BL655**		crashed near Spilsby, Lancs.	1.7.43
				Lincolnshire Aviation Heritage Centre, East Kirby	.90/92
				(wreck recov. 90; display unveiled 10.91)	
CBAF. 1806	F Mk. Vb	**BL688**		Peter Wood, Twyford, Bucks	90/95
				(full fuselage rest. to airworthy condition)	
				fuse. rep dest. by fire Twyford	2.6.96
CBAF. 2461 •	F Mk. Vb	**BM597**		RAF Hednesford: gate guard	
				RAF Bridgnorth: gate guard	60/62
				RAF Church Fenton: gate guard	66/75
				RAF Henlow	.67/68
				(static scenes, movie "Battle of Britain" .68)	
				RAF Linton-on-Ouse	.75/79
				RAF Church Fenton: gate guard	9.79/88
				Historic Flying Ltd, Cambridge	6.88

			G-MKVB	Historic Flying Ltd, Audley End Historic Aircraft Collection, (rest. to fly, Audley End 93/96)	2.5.89/93 94/96
- •	F Mk. Vc	**BR108**		shot down by Bf109, in sea near Gozo, Malta recov. by RAF Luqua team National War Museum, Fort St Elmo, Malta (fuselage and wing sections only: see EN199)	8.7.42 .73 5.75/95
- •	F Mk. Vc	**BR545**		(to RAAF as A58-51): BOC ditched, Prince Regent River, Kimberly WA RAAF Museum, RAAF Point Cook VIC (hulk recov. from river crash site 12.87, stored)	10.42 24.12.43 .87/95
GAL/R/6S 160931•	F Mk. IX	**BR601**		(to SAAF as 5631): BOC Harold Barnett/South African Metal & Machinery Co, Salt River, Cape Town (displ. on pole at scrapyard as "PV260/DB-P", later static rest. Cape Town) auctioned in London UK Warbirds of GB Ltd. (arr. dism. Thruxton 6.7.89 for rest. to fly, stored dism. Biggin Hill 92) Mike Araldi/Jet Cap Aviation, Lakeland FL	13.3.49 - 10.3.55/87 31.10.87 10.87/89 94/96
- •	F Mk. Vc	**BS164**		(to RAAF as A58-63): BOC midair collision, crashed nr. Strauss Strip NT Peter Croser, Melbourne VIC (rest project, parts recov. ex crash site NT)	11.42 1.44 91/96
6S/ 199407 •	F Mk. Vc	**BS199**		(to RAAF as A58-81): BOC crashed during combat, Millingimbi NT wreck recov. by Langdon Badger, Adelaide SA Robert L. Eastgate, Melbourne VIC (composite rest. project, RAAF Point Cook VIC)	10.42 10.5.43 83/96
-	F Mk. Vc	**BS231**		(to RAAF as A58-92): BOC missing on operations, Pt Charles NT Aviation Society of NT, Darwin NT: displ. (substantial remains recov. ex crash site)	10.42 3.43 90/96
CBAF. 196667	F Mk. IXb	**BS464**		(to French Air Force as BS464): del. Musee de l'Air, Chalais-Meudon, Paris Musee de l'Air, Paris-Le Bourget destroyed in hangar fire, Le Bourget	25.6.46 12.49/69 73/90 17.5.90
WWA. 2822 •	F Mk. Vc	**EE606**	 G-MKVC	(to RAAF as A58-106): BOC 11.42: SOC parts recov. from farm Oakey QLD Charles Church (Spitfires) Ltd, Winchester (rest. project Micheldever, adopted id. of EE606; ff 20.11.88 as "EE606/D-B") crashed dest., near Blackbushe (Church k.) Warbirds of GB Ltd: wreck wreck sold Derby UK	5.46 18.5.88/89 1.7.89 91/92 6.92/96
WASP/ 20/484 •	F Mk. Vc	**EE853**		(to RAAF as A58-146): BOC dam. landing, Kiriwina, Solomon Islands Langdon Badger, Unley Park, Adelaide, SA (recov. ex Goodenough Island, shipped to Adelaide-Parafield, arr. 7.5.74 for static rest: displ. at owner's home as "RAAF EE853/UP-O")	4.43 28.8.43 .74/96
WWA. 3832 •	F Mk. Vc	**EF545**	 ZK-MKV (1	(to RAAF as A58-149): BOC 5.43: SOC N. Monty Armstrong, Auckland NZ (burnt hulk recov. ex Kiriwina , Solomon Islands) J. Shivas, Ashburton NZ G. S. Smith, Auckland: reg. res. Don J. Subritzky, Auckland-Dairy Flat NZ (parts used in JG 891 rest. project) Chris Warrilow, Woburn Green UK: parts	12.43 .74 84 7.11.83 86/95 92/96

c/n	Model	Serial	Registration	History	Date
6S/ 240837 •	F Mk. IXe	EN145		(to Italian AF as MM4116) (to IDFAF as 20-78) Ramat David AB, Israel: displ. (arr. Carmiel 29.5.89 for rest. for IDFAFM) IDFAF Museum, Be'er Sheva AB: arr. (displ. as "IDFAF 78")	26.6.46 60/85 .90/95
- •	F Mk. IXe	EN199		blown over by gale, RAF Luqua, Malta (hulk stripped for parts, wings to UK: fuse hulk stored in Civil Defence yard, Malta) Palace Armoury, Valletta, Malta: hulk National War Museum, Fort St Elmo, Malta (fuse only: static rest. Attard, Malta 93, using parts from BR108 & EN976 recov. ex sea 2.4.93; rolled-out complete as "EN199" 5.95)	12.46 69 90/96
6S/ 197707 •	F Mk. XII	EN224	 G-FXII	College of Aeronautics, Cranfield Peter R. Arnold, Newport Pagnell: fuse parts. Peter R. Arnold, Newport Pagnell (long-term rest. project)	4.7.46/60 88 4.12.89/96
6S/ 171652 •	F Mk. VIIc	EN474		(to USAAF as EN474: later FE-400) NASM: stored Park Ridge IL & Silver Hill MD NASM, Washington DC: displ.	3.43 .47/69 76/96
CBAF. 2403 •	LF Mk. Vb	EP120	 G-LFVB	RAF Wilmslow RAF Bircham Newton RAF Boulmer RAF Henlow (static scenes, movie "Battle of Britain" .68) RAF Wattisham: gate guard RAF St Athan (stored pending disposal) The Fighter Collection, Duxford: arr. Patina Ltd/op The Fighter Collection, Duxford (rest. Audley End, ff 12.9.95 "EP120/AE-A")	.55/60 62 .64/67 67/68 .68/89 .89/93 1.93/94 9.5.94/96
6S/ 238666 •	F Mk. VIII	JF294		flown Cairo-Cape Town, for exhibition use (to SAAF as 5501) : exhibition use only South African National Museum of Military History, Saxonwold, Johannesburg (displ. as "SAAF 5501")	3.44 11.48/96
-	LF Mk. VIII	JF620		(to RAAF as A58-300): BOC midair collision with A58-364, crashed near Truscott Strip, Kimberly WA John Haslett, Darwin NT: wreck recov. East Point Artilliary Museum, Darwin NT Peter Sledge & Gary Cooper, Sydney NSW (components used in rest. projects: RR232 & RM797 in Australia, TE294 in South Africa)	11.43/44 16.11.44 c72 73/74 .74
6S/ 399579 •	LF Mk. VIII	JG267		(to RAAF as A58-377): BOC forced landing on reef, Point Blaze NT Darwin Aviation Museum, Darwin NT: recov.	1.44 3.11.44 .85/95
6S/ 445748 •	LF Mk. VIII	JG355		(to RAAF as A58-359): BOC forced landing, near Daly Waters NT Langdon Badger, Adelaide SA (wreckage recov. ex crash site NT) Pearce Dunn/Warbirds Aviation Museum, Mildura VIC: stored Jeff Trappett, Morwell VIC: stored Robert L. Eastgate, Melbourne VIC (composite rest. project, RAAF Point Cook VIC)	1.44 6.44 88/96
HAI/ • 6S/196330	LF Mk. VIII	JG484		(to RAAF as A58-408): BOC 5.44: SOC Noel Smoothie, Ningi QLD	5.46 93/96

C/n	Type	Serial	Regn	History	Date
				(substantial components: rest. project)	
- •	F Mk Vc	**JG891**		(to RAAF as A58-178): BOC	4.43
				crashed landing Kiriwina, Solomon Islands	11.1.45
				N. Monty Armstrong, Auckland NZ	.74
				(stripped hulk recov. from Kiriwina .74)	
			ZK-MKV(2	Don J. Subritzky, Auckland-Dairy Flat	.74/96
				(composite rest. to fly, Dairy Flat, using	
				parts from EF545 also from Kiriwina)	
CBAF. 4690 •	F Mk. Vc	**JK448**		(to Yugoslav AF as 9486)	
				Military Museum, Kalemagden Park, Belgrade	58/61
				Yugoslavian Aviation Museum, Belgrade	84/96
				(displ. as "9486", later "JK808/B")	
SMAF 4338 •	F Mk. 21	**LA198**		Air Training Corps, Portiswell, Worcester	19.2.54/67
				RAF Henlow	.67/68
				(static scenes, movie "Battle of Britain" .68)	
				RAF Locking: displ.	.69/86
				RAF Leuchars: gate guard	3.86/89
				RAF St Athan (stored pending disposal)	.89/95
				RAF Museum Store, RAF Cardington	96
SMAF 4371 •	F Mk. 21	**LA226**		Air Training Corps, Albrighton, Staffs	.54/58
				RAF Little Rissington	9.2.58/67
				RAF Henlow: for movie "Battle of Britain"	.67/68
				Vickers South Marston Works: displ.	.68/84
				Vickers-Armstrongs Ltd	84/92
				RAF Memorial Chapel, Biggin Hill: loan	.84/87
				RAF Shawbury: stored	89/92
				RAF Museum Store, RAF Cardington	96
SMAF 4388 •	F Mk. 21	**LA255**		RAF Cardington	60/62
				RAF West Raynham	64/67
				RAF Henlow : for film *Battle of Britain*"	.67
				RAF Wittering: displ. as "LA255/JX-U"	69/96
SMAF 19989 •	Seafire F. 46	**LA546**		Daniel Clark & Co, Carlisle (as scrap)	c51/66
				recov ex scrapyard by J. D. Kay/Manchester	
				Tankers Ltd, Charnock Richard, Lancs	.66
				Neville Franklin & Peter R. Arnold	.73
				Peter R. Arnold, Redbourn: bulkhead	.73/86
				Craig Charleston, Colchester	88/96
SMAF 19985 •	Seafire F. 46	**LA564**		Daniel Clark & Co, Carlisle (as scrap)	c51/66
				recov. ex scrapyard by J. D. Kay/Manchester	
				Tankers Ltd, Charnock Richard, Lancs	.66
				Neville Franklin & Peter R. Arnold, Newark	12.71/73
				Peter R. Arnold, Redbourn/Newport Pagnell	.73/96
				(long-term rest. project)	
CBAF 5056 •	F Mk. IX	**LZ842**		(to SAAF as ....)	
				South African Metal & Machinery Co,	
				Salt River, Cape Town, South Africa	.54/69
				(forward fuse. hulk recov. by Larry Barnett,	
				Johannesberg .69)	
				SAAF Museum: stored Lanseria AB	78/86
				Steve W.Atkins & Chris Warrillow, Oxford UK	89
				Ross Campbell, Toowoomba QLD: fuse.	91/96
				(composite static rest. project)	
- •	F Mk. Vc	**MA353**		(to RAAF as A58-232): BOC	8.43
				missing on testflight from Strauss Strip NT	4.44
				John Haslett, Darwin NT	9.69/75
				(recov. from crash site near Darwin NT 9.69)	
				Darwin Air Museum NT: engine & wing parts	80/93
				Peter Croser, Melbourne: fuse. hulk	93/95
- •	HF Mk.IXe	**MA793**		(to USAAF as MA793): BOC 31.10.43: SOC	5.44
				(to SAAF as 5601): shipped, arr.	30.9.48

				Meerhof Hospital for Handicapped Children, Pretoria: playground	27.4.54/67
				Larry Barnett & Alan Lurie, Johannesburg (rebuilt, ff. Johannesburg-Jan Smuts 29.9.75 as "SAAF PT672/WR-RR")	.67/86
				loan: SAAF, Lanseria AB : displ. flying	.76/86
			N930LB	Larry Barnett International California Inc, Los Angeles CA (shipped Chino, ff 1.1.87)	14.8.86/95
				op: Museum of Flying, Santa Monica CA (flies as "RAF EN398/JE-J")	8.86/96
- •	F Mk Vc	**MA863**		(to RAAF as A58-246): BOC	10.43
				crash landing , Lake Tarang VIC	8.45
				Richard E. Hourigan/Moorabbin Air Museum, Melbourne VIC : hulk recov. ex farm	
				Ian A. Whitney, Romsey VIC : rest. to fly	.75/96
6S/ 65239292 •	Seafire LF. II**c**	**MB293**		National War Museum, Fort St Elmo, Malta (wreck recov. ex sea off coast of Malta 25.4.94) (stored museum rest. facility Takali, Malta)	.94/95
HAI/6S/ 196387 •	LF Mk. VIIIc	**MD228**		(to RAAF as A58-445): BOC 4.44: SOC	11.48
				RAAF Oakey QLD: storage, scrapped	
				Les Arthur, Toowoomba QLD (parts recov. ex farm, near Oakey QLD)	
				Robert L. Eastgate, Melbourne VIC: project	93/96
- •	LF Mk. VIIIc	**MD338**		(to RAAF as A58-467): BOC 5.44: SOC	10.45
				broken-up and buried, Gorrie Strip NT: "ZP-S" (hulk excavated c70, with parts LV750/A58-471 & MT682/A58-529: stored Darwin NT)	
			VH-ZPY	Alec Wilson, Frome Downs Station, Yunta SA (long-term rest. to fly, Melbourne VIC) (note: prev. incorrectly identified as MT834)	88/96
CBAF. IX490 •	LF Mk. IXe	**MH350**		(to R NoAF as BM-A, later FN-M): BOC	8.11.45
				last flight 15.11.51; stored Vaernes AB	.51/61
				Bodo AB, Norway: displ. as "FN-T"	5.61/82
				Norwegian Armed Forces Museum, Akershus Castle, Oslo	8.82/96
CBAF. IX533 •	LF Mk.IXb	**MH415**		(to R Netherlands AF as H-108, later H-65)	6.47/53
				shipped to Java N.E.I.	5.47/50
				(to Belgian AF as SM40): del.	8.4.53/56
			OO-ARD	COGEA Nouvelle, Ostend	15.6.56/61
				Rousseau Aviation, Dinard, France (flew in film *The Longest Day* .61)	61/66
			G-AVDJ	T. G. Mahaddie/Film Aviation Services, Elstree	12.66/68
				Spitfire Productions Ltd, Duxford (flew in film *Battle of Britain* .68)	1.68
			N415MH	Wilson C. Edwards, Big Spring TX (shipped ex Bovington, arr. Houston 1.69, rest. ff .73; stored Big Spring TX 96)	11.68/96
CBAF. IX552 •	LF Mk. IXb	**MH434**		(to R Netherlands AF as H-105, later H-68)	19.2.47/53
				shipped to Java N.E.I.	5.47/50
				crash landing Semarang, Java (shipped to Holland, rebuilt, ff 10.3.53)	7.5.49
				(to Belgian AF as SM41): del.	9.10.53/54
				accident, retired	19.3.54
			OO-ARA	COGEA Nouvelle, Ostend	23.3.56/63
			G-ASJV	Tim A. Davies, Elstree: del.	29.6.63/67
				T: G. Mahaddie/Film Aviation Services, Elstree (flew in film *Battle of Britain* .68)	11.67/69
				Adrian C. Swire, Booker & Duxford	2.69/83

c/n	Mark	Serial	Reg	History	Date
				Ray G. Hanna/Nalfire Aviation Ltd, Duxford	14.4.83
				Old Flying Machine Co, Duxford	87/96
				complete rebuild Duxford	95
				(flies as "MH434/ZD-B")	
CBAF. 5589 •	F Mk. IX	**MH603**		(to SAAF as ......)	
				John Sykes, Oxford, UK: major parts	89
				Joe Scogna, Fort Collins CO: rest. project	93/96
CBAF. IX907 •	LF Mk. IXc	**MJ143**		(to R Netherlands AF as H-1, 3W-1): del.	17.6.46
				retired 4.6.54; stored Gilze-Rijen AB	7.54/60
				Aeroplanorama Museum, Amsterdam-Schipol	3.60/68
				Militaire Luchtvaart Museum, Soesterberg AB	6.68/95
CBAF. IX970 •	LF Mk. IXc	**MJ271**		(to R Netherlands AF as H-8, 3W-8): del.	25.11.46
				Volkel AB : decoy use	10.54/57
				War Museum, Delfzijl: displ.	6.1.59/73
				(removed 4.4.73 for rest. by Anthony Fokker Technical School, Den Haag, Holland .73/78)	
				Aviodome Museum, Amsterdam-Schiphol	22.3.78/95
				(displ. as "MH424/H-53")	
CBAF. 7722 •	LF Mk. IX Tr Mk. 9	**MJ627**		(to Irish Air Corps as 158): del.	5.6.51
				J. Crewdson/Film Aviation Services Ltd, Biggin Hill	.63/64
				(arr. dism. Biggin Hill 13.11.63, stored dism.)	
			G-ASOZ	Film Aviation Services Ltd, Elstree	19.2.64
				Tim A. Davies, Elstree (stored dism.)	9.64/67
				John Fairey, Stockbridge (stored dism.)	12.67/76
				Maurice Bayliss (rest. begun at Kenilworth)	.76/78
			G-BMSB	Maurice S. & Peter K. Bayliss, Coventry	3.5.78/96
				(rest. Coventry, ff 8.11.93 as "MJ627/9G-P")	
				(c/n also quoted as 6S/R/749433)	
CBAF. 7243 •	LF Mk. IXe	**MJ730**		(to Italian AF as MM4094)	27.6.46
				(to IDFAF as 0606: later 20-66): del.	21.1.55
				hulk recov. ex kibbutz Kabri, Israel by Robs Lamplough; arr. Nailsworth, Glos	6.78/80
				Aero Vintage Ltd, Hastings	10.80/83
				(rest. commenced 80)	
			G-FEDX	ntu: Fred Smith/Federal Express, Memphis TN	4.82
			G-BLAS	Aero Vintage Ltd, St Leonards	11.83/88
				David W. Pennell, East Midlands	88/89
				(ff East Midlands 12.11.88)	
			G-HFIX	David W. Pennell, Gloucester	22.8.89/96
				(flies as "MJ730/GZ-?")	
CBAF. IX1285 •	LF Mk. IXc	**MJ755**		(to R Hellenic AF as MJ755)	27.2.47
				last flight 8.9.53; stored Hellenikon AB	
				Tatoi AB, Dekelia Greece: displ.	72/78
				Hellenic War Museum, Athens	85/91
				Hellenic Air Force Museum, Tatoi AB	94/96
				(static rest. Tatoi AB 96)	
CBAF. 7269 •	LF Mk. IX Tr Mk. 9	**MJ772**		(to Irish Air Corps as 159): del.	5.6.51/63
				J. Crewdson/Film Aviation Services, Biggin Hill: stored dism.	.63
				COGEA Nouvelles, Ostend Belgium	3.64/65
				(airfreighted to Ostend 1.4.64: stored dism.)	
				N. A. W. Samuelson, Elstree	.65/66
				(shipped ex Belgium; rest. Elstree, ff 7.67)	
			G-AVAV	N. A. W. Samuelson, Elstree	8.11.66/69
				(flown in film "Battle of Britain" .68)	
				landing accident, Little Straughton (repaired)	9.7.68
				Sir W. J. D. Roberts, Shoreham	12.69/71
				Sir W. J. D. Roberts/Strathallan Collection, Auchterader, Scotland	12.71/74
			N8R (2	Doug Champlin/Windward Aviation, Enid OK	12.74/80
				Champlin Fighter Museum, Mesa AZ	.80/96
				dam. ldg. Amarillo TX, on ferry flight to Mesa	22.7.80

C/n	Type	Serial	Reg.	History	Date
				(rebuilt Mesa single-seat config, ff 10.85)	
CBAF. IX1301 •	LF Mk. IXc	**MJ783**		(to Belgian AF as SM15): BOC	3.2.48
				Musee de l'Armee et d'Histoire Militaire/	
				Palais du Cinquantenaire, Brussels: stored	1.52/78
				Musee Royal de l'Armee, Brussels	80/96
				(displ. as "MJ360/GE-B")	
CBAF. IX1514	LF Mk. IXc	MK297		(to R Netherlands AF as H-116: later H-55)	6.47/52
				shipped to Java, N. E. I.	5.47/50
				(to Belgian AF as SM43): del.	16.6.53/54
				accident, retired	10.3.54
			OO-ARB	COGEA Nouvelle, Ostend	5.5.56/64
				(flew in movie "The Longest Day" .61)	
			G-ASSD	J. Crewdson/Film Aviation Services Ltd,	
				Biggin Hill: del.	4.64/65
				R. A. Wale, London	3.65
			N11RS	ntu: Confederate Air Force, Mercedes TX	5.65
				(remained in UK & France for filming work)	
			G-ASSD	J. Crewdson/Film Aviation Services Ltd	5.66
				G. A. Rich, Henlow	9.66/68
				dam. North Weald, filming "Battle of Britain"	17.5.68
			N1882	Aerosmith Corp, Dallas TX/Confederate AF	12.68/73
				(shipped Bovington to Houston TX 11.68)	
			N9BL	Confederate Air Force, Harlingen TX	20.6.73/90
				dam. forced landing ag. strip TX (repaired)	5.81
			N11RS	ntu: Confederate Air Force, Harlingen TX	86
			N9BL	Confederate Air Force, Harlingen/Midland TX	86/93
				dest. in hangar fire, Hamilton ONT	15.2.93
CBAF. IX1561 •	LF Mk. IXc	**MK356**		RAF Hawkinge (displ. as "M5690","MK365")	.51/61
				RAF Bicester	.62
				RAF Locking	66/67
				RAF Henlow	.67/69
				(static scenes, film *Battle of Britain* .68)	
				RAF Museum, RAF St Athan	18.8.69/96
				(rest. to fly, RAF St Athan 94/96)	
CBAF. IX1732 •	LF Mk. IXc	**MK732**		(to R Netherlands AF as H-25, 3W-17): del.	27.6.48/54
				Eindhoven AB: decoy use	30.6.54/56
				RAF Oldenburg, West Germany: displ.	.56/57
				RAF Aldhorn, West Germany	
				RAF Gutersloh, West Germany: gate guard	60/69
				RAF Brize Norton: arr. airfreighted	27.6.69
				RAF St Athan	10.7.69/70
				RAF Bicester: arr., stored dism.	3.12.70/74
				RAF Coltishall: B of B Flight spares source	10.74
				RAF Coningsby	78
				RAF St. Athan: arr., stored dism. stripped	8.79
				RAF Abingdon: further parts removal	9.80
				RAF St. Athan: stripped hulk stored	.80/84
				RNAF 322 Squadron, Gilze-Rijen AB	30.8.83/86
				(arr. Schiphol 13.4.84, displ. Schiphol 84/85; to Gilze-Rijen AB for rest. 29.11.85)	
				Dutch Spitfire Flight, Deelen AB	89/94
			G-HVDM	DSF (Guernsey) Ltd, Guernsey	18.1.91/95
				(rest. Deelen AB, shipped to Battle UK 1.10.92, ff Lydd 10.6.93 as "H-25/MK732/Baby Bea V", flies as "MK732/OU-U/Baby Bea V")	
				dam. gear collapsed landing, Manston	26.8.95
CBAF. IX1780 •	LF Mk. IX	**MK805**		(to Italian AF/AMI as MK805)	27.6.46
				(to Italian AF/AMI as MM4084)	19.12.47
				displ. in town, Nettuno, Italy	
				Foce Verde Artillery School, Nettuno: on pole	58/76
				Museu Storico Dell'Aeronautica Militaire Italiana, Vigna di Valle AB	.76/95
				(rest. Lecce AB .76/89 as "MM4079/A-32"	

				final roll-out 14.7.89 as "A-32", later "MK805")	
CBAF. IX1875 •	LF Mk. IXc	**MK912**		(to R Netherlands AF as H-119: later H-59)	7.46/53
				shipped to Java, N.E.I	5.47/50
				(to Belgian AF as SM29): del.	4.6.52
				accident, retired	17.6.53
				BAF Technical School, Saffraenberg: displ.	8.55/88
				Musee Royal de l'Armee, Brussels	.88
				Guy Black/Historic Aircraft Collection: arr.	22.6.89
			G-BRRA	Historic Aircraft Collection Ltd,	10.89/93
				stored Paddock Wood, Kent 93/96)	
CBAF. IX1886 •	LF Mk.IXc	**MK923**		(to R Netherlands AF as H-104, later H-61)	7.46
				shipped to Java, N.E.I.	5.47/50
				(to Belgian AF as SM37): del.	25.2.52/56
			OO-ARF	COGEA Nouvelle, Ostend	25.4.58/63
				(flown in film "Longest Day", France .61)	
			N93081	Clifford P. Robertson, Santa Ana CA	.63/66
				(del. to Biggin Hill 17.11.63, airfreighted to USA)	
				(displ. Tallmantz/Movieland of Air Museum 64/67)	
			N521R	Cliff Robertson & Jerry Billing, Los Angeles CA	
				& Windsor ONT (flies as "MK923/5J-Z")	2.66/96
CBAF. 8125 •	LF Mk.IXc	**MK959**		(to R Netherlands AF as H-15, 3W-15): del.	26.9.46
				Volkel AB & Eindhoven AB : decoy use	54
				Eindhoven AB : displ. on pole	.55/87
				(displ. as "MJ289", later "MK959/H-15")	
				Dutch Spitfire Flight, Deelen AB: stored	.93
				Raybourne Thompson, Houston TX	95/96
CBAF. IX1892 •	LF Mk. IXe S.89	**ML119**		(to Czech AF as ML119)	6.12.46
				(to IDFAF as 20-20)	5.49
				(to Burmese AF as UB441)	2.55
				Mingaladon AB, Rangoon: displ.	65/89
				Aungsan Park, Rangoon: displ.	91/93
				Mingaladon AB, Rangoon: stored	94/96
- •	LF Mk. IXe	**ML196**		(to SAAF as ....)	
				South African Metal & Machinery Co,	
				Salt River, Cape Town, South Africa	54
				SAAF Museum, Snake Valley AB: hulk stored	81
				Graham McDonald, Durban: rest. project	95/96
CBAF. 8342 •	HF Mk. IXc	**ML255**		(to SAAF as 5563): del.	16.11.48
				dam. collision, Ysterplaat AB : SOC	22.1.54
				derelict hulk held Snake Valley, Pretoria	81
				SAAF Museum : static rest.	
				Museo do Ar, Alverca AB, Lisbon Portugal	.89/96
				(displ. as "FA Portuguesa ML255/MR-2")	
CBAF. 8463 •	LF Mk. IXe Tr Mk. 9	**ML407**		(to Irish Air Corps as 162): del.	30.7.51/68
				to inst. airframe; stored dism. Baldonnel AB	62/68
				N. A. W. Samuelson, Cricklewood, London	3.68/70
				(stored dism., Cricklewood, North London 68/70)	
				Sir W. J. D. Roberts, Shoreham, later	
				Strathallan Collection, Scotland (stored dism.)	4.70/79
				E. Nick Grace, St Merryn, Cornwall: arr.	9.8.79
			G-LFIX	E. Nick Grace/Island Trading Ltd, St Merryn	1.2.80/85
				(rest. St Merryn, ff 16.4.85)	
				Nick Grace & Chris Horsely, Middle Wallop	.85/89
				(landing accident, Southend 5.3.86: repaired)	
				Carolyn S. Grace, Winchester/Duxford	26.5.89/96
				(flies as "ML407/NL-D" (port), "OU-V" (stbd)	
6S/ 730116 •	LF Mk. IXc Tr Mk. 9	**ML417**		(to Indian AF as HS543)	.48
				Indian AF Museum, Palam AB: stored unrest.	67/71
				Senator Norman E. Gaar, Kansas City MO	4.71/80
				(shipped to USA 3.72, rest. begun Ft.Collins CO)	
				B. J. Stephen Grey, Duxford UK	11.6.80
				(shipped to UK, partly rest., arr. 7.8.80)	

c/n	Mark	Serial	Reg.	History	Dates
			G-BJSG	The Fighter Collection, Duxford	29.1.81/95
				(rest. as Mk.IXc single seater completed Booker, ff 10.2.84 as "ML417/2I-T")	
				(new c/n 6S-735188 when conv. to Tr.9)	
CBAF. IX2131 •	LF Mk. IXc	**ML427**		Vickers Castle Bromwich : gate guard	8.54/58
				Museum of Science & Industry, Birmingham	.58/95
				(displ. as "ML427/ST-A")	
6S/ 442296 •	LF Mk. VIIIc	**MT719**		(to Indian AF as HS...)	29.12.47
				to instructional airframe "T17"/Code 87	
				hulk recov. ex Jaipur AB by Ormond & Wensley	
				Haydon-Baillie, Duxford UK	.78
			I-SPIT	Franco Actis, Turin, Italy: shipped ex UK	12.79/88
				(rest. Vergiate, ff 27.10.82 as "MT719/YB-J")	
				Reynard Racing Cars: del.	5.11.88/89
			G-VIII	Reynard Racing Cars Ltd, Bicester	27.4.89/91
				Aircraft Investments Ltd	93
				(sold to USA, crated ex Micheldever 25.6.93)	
			N719MT	Cavanaugh Flight Museum, Dallas-Addison TX (flies as "MT719/YB-J")	10.8.93/96
6S/ 729058 •	LF Mk. VIIIc Tr Mk. 8	**MT818**	G-AIDN	Vickers-Armstrongs Ltd, Eastleigh	8.46/56
				(prototype 2-seat trainer Mk.8, ff 9.46 as N32)	
				(wfu, stored at Chilbolton 52/56)	
				Vivian H. Bellamy, Eastleigh	8.56/63
				John S. Fairey, Eastleigh, later Andover	8.63/67
				John S. Fairey & Tim Davies, Andover	.67/76
				M. S. Bayliss, Baginton	.76/78
				George F. Miller, Baginton/Dinas Powis	9.77/83
				dam. gear collapsed landing, Baginton	6.2.78
				(rebuilt .82 as "MT818/G-M", then shipped to TX)	
				George F. Miller, Houston TX	.83/86
			N58JE	Erickson Aircrane Inc, Medford OR	7.86/96
				(rest. completed, ff 4.87 as "MT818/G-M")	
6S/ 643779 •	FR Mk. XIVe	**MT847**		RAF Warton : gate guard	5.52
				RAF Freckleton	.55/62
				RAF Middleton St. George	
				RAF Weeton	c63
				RAF Cosford : displ. on pylon	.64/78
				RAF Museum, RAF Cosford	79/95
				Museum of Science & Industry, Manchester	3.95/96
				(arr. 22.3.95, displ. as "MT847/AX-H")	
6S/ 583793 •	HF Mk. VIIIc	**MV154**		(to RAAF as A58-671): BOC 9.12.44: SOC	6.10.48
				Sydney Technical College, Ultimo NSW	49/61
				A. J. R. Oates, Sydney NSW	.61
				Sid Marshall, Sydney-Bankstown NSW	63/75
				(open storage in yard, Bankstown Airport 63/75)	
				Jack P. Davidson, Bankstown NSW	75/77
				Brian A. Simpson, Sydney NSW	5.77
				Robert J. Lamplough, Duxford UK	9.79/82
				(shipped to UK ex Sydney 18.9.79)	
			G-BKMI	Fighter Wing Display Team Ltd, Duxford	23.12.82
				R. J. Lamplough, North Weald	85/96
				(rest. John Hart and team Huntingdon & Filton, ff 28.5.94 "MT928/ZX-M")	
6S/ 581740 •	HF Mk VIIIc	**MV239**		(to RAAF as A58-758): BOC	26.6.45
				Sydney Technical College, Ultimo NSW	9.49/61
				A. J. R. Oates, Sydney	.61
				Sid Marshall, Sydney-Bankstown NSW	63/75
				(open storage in yard, Bankstown Airport 63/73)	
				Camden Museum of Aviation NSW: loan, arr.	29.7.72/82
				(static rest. Camden: displ. as "MV239")	
				Jack P. Davidson, Bankstown/The Oaks NSW	75/82
			VH-HET	Col Pay, Scone NSW	6.83/96

				(rest. Scone, ff 29.12.85 as "A58-758")	
6S/ 649170 •	F Mk.XIVc	**MV246**		(to Belgian AF as SG55): BOC	24.8.48
				Musee Royal de l'Armee, Brussels	.49/95
				(composite: assembled Coxide AB .49 using parts of SG37/RM860 & SG46 which collided 14.1.49; displ. as "SG55/GE-R")	
6S/ 649186 •	FR Mk. XIVe	**MV262**		(to Indian AF as "42")	12.47
				National Air Cadet Corps, Calcutta	.77
				hulk recov. by Ormond & Wensley	
				Haydon-Baillie, Duxford UK	.78
				Warbirds of GB, Blackbushe	.78/85
				(arr. crated Blackbushe 26.5.78: rest. commenced)	
				B. J. Stephen Grey, Duxford	.85
				Charles Church (Spitfires) Ltd, Winchester	8.86
			G-CCVV	Charles Church (Spitfires) Ltd, Winchester	18.5.88/89
				(rest. commenced Winchester, not completed)	
				The Fighter Collection, Duxford: stored	92
				Kermit A. Weeks, Tamiami FL	10.92/96
				(stored Booker UK 96 pending rest.)	
6S/ 649205 •	FR Mk. XIVe	**MV293**		(to Indian AF as "48")	12.47
				to "T-20" IAF Technical College, Jalahalli	
				recov. from Bangalore by Warbirds of GB Ltd	.78
				(arr. crated Blackbushe 26.5.78)	
			G-BGHB	ntu: Warbirds of GB Ltd, Blackbushe	29.12.78
			G-SPIT	Warbirds of GB Ltd, Blackbushe	2.3.79/85
				The Fighter Collection, Duxford	9.85/96
				(rest. Duxford, ff 14.8.92 as "MV293/OI-C")	
- •	HF Mk. VIII	**MV321**		(to RAAF as A58-642): BOC 11.44: SOC	11.48
				Bill Martin/Darling Downs Aviation Museum, Oakey QLD	89/92
				(rest. project, parts recov. ex farm Oakey QLD)	
				Noel Smoothie, Ningi QLD	96
- •	FR Mk. XIVc	**MV370**		(to Indian AF as HS.......)	12.47
				to instructional airframe "T-44"	
				hulk recov. ex Nagpur AB by Ormond & Wensley	
				Haydon-Baillie, Duxford UK	.77
				Alan & Keith Wickenden, Hemel Hempstead	.78
			G-FXIV	A. K. & K. W. Wickenden & Michael Connor, Buckwish Farm, Henfield (stored dism.)	11.4.80/83
				Paul Raymond/Whitehall Theatre of War	6.83/85
				(static rest., displ. as "MV370/AV-L")	
				Robs Lamplough, North Weald: at auction	5.6.85/91
				Old Flying Machine Co, Duxford	.91/92
				(static rest., Duxford: for German museum)	
				Luftfahrtmuseum, Laatzen, Hanover, Germany	92/96
				(displ. as "MV370/EB-Q")	
CBAF. IX2161 •	HF Mk.IXc	**NH188**		(to R Netherlands AF as H-109, later H-64)	5.47/52
				shipped to Java, N.E.I., arr. Batavia	22.7.47/50
				(to Belgian AF as SM39): del.	22.4.53/54
				accident, retired	12.4.54
			OO-ARC	COGEA Nouvelle, Ostend	25.5.56/61
			CF-NUS	John N. Paterson, Fort William ONT	8.61/64
				(shipped UK-Canada, ff 13.2.62: retired 7.6.64)	
				Canadian National Aeronautical Collection, Rockcliffe ONT: displ. as "NH188/AU-H"	6.6.64/82
				National Aviation Museum, Rockcliffe ONT	9.82/96
CBAF. IX2200 •	LF Mk.IXe	**NH238**		(to R Netherlands AF as H-103, later H-60)	30.5.47/53
				shipped to Java, N.E.I., arr. Batavia	22.7.47/50
				(to Belgian AF as SM36): del.	29.1.53/56
			OO-ARE	COGEA Nouvelles, Ostend	8.9.56/61
				Beverley Snook/Trans Global Aviation Supply, Southend UK: del.	27.5.61
				wing dam. ground fuel explosion, Elstree UK	2.6.61

				Taskers of Andover Ltd UK	18.7.61/69
				(displ. company museum, on RAF transporter)	
				Thomas H. Pasteur, Eastleigh UK	22.2.69
			N238V	Ed Jurist & Bruce Farkas/CAF, Sugarland TX	3.7.69/75
				(shipped from UK, arr. Galveston TX 14.6.70;	
				rest. Sugarland TX, ff 22.8.72 as "EN398")	
				David C. Tallichet/ MARC, Chino CA	4.75/79
				Douglas W. Arnold, Blackbushe UK	.79/83
			G-MKIX	Warbirds of GB Ltd, Blackbushe	12.12.83
				(shipped to UK, rest., ff Blackbushe 6.5.84)	
				Warbirds of GB Ltd, Biggin Hill	88/93
- •	HF Mk. IXc	**NH417**		(to RDAF as 41-401): del. 11.1.49: SOC	13.4.51
				Tojhusmuseet, Copenhagen	.51/93
				Danish Technical Museum, Elsinore (loan)	.75/76
				RDAF Historical Section: stored Vaerlose AB	78
				Egeskov Veteranmuseum, Kvaerndrup (loan)	82/85
				Danmarks Flyvemuseum, Billund (loan)	93/96
6S/ 326987 •	LF Mk. VIIIc	**NH631**		(to Indian AF as NH631)	31.12.47
				IAF Museum, Palam AB	67/85
				IAF Historic Flight, Palam AB, New Delhi	88/95
				(maintained airworthy, displ. as "NH631")	
6S/ 583887 •	FR Mk. XIVe	**NH749**		(to Indian AF as ....)	31.12.47
				to instructional airframe "T3"/Code 54	
				hulk recov. ex Patna AB by Ormond & Wensley	
				Haydon-Baillie, Duxford UK	.77
				Alan & Keith Wickenden, Hemel Hempstead	.78/80
			G-MXIV	Keith W. & Alan W. Wickenden, Cranfield	11.4.80/85
				(rest. Cranfield, ff 9.4.83 as "NH749/L")	
			N749DP	David G. Price, Portland OR	4.3.85/95
				(shipped to Chino CA 4.85, ff Chino 24.7.85)	
				Museum of Flying,	
				Santa Monica CA (flies as "RAF H749/L")	88/96
6S/ 648269 •	FR Mk. XIV	**NH799**		(to Indian AF as ....)	31.12.47
				recov. ex India by Warbirds of GB Ltd,	
				Blackbushe UK: arr. dism.	c81/85
				(stored dism., Blackbushe & Bitteswell 81/85)	
				The Fighter Collection, Duxford	.86/93
				(rest. Duxford, later Audley End 86/94)	
			G-BUZU	Patina Ltd, Duxford	1.7.93/94
				Alpine Fighter Collection, Wanaka NZ	1.94
				(ff Audley End 21.1.94 as "NH799/AP-V":	
				dep. Duxford crated for NZ 14.2.94)	
			ZK-XIV	Alpine Fighter Collection, Wanaka	28.3.94/96
				badly damaged take off accident Wanaka	2.1.96
				aircraft salvage for sale	3.96
6S/ 648296 •	FR Mk. XIVc	**NH904**		(to Belgian AF as SG108)	9.4.51
				Oscar Dewachter Scrapyard, Ostend Belgium	57/66
				(displ. on roof: wings axed off)	
				Bunny Brooks, Hoylake, Cheshire UK: shipped	.66/68
				(fitted wings RM694, static displ. at garage)	
				T. G. "Hamish" Mahaddie, RAF Henlow	.68
				(stored dism. Henlow, for film *Battle of Britain*)	
				Jeff Hawke: rest. commenced Henlow	69
				Sir W. J. D. Roberts/Strathallan Collection	8.71/79
				(stored dism. Flimwell, arr. Strathallan 1.77)	
			G-FIRE	Spencer R. Flack/Classic Air Displays,Elstree	1.79/88
				(arr. Elstree for rest., ff Elstree 14.3.81)	
				B. J. Stephen Grey, Duxford	.88
				(crated at Duxford 12.88, shipped to USA)	
			N8118J	Planes of Fame East,	
				Minneapolis-Flying Cloud MN	1.89/91
			N114BP	Robert J. Pond, Eden Prairie MN	4.91/96

			(flies as "W2-P")	
6S/ 417723 •	PR Mk. XI	**PA908**	(to Indian AF as M342)	
			offered for sale by IAF at Poona AB, India	.84
			Carl Enzenhofer, John Wilson & Jeet Mehal, Vancouver BC: arr. by ship Vancouver	8.2.85
			USAFM, Wright-Patterson AFB, Dayton OH	86/96
			(static rest. Van Nuys CA 91/93 for USAFM, as PR.XI "USAAF MB950": arr. dism. USAFM 4.93)	
SMAF. 15826	F Mk. 22	PK350	(to Southern Rhodesian AF as SR.64): del.	28.3.51/54
			(to Royal Rhodesian AF as RRAF64)	10.54
			retired: last flight	18.12.54
			New Sarum AB, Rhodesia : displ. on pole	.55/77
			Capt. Jack Malloch/Air Trans Africa, Salisbury/Harare, Zimbabwe	.77/82
			(rest. Salisbury: ff 28.3.80 as "PK350/JM-M")	
			crashed dest., Goromorzi, near Harare, Zimbabwe (Malloch k.)	26.3.82
CBAF. 44 •	F Mk. 22	**PK355**	(to Southern Rhodesian AF as SR.65): del.	28.3.51/54
			(to Royal Rhodesian AF as RRAF65)	10.54
			Bulawayo Museum: displ.	
			Thornhill AB, Rhodesia: displ. on pole	78
			Zimbabwe Air Force Museum, New Sarum AB	81/90
			National Museum, Gweru, Zimbabwe	.93/95
			(stored pending static rest.)	
			adv. for sale, as is, Zimbabwe: French broker	9.95
CBAF. 70 •	F Mk. 22	**PK481**	RAFA, Brighton & Hove Branch UK: displ.	9.55/58
			RAAF Association, Perth WA	5.8.58
			(shipped arr. 9.6.59, displ. on pole in city as "PK481/AF-A" .59/70, to pole Bullcreek 13.3.71; outside displ. replaced by fibreglass replica .85)	
			RAAF Assoc. Aviation Museum, Bullcreek WA	.85/96
CBAF. 189 •	F Mk. 22	**PK624**	RAF North Weald : gate guard	58
			RAF Uxbridge (displ. as "WP916")	60
			RAF Northolt	.63/68
			RAF Henlow : for movie "Battle of Britain"	.68
			RAF Abingdon: gate guard	23.7.70/89
			RAF St Athan: stored pending disposal	.89/94
			The Fighter Collection, Duxford: arr. dism.	.94/96
			(Duxford pending restoration to fly)	
CBAF. 217 •	F Mk. 22	**PK664**	RAF Waterbeach : gate guard	
			RAF West Raynham	
			RAF Binbrook: gate guard	5.62/67
			RAF Henlow: for movie "Battle of Britain"	.67/68
			RAF Binbrook: gate guard	.68/88
			RAF St Athan (stored pending disposal)	.89/96
CBAF. 236 •	F Mk. 24	**PK683**	RAF Changi, Singapore : gate guard	54/69
			(rest. RAF Seletar, Singapore .69 for displ. duties)	
			RAF Bicester: arr. by RAF Belfast	16.4.70/72
			RAF Kemble	30.6.72
			RAF Museum, RAF Colerne	11.72/75
			RAF Shawbury	21.8.75
			R. J. Mitchell Museum, Southampton	7.2.76/84
			Hall of Aviation, Southampton	5.84/96
CBAF. 61 255 •	F Mk. 24	**PK724**	RAF Norton: gate guard	4.11.54/
			RAF Gaydon	1.12.61/70
			RAF Henlow: for film *Battle of Britain*	.67/68
			RAF Finningley	20.2.70
			RAF Museum, Hendon	2.4.71/96
- •	LF Mk. IXe	**PL344**	Anthony Fokker Technical School, Holland	
			(dism., Holland, various parts sold)	
			Charles Church (Spitfires) Ltd, Andover: hulk	.85/88

c/n	Type	Serial	Reg.	Owner / history	Date
			G-IXCC	Charles Church (Spitfires) Ltd, Winchester	18.5.88/92
				(rest. Winchester, ff 11.3.91)	
				Kermit A. Weeks, Tamiami FL	10.92/96
				(rest. to fly Booker UK 96 as "PL344/Y2-P")	
6S/ 504719 •	PR Mk. XI	**PL965**		(to R Netherlands AF as PL965): del.	8.7.47
				RNAF School of Technical Training, Deelen AB	22.7.47/52
				Deelen AB : displ.	.52/60
				National War & Resistance Museum, Overloon AB, Netherlands	11.60/87
				E. Nick Grace, Chichester UK	.86
				Chris Horsley/Medway Aircraft Preservation Society: arr. Rochester for rebuild	2.87/92
			G-MKXI	Christopher P. B. Horsley, Chichester	11.89/95
				(rest. Rochester 87/92 as "USAAF PL965/R", ff Rochester 23.12.92)	
				op: Old Flying Machine Company, Duxford	93/96
6S/ 583719 •	PR Mk. XI	**PL979**		(to RNoAF as PL979/A-ZB): del.	31.7.47
				last flew 25.3.54; stored Rygge AB	60/81
				R Norwegian AF Collection/Forsvarsnuseet Flysamlingn, Gardermoen AB	7.81/96
6S/ 583723 •	PR Mk. XI	**PL983**		Vickers-Armstrongs Ltd, Eastleigh (loan)	22.7.47
			NC74138	US Embassy, Air Attache, Hendon UK: del.	27.1.48
				Vickers-Armstrongs Ltd, Eastleigh	.49
				Shuttleworth Trust, Old Warden: del.	.50/83
				(static displ. 50/75, trucked to Duxford 30.8.75: rest. to fly Duxford 75/83)	
				Roland Fraissinet, Marseilles, France	14.4.83
			G-PRXI	Roland Fraissinet, East Midlands Airport UK	6.6.83/87
				(rest. completed, ff. East Midlands 17.7.84)	
				Warbirds of GB Ltd.	1.10.87/93
6S/ 683524 •	PR Mk. XIX	**PM627**		(to Indian AF as HS964)	.53
				Indian AF Museum, Palam AB: stored unrest.	.67/69
				John Weir/Canadian Fighter Pilots Association, Downsview ONT: arr. dism. in C-130	3.2.71/82
				(static rest., displ. as "PM627/YO-X & DB-X")	
				Canadian National Exhibition, Toronto ONT	.72/73
				Ontario Science Centre, Toronto ONT: displ.	11.73/78
				Can. Warplane Heritage, Hamilton ONT: displ.	80
				David C. Tallichet/MARC, Chino CA	.82
				Flygvapenmuseum, Linkoping, Sweden	10.82/96
				(airfreighted to Sweden by C-130 22.10.82, rest. and displ. as "RSwAF Fv31051")	
6S/ 683527 •	PR Mk. XIX	**PM630**		(to R Thai AF as PM630)	8.54
				Technical School, Trat, Thailand: displ.	60/86
				R Thai AF Thai Air Classics/Tango Squadron	96
				(static rest. completed Bangkok-Don Muang 95)	
6S/ 683528 •	PR Mk. XIX	**PM631**		RAF Memorial Flight, RAF Biggin Hill: del.	14.6.57/61
				RAF Battle of Britain Memorial Flight	11.3.61/96
6S/ 687107 •	PR Mk. XIX	**PM651**		Rolls-Royce Ltd, Hucknall: gate guard	.54
				RAF Andover	3.57/62
				RAF Benson	66/67
				RAF Henlow	.67/68
				(static scenes, film *Battle of Britain* .68)	
				RAF Bicester: travelling exhibit	70/71
				RAF Benson: gate guard	.71/88
				RAF Museum, Hendon	.89/91
				RAF Museum, St.Athan	12.91/95
				RAF Museum Store, RAF Cardington	.95
- •	Seafire	**PP972**		(to Aeronavale as 12F.2 later 1F.9)	.48

c/n	Type	Serial	Reg.	History	Date
	LF. IIIc			op. from carrier "Arromanches", Indo China	48/49
				Hyeres AB: instructional airframe	.49
				Jean Frelaut, Vannes-Meucon	.70/88
				(recov. from scrap yard, Gavres, near Lorient .70, static rest. as "PP972/1.F.9")	
				Musee de la Resistance, St Marcel: loan	.82/84
				Warbirds of GB Ltd, Biggin Hill	.88/92
				(rest. Thruxton, East Midlands & Audley End 88/96)	
			G-BUAR	Precious Metals Ltd, Bournemouth	21.1.92
CO. 9621 •	Seafire F. XV	**PR376**		(to Union of Burma AF as UB409)	
				Meiktila AB, Burma: displ.	70/89
				Mingaladon AB, Rangoon: stored	95/96
CO 9675 •	Seafire F XV	**PR422**		(to Burmese AF as UB415)	
				Meiktila AB, Burma: stored	88/96
CO. 9673 •	Seafire F. XV	**PR451**		(to RCN as PR451): BOC 1.6.46: SOC	25.5.49
				Southern Alberta Institute of Technology	c50
				HMCS Tecumseh, Calgary ALTA	.61/84
				(gate guard: displ. as "PR425/TG-B")	
				Aero Space Museum of Calgary ALTA	.84/85
				(rest., displ. as "VG-AA-N")	
				CAFB Tecumseh, Calgary ALTA (displ.)	88/96
COA. 30621 •	Seafire F. XV	**PR503**		(to RCN as PR503): BOC 1.6.46: SOC	5.4.50
				Shearwater CFB NS: derelict hulk	58
				Peter Myers: rest., stored Bedford NS	.58/64
				EAA/Dartmouth, Nova Scotia Chapter	.66
				Dennis J. Bradley, Buttonville ONT: stored	70/72
			C-GCWK	ntu: D. J. Bradley/Canadian Warplane Heritage, Hamilton ONT: long-term rest.	85/92
				Courtesy Aircraft, Rockford IL	.92
				(offered for sale, incomplete rest. project)	
			N535R	Amjet Aircraft Corp, St Paul MN	.93/96
				(rest. to fly, St Paul-Anoka County 93/96)	
6S/ 637129 •	PR Mk. XIX	**PS836**		(to R Thai AF as U14-27/97)	26.6.54
				technical school, Chiang Mei: inst. airframe	78
				derelict: rep. purchased by British collector	c79
				stored dism. stripped, Chiang Mei, Thailand	80/86
				RTAF Thai Air Classics/Tango Squadron, Chiang Mei AB: rest. to fly	92/95
				(rest. Chiang Mei AB 92, rest. by Thai Airways Bangkok-Don Muang 93/96)	
6S/ 594677 •	PR Mk. XIX	**PS853**		RAF Memorial Flight, RAF Biggin Hill: del.	14.6.57
				RAF West Raynham: gate guard	.60/64
				RAF Battle of Britain Memorial Flight	14.4.64/95
				(flew in movie "Battle of Britain" .68)	
				Euan C. English, North Weald: del.	17.2.95
			G-MXIX	Mrs.E.C.. English, North Weald	23.2.95
			G RRGN	sold	2.96
6S/ 585110 •	PR Mk. XIX	**PS890**		(to R Thai AF as U14-26/97)	26.6.54/62
				Ed Maloney/The Air Museum, Claremont CA	.62/70
				(donated by King Bhumiphol of Siam, airfreighted by Flying Tigers L-1049 to Burbank CA .62)	
				Planes of Fame Museum, Chino CA	71/96
				(stored Chino 80/93: rest. to fly Chino 94/96)	
6S/ 585121 •	PR Mk. XIX	**PS915**		RAF Memorial Flight, RAF Biggin Hill: del.	6.57
				RAF West Malling: gate guard	31.8.57/60
				RAF Leuchars: gate guard	66/75
				RAF Henlow: for movie "Battle of Britain"	.67/68
				RAF Brawdy: gate guard	.75/84
				RAF Battle of Britain Memorial Flight	.84/96
				(rest. Salmesbury, ff 20.11.86)	
				major service Historic Flying Audley End	2.96

c/n	Type	Serial	Reg.	History	Date
- •	HF Mk. IXe	**PT462**		(to Italian AF as MM4100)	27.6.46
				(to IDFAF as 0607: later 20-67 "4X-FOM")	4.52
				Robs Lamplough, Duxford UK	.83/84
				(hulk of forward fuselage recov. ex town dump Gaza Strip, Israel .83, arr. Fowlemere UK 5.83)	
				Charles Church, Winchester UK	7.84
			G-CTIX	Charles Church (Spitfires) Ltd, Winchester	9.4.85/94
				(rest. Winchester as Tr.9: ff 25.7.87)	
				op: Dick Melton Aviation, Winchester	91/94
			N462JC	Jet Cap Aviation, Lakeland FL	25.7.94/96
				(flies as "PT462/SW-A")	
			G-CTIX	A.A. HODGSON	1998
CBAF. 2716 •	HF Mk. IXe	**PT601**		(to SAAF as 5573)	
				components stored Lanseria AB, South Africa	78/86
CBAF. 9590 •	LF Mk. IX Tr Mk. IXc	**PV202**		(to Irish Air Corps as 161): del.	29.6.51/68
				N.A.W. Samuelson, Cricklewood	4.3.68
				(stored dism., Cricklewood, North London)	
				Sir W. J. D. Roberts/Strathallan Collection	4.70/79
				(stored dism., Flimwell & Strathallan 70/79)	
				E. Nick Grace, St. Merryn	9.8.79
			G-BHGH	ntu: Steve W. Atkins, Battle Sussex	10.10.79
			G-TRIX	Steve W. Atkins, Saffron Walden	2.7.80/90
				Richard Parker	5.90/91
				(rest. Battle 79/90, ff Dunsfold 23.2.90)	
				Rick A. Roberts, Goodwood	.91/94
CBAF. IX3128 •	F Mk. IX	**PV270**		(to Italian AF as MM4014)	27.6.46
				(to IDFAF as 20-..)	
				(to Burmese AF as UB424)	
				Hmawbi AB, Rangoon: displ. on pole: "UB425"	70/90
				Mingaladon AB, Rangoon: stored	94/96
CBAF. 9746 •	F Mk. IX	**RK858**		recov. ex crash site Russia	
				The Fighter Collection, Duxford UK	92/95
6S/ 432263	F Mk. XIVc	RM689	G-ALGT	Rolls-Royce Ltd, Hucknall/Castle Donnington	19.2.49/92
				(CofA Hucknall 8.6.50)	
				(flown in film *Battle of Britain* .68)	
				(flew as "RM619/AP-D", later "RM689/MN-E")	
				crashed dest. during airshow, Woodford	27.6.92
6S/ 432268 •	F Mk. XIV	**RM694**		RAF Hornchurch	50/60
				RAF Bicester	64
				RAF Dishforth, for disposal as scrap	
				A. H. 'Bunny' Brooks, Hoylake, Cheshire	.66
				(wings used to rest. NH904 for static displ.)	
				J. Denis Kay/Manchester Tankers Ltd, Charnock Richard, Lancs. (fuse. only)	.66/68
				(fuse. at Henlow .67 for film "Battle of Britain")	
				A. W. Francis, Southend	1.68
				John Lowe & Larry Matt, Riverside IL	c72/81
				(rest project: wings from various sources: stored Victory Air Museum, Mundelein IL)	
				Warbirds of GB Ltd, Bitteswell	.85
				Don L. Knapp/DK Precision, Ft. Lauderdale FL	89
				Vern Schuppan: stored Florida	95/96
6S/ 534585 •	F MK. XIVe	**RM797**		(to R Thai AF as U14-16/93)	.50
				displ. Province Administration building, Surin	50s
				derelict, Surin, Thailand: recov. by Garry Cooper, Hong Kong/Sydney NSW	24.5.73/77
				(airfreighted to Darwin NT 19.8.73: stored)	
				dam. during Cyclone "Tracy", Darwin NT	25.12.74
			VH-XIV	Garry Cooper, Sydney NSW: reg. res.	77/96
				(rest. project Darwin, then Albury NSW)	
6S/	F Mk. XIV	**RM873**		(to R Thai AF as U14-5/93)	11.50

C/n	Mark	Serial	Reg.	History	Date
432296 •				Sawankalok, Thailand: displ.	
				(mainplane to P. Sledge, Australia for RR232 .81,	
				fuse. stored, Sawankalok, Thailand 85)	
				R Thai AF Thai Air Classics/Tango Squadron	96
				(rest. project Chiang Mei AB 93/94,	
				stored Bangkok-Don Muang 96)	
6S/ 432331 •	FR Mk. XIVc	**RM921**		(to Belgian AF as SG57): BOC	8.48
				Florrenes AB, Belgium: displ. on pole	c55/87
				(static rest. 86/92 as "RL-D")	
				Florrenes AB: displ. as "SG57/RL-D"	24.7.92/96
6S/ 381758 •	FR Mk. XIVe	**RM927**		(to Belgian AF as SG25): BOC	14.11.47
				Oscar Dewachter Scrapyard, Ostend Belgium	57/67
				(displ. on roof: wings axed off)	
				J. Denis Kay/Manchester Tankers Ltd,	
				Charnock Richard, Lancs: arr. by road	4.3.67/69
				A. W. Francis, Southend: arr. by road	22.3.69
				John Lowe & Larry Matt, Riverside IL	.69/81
				(stored at Victory Air Museum, Mundelein IL)	
				Larry Matt, Chicago IL	82/85
				(rest. commenced, using wings ex IAF HS649)	
				Don L. Knapp/DK Precision, Ft. Lauderdale FL	87
				Vern Schuppan: stored Florida	95/96
6S/ 663417 •	F Mk. XIVe	**RN201**		(to Belgian AF as SG31): del.	19.2.48
				Beauvechain AB, Belgium: displ. on pole "SG3"	53/90
				Guy Black/Historic Aircraft Collection: arr.	3.5.90
			G-BSKP	Historic Aircraft Collection Ltd,	27.6.90/96
				(stored Paddock Wood, Kent,	96
- •	HF Mk. IXc	**RR232**		(to SAAF as 5632): BOC 5.49: SOC	16.1.54
				South African Metal & Machinery Co,	
				Salt River, Cape Town, South Africa	.54
				recov. Larry Barnett & Alan Lurie, Johannesberg	
				(tail section used to rebuild MA793)	
				Peter Sledge, Sydney NSW (fuse. only)	.76/86
				(fuse. shipped ex S.Africa 12.76, static rest.	
				RAAF Pt.Cook VIC & Sydney NSW, using parts	
				from wartime crash sites and mainplane of	
				RM873 ex Thailand, tail of MK732 ex UK)	
				rest. completed, rolled-out Bankstown NSW	14.10.84
				loan RAN Museum, Nowra NAS NSW	85/86
				Charles Church, Micheldever UK	.86/89
				(shipped to UK, arr. Micheldever 13.1.87)	
			G-BRSF	Sussex Spraying Services Ltd, Shoreham	11.89/96
				stored for sale, struck-off reg.	23.6.94
CBAF. IX3310 •	LF Mk. XVIe	**RR263**		RAF Kenley: gate guard: "TB597/GW-B"	55/67
				presented French Air Force: displ. Tours AB	5.67/77
				(airfreighted to Tours AB by RAF Beverley 5.67,	
				displ. as "TB597": rep. flown at Tours 20.5.77)	
				Musee de l'Air, Paris-Le Bourget	.78/95
				(displ. as "TB597/GW-B")	
CBAF. IX4640 •	LF Mk. XVIe	**RW382**		RAF Leconfield: gate guard as "RW729"	.57/73
				RAF Henlow	.67/68
				(static scenes, film "Battle of Britain" .68)	
				RAF Uxbridge: arr., displ. on pole	4.4.73/88
				Tim Routis/Historic Flying Ltd, Cambridge	8.88/89
				(collected ex RAF Uxbridge 26.8.88)	
				David C. Tallichet/MARC, Chino CA	.89/94
			G-XVIA	Historic Flying Ltd, Audley End	2.7.91/94
				(ff Audley End 3.7.91 as "RW382/NG-C")	
				David C. Tallichet/MARC, Chino CA	91/94
				Barry Jackson MAN Canada	.94/95
				(based UK 91/95, del. Audley End 13.2.95 for	
				dism. for export to USA): struck-off reg.	17.3.95
			N382RW	Bernie Jackson CA & Barry Jackson MAN	8.95/96
				A/C CRASHED, BLUE RIVER CANYON, NEVADA. USA 6/6/98	

CBAF. IX4644 •	LF Mk. XVIe	**RW386**		RAF Halton: displ. as "RF114"	30.8.57/82
				Warbirds of GB Ltd, Blackbushe	.82
			G-BXVI	Warbirds of GB Ltd, Blackbushe	27.12.84
				Warbirds of GB Ltd. (rest. "RW386/NG-D")	85/94
CBAF. IX4646 •	LF Mk. XVIe	**RW388**		RAF Colerne	2.52/60
				RAF Benson	
				RAF Andover	63/67
				RAF Bicester	68/72
				City Museum, Stoke-on-Trent (displ. as "RW388/U4-U")	15.2.72/96
CBAF. IX4651 •	LF Mk. XVIe	**RW393**		RAF Turnhouse: gate guard "XT-A"	8.56/89
				RAF St Athan: stored pending disposal	.89/95
				RAF Museum, RAF Cosford: arr. (displ. as "RW393/XT-A")	1.5.95/96
- •	Seafire L. III	**RX168**		(to Irish Air Corps as 157)	
				Chris Warrillow, High Wycombe (rest. to fly, Dunsfold 91)	89/91
			G-BWEM	Christopher J. Warrilow, High Wycombe	28.6.95/96
CBAF. IX4656 •	LF Mk. XVIe	**SL542**		RAF Horsham St. Faith : gate guard	5.57
				RAF Coltishall : displ. on pole	66/88
				RAF St Athan (stored pending disposal)	.89/92
				Jeet Mahal, Vancouver BC	.92
			N2289J	Pegasus Investments Inc, West Palm Beach FL	11.5.94/96
CBAF. IX4688 •	LF Mk. XVIe	**SL574**		RAF Bentley Priory	11.61/86
				RAF Henlow" (static scenes, film *Battle of Britain*" .68)	.67/69
				RAF Halton: static rest.	.86/89
				American Eagle Squadron/San Diego Aerospace Museum, San Diego CA (still in UK awaiting shipment to USA 89;	.86/95
				displ. SDAM by 92 as "SL574/MD-T")	96
CBAF. IX4701 •	LF Mk. XVIe	**SL674**		RAF Memorial Chapel, Biggin Hill: del.	11.9.54/89
				RAF St Athan: stored pending disposal	3.89/95
				RAF Museum Store, RAF Cardington	95
CBAF. IX4756 •	LF Mk. XVIe	**SL721**		F. M. Wilcock, Swandean Garage, Worthing (arr. Worthing 11.54 ex storage RAF Lyneham, displ. at garage, engine run-up regularly)	11.54/65
				RAF Thorney Island: loan, briefly flown	9.58
				Beaulieu Motor Museum: loan, arr.	6.10.58/65
				Monty Thackray/M. D. Thackray Ltd	9.7.65/66
				William D. Ross, Chicago IL (rest. Atlanta GA, ff 11.5.67 as "SL721/JM-R")	12.65/67
			N8R (1	William D. Ross, Du Page IL	.67/73
			G-BAUP	Doug W. Arnold/Fairoaks Aviation Services (shipped, arr. Leavesden 28.3.73, assembled Blackbushe, flew as "SL721/DA")	4.4.73/77
			N8WK	Woodson K. Woods, Scottsdale AZ (shipped ex UK 8.77, ff Deer Valley AZ 18.9.77)	21.7.77/82
			N721WK	Woodson K. Woods/Aero Meridian Corp/ Carefree Flying Museum, Scottsdale AZ	2.82/95
				San Diego Aerospace Museum CA: loan, arr. (trucked San Diego-Ft Collins CO .90 for rest., del. Scottsdale AZ 23.2.92 as "SL721/WK-W")	21.2.83/90
				dam. landing Albuquerque NM (trucked out)	7.10.95
CBAF. IX3495 •	LF Mk. XVIe	**SM411**		RAF Wattisham	8.55/67
				RAF Henlow (taxy scenes, film *Battle of Britain* .68)	.67/70

c/n	Model	Serial	Reg.	History	Date
				RAF Bicester: travelling exhibit	2.70/71
				RAF Museum, RAF Abingdon	76/78
				Aviation & Space Museum, Krakow, Poland	.78/95
				(displ. as "SM411/AU-Y")	
CBAF. 10164 •	HF Mk. IX	**SM520**		(to SAAF as ....)	
				South African Metal & Machinery Co,	
				Salt River, Cape Town	54
				SAAF Museum, Snake Valley AB: hulk	81
				Steve W. Atkins, Oxford, UK	
				Alan Dunkerly, Oxford UK: rest. project	93/96
- •	Mk. IX	**SM639**		(to Soviet AF as ....)	
				(recov. ex surface crash site, Russia)	
				AJD Engineering, Milden, Suffolk	95
				Chris Lawrence, Norfolk	.95
6S/ 663452 •	F Mk. XIVc	**SM832**		(to Indian AF as ....)	7.47
				Indian Military Academy, Dehra Dun, India	72/78
				recov. from India by Ormond &	
				Wensley Haydon-Baillie, Duxford UK	.78
			G-WWII	Warbirds of GB, Blackbushe	9.7.79/85
				(rest. as Mk. VIII commenced Blackbushe & Bitteswell)	
				The Fighter Collection, Duxford	8.86
				Charles Church (Spitfires) Ltd, Micheldever	11.88/91
				(rest. to Mk. XIV continued Winchester)	
				The Fighter Collection, Duxford	11.91/96
				(rest. Audley End, completed Duxford,	
				ff Duxford 22.5.95 as "SM832/YB-A")	
6S/ • 672224	FR Mk. XVIIIe	**SM845**		(to Indian AF as HS687)	31.12.47
				hulk recov. from Kalaikunda AB by Ormond &	
				Wensley Haydon-Baillie, Duxford UK	.77
				Marshall Moss & Richard A. Boolootian,	
				Lancaster CA	.78/81
				(stored crated Lancaster-Fox Field CA 79/80)	
				MARC, Chino CA	c81/87
				(rest. commenced Tulsa OK later Casper WY)	
				Adrian Reynard, Kidlington UK	88/92
				(shipped to UK for rebuild)	
			G-BUOS	Park Avenue Investments Ltd,	
				Witney	10.92/96
				(rest. to fly, Audley End 92/96)	
6S/ 662808 •	FR Mk. XIVe	**SM914**		(to R Thai AF as U14-1/93)	.50
				R Thai AF Museum, Don Muang AB, Bangkok	.54/96
6S/ 663052 •	FR Mk. XVIIIe	**SM969**		(to Indian AF as HS877)	21.7.49
				Indian AF Western Air Command HQ,	
				Delhi Cantonment: displ.	72/78
				recov. by Ormond & Wensley Haydon-Baillie,	
				Duxford UK	.78
				Doug Arnold, Blackbushe: arr crated	5.78
			G-BRAF	Warbirds of GB Ltd, Blackbushe	12.78/85
				(rest. Blackbushe, ff 12.10.85 "SM969/D-A")	
				Warbirds of GB Ltd, Bitteswell/Biggin Hill	.85/93
				(del. Biggin Hill-Bournemouth for storage 20.11.92)	
6S/ 643887 •	F Mk. XVIIIe	**SM986**		(to Indian AF as HS986)	30.6.49
				IAF Museum, Palam AB, New Delhi	.67/95
WASE1 4106 •	Seafire F XV	**SR462**		(to Burmese AF as UB414)	
				Hmawbi AB, Rangoon: gate guard "UB415"	70/85
				Mingaladon AB, Rangoon: stored	94/95
WASP 4417 •	F Mk. XV	**SW800**		Peter Croser, Melbourne VIC	91/96
				(rest. project)	
WASE1 5325 •	Seafire F XVII	**SX137**		RNAS Yeovilton: flying & static displ.	12.8.58/64
				(displ. as "W9132/TT-C/Suzy")	

c/n	Type	Serial	Reg	History	Date
				Fleet Air Arm Museum, RNAS Yeovilton	.64/96
				(displ. as "RNFAA SX137")	
- •	Seafire F XVII	**SX300**		Peter R. Arnold, Newport Pagnell : fuse only	.73
				(recov. from scrapyard, Warrington .73)	
				John Berkeley/Midlands Aircraft Preservation Society, Warwick	82/96
				(long-term composite rest. project)	
FLWA/ 25488 •	Seafire F XVII	**SX336**		Peter R. Arnold, Newport Pagnell : fuse only .73	
				(recov. from scrapyard, Warrington .73)	
				Neville Franklin	.73
				Craig Charleston, Hemel Hempstead	78
				Peter J. Wood, Twyford, Bucks	80/89
			G-BRMG	Peter J. Wood, Twyford, Bucks	19.9.89/96
				(rest. project)	
CBAF. 10372 •	LF Mk. IX	**TA805**		(to SAAF as .....)	
				South African Metal & Machinery Co, Salt River, Cape Town	54
				SAAF Museum, Snake Valley AB: fuse. hulk	81
				Steve W. Atkins, Oxford, UK	89/95
				(rest. project, stored Isle-of-Wight 95)	
CBAF. IX3807 •	LF Mk. XVIe	**TB252**		RAF Odiham: gate guard	12.9.55/59
				RAF Acklington	8.59/67
				RAF Boulmer	7.69
				RAF Leuchars: gate guard	12.69/86
				RAF Bentley Priory: gate guard	4.86/88
				Tim Routsis/Historic Flying Ltd, Cambridge	6.88/92
				(collected ex gate guard Bentley Priory 9.11.88)	
			G-XVIE	Historic Flying Ltd, Audley End	3.7.92
				Nicholas Springer	95/96
				(stored Audley End 93/96)	
- •	LF Mk. XVIe	**TB382**		RAF Thornaby	.55
				RAF Middleton St George	7.57/62
				RAF Hospital, Ely	66/67
				RAF Henlow	18.2.67/68
				(taxy scenes, movie "Battle of Britain" .68)	
				RAF Museum Store, RAF Henlow	74
				RAF Abingdon : travelling exhibit "X4277"	77/90
				displ. West Midlands as "MK673"	95/96
CBAF. IX4113 •	LF Mk. XVIe	**TB752**		RAF Kenley, for movie "Reach for the Sky"	55
				RAF Manston: gate guard, then displ. inside	28.9.55/96
				(displ. as "TB752/KH-Z")	
CBAF. 10895 •	LF Mk. XVIe	**TB863**		Metro-Goldwyn-Meyer, Pinewood Studios UK	.55/68
				(used in movie "Reach for the Sky" .55)	
				(stored Pinewood Studios 56/67)	
				(dism. for spares, Henlow .68)	
				A. William Francis, Southend: rest. project	12.68/82
				(rest. at owner's home and at HAM Southend)	
				Historic Aircraft Museum, Southend: displ.	72
			G-CDAN	J. Parkes & A. W. Francis, Booker	30.11.82
				The Fighter Collection, Duxford	.84/88
				Tim Wallis, Wanaka NZ	.87
				(ff Duxford 14.9.88: shipped to NZ 13.10.88)	
			ZK-XVI	Tim Wallis/Alpine Fighter Collection, Wanaka	17.1.89/96
				dam. forced landing, Waipukarau NZ (repaired)	29.1.89
				dam. landing, Woodbourne NZ (repaired)	18.11.92
				(flies as "TB863/FU-P")	
- •	LF Mk. XVIe	**TB885**		RAF Kenley : fire fighting practice	55
				background views, film "Reach for the Sky"	9.55
				buried fire dump, RAF Kenley	.59/82
				Shoreham Aircraft Pres. Society: excavated	4.82

				Lashenden Air Warfare Museum, Sevenoaks	85
				Shoreham Aircraft Museum, Shoreham	91
				(long-term rest. for static displ.)	
CBAF. IX4218 •	LF Mk. XVIe	**TD135**		Air Training Corps, Tynemouth, Newcastle	51/63
				RAF Dishforth : for sale as scrap	63/64
				Percy Sheppard/The Spitfire Inn, Leominster	.64/75
				Worral Granger/Connie Motors	.75
				Larry Higgins/Thunderbird Aviation, Deer Valley AZ	.75
				David Boyd & Hurley Bowler, Tulsa OK	.76
				Ray Stutsman, Elkhart IN	85/86
				William C. Anderson, Geneseo NY	20.1.86/96
				(long-term rebuild, Palmyra & Geneseo NY)	
CBAF. IX4262 •	LF Mk. XVIe	**TD248**		RAF Hooton Park: gate guard, arr.	4.10.55/59
				RAF Sealand: gate guard	8.4.59/67
				RAF Henlow : for movie "Battle of Britain"	.67/68
				RAF Sealand : gate guard on plinth	.68/88
				Historic Flying Ltd, Cambridge	6.88
				Eddie Coventry, Earls Colne	8.88
				(trucked Audley End ex RAF Sealand 14.10.88)	
			G-OXVI	Eddie Coventry/BAC Aviation Ltd, Earls Colne	22.8.89/96
				(rest. Audley End, ff 10.11.92 as "TD248/D")	
				Mr. Bos, op Stampe Centre, Belgium	96
- •	F Mk. IX	**TD314**		(to SAAF as ....)	12.5.48
				South African Metal & Machinery Co, Salt River, Cape Town	c54
				Larry Barnett, Johannesburg: hulk recov.	69/72
				Pat Swonnell, Vancouver BC	.78/81
				(fuse. hulk arr. Vancouver by ship 11.4.79)	
				Matt Sattler, Carp ONT later Vancouver BC	85/96
				(long-term rest. project: fuse. to UK .95)	
CBAF. X4394 •	LF Mk. XVIe	**TE184**		Air Training Corps, Royton, Lancs	.52/67
				RAF Bicester	2.67
				RAF Henlow: for film *Battle of Britain*	67
				RAF Finningley Museum Collection	69
				RAF Aldergrove	.71/77
				Ulster Folk & Transport Museum, Holywood	3.77/86
				E. Nick Grace, St. Merryn	.86/88
			G-MXVI	Myrick Aviation Services, Castle Donington	17.2.89/94
				(rest. East Midlands, ff 23.11.90)	
				sold	96
BAF. 1274 •	F Mk. IXe	**TE213**		(to SAAF as 5518)	8.47
				Waterkloof AB : displ. on pole	.54/79
				(displ. as "5518", "W5581", later "W5518")	
				SAAF Museum, Swartkop AB	29.3.79/95
				SAAF Historic Flight	90/96
				(rest., ff 5.10.95 as "SAAF 5553/AX-K")	
BAF X4424 •	LF Mk. XVIe	**TE214**		RAF Ternhill: displ. as "TE353"	56/60
				loaned RCAF: displ. Parliament Hill, Ottawa	.60
				RCAF Mountain View ONT: stored	.60/62
				RCAF BOC at Trenton ONT	10.1.63
				Canadian War Museum, Ottawa ONT ("DN-T")	.66/93
				Western Canada Avtn Museum, Winnipeg: loan	12.88/96
BAF 1414 •	LF Mk. XVIe	**TE288**		RAF Rufforth	.55/59
				(flew in film "*Reach for the Sky*" 8.55)	
				RAF Church Fenton	7.59/61
				RAF Dishforth	9.61/63
				Brevet Club, Canterbury NZ	.62/84
				(shipped to NZ, arr. 28.6.63: displ. on plinth)	
				(replaced by fibreglass replica "TE283" .84)	
				(static rest. Woodbourne AB 84/86)	
				RNZAF Museum, Wigram AB: displ. as "OU-V"	.84/96

- •	HF Mk. IX	**TE294**		(to SAAF as ....)	
				Mark de Vries, Bryanston, South Africa	81/96
				(rest. project at Honeydew, South Africa)	
CBAF. IX4494 •	LF Mk. IXe Tr Mk. IXc	**TE308**		(to Irish Air Corps as 163): del.	30.7.51/68
				instructional airframe, Baldonnel AB, Eire	.61/68
			G-AWGB	N. A. W. Samuelson/Samuelson Film Services	
				Elstree : del. ex Baldonnel	8.5.68/69
				(flown in film *Battle of Britain* .68)	
				Sir W. J. D. Roberts, Shoreham	12.69/70
				Don Plumb, Windsor ONT	16.7.70
				(shipped to Toronto ONT, arr. 9.10.70)	
			CF-RAF	Don Plumb, Windsor ONT	12.70/73
				C-FRAFDon Plumb, Windsor ONT	75
				(conv. to single seater)	
			N92477	Thomas J. Watson/Owls Head Transport	
				Museum, Owls Head ME	.75/79
			N308WK	Woodson K. Woods, Scottsdale AZ	7.10.79/82
				(conv. back to Tr.IX two-seater config., displ.	
				Carefree Aviation Museum, Scottsdale AZ)	
				Aero Meridian Corp, Scottsdale AZ	11.1.82
				William S. Greenwood, Aspen CO	8.83/96
				(flies as "TE308/RJ-M")	
CBAF. IX4497 •	LF Mk. XVIe	**TE311**		RAF Tangmere: gate guard	11.8.55/67
				RAF Henlow	.67
				(taxy scenes, film *Battle of Britain*" .68)	
				RAF Benson	9.68/77
				RAF Abingdon : travelling display exhibit	77/90
				SERCO, West Midlands	
				Bayeux Museum, France: loan,"MK178/LZ-V"	94/96
CBAF. 11446 •	LF Mk. XVIe	**TE330**		RAF North Weald Station Flight	13.3.58
				USAF Academy, Colorado Springs CO	7.58
				(del. ex RAF Odiham by C-124 7.58)	
				USAFM, Wright-Patterson AFB, Dayton OH	61/96
CBAF. 11470 •	LF Mk. XVIe	**TE356**		RAF Bicester	52/67
				RAF Henlow	.67/68
				(taxy scenes, movie "Battle of Britain" .68)	
				RAF Kemble	5.69
				RAF Little Rissington	4.12.70/76
				RAF Cranwell	20.4.76/78
				RAF Leeming : displ. on pole	.78/86
				Warbirds of GB Ltd, Bitteswell	.86
			G-SXVI	Warbirds of GB Ltd, Biggin Hill	25.2.87/90
				(rest. East Midlands : ff 16.12.87)	
			N356EV	Evergreen Ventures Inc,	
				McMinnville OR	1.90
			N356TE	Evergreen Heritage Collection, Marana AZ	4.90/96
				(flies as RAF TE356/D-DE/*Carolyn*)	
CBAF. 11485 •	LF Mk. XVIe	**TE384**		RAF Wymeswold: instructional airframe	8.55
				RAF Syerston : instructional airframe	11.57/67
				RAF Henlow	.67/68
				(taxy scenes, film *Battle of Britain*" .68)	
				RAFM Store, Henlow	10.68/72
				Hockey Treloar, Sydney NSW	.72/83
				(airfreighted to Australia by RAF Belfast 12.72,	
				open storage Canberra ACT 73/83)	
				Camden Museum of Aviation NSW: loan, arr.	24.4.75
				H. Treloar & Jim Czerwinski, Toowoomba QLD	9.83/95
				(trucked to Toowoomba 9.83, rest. commenced)	
			VH-XVI	Jim F. Czerwinski, Toowoomba QLD	5.10.88/96
				(ff Toowoomba 6.10.88, flies as "TE384/XVI")	
CBAF.	LF Mk. XVIe	**TE392**		RAF Wellesbourne Mountford: gate guard	.52/61

IX4551 •				RAF Waterbeach: gate guard	9.61/66
				RAF Kemble	3.66/70
				RAF Hereford: gate guard	19.2.70/84
				Warbirds of GB Ltd, Blackbushe	.84/85
				Warbirds of GB Ltd, Bitteswell/Biggin Hill	.85/92
				(arr. dism. Thruxton 6.7.89 for rest., stored dism. Biggin Hill 92)	
				Jet Cap Aviation, Lakeland FL	93/96
CBAF IX4590 •	LF Mk. XVIe	**TE456**		flew in film *Reach for the Sky*	8.55
				Domain War Memorial Museum, Auckland NZ	.56/95
				(displ. as "TE456/43")	
CBAF IX4596 •	LF Mk. XVIe	**TE462**		RAF Ouston : gate guard	19.8.55/70
				Museum of Flight, East Fortune, Scotland	19.2.71/96
CBAF. IX4610 •	LF Mk. XVIe	TE476		RAF Battle of Britain Flight	1.3.58/60
				RAF Neatishead: displ.	1.60/67
				RAF Henlow	2.67/68
				(taxy scenes, movie "Battle of Britain" .68)	
				RAF Northolt: gate guard	2.6.70/88
				Historic Flying Ltd, Rayne	6.88
			G-XVIB	Historic Flying Ltd, Cambridge	3.7.89/90
				Weeks Air Museum, Tamiami FL (stored)	1.2.90
			N476TE	Kermit A. Weeks ,Tamiami FL	4.91/96
				(shipped FL to UK 5.92, for rest. at Booker)	
			G-XVIB	Personal Plane Services, Booker	3.5.94
				(rest. Booker, ff 20.6.95 as "TE476/GE-D", dism. Booker 9.95 for shipping to Florida)	
SH/CBAF. IX558 •	LF Mk. IXe	TE517		(to Czech AF as TE517): del.	20.8.45/48
				(to IDFAF as 20-46)	.48/54
				(hulk recov. from kibbutz, Gaaton, Israel by Robert J. Lamplough : arr. Duxford 3.77)	
			G-BIXP	Robs Lamplough, Duxford	3.7.81/84
				(rest. commenced Bristol)	
				Charles Church, Micheldever: rest. project	8.84
			G-CCIX	Charles Church (Spitfires) Ltd, Winchester	9.4.85/92
				(rest. to fly, Micheldever)	
				Kermit A. Weeks, Tamiami FL	10.92/96
				(stored Booker UK 96)	
17-1351•	LF Mk. IXe	TE554		(to Czech AF as A-708): del.	20.8.45/48
				(to IDFAF as 20-57) "4X-FOG"	.48/55
				retired, stored for displ. flying	.55
				IDFAF Museum, Ramat David AB	
				Israeli Air Force Museum, Be'er Sheva AB	76/96
				(airworthy, glossy black sc. "IDFAF 57")	
CBAF. 11397 •	LF Mk. IXe	TE565		(to Czech AF as A-712)	.45
				Narodni Technicke Museum, Prague	22.5.50/70
				Military Museum, Kbely Airport, Prague	70/94
				(displ. as "TE565/NN-N")	
17-1363•	LF Mk. IX	**TE566**		(to Czech AF as TE566)	8.45
				(to IDFAF as 20-32) "4X-FOB"	.49
				hulk recov. from kibbutz at Alonim, Israel by Robert J. Lamplough: arr. Duxford	12.76/81
				Aero Vintage Ltd, St Leonards	.81
			G-BLCK	Aero Vintage Ltd,	11.83/86
				Historic Aircraft Collection Ltd	5.3.87/96
				(rest. Audley End, ff 2.7.92 "Czech marks TE566/DU-A")	
6S/ 676368 •	FR Mk. XVIIIe	**TP276**		(to Indian AF as HS653)	31.12.47
				hulk recov. from Barakpor AB by Ormond & Wensley Haydon-Baillie, Duxford UK	.77
				Rudolph A. Frasca/Antiques & Classics Inc, Champaign IL: rest. project	.78/86
				Rudy Frasca/Frasca Air Museum, Urbana IL	86/96

Constr. No.	Model	Serial	Reg.	History	Date
				(rest. project, Urbana IL 92/96)	
6S/ 676372 •	FR Mk. XVIIIe	**TP280**		(to Indian AF as HS654)	31.12.47
				hulk recov. from Kalaikunda AB by Ormond & Wensley Haydon-Baillie, Duxford UK	.77
				Rudolph A. Frasca/Antiques & Classics Inc, Champaign IL	.78/94
			G-BTXE	Historic Flying Ltd, Audley End	23.10.91
				(shipped to UK .91 for completion of rest.: rest. Audley End, ff 5.7.92; shipped USA 9.92)	
			N280TP	Rudy Frasca/Frasca Air Museum, Urbana IL	2.2.93/96
				(flies as "TP280/Z")	
6S/ 672268 •	FR Mk. XVIII	**TP285**		(to Indian AF as HS649)	
				hulk recov. from Kalaikunda AB by Ormond & Wensley Haydon-Baillie, Duxford UK	.77
				Alan & Keith Wickenden, Hemel Hempstead	.78/81
				Spencer R. Flack, Elstree	
				Aero Vintage Ltd	
				S.W.Atkins/Vintage Airworks Ltd,St Leonards	85
				(wings to RM927 in USA; fuse. rebuilt as Mk.XIV)	
				E. Nick Grace & Chris P. Horsley, Chichester	86
				(composite rebuild: wings ex SAAF & USA)	
				National War & Resistance Museum, Overloon, Netherlands (displ. as "NH649")	.86/93
				(note: id. TP285 unconf., believed correct)	
6S/ 676390	FR Mk. XVIIIe	TP298		(to Indian AF as HS662)	31.12.47
				hulk recov. from Kalaikunda AB by Ormond & Wensley Haydon-Baillie, Duxford UK	.77
				Marshall Moss & Richard A. Boolootian, Lancaster CA	.78/81
				(stored crated Lancaster-Fox Field CA 79/80)	
				David C. Tallichet/MARC, Chino CA	c81/91
				(rebuild Tulsa OK, later Casper WY; shipped to UK, rebuild Colchester .88/90)	
			N41702	MARC, Chino CA	1.7.91/94
				(shipped back to USA 12.90, final rest. Chino CA; ff Chino 6.7.92 as "TP298/T-UM")	
				John Briet, Denver CO: del. ex Chino	19.1.94
				crashed dest., struck mountain Geyser MT	19.5.94
HAI/6S/ 663145 •	F Mk. XVIII	**TP367**		(to Indian AF as HS669)	
				Indian Institute of Technology, Kahragpur	
				Jeet Mahal, Vancouver BC	79/94
				(export difficulties: remained in India)	
				(shipped ex India, arr. Sandy, Beds UK 17.8.94;	
6S/ 676505 •	FR Mk. XIVe	**TZ138**		shipped to Canada for winterisation trials	16.11.45
			CF-GMZ	Imperial Oil Co, Edmonton ALTA (race #80)	.48/49
				J. H. G. McArthur (race #80)	.49
			N20E	Fulgencio Batista, Hollywood FL	51
				dam. in Florida by Castro supporters	1.6.51
				US Customs Service, Miami FL	
				Exporters Service Inc	52
				(to AMD/FA Dominicana): not del.	.52
				dam. ground collision by vehicle prior to del.	.52
				Lloyd B. Milner, Minneapolis MN	.60
				John L. Russell	
				M. W. Fairbrother, Rosemont MN	.60
			N5505A	Harvey J. Ferguson, McAllen TX / CAF	.63/68
				Charles H. Leidal, Fergus Falls MN	69/70
				(stored/rest. 50/70: ff 5.70)	
				dam. in forced landing, Mexico	5.70
				Jack Arnold, Brantford ONT	.71
				(by road ex Mexico to ONT .71: rest. static displ.)	
				Max R. Hoffman, Fort Collins CO	.71/72
				Don Plumb, Windsor ONT	6.74

c/n	Model	Mil ID	Civil Reg	History	Dates
				Ray Jones, Pontiac MI	78
			N138TZ	ntu: Leonard A. Tanner, New Braintree CT	79/87
				Bradley Air Museum, Windsor Locks CT: loan	79/81
			N5505A	Don L. Knapp/DK Precision, Ft. Lauderdale FL	.88
			N180RB	ntu: Don L. Knapp, Fort Lauderdale FL	11.88/90
			N5505A	Lone Star Flight Museum, Galveston TX	.90/91
				Bill Destefani, Bakersfield CA	.91/94
				(dism. rest. project since last flight 5.70; trucked from TX to Shafter CA 1.92 restoration Shafter as "TZ138")	
6S/ 676555 •	F Mk. XVIII	**TZ219**		(to Indian AF as HS683)	
				IAF Technical School, Chandigarh, Punjab	60/96
				(painted as "IAF HS674")	
SMAF. 21567 •	F Mk. 24	**VN485**		Royal Hong Kong Auxiliary AF, Kai Tak	31.5.52
				last flight 21.4.55; stored/displ. Kai Tak	7.55/89
				Imperial War Museum, Duxford UK: arr.	7.89/96
6S/ 73229 •	Seafire FR.47	**VP441**		Air Training Corps, Saltash, Devon	c55/65
				recov. Malcolm D. N. Fisher/Historic Aircraft Preservation Society: displ. RNAS Culdrose	65
				HAPS/Reflectair Museum, Blackpool	69/72
				Personal Plane Services, Booker	4.72
			N47SF	John J.Stokes/Rebel Aviation,San Antonio TX	75/80
				Confederate Air Force, Harlingen/Midland TX	4.12.80/96
				(stored dism. Midland TX, pending rest. to fly)	
				Nelson Ezell, Breckenridge TX	.95
- •	HF Mk. VIII	**-**		(to RAAF as A58-.....)	
				N. Monty Armstrong, Auckland NZ	.74
				(fuse. hulk recov. from Kiriwina, Solomon Islands)	
				Barry Coran, Melbourne VIC	80/96
				(composite static rest. RAAF Pt. Cook 80/95: rolled-out complete 2.95 as "R6915/PR-U")	
SH/CBAF. IX550 •	LF Mk. IXe S.89	**TE5..**		(to Czech AF as ...)	
				(to IDFAF as 20-..)	
				(to Union of Burma AF as UB421): del.	27.9.54
				Burmese Air Force Museum, Meiktila AB	88/90
				Mingaladon AB, Rangoon: stored	94/96
				Burma War Museum, Rangoon: displ.	.95
CBAF. IX558 •	LF Mk. IXe S.89	**TE5..**		(to Czech AF as TE5..)	
				(to IDFAF as 20-38)	
				IDFAF Museum Collection	73
				Hazor AB, Israel (displ. as "105")	78/90
- •	LF Mk. IXe	-		(to IDFAF as 20-..)	
				(to Union of Burma AF as UB425): del.	1.10.54
				King Mindon's Palace, Mandalay: displ.	81/90
				Mingaladon AB, Rangoon: stored "UB424"	94/96
- •	F Mk. IX	-		(to Burmese AF as UB431)	.56
				Aung Sang Park, Royal Lakes, Rangoon, Burma	60/75
				dam. by storm, scrapped	c75
-	PR Mk. IV	-		(to Soviet AF as ....)	
				R Norwegian AF Collection/Forsvarsnuseet Flysamlingn, Gardermoen AB: stored	.89/96
				(recov. ex crash site Norway 8.89)	
				(id. orig. rep. as BP889, since disproved)	

VICKERS SUPERMARINE STRANRAER

c/n	Mil ID	Civil Reg	History	Dates
CV-205 •	**RCAF915**		RCAF BOC 27.9.39: SOC	7.2.45
		CF-BYJ	Siple Air Transport, Montreal QUE	12.44/47
			Queen Charlotte Airlines "Nootka Queen"	.47/49
			dam. water landing, Ceepeecee BC	19.3.48
			crashed landing, sank, Belize Inlet BC	24.12.49

c/n	Version	Serial	Regn	History	Date
				Canadian Museum of Flight & Transportation, Vancouver BC: hulk recov.	.84
CV-209 •		RCAF920		RCAF BOC 28.11.40: SOC	10.5.44
			CF-BXO	Labrador Mining & Exploration Co Ltd	10.5.44/47
				E. Lando, Vancouver	23.4.47
				Queen Charlotte Airlines "Alaska Queen"	28.5.47/56
				dam. water takeoff, Vancouver-Sea Island	30.4.49
				dam. landing, Sullivan Bay BC	2.52
				(wfu Vancouver, open storage 54/58)	
				Stranraer Aerial Enterprises Ltd	28.6.62/63
				leased: Pacific Western Airlines	.63
				(wfu Vancouver, open storage 68)	
				Fortune Films Ltd	70
				RAF Museum, Hendon	72/96
				(displ. as "RCAF 920/QN")	

VICKERS SUPERMARINE WALRUS

c/n	Version	Serial	Regn	History	Date
6S/ 21840 •	Mk. I	L2301		(to Irish Air Corps as N18): del.	3.3.39/45
			EI-ACC	ntu: Aer Lingus, Dublin	28.8.45/46
			G-AIZG	R. G. Kellett, Biggin Hill	12.46/48
				(del. to Biggin Hill 3.47, sold for scrap .47: open storage dism. scrapyard Thame .47/64)	
				Historical Aircraft Pres. Society: recov.	.63
				Fleet Air Arm Museum, RNAS Yeovilton	.63/96
				(arr. RNAS Arbroath 1.64 for static rest., handed over FAA Museum 12.66, displ. as "L2301")	
2S/ 5591 •	Mk. I	W2718		Somerton Airways, Cowes IoW	4.46/47
				(not conv., broken-up for scrap: fuselage later conv. into car & caravan)	
				Hall of Aviation, Southampton: as caravan	88/89
				Dick Melton Aviation, Winchester: arr.	10.89
			G-RNLI	Richard E. Melton, Basingstoke	12.90/96
				(rest. to fly Winchester , later Norfolk)	
- •	Mk. II	HD874		(to RAAF as HD874): BOC 9.43: SOC	12.47
				wrecked by storm, Heard Island, Antarctica	21.12.47
				fuselage recov. by MV "Cape Pillar"	27.3.80
				RAAF Museum, RAAF Point Cook VIC	.80/96
				(under rest. Pt Cook to planned taxy condition)	
- •	Seagull V	A2-4		Eric E. McIllree/Amphibious Airways, Rabaul	3.10.46
			VH-ALB	ntu: Eric E. McIllree, Sydney NSW: stored	12.3.51
				Peter J. Gibbes, Melbourne VIC: stored	.52/60
			VH-ALB	P. J. Gibbes/Amphair Pty Ltd, Melbourne VIC	14.4.60/62
				(CofA 4.60, fitted 7 passenger seats)	
				Barrier Reef Flying Boat Service, Mackay QLD	14.9.62/63
				Hockey Treloar/Yerramba Estates, Sydney	17.9.64/72
				forced landing, Terrigal NSW	30.1.66
				crashed takeoff, Taree NSW	27.1.70
				(open storage, dism., Bankstown NSW 70/72)	
				RAF Museum Store, RAF Wyton: airfreighted	3.73
				(static rest. RAF Wyton & Cardington 73/79)	
				RAF Museum, Hendon: displ. as "A2-4"	.79/96

VICKERS WELLINGTON

c/n	Version	Serial	Regn	History	Date
- •	Mk. 1a	L7775		South Yorkshire Aircraft Museum, Firbeck	.86/89
				(recov. from crash site, Braemar, Scotland; static rest. project)	
- •	Mk. 1a	N2980		crashed into Loch Ness, Scotland	31.12.40
				(recov. from Loch Ness 21.9.85)	
				Brooklands Museum, Weybridge: arr.	12.85/96

c/n	Type	Serial	Regn	History	Date
				(100,000 hours complete static rest. by 95)	
- •	Mk. X T Mk. 10	**MF628**		flew in film *The Dam Busters*	.54
				Vickers Armstrong Ltd, Weybridge	.55
				Royal Aeronautical Society/Nash Collection, stored Heathrow	.56
				RAF Air Historical Branch, RAF Biggin Hill	60/64
				RAF Museum, RAF Abingdon, RAF St. Athan	
				RAF Museum Store, RAF Henlow	69
				RAF Museum, Hendon	.72/96

VOUGHT F4U/GOODYEAR FG-1D CORSAIR

c/n	Type	Serial	Regn	History	Date
5203 •	F4U-1A	**Bu10508**		(to RNZAF as NZ5527)	
				crashed landing Ardmore AB, Auckland	1.45
				Technical Training School, Nelson as INST106	
				John R. Smith, Mapua, Nelson NZ	
				(recov. as a collection of axed components)	
				Ross Jowitt, Auckland-Ardmore NZ: stored	89/95
				(rest. project: parts of F4U-1A NZ5503)	
2495 •	FG-1A	**Bu13459**		USMC Museum, MCAS Quantico VA	74/94
				(displ. as "13486/86")	
1871 •	FG-1D Mk. IV	**Bu14862**		(to Royal Navy FAA as KD431)	
				College of Aeronautics, Cranfield	12.46/63
				Historical Aircraft Preservation Society	5.63
				Fleet Air Arm Museum, RNAS Yeovilton	.63/95
				(displ. as "KD431/E2-M")	
- •	F4U-1A	**Bu17799**		MGM Studios, Culver City CA: movie prop	60/70
				(derelict, unconv., MGM backlot 70)	
				Ed Maloney/The Air Museum, Ontario CA	.70
			N83782	Planes of Fame, Chino CA	9.77/95
				(rest. Chino 76/77, ff .77 as "17799/WS-80")	
				(USCR quotes id. 3884, also rep. as Bu56198)	
4078 •	F4U-1A	**Bu17995**		displ. as war memorial, Provo UT	
				derelict in junk yard, Provo UT	65
				Harry S. Doan, Daytona Beach FL	c66
			N90285	Doan Helicopters, Daytona Beach	82/89
				(rebuilt 65/82: ff 3.82 Daytona Beach)	
				crashed into sea, New Smyrna Beach FL	8.5.83
				(rebuilt 84/89 New Smyrna Beach: ff 11.3.89)	
				Roy M. Stafford, Jacksonville FL	.89
				Don Knapp/D. K. Precision, Fort Lauderdale FL	7.89/90
			ZK-FUI	Alpine Fighter Collection, Wanaka	.90/95
				(shipped to NZ, ff 20.10.91 as RNZAF NZ5201)	
5247 •	F4U-1A	**Bu50000**		(to RNZAF as NZ5503)	
				Rukuhia Salvage Co, Hamilton NZ: as scrap	.48
				Asplin's Supplies, Rukahia NZ: scrapyard	60/77
				(fuse. hulk and components moved to Auckland .77)	
				Ross Jowitt, Auckland-Ardmore NZ: stored	89/95
				(rest. project: using parts of F4U-1A NZ5527)	
5622 •	F4U-1A	**Bu50375**		NAS Norman OK: stored for museum use: SOC	30.4.46
				NAS Norfolk VA: stored	58/60
				NASM, Silver Hill MD	.60/94
				(rest., 10.80 as "50375/56/*Sun Setter*)	
				VA Air & Space Centre, Hampton VA: loan	93/94
- •	FG-1D	**Bu67070**		NAS Litchfield Park AZ: stored	57
				(to FA Salvadorena as FAS 201)	.57
				John Roxbury, Princeton MN	88
				(under rest. 88)	
- •	FG-1D	**Bu67087**		(to FA Salvadorena as FAS....)	
				Chuck Wentworth/Antique Aero, Rialto CA	88/93

				(rest. Rialto CA 88/95, due to fly .95"USN/8")	
			N11Y	reg.	7.95
- •	FG-1D	**Bu67089**		NAS Jacksonville FL: stored	.53/58
				disposal, Queen City Salvage, Jacksonville FL	.58
			N4716C	Queen City Salvage Inc, Charlotte NC	64/69
				Earl E. Ware/Harran Aircraft Sales, Jacksonville FL	.75/77
			N4715C	Knight Aircraft Corporation	1.77/81
				Don C. Davis/Tired Iron Racing Team, Casper WY (race #82/"Wart Hog")	.81/86
				Gary Meermans, Long Beach CA	.86/87
			N97GM	Gary Meermans, Chino CA	3.87/94
				(flew as "VF-53/"Sky Boss")	
			N83JC	F4U Inc, New York NY	1.94/96
2490 •	FG-1D	**Bu76628**		forced landed, Hawaii	
				Ted Darcy, Kailua HI: recov. ex crash site	.85/86
				Robert J. Odegaard, Kindred ND	.87/90
				Kevin M. Hooey, Corning NY (hulk)	5.90
			N7171K	Kevin M. Hooey, Corning NY (rest. project)	12.90/96
			N32076	reg. res.	2.94
- •	XF4U-4	**Bu80759**		NAS Norfolk VA: stored	65
				Bradley Air Museum, Windsor Locks CT	.65/81
				New England Air Museum, Windsor Locks CT	81/90
7889 •	F4U-4	**Bu81164**		crashed, NALF Charlestown RI	27.1.50
				wreck buried, NALF Charlestown RI	.50/77
				hulk recov. by New England Air Museum, Windsor Locks CT	.77/87
				Gerald S. Beck/Tri-State Aviation, Wahpeton ND	1.87
			N5014	Robert J. Odegaard, Kindred ND	17.3.87/96
				(rest. project)	
8140 •	F4U-4	**Bu81415**	N5219V	Robert Bean, Hereford AZ	59/69
				(open storage, Blythe CA "USN Olathe/K7"	66/69,
				at Tucson AZ 6.73, dism. unconv.)	
				Korean War Museum, Seoul, South Korea	74/90
				(displ. as "US Marines/WR-22")	
8423 •	F4U-4	**Bu81698**	N3763A	Joe Arnold, Mulberry AR	77
			N53JB	John MacGuire, Fort Hancock TX	10.80/90
				War Eagles Air Museum, Santa Teresa NM	90/96
				El Paso Community Foundation, El Paso TX	3.95
				(flies as "Marines/81698/JM98" later "JM53")	
8582 •	F4U-4	**Bu81857**		crashed, NALF Charlestown RI	21.1.50
				wreck buried, NALF Charlestown RI	.50/77
				hulk recov. by New England Air Museum, Windsor Locks CT	.77/87
			N5081	Robert J. Odegaard, Kindred ND	1.87/96
				(long-term rest. to fly, Kindred ND 94)	
7240 •	F4U-1D	**Bu82811**		War Memorial Museum of Virginia, Newport News VA	79
				Confederate Air Force, Virginia Beach VA	88
				(rest. project)	
7279 •	F4U-1D	**Bu82850**		Walter Soplata Collection, Newbury OH	85
2667	FG-1D	Bu87853	N9152Z	Malcolm L. Miller, Carpinteria CA	64/70
2840 •	FG-1D	**Bu88026**		Walter Soplata Collection, Newbury OH	65/88
				(unconv. "USN 00")	

2890	FG-1D	Bu88076	N8051E	Queen City Salvage Inc, Charlotte NC	64/70
2900 •	FG-1D	Bu88086	NX63382	Vought Company (executive transport)	
				(Bendix racer #90/*Joe*; later #99)	46/49
			N63382	Paul Mantz, Orange County CA	55/63
				Tallmantz Aviation/International Flight & Space Museum, Orange County CA: displ.	63/67
				Rosen Novak Auto Co, Omaha NE	66
				(remained displ. at Tallmantz Collection)	
				Jack M. Spanich, Detroit MI	.69/77
				Weeks Air Mus., Tamiami FL	3.84/95
				(rest., ff .90 as "USN G5")	
2904 •	FG-1D	**Bu88090**		(to RNZAF as NZ5612)	
				Asplin's Supplies, Rukahia NZ: scrapyard	5.49/71
				Asplin's Garage, Hamilton NZ: displ.	69/71
				John Chambers, Auckland NZ: rest. project	69
				Museum of Transport & Technology, Auckland	.72/74
				Ross Jowitt, Auckland-Ardmore NZ: stored	74/96
				(rest. project, using F4U-1A NZ5503: que se)	
3111 •	FG-1D	**Bu88297**		USN disposal, to scrap metal dealer	23.1.59
			N9154Z	Frank G. Tallman, Orange County CA	9.1.60
				Tallmantz Collection, Orange County CA	
				(displ. unconv. "Columbus/C" .60/68)	
				Rosen Novak Autos, Omaha NE	66
				sold at auction, Orange County CA	29.5.68
				Johan M. Larsen, Minneapolis MN	69/72
				Minnesota Aircraft Museum, Minneapolis MN	73/75
			N8297	Louis E. Antonacci, Hampshire IL	80/86
				The Fighter Collection, Duxford	3.86/91
				(shipped from US to Rotterdam: arr. 21.4.86)	
			G-FGID	The Fighter Collection, Duxford	1.11.91/96
				(flies as "88297/29")	
3117 •	FG-1D	**Bu88303**	N6594D	Gene M. Strine, Middletown PA	56/66
				William C. Whitesell/ Flying W Ranch Airpark, Medford NJ	.66
			N700G	Flying W Ranch Airpark, Medford NJ	69/71
				Doug Champlin/Windward Aviation, Enid OK	.71/79
				Champlin Fighter Museum, Mesa AZ	81/84
				Larry D. Rose, Peoria AZ	87/92
				Laurie A. Shipley, Malvern PA	2.95
				(flies as "Marines WA-22")	
3178	FG-1D	Bu88364	N8054E	Queen City Salvage Inc, Charlotte NC	64/70
3182 •	FG-1D	**Bu88368**		recov. good condition ex Lake Washington WA	14.6.84
				Patriots Point Naval & Maritime Museum, Charleston SC	
				(static rest Paine Field WA 84,	.84/93
				displ. on carrier USS Yorktown as "88368/21")	
3196 •	FG-1D	**Bu88382**		midair collision, crashed Lake Washington WA	29.7.50
				recov. from lake, in good condition	8.83
				Museum of Flight, Seattle-Boeing Field WA	.83/95
				(static rest. Jerome ID, trucked to Seattle .92;	
				displ. as "USN 88382/S89")	
3205 •	FG-1D	**Bu88391**		(to RNZAF as NZ5648): BOC 17.8.45: SOC	9.5.49
				Asplin's Supplies, Rukahia NZ: scrapyard	5.49/70
				Asplin's Garage, Hamilton NZ: displ.	54/65
				(rest. taxy condition, Waikato Aero Club .62/63)	
				Museum of Transport & Technology, Auckland	65/71
				(displ. as "NZ5611/Josephine II")	
				Ed A. Jurist, Nyack NY	.70
				(shipped Auckland - Vancouver 10.71; impounded	
				by Canadian Customs, stored Vancouver 72/73)	
				Duane Egli, Harlingen TX	73
				Jim Landry & Pat Palmer, Seattle WA	.73/82

			N55JP	Jim Landry & Pat Palmer, Seattle WA	.82
				(rest. Paine Field WA, ff 17.7.82)	
				Sky Garden Centre Inc, Seattle WA	84
				Peter W. Thelen, Fort Lauderdale FL	85
				Robert L. Waltrip/Lone Star Flight Museum,	
				Houston-Hobby TX	7.85/88
				Warbirds of GB Ltd, Biggin Hill	.88/91
				(shipped to UK 4.89, flew as "17640/*Big Hog*")	
				Old Flying Machine Co, Duxford	.91/95
				Classic Flying Machines Ltd, King City CA	92/96
				(flies as "RNZAF NZ5648")	
				(id. also rep. as Bu88439, FAA quotes "P32823")	
3267	FG-1D	Bu88453	N7756B	Queen City Salvage Inc, Charlotte NC	64/70
3274 •	FG-1D	**Bu92013**	N1978M	Stephen J. Linsenmeyer, Monroe MI	63/64
				Robert Gardner/Damn Yankee Air Force,	
				Hartfield MA	65/67
				Arnold R. (Bob) Tefft, Wakeman OH	69
				USMC Museum, MCAS Quantico VA	
				USNAM, NAS Pensacola FL	75/90
				Patriots Point Dev. Authority, Charleston SC	79
				(heli-lift NAS Pensacola-Smyrna TX 5.80 for	
				rest. by Stones River Air Service)	
				USNAM, Washington Navy Yard DC: loan	88/96
3291	FG-1D	Bu92030	N8052E	Queen City Salvage Inc, Charlotte NC	64/70
3311 •	FG-1D	**Bu92050**	N6604C	Aero Enterprises Inc, La Porte IN	63
				Robert Mitchum, Broomfield CO	.63/66
			N194G	Robert Mitchum, Broomfield CO (race #94)	69
				Aero Inc, Broomfield CO	70/72
				James R. Axtell, Denver CO (race #94)	1.77/96
3342	FG-1D	Bu92081	N4719C	James T. Lambert, Clarksdale MS	63/65
				Lou Kaufman	65
				crashed racing, Lancaster CA	6.65
				James T. Lambert, Clarksdale MS	72
3346 •	FG-1D	**Bu92085**		Naval Reserve HQ, Lincoln NE	73
				(held dism., ex city park displ.)	
				Pima County Air Museum, Tucson AZ	73/76
				USMC Museum, Quantico VA : loaned to	
				Selfridge ANGB Museum, Selfridge ANGB MI	79/94
				(displ. as "Marines 92085/LE-09")	
3356 •	FG-1D	**Bu92095**		NAS Litchfield Park AZ: stored	57
				(to FA Salvadorena as FAS...)	.57/75
				Terry Randal/ Har-Ran Aviation, Tulsa OK	.75
				(ferried El Salvador-San Marcos TX .75)	
			N62344	John J. Stokes, San Marcos TX	.75/77
			N67HP	Howard E. Pardue, Breckenridge TX	9.77/90
				(flew as "Marines/HP-67")	
				Evergreen International Airlines/747 Inc/	
				Evergreen Heritage Collection, Marana AZ	19.5.90/96
				(flies as USN 92095/4/*Ruthless II*)	
				(prev. rep. ex FAS220, but see Bu92697)	
3367 •	FG-1D	Bu92106		stored unconv., Brewster WA	74
			N6897	David C. Tallichet/MARC, Chino CA	75/88
				(flew as VMF-214/WE/*Blacksheep*)	
				struck-off reg.	4.89
				Jerry Couers, Chicago	
				(stored Jerome ID 91/92 pending rest.)	
3393 •	FG-1D	**Bu92132**	**N3466G**	Ed Maloney/The Air Museum, Claremont CA	
				later Ontario CA: displ. as USN "29"	58/73
				David C. Tallichet/MARC, Chino CA	.73/94

Continued on Page 659

				(stored Chino CA as "Bu34666" 88/92)	
				Henry J. "Butch" Schroeder/	
				Midwest Aviation Museum, Danville IL	3.94/95
				(rest. to fly, Danville IL)	
3507 •	FG-1D	**Bu92246**	N8050E	David B. Robinson, Miami FL	63/64
				James R. Spletstoser, Fort Pierce FL	66
			N766JD	Joseph T. Norris/Air & Space Museum,	
				Charlottesville VA	69/70
				Bentwing Aircraft, Plant City FL	72/77
				USNAM, NAS Pensacola FL	79/94
				(displ. as "92246/86")	
3647	FG-1D	Bu92386	N8053E	Queen City Salvage Inc, Charlotte NC	63/70
3660 •	FG-1D	**Bu92399**	N4717C	Queen City Salvage Inc, Charlotte NC	63/64
			N448AG	Alvin T. George, Atlanta GA	66/69
				crashed on take-off, NAS Norfolk VA	
				USMC Museum, MCAS Quantico VA: wreck	69/72
				Harry S. Doan, Daytona Beach FL	70/87
				John C. Hooper, Harvey LA	88/90
				William J. Hooper, Harvey LA	92
				Charles A. Osborn/Blue Sky Aviation,	
				Louisville KY & Sellersburg IN	7.94/95
				Vintage Fighters Inc, Sellersburg IN	95
				(flies as "USN 17")	
3694	FG-1D	**Bu92433**	**N3440G**	Frank. G. Tallman/Movieland of the Air Museum,	
				Orange County CA	60/69
				I. N. Burchinall Jr, Paris TX	70/78
				rep. dest. in hangar fire, Dallas-Addison TX	.79
				sale rep., Addison TX: USCR	84/96
3697 •	FG-1D	**Bu92436**	N3470G	Ed Maloney/The Air Museum, Ontario CA	63/73
			CF-JJW	Canadian Warplane Heritage, Hamilton ONT	15.10.73
				(flew as "VMF-112/"Wolf Pack")	
			C-GCWX	Canadian Warplane Heritage, Hamilton ONT	74/96
				(flies as "KD658/115X")	
3721 •	FG-1D	**Bu92460**		NAS Litchfield Park AZ: stored	57
				(to FA Salvadorena as FAS 207)	.57/69
				donated by FAS to Sikorsky Memorial CT	.69
				displ. on pole at airport, Bridgeport CT	.69/92
				(displ. as "USMC/217")	
3729 •	FG-1D	**Bu92468**		NAS Litchfield Park AZ: stored	60
				sold, towed to Buckeye AZ and stored until	60
			N9964Z	Marvin L. Gardner/CAF, Mercedes TX	.60/75
				crashed, Olathe KS	.74
				Confederate Air Force, Harlingen/Midland TX	8.5.75/95
				(rebuilt by LTV Corp 74/81, redel. 3.81)	
				cr., forced landing, Forney TX (rebuilt)	14.4.82
				(flies as "USN 13/USS Essex")	
3732 •	FG-1D	**Bu92471**		Harry & Diane Tope, Mount Pleasant MI	90/93
				(under rest. Kalamazoo MI 92/93)	
				Ray Dieckman, Chino, CA	3.96
3750 •	FG-1D	**Bu92489**		NAS Litchfield Park AZ: stored	57
				(to FA Salvadorena as FAS 208)	.57
				Frank Arrufat, Los Angeles CA	88
				(id. quoted as "FAS 409": rest. project)	
3769 •	FG-1D	**Bu92508**	N7225C	Carl J. Lutt, Hayward CA	63/64
				H. A. Matteri, Santa Rosa CA	66
				Valley Air Service, Sunnyside WA	69
				Knickerbocker Aviation, Stratford CT	70
			N46WB	Whittington Bros, Fort Lauderdale FL	76
			N46LF	Louis E. Fischer, Miami FL	1.77
			N70RP	ntu: Robert P. Lammerts, Oklahoma City OK	5.79

c/n		Type	Bu	Reg	Owner	Date
				N46LF	Robert P. Lammerts, Oklahoma City OK	79/84
				N46RL	Robert P. Lammerts, Oklahoma City OK	4.84/90
					Dee Ring Inc, Dallas TX	92
					T T M Inc, Oklahoma City OK	3.95
					(flies as "Marines/L-46")	
3770	•	FG-1D	**Bu92509**	N9150Z	Malcolm L. Miller, Carpinteria CA	63/64
					David W. Slica, Sylmar CA	66
				N92509	David W. Slica, Sylmar CA	69/70
					John H. Van Andel, Stanford CT	1.71/74
					Preston Parish/Kalamazoo Aviation History Museum, Kalamazoo MI	77
				N9PP	ntu: Preston Parish, Kalamazoo MI	4.78
				N3PP	Preston Parish/Kalamazoo Aviation History Museum, Kalamazoo MI	8.79/96
					(flies as "USN 92509/611")	
3787	•	FG-1D	**Bu92526**		S. & Y. Degani	
				N....	Fouga International Inc: reg. candidate	26.2.93
3890	•	FG-1D	**Bu92629**		NAS Litchfield Park AZ: stored	57
					(to FA Salvadorena as FAS 215)	.57
				N62290	Har-Ran Aviation, Tulsa OK	.75
					John J. Stokes, San Marcos TX	.75/77
					(del. San Marcos by 2.75, rest. as "USS Essex")	
					Robert Friedman, Waukegan IL	.77
					Wayne Williams, Garland TX	.79
					Ray Jones	82
					Planes of Fame East, Minneapolis-Flying Cloud MN	83/95
					landing accident, Crystal MN (rebuilt)	3.8.83
					(flies as "USS Essex/S-301")	
					(id. prev. rep. as Bu92529: not del. El Salvador)	
3958	•	FG-1D	**Bu92697**		NAS Litchfield Park AZ: stored	57
					(to FA Salvadorena as FAS 220)	.57/92
					rest. by FAS, Ilapongo AB as "FAES 220"	91/92
					Ace Enterprises Co, Honduras	92
					(offered for sale, complete, TT 2224 hrs)	
					rep. sold to USA, stored Miami FL	93
					(sale paperwork quotes FAS 220 c/n 3356: see 3356 above)	
9039	•	F4U-4	**Bu96885**		Earl Ware, Jacksonville FL	81/88
					(rest. project)	
9149	•	F4U-4	**Bu96995**	N5221V	Robert Bean, Hereford AZ	
					(to FA Hondurena as 614)	.60/78
					Hollywood Wings, Long Beach CA: recov.	.78
				N4908M	Robert L. Ferguson & Howard E. Pardue, Breckenridge TX	79
					J. K. (Buck) Ridley, Abilene/Breckenridge TX	80/89
				OE-EAS	Siegfried Angerer/Tyrolean Jet Service, Innsbruck	1.90/94
					(shipped to Austria, flies as USN "BR-37")	
9296	•	F4U-4	**Bu97142**	N3771A	Robert Bean, Hereford AZ	59
					stored unconv., Moseley Field, Phoenix AZ	67/69
					Arthur W. McDonnell, Mojave CA	78/80
					(outside storage unconv., in pale grey sc. Mojave "USN Seattle/10" 10.78: static rest. 78/80)	
					USMC Museum, MCAS Quantico VA	88/94
					Pima County Air Museum, Tucson AZ: loan	88/94
					(rep. displ. as "Marines 97349")	
9297	•	F4U-4	**Bu97143**	N96042	sale rep.	77
					Charles T. Unkle, Homestead FL	84
				N713JT	Joseph O. Tobul, Pittsburgh PA	2.85/95

				(10 year rest., ff .92 as "Navy JT416")	
				forced landing, crashed: badly dam.	c5.93
9413 •	F4U-4	**Bu97259**	N3728A	Robert Bean, Hereford AZ	
			N6667	Eugene H. Akers, Lancaster CA	66/73
				(racer #100; #22/*Lancer Two*)	
				Wilson C. Edwards, Big Spring TX	.74/81
				EAA Aviation Foundation, Oshkosh WI	12.81/95
				(del. Oshosh 5.82, rest. .93 as "USN 13")	
9418 •	F4U-4	**Bu97264**	**N5218V**	Robert Bean, Hereford AZ (USN/"K11")	59
				(stored unconv. Phoenix-Moseley Field AZ 67/69;	
				stored unconv., Tucson AZ 73)	
				Pacific Warbirds Museum, Half Moon Bay CA	73
				Eugene H. Akers, San Diego & Ramona CA	77/90
				(rest. Ramona CA, flies as USN *Ghost Riders*)	
				H & H Aircraft Sales, Pinedale WY	92
				Charles R. (Chuck) Hall, Pinedale WY	4.94/95
9434 •	F4U-4	**Bu97280**		Robert Bean, Hereford AZ	
				(to FA Hondurena as 615)	.61/78
				Hollywood Wings, Long Beach CA: recov.	.78
			N49092	Robert L. Ferguson & Howard E. Pardue,	
				Breckenridge TX	79
				Robert F. Yancy, Klamath Falls OR : del.	4.7.80/88
				(flew as USN "S-101/"*Old Blue*")	
				Warbirds of GB Ltd, Biggin Hill	1.88/92
				(shipped to UK, arr. Biggin Hill 19.2.88)	
				struck-off reg.	12.88
				ret. to Ft. Lauderdale FL	3.92
			N712RD	ISRMS Inc, Land-o-Lakes FL	6.92
				Cavanaugh Flight Museum, Dallas-Addison TX	8.94/96
				(flies as "USN 97280/N206")	
9440 •	F4U-4	**Bu97286**	**N5215V**	Robert Bean, Hereford AZ	59/72
				(stored unconv. Blythe CA "Olathe/K5" 63/72)	
				Merle B. Gustafson, Tallulah LA	.72/84
				(trucked to LA ex Blythe 11.72, rest. ff 8.73)	
				Robby R. Jones, Minter City MS	87/88
				Weeks Air Mus., Tamiami FL	3.90/95
				(flew as "97286/G5/*Angel of Okinawa*")	
				dam. Tamiami FL, by Hurricane "Andrew"	24.8.92
9442 •	F4U-4	**Bu97288**		Robert Bean, Hereford AZ	59
				(to FA Hondurena as 612)	.60/78
				Hollywood Wings, Long Beach CA: recov.	.78
			N4907M	Robert L. Ferguson & Howard E. Pardue,	
				Breckenridge TX	79
				Joseph J. Bellantoni, Bridgeport CT	6.80/84
				crashed, Stratford CT (repaired)	7.6.81
				Joseph J. Bellantoni, Port Chester NY	84/95
9456 •	F4U-4	**Bu97302**	N3764A	Bob Bean, Hereford AZ ("Seattle/T4")	
				(stored unconv. Phoenix-Moseley Field AZ 67/69,	
				stored dism., Tucson Airport AZ 73)	
			N68HP	Howard E. Pardue/Breckenridge Aviation	
				Museum, Breckenridge TX	2.79/95
				(rest. Breckenridge by Bean, flew as "Marines/HP-68")	
				accident, forced landing, nr. Breckenridge TX	1.4.93
				(rebuild to fly, Breckenridge TX)	
9474 •	F4U-4	**Bu97320**		Robert Bean, Hereford AZ	59
				(to FA Hondurena as 616)	.60
				John Roxbury, Princeton MN	88
				Gerald S. Beck/Tri-State Warbird Collection,	
				Wahpeton ND	.88/94
				(stored Wahpeton ND 92/94, pending rest.)	
				US reg. candidate	4.11.94
9484	F4U-4	**Bu97330**	**N5222V**	Robert Bean, Hereford AZ	59

				(stored unconv. Phoenix-Moseley Field AZ 67/69, stored Tucson Airport AZ 6.73, "USN Olathe/N5")	
				William Barnes, Lancaster CA	77
				Shouling M. Barnes, Lancaster CA	84
				Jack A. Erickson/Erickson Air Crane Co, Central Point OR	86/91
				crashed, dest., Chilquin OR (pilot baled out)	2.8.91
				Craig M. McBurney, Boca Raton FL	1.95
9503 •	F4U-4	**Bu97349**		Robert Bean, Hereford AZ	7.56
				(stored unconv. Phoenix-Moseley Field AZ 67/69)	
				Tucson Inn, Tucson AZ	73/76
				(displ. on pole as "Marines/MR")	
				Arthur W. McDonnell, Mojave CA	78/79
				(dism. unconv., in dk bl sc. Mojave CA still Marines/MR" 10.78: static rest. 78/80)	
				USMC Museum, Quantico VA	.79
				Pima County Air Museum, Tucson AZ: loan	.79/83
			N4802X	USNAM, NAS Pensacola FL	4.84/94
				(displ. as "97349/WR-18", later "Marines/86")	
9513 •	F4U-4B	**Bu97359**	N5213V	Robert Bean, Hereford AZ	59
				(stored unconv. Phoenix-Moseley Field AZ 67/69, stored dism., Tucson Airport AZ 73)	
			N97359	Thomas Friedkin/Cinema Air, Houston TX	76/77
				(flew in TV series " *Ba Ba Black Sheep*")	76
			N240CA	Cinema Air, Houston TX	4.80/88
				Merlin Aire Ltd, King City CA	88
				Classic Flying Machines Ltd, King City CA	90/92
				op: Old Flying Machine Co, Duxford	4.88/92
				(shipped. to UK, arr. Duxford 17.4.88, flew as "RNZAF NZ5628"; shipped to USA 3.92)	
				Norm Lewis/Lewis Aviation, Louisville KY	9.92/96
				(flies as "USN F112")	
9523 •	F4U-4	**Bu97369**	**N5214V**	Robert Bean, Hereford AZ	59
				(stored unconv. Phoenix-Moseley Field AZ 67/69, stored dism., Tucson Airport AZ 73)	
				Arthur W. McDonnell, Mojave CA	74/75
				(static rest. Mojave CA 74/75)	
				USMC Museum, MCAS Quantico VA	75/94
9542 •	F4U-4	Bu97388		Robert Bean, Hereford AZ	59
				(to FA Hondurena as 610)	.60
				Earl Ware, Jacksonville FL	81
				(noted in yard,"FAH 610", Jacksonville FL 81)	
				Gerald S. Beck/Tri-State Warbird Collection, Wahpeton ND	.82/94
				(rest. Wahpeton ND)	
				US reg. candidate	4.11.94
9543	F4U-4	Bu97389		Robert Bean, Hereford AZ	59
				(stored unconv., Phoenix-Moseley Field AZ 67/69)	
				stored dism., Tucson Airport AZ	73
9544 •	F4U-4B	**Bu97390**		Robert Bean, Hereford AZ	59
				(stored unconv. Phoenix-Moseley Field AZ 67/69, noted Tucson AZ 6.73, unconv. USN "Olathe/90")	
			N47991	Yankee Air Corps, Chino CA	4.84/91
				Yanks Air Museum, Chino CA	91/95
				(stored Chino, pending rest. to fly)	
- •	F4U-5	**Bu121794**		(to Argentine Navy as 0384)	.58
				Bahia Blanca AB, Argentina: displ.	91
				Museo de la Aviacion Naval, Rio Parana Delta AB, Buenos Aires	
				(displ. as "3-A-211/121794")	94/95

	Type	Serial	Reg	History	Date
- •	F4U-5	**Bu121859**	**N4993V**	reg. res.	11.78/92
- •	F4U-5N	**Bu121881**		(to Argentine Navy as ......)	
				displ. on pole in park, Argentina	80/90
				Don Knapp, Fort Lauderdale FL	90
				Lone Star Flight Museum, Galveston TX	.90/93
				(recov. ex Argentina .90; rest. Breckenridge TX 91/94, ff .94 as "USN 121881/RW21")	
			N43RW	Lone Star Flight Museum, Galveston TX	9.93/96
- •	F4U-5P F4U-5N	**Bu122179**		(to FA Hondurena as 604): del.	3.56/78
				Hollywood Wings, Long Beach CA: recov.	.78
			N4903M	Robert L. Ferguson & Howard E. Pardue, Breckenridge TX	79
				Barry A. Landy, Fairfield NJ	80
				Barry Lansing, Mike Collier, Jack Goulding, Foy Midkiff/Banner Inc, Lubbock TX	.83/84
				(flew as "Marines/BL-13")	
				crashed near Houston TX	3.84
				Peter W. Thelen, Fort Lauderdale FL: rebuilt	12.86/87
			N179PT	Peter W. Thelen, Fort Lauderdale FL	10.87/88
			N179NP	Warbirds of GB Ltd, Biggin Hill	14.8.88/90
				(arr. Biggin Hill on del. ex USA 16.8.88)	
			N179PT	Peter W. Thelen, Fort Lauderdale FL	90/95
				op: Warbirds of GB Ltd, Bournemouth UK	88/92
- •	F4U-5P F4U-5N	**Bu122184**		NAS Litchfield Park AZ: stored, SOC	3.56
			N3764A	Bob Bean, Hereford AZ	.56
				(to FA Hondurena as 605): del.	3.56/78
			N4901E (1	ntu: Hollywood Wings, Long Beach CA: recov.	.78
			N49051(2	Hollywood Wings, Long Beach CA	.78
				Robert L. Ferguson & Howard E. Pardue, Breckenridge TX	.79
			N65HP	Howard E. Pardue, Breckenridge TX	2.79/87
				Robert J. Ready/Exec Aviation, Cincinatti OH	11.87
			N65WF	Exec Aviation Inc, Cincinatti OH	2.88/92
				(dep. Breckenridge on del. to Ohio 21.7.88, flew as "Marines/WF-6")	
				James E. Smith, Fortine MT	8.92/95
				(note: FAH 600/605 may have transposed US regs: FAH600 del. US as N4901E)	
- •	F4U-5P F4U-5NL	**Bu122189**		NTS Bainbridge GA: stored	
				USNAM, NAS Pensacola FL	65/76
				USMC Museum, MCAS El Toro CA	88/94
				(displ. as USMC "122189/WF15")	
- •	F4U-5NL	**Bu124447**		(to FA Hondurena as 602): del.	3.56/78
				Hollywood Wings, Long Beach CA: recov.	.78
				(rep. recov. as collection of components; rest. Van Nuys CA, later Chino CA 81/87)	
			N100CV	Glen Hyde, Dallas TX (ff Chino 21.1.87)	10.84/88
				IR3T Inc, Roanoke TX/Pahrump NV: USCR	.88/92
				USMC Museum, MCAS Quantico VA	7.88/94
				(del. El Toro MCAS ex Breckenridge TX 20.7.88)	
				Mid America Air Museum, Liberal KS: loan	93/94
- •	F4U-5NL	**Bu124486**	N52...V	Robert Bean, Hereford AZ	
				(to FA Hondurena as 606): del.	3.56/78
				Hollywood Wings, Long Beach CA: recov.	.78
			N49068	Robert L. Ferguson & Howard E. Pardue, Breckenridge TX	.79
				Phil Dear, Jackson MS	80/84
				McGehee Air Inc, McGehee AR	87
				(flew as 124453/NP-21/*Annie Mo*)	
				Sherman Aircraft Sales, West Palm Beach FL	88
				Richard Bertea, Chino CA	9.88/95
				(flies as "124486/Marines/RB14")	

-	•	F4U-5NL	**Bu124493**		(to FA Hondurena as 608): del.	3.56
					Walt Disney Studios: composite rest. project	
					RNZAF Museum, Wigram AB: arr. by sea	9.87/95
					(exchange deal for use of RNZAF A-4s in movie:	
					static rest. project, using parts from other	
					aircraft including FAH 613 & N4903M/"BL13":	
					stored whole, pending exchange for early model)	
-	•	F4U-5NL	**Bu124541**		(to Argentine Navy as 0433/2-A-202,	
					later 0433/3-A-204): del.	.57
					Museo de la Aviacion Naval,	
					Rio Parana Delta AB, Buenos Aires	69/91
					sold	.91
					rep. rest. project France	94/96
-	•	F4U-5NL	**Bu124569**		(to FA Hondurena as 601): del.	3.56/78
					Hollywood Wings, Long Beach CA: recov.	.78
				N4901W	Robert L. Ferguson & Howard E. Pardue,	
					Breckenridge TX	.79
					Robert L. Ferguson, Wellesley MA	80/82
					Sherman Aircraft Sales,West Palm Beach FL	83
					Bruce Lockwood, Juneau AK	3.83
					Alan Preston/Preston Air Museum, Dallas TX	.84/87
					David K. Burnap, Dayton OH	9.87/96
					(flies as "USN/RF-12/Old *Deadeye*")	
					(USCR quotes id. Bu124560)	
-	•	F4U-5NL	**Bu124692**		(to FA Hondurena as FAH...)	
					Collings Foundation, Stowe MA	88/93
					(rest. to fly)	
-	•	F4U-5NL	**Bu124724**		(to FA Hondurena as 600): del.	3.56/78
					Hollywood Wings, Long Beach CA: recov.	.78
					crash landing on del. flight, Belize	.78
				N49051 (1	ntu	
				N4901E (2	Robert L. Ferguson & Howard E. Pardue,	
					j11	
					Breckenridge TX	.79/80
					Ralph C. Parker, Wichita Falls TX	.84/86
					Amicale Jean Baptiste Salis, La Ferte-Alais	3.86
					shipped to Amsterdam, Holland : arr.	21.4.86
				F-AZEG	Jean Salis/Salis Collection, La Ferte-Alais	12.86/93
					(flies as USN "124724/P-22")	
					(note: FAH 600/605 may have transposed US regs:	
					FAH 600 painted as N4901E on del. Long Beach 80)	
-		F4U-7	Bu133693		(to Aeronavale as 693)	
				CF-VUM	Lynn Garrison/The Air Museum of Canada,	
					Calgary ALTA	67/68
				N693M	Lynn Garrison/American Aerospace & Military	
					Museum, Pomona CA	68/70
					Robert E. Guilford, Beverly Hills CA (race #3)	.70/71
				N33693	Robert E. Guilford, Beverly Hills CA	.71/84
					(race #3 ; #93/"WR-93/*Blue Max*")	
					G & R Aviation Enterprises, Santa Monica CA	84/87
					crashed dest., San Diego-Brown Field CA	10.5.87
					(c/n quoted as 1531)	
-	•	F4U-7	Bu133704		(to Aeronavale as 704)	
					USNAM, NAS Pensacola FL	65/72
					USS Alabama Memorial Park, Mobile AL	77/94
					(displ. as "Marines/129359/LD-15")	
965	•	F4U-7	**Bu133714**		(to Aeronavale as 714)	
				N33714	USMC Museum, Quantico VA	69/70
					Dean J. Ortner, Wakeman OH	71/72
					John J. Schafhausen, Hayden Lake WA	.73/77
					(flew as "Aeronavale 965")	

			C-GWFU	Blain Fowler, Camrose ALTA	10.83/93
				(flies as *Alberta Blue*)	
- •	F4U-7	**Bu133722**		(to Aeronavale as 722)	
				inst. airframe Mourillan-Toulon AB, France	64/73
			N1337A	Gary L. Harris, Oakland CA	.74/84
				(shipped to San Francisco .74, rebuilt	
				Half Moon Bay CA, ff. 22.8.76)	
				Lindsey Walton, Duxford UK: lease, del.	7.8.82/93
				(flew as Aeronavale "133722/15F.22")	
				Harold E. Kindsvoter, Clovis CA	87/93
				Jack A. Erickson, Medford OR	4.93/95
				(dep. Duxford crated 5.4.93 for shipping to USA)	
-	F4U-1D	-		used as movie prop., Hollywood CA	
				Ed Maloney/The Air Museum, Ontario CA	59/69
				(displ. fuse. only, unrest. mil. scheme)	
	Super			(rebuilt Chino .82 mod. racer #1, P&W R4360)	
	Corsair		N31518	Planes of Fame, Chino CA	11.82/83
				Steve Hinton/Fighter Rebuilders, Chino CA	5.83/94
				crashed dest., Williams AFB AZ	19.3.94
	FG			Goodyear World of Rubber, Akron OH	52/74
				(displ. Goodyear blimp hangar "USN/F-9")	
				Arthur W. McDonnell, Mojave CA	.75
				arr. by road for rebuild, Mojave CA	2.75
				(to Argentine Navy as ....)	
				displ. on pole, Trelew AB, Argentina	91
				(displ. as "2-A-202")	
				(to Argentine Navy as 3-A-202)	
				dumped, complete, Navy base Argentina	87
				(to FA Hondurena as 609): del.	3.56/80
				FA Hondurena Museum	.80/93
	F4			(to FA Hondurena as 611)	.60
				Earl Ware, Jacksonville FL	81
				(hulk in yard, "FAH 611", Jacksonville FL 81)	
				Ray Adams, Melbourne FL	85/90
				(rest. to fly, Titusville FL)	
	U-4	-		(to FA Hondurena as 617)	.60
				Earl Ware, Jacksonville FL	81
				hulk in yard, "FAH 617", Jacksonville FL	81
- •	F4U-4	-		(to FA Hondurena as 692)	.60
				Earl Ware, Jacksonville FL	81
				hulk in yard, "FAH 692", Jacksonville FL	81
- •	F4U	-		USMC Museum	79
				(rep. ex storage in rafters of dirigible hangar,	
				MCAS El Toro CA)	
				(static rest. Chino CA 79/81; completed fuse.	
				trucked ex Chino 1.82 to USMCM)	
				(rep. rebuild combined with Bu124447: see above)	

VOUGHT/GOODYEAR F2G CORSAIR

6163 •	F2G-1D	**Bu88454**		NASM, Washington DC	
				NAS Norfolk VA: stored in container	c48/66
				Bradley Air Museum, Windsor Locks CT	65/66
				loan: MCAS Museum, MCAS Quantico VA	68/72
			N4324	Walter E. Ohlrich, Norfolk VA	73/74
				(res. race #50 : civil conv. at Newport News	
				not completed)	
				USMC Museum, Quantico VA	74
				Doug Champlin Collection, Enid OK	.74
				USS Intrepid Museum, New York NY	76
				ferried NAS Norfolk - Enid OK	c77

c/n		Type	Serial	Reg.	History	Date
					Champlin Fighter Museum,	
					Mesa AZ (flies as "NATC/454")	.78/96
6166	•	F2G-1	**Bu88457**	**NX5588N(2**	Cook Cleland (race #57)	.49
					Cook Cleland Air Svce, Willoughby OH: USCR	66/69
					dism. hulk stored, Van Sant PA	72/80
					Harry S. Doan/Doan Helicopters,	
					Daytona Beach FL (dism.)	1.83/88
					D. K. Precision, Ft Lauderdale FL	2.89/90
					Lone Star Flight Museum, Galveston TX	.90/96
					(stored dism., pending rest. to fly)	
6172	•	F2G-2	**Bu88463**	NX5577N	Cook Cleland (race #74)	.46/47
					Dick Beckler (race #74)	.48/49
					Walter Soplata Collection, Newbury OH	65/88
					(Goodyear Production c/n 10)	

VOUGHT OS2U KINGFISHER

c/n		Type	Serial	Reg.	History	Date
-	•	OS2U-2	**Bu3073**		crashed, Mount Buxton, Calvert Island BC	20.8.42/64
					Air Museum of Canada, Calgary ALTA: recov.	.64/67
					USNAM, NAS Pensacola FL	68/94
					(rest. at Vought factory, Dallas TX .69/71)	
					USS North Carolina Battleship Memorial,	
					Wilmington NC : "55", unveiled	25.6.71/96
2400	•	OS2U-3	**Bu5909**		NASM, Silver Hill MD	65/68
					USS Massachusetts Battleship Memorial,	
					Fall River MA: loan	71/76
					NASM, Silver Hill MD	86/96
-	•	OS2U-3	**Bu5926**		(to Uraguayan Navy as A-752)	
					Laguna-del-Sauce Naval Air Base, Uraguay	64/71
					USNAM, NAS Pensacola FL	.71/94
					(displ. as "USN Bu5926/2")	
-	•	OS2U-3	**Bu59...**		(to FA Chile as 314)	
					Quintero AB, Valparaiso, Chile : displ.	71/73
					FAC Museum, Los Cerillos AB: static rest.	92
2475	•	OS2U-3	**Bu09418**		(to Dutch Navy/MLD as V-8)	
					shipped to NEI, diverted to Australia	4.42
					(to RAAF as A48-2)	
					disposal ex RAAF Lake Boga, to farmer	.48
					Pearce Dunn/Warbirds Air Museum,	
					Mildura VIC	.68/87
					(fuse. & floats recov. ex farm, Merbein VIC)	
					John Bell/Whaling Museum, Albany WA	.87/95
					(substantially rest. for static displ.)	
-	•	OS2U-3	-		(to Cuban Navy as ....)	
					Museum of The Revolution, Havana	76/94
					(landplane, displ. as *Marina*)	
-	•	OS2U-3	-		(to FA Mexicana as 03)	
					FAM Base Santa Margarita: stored, landplane	
					arr. by C-119, Mazatlan-Brookley AFB AL	11.64
					(static rest. Brookley AFB AL .64/65)	
					USS Alabama Battleship Memorial, Mobile AL	.65/94
					(displ. on ship's catapult as "Bu0951/60";	
					under rest. 93/94 after hurricane dam.)	
					(manufacturers plate: CV59250; built 14.2.42)	
-	•	OS2U-3	-		rep. recov. ex crash site, northern California	
					Yanks Air Museum, Chino CA	93/95
					(dism. hulk stored Chino 94/95)	

-	•	OS2U	-		forced landing, Everglades FL	.43
					Jay R. Wisler, Tampa FL: hulk recov.	.90/94
-	•	OS2U	-		NASM, Washington DC	
					(crash hulk recov. ex Alaska: parts to Bu5909)	
					New England Air Museum, Windsor Locks CT	87/89
					(fuse. hulk and parts: no wings)	
					to new owner in parts exchange deal	.89

VULTEE A-31 VENGEANCE

-	•	A-31	**41-31047**		(to RAF as EZ999)	
		Mk. Ia			(to RAAF as EZ999)	
					Sydney Technical College, Ultimo NSW	50/63
					Camden Museum of Aviation, Camden NSW	
					later Narellan NSW	5.63/95
					(displ. as RAAF EZ999/NH-V/*Dina Might*,	
					ground engine runs carried out)	
-	•	Mk. II	**AF929**		(to RAAF as A27-247) BOC 24.4.43 : SOC	22.6.48
					John Bell, Albany WA: hulk, open storage	.66/72
					(recov. from scrapyard, Kalgoorlie WA .66)	
					RAAF Assoc. Museum, Bullcreek, Perth WA	.72/92
					John Bell/Whaleworld Museum, Albany WA	.92/95
					(static rest. project Bullcreek, using parts from	
					A27-247/5J-G & A-27-..../NV-D ex scrapyards:	
					project trucked to Albany 5.10.92)	

WESTLAND LYSANDER

-	•	Mk. III	**R9125**		RAF Museum Store, RAF Henlow	69
					RAF Museum, Hendon	73/95
					(displ. as "R9125/LX-L")	
-	•	Mk.IIIa	**V9300**		(to RCAF as 1558): BOC27.1.42: SOC	1.10.46
					Don Bradshaw, Saskatoon SASK	
					(recov. ex farm, Harris SASK .73)	
				G-LIZY	British Aerial Museum,	
					Duxford UK : arr. dism. Duxford	11.82/90
					Imperial War Museum, Duxford	91/95
					(static rest. Duxford, unveiled 10.93 "V9673/MA-J")	
Y1363	•	Mk.IIIa	**V9312**		(to RCAF as V9312): BOC 22.10.42: SOC	1.10.46
		Mk.IIITT			Harry Whereatt/Whereatt's Warbirds,	
					Assiniboia SASK	72/88
					(recov. derelict ex farm, Meyvoune SASK)	
				N3093K	Weeks Air Museum,	
					Tamiami FL : rest. project	12.8.91/96
-	•	Mk. IIIa	**V9415**		(to RCAF as 1589): BOC	17.2.42
		Mk. IIITT			(stored for future museum use .46)	
					Canadian National Aeronautical Collection,	
					Rockcliffe ONT	65/67
					Indian Air Force Museum, Palam, New Delhi	10.67/90
					(displ. as "IAF 1589")	
Y1530	•	Mk. IIIa	**V9546**		(to RCAF as V9546): BOC 22.10.42: SOC	1.10.46
		Mk. TTIIIA			Wes Agnew, Hartney MAN	
					(recov. from farm, Cabri SASK)	
					Musee Royal de l'Armee, Brussels : stored	.71/82
					Sabena Old Timers Foundation, Brussels	7.82
				OO-SOT	Sabena Old Timers, Zaventem	11.9.87/96
					(arr. for rest. Brussels 10.82, using parts of	
					RCAF2341,2360,2442: ff 27.8.88"2442/MA-D")	
					forced landing nr. Florennes AB (repaired)	4.9.88
Y1536	•	Mk. IIIa	**V9552**		(to RCAF as 1582): BOC 17.2.42: SOC	22.8.46
					Wes Agnew, Hartney MAN	71

				(recov. from farm, Stroughton SASK)	
				Sir William Roberts/Strathallan Aircraft Collection, Auchterader, Scotland: arr. dism.	10.71
			G-AZWT	Sir W. J. D. Roberts, Auchterader, Scotland	9.6.72/93
				(rest. Strathallan, ff 14.12.79 "V9441/AR-A")	
				(id. also quoted as RCAF 2355: small parts only)	
Y1399 •	Mk. IIIa	-		(to RCAF as ......)	
				Vince O'Connor, Uxbridge ONT	
				(fuse. only, wings from RCAF2404)	
				Peter Dimond, Portsmouth UK	92
1176 •	Mk. IIIa	**RCAF**		David C. Tallichet/ MARC, Chino CA	.72/93
				(railed to Ontario CA .72, stored Chino CA)	
				Air Heritage Inc, Beaver Falls PA: lsd.	91/93
				(stored Beaver Falls PA, planned rest. to fly)	
1181 •	Mk. IIIa	**RCAF2341**		RCAF BOC 27.4.42: SOC	1.10.46
				Ed Zalesky/Canadian Museum of Flight & Transportation, Vancouver BC	79/88
				(hulk recov. ex farm, Riverhurst SASK)	
				Ed & Rose Zalesky, Surrey BC	88/95
1183 •	Mk. IIIa	**RCAF2344**		RCAF BOC 28.4.42: SOC	1.10.46
				Ed Zalesky/Canadian Museum of Flight & Transportation, Vancouver BC	79/88
				(hulk recov. ex farm, Gull Lake SASK)	
				Ed & Rose Zalesky, Surrey BC	88/95
1185 •	Mk. IIIa	**RCAF2346**		RCAF BOC 24.6.42: SOC	15.1.47
				Ernie Simmons, Tillsonburg ONT	.45/57
				F. D. Emmorey, Montreal QUE: rest. project	69
				Dolph Overton, Kenley NC: stored	
			N7791	Dwight Brooks, Van Nuys CA	.73/75
				(rebuilt Van Nuys CA, using parts from RCAF 2366: ff 3.7.74 as "N7791/AC-B")	
				NASM: loan USAFM, Wright-Patterson AFB OH	79/92
				(displ. as "N7791/AC-B")	
1194 •	Mk. IIIa	**RCAF2349**		RCAF BOC 30.4.42: SOC	1.10.46
				Wes Agnew, Hartney MAN	
				(recov. from farm, Cabri SASK)	
				Tim Inman, Beasley TX/Confederate AF	80
				Ed Zalesky/Canadian Museum of Flight & Transportation, Vancouver BC	5.80/92
				(basis of composite static rest. for "Expo 86")	
1202 •	Mk. IIIa	**RCAF2363**		RCAF BOC 5.6.42: SOC	1.10.46
			C-GCWL	Canadian Warplane Heritage, Mount Hope ONT	83/88
			N1274	Friends of CWH, Tonawanda NY	4.89/95
				(rest. to fly, Niagara Falls NY)	
1205 •	Mk. IIIa	**RCAF2364**		RCAF BOC 5.6.42: SOC	1.10.46
				Martin Riehl, Calgary ALTA	69/72
				(recov. ex farm, Weyburn SASK .72)	
				Arny Carnegie, Edmonton ALTA	.72
				Dwight Brooks, Van Nuys CA	1.73/74
				(spare airframe for rebuild of RCAF 2346)	
				Friends of CWH, Tonaswanda NY	85
				(spare airframe for rebuild of RCAF 2363)	
			C-GCWW	Canadian Warplane Heritage, Hamilton ONT	85/92
				(rest. project: RCAF serial also poss. 2366)	
1206 •	Mk. IIIa	**RCAF2365**		RCAF BOC 23.6.42: SOC	22.8.46
				Air Museum of Calgary ALTA: listed	69
				Martin Riehl, Calgary ALTA	72/77
				(recov. ex farm, Weyburn SASK .72)	
				Harry Whereatt, Assiniboia SASK	.77/92

1209 •	Mk. IIIa	RCAF2367		RCAF BOC 23.6.47: SOC	22.8.46
				Air Museum of Calgary ALTA: listed	69
				Martin Riehl, Calgary ALTA	72/77
				(recov. ex farm, Weyburn SASK .72)	
				Harry Whereatt, Assiniboia SASK	.77/92
				(RCAF serial also poss. 2366)	
1216 •	Mk. IIIa	RCAF2374		RCAF BOC 23.6.42: SOC	25.11.46
				Capt. Bernard M. Lapointe, RCAF Winnipeg	66/68
				(rest. Winnipeg from three derelict airframes recov. from MAN farms : ff 29.12.67)	
				Canadian National Aeronautical Collection, Rockcliffe AB ONT	.68/82
				National Aviation Museum, Rockcliffe ONT	9.82/93
				(displ. as "RCAF R9003")	
1217 •	Mk. IIIa	RCAF2375		RCAF BOC 23.6.42: SOC	22.8.46
				Wes Agnew, Hartney MAN	
				Commonwealth Air Training Plan Museum, Brandon MAN	88/92
1218 •	Mk. IIIa	RCAF2376		RCAF BOC 23.6.42: SOC	22.8.46
				G & M Aircraft, St. Albert ALTA	85
				Ed Zalesky/Canadian Museum of Flight & Transportation, Vancouver BC : arr.	7.85
				Ed & Rose Zalesky, Surrey BC	88/95
1222 •	Mk. IIIa	RCAF2381		RCAF BOC 26.6.42: SOC	1.5.46
				G & M Aircraft, St. Albert ALTA	85
				Ed Zalesky/Canadian Museum of Flight & Transportation, Vancouver BC : arr.	7.85
				fuse. only: dam. in truck crash during recov.	18.7.85
				Ed & Rose Zalesky, Surrey BC	88/95
				(id. also quoted as RCAF 2383)	
1244 •	Mk. IIIA	RCAF		Wes Agnew, Hartney MAN	
				(recov. from farm, Nipiwan MAN)	
				Joe Gertler, New York NY	71
				Philip A. Mann, Booker	.71/75
			G-BCWL	Philip A. Mann, Booker	9.9.75/79
				(composite rest. Booker .72/77, using parts of RCAF2341, 2349, 2391: ff Booker 26.5.77)	
				Warbirds of GB Ltd, Blackbushe	9.5.79/85
				forced landing, overturned, Whitchford	21.8.83
				Brian Woodford/Wessex Aviation & Transport, Henstridge	2.85/95
				(arr. Booker 5.85 ex Hamble for rebuild, ff 18.9.87)	
				op Aircraft Restoration Co. Duxford	11.95/96
-	Mk. IIIA	RCAF		derelict hulk recov. ex farm Canada	
				Eric Vormezeele, Braaschaat, Belgium	84/85
				Musee de l'Air, Paris-Le Bourget	21.8.85/90
				dest. in museum hangar fire, Le Bourget	17.5.90
				(id. rep. as "RCAF 1589": see above)	

Yakovlev Let-C.11

102146 •	LET C.11	-		(to Egyptian AF as ....)	56/84
				Jean-Baptiste Salis/Salis Aviation, La Ferte-Alais, France: recov.	.84
				(total 41 C.11s: shipped France ex Egypt .84)	
			N2124X	Joseph R. Haley, El Segundo CA later East Sound WA	8.89/95
				(rebuilt Chino CA .89 racer with R-2000, race #111/*Defector*, later all-black sc., flies painted as N2421X in 95)	

c/n	Type	Mil. ID	Reg.	History	Date
105022 •	LET C.11	-		(to Egyptian AF as ....)	
				Salis Aviation, La Ferte-Alais, France: recov.	.84
			N7030U	Jeff Thomas/Vintage Wings, Anchorage AK	7.89
			N711JT	Vintage Wings, Anchorage AK	10.89/95
170101 •	LET C.11	-		(to Egyptian AF as 533)	
				Salis Aviation, La Ferte-Alais, France: recov.	.84
				The Fighter Collection, Duxford UK	.88
			G-BTHD	The Fighter Collection, Duxford	7.3.91/95
	Yak-3U repl.			(to Russia .91/95 for rebuild as Yak-3U, with Allison engine)	
170103 •	LET C.11	-	**G-BWFU**	M. Rusche, Hanover Germany	26.7.95
				rebuild LittleGransden with Yak U.K	95/96
170406 •	LET C.11	-		(to Egyptian AF as ....)	
				Salis Aviation, La Ferte-Alais, France: recov.	.84
				Frank Day, Bloomfield Hills MI	86/93
				Tom Dodson/Tulsa Warbirds, Tulsa OK	.93/94
	Yak-3UA repl.		**N33UA**	Tulsa Warbirds Inc, Tulsa OK	12.94/95
				(rebuild as Yak-3 replica 90/95)	
171101 •	LET C.11	1701		(to Czech AF as 1701)	
				(to Egyptian AF as 590): del.	.59
				defected to Israel, stored by IDFAF	.64/77
				recov. by Robs Lamplough : shipped to UK	.77
			G-KYAK	Robs Lamplough, Duxford/North Weald	12.78/92
				(rest. Duxford, ff 29.4.81 in Soviet AF sc.)	
				dam. forced landing, near Duxford (rebuilt)	21.10.84
				C. Jacquard, Dijon: del. ex North Weald	1.92
			F-AZHQ	Flying Legends, Dijon-Longvic	11.5.92/93
				Ste. Yak Warbird Ltd, Dijon-Longvic	93/94
				The Fighter Collection, Duxford UK	6.94
			G-KYAK	The Fighter Collection, Duxford	4.1.95
				(flies as "Soviet AF 36")	
171103 •	LET C.11	-		(to Egyptian AF as ....)	
				Salis Aviation, La Ferte-Alais, France: recov.	.84
			G-IYAK	Eddie K. Coventry, Earls Colne	12.1.94
171205 •	LET C.11	-	OK-KIH	Czech Government: reg. for del.	.64
				(to Egyptian AF as 705)	
				Salis Aviation, La Ferte-Alais, France: recov.	.84
			G-OYAK	Eddie K. Coventry, Earls Colne	25.2.88/94
				(rest. Earls Colne, ff 18.11.90 as "Soviet AF 27")	
				(c/n also quoted as 690120, also rep. ex EAF 205, or 097: confirmed as EAF 705)	
171304 •	LET C.11	-		(to Czech AF as 171304)	
				Salis Aviation, La Ferte-Alais, France: recov.	.84
				Planes of Fame Museum, Chino CA	90/93
171306 •	LET C.11	-		(to Czech AF as 171306)	
				Salis Aviation, La Ferte-Alais, France: recov.	.84
				Planes of Fame Museum, Chino CA	90/93
171312 •	LET C.11	-	OK-JIK	Czech Government: reg. for del.	.64
				(to Egyptian AF as ...)	
				Salis Aviation, La Ferte-Alais, France: recov.	.84
				Tony Bianchi, Booker : arr. dism. for rest.	5.5.89/92
			G-BTZE	Bianchi Aviation Film Services Ltd, Booker	11.2.92/96
				(under rest. Booker 92/95)	
171314 •	LET C.11	-		(to Egyptian AF as.........)	.55
				Salis Aviation, La Ferte-Alais, France: recov.	.84
				Paul Franceschi, Le Castellet, near Marseille	.85/96
				(under rest. 87/96)	

171521 •	LET C.11	-		(to Egyptian AF as ....)	
				Salis Aviation, La Ferte-Alais, France: recov.	.84
				John W. Houston, Harlingen TX	
				Ascher Ward, Van Nuys CA	88
			N134JK	Joe Kasparoff, Van Nuys CA	5.88/95
				(rebuilt Van Nuys as mod. racer with R-3350, ff Mojave 11.8.88; race #97/*Mr Awesome*)	
				Darryl Greenamyer, Van Nuys CA	8.89
				(further racing mods., including T-33 tail)	
				crashed, Reno NV	11.8.89
				Roger Van Grote & Dale Williamson TX	95/96
				(being rebuilt Denton TX 95 as R-3350 racer)	
171529 •	LET C.11	-		(to Egyptian AF as ....)	
				Salis Aviation, La Ferte-Alais, France: recov.	.84/87
			N21241	Daniel M. McCue, Somersworth NH	.87/89
				(crated from France to USA .87)	
			N11MQ	Daniel M. McCue/Warbirds East, Somersworth NH	7.89/96
				(rebuilt Live Oak FL with P&W R2000, ff. 3.90)	
				(FAA quote id."Yak-11-01M": flies in Soviet AF sc.)	
172503 • 25111/ 19	LET C.11	-		(to Egyptian AF as ....)	
				Salis Aviation, La Ferte-Alais, France: recov.	.84
				Gerard Chambert, La Ferte-Alais: rest.	88/93
			F-AZOK	Gerard Chambert, J-P Toutblanc & Patrick Falloux, La Ferte-Alais	3.6.93
				(rest. La Ferte-Alais, ff .93 as "Soviet 37")	
172521 •	LET C.11	-		(to Egyptian AF as ....)	
				Salis Aviation, La Ferte-Alais, France: recov.	.84
				Jean-Marie Garric, Mercedes TX	87/90
				Jean-Marie Garric, Mercedes TX : candidate	23.3.90
			N111YK	Robert G. Chinnery, Independence MO	5.90/95
172612 •	LET C.11	-		(to Egyptian AF as ....)	
				Salis Aviation, La Ferte-Alais, France: recov.	.84
				Don C.Talley & C.A.Barnes, Longview TX	88
			N9YK	Don Talley/Talleys Warbirds, Longview TX	3.89/95
	Yak-9 repl.			(rebuilt as single-seat Yak-9 replica, ff 20.9.91 as "Soviet AF 11")	
				Tom Everhart, Taylorsville KY	.95
172623 •	LET C.11	-		(to Egyptian AF as 543)	.56
				Salis Aviation, La Ferte-Alais, France: recov.	.84
				(arr. dism. Booker UK 23.4.86 from France)	
			G-BTUB	Yak UK, Little Gransden	29.8.91/95
				(rest. Little Gransden, ff 13.5.94)	
				(id. also quoted as "039")	
172701 •	LET C.11	-	OK-KIE	Czech Government: for del. to Egyptian AF	.64
				forced landing on del., Philia, Cyprus	27.3.64
				impounded by RAF Cyprus: stored dism.	3.64/70
			G-AYAK	Philip A. Mann, Booker	31.3.70/76
				(shipped to UK .70, rest. Booker, ff 6.72)	
				Robs Lamplough, Duxford	
				Anthony E. Hutton,	.76/83
				(shipped to US .82 for sales tour, at Oshkosh 8.82: shipped back to UK .83)	
				Aero Vintage Ltd, Lydd	11.2.83/84
			N11YK	Heliflight Inc, Fort Lauderdale FL	7.6.84
				Weeks Air Museum, Tamiami FL (flew as "Soviet AF 14")	4.85/96
				dam. by Hurricane Andrew, Tamiami	24.8.92
172809 •	LET C.11	-		(to Egyptian AF as ....)	
				Salis Aviation, La Ferte-Alais, France: recov.	.84
				Yves Jean-Marie Garric, Mercedes TX	87/93
			N3UA	Yves Jean-Marie Garric, Harlingen TX	1.93/95
	Yak-3 repl.			(rebuilt as single-seat Yak-3UA replica,	

				ff Harlingen TX 16.2.93 as "Soviet AF 6")	
1701231•	LET C.11	-		(to Egyptian AF as ....)	
				Salis Aviation, La Ferte-Alais, France: recov.	.84
			N11SN	Neil R. Anderson, Fort Worth TX	3.86/90
				The Old Flying Machine Company,	
				Duxford UK : arr. dism.	17.3.90/92
				(flies in Soviet AF sc.)	
	Yak. 3U			(to Russia .91 for conv. to Yak 3U .91/96)	
				struck-off USCR	5.93
			G-BUXZ	Old Flying Machine Company, Duxford	.93/96
458519 •	LET C.11	-		(to Egyptian AF as ....)	
				Salis Aviation, La Ferte-Alais, France: recov.	.84
			N11YH	Jim H. McKinstry, Longmont CO	1.86/95
8492250•	LET C.11	-		(to Egyptian AF as ....)	
				Salis Aviation, La Ferte-Alais, France: recov.	.84
			N5YK	Tom Everhart, Louisville KY	87/90
25111/ 02 •	LET C.11	-		(to Egyptian AF as ....)	
				Salis Aviation, La Ferte-Alais, France: recov.	.84
			F-AZFJ	Jean-Baptiste Salis Collection, La Ferte-Alais	6.88/90
				H. R. Capel, La Ferte-Alais	93
				(flies as "Soviet AF 29")	
25111/ 03 •	LET C.11	-		(to Egyptian AF as 539)	
				Salis Aviation, La Ferte-Alais, France: recov.	.84
			F-YAKA	reg. for test flying	
			F-AZJB	Aero Retro, St.Rambert	29.8.88/94
				(also rep. ex EAF533)	
25111/ 05 •	LET C.11	-		(to Egyptian AF as ....)	
				Salis Aviation, La Ferte-Alais, France: recov.	.84
			F-AZNN	Pierre Dague, La Ferte-Alais	5.87/93
				(first of the Egyptian Yak 11s to fly, rest.	
				La Ferte-Alais as single-seat Yak 3, ff 5.87)	
				(flies as "Soviet AF 14")	
25111/ 06 •	LET C.11	-		(to Egyptian AF as ....)	
				Salis Aviation, La Ferte-Alais, France: recov.	.84
			F-AZFB	H. R. Capel, La Ferte-Alais	.87/93
25111/ 08 •	LET C.11	-		(to Egyptian AF as ....)	
				Salis Aviation, La Ferte-Alais, France: recov.	.84
			F-AZPA	Amicale Jean-Baptiste Salis, La Ferte-Alais	5.9.90/93
25111/ 20 •	LET C.11	-		(to Egyptian AF as ....)	
				Salis Aviation, La Ferte-Alais, France: recov.	.84
			N18AW	Ascher Ward, Van Nuys CA	87/88
				Thomas L. Camp, San Francisco CA	5.89/95
				(rebuilt with R2800; race #58/*Maniyak*	
				later #00 *Mr. Awful*)	
25111/ 25 •	LET C.11	-		(to Egyptian AF as ....)	
				Salis Aviation, La Ferte-Alais, France: recov.	.84
				Robert J. Pond, Minneapolis MN	.85
			N25YK	Planes of Fame East,	
				Plymouth MN	5.88/96
				(rest. Chino CA with R-1830: ff Chino 4.87,	
				flies as "Soviet AF 27")	
- •	LET C.11	-		(to Egyptian AF as ....)	
				Salis Aviation, La Ferte-Alais, France: recov.	.84
			N3YK	John W. Houston/Texas Air Museum,	
				Rio Hondo TX	12.85/92
	Yak 3UA repl.			Tom Dodson/Tulsa Warbirds Inc, Tulsa OK	11.94/95

c/n		Type		Reg.	History	Date
					(rebuild 90/96 as Yak-3 replica)	
					(USCR quotes id. "Y337")	
-	•	LET C.11	-		(to Egyptian AF as ....)	
					Salis Aviation, La Ferte-Alais, France: recov.	.84
				N7YK	Frank Day, Bloomfield Hills MI: reg. res.	90/96
		Yak-9 repl.			(conv. to Yak 9UTI rep., Allison engine)	
					(USCR quotes id. "51-24")	
-	•	LET C.11	-		(to Egyptian AF as ....)	
					Salis Aviation, La Ferte-Alais, France: recov.	.84
				N5940	Robert F. Yancey, Klamath Falls OR	4.87/96
					(USCR quotes id. "210")	
-	•	LET C.11	-		(to Egyptian AF as ....)	
					Salis Aviation, La Ferte-Alais, France: recov.	.84
				N5942	Robert F. Yancey, Klamath Falls OR	4.87/89
-	•	LET C.11	-		(to Egyptian AF as 407)	
					Salis Aviation, La Ferte-Alais, France: recov.	.84
				N5943	Robert F. Yancey, Klamath Falls OR	4.87/96
					(rebuilt with R-2800; race #101/"*Perestroika*)	
					(USCR quotes id. "407")	
-	•	LET C.11	-		(to Egyptian AF as ......)	
					Salis Aviation, La Ferte-Alais, France: recov.	.84
				N5945	Robert F. Yancey, Klamath Falls OR	4.87
-	•	LET C.11	-		(to Egyptian AF as 079)	
					Salis Aviation, La Ferte-Alais, France: recov.	.84
					BAP Air, Charleroi, Belgium : arr. dism.	.85
				OO-YAK	BAP Air, Charleroi/Temploux	24.3.86
					M. Adge	87/96
					(rest. Gosselies-Charleroi, ff 12.5.88 as "12")	
-	•	LET C.11	-		(to Egyptian AF as ....)	
					Salis Aviation, La Ferte-Alais, France: recov.	.84
					Jean-Baptiste Salis, La Ferte-Alais: rest.	87
-	•	LET C.11	-		(to Egyptian AF as ....)	
					Salis Aviation, La Ferte-Alais, France: recov.	.84
					Aero Retro, St. Rambert-d'Albon	87
-	•	LET C.11	-		(to Egyptian AF as ....)	
					Salis Aviation, La Ferte-Alais, France: recov.	.84
					Philip Joyet, Lausanne, Switzerland	87
					J. F. Perrin, Lausanne, Switzerland	88
-	•	LET C.11	-		(to Egyptian AF as ....)	
					Salis Aviation, La Ferte-Alais, France: recov.	.84
					Dale Clark, Chino CA	88
-	•	LET C.11	-		(to Egyptian AF as ....)	
					Salis Aviation, La Ferte-Alais, France: recov.	.84
					Planes of Fame East,	
					Minneapolis MN	.85
					(prob. the Yak.11 in open storage, complete,	
					Planes of Fame compound, Chino CA 89/92)	
-	•	LET C.11	-	OK-JZE	Museum of Aviation & Cosmonautics, Kbely	89/91
					(rest. 89/91, ff 27.11.91)	
9/04623	•	LET C.11	-		(to Romanian AF as ....)	
					Alain Capel/Capel Aviation, La Ferte-Alais	92/94
					(rebuilt Romania as Yak3UTI-PN with R1830,	
					ff 15.4.94 as "1")	
		Yak 3UTI		F-AZIM	Capel Aviation, La Ferte-Alais	5.94/95
					(del. ex Craiova, Romania, arr. 30.5.94)	

Yakovlev Let C-11

C/n	Type		Reg	History	Date
- •	Yak-11	-	**F-AZIO**	B. Charbonnel & J-F Chalumeau,	
				Lons-le Saunier: reg. res.	.94
- •	Yak-11	-	**F-AZIR**	Capel Aviation, La Ferte-Alais: reg. res.	.94
760806 •	Yak 11	-		(to Soviet AF as 08)	
			LY-AKZ	based Angleholm, Sweden	.93
- •	Yak 11	-		(to Romanian AF as ......)	
				Capel Aviation, La Ferte-Alais, France	
				(rebuilt Romania with R1830)	
				Joseph R. Haley, El Segundo CA: ordered	.93

Yakovlev Yak-3

C/n	Type		Reg	History	Date
- •	Yak-3UA	-		Gunnell Aviation, Santa Monica CA	91/93
	new production			Museum of Flying, Santa Monica CA	8.91/93
				(on loan from Yakovlev OKB, arr. dism. 8.91)	
				(c/n "115450123" painted on fuselage)	
0470101•	Yak-3UA	-		Gunnell Aviation, Santa Monica CA	93
	new production			(built by Yakovlev, Orenburg, Russia 91/93:	
				new production run of 20 Model 3UAs)	
				displ. Paris Air Show, France	6.93
			N854DP	reg.	7.95
0470102•	Yak-3UA	-		Gunnell Aviation, Santa Monica CA	93
	new production			(built by Yakovlev, Orenburg, Russia 91/93:	
			N915LP	Bruce Lockwood/Flight Magic Inc,	
				Pacific Palisades CA	10.6.94
				(US certification test flying, Mojave CA 7.94)	
				Alpine USA Ltd, Wilmington DE	10.94/95
			ZK-YAK	Alpine Fighter Collection, Wanaka : reg. res.	.94/96
				(shipped NZ, arr. Wanaka 11.94, ff 7.1.95)	
0470103•	Yak-3UA	-		Gunnell Aviation, Santa Monica CA	93
	new production			(built by Yakovlev, Orenburg, Russia 91/93:	
				production run of 20 Model 3UAs: Allison V1710)	
			N494DJ	Bruce Lockwood/Flight Magic Inc,	
				Pacific Palisades CA	10.6.94/96
				(US certification test flying,	
				Mojave CA 7.94,	
				raced at Reno NV 9.94 race #12)	
- •	Yak-3	-		technical school, Russia: inst. airframe	
				Eddie Coventry, Earls Colne UK	94
				(arr. Suffolk UK 7.94, stored pending rest.)	
- •	Yak-3	-		Musee de l'Air, Paris-Le Bourget	73/95
				(displ. as "Soviet AF 4")	
- •	Yak-3	-		Plovdiv Museum, Bulgaria: displ. as "23"	95

Yakovlev Yak-9

C/n	Type		Reg	History	Date
- •	Yak 9P	-		Naval Military Museum, Gydnia, Poland	83
- •	Yak 9U	-		Polish Army Museum, Warsaw	68/83
0815346•	Yak-9U	-		Champlin Fighter Museum, Mesa AZ: arr.	3.95
				(recov. dam. ex long term storage Siberia,	
				rest. to airworthy Moscow 92/94)	
				(shipped ex Russia, displ. as "Soviet AF 36")	
3267 •	Yak 9U	-		Plovdiv Museum, Bulgaria: displ. as "7"	95

ARADO Ar 234 BLITZ

c/n	Type	Identity	Reg	History	Date
Nr623167•	Ar 234B-2	Nr140312		KG76: captured Stavenger, Norway	.45
				shipped to USA ex France on *HMS Reaper*	7.45
				(to USAAF as FE-1010/T2-1010)	.45/46
				Smithsonian Institute: stored Park Ridge IL	.46
				NASM, Silver Hill MD	72/96
				(rest. .89, displ. as "140312/F1+GS")	

ARADO Ar 199

c/n	Type	Identity	Reg	History	Date
WNr3673...•	Ar 199 A-0			10 Seenotstaffel.	
				damaged on Lake Wesnej.	13.08.42
				recov . ex crash site Russia	94
				Kolair Inc, Roswell GA	94
				(crash hulk offered for sale as rest. project:	
				date built 24.3.39)	

BREWSTER F2A BUFFALO

c/n	Type	Identity	Reg	History	Date
632567 •	F2A Humu	**HM-671**		(Finnish AF HM-671): ff	8.8.44
				wfu after last flight	28.3.45
				Aviation Museum of Central Finland,	
				Tivkakoski AB: displ. complete as "HM-671"	

BLOHM-VOSS Bv 155

c/n	Type	Identity	Reg	History	Date
V2 •	Bv 155B-V2			captured unfinished, Finkenwerder works	5.45
				Royal Aircraft Establishment, Farnborough	.45
				(shipped to UK, arr. Farnborough 20.10.45;	
				shipped to New York 1.46)	
				(to USAAF as FE-505/T2-505)	.46
				Smithsonian Institute, stored Park Ridge IL. 21.8.46	
				NASM, Silver Hill MD	66/94

CURTISS F15C

c/n	Type	Identity	Reg	History	Date
- •	XF15C-1	**Bu01215**		New England Air Museum, Windsor Locks CT	87/92
				(fully rest. : displ. as USN "NATC/215")	

DORNIER Do 335 PFEIL

c/n	Type	Identity	Reg	History	Date
Nr240102•	Do 335A-02			"VG+PH" captured Oberpfaffenhofen,Munich	22.4.45
				shipped to USA ex France on *HMS Reaper*	7.45
				(to USN as Bu121447)	
				NAS Patuxent River MD; flight tests	.45/46
				NASM, NAS Norfolk VA: stored	.47/61
				NASM, stored Silver Hill MD	.61/74
				Deutsches Museum, Munich: loan	.74/86
				(airfreighted to Germany 11.10.74, rest. by	
				Dornier, Oberpfaffenhofen as "102/VG+PH")	
				NASM, Silver Hill MD	90/94

DOUGLAS BTD DESTROYER

c/n	Type	Identity	Reg	History	Date
1891 •	BTD-1	**Bu04959**		NAS Norfolk VA: stored	65/75
				(dism. for transportation NAS Norfolk VA .75)	
				USNAM, NAS Pensacola FL	87/95
				Florence Air & Missile Museum SC: loan	87/95
			N7035U	USNAM, NAS Pensacola FL	11.93/96

DOUGLAS A2D SKYSHARK

c/n	Type	Identity	Reg	History	Date
7596 •	XA2D-1	**Bu125485**		Ed Maloney/The Air Museum, Ontario CA	65/76
				(recov. from fire dump, LAX Airport CA)	
				David C. Tallichet/Yesterdays Air Force,	
				Chino CA	78/87
				John Muszala/Pacific Fighters, Chino CA	88/96
				(rest. project, Chino CA)	

FOCKE-WULF Fw 189

c/n	Type	Identity	Reg	History	Date
Nr0112100•	Fw 189A-1			1(H)/32: "V7+1H"	
	Fw 189A-2			shot down, Łouhki, eastern Finland 4.5.43	
				(hulk recov. from crash site, Russia 1.92)	
				Jim Pearce/Sussex Spraying Services,	
				Shoreham UK	2.92/94
				(arr. Hull Docks 18.2.92, rest. project;	
				displ. unrest. Biggin Hill 9.95,	
				planned rest. to fly, Czech Republic)	

GENERAL MOTORS P-75 EAGLE

c/n	Type	Identity	Reg	History	Date
| •	P-75A	**44-44553**		NASM, Silver Hill MD	
				USAFM, Wright-Patterson AFB, Dayton OH	.77/92

GLOSTER GAUNTLET

c/n	Type	Identity	Reg	History	Date
G.5/ 35957 •	Mk. II	**K5271**		(to Finnish AF as GT-400)	
				(shipped to Sweden, flown to Finland 12.4.40)	
				Alpo Hinktikka	.75

				(hulk recov. ex farm Juupajoki, Finland 11.75)	
				Hallinportti Aviation Museum, Halli AB	.76/96
			OH-XGT	Lentotekniikan Kilta ry, Halli AB	21.6.82
				(rest. Halli AB .76/82, ff 10.5.82;	
				displ. as "Finnish AF GT-400")	
HEINKEL He 46					
Nr846	He 46D			captured Chateauroux AB, France	8.44
				(to Armee de l'Air as .....)	
				Musee des Trois Guerres, Chateau de Diors,	
				Indre, Francee: displ.	60/70
				Musee de l'Air et de l'Espace, Villacoublay	79/84
				Musee de l'Air, Paris-Le Bourget : stored	90
				dest. by fire, museum hangar Le Bourget	17.5.90
HEINKEL He 219					
Nr290202•	He 219A			captured Grove, Denmark	
				shipped to USA ex France on HMS Reaper	7.45
				(to USAAF as FE-614/T2-614)	.45/46
				Smithsonian Institute, stored Park Ridge IL	17.9.46
				NASM, Silver Hill MD	65/96
HORTON BROS. Ho 229					
V3 •	Ho 229V3			captured Gotha works, Fredrichsroda	4.45
				construction not completed, shipped to USA	.45
				(to USAAF as FE-490/T2-490)	
				Smithsonian Institute, stored Park Ridge IL	.46
				NASM, Silver Hill MD	66/96
JUNKERS Ju 388					
Nr560049•	Ju 388L-1			captured at Merseburg Werks	5.45
				shipped to USA ex France on HMS Reaper	7.45
				(to USAAF as FE-4010/T2-4010)	.45/46
				Smithsonian Institute, stored Park Ridge IL	26.9.46
				NASM, Silver Hill MD	72/94
JUNKERS Ju 86					
0860412 •	Ju 86K-4			(to R Swedish AF as Fv155)	
	Tp-73			Flygvapenmuseum, Linkoping, Sweden	60/94
KAWANISHI H8K("EMILY")					
426 •	H8K2			captured Takuma, Shikoku	.45
				(flown to Yokosuka 13.11.45, shipped to USA	
				on seaplane tender USS Cumberland Sound 11.45)	
				(to USN as "T-31"): flying trials	
				Smithsonian Institute: stored NAS Norfolk	45/79
				Museum of Maritime Science, Tokyo, Japan	.79/94
				(shipped Tokyo, arr. 12.7.79 ex NAS Norfolk)	
NORTH AMERICAN P-64					
68-3061 •	NA-68			(built as NA-68 for Siam: impressed by USAAC)	
	P-64	**41-19085**	NX37498	Jack Canary/Phoenix Aviation Inc,Phoenix AZ	.46/48
	RP-64			(operated with rain-making mods.)	
				Charles Barnes/Precipitation Control Corp,	
				Phoenix AZ	.49/50
			XB-KUU	Precipitation Control Corp	52/59
				(returned USA, stored Long Beach CA 59/62)	
			N68822	(under rest. Riverside-Flabob Airport CA 63)	
				Paul Poberezny/EAA, Milwaukee WI	1.64
				(dep. Flabob on del. 26.5.64, rest. ff 24.7.65)	
			N840	EAA Air Museum, Hales Corner/Oshkosh WI	66/95
NORTHROP P-56					
- •	XP-56	**42-38353**		NASM, Silver Hill MD	65/74
				loan: USAFM, Wright-Patterson AFB OH	7
SAVOIA MARCHETTI SM.82 MARSUPIALE					
- •	SM.82PW	**MM61187**		Museo Aeronautico Caproni di Taliedo, Milan	75
				Museo Storico dell'Aeronautica Militaire	
				Italiana, Vigna di Valle AB	80/92
				(displ. as "MM61850/14")	
VOUGHT F7U CUTLASS					
- •	F7U-3	**Bu129554**		City of Bridgeport CT	
				T.E. Cathcart: reg. candidate	7.94
VOUGHT SB2U VINDICATOR					
-	SB2U-2	**Bu1383**		ditched Lake Michigan, off carrier"Wolverine"	21.6.43
				USNAM, NAS Pensacola FL (static rest.)	.90/94
				(recov. from Lake Michigan 10.90 for USNAM)	
YAKOVLEV Yak-1					
8188 •	Yak-1	**1342**		(to Soviet AF as 1342)	
				recov. ex lake, Northern Russia	c90
				Historic Aircraft Collection : imported to UK	8.91
			G-BTZD	Historic Aircraft Collection,(rest. to fly, •	

AERO VODOCHY L-29 DELFIN

C/n	Type	Reg	History	Date
093734 •	L-29L		(to Soviet AF as ...)	
		N8164C	Thrust Inc, Brooklyn Park MN	17.4.95
194150 •	L-29L		(to Soviet AF as 34)	
			(noted stored Minneapolis-Crystal MN 95)	
		N88LK	reg.	7.95
194340 •	L-29L		(to Soviet AF as 15)	
		N4097P	C & P Aviation Services, Blaine MN	3.5.95
		N321CP	C & P Aviation Services, Blaine MN	11.5.95
194557 •	L-29L		(to Soviet AF as 76)	
		N82608	Warren A. Pietsch, Minot ND	25.4.95
290105 •	L-29		(to Czech AF as 0105)	
		N82171	Stephan Hornak, Palm Springs CA	21.6.95
290909 •	L-29		reg. candidate USCR	30.8.89
		N5959L	Delfin Group Inc, Santa Paula CA	4.90/92
			Mil Air Inc, Hidden Hills CA	6.92/95
294677 •	L-29A		(to Soviet AF as ....)	
		N40973	Walter A. Wootton, Harlingen TX	16.5.95
294856 •	L-29A		(to Soviet AF as ...)	
		N129BE	Edward L. Erickson, Minneapolis MN	21.4.95
490902 •	L-29		reg. candidate USCR	30.8.89
		N3939L	Mira Slovak Aerobatics Inc, Santa Paula CA	4.90/93
			Larry Salganek/Fantasy Fighters Inc, Santa Fe NM	8.94/95
490925 •	L-29		(Soviet AF as .....)	
			Action Products Inc	93/94
			Quonset Air Museum, Quonset Point RI: loan	8.93/94
			Divis Ltd	
		N7857Y	Aero Delphin Ltd, Wilmington DE	24.6.94/95
491119 •	L-29S		(to Soviet AF as Red 37)	
			Jeff Rosenbloom, Cumbernauld, Scotland	93/94
			(noted stored Cumbernauld 9.93/95)	
491165 •	L-29S		(to Soviet AF as Red 40)	
			Jeff Rosenbloom, Cumbernauld, Scotland	93/94
			(noted stored Cumbernauld 7.93/95)	
491174 •	L-29L		(to Soviet AF as 52)	
			(noted stored Minneapolis-Crystal MN 95)	
491273 •	L-29S		(to Soviet AF as Red 51)	
			Jeff Rosenbloom, Cumbernauld, Scotland	93
			(noted stored dism., Cumbernauld 9.93; trucked to Hawarden 12.93)	
591234 •	L-29	**N62187**	(to Czech AF as 1234)	
			Aero Delfin Group Inc, Santa Paula CA	19.4.93/95
591235 •	L-29		(to Czech AF as 1235)	
		OK-TYP	noted at Prague	8.92
			Pino Valenti/Nucleo Acrobatica Parmense, Parma, Italy	.94/95
591238 •	L-29	**N3159Y**	Mira Slovak Aerobatics Inc, Santa Paula CA	10.9.91/92

			Al Swafford, Bakersfield CA	12.94/95
591311 •	L-29		(to Indonesian AF/TNI-AU as A-2901, LL2901)	
		N7150M	Erickson Air Crane Co, Medford OR	10.1.90/95
591312 •	L-29		(to Indonesian AF/TNI-AU as A-2902, LL2902)	
			Indonesian Air Force Museum, Yogyakarta	89/90
		N7150J	Erickson Air Crane Co, Medford OR	10.1.90/95
591317 •	L-29		(to Indonesian AF/TNI-AU as A-2907, LL2907)	
		N7150D	Erickson Air Crane Co, Medford OR	10.1.90/95
591318 •	L-29		(to Indonesian AF/TNI-AU as A-2908, LL2908)	
			Indonesian Air Force Museum, Yogyakarta	88
			gate guard: Adisutjipto AB, Yogyakarta	88
		N7150A	Erickson Air Crane Co, Medford OR	10.1.90/95
591319 •	L-29		(to Indonesian AF/TNI-AU as A-2909, LL2909)	
		N7149Z	Erickson Air Crane Co, Medford OR	10.1.90
			Robert F. Yancey, Klamath Falls OR	92
			Gordon P. Richardson, Aurora OR	10.93/95
591322 •	L-29		(to Indonesian AF/TNI-AU as A-2912, LL2912)	
		N7149X	Erickson Air Crane Co, Medford OR	10.1.90/92
			Robert F. Yancey, Klamath Falls OR	9.92/95
591324 •	L-29		(to Indonesian AF/TNI-AU as A-2914, LL2914)	
		N7149J	Erickson Air Crane Co, Central Point OR	6.3.90
			Robert F. Yancey, Medford OR	92
			Rand Harris, Byron CA	2.94/95
591326 •	L-29		(to Czech AF as 1326)	
		N70750	Aero Delfin Group Inc, Santa Paula CA	2.6.93/95
591327 •	L-29		(to Czech AF as 1327)	
591328 • N7149E	L-29		(to Indonesian AF/TNI-AU as A-2918, LL2918)	
			Erickson Air Crane Co, Medford OR	10.1.90/95
591330 •	L-29	N62188	Aero Delfin Group Inc, Santa Paula CA	19.4.93/95
591378 •	L-29S		(to Hungarian Af as 378)	
			(to Soviet AF as Red 09)	.84
		YL-PAD	Jeff Rosenbloom, Cumbernauld, Scotland	93/94
			(noted stored Cumbernauld 9.93/95)	
591408 •	L-29		(to Czech AF as 1408)	
		N7082K	Aero Delfin Group Inc, Santa Paula CA	13.7.93/95
591416 •	L-29		(to Czech AF as 1416)	
		N7082P	Aero Delfin Group Inc, Santa Paula CA	13.7.93/95
591419 •	L-29		(to Czech AF as 1419)	
		N6216T	Aero Delfin Group Inc, Santa Paula CA	19.4.93/95
591427 •	L-29S		(to Soviet AF as ....)	
			(shipped ex Russia, arr. Chino CA 8.93)	
		N154MM	Michael D. McCluskey, Torrance CA	10.93/95
591429 •	L-29A		(to Soviet AF as 29)	
		RA-1429	Stu Davidson, Seaview, South Africa	.95
591607 •	L-29S		(to Soviet AF as ....)	
			(shipped ex Russia, arr. Chino CA 8.93)	
		N65BR	Robert Russell, Darby MT	7.1.94/95
591627 •	L-29A		(to Soviet AF as ....)	
		N81637	Paul J. Weske, Crystal MN	4.5.95
591635 •	L-29		(to Czech AF as 1635): stored Kbely AB	

c/n	Type	Reg	Owner	Date
			European Sport Aviation	94
		N41PK (1	ntu: Paul E. Isaakson, Amery WI	.94
		N11CZ	Paul E. Isaakson, Amery WI	23.5.94
			Karl S. Scriba, Amery WI	1.95
591636 •	L-29S		(to Soviet AF as Red 06)	
			Jeff Rosenbloom, Cumbernauld, Scotland	93
			(arr. dism. Cumbernauld 12.8.93, stored 93/95)	
591694 •	L-29		(to Soviet AF as ...)	
		N162SB	Stephen F. Boyce, Missoula MT	1.95
591699 •	L-29		(to Soviet AF as 79)	
		N179EP	Frank E. (Ed) Park, La Canada CA	5.10.93/95
			(civil conv. at Chino CA 1.94)	
591705 •	L-29		(to Czech AF as 1705)	
		N47JJ	John R. Jagusch, Cayton WI	20.5.94/95
591706 •	L-29		(to Czech AF as 1706)	
		N70753	Aero Delfin Group Inc, Santa Paula CA	2.6.93/95
591707 •	L-29A		(to Soviet AF as 55)	
		RA-1707	Stu Davidson, Seaview, South Africa	.95
591721 •	L-29		(to Czech AF as 1721): stored Kbely AB	
			European Sport Aviation	94
		N70WG	William R. Geipel, Deer Park WI	18.5.94
			David C. Tune, Nashville TN	4.95
		N42NE	rereg. res.	4.95
591722 •	L-29		(to Czech AF as 1722): stored Kbely AB	
			European Sport Aviation	94
		N52BS	William R. Geipel, Deer Park WI	18.5.94/95
591771 •	L-29S		(to Soviet AF as Red 18)	
			Jeff Rosenbloom, Cumbernauld, Scotland	93
			(noted stored dism., Cumbernauld 7.93, trucked out to Hawarden 12.93)	
691895 •	L-29L		(to Soviet AF as 28)	
		N82697	Amjet Aircraft Corp, St Paul MN	26.5.95
691902 •	L-29		(to Czech AF as 1902): stored Kbely AB	
			European Sport Aviation	94
		N41PK (2	Paul E. Isaakson, Amery WI	5.94/95
691927 •	L-29		(to Czech Republic AF as 1927)	
			(noted stored Kbely AB, Czech Republic 9.92)	
			European Sport Aviation	94
			C. W. Robertson, Belleville MI: reg. candidate	1.6.94
		N321RW	Richard G. Worringer, Bloomington MN	14.9.94/95
792383 •	L-29L		(to Soviet AF as ...)	
		N919WW	Westling Leasing Inc, Princeton MN	18.4.95
792396 •	L-29L		(to Soviet AF as 66)	
		N40976	C & P Aviation Services, Blaine MN	3.5.95
		N331CP	C & P Aviation Services, Blaine MN	11.5.95
792405 •	L-29		(to Czech AF as 2405)	
		N29AD	Aero Taxi Inc, New Castle DE	7.91/92
			Joseph J. Gano, Wilmington DE	9.94/95
792413 •	L-29A		(to Soviet AF as 38)	
		N19HW	John F. Huls, St. Cloud MN	10.5.95
792603 •	L-29RS		(to Slovakina AF as 2603): stored Trencin	
		N29RZ	Aztec Capital Corp, Coconut Grove FL	5.5.95
792607 •	L-29		(to Czech AF as 2607)	
		N229DJ	Aero Taxi Inc, New Castle DE	18.2.93/95

792661•	L-29L		(to Soviet AF as ...)	
		N82601	Clyde E. Barton, Angleton TX	18.4.95
892806 •	L-29R		(to Czech AF as 2806)	
		N29DJ	Aero Taxi Inc, New Castle DE	6.92/95
892813 •	L-29R		(to Czech AF as 2813)	
		N31088	Mira Slovak Aerobatics Inc, Santa Paula CA	5.7.91/92
			Aero Delfin Group Inc, Santa Paula CA	2.94/95
892814 •	L-29R		(to Czech AF as 2814): stored Vodochody AB	91
		N12DN	Aero Taxi Inc, New Castle DE	10.3.92
		N7076N	Aero Delfin Group Inc, Santa Paula CA	2.6.93/95
892815 •	L-29R		(to Czech AF as 2815): stored Vodochody AB	
			Mira Slovak Aerobatics Inc, Santa Paula CA	.90/91
		N7076R	Aero Delfin Group Inc, Santa Paula CA	2.6.93/95
892817 •	L-29R		(to Czech AF as 2817)	
		N3098E	Mira Slovak Aerobatics Inc, Santa Paula CA	28.8.91/92
			Aero Delfin Group Inc, Santa Paula CA	5.92/95
892819 •	L-29R		(to Czech AF as 2819): stored Vodochody AB	
		N7075Z	Aero Delfin Group Inc, Santa Paula CA	2.6.93/95
		N19CZ	re-reg.	8.95
892820 •	L-29R		(to Czech AF as 2820): stored Vodochody AB	
		N7076J	Aero Delfin Group Inc, Santa Paula CA	2.6.93/95
892824 •	L-29R		(to Czech AF as 2824): stored Vodochody AB	
		N7076G	Aero Delfin Group Inc, Santa Paula CA	2.6.93/95
892825 •	L-29R		(to Czech AF as 2825)	
		N2825Q	Don G. Misevic, Stevensville MT	22.7.92/95
892830 •	L-29R		(to Czech AF as 2830): stored Vodochody AB	
		N70759	Aero Delfin Group Inc, Santa Paula CA	2.6.93/95
		N82674	re-reg.	8.95
892847 •	L-29R		(to Czech Republic AF as 2847): stored Kbely AB	
			European Sport Aviation	94
			Carroll C. Hemming: US reg. candidate	30.6.94
		N97869	Carroll C. Hemming, Edina MN	11.10.94
			reg. pending, Modesto CA	95
892849 •	L-29R		(to Czech Republic AF as 2849): stored Kbely AB	
			European Sport Aviation	94
			Carroll C. Hemming, Edina MN: candidate	7.6.94
		N98476	Charles W. Robertson, Belleville MI	14.9.94
			Floating Czech Inc, Chesterton IN	6.95
993219 •	L-29A		(to Soviet AF as 30)	
		N495D	Delta Alpha Sierra Inc, Golden CO	3.5.95
993230 •	L-29		(to Czech Republic AF as 3230)	
			European Sport Aviation	94
			ESA Inc: US reg. candidate	1.7.94
		N3624G	Thomas M. Gray, River Falls WI	14.9.94/95
993243 •	L-29A		(to Czech AF as 3243): stored Kbely AB	
			European Sport Aviation	94
		N5283Y	William R. Geipel, Deer Park WI	18.5.94
			R. G. Westphal, Eau Claire WI	9.94/95
		N39DE	R. G. Westphal, Eau Claire WI	7.95
- •	L-29		(to Czech AF as ....)	
		OK-XXA	Mira Slovak Aerobatics Inc, Santa Paula CA	.90/91
			(testflown Vodochody, Czechoslovakia .90,	
			flown at airshow Madera CA 8.91)	

c/n	Type	Reg.	History	Date
132020 •	L-39C		(to Estonian AF as ......)	
			Jerssco Ltd	
		N339DM	Warplanes Inc, South Burlington VT	6.94
			Ward Leasing Co, Jersey Shore PA	1.95
232218 •	L-39C		(to Soviet AF as 91)	
			(to Estonian AF as .....)	
		ES-YLC	Computaplane, North Weald UK: del.	20.4.95
232314 •	L-39ZO		(to Libyan AF 2314)	
			captured Ouadi Doum AB by Chad Army	22.3.87
		N4313Y	ntu: Avstar Inc, Seattle WA	5.4.91
		N162JC	Avstar Inc, Seattle WA	4.91
			Robs Lamplough, North Weald UK: del.	6.6.91
			sale rep., Zurich, Switzerland	11.91/92
		N39VC	John V. Crocker/Pegasus Aviation, Ione CA	7.92/95
232337 •	L-39ZO		(to Libyan AF 2337)	
			captured Ouadi Doum AB by Chad Army	22.3.87
		N4312X	ntu: Avstar Inc, Seattle WA	5.4.91
		N159JC	Avstar Inc, Seattle WA	4.91
			Robs Lamplough, North Weald UK: del.	7.91
			sale rep., Zurich, Switzerland	92
		N40VC	John V. Crocker/Pegasus Aviation, Ione CA	8.92
		G-OTAF	Robs Lamplough & A. J. E. Smith, North Weald	9.2.95
			(based North Weald UK 7.91/95)	
332628 •	L-39TC		Kyrghyzstan Government	
			D. M. Barnell: US reg. candidate	23.5.94
		N5835H	Dwight M. Barnell/Starfighter International, Mineral Wells TX	20.9.94
			Charles Kalko, Edison NJ	12.94/95
			N39XX	
			Charles Kalko, Edison NJ	2.95
332639 •	L-39C		Kyrghyzstan Government	
			US reg. candidate	7.93
			Musket Ltd	
			D. M. Barnell, Mineral Wells TX: candidate	23.5.94
		N94BF	International Aviation Group, Van Nuys CA	27.6.94/95
332744 •	L-39C		(to Soviet AF as 08, later 75)	
			(to Estonian AF as .....)	
		ES-YLD	Computaplane, North Weald UK: del.	23.4.95
430218 •	L-39	**N139BJ**	reg.	8.95
432826 •	L-39TC		Kyrghyzstan Government	
			D. M. Barnell: US reg. candidate	23.5.94
		N5846V	Dwight M. Barnell/Starfighter International Inc, Mineral Wells TX	20.9.94
			Fort Wayne Air Service, Fort Wayne IN	5.95
432827 •	L-39TC		Kyrghyzstan Government	
			D. M. Barnell: US reg. candidate	23.5.94
		N3958J	Dwight M. Barnell/Starfighter International Inc, Mineral Wells TX	20.9.94
			Elmo E. Hahn, Muskegon MI	3.95
432831 •	L-39TC		Kyrghyzstan Government	
			D. M. Barnell: US reg. candidate	23.5.94
		N4570B	Dwight M. Barnell/Starfighter International Inc, Mineral Wells TX	20.9.94/95
			Cambar Inc, Mineral Wells TX	5.95
32845 •	L-39TC		Kyrghyzstan Government	
			D. M. Barnell: US reg. candidate	23.5.94
		N4895B	Dwight M. Barnell/Starfighter International Inc, Mineral Wells TX	20.9.94

		N39EP (2	Esper A. Petersen, Gurnee IL	11.94/95
432846 •	L-39TC		Kyrghyzstan Government	
			D. M. Barnell: US reg. candidate	23.5.94
		N7868M	Dwight M. Barnell/Starfighter International Inc, Mineral Wells TX	20.9.94/95
			Cambar Inc, Mineral Wells TX	5.95
432849 •	L-39TC		Kyrghyzstan Government	
			D. M. Barnell: US reg. candidate	23.5.94
		N6743D	Dwight M. Barnell/Starfighter International Inc, Mineral Wells TX	20.9.94/95
			Cambar Inc, Mineral Wells TX	5.95
432929 •	L-39TC		Kyrghyzstan Government	
			D. M. Barnell: US reg. candidate	23.5.94
		N3467N	Dwight M. Barnell/Starfighter International Inc, Mineral Wells TX	20.9.94
			Southern Aircraft Leasing, Rockville MD	5.95
432934 •	L-39TC		Kyrghyzstan Government	
			D. M. Barnell: US reg. candidate	23.5.94
		N2475B	D. M. Barnell/Starfighter International Inc, Mineral Wells TX	20.9.94
			Simulation Systems Inc, Anahola HI	5.95
433105 •	L-39ZO		(to Iraq AF as 3105)	
			Letecke Opravovne Trencin Statny	
		N332BH	Air Displays International Inc, Fernandina Beach FL	14.7.93/95
433108 •	L-39ZO		(to Iraq AF as 3108)	
			Letecke Opravovne Trencin Statny	
		N303BH	Air Displays International Inc, Fernandina Beach FL	14.7.93/95
433110 •	L-39ZO		(to Iraq AF as 3110)	
			Letecke Opravovne Trencin Statny	
		N334BH	Air Displays International Inc, Fernandina Beach FL	14.7.93/95
533216 •	L-39ZO		(to Czech AF as ....)	
		OK-186	del. Prague to USA, via Prestwick	29.7.91
		N92JJ	Avstar Inc, Seattle WA	2.92/95
533520 •	L-39TC		Kyrghyzstan Government	
			D. M. Barnell: US reg. candidate	23.5.94
		N6784B	Dwight M. Barnell/Starfighter International Inc, Mineral Wells TX	20.9.94
			Michael Clarke, Prescott AZ	2.95
630742 •	L-39C		(to Czech AF as ....)	
		OK-002	VZLU	
		OK-GXA	noted La Ferte Alais, France	8.91
731003 •	L-39ZA		(to Luftwaffe as 28+03)	
		F-GOJS	flying on permit, France	.94/95
812041 •	L-39CT		(to Soviet AF as ......)	
		N39MQ	Dan McCue/Warbirds East, Somersworth NH	11.92/93
		N39LE	Lou Edmondson/Lou Air, Tierra Verda FL	7.94/95
			(id. also quoted as 132041)	
931332 •	L-39TC		Kyrghyzstan Government	
			D. M. Barnell: US reg. candidate	23.5.94
		N4679B	Dwight M. Barnell/Starfighter International Inc, Mineral Wells TX	20.9.94
			Rotorall Corp, Ann Arbor MI	3.95
931341 •	L-39TC		Kyrghyzstan Government	
			D. M. Barnell: US reg. candidate	23.5.94

c/n	Type	Serial	Reg	History	Date
			N7806J	Dwight M. Barnell/Starfighter International Inc, Mineral Wells TX	20.9.94/95
				Cambar Inc, Mineral Wells TX	5.95
931528 •	L-39TC			Kyrghyzstan Government	
				D. M. Barnell: US reg. candidate	23.5.94
			N3468V	Dwight M. Barnell/Starfighter International Inc, Mineral Wells TX	20.9.94
				Cambar Inc, Mineral Wells TX	5.95
931529 •	L-39TC			Kyrghyzstan Government	
				D. M. Barnell: US reg. candidate	23.5.94
			N5683D	D. M. Barnell/Starfighter International, Mineral Wells TX	20.9.94
				International Jets Inc, Gadsden AL	4.95
..3549 •	L-39ZO			(to Libyan AF 3549)	
				captured Ouadi Doum AB by Chad Army	22.3.87
			N4312C	ntu: Avstar Inc, Seattle WA	5.4.91
			N157JC	Avstar Inc, Seattle WA	4.91/95
				(noted at Paris-Le Bourget 8.91)	
..8021 •	L-39		**N39EP (1**	reg. res. only: struck-off USCR	10.94
..8201 •	L-39ZO			(to Libyan AF 8201)	
				captured Ouadi Doum AB by Chad Army	22.3.87
			N4312E	ntu: Avstar Inc, Seattle WA	5.4.91
			N158JC	Avstar Inc, Seattle WA	4.91/95
				Robs Lamplough, North Weald UK: del.	6.6.91
..8211 •	L-39ZO			(to Libyan AF 8211)	
				captured Ouadi Doum AB by Chad Army	22.3.87
			N43129	ntu: Avstar Inc, Seattle WA	5.4.91
			N160JC	Avstar Inc, Seattle WA	4.91/95
				(noted at Paris-Le Bourget 8.91)	
..8212 •	L-39ZO			(to Libyan AF 8212)	
				captured Ouadi Doum AB by Chad Army	22.3.87
			N4313T	ntu: Avstar Inc, Seattle WA	5.4.91
			N161JC	Avstar Inc, Seattle WA	4.91/95
				(noted at Paris-Le Bourget 8.91)	
..8229 •	L-39ZO			(to Libyan AF 8229)	
				captured Ouadi Doum AB by Chad Army	22.3.87
			N4313Z	ntu: Avstar Inc, Seattle WA	5.4.91
			N163JC	Avstar Inc, Seattle WA	4.91/95
				(noted at Paris-Le Bourget 8.91)	
- •	L-39ZO			(to Libyan as .....)	
				captured Ouadi Doum AB by Chad Army	22.3.87
			F-ZVLS	Michel Bidoux : arr Toussus-le Noble	7.91
				(noted Toussus 6.93)	
X-24 •	L-39MS		**OK-182**	Aero Vodochody	92

AVRO 698 VULCAN

c/n	Type	Serial	Reg	History	Date
- •	B Mk. 2 / K Mk. 2	**XH558**		RAF Vulcan Display Flight	.86/93
				David Walton Ltd, Bruntingthorpe: del.	23.3.93/95
			G-VLCN	C. Walton Ltd, Bruntingthorpe	6.2.95
- •	B Mk. 2	**XL426**		RAF Vulcan Display Flight	80/85
				Roy E. Jacobsen/Vulcan Memorial Flight, Southend: del.	19.12.86
			G-VJET	Vulcan Memorial Flight, Southend	7.7.87/93
				Vulcan Restoration Trust, Southend	28.7.93/95
- •	B Mk. 2	**XM575**	G-BLMC	Loughborough & Leicester Aircraft Museum, East Midlands Airport: del.	21.8.83/85
				East Midlands Aeropark Centre: displ.	87/95

Avro Vulcan

c/n	Model	Serial	Reg	Owner	Date
- •	B Mk. 2	XM655	G-VULC	Roy E. Jacobsen/Vulcan Memorial Flight, Wellesbourne Mountford: del.	11.2.84
			N655AV	ntu: Jeff Hawke/Visionair Inc, Miami FL	3.9.85
			G-VULC	Roy E. Jacobsen/Vulcan Memorial Flight, Wellesbourne Mountford	25.9.87/92
				Radar Moor Ltd, Wellesbourne Mountford	.92/93

BAC /Hunting Jet Provost/BAC Strikemaster

c/n	Model	Serial	Reg	Owner	Date
HPAL.6 61 P84/6 •	T Mk. 1		**G-AOBU**	Hunting Percival Aircraft Ltd, Luton: CofA	25.5.55/
				Shuttleworth Trust, Old Warden	4.61/90
				Loughborough University: inst. airframe, loan	.61/90
				Tim J. Manna/Kennett Aviation, Cranfield (trucked to Old Warden 1.91, stored Thatcham .91, trucked Winchester 9.91 to commence rest., arr. Cranfield 16.9.93, ff Cranfield 22.5.94)	.90/95
P.84/12 •	T Mk. 2		G-AOHD	Hunting Percival Aircraft Ltd	3.56/59
				(to RAAF as A99-001)	5.59/62
				Sydney Technical College, Ultimo NSW	.62/80
				Richard E. Hourigan, Melbourne VIC	83
				RAAF Museum, RAAF Point Cook VIC	85/95
- •	T Mk. 3 T Mk. 3A	**XM349**		Global Aviation Ltd, Binbrook	11.93/94
- •	T Mk. 3 T Mk. 3A	**XM352**		Global Aviation Ltd, Binbrook	11.93/94
				Lance Toland Associates, Griffin GA	.94
			N35378	William A. McClure, Cookeville TN	11.94/95
- •	T Mk. 3 T Mk. 3A	**XM357**		Global Aviation Ltd, Binbrook	11.93/94
				Lance Toland Assoc., Griffin GA	.94
			N27357	William A. McClure, Cookeville TN: candidate	12.7.94
- •	T Mk. 3 T Mk. 3A	**XM365**		Global Aviation Ltd, Binbrook (stored dism. Binbrook 94/95)	11.93/94
PAC/W 6327 •	T Mk. 3 T Mk. 3A	**XM370**		Global Aviation Ltd, Binbrook	11.93
			G-BVSP	T. Haysleden, Rotherham	31.8.94
				Special Scope Group, Oldham UK	1.9.95
K84-001001 •	T Mk. 3 T Mk. 3A	**XM371**		RAF Halton: inst. airframe	91/92
				Pounds Marine Shipping Ltd	
			N4427Q	Barry Simpson Aircraft Sales, Fountain CO	10.92
				Charles B. Simpson, Colorado Springs CO (id. also quoted as PAC/W/6328)	4.93/95
PAC/W 6601 •	T Mk. 3 T Mk. 3A	**XM374**	**N374XM**	Fred Flaquer, Rifle CO	11.4.95
PAC/W 6603 •	T Mk. 3 T Mk. 3A	**XM376**		Global Aviation Ltd, Binbrook	11.93/95
			G-BWDR	Global Aviation Ltd, Binbrook	6.6.95
PAC/W 6605 •	T Mk. 3 T Mk. 3A	**XM378**		Global Aviation Ltd, Binbrook	11.93/95
				Lance Toland Associates, Griffin GA	.95
PAC/W 6614 •	T Mk. 3 T Mk. 3A	**XM387**		Global Aviation Ltd, Binbrook	11.93/94
				Biggles Air Inc, New Castle CO	.94/95
			N387TW	Iowa Birds of Pray Inc	19.7.95
K84-03/ •	T Mk. 3 T Mk. 3A	**XM405**	**G-TORE**	Butane Buzzard Aviation, North Weald	14.6.91/95 6523/4
- •	T Mk. 3 T Mk. 3A	**XM412**		Global Aviation Ltd, Binbrook	11.93/95
				Lance Toland Associates, Griffin GA	.95
- •	T Mk. 3 T Mk. 3A	**XM424**		Global Aviation Ltd, Binbrook UK	11.93/95
			G-BWDS	Global Aviation Ltd, Binbrook (c/n quoted as 932)	12.6.95

- •	T Mk. 3 T Mk. 3A	**XM455**		Global Aviation Ltd, Binbrook (stored Binbrook 95)	11.93/95
K84-03 6579/2 •	T Mk. 3 T Mk. 3A	**XM459**		Global Aviation Ltd, Binbrook (stored Binbrook 95)	11.93/95
K84-03/ 6579/4 •	T Mk. 3 T Mk. 3A	**XM461**	 **N6204H**	RAF Linton-on-Ouse: sold at RAF auction Magnificent Obsessions Ltd, Grimsby UK Lance Toland Associates, Griffin GA Pike Aviation Inc, Troy AL: USCR Paul Hunt, Senoia GA (rep. actually XN461: rep. XN461/XM461 swapped ids. during RAF service)	10.91 9.92 2.93/95 2.6.93/94
- •	T Mk. 3 T Mk. 3A	**XM466**	 **N7075U**	RAF Linton-on-Ouse: operational Magnificent Obsessions Ltd, Grimsby UK Lance Toland Associates, Griffin GA KW Plastics Inc, Troy AL Paul Hunt, Senoia GA/Memphis TN	92 2.6.93 2.6.93/95
- •	T Mk. 3 T Mk. 3A	**XM470**		Global Aviation Ltd, Binbrook (stored Binbrook 95)	11.93/95
- •	T Mk. 3A	**XM473**	**G-TINY**	reg. res: noted Norwich	2.95
PAC/W 9286	T Mk. 3 T Mk. 3A	**XM478**		Global Aviation Ltd, Binbrook (stored Binbrook 95)	11.93/95
PAC/W 9287 •	T Mk. 3 T Mk. 3A	**XM479**	 **G-BVEZ**	RAF Linton-on-Louse, 7141 hrs: last flew sold at RAFauction Magnificent Obsessions Ltd, Grimsby	29.1.93 8.7.93 13.10.93
PAC/W 949267 •	T Mk. 3 T Mk. 3A	**XN459**		Global Aviation Ltd, Binbrook (stored Binbrook 95)	11.93/95
PAC/W 949268 •	T Mk. 3 T Mk. 3A	**XN460**	 **N460XN**	Global Aviation Ltd, Binbrook Lance Toland Associates, Griffin GA Mark Johnson, Broomfield CO	11.93/94 21.6.94
PAC/W 949269 •	T Mk. 3 T Mk. 3A	**XN461**	 **G-BVBE**	RAF Linton-on-Ouse, 8425 hrs: last flew sold at RAF auction R. E. Todd, Doncaster (rep. actually XM461: XN461/XM461 rep. swapped ids. during RAF service)	29.1.93 8.7.93 21.7.93
PAC/W • 949278	T Mk. 3 T Mk. 3A	**XN470**		Global Aviation Ltd, Binbrook (stored Binbrook 95)	11.93/95
PAC/W 949279 •	T Mk. 3 T Mk. 3A	**XN471**	**N471XN**	Downbird UK Ltd, Stoke-on-Trent Astre Aire, Aurora CO Jet Provost Partnership, Aurora CO (rep. actually XM471: XN471/XM471 rep. swapped ids. during RAF service)	 7.93 7.7.93/95
PAC/W 10159 •	T Mk. 3 T Mk. 3A	**XN498**		Global Aviation Ltd, Binbrook (stored Binbrook 95)	11.93/95
PAC/W 10160 •	T Mk. 3 T Mk. 3A	**XN499**	 **N7075X**	Magnificent Obsessions Ltd, Grimsby UK Lance P. Toland, Griffin GA: arr. dism. KW Plastics Inc, Troy AL	 .93 2.6.93/95
PAC/W 10163 •	T Mk. 3 T Mk. 3A	**XN502**	 **N502GW**	Global Aviation Ltd, Binbrook George Wragg, Gainesville GA	11.93/94 1.95
PAC/W 11795 •	T Mk. 3 T Mk. 3A	**XN506**	**N77506**	Biggles Air Inc, New Castle CO	5.93/95
PAC/W 10799 •	T Mk. 3 T Mk. 3A	**XN510**		Global Aviation Ltd, Binbrook (stored Binbrook 95)	11.93/95

c/n	Model	Serial	Reg.	History	Date
PAC/W 11803 •	T Mk. 3 T Mk. 3A	XN548	 N4421B	RAF Halton: inst. airframe reg. Richard D. Janitell, Colorado Springs CO	91/92 9.92 4.93/95
- •	T Mk. 3 T Mk. 3A	XN552	 N68354	Global Aviation Ltd, Binbrook UK Lance Toland Assoc., Griffin GA: candidate	11.93/94 12.7.94
- •	T Mk. 3 T Mk. 3A	XN553	N57553	Biggles Air Inc, New Castle CO Cyndee One Inc, Encino CA (stored unconv., Van Nuys CA 2-5.95)	25.4.94 25.4.94/95
PAC/W 13891 •	T Mk. 3	XN606	N606RA	Rudd Aviation, Basalt CO	5.93/95
PAC/W 13893 •	T Mk. 3 T Mk. 3A	XN629	G-BVEG	Magnificent Obsessions Ltd, Grimsby Tom Moloney, North Weald: del. canopy dam. by ejection seat exit, Colchester op: Transair, North Weald	19.8.93 2.4.94 3.4.94 95
PAC/W 13901 •	T Mk. 3	XN637	G-BKOU	Sandy Topen/Vintage Aircraft Team,Cranfield (arr. Cranfield 3.85 ex storage Bushey, rest. Cranfield, flies as "XN637")	17.2.83/93
- •	T Mk. 3A	XN640	 N640XN	RAF Cosford: inst. airframe Global Aviation Ltd, Binbrook UK Plane Old PBJ Inc, Bloomfield CO	 11.93/94 21.6.94/95
- •	T Mk. 4	XP547		Global Aviation Ltd, Binbrook UK (stored Binbrook 95)	11.93/95
- •	T Mk. 4	XP567	 N8272M	RAF Halton: inst. airframe Richard J. Everett, Ipswich UK Randall K. Hames, Gaffney SC	84/86 94 9.5.95
PAC/W 17635 •	T Mk. 4 T Mk. 52A	XP666	 G-JETP	British Aircraft Corp: for conv. to T.52A (to South Arabian AF as 105) (to South Yemen AF as 105) (to Republic of Singapore AF as 355) Mike Carlton/Brencham Historic Aircraft Co/ Hunter One Collection, Hurn (shipped ex Singapore 11.83, rest. Hurn, ff .85) LGH Aviation Ltd, Hurn op. Jet Heritage/Hunter Wing, Hurn Savvas Constantinides, Paphos, Cyprus struck-off UK reg, sold to Cyrpus (dep. Hurn 27.5.93 on del. Cyprus)	30.8.67 .67 .78/80 12.83/87 1.10.87/92 19.9.92/93 11.3.93
PAC/W 17641 •	T Mk. 4	XP672	 G-RAFI	RAF Halton: inst. airframe R. MacGregor Muir, Ramsey IoM	84/92 18.12.92
- •	T Mk. 4	XR643		RAF Halton: inst. airframe International Air Parts, Sydney NSW (arr. dism. Sydney-Bankstown "8516M" 3.93)	84/92 .92/93
- •	T Mk. 4	XR653		RAF Halton: inst. airframe International Air Parts, Sydney NSW (arr. dism. Sydney-Bankstown "9035M" 3.93)	.91/92 .92/93
PAC/W 19987 •	T Mk. 4	XR674	 G-TOMG	RAF Halton: inst. airframe Rory McCarthy, North Weald Gosh That's Aviation Ltd, North Weald (del. North Weald 27.10.94, rest. to fly)	92 94 31.8.94
PAC/W 19992 •	T Mk. 4	XR679	 G-BWGT	Global Aviation Ltd, Binbrook Global Aviation Ltd, Binbrook	11.93/95 21.8.95
- •	T Mk. 4	XR701	N8272W	Randall K. Hames, Gaffney SC	9.5.95
- •	T Mk. 4	XR704		RAF Halton: inst. airframe	84/86

c/n	Type	Serial	Reg	History	Date
			N8272Y	Randall K. Hames, Gaffney SC	9.5.95
- •	T Mk. 4	XS178		RAF Cosford: inst. airframe	
				Global Aviation Ltd, Binbrook UK	11.93/94
				Project Jet Provost, Devenport TAS	.94
				(shipped, arr. dism. Devenport 5.94)	
			VH-JPP	F. Ray Edington, Launceston TAS	13.2.95
				(rest. Devenport TAS, ff 3.6.95)	
				(c/n quoted as "PAC/W/281663")	
- •	T Mk. 4	XS210		RAF Halton: inst. airframe	74/92
				International Air Parts, Sydney NSW: dism.	.93/95
				(arr. dism. Sydney-Bankstown "8239M" 3.93)	
PAC/W 23896 •	T Mk. 4	XS219		RAF Cosford: inst. airframe	4.89/92
				Global Aviation Ltd, Binbrook UK	94
			N219JP	Biggles Air Inc, New Castle CO	27.5.94/95
PAC/W 23905 •	T Mk. 4 T Mk. 52A	XS228		British Aircraft Corp: for conv. to T.52A	18.1.67
				(to South Arabian AF as 104) : del.	16.10.67
				(to South Yemen AF as 104)	
				(to Republic of Singapore AF as 352): BOC	2.75/81
				wfu, last flight Singapore: stored	14.10.81
			G-PROV	Mike Carlton/Brencham Historic Aircraft Co/	
				Hunter One Collection, Hurn	12.83/87
				(shipped ex Singapore 11.83, ff Hurn 23.11.84)	
				LGH Aviation Ltd, Hurn	1.10.87/93
				op. Jet Heritage/Hunter Wing, Hurn	
				Rory McCarthy, North Weald: del ex Hurn	12.3.93/95
PAC/W 23907 •	T Mk. 4 T Mk. 5	XS230		prototype T Mk.5: ff Warton	28.2.67
				sold at RAF auction	26.11.94
			G-BVWF	Transair (UK) Ltd, North Weald	7.12.94/95
				(del. to North Weald 21.12.94)	
				op: Transair Pilot Shop, North Weald	95
BAC/ 166 •	T Mk. 4 T Mk. 5	XS231	G-ATAJ	British Aircraft Corporation, Preston: ff	16.3.65
				(to prototype BAC.166, ff 7.67)	
				(to RAF as Strikemaster XS231)	
				stored dism. Bruntingthorpe	94/95
EEP/JP/ 951 •	T Mk. 5 T Mk. 5A	XW287		Global Aviation Ltd, Binbrook UK	11.93
				Lance P. Toland Associates, Griffin GA	94
			N4107K	Ted Thomas, Birmingham AL	12.7.94
				Truman A. Thomas, Cropwell AL	11.94/95
			N900SA	Truman A. Thomas, Cropwell AL	8.95
EEP/JP/ 953 •	T Mk. 5 T Mk. 5A	XW289	G-BVXT	Global Aviation Ltd, Binbrook	18.1.95
			G-JPVA	Tim J. Manna/Kennett Aviation, Cranfield	22.2.95
				(del. Cranfield ex Binbrook 18.2.95)	
EEP/JP/ 955 •	T Mk. 5 T Mk. 5A	XW291		Global Aviation Ltd, Binbrook	18.1.95
EEP/JP/ 957 •	T Mk. 5	XW293	G-BWCS	C. P.Allen/Downbird UK Ltd, Stoke-on-Trent	28.4.95
				(del. RAF Shawbury to Tatenhill 24.5.95)	
EEP/JP/ 959 •	T Mk. 5 T Mk. 5A	XW295		International Air Parts, Sydney NSW: dism.	.92/95
				(arr. dism. Sydney-Bankstown "XW295/29" 6.93)	
EEP/JP/ 960 •	T Mk. 5 T Mk. 5A	XW296		Global Aviation Ltd, Binbrook UK	11.93
				Lance P. Toland Associates, Griffin GA	94
			N4107G	Rudy Beaver, Gadsen AL: reg. candidate	12.7.94
EEP/JP/ 966 •	T Mk. 5 T Mk. 5A	XW302		Global Aviation Ltd, Binbrook	11.93/95
				Lance P. Toland Associates, Griffin GA	.95
EEP/JP/ 969 •	T Mk. 5 T Mk. 5A	XW305		Global Aviation Ltd, Binbrook	11.93
EEP/JP 971 •	T Mk. 5 T Mk. 5A	XW307		Global Aviation Ltd, Binbrook UK	11.93
				Lance P. Toland Associates, Griffin GA	94

			N4107U	Jon Galt Bowman, Seattle WA	12.7.94/95
EEP/JP 974 •	T Mk. 5A	XW310		sold RAF auction, ex storage RAF Shawbury	8.7.93
			G-BWGS	J. S. Everett, Ipswich	18.8.95
EEP/JP 977 •	T Mk. 5A	XW313		RAF Linton-on-Ouse: storage	93
				Global Aviation Ltd, Binbrook	11.93
			G-BVTB	Global Aviation Ltd, Binbrook	7.9.94/95
				Dick J. Everett, Ipswitch	.95
			N313RH	Randall K. Hames, Gaffney SC	6.95
				(dism. Ipswich 6.95 for shipping to USA)	
EEP/JP/ 980 •	T Mk. 3A T Mk. 5A	XW316		sold RAF auction, ex storage RAF Cranwell	.93
				Downbird UK Ltd, Stoke-on-Trent	.93
			N316HC	Astre Aire, Aurora CO	7.7.93
				Quando Inc, Scottsdale AZ	7.93/95
EEP/JP/ 983 •	T Mk. 5 T Mk. 5A	XW319		Global Aviation Ltd, Binbrook UK	11.93
				Lance P. Toland Associates, Griffin GA	94
			N8087V	reg. res.	3.95
EEP/JP/ 986 •	T Mk. 5 T Mk. 5A	XW322		RAF Shawbury: wfu, stored	
				Global Aviation Ltd, Binbrook UK	11.93/94
				Lance Toland Associates, Griffin GA	.94
				(shipped ex Binbrook .94)	
			N8086U	Impex Aero Ltd, Wilmington DE	8.3.95
EEP/JP/ 989 •	T Mk. 5 T Mk. 5A	XW325		Global Aviation Ltd, Binbrook	11.93/95
			G-BWGF	Global Aviation Ltd, Binbrook	10.8.95
EEP/JP/ 990 •	T Mk. 5 T Mk. 5A	XW326		retired RAF Shawbury, 4586 hrs: last flew	10.88
				sold RAF auction, ex storage RAF Shawbury	8.7.93
				dism. Ipswich UK, rep. for shipping to USA	6.95
EEP/JP/ 996 •	T Mk. 5 T Mk. 5A	XW332		sold RAF auction, ex storage RAF Cranwell	.93
				Downbird UK Ltd, Stoke-on-Trent	.93
				Astre Aire, Aurora CO	7.93
			N332RC	Grand Touring Cars Inc,Scottsdale AZ	12.7.93/95
EEP/JP/ 997 •	T Mk. 5 T Mk. 5A	XW333		RAF Shawbury: wfu, stored	93
				Global Aviation Ltd, Binbrook	11.93
			G-BVTC	Global Aviation Ltd, Binbrook	7.9.94/95
EEP/JP/ 998 •	T Mk.5 T Mk. 5A	XW334		sold RAF auction, ex storage RAF Cranwell	.93
				Downbird UK Ltd, Stoke-on-Trent	.93
				Denver Aerospace Museum, Aurora CO	93
				Astre Aire, Aurora CO	7.93
			N334XW	C. Allen/Grand Touring Cars	12.7.93
				Reed L. Dalton, Aurora CO	5.95
EEP/JP/ 1000 •	T Mk. 5 T Mk. 5A	XW336		RAF Shawbury: wfu, stored	
				Global Aviation Ltd, Binbrook UK	11.93
				Lance P. Toland Associates, Griffin GA	94
			N8089U	Impex Aero Ltd, Wilmington DE	8.3.95
EEP/JP/ 1004 •	T Mk. 5 T Mk. 5A	XW354		Global Aviation Ltd, Binbrook UK	11.93
				(trucked ex RAF Shawbury: shipped to USA .93)	
			N300LT	Lance P. Toland, Griffin GA	14.2.94
				(noted dism. Griffin GA 3.94)	
				Wiley Sanders, Troy AL	94
				Kenneth N. Campbell/KW Plastics, Troy AL	4.94/95
EEP/JP/ 1005 •	T Mk. 5 T Mk. 5A	XW355		retired RAF Shawbury, 6353 hrs: last flew	10.88
				sold RAF auction, ex storage RAF Shawbury	8.7.93
				Downbird UK Ltd, Tatenhill	95
EEP/JP/ 1007 •	T Mk. 5 T Mk. 5A	XW357		International Air Parts, Sydney NSW	.92/93
				(arr. dism. Sydney-Bankstown "XW357/5" 3.93)	
EEP/JP/	T Mk. 5	XW359		Global Aviation Ltd, Binbrook UK	11.93

C/n	Type	Serial	Reg	History	Date
1009 •	T Mk. 5A			(trucked ex RAF Shawbury: shipped to USA .93)	
			N400LT	Lance P. Toland, Griffin GA	14.2.94
				(noted dism. Griffin GA 3.94)	
				Wiley Sanders, Troy AL	94
				Kenneth N. Campbell/KW Plastics, Troy AL	4.94/95
EEP/JP/ 1012 •	T Mk. 5 T Mk. 5A	XW362		International Air Parts, Sydney NSW: dism.	.92/95
				(arr. dism. Sydney-Bankstown "XW362/17" 3.93)	
EEP/JP/ 1018 •	T Mk. 5 T Mk. 5A	XW368		Global Aviation Ltd, Binbrook UK	11.93
				(trucked ex RAF Shawbury: shipped to USA .93)	
			N600LT	Lance P. Toland, Griffin GA	14.2.94
				Wiley Sanders, Troy AL	94
				Robert Delvalle, Brooksville FL	.94
				ISRMS, Land-o-Lakes FL	27.5.94/95
			N183HJ	rereg. res: ISRMS, Land-o-Lakes FL	1.8.94
EEP/JP/ 1019 •	T Mk. 5 T Mk. 5A	XW369		Global Aviation Ltd, Binbrook UK	11.93
				(trucked ex RAF Shawbury: shipped to USA .93)	
			N800LT	Lance P. Toland, Griffin GA	14.2.94
				(assembled Griffin GA, ff .94)	
				David Weininger, Santa Fe NM	6.95
EEP/JP/ •	T Mk. 5 T Mk. 5A	XW372		Global Aviation Ltd, Binbrook UK	11.93/95 1022
				(stored Binbrook 95)	
EEP/JP/ 1023 •	T Mk. 5 T Mk. 5A	XW373		sold RAF auction, ex storage RAF Cranwell	.93
				Downbird UK Ltd, Stoke-on-Trent	.93
			N373XW	C. Allen/Grand Touring Cars	7.7.93
				Astre Aire, Aurora CO	7.93
				Jet Provost Partnership, Aurora CO	9.8.93
				Astre Aire, Aurora CO	5.95
EEP/JP/ 1024 •	T Mk. 5 T Mk. 5A	XW374		International Air Parts, Sydney NSW	.92/95
				(arr. dism. Sydney-Bankstown 3.93)	
				stored assembled "XW374/38" 93/95)	
EEP/JP/ 1028 •	T Mk. 5 T Mk. 5A	XW406		Denver Aerospace Museum, Aurora CO	5.91/93
EEP/JP/ 1030 •	T Mk. 5 T Mk. 5A	XW408		International Air Parts, Sydney NSW: dism.	.92/95
				(arr. dism. Sydney-Bankstown "XW408/24" 3.93)	
EEP/JP/ 1034 •	T Mk. 5A	XW412		RAF Shawbury: wfu, stored	
				Global Aviation Ltd, Binbrook UK	11.93
				Lance P. Toland Associates, Griffin GA	94
			N8088V	Impex Aero Ltd, Wilmington DE	8.3.95
EEP/JP/ 1037 •	T Mk. 5A	XW415		Global Aviation Ltd, Binbrook UK	11.93
				(trucked ex RAF Shawbury: shipped to USA .93)	
			N900LT	Lance P. Toland, Griffin GA	14.2.94
				Pike Aviation, Troy Al	4.94/95
EEP/JP/ 1044 •	T Mk. 5A	XW422		Global Aviation Ltd, Binbrook UK	11.93/95
			G-BWEB	James S. Everett, Aylesbury	19.6.95
EEP/JP/ 1050 •	T Mk. 5A	XW428	N4311M	Randall K. Hames, Cliffside NC	12.94/95
EEP/JP/ 1051 •	T Mk. 5A	XW429		Global Aviation Ltd, Binbrook UK	11.93
EEP/JP/ 1053 •	T Mk. 5 T Mk. 5A T Mk. 5B	XW431		RAF Shawbury: stored	3.93/95
			G-BWBS	C. P.Allen/Downbird UK Ltd, Tatenhill	13.4.95
				(del. RAF Shawbury to Tatenhill 25.5.95)	
EEP/JP/ 1055 •	T Mk. 5A	XW433		Global Aviation Ltd, Binbrook UK	11.93/94
			G-JPRO	Ruddington Aviation Ltd, Edwalton	10.8.95
EEP/JP/ 1057 •	T Mk. 5 T Mk. 5A	XW435		International Air Parts, Sydney NSW:, dism.	.92/95
				(arr. dism. Sydney-Bankstown "XW435/4" 6.93)	

EEP/JP/ 1059 •	T Mk. 5 T Mk. 5A T Mk. 5B	**XW437**		RAF Shawbury: wfu, stored Global Aviation Ltd, Binbrook UK Lance P. Toland Associates, Griffin GA	 11.93 94
			N80873	Impex Aero Ltd, Wilmington DE	8.3.95
- •	T Mk. 4 T Mk. 52			(to Republic of Singapore AF as 350) International Air Parts, Sydney NSW: dism. (arr dism. Sydney-Bankstown NSW 7.92)	 .92/95
- •	T Mk. 4 T Mk.52			(to Republic of Singapore AF as 354) International Air Parts, Sydney NSW: dism. (arr dism. Sydney-Bankstown NSW 7.92)	 .92/93
- •	T Mk. 4 T Mk. 52			(to Republic of Singapore AF as 356) International Air Parts, Sydney NSW (arr. dism. Sydney-Bankstown NSW 7.92) Project Jet Provost, Devenport TAS (rest. to fly, Devenport TAS .92/94)	 .92 .92/95
EEP/JP/ 165 •	Mk. 81		G-AXEF	British Aircraft Corporation, Preston (to South Yemen AF as 503): del. (to Republic of Singapore AF as 322) International Air Parts, Sydney NSW Wally Fisk/Amjet Aircraft Corp, St Paul MN	24.4.69 7.69/76 .76/88 .88 90/92
			N167SM	Wally Fisk/Amclyde Engineered Products Inc, St Paul-Anoka County MN (rest., CofA 2.2.94, flies as "Kenya AF 322")	21.7.93/95
EEP/JP/ 168 •	Mk. 81		G-AXFX	British Aircraft Corporation, Preston (to South Yemen AF as 504): del. (to Republic of Singapore AF as 323) International Air Parts, Sydney NSW Wally Fisk/Amjet Aircraft Corp, St Paul MN	21.5.69 7.69/76 .76/88 .88 90/92
			N21419	Amclyde Engineered Products Inc, St Paul MN	6.12.93/95
EEP/JP 404 •	Mk. 82			(to Oman AF as 402) (to Republic of Singapore AF as 327): del. International Air Parts, Sydney NSW Wally Fisk/Amjet Aircraft Corp, St Paul MN	1.69/77 27.2.77/88 .88 90/92
			N2143J	Amclyde Engineered Products Inc, St Paul MN	6.12.93/95
EEP/JP 406 •	Mk. 82			(to Oman AF as 404) (to Republic of Singapore AF as 328): del. International Air Parts, Sydney NSW Wally Fisk/Amjet Aircraft Corp, St Paul MN	3.69/77 27.2.77/88 .88 90/92
			N21444	Amclyde Engineered Products Inc, St Paul MN	6.12.93/95
EEP/JP 949 •	Mk. 82			(to Oman AF as 407) (to Republic of Singapore AF as 329): del. International Air Parts, Sydney NSW Wally Fisk/Amjet Aircraft Corp, St Paul MN (noted Chandler Memorial AZ "329" 10.91/93)	6.69/77 27.2.77/88 .88 90/92
			N167X	David J. Lofstrom, Chandler AZ Strikemaster Corp, Dover DE	29.4.93 5.94/95
EEP/JP/ 1924 •	Mk. 84			(to Republic of Singapore AF as 304): del. International Air Parts, Sydney NSW Wally Fisk/Amjet Aircraft Corp, St Paul MN	10.69/89 .88 90/92
			N2145V	Amclyde Engineered Products Inc, St Paul MN Hancock Mechanical Services, Louisville KY	6.12.93/94 4.95
EEP/JP/ 1925 •	Mk. 84			(to Republic of Singapore AF as 305): del. International Air Parts, Sydney NSW Wally Fisk/Amjet Aircraft Corp, St Paul MN	10.69/89 .88 90/92
			N21451	Amclyde Engineered Products Inc, St Paul MN	6.12.93/95
EEP/JP/ 1928 •	Mk. 84			(to Republic of Singapore AF as 308): del. International Air Parts, Sydney NSW Wally Fisk/Amjet Aircraft Corp, St Paul MN	19.3.70/89 .88 90/92
			N2146G	Amclyde Engineered Products Inc, St Paul MN	6.12.93/95

EEP/JP 1930 •	Mk. 84		(to Republic of Singapore AF as 310): del.	5.70/89
			International Air Parts, Sydney NSW	.88
			Wally Fisk/Amjet Aircraft Corp, St Paul MN	90/92
		N2146J	Amclyde Engineered Products Inc, St Paul MN	6.12.93/95
EEP/JP/ 1931 •	Mk. 84		(to Republic of Singapore AF as 311): del.	5.70/89
			International Air Parts, Sydney NSW	.88
			Wally Fisk/Amjet Aircraft Corp, St Paul MN	90/92
		N2146S	Amclyde Engineered Products Inc, St Paul MN	6.12.93/94
		G-SARK	Sark International Airways, Bournemouth	13.1.95
			(arr. dism. Biggin Hill 11.94)	
EEP/JP/ 1932 •	Mk. 84		(to Republic of Singapore AF as 312): del.	13.7.70/89
			International Air Parts, Sydney NSW	.88
			Wally Fisk/Amjet Aircraft Corp, St Paul MN	90/92
		N167BC	reg.	7.95
EEP/JP/ 1934 •	Mk. 84	G-AYHS	British Aircraft Corporation, Preston	22.7.70
			(demonstrator Farnborough Air Show 9.70)	
			(to Republic of Singapore AF as 314): del.	28.9.70/89
			International Air Parts, Sydney NSW	.88
			Wally Fisk/Amjet Aircraft Corp, St Paul MN	90/92
		N21463	Amclyde Engineered Products Inc, St Paul MN	6.12.93/95
EEP/JP/ 1935 •	Mk. 84	G-AYHT	British Aircraft Corporation, Preston	22.7.70
			(demonstrator Farnborough Air Show 9.70)	
			(to Republic of Singapore AF as 315): del.	9.10.70/89
			Steve Ferris/International Air Parts, Sydney NSW	.88/92
		VH-AKY	Steve Ferris, Sydney-Bankstown NSW	7.10.92/95
			(rest. Bankstown, ff 10.10.92 as "RSAF 315")	
			dam. wheels-up landing, Bankstown (repaired)	26.1.95
EEP/JP 1942 •	Mk. 82		(to Oman AF as 408)	12.69/77
			(to Republic of Singapore AF as 330): del.	27.2.77/88
			International Air Parts, Sydney NSW	.88
			Wally Fisk/Amjet Aircraft Corp, St Paul MN	90/92
		N2147S	Amclyde Engineered Products Inc, St Paul MN	6.12.93/95
EEP/JP 1943 •	Mk. 82		(to Oman AF as 409)	12.69
			(to Republic of Singapore AF as 331): del.	27.2.77/88
			International Air Parts, Sydney NSW	.88
			Wally Fisk/Amjet Aircraft Corp, St Paul MN	90/92
		N331MM	Michael T. McComsley, Monrovia CA	12.7.93/95
68 (PS174)	Mk. 83	G-AYVK	British Aircraft Corporation, Warton	5.4.71
			(to Kuwaiti AF as 120): del.	2.7.71
			ret. to UK, stored Samlesbury	7.10.86
69 PS175)	Mk. 83	G-AYVL	British Aircraft Corporation, Warton	5.4.71 (
			(to Kuwaiti AF as 121): del.	2.7.71
			ret. to UK, stored Samlesbury	7.10.86
70 (PS164)	Mk. 87	G-AYHR	British Aircraft Corporation, Warton	22.7.70
			(to Kenyan AF as KAF.601): del.	10.1.71
301 •	Mk. 88		(to RNZAF as NZ6361)	73/93
			International Air Parts, Sydney NSW	6.93
			(arr. dism. Bankstown 7.7.93, stored 7.93/94)	
		VH-ZEP	D. G. Smith/International Air Parts, Sydney	9.6.95
			(rest. to fly, Sydney-Bankstown .95)	
EEP/JP 3234 • **(302)**	Mk. 88		(to RNZAF as NZ6362)	73/93
			International Air Parts, Sydney NSW	6.93
			(arr. Bankstown dism. 8.7.93 ex NZ)	
		VH-AGI	International Air Parts, Sydney-Bankstown	9.9.93/94
			Neville Hyder, Busselton WA	3.94/95
			(rest. Bankstown, ff 28.5.94 as "NZ6362")	
303 •	Mk. 88	G-AZXJ	British Aircraft Corporation, Warton	28.6.72
			(to RNZAF as NZ6363)	10.7.72/93
			International Air Parts, Sydney NSW	6.93/95

Flying Jets is a serious business -
we are serious about our business!

Your Jet Warbird Headquarters

				(noted stored dism. Bankstown 8.93/95)	
EEP/JP/ 3236 • (304)	Mk. 88		G-AZXK	British Aircraft Corporation, Warton	28.6.72
				(to RNZAF as NZ6364)	12.9.72/93
				International Air Parts, Sydney NSW	6.93
				(arr. Bankstown dism. 7.7.93 ex NZ; repacked 23.9.93 for shipping to USA)	
			N6364Z	Falcon Helicopters, Lees Summit MO	8.2.95
305	Mk. 88		G-AZYN	British Aircraft Corporation, Warton	13.7.72
				(to RNZAF as NZ6365)	9.72
310 •	Mk. 88			(to RNZAF as NZ6370)	73/93
				International Air Parts, Sydney NSW	6.93
				(arr. dism. Bankstown 8.7.93, stored 7.93/94)	
			VH-RBA	reg. res: being rest. Sydney-Bankstown	95
311	Mk. 89		G-AZXL	British Aircraft Corporation, Warton	28.6.72
				(to FA Ecuadoriana as T-243)	10.7.72
				crashed, written-off	14.10.81
323	Mk. 82A		**G-BAWE**	British Aircraft Corporation, Warton	18.4.73
				(to Muscat & Oman AF as 417): del.	8.6.73
324	Mk. 82A		**G-BAWF**	British Aircraft Corporation, Warton	18.4.73
				(to Muscat & Oman AF as 418): del.	8.6.73
341 •	Mk. 88			(to RNZAF as NZ6371)	73/93
				International Air Parts, Sydney NSW: dism.	6.93/95
				(arr. dism. Bankstown 7.7.93, stored 93/95)	
EEP/JP/ 3871 • (342)	Mk. 88			(to RNZAF as NZ6372)	73/93
				International Air Parts, Sydney NSW	6.93
				(arr. dism. Sydney-Bankstown 8.7.93)	
				John Pierce, Bendigo VIC	11.93/94
				(trucked Bendigo ex Bankstown 11.93 for rest.)	
			VH-LLD	John Pierce, Watchem VIC	11.94/95
PS355	Mk. 80A		G-BECI	British Aircraft Corporation, Warton	27.7.76
				(to R Saudi AF as 1124)	.76
PS364	Mk. 80		G-BESY	British Aircraft Corporation, Preston	26.4.77
				(to R Saudi AF as 1133): del.	7.7.77
PS365	Mk. 80		G-BESZ	British Aircraft Corporation, Preston	26.4.77
				(to R Saudi AF as 1134): del.	7.7.77
PS366	Mk. 80A		G-BFOO	British Aircraft Corporation, Preston	22.3.78
				(to R Saudi AF as 1135): del.	2.5.78
PS367	Mk. 8...		G-BIDB	British Aerospace, Hurn	15.9.80
				(to Sudanese AF as ....)	.80
PS368	Mk. 8...		G-BIHZ	British Aerospace, Hurn	5.2.81
				(to Sudanese AF as ....)	.81

BELL P-59 AIRACOMET

27-10 •	YP-59A	**42-108777**		CA Polytechnic Institute, San Luis Obispo CA	
				Maloney/The Air Museum, Claremont CA	3.58/60
				The Air Museum, Ontario later Chino CA	60/95
				(rest. to fly, Chino 91/94)	
				Planes of Fame, Chino CA: reg. candidate	5.92
27-17 •	XP-59A	**42-108784**		Smithsonian Institute, Washington DC	.45/58
				NASM, Silver Hill MD: stored	.58/76
				NASM, Washington DC	.76/93
				(displ. as *Miss Fire*/1)	

27-22 •	P-59A	**44-22614**		Hancock College Aeronautics, Santa Maria CA (noted Van Nuys CA, USAF "88", 3.50) Los Angeles Trade Technical School Jack P. Hardwick, El Monte CA: stored yard Ascher Ward, Van Nuys CA USAFM, Edwards AFB CA: arr dism. USAFM, March AFB CA (displ. as "422614/88")	.48/49 .60/76 .76 15.2.78 .78/95
27-41 •	P-59B	**44-22633**		derelict on target range, Edwards AFB CA USAFM, Edwards AFB CA (displ. on pedestal as XP-59 *Reluctant Robot*, later rest. and displ. as "422633")	 69/94
27-58 •	P-59B	**44-22650**		Kirtland AFB NM: displ. USAFM, Wright-Patterson AFB, Dayton OH (airfreighted Kirtland-WP by C124 .56)	50/56 2.56/92
27-64 •	P-59B	**44-22656**		(to USN as Bu64108) Purdue University: instrument tests Harold Warp Pioneer Village, Minden NE	 65/94

Blackburn/HSA Buccaneer

- •	S. 2B	**XX894**		RAF St Athan: arr. for storage Vintage Aircraft Team, Bruntingthorpe (arr. Bruntingthorpe 29.10.94, maintained to taxiing standard 95)	7.4.94 10.94/95
- •	S. 2B	**XX897**	 G-BUCC	Defence Research Agency, RAF Bedford (fitted with Tornado nose): sold at auction Source Classic Jet Flight, Hurn: reg. res. (del. Bedford-Hurn 19.8.93)	93 8.7.93 8.7.93

Canadair CL-41 Tutor/Tebuan

-	CL-41R		CF-LTV-X	Canadair Ltd, Montreal QUE: prototype	
1	CL-41R		CF-LTW	Canadair Ltd, Montreal QUE	63/66
2	CL-41R		CF-LTX-X	Canadair Ltd, Montreal QUE (testflown with CF-104 nose) Aero Composites Canada, Bradford ONT (rest. to fly, Bradford ONT 95 : F-104 nose)	65/66 95
1072	CL-41A	**CAF114072**	C-GVQX	Canadair Ltd, Montreal QUE (Challenger chase plane, based Mojave CA) struck-off reg.	81/83 11.83
2201 •	CL-41G		 N21527 **N401AG**	(to R Malaysian AF as FM2208, M22-08) Avstar Inc, Seattle WA (noted dism. ex shipping, Arlington WA 4.90) Aero Flight Services, Ypsilanti MI (op as "Aero Group Jet Team") ATLO Inc, Dover DE	 12.89/90 1.91/92 5.95
2202 •	CL-41G		 N2153R **N402AG**	(to R Malaysian AF as FM2209, M22-09) Avstar Inc, Seattle WA (noted dism. ex shipping, Arlington WA 4.90) Aero Flight Services, Ypsilanti MI ALT Inc, Derry NH Aero Flight Services, Ypsilanti MI (op. as "Aero Group Jet Team")	 12.89/90 1.91/92 92 27.4.92/95
2205 •	CL-41G		 N2153V **N403AG**	(to R Malaysian AF as FM2211, M22-11) Avstar Inc, Seattle WA (noted dism. ex shipping, Arlington WA 4.90) Aero Flight Services, Ypsilanti MI ALT Inc, Derry NH	 12.89/90 91/92 11.5.92/95
-	CL-41A		CF-OUM	noted in UK - Canada air race, Abingdon UK	71

c/n	Type	Serial	Reg.	History	Date
40026 •	T-37B	**55-4312**		disposal by US Government Surplus Agency	.77
	A-37A	**67-14510**	**N91RW**	Lone Star Flight Museum, Galveston TX	6.92/95
				(rest. Phoenix AZ, ff .94 as "USAF 14510/EK")	
40046 •	T-37B	**56-3474**			
	A-37A	**67-14528**	**N128RA**	Condor Corp, Milwaukee WI	29.8.89/95
40051 •	T-37B	**56-3479**			
	A-37A	**67-14532**	**N132RA**	Condor Corp, Milwaukee WI	29.8.89/95
40053	T-37B	**56-3480**		(to FA Panamena as ....)	
				recov. ex Panama by David Brady	c85
			N120DB	David Brady, Cartersville GA	8.87/91
				(flew as "USAF 63480/Georgia Tweet")	
				crashed after mid-air collision with A-26,	
				near Cartersville GA (David Brady k.)	7.6.91
40054 •	T-37B	**56-3481**			
	A-37A	**67-14533**	**N133RA**	Condor Corp, Milwaukee WI	29.8.89/95
40055 •	T-37B	**56-3482**			
	A-37A	**67-14534**	N134RA	Condor Corp, Milwaukee WI	29.8.89/91
			N534RW	Lone Star Flight Museum, Galveston TX	91/95
				(reg. res: rest. to fly 94/95)	
40056 •	T-37B	**56-3483**	**N3757U**	Thunderbird Aviation Inc, Deer Valley AZ	14.4.80/95
	A-37A	**67-14535**			
40057 •	T-37B	**56-3484**			
	A-37A	**67-14536**	**N136RA**	Condor Corp, Milwaukee WI	29.8.89/95
40059 •	T-37B	**56-3486**	**N3757Z**	Thunderbird Aviation Inc, Deer Valley AZ	14.4.80/91
	A-37A	**67-14537**		struck-off USCR	21.3.91
40060 •	T-37B	**56-3487**			
	A-37A	**67-14538**	**N138RA**	Condor Corp, Milwaukee WI	29.8.89/95
40087 •	T-37B	**56-3515**		(to FA Peru as ....)	
			N7154Y	Air Acres Museum, Cartersville GA	13.9.90/94
				(FAP446, 458, 492, 494 at Cartersville 12.90)	
				Reva J. Brady, Cartersville GA	3.92/95
40152 •	T-37B	**56-3580**		(to FA Peru as ....)	
			N6528G	Air Acres Museum, Cartersville GA (displ.)	13.9.90/94
				Reva J. Brady, Cartersville GA	3.92/95
-	T-37B	**60-0084**	**N807NA**	NASA, NAS Moffett Field CA	81
40974 •	T-37C	**66-13618**		(to FA Peru as ....)	
			N7154W	Air Acres Museum, Cartersville GA (displ.)	13.9.90/94
				Reva J. Brady, Cartersville GA	3.92
				sale rep., Huntington Beach CA: USCR	95
40976 •	T-37C	**66-13620**		(to FA Peru as ....)	
			N6527M	Air Acres Museum, Cartersville GA (displ.)	13.9.90/94
				Reva J. Brady, Cartersville GA	3.92/95
41049 •	T-37C	-	N7081C	del. reg. to FAB: built	22.7.68
				(to FA Brasileira as 0897)	.68
				Museu Aerospacial, Campo dos Afonsos	.91
				Stacy Prineas, Redmond OR	.91
				(shipped to US via Honduras, offered at auction,	
				dism. unconv., Santa Monica CA 10.91)	
			N7081C	Edward H. Wachs, Harrison MT	10.91/95
				(stored Ennis-Big Sky Airpark MT, pending rest. 92)	
41061	T-37C	-	N7091C	Cessna Aircraft, Wichita KS	
				(to FA Brasileira as 0901)	
			N5435M	reg. res. (but written-off in FAB service)	.79

c/n	Type	Serial	Reg	History	Date
41221 •	T-37C	-	N5431M	Cessna Aircraft, Wichita KS	
				(to FA Brasileira as 0931)	
				to FAB instructional airframe	
				Museu Aerospacial, Campo dos Afonsos	91
			N3127M	Edward H. Wachs, Harrison MT	10.91/95
				(stored dism., Ennis MT 92)	
43019 •	A-37B	**67-14794**		(to SVNAF as 67-14794)	
				(captured by NVNAF as ....)	
				Noel R. Vinson/Australian Aviation Facilities,	
				Sydney-Bankstown Airport NSW: stored	.89/94
43035 •	A-37B	**67-14810**		(to SVNAF as 67-14810)	
				(captured by NVNAF as ....)	
				(recov. by Australia Vietnam Holdings Pty Ltd:	
				shipped to Darwin ex Saigon 11.92)	
				Guido Zuccoli, Darwin NT	.92/95
				(rest. to fly, Darwin 92/93)	
43068 •	A-37A	**68-7921**		(to SVNAF as 68-7921)	
				(captured by NVNAF as ....)	
				Col Pay, Scone NSW	.89
				(recov. from Bien Hoa AB, Saigon, Vietnam:	
				shipped to Australia, arr. Sydney 11.89)	
				Noel R. Vinson/Australian Aviation Facilities,	
				Bankstown Airport, Sydney NSW: stored	.89/94
43130 •	A-37B	**68-10779**		(to SVNAF as 68-10779)	
				(captured by NVNAF as ....)	
				(recov. by Australia Vietnam Holdings Pty Ltd:	
				shipped to Sydney ex Saigon 2.93)	
				Michael Silva, Sydney NSW	.93/94
			VH-XVA	Michael Silva/North Western Aviation Service,	
				Sydney NSW	15.6.94/95
				(rest. Sydney-Bankstown, ff 9.6.94)	
43156 •	A-37B	**68-10805**		(to SVNAF as 68-10805)	
				(captured by NVNAF as ....)	
				(recov. from Bien Hoa AB, Vietnam by Col Pay,	
				Scone NSW : arr. Sydney by ship 11.89)	
				David Lowy, Sydney NSW	.89/92
			VH-DLO	David Lowy/DL Aviation, Sydney NSW	29.4.92/95
				(rest. Scone NSW, ff 1.5.92)	
43158 •	A-37B	**68-10807**		(to SVNAF as 68-10807)	
				(captured by NVNAF as ....)	
				Col Pay, Scone NSW	.89
				(recov. ex Bien Hoa AB, Saigon, Vietnam:	
				shipped to Australia, arr. Sydney11.89)	
				Hugh Farris,Ivanhoe Station, Wee Waa NSW	90/95
				(arr."Ivanhoe 3.91 ex Scone: rest. project)	
43226 •	A-37A	**69-6381**		(to SVNAF as 69-6381)	
				(captured by NVNAF as ....)	
				Col Pay, Scone NSW	.89
				(recov. ex Bien Hoa AB, Saigon, Vietnam:	
				shipped to Australia, arr. Sydney11.89)	
				Noel R. Vinson/Australian Aviation Facilities,	
				Sydney-Bankstown Airport NSW: stored	.89/94
43255 •	A-37B	**69-6410**		(to SVNAF as 69-6410)	
				(captured by NVNAF as ....)	
				Col Pay, Scone NSW	.89
				(recov. ex Bien Hoa AB, Saigon, Vietnam:	
				shipped to Australia, arr. Sydney 10.89)	
				Noel R. Vinson/Australian Aviation Facilities,	
				Sydney-Bankstown Airport NSW: stored	.89/94
43284 •	A-37B	**69-6439**		(to SVNAF as 69-6439)	
				(captured by NVNAF as ....)	
				Col Pay/Pays Air Service, Scone NSW	.89/95

				(recov. ex Bien Hoa AB, Saigon, Vietnam:	
				shipped to Australia, arr. 10.89, rest. Scone 94)	
43311 •	A-37B	**70-1296**		(to SVNAF as 70-1296)	
				(captured by NVNAF as 256)	
			ZK-ITL	Bruce Black, Auckland NZ: reg. res.	92/95
				(rest. to fly, Auckland-Ardmore 94)	
43328 •	A-37B	**71-0790**		(to SVNAF as 71-0790)	
				(captured by NVNAF as ....)	
				M. Perrin, La Ferte-Alais, France: arr dism.	5.90
43331 •	A-37B	**71-0793**		(to SVNAF as 71-0793)	
				(captured by NVNAF as ....)	
				Col Pay/Pays Air Service, Scone NSW	.89/95
				(recov. ex Bien Hoa AB, Saigon, Vietnam:	
				shipped Australia, arr. 10.89, stored Scone 94)	
43370 •	A-37B	**71-0832**		(to SVNAF as 71-0832)	
				(captured by NVNAF as ....)	
				Noel R. Vinson/Australian Aviation Facilities,	
				Sydney-Bankstown Airport NSW: stored	.89/94
43372 •	A-37B	**71-0834**		(to SVNAF as 71-0834)	
				(captured by NVNAF as ....)	
				M. Perrin, La Ferte-Alais, France: arr dism.	5.90
43392 •	A-37B	**71-0854**		(to SVNAF as 71-0854)	
				(captured by NVNAF as 854)	
				Bruce Black, Auckland, New Zealand	.91/92
				(recov. ex open storage Bien Hoa AB, Vietnam)	
			ZK-JTL	Jet Trainers Ltd/NZ Warbirds Association,	
				Auckland-Ardmore	2.7.92/95
				(rest. Ardmore, ff 2.94 as "54")	

DeHavilland DH100/115 Vampire

EEP 42310 •	F Mk. 3	**RCAF17018**	**N6881D**	Merle C. Zuehlke/Fliteways Inc, West Bend WI	.57/58
				Dave White, Carpenteria CA	63
				William H. Boyce, Pomona CA	66
				(stored, derelict, Santa Barbara CA 66)	
				Roland G. Holmes Company, Long Beach CA	69
				Ed Maloney/The Air Museum, Chino CA: dism.	77/92
				Fighter Jets Museum, Chino CA	92/95
				(displ. in RAF sc as "018")	
EEP 42312 •	F Mk. 3	**RCAF17020**	**N6863D**	Merle C. Zuehlke/Fliteways Inc, West Bend WI	.57/58
				James Cook, Milwaukee WI	66/69
				Gateway Technical Institute, Kenosha WI	74/77
				Crosby Enterprises Inc, Milwaukee WI	
				Canadian Warplane Heritage, Hamilton ONT	81/84
				(stored dism., Hamilton ONT)	
				Reynolds Aviation Museum, Wetaskiwin ALTA	88/92
- •	F Mk. 3	**RCAF17031**	**N41J**	Stinson Field Aircraft, San Antonio TX	.56/59
				W. H. Boyce, Ramona CA	66
				Roland G Holmes, Long Beach CA	69
				(open storage, derelict, Long Beach CA 69/72)	
				Western Aerospace Museum, Lancaster CA	73
				Albert C. Hansen, Mojave CA	77/82
				Bill Lamberton/Pacific Flying Service,	
				Everett-Paine Field WA	.82/95
				(8 year rest., ff Arlington WA 12.4.91,	
				flies as "17031/SL-031")	
EEP 42376 •	F Mk. 3	**RCAF17058**	**N6860D**	Merle C. Zuehlke/Fliteways Inc, West Bend WI	4.3.58
				Dewey-Shepard Boiler Co, Peru IN	
				George D. Arnold, Peru IN	66/69
				Calgary Air Museum, Calgary ALTA : dism.	c68
				Don Campbell, Kapuskasing ONT : dism.	.70/82

				Canadian Museum of Flight & Transportation	
				Vancouver BC: arr. dism.	19.9.82/92
EEP 42380 •	F Mk. 3	**RCAF17062**	**N6885D**	Merle C. Zuehlke/Fliteways Inc, West Bend WI	.57/58
				E. H. Roybal, Livermore CA	66/69
				(noted derelict, Santa Ana CA 6.73)	
				Letcher & Associates, Lancaster CA	.73/81
				stored dism., Mojave CA	74/81
EEP 42387 •	F Mk. 3	**RCAF17069**	N6877D	Merle C. Zuehlke/Fliteways Inc, West Bend WI	.57/59
				Ken Cook Publishing Co, Milwaukee WI	60/63
			CF-RLK	Milt Harradance, Calgary ALTA	.64/65
				Centennial Planetarium, Calgary ALTA	72/88
				Calgary Air & Space Museum, Calgary ALTA	88/94
EEP 42389 •	F Mk. 3	**RCAF17071**	**N6883D**	Merle C. Zuehlke/Fliteways Inc, West Bend WI	.57/58
				E. H. Roybal, Livermore CA	66/69
				(noted derelict, Santa Ana CA 6.73)	
				Letcher & Associates, Lancaster CA	.73/77
				(stored dism., Mojave CA 74/79)	
				Flight Research Inc, State College MS	86/92
				Reynolds Aviation Museum, Wetaskiwin ALTA	92
				struck-off USCR	10.4.92
EEP 42390 •	F Mk. 3	**RCAF17072**	**N6878D**	Merle C. Zuehlke/Fliteways Inc, West Bend WI	.57/58
				John E. Morgan, Pittsburg PA	.58
				(flew as *Johny Rocket*)	
				Frank G. Tallman, Orange County CA	.59
				displ. Movieland of the Air : *Golden Eagle*	59/68
				Rosen Novak Auto Co, Omaha NE	66/68
				(sold at Tallmantz auction 29.5.68)	
				James F. Brucker, Somis CA	29.5.68/69
				Jet Craft Inc , Las Vegas NV	70
				(planned conv. to 8 passenger Mystery Jet)	
				Pete Regina, Van Nuys CA : del.	12.70/73
				(rest. Van Nuys, ff 8.4.72 as "VN68/YG")	
				Al Letcher & Associates, Lancaster CA	.73/81
				John T. Downing, Cumming GA	86
				Greater Leasing Inc, Marietta GA	12.87
				Randall K. Hames, Gaffney SC	4.88/89
				John Travolta/Atlo Inc, Studio City CA	10.89/92
				sale rep., Fort Lauderdale FL	95
V0674 •	FB Mk. 9	-		(to SAAF as 251)	
				(to R Rhodesian AF/Zimbabwe AF as R1378)	
				wfu Gwelo AB, open storage	80/88
				Hosking/Judy Pay syndicate, Melbourne VIC	.88/95
				(shipped dism., arr. Melbourne VIC 12.88)	
V0583 •	FB Mk. 9	-		(to SAAF as 216)	
				(to R Rhodesian AF/Zimbabwe AF as R1829)	
				wfu Gwelo AB, open storage	80/88
				Hosking/Judy Pay syndicate, Melbourne VIC	.88/95
				(shipped dism., arr. Melbourne VIC 12.88)	
V0252 •	FB Mk. 9	-		(to SAAF as 252)	
				(to R Rhodesian AF/Zimbabwe AF as R1832)	
				wfu Gwelo AB, open storage	80/88
				Hosking/Judy Pay syndicate, Melbourne VIC	.88/95
				(shipped dism., arr. Melbourne VIC 12.88)	
- •	FB Mk. 9	-		(to R Rhodesian AF: Zimbabwe AF as R1835)	
				wfu Gwelo AB, open storage	80/88
				Hosking/Judy Pay syndicate, Melbourne VIC	.88/95
				(shipped dism., arr. Melbourne VIC 12.88)	
V0489 •	FB Mk. 9	-		(to SAAF as 211)	
				(to R Rhodesian AF/Zimbabwe AF as R1828)	
				wfu Gwelo AB, open storage	80/88
				Hosking/Judy Pay syndicate, Melbourne VIC	.88/95
				(shipped dism., arr. Melbourne VIC 12.88)	
22100 •	FB Mk. 9	**WL505**		RAF Museum, RAF St Athan	87/89

				D. G. Jones : sold at auction	21.4.89
			G-FBIX	D. G. Jones, Bridgend, Wales	24.7.91/92
				(rest. to fly, Cranfield)	
V06725	FB Mk. 50			(to R Swedish AF as Fv28326): BOC	10.51/57
	J 28B			Nordenfeldt & Co, Stockholm, Sweden	12.57
			N2323	Interarmco USA	2.58/60
				struck-off USCR	5.60
				(to Finnish AF for parts)	.60
				Koskue Camping Ground, Finland: displ.	74
15127 •	T Mk. 11	**WZ507**		Solway Aviation Society, Carlisle Airport	76/79
				J. Turnbull, S. Topen, J. Chilling, Cranfield	.79
			G-VTII	Vintage Aircraft Team, Cranfield	
				later Bruntingthorpe	9.1.80/95
				(rest. Cranfield, ff 17.2.80; flies as "WZ507")	
15133 •	T Mk. 11	**WZ513**		(to Swiss AF as U-1238)	
	T Mk. 55			sold at auction, Dubendorf AB	23.3.91
				NFZ-Flyg AB: del. to Eskilstuna, Sweden	23.5.91
			SE-DXU	NFZ-Flyg AB, Eskilstuna	10.91/93
				Team Vampire Sweden AB, Eskilstuna	.93/95
				Eskilstuna Flygmuseum AB, Eskilstuna	.95
				(flies as "RSwAF F14-S")	
15112 •	T Mk. 11	**WZ553**		Merseyside Aviation Society, Liverpool	
				Phoenix Aviation Museum, Bruntingthorpe	84/86
				(stored dism. Loughborough, Bruntingthorpe)	
				Newark Air Museum, Newark	
				Vintage Aircraft Team, Cranfield	
			G-DHYY	Lindsay Wood Promotions Ltd, Bournemouth	17.3.95
- •	T Mk. 11	**XD538**	N70877	Laub America Corp, Carmel CA	11.77/86
				(noted Marana AZ as "N77087" 10.84)	
				Wesley D. O'Dell, Dana Point CA	8.87
				William G. Dilley/Spectra Sonics, Ogden UT	2.88/92
			N675LF	ntu: Gregory Dilley, Ogden UT	7.88
			N70877	William G. Dilley, Ogden UT	7.88/95
15621 •	T Mk. 11	**XE920**		RAF Scampton: sold at auction	3.92
				Allied Aeroplane Collection, RAF Sealand	93
				Vampire Support Team	95
				(rest. to fly Sealand 93/95: taxy trials 3.95)	
			G-VMPR	J. N. Kerr & Jacquelyn Jones, Hawarden	13.3.95
- •	T Mk. 11	**XE956**		St Albans College of Education: inst airframe	80/92
				deHavilland Aviation Ltd, Bridgend UK	.92/95
			G-OBLN	deHavilland Aviation Ltd, Bridgend UK	.92/95
15641 •	Sea Vamp.	**XG766**		(to RAN as XG766; N6-766): BOC	8.59/71
	T Mk. 22			disposal ex NAS Nowra NSW (TT1514)	16.9.71
				Chewing Gum Field Air Mus.,Tallebudgera QLD	23.3.72/87
			VH-RAN	Kim Rolph-Smith, Brisbane QLD: reg. res.	9.87/89
				Ian Aviation, Sydney-Bankstown NSW	90/94
				Paul Bredereck/Tamair, Tamworth NSW	4.94/95
				(stored Archerfield QLD 90/94, trucked to Tamworth NSW 12.4.94: rest. to fly)	
15679 •	T Mk. 11	**XH271**		(to RNZAF as NZ5709)	
			ZK-TII	G. S. Smith, Auckland: reg. res.	7.11.83/89
				(stored Auckland-Ardmore 94)	
- •	T Mk. 11	**XK623**		North Manchester College, Moston: inst. airfr.	80/84
			G-VAMP	ntu: Mike Carlton/Brencham Historic Aircraft/	
				Hunter One Collection, Hurn: planned rest.	.84/86
				Snowdon Mountain Aviation Mus., Caernarfon	.86/90
15765 •	T Mk. 55			(to Irish Air Corps as 186)	
				noted on dump, Casement AB, Ireland	78
			N4861K	Laub America Corp, Carmel CA	11.79/87
				(noted stored as IAC 186, Tucson AZ 11.81)	

				Wesley D. O'Dell, Dana Point CA	8.87
				William G. Dilley/Spectra Sonics, Ogden UT	7.88/95
4123 •	T Mk. 35	**A79-602**		disposal ex RAAF Laverton VIC (TT 2925)	17.6.70
			N11920	Westair International, Broomfield CO: USCR	7.70/95
				not imported to USA	
				Pearce Dunn/Warbirds Aviation Museum, Mildura VIC	80/83
				Lincoln Nitschke/Military & Historic Aircraft Collection, Parafield/Greenock SA	9.83/92
4135 •	T Mk. 35	**A79-613**		disposal ex RAAF Laverton VIC (TT2894)	17.6.70
			N11921	Westair International, Broomfield CO	7.70/71
				Arthur W. McDonnell, Mojave CA	.72
				Ascher Ward, Van Nuys CA	82/83
				Alan G. Preston, Dallas TX	7.83
				Preston Air Museum, Dallas TX	3.86
				J. Duncan/Microjet Airshows, Miami FL	86
				William G. Dilley/Spectra Sonics, Ogden UT	2.87/95
4138 •	T Mk. 35	**A79-616**		disposal ex RAAF Laverton VIC (TT1945)	17.6.70
			N11922	Westair International, Broomfield CO	7.70/71
				(open storage, dism., nr RAAF Laverton 6.71)	
				Curtis Everett, Gretra LA	76
				stored unconv. dism., Tucson AZ	76/78
				James F. Moody, Atascadero CA	2.84/95
4139 •	T Mk. 35	**A79-617**		disposal ex RAAF Laverton VIC (TT2809)	17.6.70
			N11923	Westair International, Broomfield CO	7.70/72
				(open storage, dism., nr RAAF Laverton 6.71)	
				Arthur W. McDonnell, Lancaster CA	76/82
				Firebird Enterprises, Middlefield OH	6.84/88
				Ohio Associated Enterprises, Painesville OH	7.88/95
4140 •	T Mk. 35	**A79-618**		disposal ex RAAF Laverton VIC (TT2605)	17.6.70
			N11924	Westair International, Broomfield CO	7.70/72
				Robert A. Mitchum, Broomfield CO	.72
				Crosby Enterprises Inc, Wauwatosa WI	76
				Vampire Mk.35W Inc, Miami FL	3.84
				Preston Air Museum Inc, Dallas TX	2.85/86
				J. Duncan/Microjet Airshows, Miami FL	4.86/88
				Sherman Aircraft Sales, West Palm Beach FL	2.88
				Red Stevenson, Haskell OK	5.89
				Ernest J. Saviano, Arlington TX : *Shamu*	1.90
				Charles B. Yates, Woodstock VT	10.93/95
4146 •	T Mk. 35	**A79-624**		disposal ex RAAF Laverton VIC (TT2475)	17.6.70
			N11925	Westair International, Broomfield CO	7.70/72
				(noted under assembly, Oakland CA 2.71)	
				Mercer Aviation, Kalamazoo MI	72
				Lawrence W. Borret, Las Vegas NV	76
				(noted derelict, Van Nuys CA 78)	
	Mystery Jet			Jetcraft Inc, Las Vegas NV	
				(conv. Las Vegas: 8-seater Jetcraft Mystery Jet)	
				Don Bateman, Las Vegas NV	11.80/95
				(open storage, Henderson-Sky Harbour NV 90/94)	
4153 •	T Mk. 35	**A79-631**		disposal ex RAAF Laverton VIC (TT2636)	17.6.70
			N11926	Westair International, Broomfield CO	7.70/72
				(open storage, dism., nr RAAF Laverton 6.71)	
				Edwin Dye, Devine TX	76
				Wayne Dye Inc, Helotes TX	18.8.78/87
				Charles R. Parnell/Mission Motors, Universal City TX	1.87/90
				Combat Jets Flying Museum, Houston TX (flies in Zimbabwe AF sc.)	.90/92
				EAA Aviation Foundation, Oshkosh WI	.92/95
4157 •	T Mk. 35	**A79-635**		disposal ex RAAF Laverton VIC (TT1964)	17.6.70
			N11927	Westair International, Broomfield CO	7.70/72
			N35DS	Dennis M. Sherman, West Palm Beach FL	72
				Country Club Investment Co, Fairmont WV	4.77/95

c/n		Model	ID	Reg	Owner / History	Date
4158	•	T Mk. 35	**A79-636**		RAAF Museum, RAAF Point Cook VIC	75/88
				VH-HLF	RAAF Heritage Flight, RAAF Point Cook VIC	25.2.88/95
					(ff RAAF Laverton VIC 28.2.88 as "A79-636")	
4159	•	T Mk. 35	**A79-637**		disposal ex RAAF Laverton VIC (TT1944)	17.6.70
					Arnold J. Glass/Arnjul Ltd, Bankstown NSW	7.70
					Jeremy Flynn/Jecani Pty Ltd, Sydney NSW	80/92
					(stored Sydney-Bankstown, rest. project)	
4161	•	T Mk. 35	**A79-639**		disposal ex RAAF Laverton VIC (TT2627)	17.6.70
				N11928	Westair International, Broomfield CO: USCR	7.70
					(open storage, dism., nr RAAF Laverton 6.71)	
					Patrick Donovan, Seattle WA	84
					Museum of Flight, Seattle WA: stored dism.	.84/94
4166	•	T Mk. 35	**A79-644**		disposal ex RAAF Laverton VIC (TT2514)	17.6.70
				N11929	Westair International, Broomfield CO	7.70/72
					Dayton Air Taxi, Dayton OH	76/87
					Indiana Museum of Military History, Indianapolis IN	.87/95
4167	•	T Mk. 35	**A79-645**		disposal ex RAAF Laverton VIC (TT2716)	17.6.70
				N11930	Westair International, Broomfield CO	7.70/72
					Bass Aero Unlimited, Corpus Chrstii TX	.72
					Age Leasing Corp	25.3.74
					John O. Sheeran, Plum City WI	76
					Arthur W. McDonnell & Richard M. Vartanian, Mojave CA	5.1.78
					Edward C. Stead, Bedford & Manchester NH	1.83/95
					(flies as "RAF `WH930/ES930")	
4168	•	T Mk. 35	**A79-646**		disposal ex RAAF Laverton VIC (TT1024)	17.6.70
				N11931	Westair International, Broomfield CO	7.70/72
					Robert R. Redding, Houston TX	72
					Redding International Inc, Houston TX	84/86
					Rick E. Sharpe, Manvel TX	87/88
					FOAG Inc, Breckenridge TX	6.89/92
					Douglas F. Hollstrom, Cheboygan MI	12.93/94
				N4445D	Douglas F. Hollstrom, Cheboygan MI	8.94/95
4171	•	T Mk. 35	**A79-649**		disposal ex RAAF Laverton VIC (TT2536)	17.6.70
					Arnold J. Glass/Arnjul Ltd, Bankstown NSW	7.70/80
				VH-ICP	Jeremy Flynn/Jecani Pty Ltd, Sydney NSW	26.9.86/90
					(rest. Bankstown NSW, ff 19.9.86 "A79-649")	
				ZK-VAM	Ross Ewing/Vampire Syndicate, Ardmore	11.90/95
					(del. to NZ via Brisbane 20.11.90)	
4176	•	T Mk. 35	**A79-654**		disposal ex RAAF Laverton VIC (TT1998)	17.6.70
				N11932	Westair International, Broomfield CO	7.70/71
					Mercer Aviation, Kalamazoo MI	72
					Jimmie Moe	22.7.74
					Don Bateman, Las Vegas NV	74/84
					(open storage, Van Nuys CA 79)	
					Mark E. Foster, Aurora CO	86
					Bill Lamberton, Mercer Island WA	2.87/89
					Bill Lamberton/Jet Jockey Squadron Inc, Mercer Island WA	5.89/91
					Bill Lamberton/Pacific Flying Services, Mercer Island WA	7.91/95
4179	•	T Mk. 35	**A79-657**		disposal ex RAAF Laverton VIC (TT1948)	17.6.70
				N11933	Westair International, Broomfield CO	7.70/72
					Bradley Air Museum, Windsor Locks CT	74/84
					New England Air Museum, Windsor Locks CT	.84/89
					Alex Louis, Rockland ME	.89
				N6528Z	Alex Daphne Louis, Rockland ME	11.90/95
-	•	T Mk. 55			(to Indian AF as BY385)	
				N172LA	Lance Aircraft Supply Inc, Dallas TX	12.86/90
					Allen Dunn & Frank Kirchoff/	

c/n		Version	Serial	Registration	Owner / History	Dates
					A & F Entertainment Inc, Wilmington DE	2.90/95
-	•	T Mk. 55			(to Indian AF as IB882)	
				N173LA	Lance Aircraft Supply Inc, Dallas TX	12.86/89
					Reid Moorhead, Alhambra CA	7.89/90
					sale rep: USCR (rest. to fly, Chino CA 92)	92/95
-	•	T Mk. 55			(to Indian AF as IB1686)	
				N174LA	Lance Aircraft Supply Inc, Dallas TX	12.86/88
					Donald L. Fitzgerald, Aloha OR	4.88/95
-	•	T Mk. 11			(to R Rhodesian AF/Zimbabwe AF as R2424)	
					Hosking/Judy Pay syndicate, Melbourne VIC	.88/95
					(shipped dism., arr. Melbourne VIC 12.88)	
-	•	T Mk. 11			(to R Rhodesian AF/Zimbabwe AF as R4221)	
					Hosking/Judy Pay syndicate, Melbourne VIC	.88/92
					(shipped to Melbourne 12.88; rest. Tyabb VIC as "RRAF119/4221")	
				VH-ZVZ	Judy Pay/Mount Sherman Pty Ltd, Tyabb VIC	4.5.92/95
					(trucked Tyabb-Sale VIC 3.93 : rest. complete, not flown: stored Sale VIC 93/95)	
-	•	FB Mk. 6	**J-1082**		E. Wildhaber AG, Altenrhein: at auction	23.1.91
				HB-RVE	Wildhaber Sammlung, Altenrhein AB	30.8.91/93
					(flies as "J-1082")	
610	•	FB Mk. 6	**J-1101**		sold at auction, Dubendorf AB	23.1.91
				F-AZHY	Bernard Vurpillot, Le Havre	.91/92
					Y. Duval/Aerospeciale, Rennes	6.11.92/93
					(flies as French AF Mistral "DY-6")	
611	•	FB Mk. 6	**J-1102**		sold at auction, Dubendorf AB	23.1.91
					Heinrich Weisskopf, Switzerland	23.1.91
					(del. to North Weald UK 3.10.91: then crated)	
					Kermit A. Weeks, Tamiami FL	.91
					(shipped ex UK to Fort Lauderdale FL 10.91)	
				N100VJ	Vampire Aeronautical Corp, Delray Beach FL	12.91/92
					Richard E. Thompson, Kissimmee FL	5.93/95
					(rest. standard nose, flies as "RAF WA602/A")	
612	•	FB Mk. 6	**J-1103**		sold at auction, Dubendorf AB	23.1.91
				HB-RVH	Air Vampire SA, Sion	21.1.92
615	•	FB Mk. 6	**J-1106**		sold at auction, Dubendorf AB	23.1.91
				HB-RVO	Pegus AG, Altenrhein	15.6.94
				G-BVPO	R.V. Aviation Ltd, Bournemouth-Hurn: del.	30.6.94/95
					(rest. Hurn, ff 22.12.94 in RJAF sc.)	
					op: Royal Jordanian Air Force Historic Flight	
624	•	FB Mk. 6	**J-1115**		sold at auction, Dubendorf AB	23.1.91
					Jean Salis, La Ferte-Alais, France	23.1.91
					Bernard Vurpillot/Amicale J-B Salis	.91/92
				F-AZHX	Bernard Vurpillot, Le Havre	22.5.92/93
					(flies as French AF "VZ152/4-LH")	
630		FB Mk. 6	J-1121		sold at auction, Dubendorf AB	23.1.91
				HB-RVD	ntu	
				SE-DXZ	Christer C. Andskar, Sundbyberg	16.6.92
					(del. to Eskilstuna, Sweden 7.5.92)	
					crashed dest., Nackhall, Sweden: pilot ejected	6.7.93
636	•	FB Mk. 6	**J-1127**		sold at auction, Dubendorf AB	23.1.91
					Aero Dima, Nantes	.91
				F-AZOO	Aerodima Radio Air Service, Melun-Villaroche	14.8.92/93
638	•	FB Mk. 6	**J-1129**		sold at auction, Dubendorf AB	23.1.91
					(del. Dubendorf to Duxford UK 28.8.91)	
					Worldwide Jet Management, Chino CA	91
					sold to USA: crated ex Duxford	20.9.91
				N4024S	Ray Dieckman/The Air Museum, Chino CA	19.2.92/95

c/n		Type	Serial	Reg.	History	Date
649	•	FB Mk. 6	**J-1140**		sold at auction, Dubendorf AB	23.1.91
				N3160Y	Kermit A. Weeks/Weeks Air Museum, Tamiami FL	23.1.91/94
					(del. North Weald UK 11.9.91: crated to USA)	
652	•	FB Mk. 6	**J-1143**		sold at auction, Dubendorf AB	23.1.91
				F-AZHI	Yves Duval/Aerospeciale, Rennes: reg. res.	.91/93
655	•	FB Mk. 6	**J-1146**		Oyvind Ellingsen, Oslo Norway: at auction	23.1.91
					(del. Oslo 3.7.91 ex Dubendorf AB)	
				LN-17	Oyvind Ellingsen/Warbirds of Norway, Oslo	6.92/95
				LN-JET	res: Oyvind Ellingsen, Gardermoen AB	.92/95
					(rest. Gardermoen AB, ff 14.5.93 as LN-17, flies as RNoAF ZK-P/*Pinocchio*)	
658	•	FB Mk. 6	**J-1149**		sold at auction, Dubendorf AB	23.1.91
					Jet Heritage/Hunter Wing Ltd, Hurn	23.1.91
				G-SWIS	Hunter Wing Ltd, Hurn: del. ex Sion	10.5.91/94
661	•	FB Mk. 6	**J-1152**		sold at auction, Dubendorf AB	23.1.91
					(del. Dubendorf to Duxford UK 28.8.91)	
					sold to USA, crated ex Duxford	20.9.91
				N152RD	Ray Dieckman/Air Museum, Chino CA	19.2.92/95
					(shipped to Chino CA, ff 21.3.92 as "J-1152", flies as camouflaged "RAF NX152")	
664	•	FB Mk. 6	**J-1155**		sold at auction, Dubendorf AB	23.1.91
				F-AZHZ (1	Gilbert Villa, Nimes-Garons: reg. res.	.92/93
					Musee de l'Air, Paris-Le Bourget	93
668	•	FB Mk. 6	**J-1159**		sold at auction, Dubendorf AB	23.1.91
					Gerald Marie-Berger/Assoc. Varoise Avions de Collection, Cuers-Pierrefeu	9.91/92
				F-AZHJ	Assoc. Varoise Avions de Collection, Cuers	22.5.92/93
					(flies as "French AF VZ221/4-LF/7-BA")	
676	•	FB Mk. 6	**J-1167**		sold at auction, Dubendorf AB	23.1.91
					Sandy Topen, Cranfield	23.1.91/92
					(del. to Cranfield 8.8.91 as J-1167)	
				G-MKVI	Sandy Topen/Vintage Aircraft Team, Cranfield later Bruntingthorpe	2.6.92/95
					(rest. Cranfield, ff 20.7.93 as "RAF VZ304/A-T")	
682	•	FB Mk. 6	**J-1173**		sold at auction, Dubendorf AB	23.1.91
					Don Woods, Southampton	23.1.91
				G-DHXX	Lindsay Wood Promotions Ltd, Cranfield: del.	7.8.91/92
687	•	FB Mk. 6	**J-1178**		sold at auction, Dubendorf AB	23.1.91
					Michael Pont/Musee du Chateau de Savigny, Chateau de Savigny, Dijon France:	.91/92
					(displ.: maintained airworthy)	
693	•	FB Mk. 6	**J-1184**		sold at auction, Dubendorf AB	23.1.91
					Scandinavian Historic Flight, Norrkoping	23.1.91
					(del. Norrkoping 22.5.91, flies as "RSwAF F9/G")	
				SE-DXY	Scandinavian Historic Flight, Norrkoping	15.8.91/95
				OY-VAM	ntu: Scandinavian Historic Flight	14.3.94
				SE-DXY	Scandinavian Historic Flight, Solna, Sweden	94/95
700	•	FB Mk. 6	**J-1191**		sold at auction, Dubendorf AB	23.1.91
					del. to Nimes-Garons, France	.91
				F-AZIK	Association Cercle de Chasse de Nangis, Melun	12.93/95
701	•	FB Mk. 6	**J-1192**		sold at auction, Dubendorf AB	23.1.91
					del. to Sion, Switzerland : rest. to fly	.91
				F-AZOP	Association Warbird, Melun-Villaroche	1.7.93
					(flies as "French AF Mistral 192/M-DU")	
705	•	FB Mk. 6	**J-1196**		sold at auction, Dubendorf AB	23.1.91
					del. to Nimes, France	.91
					Christer C. Andskar, Sundbyberg, Sweden	.93/94

c/n	Type	Serial	Reg.	History	Date
				(del. to Norrkoping, Sweden 4.94)	
			SE-DXS	Christer C. Andskar, Sundbyberg	18.8.94/95
				(rest., flies as "R SwAF F5-A")	
706 •	FB Mk. 6	**J-1197**		sold at auction, Dubendorf AB	23.1.91
			HB-RVN	C. Dvorak, Altenrhein	10.8.93
708 •	FB Mk. 6	**J-1199**		J. L. Langeard & J. deRaineri/Association Atlantic, Caen: at auction Dubendorf AB	23.1.91/92
				(del. Caen-Carpiquet 17.7.91 ex Sion)	
			F-AZHH	J. deRaineri, Caen-Carpiquet	14.8.92/93
864 •	T Mk. 55	**U-1204**		sold at auction, Dubendorf AB	23.3.91
				Gilbert Villa, Nimes-Garons, France	.91
			F-AZHZ (2	Cercle de Chasse de Nangis, Melun	23.6.94
				(flies as Mistral "Aeronavale 204/16F-27")	
866 •	T Mk. 55	**U-1206**		sold at auction, Dubendorf AB	23.3.91
				(del. to North Weald UK 11.9.91: then crated)	
				Kermit A. Weeks, Tamiami FL	.91
				(shipped to Fort Lauderdale FL ex UK 11.11.91)	
			N115DH	Vampire Aeronautical Corp, Delray Beach FL	12.91/92
				R. Brinkman, San Antonio TX	4.94/95
868 •	T Mk. 55	**U-1208**		sold at auction, Dubendorf AB	23.3.91
			HB-RVF	A-Jet Ltd, Altenrhein AB	3.9.91/92
				Wildhaber Sammlung, Altenrhein AB	93
870 •	T Mk. 55	**U-1210**		sold at auction, Dubendorf AB	23.3.91
			F-AZHU	Yves Duval/Aerospeciale, Rennes-St. Jaques	12.91/93
872 •	T Mk. 55	**U-1212**		sold at auction, Dubendorf AB	23.3.91
				NFZ-Flyg AB: del. to Eskilstuna, Sweden	23.5.91
			SE-DXT	NFZ-Flyg AB, Eskilstuna	10.91/93
				Team Vampire Sweden AB, Eskilstuna	.93/95
				Eskilstuna Flygmuseum AB, Eskilstuna	.95
55973 •	T Mk. 55	**U-1213**		sold at auction, Dubendorf AB	23.3.91
			N935HW	Paul McMinn/IMP Inc, Coatesville PA	20.8.91/95
				(del. to USA, ex Cranfield UK 16.9.91)	
55092 •	T Mk. 55	**U-1214**		sold at auction, Dubendorf AB	23.3.91
				Don Woods, Southampton	23.3.91
			G-DHVV	Lindsay Wood Promotions Ltd, Cranfield	5.9.91/92
975 •	T Mk. 55	**U-1215**		sold at auction, Dubendorf AB	23.3.91
				Jet Heritage/Hunter Wing Ltd, Hurn	23.3.91
			G-HELV	Hunter Wing Ltd, Hurn: del.	28.8.91/94
				(rest. Bournemouth-Hurn, ff 13.10.92)	
976 •	T Mk. 55	**U-1216**		RAF Benevolent Fund: del. Boscombe Down	6.90/94
				(taken on RAF charge as ZH563)	
				(stored RAF Boscombe Down "ZH563": for sale)	
			G-BVLM	R.V. Aviation Ltd, Bournemouth-Hurn	6.4.94/95
				op: Royal Jordanian Air Force Historic Flight	
				(flies as "R Jordanian AF 209")	
978 •	T Mk. 55	**U-1218**		sold at auction, Dubendorf AB	23.3.91
				Monte Tamaro SA, Rivera, Switzerland	.91/92
979 •	T Mk. 55	**U-1219**		sold at auction, Dubendorf AB	23.3.91
				Don Woods, Southampton	23.3.91
			G-DHWW	Lindsay Wood Promotions Ltd, Cranfield	5.9.91/92
980 •	T Mk. 55	**U-1220**		sold at auction, Dubendorf AB	23.3.91
				Randall K. Hames, Cliffside NC	23.3.91
			N391RH	Randall K. Hames, Gaffney SC	6.8.91/92
				(del. to USA, ex Cranfield UK 16.9.91)	
				Gabriel Vidal, Miami FL	1.93/95
981 •	T Mk. 55	**U-1221**		Swedish Air Force Museum: del. Ljungbhyed	14.8.90
			SE-DXV	Ljungbyheds Aeronautiska Sallskap/	

c/n		Type	Mil. ID	Reg.	History	Date
					Scandinavian Historic Flight, Ljungbhyed	22.8.91/95
					(flies as "R SwAF F5-105")	
983	•	T Mk. 55	**U-1223**		sold at auction, Dubendorf AB	23.3.91
				F-AZHV	Yves Duval/Aerospeciale, Rennes: reg. res.	.91/93
985	•	T Mk. 55	**U-1225**		sold at auction, Dubendorf AB	23.3.91
				HB-RVM	H. Weidmann, Altenrhein	30.6.92
986	•	T Mk. 55	**U-1226**		sold at auction, Dubendorf AB	23.3.91
					Jacques Lacombe, Laval QUE	92/93
					(del. ex storage Montreal to NC .93)	
				N593RH	Randall K. Hames, Cliffside NC	7.93
					Wade H. McDuffie, Cheraw SC	8.93/95
987	•	T Mk. 55	**U-1227**		sold at auction, Dubendorf AB	23.3.91
					Gilbert Villa, Nimes-Garons, France : del.	.91
988	•	T Mk. 55	**U-1228**		sold at auction, Dubendorf AB	23.3.91
				HB-RVJ	Custox AG, Bern	.91
989	•	T Mk. 55	**U-1229**		sold at auction, Dubendorf AB	23.3.91
					Y. Descamps, Cannes-Mandelieu	.91/92
				F-AZGU	J. Carlton, Cannes	10.9.92/93
990	•	T Mk. 55	**U-1230**		sold at auction, Dubendorf AB	23.3.91
					Don Woods, Southampton	23.3.91
				G-DHZZ	Lindsay Wood Promotions Ltd, Cranfield: del.	7.8.91/92
993	•	T Mk. 55	**U-1233**		sold at auction, Dubendorf AB	23.3.91
				HB-RVK	K. Fasnacht, Sion	9.4.92
994	•	T Mk. 55	**U-1234**		sold at auction, Dubendorf AB	23.3.91
					H. Weisskopff, Switzerland	.91
					Aces High Ltd, North Weald UK : del.	3.10.91/92
					Weeks Air Museum, Tamiami FL	94
DHP/ 44352	•	T Mk. 55	**U-1235**		sold at auction, Dubendorf AB	23.3.91
				HB-RVI	Air Vampire SA, Sion	9.9.91/92
DHP/ 40303	•	T Mk. 11 / T Mk. 55	**U-1236**		sold at auction, Dubendorf AB	23.3.91
					Flygexpo Vasteras AB: del. Vasteras, Sweden	23.5.91
				SE-DXX	Flygexpo/Swedish Veteran Wing, Vasteras	4.91/95
					(flies as "RSwAF F14-G")	
22277	•	T Mk. 55	**U-1237**		sold at auction, Dubendorf AB	23.3.91
					(del. to Charleroi, Belgium 28.8.91,	
					rest. to fly, Gosselies 10.91/92)	
				N4368F	Collette M. Fossez-Sumner, Brooklyn NY	17.3.92
					(to be based Belgium)	
				OO-KGS	Carolo Vampire Association, Gosselies	2.93

DEHAVILLAND DH112 VENOM/SEA VENOM

c/n		Type	Mil. ID	Reg.	History	Date
12364	•	NF Mk. 51			(to R Swedish AF as Fv33015)	
		J33		SE-DCA	Svensk Flygtjanst AB, Stockholm-Bromma	.58/69
					op: Swedair Ltd: target tug	
					Flygvapenmuseum, Linkoping, Sweden	84/92
12374	•	NF Mk. 51			(to R Swedish AF as Fv33025)	
J33				SE-DCD	Svensk Flygtjanst AB, Stockholm-Bromma	.58/69
					op: Swedair Ltd: target tug	
					Flygvapenmuseum, Linkoping, Sweden	.69/92
12752	•	Sea Venom	**WZ895**		(to RAN as WZ895): BOC	27.2.56/74
		FAW Mk. 53			(arr. on carrier HMAS Melbourne 4.56)	
					Nowra NAS: retired as ground inst. airframe	5.66/74
					Naval Aviation Museum, Nowra NAS NSW	.74
				VH-NVV	RAN Historic Flight, Nowra NAS NSW	.85/94
					(long-term rest. to fly: first taxying trials	

				Nowra 2.83 as "WZ895/NW870/M")	
12760 •	Sea Venom FAW Mk. 53	**WZ903**		(to RAN as WZ903): BOC (arr. on carrier HMAS Melbourne 4.56) Pearce Dunn/Warbirds Aviation Museum, Mildura VIC (trucked ex Nowra NAS, displ. "WZ903/NW871/M") Sanders Aircraft, Chino CA	27.2.56/70 12.70/89 .89/93
12786 •	Sea Venom FAW Mk. 53 TT. Mk. 53	**WZ944**	 **N7022H**	(to RAN as WZ944, later N4-944): BOC (arr. on carrier HMAS Melbourne 4.56) Pearce Dunn/Warbirds Aviation Museum, Mildura VIC (trucked ex Nowra NAS, displ. "WZ944/NW873") Dennis Sanders/Sanders Aircraft, Chino CA Sanders Aircraft, Chino CA (rest. Chino 92/95, visited Oshkosh 8.95) Amjet Aircraft Corp, St Paul MN	27.2.56/70 72/89 .89/93 5.93/95 .95
733 •	FB Mk. 1 FB Mk. 50 (Swiss)	**J-1523**	**G-VENI**	Source Premium & Promotional Consultants Ltd, Weybridge: del. Cranfield op: Source Classic Jet Flight, Bournemouth (flies as "RAF WE402")	 9.6.84/95 94/95
737 •	FB Mk. 1 FB Mk. 50	**J-1527**	**N9196M**	Westair International USA Inc, Monument CO M & M Aircraft Sales Co, Broomfield CO	11.87/90 4.91/95
749 •	FB Mk. 1 FB Mk. 50	**J-1539**	**G-BMOD**	ntu : stored Locarno, Switzerland	90
752 •	FB Mk. 1 FB Mk. 50	**J-1542**	**G-GONE**	Philip Meeson & Elsdon Davies/Glylynn Ltd, Hurn: del. op: Jet Heritage Collection Ltd, Hurn Venom Jet Promotions Ltd, Hurn John E. Davies, Bournmouth-Hurn	 20.9.84/89 84/94 20.2.89 22.2.91/94
783 •	FB Mk. 1 FB Mk. 50	**J-1573**	G-BMOB HB-RVB **G-VICI**	ntu Tarmac Aviation Gordold, Altenrhein Lindsay Wood Promotions Ltd, Bournemouth op: Source Classic Jet Flight, Bournemouth	 4.89 6.2.95 95
811 •	FB Mk. 1 FB Mk. 50	**J-1601**	**G-VIDI**	Source Premium & Promotional Consultants Ltd, Weybridge: del. Cranfield (rest. Cranfield, ff 12.94 as "RAF WE275") op: Source Classic Jet Flight, Bournemouth	 9.6.84/95 94/95
815 •	FB Mk. 1 FB Mk. 50	**J-1605**	G-BLID	Aces High Ltd, Duxford: del. Peter F. A. Hoar, Duxford Peter G. Vallance/Vallance By-Ways Museum, Charlwood : static displ., arr.	20.9.84/86 89 1.90/95
821 •	FB Mk. 1 FB Mk. 50	**J-1611**	**G-BMOC**	ntu : stored Locarno, Switzerland	90
824 •	FB Mk 1 FB Mk. 50	**J-1614**	**G-BLIE**	Aces High Ltd, Duxford R. Everett/Air Charter Scotland,Glasgow:del.	28.2.85 27.2.85/91
826 •	FB Mk. 1 FB Mk. 50	**J-1616**	G-BLIF **N202DM**	Aces High Ltd, Duxford (del. Dubendorf-Duxford 5.7.84; loaned Imperial War Museum, Duxford 84/85) Dean Martin/Warplanes Inc, Burlington VT Red Stevenson, Haskell OK CATS Inc, Eugene OR Dolphin Oil Ltd, Eugene OR ACE Ltd, Houston TX David L. Van Liere, Muncie IN	28.9.84 4.86/88 2.89/90 1.90 5.90 92 2.94/95
840 •	FB Mk. 1R FB Mk. 50	J-1630	**HB-RVA**	Halos AG/Foundation Pour Le Maintien du Patrimoine Aeronautique, Lausanne: del. (ff 22.6.88 Altenrhein AB: flies as "J-1630") Wildhaber Sammlung, Altenrhein AB	 14.7.84/89 93

c/n		Type	Serial	Reg.	History	Date
841	•	FB Mk. 1R FB Mk. 50	J-1631	**HB-RVC**	Foundation pour le Maintien du Patrimoine Aeronautique - FMPA, Sion (rest. Sion, ff 20.4.90)	 88/93
842	•	FB Mk. 1R FB Mk. 50	J-1632	**G-VNOM**	A. Topen/Vintage Aircraft Team, Cranfield (del. Dubendorf-Cranfield 5.7.84) stored unconv. Cranfield: struck-off reg.	13.7.84/91 25.3.91
844	•	FB Mk. 1R FB Mk. 50	J-1634	 **ZK-VNM (1**	Aces High Ltd, Duxford UK: del. Trevor Bland/NZ Warbirds Inc, Ardmore (shipped NZ, ff Whenuapai 29.8.87 as "RAF WE434") crashed Auckland-Ardmore NZ (stored dam. Ardmore 92/95)	27.2.85 8.1.87/91 16.12.91
883	•	FB Mk. 4 FB Mk. 54	J-1730	G-BLIA **N402DM**	Aces High Ltd, Duxford: del. Dean Martin/Warplanes Inc, Burlington VT Gene F. Fisher, Boiling Springs PA David L. Van Liere, Huntington IN (flies as "J-1730")	8.6.84 1.11.84/86 .86/92 1.94/95
917	•	FB Mk. 4 FB Mk. 54	J-1747	G-BLIB N5471V **N747J**	Aces High Ltd, Duxford: del. Warplanes Inc, East Middlebury VT James W Goodwin, Rutland VT Venom Partners Inc, Campbell CA Ernest J. Saviano, Arlington TX David L. Vanliere, Huntington IN Curtis E. Farley, St Petersburg FL	8.6.84 31.8.84/86 12.86/87 1.89 5.90 1.92 1.94/95
928	•	FB Mk. 4 FB Mk. 54	J-1758	G-BLSD N203DM **G-BLSD**	Aces High Ltd, Duxford (del. Cranfield 30.4.85 ex Dubendorf AB, crated at Cranfield 8.85) Dean Martin/Warplanes Inc, Burlington VT (not shipped to USA, stored North Weald 86/88) Aces High Ltd, North Weald	20.5.85 4.4.86 22.4.88/93
933		FB Mk. 4 FB Mk. 54	J-1763	G-BLSE N902DM	Aces High Ltd, Duxford (del. Cranfield 30.4.85 ex Dubendorf AB, crated at Cranfield 12.85, shipped to USA) Warplanes Inc, East Middlebury VT Classic Fighters Inc, Argyle TX George Dubick Bill Harrison, Tulsa OK Ernest J. Salviano, Arlington TX crashed, dest., Muskogee OK (Saviano k.)	20.5.85 8.85/86 6.86 89/90 4.90 8.6.90
960	•	FB Mk. 4 FB Mk. 54	**J-1790**	G-VENM **G-BLKA**	ntu: A. "Sandy" Topen, Cranfield (del. Cranfield 5.7.84 ex Dubendorf AB) Sandy Topen/Vintage Aircraft Team, Cranfield later Bruntingthorpe (ff Cranfield 1.12.84: flies as "RAF WR410/N")	7.84 13.7.84/96
969	•	FB Mk. 54 FB Mk. 4	**J-1799**	G-BLIC N502DM **ZK-VNM (2**	Aces High Ltd, Duxford (del. Dubendorf - Duxford 5.7.84) Dean Martin/Warplanes Inc, Burlington VT Maintenance One, Essex Junction VT sale rep., Klamath Falls OR reg. pending, Visalia CA Rural Aviation Ltd/Flightwatch, Ardmore (shipped to NZ, ff Auckland-Ardmore 23.1.93, flies in all red sc. "J-1799")	13.7.84 7.6.85 1.86 90 92 7.92/96

Douglas A-4 Skyhawk

c/n		Type	Serial	Reg.	History	Date
11366	•	A4D-2 A-4B	**Bu142112**	N3E **N41CJ**	Jim Robinson/Combat Jets Flying Museum, Houston TX (ex tech. school, rebuilt Chino CA, ff 12.4.89) (flies as "148609/USS Bon Homme Richard") EAA Aviation Foundation, Oshkosh WI: del. EAA Aviation Foundation, Oshkosh WI	 1.87/92 5.92/93 9.93/96

11370	A4D-2	**Bu142116**	N116MD	US Navy/McDonnell Douglas, Long Beach CA	77
	A-4B				
11420 •	A4D-2	**Bu142166**	**N5548**	George T. Baker Aviation School, Miami FL	9.71/95
	A-4B			(USCR quotes id. A11-32)	
11967 •	A4D-2	**Bu142905**	**N905MD**	US Navy/McDonnell Douglas, Long Beach CA	77
	A-4B			San Diego Aeropace Museum, San Diego CA	79/94
12377 •	A4D-2N	**Bu145131**		Tom Reilly Vintage Aircraft, Kissimmee FL	90/94
	A-4C		**N2262Z**	American Warplane Heritage: reg. candidate	5.94
				Donald C. Rounds, Manchester TN	16.9.94/95
12764 •	A4D-2N	**Bu148571**	N53996		76
	A-4C		N401FS	US Navy/Flight Systems Inc, Mojave CA	1.77/81
				Davis-Monthan AFB AZ: storage	23.10.81
				Pima County Air Museum, Tucson AZ	.82/93
12841 •	A4D-2N	**Bu149516**	N402FS	US Navy/Flight Systems Inc, Mojave CA	1.77/86
	A-4C			retired .84, struck-off USCR	1.86
	A-4L			RNZAF Museum, Wigram AB NZ: arr.	1.88/96
				(displ. as A-4K "RNZAF NZ6207")	
12997 •	A4D-2N	**Bu150586**	N403FS	US Navy/Flight Systems Inc, Mojave CA	1.77/86
	A-4C			struck-off USCR	1.86
	A-4L			MCAM, Yuma MCAS AZ	93
- •	TA-4J	**Bu158128**		USNAM, NAS Pensacola FL	
			N3203Z	Stacy N. Prineas, Redmond OR: candidate	90/91
			N128TA	Stacy N. Prineas, Seattle WA	11.91/92
				Donald C. Rounds, Manchester TN	16.3.92
				Betty L. Welcome, Kirkland WA	2.93/96
14213 •	TA-4J	**Bu158176**	**N141TA**	Stacy N. Prineas, Redmond OR	8.95
- •	TA-4J	**Bu158471**		Tom Reilly Vintage Aircraft, Kissimmee FL	90/94
				(rest. to fly, Kissimmee FL 91)	
-	A-4A	-		Pascal Mahvi, Chino CA	c78/84
				(recov. ex gate guard USN Base, rest. Chino 82/86,	
				flew as "A-4A 14219")	
			N444AV	Pascal Mahvi/Aeronautical Test Vehicles Inc,	
				Newport Beach CA	10.84
				Guy Neeley/Advanced Aero Enterprises Inc,	
				Newport Beach CA	86/87
				crashed dest., California City CA (Neeley k.)	4.6.87
				(USCR quotes id. "14219")	
- •	A4D-2	-	**N21NB**	Morris Cannan, San Antonio TX	8.87/95
				op: Sierra Hotel Inc, Dallas-Addison TX	
				(USCR quotes id. 011, flies as "RAN 011")	
-	A-4	-	N115MD	US Navy, Long Beach CA	
			N900MD	US Navy, Long Beach CA	75
- •	TA-4J	-	**N91KD**	John Dilley/Fort Wayne Air Service,	
				Fort Wayne IN	90/91
				Betty L. Welcome, Redmond WA	2.91/95
				(USCR quotes id. "921001")	
- •	A-4P	-		(to FA Argentina as C-205)	
				noted, dism. in compound, Ontario CA	11.95
- •	A-4P	-		(to FA Argentina as C-212)	
				noted, dism. in compound, Ontario CA	11.95
- •	A-4P	-		(to FA Argentina as C-218)	
				noted, dism. in compound, Ontario CA	11.95
- •	A-4P	-		(to FA Argentina as C-219)	
				noted, dism. in compound, Ontario CA	11.95

c/n	Type	Serial	Reg.	Owner / Notes	Date
- •	A-4P	-		(to FA Argentina as C-222)	
				noted, dism. in compound, Ontario CA	11.95
- •	A-4P	-		(to FA Argentina as C-230)	
				noted, dism. in compound, Ontario CA	11.95
- •	A-4P	-		(to FA Argentina as C-233)	
				noted, dism. in compound, Ontario CA	11.95
- •	A-4P	-		(to FA Argentina as C-237)	
				noted, dism. in compound, Ontario CA	11.95
- •	A-4P	-		(to FA Argentina as C-240)	
				noted, dism. in compound, Ontario CA	11.95
- •	A-4P	-		(to FA Argentina as C-249)	
				noted, dism. in compound, Ontario CA	11.95
- •	A-4P	-		(to FA Argentina as C-2....)	
				noted, dism. in compound, Ontario CA	11.95
- •	A-4P	-		(to FA Argentina as C-2....)	
				noted, dism. in compound, Ontario CA	11.95
- •	A-4B	-		Frank J. Wright, Joliet IL	.90/92
				(rest. to fly, Joliet IL 90/92)	

English Electric/BAC Lightning

c/n	Type	Serial	Reg.	Owner / Notes	Date
95011 •	T Mk. 5	**XS451**		Peter F. A. Hoare/Militair, Cranfield	.87/88
				A.Topen/Vintage Aircraft Team, Cranfield	88/89
			G-LTNG	Barry J. Pover/Lightning Flying Club,	
				Plymouth: arr. dism.	12.9.89/95
				(rest. Plymouth, due to fly .94)	
95012 •	T Mk.5	**XS452**		Arnold J. Glass/Ruanil Investments Ltd,	
				Cranfield: del. ex RAF Binbrook	1.7.88
			G-BPFE	Arnold J. Glass/Ruanil Investments Ltd,	
				Cranfield	10.88/93
				(open storage Cranfield 92/93)	
				Tony Hulls, Cranfield: sold at auction	11.93/95
				(rest. to fly, taxy trials 2.95)	
95018 •	T Mk. 5	**XS458**		Arnold J. Glass/Ruanil Investments Ltd,	
				Cranfield: del. ex RAF Binbrook	29.6.88/93
				(open storage Cranfield 92/95)	
				Savvas Constantinides, Cyprus: at auction	11.93/95
95021	T Mk. 5	XV328		Arnold J. Glass/Ruanil Investments Ltd,	
				Cranfield: del. ex RAF Binbrook	29.6.88/93
				(open storage Cranfield 92/94)	
				auctioned 26.11.93, broken-up Cranfield	12.94
95113	F Mk. 2A	XN734		BAC Ltd, Saudi Support School, Warton: del	26.6.73/86
	F Mk. 3A		G-BNCA	Aces High Ltd, North Weald UK	10.12.86
				Peter F. A. Hoare/Militair, Cranfield: arr.	31.10.87
				A. Topen/Vintage Aircraft Team, Cranfield	10.87/92
				(open storage Cranfield 92/94)	
				broken-up Cranfield	12.94
95116 •	F Mk. 6	**XP693**		op: British Aerospace, Warton: wfu last flight	16.12.92
			G-FSIX	Barry J. Pover/Lighting Flying Club,	
				Plymouth	12.92/95
				(del. Exeter ex Warton 23.12.92, rest. to fly)	
95207 •	F Mk. 6	**XR724**		British Aircraft Corp, Shawbury: retired	.90
			G-BTSY	Barry Pover/Lightning Association, Callington	25.7.91/92
				(del. Shawbury-Binbrook 23.7.92)	
- •	F Mk. 6	**XR728**		Lightning Preservation Group, Bruntingthorpe	6.88/95

				(del. Bruntingthorpe ex RAF Binbrook 24.6.88, maintained, engine runs, Bruntingthorpe 94)	
- •	F Mk. 3	**XR755**		Castle Air, Cornwall: arr. dism ex Binbrook	24.6.88/90
95238 •	F Mk. 6	**XR773**		op: British Aerospace, Warton: wfu last flight	16.12.92
			G-OPIB	Barry J. Pover/Lighting Flying Club, Plymouth:	12.92/95
				(del. Exeter ex Warton 23.12.92, rest. to fly 94)	
95244	F Mk. 6	XS898		Arnold J. Glass/Ruanil Investments Ltd, Cranfield: del. ex RAF Binbrook	30.6.88/94
				(open storage Cranfield 92/94)	
				auctioned 26.11.93, broken-up Cranfield	12.94
95245	F Mk. 6	XS899		Arnold J. Glass/Ruanil Investments Ltd, Cranfield: del.	29.6.88/93
				(open storage Cranfield 92/94)	
				auctioned 26.11.93, broken-up Cranfield	12.94
- •	T Mk. 6	**XS904**		(op. BAe Warton, last flight 16.12.92)	
				Lightning Preservation Group, Bruntingthorpe	12.92/95
				(del. Bruntingthorpe ex Warton 21.1.93)	
95256	F Mk. 6	XS923		Arnold J. Glass/Ruanil Investments Ltd, Cranfield: del.	30.6.88/93
				(open storage Cranfield 92/94)	
				auctioned 26.11.93, broken-up Cranfield	12.94
-	F Mk. 53		G-AWON	British Aircraft Corporation, Preston	9.8.68
				(to R Saudi AF as 53-686): del.	9.68
				(to RAF as ZF592)	
				open storage, BAe Warton	87
95293	F Mk. 53		G-AWOO	British Aircraft Corporation, Preston	9.8.68
				(to R Saudi AF as 53-687): del.	9.68
95311	F Mk. 53		G-AXEE	British Aircraft Corporation, Preston	24.4.69
				(to Kuwaiti AF as K418): del.	7.69
95312	F Mk. 53		G-AXFW	British Aircraft Corporation, Preston	21.5.69
				(to Kuwaiti AF as K419): del.	7.69

FOLLAND GNAT/HINDUSTAN HF24 ADJEET

GT005 •	Mk. 1	**IE1076**		(to Indian AF as IE1076)	.59
				(assembled by Hindustan Aircraft, Bangalore)	
				David C. Tallichet/MARC, Chino CA	86/94
				(stored dism., Chino 88)	
				USAFM, March AFB CA: loan	90/94
- •	HAL Mk. 1	**IE1214**		(to Indian AF as IE1214)	.62
				(built by Hindustan Aircraft, Bangalore)	
				David C. Tallichet/MARC, Chino CA	86/93
				(stored dism., Chino 88/89)	
- •	HAL Mk. 1	**IE1222**		(to Indian AF as IE1222)	.59
				(built by Hindustan Aircraft, Bangalore)	
				David C. Tallichet/MARC, Chino CA	86/93
				(stored dism., Chino 88)	
FL.507 •	T Mk. 1	**XM697**		Air Training Corps, Woking Surrey	80/89
			G-NAAT	Jet Heritage Ltd/Hunter Wing, Hurn	11.89/95
				(arr. dism. Hurn ex Woking 22.12.89, stored Hurn awaiting rest. to fly 93/95)	
				wfu, stored Hurn: struck-off reg.	10.4.95
FL.508 •	T Mk. 1	**XM698**		RAF Halton: inst. airframe	74
				RAF Exhibition Flight, RAF Abingdon	80
				RAF Museum, RAF Cosford	86
			N698XM	James E. Thompson, St Cloud FL	2.87/95

c/n	Type	Serial	Reg	Owner	Date
FL.510 •	T Mk. 1	**XM705**		RAF Bruggen: inst. airframe	80
			N705XM	James E. Thompson, St Cloud FL	2.87/95
FL.519 •	T Mk. 1	**XP504**		RAF Halton: inst. airframe: del.	4.3.78/91
				Tim J. Manna, Leavesden: at RAF auction	11.91
			G-TIMM	Tim J. Manna/Kennett Aviation, Cranfield	19.2.92/95
				(arr. by road Leavesden 16.1.92 for rest., ff Leavesden 15.11.92, flies as "XM693")	
FL.526 •	T Mk. 1	**XP511**		RAF Halton: inst. airframe	80/92
				sold at RAF auction 3.92: shipped to USA	9.92
				Downbird USA	3.11.92
			N6145X	Welcome Aviation, Redmond WA	7.93/95
FL.528 •	T Mk. 1	**XP513**		Royal Aircraft Establishment, RAF Bedford	80
			N513XP	Morey & John Darznieks/Lance Aircraft Supply, Dallas TX	3.85
			N513X	Lance Aircraft Supply Inc, Dallas TX	8.86/95
FL.529 •	T Mk. 1	**XP514**		RAF Cranwell: inst. airframe	84
				RAF Cosford: inst. airframe	.84/88
				Arnold J. Glass/Ruanill Investments,Cranfield	12.88
				(shipped to USA, ex Felixstowe Docks 2.8.89)	
			N22394	ntu	
			N7HY	Morgan Merrill/Jet 1 Inc, Alexandria VA	4.90
				McDonnell Enterprises, California City CA	3.92
				Transonic Flight Test Ltd, Los Angeles CA	10.92/95
				(noted dism., unconv., California City 11.92/94)	
FL.532 •	T Mk. 1	**XP530**		RAF Halton: inst. airframe	84/93
				sold at RAF auction	21.10.93
			N530X	Randall K. Hames, Cliffside NC	25.4.94/95
FL.535 •	T Mk. 1	**XP533**		RAF Cosford: inst. airframe: TT3652 hrs	80
				RAF Halton: inst. airframe	84/86
				sold at RAF auction 9.3.90: shipped to USA	5.90
			N533XP	NTC Group Inc, Wilmington DE	12.3.93/95
FL.536 •	T Mk. 1	**XP534**		RAF Halton: inst. airframe	84/93
				Tim J. Manna: arr. dism. Cranfield	23.11.93
			G-BVPP	Tim J. Manna/Kennett Aviation, Cranfield	22.4.94/95
				(rest. to fly Cranfield 94/95)	
FL.537	T Mk. 1	XP535		School of Aircraft Handling, RNAS Culdrose	80/87
			G-BOXP	Arnold J. Glass/Ruanil Investments, Cranfield	3.8.88
				(arr. dism. Leavesden 11.87 "SAH-1"; ff 5.8.88)	
			N1CW	Morgan Merrill/Jet 1 Inc, Alexandria VA	25.9.89/90
				(shipped to USA, ex Felixstowe Docks 2.8.89)	
				crashed dest., Mojave CA (Merrill k.)	29.9.90
FL.542 •	T Mk. 1	**XP538**		RAF Halton: inst. airframe: TT 3183 hrs	80/86
				RAF Cosford: inst. airframe	88/90
				sold at RAF auction	9.3.90
				Sporting International Ltd	
			N19GT	Pyramid Aerospace Inc, Houston TX	23.3.90
				Cinema Air Jet Centre Inc, Calsbad CA	1.91/95
				(rest. Carlsbad-Palomar CA, ff 2.94)	
FL.545 •	T Mk. 1	**XP541**		Battle Damage Repair Flight, RAF Abingdon	80
				Warbirds of GB Ltd, Biggin Hill	.86/89
			N8130Q	Robert F. Yancey, Klamath Falls OR	4.5.89
				Andrew J. McCarthy, Merrimack NH	1.92/95
FL.546 •	T Mk. 1	**XR535**		RAF Halton: inst. airframe	80/86
				Warbirds of GB Ltd, Biggin Hill	.86/89
			N8130N	Robert F. Yancey, Klamath Falls OR	4.5.89
				John Dilley/Fort Wayne Air Service IN	2.91/92
				(rest. California City CA, ff 2.92)	
				American Horizons Ltd, Fort Wayne IN	10.92/95
FL.548 •	T Mk. 1	**XR537**		RAF Cosford : inst. airframe: TT2935 hrs	80/90

				Sark Int'l Airways, Hurn: RAF auction	9.3.90
			G-NATY	Jet Heritage Ltd, Hurn	19.6.90/94
				(stored Hurn awaiting rest. to fly 94)	
FL.549 •	T Mk. 1	**XR538**		RAF Halton : inst. airframe	84/93
				sold at RAF auction	8.7.93
			G-RORI	Rory C. McCarthy, North Weald	10.93/95
				(trucked Cranfield ex Halton 10.93,	
				rest. Cranfield, ff 27.4.94)	
FL.562 •	T Mk. 1	**XR572**		School of Aircraft Handling, RNAS Culdrose	80
				Michael W. Bertz, Broomfield CO	87
				(arr. Leavesden UK dism. 11.87, "SAH-3")	
			N572XR	Michael W. Bertz, Broomfield CO	3.89/95
FL.568 •	T Mk. 1	**XR951**		RAF Halton: inst. airframe	84/86
				Warbirds of GB Ltd, Biggin Hill	.86/89
			N81298	Robert F. Yancey, Klamath Falls OR	4.5.89
				Andrew J. McCarthy, Merrimack NH	1.92/95
FL.572 •	T Mk. 1	**XR955**		School of Aircraft Handling, RNAS Culdrose	80/87
				(arr. Leavesden UK .87 "SAH-2", crated to USA)	
				Glenn Hyde, Dallas TX	90
				(rest. to fly, Chino CA 90/93)	
			N4367L	DAC International Inc, Austin TX	5.92/95
FL.577 •	T Mk. 1	**XR980**		RAF Halton: inst. airframe: del.	11.3.79/90
			N936FC	Frank Chiodo Ltd, East Islip NY	4.10.94/95
FL.578 •	T Mk. 1	**XR984**		RAF Halton: inst. airframe	80/88
				sold at RAF auction: poor condition	9.3.90
				San Diego Flight Museum, Brown Field CA	93
FL.581 •	T Mk. 1	**XR987**		RAF Cosford: inst. airframe	80/88
				Arnold J. Glass/Ruanil Investments, Cranfield	12.88
				(shipped to USA, ex Felixstowe Docks 2.8.89)	
FL.585 •	T Mk. 1	**XR991**		RAF Cranwell: inst. airframe	80
				School of Aircraft Handling, RNAS Culdrose	87
			G-BOXO	Arnold J. Glass/Ruanil Investments, Cranfield	3.8.88
				(arr. dism. Leavesden 11.87, "SAH-6";	
				shipped to USA, ex Felixstowe Docks 2.8.89)	
			N1CL	Morgan Merrill/Jet 1 Inc, Alexandria VA	7.89
			N1PT	ntu: Jet 1 Inc, Alexandria VA	10.90
			N1CL	McDonnell Enterprises, California City CA	3.92/95
			N48AM	ntu: Wally McDonnell/McDonnell Enterprises	9.92
FL.587	T Mk. 1	**XR993**		School of Aircraft Handlinbg, RNAS Culdrose	
				RAF Museum storage: offered for disposal	.86
				(arr. dism. Leavesden .87, "SAH-4", crated for USA)	
			N3XR	Gnati Inc, Wilmington DE	11.90/91
				Gary Thompson, St. Cloud FL	91
				crashed dest., Shreveland LA (Thompson k.)	9.1.91
FL.592 •	T Mk. 1	**XR998**		RAF Halton: inst. airframe	79/93
			N998XR	John R. Mulvey, Aurora CO	10.5.95
FL.594 •	T Mk. 1	**XS100**		RAF Halton: inst. airframe	80/86
			N7CV	Morgan Merrill/Jet 1 Inc, Alexandria VA	4.90
				McDonnell Enterprises, California City CA	3.92/95
				(noted dism., unconv., California City 11.92/93)	
FL.595 •	T Mk. 1	**XS101**		RAF Cranwell: inst. airframe	80
			G-GNAT	B. J. S. Grey, Duxford	14.4.82
				Arnold J. Glass/Ruanil Investments, Cranfield	29.8.83/95
FL.596 •	T Mk. 1	**XS102**		RAF Halton: inst.airframe	3.79/87
				RAF Cosford: inst. airframe: TT 3238 hrs	6.87/90
				Bob Thomson: sold at RAF auction	9.3.90
			G-MOUR	Intrepid Aviation, North Weald	16.5.90/95
				(ff Leavesden 6.91, flies as Yellowjacks "XR991")	

Folland Gnat/Hindustan HF24 Adjeet

FL.598 •	T Mk. 1	**XS104**		RAF Cosford: instructional airframe	80/88
				Ruanil Investments, Cranfield	12.88
			G-FRCE	Butane Buzzard Aviation Corp, North Weald	11.89/95
				(rest. Cranfield, ff 2.12.90)	
FL.599 •	T Mk. 1	**XS105**		RAF Cosford: inst. airframe: TT 3371 hrs	80/90
				sold at RAF auction	9.3.90
				Sporting International Ltd	
			N18GT	Pyramid Aerospace Inc, Houston TX	23.3.90
				Cinema Air Jet Centre Inc, Carlsbad CA	1.91/95
FL.601 •	T Mk. 1	**XS107**		RAF Cosford: inst. airframe: TT 2905 hrs	80/88
				sold at RAF auction 9.3.90: shipped to USA	5.90
			N107XS	NTC Group Inc, Wilmington DE	12.3.93/95
FL.603 •	T Mk. 1	**XS109**		RAF Cosford: inst. airframe	82/84
				RAF Halton: inst. airframe	.84/92
				sold at RAF auction 3.92: shipped to USA	9.92
				Downbird USA	3.11.92
			N61457	Welcome Aviation, Redmond WA	7.93/95
				(noted at Seattle-Boeing Field WA 10.93)	
FL.604 •	T Mk. 1	**XS110**		RAF Halton: inst. airframe	84/90
				sold at RAF auction: poor condition	9.3.90
			N7152Z	Jim Cullen/Westair Int'l, Broomfield CO	7.90
				International Jet Centre, Miami FL	8.90
			N110XS	Duncan Young Partnership, Miami FL	9.90/92
				International Jet Centre, Miami FL	11.93/95
- •	Ajeet	**E276**		(built by Hindustan Aircraft, Bangalore)	
				(to Indian AF as E276)	
				David C. Tallichet/MARC, Chino CA	86/93
				(stored dism. Chino 88/91)	
- •	Ajeet	**E296**		David C. Tallichet/MARC, Chino CA	86/89
				(stored dism. Chino 88/89)	
				George Perez, Reno NV	.89/93
- •	Ajeet	**E299**		David C. Tallichet/MARC, Chino CA	86/93
				(stored dism. Chino 88/91)	
- •	Ajeet	**E315**		David C. Tallichet/MARC, Chino CA	86/93

Gloster G41 Meteor

- •	F Mk. 4	**VT229**		RAF Museum, RAF Colerne	65/76
				Jeff Hawke: displ. Duxford: arr.	3.76/83
				Newark Aircraft Museum, Winthorpe: arr.	23.4.83/91
			N229VT	Kermit A. Weeks/Weeks Air Museum, Tamiami FL	8.91/95
				(shipped ex UK 8.91, stored)	
G5-361641 •	F Mk. 8	**VZ467**		RAF Brawdy: last RAF Meteor flight	22.10.74
				RAF Shawbury: "Winston", stored	84/86
				(stored as spare for RAF CFS Vintage Pair)	
			G-METE	Adrian Gjertsen/Air Support Aviation Services/ Classic Jets, Biggin Hill	5.11.91/94
				(rest. RAF Cosford, ff 11.5.94 "VZ467 Winston")	
- •	T Mk. 7	**VZ638**		Historic Aircraft Museum, Southend : arr.	12.1.72/83
			G-JETM	Mike Carlton/Brencham Historic Aircraft Ltd, Hurn : purchased at museum auction	10.5.83/87
				Aces High Ltd, North Weald	1.10.87/88
				Peter G. Vallance/Vallance By-Ways Museum, Charlwood: static displ.	.88/95

c/n		Type	Serial	Reg	History	Date
-	•	T Mk. 7	WA591		Jim Cassidy, Woodvale: stored	86/93
					Meteor Flight, Yatesbury	.93/94
					(stored Yatesbury 93/94 pending rest. to fly)	
6496	•	F Mk. 8			(to Belgian AF as EG162)	
				OO-ARU	COGEA Nouvelle, Ostende	27.8.58/61
					sold to Belgian Congo	2.3.61
					(returned to Belgian AF as EG162)	
					Dinant AB, Belgium: displ.	79
					Musee de la Citadel, Dinant, Belgium: displ.	92
-	•	NF Mk. 11 TT Mk. 20	WD592	N94749	Al Letcher & Associates, Mojave CA	12.74/88
					(del. Biggin Hill to Mojave 18-22.6.75)	
					Al Hansen & Ascher Ward, Mojave CA	.88/94
					struck-off USCR	4.1.94
					USAFM, Edwards AFB CA	.94
-	•	NF Mk. 11 TT Mk. 20	WD767		based RAAF Woomera SA: missile research	70/75
					Pearce Dunn/Warbirds Aviation Museum,	
					Mildura VIC: del. ex Woomera	7.75/94
					Don Subritzky, Auckland-Dairy Flat NZ	.94
					(shipped, arr. dism. Dairy Flat 6.94: rest. to fly)	
-	•	T Mk. 7	WF825		Jim Cassidy, Woodvale UK: stored	86/93
					Meteor Flight, Yatesbury	.93/94
					(stored Yatesbury 93/94 pending rest. to fly)	
G5-1496	•	TT Mk. 7	WF833	SE-CAS	Svensk Flygtjanst AB, Bromma: del.	29.7.55/74
					(wfu Stockholm-Bromma 4.59/74)	
					Flygvapenmuseum, Linkoping, Sweden: del.	29.7.74/92
-	•	T Mk. 7	WF877		op: Flight Refuelling Ltd, Tarrant Rushton	6.66/74
					Torbay Aircraft Museum, Higher Blagdon	2.74/78
					Mike Woodley/Aces High Ltd, North Weald	19.10.88
				G-BPOA	Aces High Ltd, North Weald	16.3.89/94
					(static displ. North Weald 94)	
G5-1525	•	T Mk. 7		G-ANSO	Gloster Aircraft Ltd, Hucclecote	12.6.54/56
					(wfu Moreton Valence 9.56/58)	
				SE-DCC	Svensk Flygtjanst AB, Bromma: del.	11.8.59
					Flygvapnets Flygmuseum, Malmslatt: del.	16.9.74
					Svedino's Bil Och Flygmuseum, Ugglarp,	
					Sweden: displ. as "WS774"	80/92
-	•	F Mk. 8	WK914		RAF Manston : fire dump	77/82
					Medway Aircraft Pres. Society, Rochester	83/88
					Old Flying Machine Co, Duxford UK	.88/93
					(arr. Duxford by road 8.8.88, rest. to fly 93)	
S4/U/2342	•	NF Mk. 11 TT Mk. 20 NF Mk. 11	WM167		Flight Refuelling Ltd, Tarrant Rushton	.65/75
					Warbirds of GB, Blackbushe: del.	12.75/84
					(conv. TT20 to NF.11, stored Blackbushe)	
				G-LOSM	Mike Carlton/Brencham Historic Aircraft Ltd/	
					Hunter One Collection, Hurn	8.6.84/87
					(del. Blackbushe - Hurn 6.7.84)	
					LGH Aviation/Jet Heritage Collection, Hurn	1.10.87/89
					Hunter Wing Ltd/Jet Heritage Collection, Hurn	3.5.89/94
					(flown from 8.84 as "WM167", rest. Hurn ff 8.91)	
AW.2163	•	NF Mk. 14	WM261	G-ARCX	Ferranti Ltd, Edinburgh-Turnhouse	8.9.60/69
					wfu Edinburgh	12.69
					Museum of Flight, East Fortune, Scotland	76/93
AW.5582	•	NF Mk. 13	WM334		(to IDFAF as 157/BK800/4X-FNB)	
				4X-BET	Israel Aircraft Industries, Tel Aviv-Lod	.71/72

				(ret. IDFAF as 157/4X-FNB)	
				Israeli Air Force Museum, Hatzerim AB	81/92
AW.	NF Mk. 11	**WM391**		(to RDAF as 51-508: later TT.20 H-508)	
5549 •	TT Mk. 20		SE-DCH	Svensk Flygtjanst AB, Stockholm-Bromma	6.8.62/69
			D-CAKU	ntu: Flugzeughandelsgesellchaft Karlsruhe	29.10.69
				(del. Malmo-Germany 15.3.69, sale to Biafra	
				aborted; abandoned Gosselies, Belgium 69/75)	
			SE-DCH	Musee Royal de l'Armee, Brussels	84
				Musee du Chateau, Savigny-les-Beaune France	92/93
AW.	NF Mk. 11	**WM395**		(to RDAF as 51-512: later TT.20 H-512)	
5562 •	TT Mk. 20		SE-DCF	Svensk Flygtjanst AB, Stockholm-Bromma	27.8.62/69
			D-CAKY	ntu: Flugzeughandelsgesellchaft Karlsruhe	29.10.69
				(del. Malmo-Germany 15.3.69, sale to Biafra	
				aborted; abandoned Gosselies, Belgium 69/75)	
			SE-DCF	Musee Royal de l'Armee, Brussels	84
				Musee du Chateau, Savigny-les-Beaune France	92/93
AW.	NF Mk. 14	**WS804**	G-AXNE	Target Towing Aircraft Co Ltd	28.8.69
5803				abandoned Bissau, Portuguese Guinea	9.69/72
				(during attempted del. flight to Biafra)	
- •	NF Mk. 14	**WS807**		RAF Watton: gate guard (on J8106593 Cpl Coggan's inventory!)	81/92
				Meteor Flight, Yatesbury	.92/94
				(trucked to Yatesbury 12.92, rest. to fly)	

GRUMMAN F9F PANTHER/COUGAR

- •	F9F-3	**Bu123072**		Air Service & Supply Co, Tulsa OK: scrap	73
			N72WP	Jack Levine & William Pryor, Pontiac MI	1.79/85
				(rest. Pontiac MI, using parts from hulk of	
				Bu127180 ex Philadelphia Navy yard, ff 30.7.83)	
				Arthur A. Wolk/Flying Warbirds Foundation,	
				Philadelphia PA	10.85/95
				(flies as "USN 123072/806V")	
- •	F9F-2B	**Bu123078**		I. N. Burchinall Jnr, Paris TX	74
			N9525A	reg. candidate	4.78
				Mark E. Foster, Aurora CO	12.84/87
				Harry S. Doan/Doan Helicopter Inc,	
				New Smyrna Beach FL (flew in USN scheme)	4.87/92
				offered for sale, Doan auction: TT 201 hrs	30.10.92
				James Cavanaugh/Cavanaugh Flight Museum,	
				Dallas-Addison TX	10.92/95
				(trucked FL to Ft Wayne IN, arr. 25.11.92,	
				rest., flies as "123078/A109")	
K.125 •	F9F-2	**Bu123420**		Travel Town, Griffith Park, Los Angeles CA	.58/90
				Eagle Field Museum, Firebaugh CA	92/93
			N32313	Joseph L. Davis, Fresno CA	30.6.94
				Kermit Weeks, Polk City FL	6.95
K.228 •	F9F-2	**Bu123526**	**N3456G**	California Airmotive, Van Nuys CA	66
				Arthur W. McDonnell & John D. Moore,	
				Lancaster/Mojave CA	13.1.66/74
				(trucked Lancaster-Fox to Mojave 2.11.70,	
				static rest. for USMCM as "123526/WL")	
				USMCM, MCAS Quantico VA	79/94
- •	F9F-5	**Bu125434**	**N1332F**	Van Dusen Airport Services	8.81
				Thomas E. Wright, Snyder TX	84/90
				Roger A. Christgau, Edina MN	9.90/95
				(USCR changed id. 125434 to "125467W")	
- •	F9F-6P	**Bu127487**	**N7993A**	John G. Johnson, Dallas TX	65/69
	RF-9F		**N9FP**	George Perez, Reno NV	77

c/n		Model	Serial	Reg	History	Date	
					I. N. Burchinall Jnr, Paris TX	78/80	
					Le Tourneau College, Longview TX	84	
					Condor Enterprises Inc	84	
					Howard Pardue/Breckenridge Aviation Museum,		
					Breckenridge TX	87	
					David H. Turlington, Greensboro NC	88	
					struck-off USCR	4.89	
					USMCAM, Cherry Point MCAS NC	94	
					(USCR quotes id. as "15")		
-	•	F9F-8P	**Bu141675**	**N9256**	Sergio Tomassoni, Buckeye AZ	76/78	RF-9J
					noted unconv. derelict, Buckeye AZ	76/78	
					rep. aircraft noted Phoenix-Deer Valley AZ	92	
-		F9F-8T	Bu142498	N24WJ	(to Argentine Navy as ....)	.62	TF-9J
					Don Whittington/World Jet Inc,		
					Fort Lauderdale FL	7.89/91	
					(rest., flew as "Marines 142498/YU")		
					crashed in sea off Louisiana coastline	31.10.91	
					(id. assumed, USCR quotes "A-20-60")		
-	•	F9F-2	-		Earl J. Ware/Ware's Mobile Home Court,		
					Jacksonville FL: stored dism.	84	
				N......	Harry S. Doan/Doan Helicopters Inc,		
					New Smyrna Beach FL: reg. candidate	4.89/92	
					offered for sale dism., Doan auction	30.10.92	
					(rep. as Bu123652 but this held by USMCM,		
					displ. at main gate MCAS El Toro CA 88/93)		

HAWKER HUNTER

c/n		Model	Serial	Reg	History	Date
-	•	F Mk. 4	**WT706**		(to FA Peru as T62-681)	2.60
		T Mk. 7			Corporacion Tecnica del Peru SA	92
		T Mk. 62		**N5196Z**	Hermes Technical International Inc, Miami FL	11.92/95
41H/		F Mk. 4	**WT722**		sold at auction, ex Royal Navy FRADU	27.7.95
670689	•	T Mk. 8C		**G-BWGN**	Barry J. Pover & B. J. Pearson, Exeter	15.8.95
-	•	F Mk. 4	**WV267**		RNAS Culdrose: stored	93
		GA. Mk.11			George Lazik, Chatsworth CA	.94
					(dism. North Weald UK 4.94 pending shipping)	
-	•	F Mk. 4	**WV272**		(to Republic of Singapore AF as 540): del.	18.7.73/94
		T Mk. 75			Geoff Moesker, Brisbane QLD	.94/95
					(shipped from Singapore to Darwin NT 7.95)	
-	•	F Mk. 4	**WV331**		(to Republic of Singapore AF as 543): del.	16.8.73/94
		GA Mk.74B			Geoff Moesker, Brisbane QLD	.94/95
					(shipped from Singapore to Darwin NT 7.95)	
					(rep. to be broken-up for spares)	
-	•	F Mk. 4	**WV386**		(to Republic of Singapore AF as 532): del.	15.12.72
		T Mk. 75			Geoff Moesker, Brisbane QLD	.94/95
					(shipped to Brisbane-Archerfield 7.95)	
41H/		F Mk. 6	**XE527**		(to Swiss AF as J-4006): del.	2.10.58/95
679902	•	F Mk. 58			Canadian Warplane Heritage, Hamilton ONT	.95
					(being dism. RAF Lyneham for Canada 7.95)	
41H/		F Mk. 6	**XE587**	**N587XE**	Andrew N. McNeil, Augusta NJ	5.3.92/95
679948	•				(ex RAE, Farnborough : shipped to US 3.92)	
41H/		F Mk. 6	**XE599**		(to Republic of Singapore AF as 535): del.	14.3.73/94
679957	•	FR Mk.10			Geoff Moesker, Brisbane QLD	.94/95
		FGA Mk.74B			(shipped from Singapore to Darwin NT 7.95)	
41H/		FGA Mk. 9	**XE611**		(to Swiss AF as J-4103): del.	17.1.72/95
679969	•	F Mk.58A		**N4103Y**	Randall K. Hames, Gaffney NC	28.6.95
					(del. Switzerland to USA, via Southend 11.9.95)	
-	•	F Mk. 6	**XE614**		(to Republic of Singapore AF as 533): del.	21.2.73/94
		FR Mk.10			Geoff Moesker, Brisbane QLD	.94/95

	FGA Mk.74B			(shipped from Singapore to Darwin NT 7.95)	
41H/ 679991 •	F Mk. 6A	**XE653**		RAF Scampton: sold at auction	26.11.94
				(rep. still in orig. 111sqdn o/a black sc.)	
			G-BVWV	Barry J. Pover, Exeter	22.12.94
				Mike Beachy-Head, Cape Town, South Africa	12.94/95
				(del. Scampton to Exeter 24.1.95)	
			ZU-AUJ	Mike Beachy-Head, Cape Town : reg. res.	.95
HABL/ 003007 •	F Mk. 4	**XE664**		(to Republic of Singapore AF as 516): del.	9.70/94
	T Mk. 8			Geoff Moesker, Brisbane QLD	.94/95
	T Mk. 75			David Philips	.95
				(shipped from Singapore to Darwin NT 7.95)	
HABL/ 003008 •	F Mk. 4	**XE665**		sold at auction, ex Royal Navy FRADU	27.7.95
	T Mk. 8C		**G-BWGM**	Barry J. Pover & B. J. Pearson, Exeter	15.8.95
HABL/ 003020 •	F Mk. 4	**XE677**		Hawker Siddeley Aircraft Ltd, Dunsfold	7.4.61/62
				Loughborough College: inst. airframe : arr.	9.1.62/89
			G-HHUN	Jet Heritage Collection/Hunter Wing Ltd, Hurn	10.89/94
				(rest. Hurn 92/94, ff 21.1.94)	
				W/O DUNSFOLD SURREY 5th JUNE 1998	
HABL/ 003028 •	F Mk. 4	**XE685**	**G-GAII**	RNAS Yeovilton: sold at auction	26.11.94
	GA. Mk. 11			Barry J. Pover, Exter	7.12.94
HABL/ 003032 •	F Mk. 4	**XE689**		sold at auction, ex Royal Navy FRADU	27.7.95
	GA Mk. 11		**G-BWGK**	Barry J. Pover & B. J. Pearson, Exeter	15.8.95
HABL/ 003038 •	F Mk. 4	**XE707**		Barry J. Pover, Exter: ex RNAS Yeovilton	12.94
	GA Mk. 11		G-BVYH	J. F.Read/Almalgamated Air Services, Exeter	31.1.95
				(due to be del. Yeovilton-Exeter 1.95)	
			N707XE	George Lazik/Hunter Flight Test Ltd,	
				Van Nuys CA	6.95
				(dep. Exeter on del. to USA 10.7.95)	
				(id. officially quoted as 41H-004048)	
HABL/R 003050 •	F Mk. 4	**XF289**		Barry J. Pover, Exter: ex RNAS Yeovilton	12.94
	T Mk. 8C		G-BVYI	J. F.Read/Almalgamated Air Services, Exeter	31.1.95
				(due to be del. Yeovilton-Exeter 1.95)	
			N289XF	George Lazik/Hunter Flight Test Ltd,	
				Van Nuys CA	6.95
				(dep. Exeter on del. to USA 10.7.95)	
				(id. officially quoted as 41H-695942)	
HABL/ 003062 •	F Mk. 4	**XF301**		RAF Shawbury: inst. airframe	
	GA Mk.11			Jet Heritage, Bournemouth-Hurn	.94/95
				(arr. dism. Bournemouth 12.94)	
				stored Bournemouth, pending export to USA	
HABL/ 003080 •	F Mk. 4	**XF319**		RAF Halton: inst. airframe	84/90
			G-BTCY	Gray Tuplin Ltd, Southall	22.1.91
				Edward C. Stead, Manchester NH	.91/92
				(shipped to Manchester NH, assembled by 9.91)	
41H/ 695946 •	F Mk. 4	**XF357**		sold at auction, ex Royal Navy FRADU	27.7.95
	T Mk. 8C		**G-BWGL**	Barry J. Pover & B. J. Pearson, Exeter	15.8.95
HABL/ 003098 •	F Mk. 4	**XF369**		(to Republic of Singapore AF as 538): del.	9.4.73/94
	FR Mk.74B			Geoff Moesker, Brisbane QLD	.94/95
				(shipped from Singapore to Darwin NT 7.95)	
- •	F Mk. 6A	**XF375**		RAF Cranwell: inst. airframe: del.	1.82/91
				Old Flying Machine Co, Duxford	.91/92
			G-BUEZ	Old Flying Machine Co, Duxford	3.4.92/95
				(rest. to fly Duxford, using parts from XJ676)	
S4/U/ 3308 •	F Mk. 6	**XF432**	G-BABM	Hawker Siddeley Aviation, Dunsfold	21.8.72
	FR Mk.10			(to Republic of Singapore AF as 526): del.	11.10.72
	FGA Mk.74B			Geoff Moesker, Brisbane QLD	.94/95
				Mike McFadden	.95
				(shipped from Singapore to Darwin NT 7.95)	

c/n	Model	Serial	Reg.	History	Date
- •	F Mk. 6 FGA Mk. 9 FR Mk. 74A	**XF437**		(to Republic of Singapore AF as 503): del. Geoff Moesker, Brisbane QLD (shipped from Singapore to Darwin NT 7.95) (under rest. Brisbane-Archerfield QLD 9.95)	24.6.71/94 .94/95
- •	F Mk. 6 FR Mk.10 FGA Mk.74B	**XF441**		(to Republic of Singapore AF as 545): del. Geoff Moesker, Brisbane QLD (shipped from Singapore to Darwin NT 7.95)	16.8.73/94 .94/95
- •	F Mk. 6 FR Mk.10 FGA Mk.74B	**XF460**		(to Republic of Singapore AF as 546): del. Geoff Moesker, Brisbane QLD (shipped from Singapore to Darwin NT 7.95)	11.10.73 .94/95
- •	F Mk. 6	**XF515**		RAF Scampton: sold by auction Global Aviation Ltd, Binbrook	12.94 12.94
S4/U/ 3362 •	F Mk. 6A	**XF516**	 **G-BVVC**	RAF Cranwell: inst. airframe P. Hellier, Maidenhead (del. Cranwell-Exeter 21.11.94 for rest.)	4.81/94 10.94
HABL/ 003118 •	F Mk. 4 T Mk. 75A	**XF950**		(to Republic of Singapore AF as 536): del. Geoff Moesker, Brisbane QLD (shipped from Singapore to Darwin NT 7.95)	13.4.73/94 .94/95
HABL/ 003119 •	F Mk. 4 T Mk. 68	**XF951**		(to Swiss AF as J-4202): del. Swiss Aviation Air Museum, Santa Teresa NM	12.74/95 .95
HABL/ 003124 •	F Mk. 4 FGA Mk.74B	**XF969**		(to Republic of Singapore AF as 529): del. Geoff Moesker, Brisbane QLD (shipped from Singapore to Darwin NT 7.95)	15.12.72 .94/95
HABL/ 003125 •	F Mk. 4 T Mk. 75A	**XF970**		(to Republic of Singapore AF as 528): del. Geoff Moesker, Brisbane QLD David Currie, Singapore: to be based Brisbane (shipped, arr. dism. Brisbane-Archerfield 1.7.95)	10.11.72 .94/95 .95
HABL/ 003129 •	F Mk. 4	**XF974**	 **G-BTCX**	RAF Halton: inst. airframe Gray Tuplin Ltd, Southall Edward C./ Stead, Manchester NH (shipped to Manchester NH, stored dism. by 9.91)	84/90 22.1.91 .91
HABL/ 003142 •	F Mk. 4 F Mk. 73B	**XF987**		(to R Jordan AF as 842) (to Sultan of Oman AF as 842) R Jordan AF Historic Flight	 94 .94
885602 •	F Mk. 6A FR. Mk. 10 F. Mk. 58A	**XG127**	 **SE-DXC**	(to Swiss AF as J-4101): del. Eskilstunas Flygmuseum AB: reg. res. (del. to Satenas AB, Sweden 24.5.95)	7.12.71/95 7.6.95
S4/U/ 3393 •	F Mk. 6A	**XG160**	 **G-BWAF**	RAF Scampton: sold by auction King Hussein of Jordan (arr. dism. Bournemouth ex Scampton 21.1.95 for rest. for R Jordanian AF Historic Flight) RV Aviation Ltd, Bournemouth	12.94 12.94 24.2.95
- •	F Mk. 6A	**XG172**		RAF Scampton: sold by auction Richard J. Everitt, Ipswich	12.94 12.94
- •	F Mk. 6 GA Mk. 9 FR Mk. 74A	**XG205**		(to Republic of Singapore AF as 506): del. Geoff Moesker, Brisbane QLD (shipped from Singapore to Darwin NT 7.95)	24.6.71/94 .94/95
- •	F Mk. 6 FGA Mk. 9 FR Mk. 74A	**XG266**		(to Republic of Singapore AF as 521): del. Geoff Moesker, Brisbane QLD (shipped from Singapore to Darwin NT 7.95)	8.6.72/94 .94/95
- •	F Mk. 6 FGA Mk. 9 FR Mk. 74A	**XG292**		(to Republic of Singapore AF as 512): del. Geoff Moesker, Brisbane QLD Jim Czerwinski, Caboolture QLD (shiped to Brisbane-Archerfield QLD 7.95)	4.8.71/94 .94/95 .95

c/n	Mark	Serial	Reg.	History	Date
- •	F Mk. 6 F Mk. 9 FGA Mk. 74	**XJ685**		(to Republic of Singapore AF as 502): del. Geoff Moesker, Brisbane QLD (shipped from Singapore to Darwin NT 7.95)	12.11.70 .94/95
- •	F Mk. 6 FGA Mk. 9 FR Mk. 74A	**XJ689**		(to Republic of Singapore AF as 517): del. Geoff Moesker, Brisbane QLD David Philips NZ (shipped to Brisbane-Archerfield 7.95)	4.8.71/94 .94/95 .95
- •	F Mk. 6 FR Mk. 10 FGA Mk. 74B	**XJ714**		(to Republic of Singapore AF as 531): del. Geoff Moesker, Brisbane QLD (shipped from Singapore to Darwin NT 7.95)	17.1.73 .94/95
HABL/ 003311 •	T Mk. 7	**XL572**	 **G-HNTR**	RAF Cosford: inst. airframe Hunter Wing Ltd: arr. dism. Hurn Hunter Wing Ltd/Jet Heritage, Hurn (rest. to fly, Brough 91: inst. airframe 93/95) Yorkshire Air Museum, Elvington: arr.	88 12.88 7.7.89/91 1.95
HABL/ 003360 •	T Mk. 7	**XL573**	 **G-BVGH**	RAF Lossiemouth: last flight RAF Shawbury: stored Barry J. Pover/Lightning Flying Club, Exeter (trucked to Exeter 12.93, rest: ff 7.5.94)	22.3.91 3.91/93 11.93/95
- •	T Mk. 7	**XL576**	 **N576NL**	Edward C. Stead, Manchester NH Northern Lights Aircraft Inc, Montgomery AL Wally Fisk/Amjet Aircraft Corp, St Paul MN	.88 6.2.89/91 1.95
-	T Mk. 7	**XL595**	 **G-BTYL**	RAF St Athan: arr. for storage Wallace Cubitt/Cubitt Aviation, Foulsham (rest. RAF Coltishall 91/92, ff 17.12.92) crashed, dest., near Sheffield (Cubitt k.)	7.84/91 10.91/93 11.6.93
41H/ 693836 •	T Mk. 7 T Mk. 8C	**XL598**	 G-BVWG **ZU-ATH**	RNAS Yeovilton: sold at auction Barry J. Pover, Cranfield Mike Beachy-Head, Cape Town, South Africa (del. Yeovilton to Exeter 1.95: dep. Ipswich on del. to SA 19.4.95) Mike Beachy-Head, Cape Town (c/n 41H-695320 also quoted)	26.11.94 8.12.94/95 12.94 5.95
- •	T Mk. 7	**XL600**	 **G-BVWN**	RNAY Fleetlands: sold at auction Grey Tuplin, Southall: stored P. J. Tuplin, Southall	4.92 4.92/94 23.12.94
41H/ 695332 •	T Mk. 8M	**XL602**	**G-BWFT**	Barry J. Pover & B. R. Pearson, Exeter (centre fuselage c/n 41H-694512)	24.7.95
41H/ 695347 •	T Mk. 7A	**XL613**	 **G-BVMF**	RAF Shawbury: stored Barry J. Pover/Lightning Flying Club, Exeter	 22.4.94/95
41H/ 695449 •	T Mk. 7	**XL617**	 G-HHNT **N617NL**	RAF Cosford: inst. airframe Hunter Wing Ltd: arr. dism. Hurn Hunter Wing Ltd/Jet Heritage, Hurn Northern Lights Aircraft Inc, Montgomery AL Grace Aire Inc, Corpus Christi TX	88 12.88 7.7.89 11.89/94 5.94/95
41H/ 695454 •	T Mk. 7	**XL621**	 **G-BNCX**	Royal Aircraft Establishment, Beford:disposal Louvaux Ltd, Hurn : del. stored Hurn 87/93, struck-off reg. (rest. to fly, Hurn 93)	.86 30.1.87 11.3.93
41H/ 695432 •	T Mk. 7	**XM126**	 **PH-NLH**	RAF ntu: (to R Netherlands AF as N-320) Dutch National Air Laboratory, Schiphol Staravia Ltd, Exeter UK: del. ex Schiphol (stored Exeter 80/86): rep. sold to USA	.59 27.1.66/80 22.1.80/86 .86
41H/ 693833 •	T Mk. 53	**35-271**		(to R Danish AF as 35-271, ET-271): del. Hawker Siddeley Aircraft Ltd, Dunsfold Blackbushe Engineering Ltd, Blackbushe	8.11.58 .76/79 .79/87

				(trucked to Blackbushe 7.79, stored 7.79/85)	
				Booker Aircraft Museum, Booker: loan, arr.	5.10.85/87
			G-BNFT	Peter F.A. Hoare/Militair, Cranfield	27.2.87
			N10271	Edward C. Stead, Bedford NH	3.87/95
- •	Mk. 51	**35-403**		(R Danish AF as 35-403, later E-403)	
				Hawker Siddeley Aircraft Ltd, Dunsfold: arr.	12.75
			N72602	Al Letcher & Associates, Mojave CA	2.78/85
				(shipped to Mojave CA: ff 23.5.78)	
				Al Hansen & Ascher Ward, Mojave CA	89/93
41H/ 680277 •	Mk. 51	**35-418**		(R Danish AF as 35-418, E-418): del.	22.6.56/74
				Hawker Siddeley Aircraft Ltd, Dunsfold: arr.	12.75/78
				Surrey & Sussex Aviation Society, Chipstead	.78
			G-HUNT	Spencer R. Flack, Elstree	5.7.78/81
				(rest. Elstree, ff 20.3.80)	
				Mike Carlton/Brencham Historic Aircraft Ltd/ Hunter One Collection, Hurn	9.81/87
				David C. Tallichet/MARC, Chino CA	1.10.87
			N50972	Jim Robinson, Houston TX	12.87
			N611JR	Jim Robinson/Combat Jets Flying Museum, Houston TX	2.88/92
				EAA Aviation Foundation, Oshkosh WI	.92/95
				(flies as "RAF WB188")	
41H/ 693749 •	T Mk. 7 T Mk. 53	**N-307**		(R Netherlands AF as N-307)	.58/67
				(to R Danish AF as ET-274)	7.3.67/73
				Hawker Siddeley Aircraft Ltd, Dunsfold: arr.	12.75
			G-BOOM	Brian R. Kay/Ambrion Aviation, Leavesden	6.10.80/82
				(rest. Leavesden, ff 24.4.81)	
				Mike Carlton/Brencham Historic Aircraft Ltd/ Hunter One Collection, Hurn	29.9.82/87
				LGH Aviation Ltd/Jet Heritage, Hurn	1.10.87/93
				Rory C. McCarthy, North Weald	11.93/94
				Royal Jordanian Air Force Historic Flight	94/95
				op: Jet Heritage for RJAFHF as "RJAF 800"	
- • J. 34	Mk. 50	**Fv34006**		(to R Swedish AF as Fv34006): BOC	21.1.56/68
				displ. Tullinge, Sweden: SOC	12.9.68
				David C. Tallichet/MARC, Chino CA	.83/87
				(airfreighted to CA by RSwAF C-130 .84)	
				Jim Robinson/Combat Jets Flying Museum, Houston TX	11.87
				Ed Stead, Manchester NH	1.88/93
				(rebuilt as T. Mk. 8 with nose of WT745)	
HABL/ 003215 •	Mk. 50 J. 34 T Mk. 68	**Fv34080**		(to R Swedish AF as Fv34080)	
				(to Swiss AF as J-4208): del.	3.6.75/95
				Golden Europe Jet Club, Stuttgart, Germany	.95
			G-HVIP	Golden Europe Jet De Lux Club Ltd	7.7.95
				(del. to Bournemouth-Hurn 16.6.95)	
H.IF.19	Mk. 66A		G-APUX	Hawker Aircraft Ltd, Dunsfold: demonstrator	24.6.59/63
				(demonstrator: built from nose from Indian AF T.66 BS369 & fuse. of Belgian AF T.6 IF-19)	
				(to Iraqi AF as 567): del.	30.5.63/64
				(to Lebanese AF as L-581)	65
				Hawker Siddeley Aircraft Ltd, Dunsfold: del.	18.12.65
	T Mk. 72			(rebuilt Dunsfold as T.72, ff 27.6.67)	
				(to Chile AF as J-718): shipped	8.67
41H/ 694926 •	F Mk. 58	**J-4021**		(Swiss AF as J-4021): del.	18.3.59/95
			G-BWIU	Historic Flyers Ltd	26.10.95
41H/ 697394 •	F Mk. 58	**J-4025**		(Swiss AF as J-4025): del.	23.3.59/95
				RAF Benevolent Fund, RAF Fairford UK	7.95
				(handed over at RAF Fairford 22.7.95)	
			G-BWKC	R. V. Aviation Ltd, Hurn	12.10.95
				op. for R Jordanian AF Historic Flight	
- •	F Mk. 58	**J-4029**		(Swiss AF as J-4029): del.	26.3.59/95
				(being dism. RAF Lyneham for Canada 7.95)	

c/n	Type	Serial	Reg	Owner / History	Date
41H/ 697397 •	F Mk. 58	**J-4030**		(Swiss AF as J-4030): del.	24.5.59/95
				Flygvapenmuseum, Malmslatt	95
			SE-DXD	Eskilstuna Flygmuseum AB: reg. res.	7.6.95
				(del. to Satenas AB, Sweden 24.5.95)	
41H/ 694936 •	F Mk. 58	**J-4031**		(Swiss AF as J-4031): del.	17.4.59/95
			G-BWFR	Old Flying Machine Co, Duxford: del.	28.6.95
				(centre fuselage c/n 41H-697398)	
- •	F Mk. 58	**J-4035**		(Swiss AF as J-4035): del.	24.4.59/95
				(del. Switzerland to Southend UK 12.7.95)	
41H/ 698741 •	F Mk. 58	**J-4058**		(Swiss AF as J-4058): del.	14.8.59/95
				R. J. Everett, Ipswich UK: del. via Southend	26.6.95
			G-BWFS	Old Flying Machine Co, Duxford UK	24.7.95
- •	F Mk. 58	**J-4059**		(Swiss AF as J-4059): del.	17.8.59/95
				(del. to Geneva 12.9.95, en route South Africa)	
41H/ 697427 •	F Mk. 58	**J-4060**		(Swiss AF as J-4060): del.	24.8.59/95
				Worldwide Jet Aircraft Museum,	
				Corona del Mar CA	.95
				(del. Switzerland to Southend UK 12.7.95)	
			N58WJ	reg.	7.95
41H/ 697428 •	F Mk. 58	**J-4061**		(Swiss AF as J-4061): del.	2.9.59/95
			N58MX	Mid Atlantic Air Museum, Reading PA	8.95
				(del. Switzerland to USA via Southend 1.9.95)	
41H/ 697433 •	F Mk. 58	**J-4066**		(Swiss AF as J-4066): del.	23.9.59/95
				Aviantic Association, Caen, France	.95
41H/ 697442 •	F Mk. 58	**J-4075**		(Swiss AF as J-4075): del.	10.59/95
				R Jordanian AF Historic Flight, Hurn UK: del.	16.6.95
			G-BWKA	R. V. Aviation Ltd, Hurn	12.10.95
				op. for R Jordanian AF Historic Flight	
41H/ 697443 •	F Mk. 58A	**J-4076**		(Swiss AF as J-4076): del.	11.59/95
			G-HONE	N. Brodie/Aeromec International Resources Ltd,	
				North Weald	23.8.95
				(del. Switzerland to North Weald 12.7.95)	
41H/ 697447 •	F Mk. 58	**J-4080**		(Swiss AF as J-4080): del.	12.59/95
			HB-RVT	reg.	7.95
41H/ 697448 •	F Mk. 58	**J-4081**		(Swiss AF as J-4081): del.	12.59/95
				R Jordanian AF Historic Flight, Hurn UK: del.	16.6.95
			G-BWKB	R. V. Aviation Ltd, Hurn	12.10.95
				op. for R Jordanian AF Historic Flight	
41H/ 697450 •	F Mk. 58	**J-4083**		(Swiss AF as J-4083): del.	12.59/95
				Jet Heritage Ltd, Bournemouth-Hurn UK: del.	16.6.95
			G-EGHH	Jet Heritage Ltd, Bournemouth-Hurn	4.7.95
41H/ 698454 •	F Mk. 58A	**J-4087**		(Swiss AF as J-4087): del.	14.1.60/95
				West London Aero Club, White Waltham UK	.95
			G-HTWO	N. Brodie/Aeromec International Resources Ltd,	
				North Weald	23.8.95
				(del. Switzerland to North Weald 12.7.95)	
XE77 •	F Mk. 58	**J-4089**		(Swiss AF as J-4089): del.	14.1.60/95
			OY-SKB	ntu: Scandinavian Historic Flight	23.2.94/95
			SE-DXA	Scandinavian Historic Flight, Solna	15.6.95
				(del. to Satenas AB, Sweden 5.5.95)	
41H/ 697457 •	F Mk. 58	**J-4090**		(Swiss AF as J-4090): del.	20.1.60/95
				Champlin Fighter Museum, Mesa AZ	.95
				(del. Switzerland to Southend UK 12.7.95)	
			G-SIAL	Sark International Airways Ltd, Hurn	2.10.95

c/n	Mark	Serial	Civil reg.	History	Date
- •	F Mk. 58	**J-4091**		(Swiss AF as J-4091): del.	22.1.60/95
				N. Martin/Phoenix Aviation, Bruntingthorpe	.95
				(del. Bruntingthorpe 13.7.95 ex RAF Lyneham)	
41H/ 697464 •	F Mk. 58	**J-4097**		(Swiss AF as J-4097): del.	23.2.60/95
				Texas AIr Command, Arlington TX	.95
				(del. Switzerland to Southend UK 12.7.95)	
			N58HH	reg.	7.95
- •	T Mk. 7 T Mk. 75			(to R Netherlands AF as N-303)	.58
				Hawker Siddeley Aviatioon Ltd, Dunsfold	
				(to Republic of Singapore AF as 500): del.	25.7.70/94
				Geoff Moesker, Brisbane QLD	.94/95
				Wally Fisk/Amjet Aircraft Corp, St Paul MN	.95
				(shipped to Brisbane-Archerfield 7.95)	

HAWKER SEA HAWK

c/n	Mark	Serial	Civil reg.	History	Date
AW6032 •	FB Mk. 3 FB Mk. 5	**WM994**		RNAS Abroath: inst. airframe	63
				College of Aeronautics, Cranfield	25.6.63
				Webborn Air Museum, Swansea : stored dism	.77/83
			G-SEAH	Nobleair Ltd c/- Fabric Air Ltd, Southend	5.4.83
				Mike Carlton/Brencham Historic Aircraft Co/ Hunter One Collection, Hurn	10.83/87
				Jet Heritage Collection, Hurn	1.10.87
				Sark International Airways/Jet Heritage	25.1.88/94
				(stored Bournemouth-Hurn 92, under rest. 93/94)	
			N994WM	Wally Fisk/Amjet Aircraft Corp, St. Paul-Anoka County MN: shipped ex Hurn	11.94/95
				(rest. to fly, Anoka County MN)	
- •	FGA Mk. 4 FGA Mk. 6	**WV795**		RAF Halton: inst. airframe	74
				Bob Poulter/Sea Hawk Rest. Group, Bath	84/86
				Jet Heritage Collection, Hurn: stored	92/94
				(static displ. Hurn 93/94)	
- •	FGA Mk. 4 FGA.Mk.6	**WV908**		Royal Naval Historic Flight Yeovilton on rebuild British Aerospace Dunsfold	95/96
AW6385 •	FGA Mk. 6	**XE489**		British Historic Aircraft Museum, Southend	20.5.67/83
				(del. Southend 20.5.67, displ. as "XE364/485J")	
			G-JETH	Mike Carlton/Brencham Ltd, Hurn	10.5.83/87
				(civil conv. not completed, displ. Hurn 86/87)	
				Peter G. Vallance/Vallance By-Ways Museum, Charlwood : static displ. as "XE364"	1.10.87/93
-	Mk.			Bernie Vajdi, Winnipeg MAN	.84

HEINKEL HE162 VOLKSJAGER/SALAMANDER

c/n	Mark	Serial	Civil reg.	History	Date
Nr120076•	He 162A-2			JG1 "Yellow 4": captured Leck, Germany	.45
				(to RAF for trials as AM 59, VH523)	.45/46
				(arr. dism. Farnbrough 15.6.45: testflown)	
				shipped to Montreal, Canada, arr.	9.9.46
				Canadian National Aviation Museum, Rockcliffe ONT	64/94
				(displ. as "JG3/77: 120076/4")	
Nr120077•	He 162A-2			2/JG1 "Red 1": captured at Leck, Germany	.45
				shipped to USA ex France on HMS Reaper	7.45
				(to USAAF as FE-489/T2-489)	
				(testflown Muroc Dry Lake Test Base CA .46)	
				University of Kansas, Lawrence KS	47
				Eddie Fisher, Kansas City KS	.48/55
				Ed Maloney/The Air Museum, Claremont CA	58/65
				(recov. ex KS, rest. and displ. as "T2-489")	
				Ed Maloney/The Air Museum, Ontario CA	65/70
				Planes of Fame Museum, Chino CA	70/95
				(displ. as "77/Nervenklau")	
Nr120086•	He 162A-2			JG1: captured Leck, Germany	.45
				(to RAF as AM 62)	.45

				arr. dism. Farnborough: not flown	22.8.45
				shipped to Montreal, Canada, arr.	9.9.46
				Canadian National Aviation Museum,	
				Rockcliffe ONT	68/94
Nr120223•	He 162A-1			JG1: captured Leck, Germany	.45
				(by rail from Germany to Nanterre AB, Paris)	
				(to Armee de l'Air as No.3)	
				Musee de l'Air, Paris-Le Bourget	70/95
Nr120227•	He 162A-2			JG1: captured Leck, Germany	.45
				(to RAF as AM 65, VN679)	.45
				(arr. dism. Farnborough 31.7.45, rep. carried	
				inside captured Arado AR 232B AM 17)	
				RAF Leconfield: storage	49
				RAF Museum, RAF Colerne	61/76
				RAF Museum, RAF St Athan	3.76/89
				RAF Museum, Hendon	.89/95
Nr120230•	He 162A-2			1/JG1 "White 23": captured Leck, Germany	.45
				(to USAAF as FE-504/T2-504)	
				Smithsonian Institute, stored Park Ridge IL	.46
				NASM, Silver Hill MD	65/94
Nr120235•	He 162A-1			JG1: captured Leck	.45
				(to RAF as AM 68): arr. dism. Farnborough	10.8.45
				RAF Cranwell: displ.	9.46/60
				Imperial War Museum, Lambeth, London	.60/94
				(rest. Duxford .86/89, ret. to Lambeth .89)	

HISPANO HA200 SAETA/HA220 SUPER SAETA

20/2 •	HA.200	**E.14-2**		(Ejercito del Air/Spanish AF, to E.14A-2)	
			N602HA	Nathaniel A. Kalt, San Antonio TX	6.85
				rep. sold to Panama	6.87
				Airfleet Corp, Omaha NE	88
				Skyway Sales Inc, Omaha NE	4.90/95
20/4 •	HA.200	**E.14-4**		(Spanish AF, to E.14A-4)	
			N604HA	Nathaniel A. Kalt, San Antonio TX	6.85
				rep. sold to Panama	6.87
				Charles J. Cannaday, Blue Ridge VA	9.90/95
20/5 •	HA.200	**E.14-5**		(Spanish AF, to E.14A-5)	
			N5486Y	Nathaniel A. Kalt, San Antonio TX	9.84
				Avstar Inc, Seattle WA	85
				Rick E. Sharpe, Houston TX	86
				Flight Research Inc, Hattiesburg MS	4.87/95
20/6 •	HA.200	**E.14-6**		(Spanish AF, to E.14A-6)	
			N606HA	Nathaniel A. Kalt, San Antonio TX	6.85
				W. Scott Kidwell, Redmond WA	2.87
				rep. sold to Panama	6.87
				Airfleet Corp, Omaha NE	88
				Bill Russell/Russair Ltd, Hillsboro OR	2.90/95
20/7 •	HA.200	**E.14-7**		(Spanish AF, to E.14A-7)	
			N607HA	Nathaniel A. Kalt, San Antonio TX	6.85
				Joseph B. Clark/Avstar Inc, Seattle WA	88/92
				Ronald Thompson, Fullerton CA/Carefree AZ	4.93/95
20/10 •	HA.200	**E.14-10**		(Spanish AF, to E.14A-10)	
			N3951G	Nathaniel A. Kalt, San Antonio TX	6.83/86
				(assembled, San Antonio TX: ff 29.11.84)	
				Rick E. Sharpe, Arcola TX	88
				Rolf F. Brunckhorst, Oxford OH	92
				Nioet Inc, Roanoke IN	11.94/95
20/11 •	HA.200A	**E.14A-11**	**N611HA**	Nathaniel A. Kalt, San Antonio TX	6.85
				W. Scott Kidwell, Redmond WA	2.87

				rep. sold to Panama	6.87
				Airfleet Corp, Omaha NE	88
				Whistlin Dixie Corp, Jacksonville FL	92
				American Society of Child Care, Titusville FL	10.93/95
20/13 •	HA.200A	**E.14A-13**	N613HA	Nathaniel A. Kalt, San Antonio TX	6.85
			N2000G	Dean Martin/Warplanes Inc, Dover DE: USCR	2.89/95
				(USCR quotes N2000G rereg N20036 8.90: see entry at end of this listing)	
20/14 •	HA.200E		EC-BBA	Hispano Aviacion, Seville	69
	HA.200A	**E.14A-14**		(ret. to Spanish AF as E.14A-14)	
			N614HA	Nathaniel A. Kalt, San Antonio TX	6.85
				Regis Herbst, Pittsburgh PA	89/92
				Joseph G. Trichter, Houston TX	10.94/95
20/15 •	HA.200A	**E.14A-15**	**N5486J**	Nathaniel A. Kalt, San Antonio TX	9.84
				Joseph B. Clark/Avstar Inc, Seattle WA	86
				Fred J. Garrison, Angleton TX	88
				Hoffman Aircraft Inc, Texico NM	92
				Saeteco Inc, Danville OH	9.92/95
20/16 •	HA.200A	**E.14A-16**	**N616HA**	Nathaniel A. Kalt, San Antonio TX	6.85
				W. Scott Kidwell, Redmond WA	2.87
				rep. sold to Panama	6.87
				Air Technics Inc, Houston TX	89
			N232DS	Donald H. Schleuter, Genesee ID	10.89/95
20/17 •	HA.200A	**E.14A-17**	**N617HA**	Nathaniel A. Kalt, San Antonio TX	6.85
				Joseph B. Clark/Avstar Inc, Seattle WA	89/92
				State of the Art Aviation Ltd, Wilmington DE	11.94/95
20/19 •	HA.200A	**E.14A-19**	**N619HA**	Nathaniel A. Kalt, San Antonio TX	6.85
				W. Scott Kidwell, Redmond WA	2.87
				James E. Johnson, Salina KS	89
				Joseph B. Clark/Avstar Inc, Seattle WA	12.91/95
20/20 •	HA.200A	**E.14A-20**	**N620HA**	Nathaniel A. Kalt, San Antonio TX	6.85
				W. Scott Kidwell, Redmond WA	2.87
				rep. sold to Panama	6.87
				Shepard Aircraft Corp, Corvallis OR	7.88/95
20/22 •	HA.200A	**E.14A-22**	N622HA	Nathaniel A. Kalt, San Antonio TX	6.85
				W. Scott Kidwell, Redmond WA	2.87
				Joseph Clark/Avstar, Seattle WA	89
				Morgan Aviation, Arlington WA	90
			N9107J	Katharine S. Gray, Simi CA	3.92
			N922SP	Edison Parker, Las Vegas NV	5.93
				Jet Enterprises Ltd, Las Vegas NV	1.93/95
20/26 •	HA.200A	**E.14A-26**	**N626HA**	Nathaniel A. Kalt, San Antonio TX	6.85
				Joseph B. Clark/Avstar Inc, Seattle WA	89/95
20/27 •	HA.200A	**E.14A-27**	**N5485G**	Nathaniel A. Kalt, San Antonio TX	9.84
				America In Motion Inc, Sherman Oaks CA	88
				(unconv., auctioned Santa Monica CA 10.91)	
				OK Aircraft Accessories, Monterey CA	10.91/95
20/28 •	HA.200A	**E.14A-28**	**N128HA**	Nathaniel A. Kalt, San Antonio TX	6.85
				Joseph B. Clark/Avstar Inc, Seattle WA	88/95
20/29 •	HA.200A	**E.14A-29**	**N629HA**	Nathaniel A. Kalt, San Antonio TX	6.85
				Joseph B. Clark/Avstar Inc, Seattle WA	9.85/92
20/31 •	HA.200A	**E.14A-31**	**N631HA**	Nathaniel A. Kalt, San Antonio TX	6.85
				Wayne E. Cozad, Xenia OH	10.88/95
20/32 •	HA.200A	**E.14A-32**	**N632HA**	Nathaniel A. Kalt, San Antonio TX	6.85
				rep. sold to Panama	6.87
				Guy Morgan, Whitestone NY	92/94
				Allen D. Morgan, Roseburg OR	9.94/95

20/33	HA.200A	**E.14A-33**	**N633HA**	Nathaniel A. Kalt, San Antonio TX	6.85
				W. Scott Kidwell, Redmond WA	2.87
				rep. sold to Panama	6.87
				crashed, dest. Tuskegee AL	26.5.90
20/34 •	HA.200A	**E.14A-34**	**N634HA**	Nathaniel A. Kalt, San Antonio TX	6.85
				W. Scott Kidwell, Redmond WA	2.87/88
				Western Wings Inc, Oakland OR	90
				Rhett E. Woods, Roseburg OR	92
				B. L. Jennings Inc, Carson City NV	5.94
20/35	HA.200A	**E.14A-35**	**N635HA**	Nathaniel A. Kalt, San Antonio TX	6.85
				W. Scott Kidwell, Redmond WA	2.87
				rep. sold to Panama	6.87
				Kenneth F. McLaughlin, Nashua NH	3.95
220/36 •	HA.220D	**C.10B-36**		(Spanish AF, to A.10B-36)	
				noted Griffin GA: "A.10B-36/214-36"	3.94
20/37 •	HA.200A	**C.10B-37**		(Spanish AF, to A.10B-37)	
			N2741P	Combat Aircraft Inc, Elkhart IN	9.82
				Southeast Whirly Birds Inc, New Canaan CT	88
				Classic Aircraft Inc, Albertville AL	1.92/95
20/42 •	HA.200A	**C.10B-42**		(Spanish AF, to AE.10B-42)	
			N3178N	Sierra Warbirds Corp, Truckee CA	5.8.91/95
20/44 •	HA.200A	**C.10B-44**		(Spanish AF, to AE.10B-44)	
			N9108R	Combat Aircraft Inc, Elkhart IN	7.87/89
				Tim Bacci/Sierra Warbirds Corp, Truckee CA	90/92
				sale rep., San Jose CA	95
20/45 •	HA.200A	**C.10B-45**		(Spanish AF, to AE.10B-45)	
			XB-FGB	Jorge Gornish & Juan EDuard, Toleca Mexico	93
20/46 •	HA.200A	**C.10B-46**		(Spanish AF, to AE.10B-46)	
			N3179K	Sierra Warbirds Corp, Truckee CA	5.8.91/92
				Wayne E. Cozad, Xenia OH	1.95
20/48 •	HA.200A	-	**N20036**	Dean Martin/Warplanes Inc, Dover DE: USCR	7.89/95
				George M. Krieger, Pound Ridge NY	91/93
				(USCR quotes id. "HA-20-48";	
				rep. rereg. ex N2000G .91: que se)	
20/50 •	HA.200D	**C.10B-50**	**EC-DXR**	M. V. Torralbo & D. Esquerdo, Cuatro Vientos	11.86
				Fundacion Infante de Orleans Museum,	
				Madrid-Cuatro Vientos	90/92
				(c/n also quoted as 20/56)	
20/53 •	HA.200D	**C.10B-53**		(Spanish AF, to AE.10B-53)	
			N3179U	Sierra Warbirds Corp, Truckee CA	5.8.91
			N390WW	William E. Wecker Associates, Novato CA	1.92/95
20/57 •	HA.200A	**C.10B-57**		(Spanish AF, to AE.10B-57)	
			N3179W	Sierra Warbirds Corp, Truckee CA	5.8.91/92
				reg. pending, Elkview WV	95
20/60 •	HA.200A	**C.10B-60**		(Spanish AF, to AE.10B-60)	
			N4551W	Combat Aircraft Inc, Elkhart IN	11.83/85
				James C. Parham, Greenville SC	10.85/95
20/61 •	HA.200A	**C.10B-61**	N3179Z	Sierra Warbirds Corp, Truckee CA	5.8.91/92
			N311AM	rereg.	10.92
			N3179Z	Ridgeaire Inc, Jacksonville TX	95
20/62 •	HA.200A	**C.10B-62**		(Spanish AF, to AE.10B-62)	
			N31792	Sierra Warbirds Corp, Truckee CA	5.8.91/92
			N105MD	rereg.	2.93
				David Dulabon, Erie PA	6.95
20/64 •	HA.200A	**C.10B-64**		(Spanish AF, to AE.10B-64)	

			N553GA	General Aviation Services, Wheeling IL	24.8.90/95
20/69 •	HA.200A	**C.10B-69**		(Spanish AF, to AE.10B-69)	
			N9123E	Combat Aircraft Inc, Elkhart IN	9.87
				David Van Liere, Huntington IN	89
				Five Star Aviation, Columbus City IN	92
				Hugh S. Brown, Titusville FL	7.92/95
20/72 •	HA.200A	**C.10B-72**		(Spanish AF, to AE.10B-72)	
			N554GA	General Aviation Services, Wheeling IL	24.8.90/92
			N797DB	Douglas W. Benson, Chico CA: USCR	23.5.94/95
				Robert G. Chinnery, Independence MO	7.94
20/74 •	HA.200A	**C.10B-74**		(Spanish AF, to AE.10B-74)	
			N31793	Sierra Warbirds Corp, Truckee CA	5.8.91/92
				James H. Beck, St Albans WV	5.94/95
20/77 •	HA.200A	**C.10B-77**		(Spanish AF, to AE.10B-77)	
			N41868	Tasair Inc, Ballwin MO	7.92/95
20/80 •	HA.200A	**C.10B-80**		(Spanish AF, to AE.10B-80)	
			N31798	Sierra Warbirds Corp, Truckee CA	5.8.91/92
				Tasair Inc, Ballwin MO	8.94/95
20/83 •	HA.200A	**C.10B-83**		(Spanish AF, to AE.10B-83)	
			N3180G	Sierra Warbirds Corp, Truckee CA	5.8.91
			N212AM	Sierra Warbirds Corp, Truckee CA	2.92
				Texas Biz-Jet Inc, Fort Worth TX	95
20/85 •	HA.200A	**A.10B-85**	**N3180T**	Sierra Warbirds Corp, Truckee CA	5.8.91/92
				Dayn R. Patterson, Oroville CA	2.95
20/87 •	HA.200A	**C.10B-87**		(Spanish AF, to AE.10B-87)	
			N3180J	Sierra Warbirds Corp, Truckee CA	5.8.91
				Frank M. Marzich, Rockford IL	3.94/95
20/89 •	HA.200A	**C.10B-89**		(Spanish AF, to AE.10B-89)	
			N9108Q	Combat Aircraft Inc, Elkhart IN	7.87/89
				Sierra Warbirds Corp, Truckee CA	1.91/95
220/94 •	HA.200D	**C.10C-94**		(Spanish AF, to AE.10B-94)	
			N3180X	Sierra Warbirds Corp, Truckee CA	5.8.91/92
				C. L. Max Inc, Dover DE	1.94/95
				(USCR quotes id. "20/94")	
220/95 •	HA.220D	**C.10C-95**		(Spanish AF, to A.10C-95)	
			N.....	Combat Aircraft Inc, Elkhart IN	93
				(flying 93 in orig. Ed'A sc. "214-095")	
220/96 •	HA.220D	**C.10C-96**		(Spanish AF, to AE.10C-96)	
			N9123N	Combat Aircraft Inc, Elkhart IN	9.87
				David Van Liere, Huntington IN	89
				Classic Aircraft Inc, Albertville AL	3.92/95
220/100•	HA.220D	**C.10C-100**		(Spanish AF, to AE.10C-100)	
			N3110P	Combat Aircraft Inc, Elkhart IN	9.7.91/92
				reg. pending, Xenia OH	95
220/112•	HA.220D	**C.10C-112**		(Spanish AF, to AE.10C-112)	
			N4280X	Combat Aircraft Inc, Elkhart IN	9.7.91/92
				Brad L. Sherk, Plymouth IN	5.95
220/113•	HA.220D	**C.10C-113**		(Spanish AF, to AE.10C-113)	
			N9122F	Combat Aircraft Inc, Elkhart IN	9.87/95
220/114•	HA.220D	**C.10C-114**		(Spanish AF, to AE.10C-114)	
			N5831Z	Combat Aircraft Inc, Elkhart IN	4.85
				struck-off USCR	5.85
			EC-DXJ	J. R. Garcia, Cuatro Vientos	5.6.85
				Aero Madrid, Cuatro Vientos	87
				(noted at Cuatro Vientos 1.87)	

- •	HA.200R.1	**XE.14-2**	**EC-ANN**	reg. for test flying	
				Museo del Aire, Cuatro Vientos AB, Madrid	78/93

LOCKHEED F-104 STARFIGHTER

1007 •	YF-104A	**55-2961**		(to NASA as NASA818)	8.56/70
	F-104A		**N818NA**	NASA, Edwards AFB CA	72/75
				NASM, Washington DC: displ.	11.75/93
1021	F-104A	56-0733	N47048	Darryl G. Greenamyer, Van Nuys CA	.75/76
			N104RB	Darryl G. Greenamyer/Red Baron Flying Service,	
				Tonopah NV	.76/79
				crashed & dest. (Greenamyer ejected)	c79
1066 •	F-104A	**56-0778**		(to R Jordanian AF as 907)	
			N66305	Air International Corp, Dallas TX	2.11.90/92
				(noted unconv. dism., Montgomery AL 6.91)	
				sale rep., Belfast ME: USCR	95
1068 •	F-104A	**56-0780**		(to R Jordanian AF as 908)	
			N66342	Air International Corp, Dallas TX	2.11.90/92
				(noted unconv. dism., Montgomery AL 6.91)	
				Fox II Inc, Fort Worth-Addison TX	3.93/95
				Cavanaugh Flight Museum, Addison TX	7.95
				(flies as "USAF 60780/FG-780")	
1074 •	F-104A	**56-0786**		(to R Jordanian AF as 909/G)	
			N66328	Air International Corp, Dallas TX	2.11.90/92
				(noted unconv. dism., Montgomery AL 6.91:	
				stored unconv., Mojave CA 92)	
				Skytech Aviation, Dallas TX	9.93/95
1078 •	F-104A	**56-0790**	**N820NA**	NASA, Edwards AFB CA	.72/78
	NF-104E			USAFM, Edwards AFB CA	88/93
				Museum of Flight, Seattle-Boeing Field WA	95
1150 •	CF-104	**RCAF12850**		(to CAF as 104850)	
	Canadair			(to R Norwegian AF as 850)	
			N104JT	Jet Tech Systems Inc, Belfast ME	3.95
4045 •	NF-104A		NASA811	NASA, Edwards AFB CA	8.63/70
			N811NA	NASA, Edwards AFB CA	71/89
				struck-off USCR	12.89
4053 •	NF-104A		NASA812	NASA, Edwards AFB CA	9.63/70
			N812NA	NASA, Edwards AFB CA	71/89
				struck-off USCR	12.89
4058	NF-104A		NASA813	NASA, Edwards AFB CA	10.63/66
				crashed	8.6.66
5008 •	F-104B	**57-1296**		(to R Jordanian AF as 901)	
			N65354	Air International Corp, Dallas TX	2.11.90/91
				(noted unconv. dism., Montgomery AL 6.91)	
				Northern Lights Aircraft, Minnetonka MN	10.6.91/94
				Thunderbird Aviation, Deer Valley AZ	11.4.94/95
5015 •	F-104B	**57-1303**	N819NA	NASA, Edwards AFB CA	78
				USAFM, McClellan AFB CA	90/93
5042	F-104D	**57-1330**		Letcher & Associates, Mojave CA	84
				Al Hansen & Ascher Ward, Mojave CA	89/90
5302 •	CF-104D	**RCAF12632**		(later CAF 104632)	
	Canadair			(to R Norwegian AF as 4632)	
				Norwegian Armed Forces Museum	
			N104NL	Northern Lights Aircraft Inc, Montgomery AL	12.88/94
				(flew in civil scheme, "Renee")	
				Thunderbird Aviation, Deer Valley AZ	11.4.94
			N166TB	Thunderbird Aviation, Deer Valley AZ	11.94/95

c/n	Type	Mil. ID	Civil Reg.	History	Date
5303 •	CF-104D	**RCAF12633**		(later CAF 104633)	
	Canadair			(to R Norwegian AF as 4633)	
				Norwegian Armed Forces Museum	
				S. Bruce Goessling/Combat Jet & Aerospace	
				Museum, Chino CA	.86/87
			N104JR	Combat Jets Flying Museum,	
				Houston TX (rest. Chino, ff 11.11.87)	8.87/92
				EAA Aviation Foundation, Oshkosh WI	5.92/95
5307 •	CF-104D	**RCAF12637**		(later CAF 104637)	
	Canadair			(to R Norwegian AF as 4637)	
				S. Bruce Goessling/Combat Jet & Aerospace	
				Museum, Chino CA	87
5419 •	F-104DJ	**16-5019**		(to JSDAF; later 36-5019)	1.64
				noted at Mojave CA	11.87
5702	TF-104G		N104L	Lockheed Aircraft Co, Palmdale CA	.61/65
				(to R Netherlands AF as D-5702)	30.5.65
5735 •	TF-104G	**61-3064**		(to Luftwaffe as KF+234; 27+33)	
			N825NA(1	NASA, Edwards AFB CA	2.7.75/80
			N824NA(2	NASA, Edwards AFB CA	16.8.84/95
5939 •	TF-104G	**66-13628**		(to Luftwaffe as KF+239; 28+09)	
			N826NA(1	NASA, Edwards AFB CA	2.7.75/78
			N825NA(2	NASA, Edwards AFB CA	16.8.84/95
7161 •	F-104G	**KE+461**		(Kreigsmarine as VA+137: later 22+79)	
	Messmt.			stored unconv., Mojave CA	92
8213 •	RF-104G	**KG+313**		(Luftwaffe, later ED+114; 24+64)	
	Fokker		N824NA(1	NASA, Edwards AFB CA	2.7.75/80
			N826NA(2	NASA, Edwards AFB CA	16.8.84/95
9007	F-104G	**63-13274**	OO-FSA (1	SABCA-Fairey SA, Gosselies, Belgium	18.7.62
	SABCA			(to USAF/Luftwaffe as 63-13274/25+26)	9.62
				crashed, dest., Luke AFB AZ	2.8.68
9016	F-104G	**FX-01**	OO-FSA (2	SABCA-Fairey SA, Gosselies, Belgium	
	SABCA			(to Belgian AF as FX-01)	
9094 •	F-104G	**FX-51**		(Belgian AF as FX-51)	
	SABCA			stored Koksijde AB, Belgium	80/88
				Warren Sessler Inc, Chino CA	.89/90
				Tom Reilly, Kissimee FL	19.5.90/91
				US reg. candidate	21.6.90
				(stored, unconv. Kissimmee FL 91)	
				Flying Tigers Museum, Kissimmee FL	93/94
				(displ. as "USAF 60813/FG-813")	
9140 •	F-104G	**FX-82**		(Belgian AF as FX-82)	
	SABCA			stored Koksijde AB, Belgium	80/88
				Planes of Fame/Fighter Jets Museum,	
				Chino CA	.89/95
9142 •	F-104G	**FX-84**		(Belgian AF as FX-84)	
	SABCA			stored Koksijde AB, Belgium	80/88
				noted unconv., Mineral Wells Airport AL	10.89
				noted unconv., Mojave CA	3.90/92

Lockheed F-80 Shooting Star

c/n	Type	Mil. ID	Civil Reg.	History	Date
1258 •	P-80A	**44-85235**		(to USN as Bu29689)	
	F-80A			Aberdeen Proving Grounds MD	
				Walter Soplata Collection, Newbury OH	85
				Rick Ropkey, Longview TX (rest. to fly)	91/93
1975 •	P-80C	**47-215**		(to FA Colombiana as 2058)	
	F-80C		**N10DM**	Richard W. Martin, Van Nuys CA	71/78
				(arr. dism. Van Nuys 3.71 for rebuild using	

				parts of T-33 N156 : not completed)	
				stored, stripped Whiteman Air Park CA by	84
				USAFM, Kulis ANGB, Anchorage AK	86/94
				(static rest. Kulis ANGB, displ. as "49-1849")	
				(note: P-80 displ. McConnell AFB KS as "47-0215")	
2073 •	P-80C	**47-1387**		(to USN as Bu33840)	
	TO-1			NASM/Smithsonian Institute, Washington DC	75
	TV-1			USNAM, NAS Pensacola FL	.75/92
	T2V-1A		**N4425N**	USNAM, NAS Pensacola FL	8.10.92/95
				(rest. as "Marines 33840" by Black Shadow Aviation, Jacksonville FL .93)	
				MCAS El Toro CA: loan, displ.	93/94
2125 •	P-80C	**48-0868**		EAA Museum, Hales Corner, later Oshkosh WI	79/88
	F-80C			(displ. as "USAF 45-8398")	
	GF-80C		**N80PP**	Paul H. Poberezny/EAA Aviation Foundation, Oshkosh WI	11.89/94
2467 •	P-80C	**49-0719**		US reg. candidate	5.8.91
	F-80C				

LOCKHEED T-33/CANADAIR CT-33 SILVER STAR

5034 •	T-33A	**49-0884**		(to RNAF as M-48)	
			N652	Consolidated Aero Export Corporation, North Hollywood CA	7.4.72
				(del. Holland to US, via Shannon 7.4.72)	
				Jim Cullen, Monument CO	76/95
5223 •	T-33A	**50-0370**		(to RNAF as M-49): BOC	5.2.64
			N651	Consolidated Aero Export Corporation, North Hollywood CA	7.4.72
				(del. Holland to US, via Shannon 7.4.72)	
				(rep. to FA Mexicana as JE-017)	
				Forbes Bigbee Manufacturing, San Ramon CA	84
				Cameron Wilke, Lubbock TX	5.84
				Allied Bank of Marble Falls, Marble Falls TX	12.86
				Courtesy Aircraft Inc, Rockford IL	1.87/88
				T Bird Partners, Van Nuys CA	9.88
				Museum of Flying, Santa Monica CA	1.92/95
				(displ. as "USAF 69330/FT-330")	
5313 •	T-33A	**51-4019**		(to USN as Bu126583)	
	TV-2		N151	FAA, Oklahoma City OK	
	T-33B		**N1519**	Schilling Technical Institute, Salina KS	66
				Kansas Technical Institute, Salina KS	69/92
				Kansas Aviation Museum, Wichita KS	92/94
				(displ. as "FAA N151")	
5315	T-33A	**51-4021**		(to USN as Bu126585)	
	TV-2		**N9126Z**	reg. res	84/92
	T-33B				
5327 •	T-33A	**51-4033**		(to USN as Bu126591)	
	TV-2		N335V	E. D. Weiner, Los Angeles CA	66/69
	T-33B		**N6633D**	E. D. Weiner, Los Angeles CA	.69
				Leroy B. Penhall, Balboa CA	72/74
				Edward O. Messick, San Antonio TX	10.74/86
				G. A. Smith, Long Beach CA	9.86/87
				Shooting Star Productions, Reno NV	6.87/95
5333 •	T-33A	**51-4039**	**N7641B**	University of Illinois, Champaign IL	78
5435 •	T-33A	**51-4141**		(to USN as Bu126617)	
	TV-2			FAA, Oklahoma City OK	.61
	T-33B		**N1118U**	Westair Inc, Broomfield CO	72
				General Industrial Supply, Muskegee OK	76
				AG Central Aircraft Inc, TX	3.83
				Stanley W. Cameron, Lubbock TX	7.83/84
				Allied Bank of Marble Falls, Marble Falls TX	12.86

				Courtesy Aircraft Inc, Rockford IL	1.87
				Lawrence S. Green, New Castle NH	87/89
				Chris Peatridge/GAE Inc, Manchester NH	9.89/95
5566	T-33A	**51-4271**	**N8682E**	Chicago Board of Education, Chicago IL	66/76
5588	T-33A	51-4293		(to USN as Bu128671)	
	TV-2		N152	FAA, Oklahoma City OK	63/73
	T-33B			crashed and dest., Elk City OK	24.1.73
5604 •	T-33A	**51-4309**	**N8683E**	Chicago Board of Education, Chicago IL	66/89
5669	T-33A	**51-4374**	**N401S**	rep. displ. Southern Illinois as 51-4374	
5678	T-33A	**51-4383**		(to l'Armee de l'Air as 14383)"338-HJ"	
			F-GBEX	OFEMA/Gyrafrance International, Frejorgues	2.83
				(to R Thai AF as .....): del.	.83
5695	T-33A	51-4405	N350S	no further information	
5797 •	T-33A	**51-4502**		(to l'Armee de l'Air as 14502)	
			F-BJDH	OFEMA/Gyrafrance International, Frejorgues	.79/80
				(to Republic of Singapore AF as 901)	17.4.80
				(del. via Bahrein 25.4.80)	
				RSAF Museum, Paya Lebar AB, Singapore	93/95
				(displ. as "RSAF 360/14502")	
				(note: F-BJDH prev. rep. as 5934/51-6602)	
5798	T-33A	**51-4503**		(to l'Armee de l'Air as 14503)	
			F-BJDZ(2	OFEMA/Gyrafrance International, Frejorgues	5.80
				(to Republic of Singapore AF as 907)	13.5.80
				(del. via Bahrein 17.5.80)	
5817	T-33A	**51-4522**		(to USN as Bu128700)	
			N9123Z	reg. pending: USCR	72
5848	T-33A	**51-6516**		(to l'Armee de l'Air as 16516)"338-HF"	
			F-GBER	OFEMA/Gyrafrance International, Frejorgues	12.82
				(to R Thai AF as .....): del.	.82
5860	T-33A	**51-6528**		(to RNAF as M-51)	.64
			N650	Consolidated Aero Export Corporation,	
				North Hollywood CA	7.4.72
				(del. Holland to US, via Shannon 7.4.72)	
5863	T-33A	**51-6531**		(to RNAF as M-55)	.64
			N649	Consolidated Aero Export Corporation,	
				North Hollywood CA	3.72
				(del. Holland to US, via Shannon 7.4.72)	
				Aero Systems Inc, Boulder CO	76/83
				struck-off USCR	4.83
				(rep. to FA Mexicana as JE-016)	
5912 •	T-33A	**51-6580**		(to USN as Bu128705)	
	TV-2		N156	FAA, Oklahoma City OK	66/69
	T-33B			(crash landing : hulk noted Van Nuys 4.71)	
			N156Y	Richard W. Martin, Van Nuys CA	72
				(parts used to rebuild Martin's F-80 N10DM,	
				Van Nuys .72)	
				Thunderbird Aviation Inc, Phoenix AZ	11.73/95
5913 •	T-33A	**51-6581**		(to USN as Bu128706)	
	TV-2		**N9124Z**	Ward E. Duncan, Satellite Beach FL	69/76
	T-33B			T-Birds Three Inc, Lubbock TX	84/92
				Carson Gilmer, San Antonio TX	2.93/95
5980	T-33A	**51-6648**		(to l'Armee de l'Air as 16648)	
			F-BJDI	OFEMA/Gyrafrance International, Frejorgues	.79/80
				(to Republic of Singapore AF as 902)	17.4.80
				(del. via Bahrein 25.4.80)	
6003	T-33A	**51-6671**		(to USN as Bu128719)	

	TV-2		**N154**	FAA, Oklahoma City OK	
	T-33B				
6166	T-33A	**51-6834**		(to l'Armee de l'Air as 16834)"5-MB","7-JD"	
			F-BJDK	OFEMA/Gyrafrance International, Frejorgues	.79
				(to Republic of Singapore AF as ...)	17.4.80
				(del. via Bahrein 25.4.80)	
6193	T-33A	51-6861	N62278	rep. displ. Dayton TN as "16861"	74
6284	T-33A	51-6952		(to l'Armee de l'Air as 16952)	
			F-BJDQ	OFEMA/Gyrafrance International, Frejorgues	5.80
				(to Republic of Singapore AF as ...)	13.5.80
				(del. via Bahrein 17.5.80)	
6285 •	T-33A	51-6953		(to RNAF as M-52)	
			N648	Consolidated Aero Export Corporation,	
				North Hollywood CA	7.4.72
				(del. Holland to US, via Shannon 7.4.72)	
				Samuel Reed, Zachary LA	76
				dam. by windstorm, parked Mojave CA	.81
				GHS Flying Inc, Bakersfield CA	84
				Preston Air Museum, Dallas TX	9.86
				Morris Cannan, San Antonio TX	12.86/87
				I. N. (Junior) Burchinall/	
				Flying Tiger Air Museum, Brookston TX	88/93
				Herbert D. Short, Houston TX	9.93/95
6288	T-33A	51-6956		(to l'Armee de l'Air as 16956)	
			F-BJDT	OFEMA/Gyrafrance International, Frejorgues	5.80
				(to Republic of Singapore AF as ...)	13.5.80
				(del. via Bahrein 17.5.80)	
6289	T-33A	51-6957		(to NASA as NASA 224)	
			N224NA	NASA: stored Davis Monthan AFB AZ by	75
6306	T-33A	51-8522		(to USN as Bu131729)	
	TV-2		N9122Z	reg. pending: USCR	72
6350 •	T-33A	**51-8566**		(to RDAF as 18566: later DT-566)	
				Autair: stored	81/82
			G-TJET	Aces High Ltd, Duxford	8.1.82/86
				(rest. Gatwick, ff 8.9.82)	
				Nigel Brendish, Cranfield	.86
				Ipswich Airport Ltd, North Weald	12.5.86
				A. S. Topen/Vintage Aircraft Team, Cranfield	88/91
				(flew as "USAF 91007/TR-007")	
			G-NASA	Sandy Topen/Vintage Aircraft Team, Cranfield	
				later Bruntingthorpe	3.6.91/95
6460	T-33A	51-8676	N31040	Greg Forbes, San Jose CA	10.75/77
				(FAA quote "aircraft constructed from parts")	
				sale rep., Palo Alto CA: USCR	12.80/95
6518 •	T-33A	**51-8734**		(to USN as Bu131770)	
	TV-2		N9121Z	Aerial Systems Co, Minneapolis MN	80
	T-33B		N59TW	Thomas E. Wright, Snyder TX	2.80/88
			N59TM	Thomas G. McCoy, Dallas TX	10.91/95
6536	T-33A	51-8752		(to l'Armee de l'Air as 18752) "338-HB"	
			F-GBEY	OFEMA/Gyrafrance International, Frejorgues	2.83
				(to R Thai AF as ....): del.	.83
6538	T-33A	51-8754		(to l'Armee de l'Air as 18754)"10-KX","8-OE"	
			F-BJDJ	OFEMA/Gyrafrance International, Frejorgues	.79/80
				(to Republic of Singapore AF as ...)	17.4.80
				(del. via Bahrein 25.4.80)	
6544	T-33A	51-8760		(to RNAF as M-53)	
			N647	Consolidated Aero Export Corporation,	
				North Hollywood CA	16.3.72/76

				(del. Holland to US, via Shannon 16.3.72)	
				Roger Wolfe, Lovelock NV	.77
				sale rep: USCR	84/95
6608 •	T-33A	51-8824		(to RNAF as M-56)	
			N646	Consolidated Aero Export Corporation, North Hollywood CA	16.3.72
				(del. Holland to US, via Shannon 16.3.72)	
				Northrop University, Inglewood CA	76/92
				inst. airframe: struck-off USCR	8.87
6638	T-33A	**51-8854**		(to USN as Bu131804)	
	TV-2		N155	FAA Oklahoma City OK	
	T-33B		**N15511**	Canadian Valley Area School, El Reno OK	76
				sale rep.	84/92
6699	T-33A	51-8915	N11986	Lewis College, Lockport IL	77
6821	T-33A	51-9037		(to Italian AF as MM51-9037)"CR-21"	
				for sale by auction, Treviso AB	25.9.86
				US reg. candidate	9.86
6882	RT-33A	51-9098	N1387N		
			N7490C	Robert V. Kavensky Co, Hollywood CA	.57/61
				(first civil T-33, built up from RT-33A wreck ex NV scrapyard 54/57, ff .57)	
			N233Y	Mechanical Products Inc, Jackson MI	63
				Florida Airmotive Sales Inc, Ft Lauderdale FL	66/69
				sale rep: USCR	84/95
6890 •	T-33A	**51-9106**	**N11987**	Lewis College, Lockport IL	72/76
				Donald R. Sharp, Pauls Valley OK	6.3.85
				Chester Dubaj, Bedford OH	87/88
				Harry W. Caplan, Pepper Pike OH	2.90/95
6911 •	T-33A	**51-9127**	N123MJ	Ralph Johnson, Richmond CA	69
				American Air Museum, Oakland CA	72/76
				Archie Baldocchi, San Francisco CA	77
				A. H. Massey, West Palm Beach FL	84
				Thunderbird Aviation, Deer Valley AZ	11.86/88
			N9127	Louis Antonacci, Hampshire IL	6.90
				Rolf F. Brunckhorst, Oxford OH	2.92/95
6912 •	T-33A	**51-9128**	**N11988**	Lewis College, Lockport IL	72/76
				Donald R. Sharp, Pauls Valley OK	6.3.85/95
6952	T-33A	51-9168		(to l'Armee de l'Air as 19168)	
			F-GBEP	OFEMA/Gyrafrance International, Frejorgues	12.82
				(to R Thai AF as .....): del.	.82
7047 •	T-33A	**51-9263**		displ. in park, Brooklyn OH	80/84
			N8042M	J. A. Krane: reg. candidate	19.4.89/92
7055 •	T-33A	**51-9271**	N16697		
			N1452	Utah University of Agriculture, Logan UT	.72/84
				struck-off USCR	3.84
				USAFM, Hill AFB UT	85/94
7086 •	T-33A	**51-9302**	N13182	Arizona State University, Tempe AZ	66/69
			N48097	Clark County School District, Las Vegas NV:	
				South Nevada Vo-Tech Centre, Las Vegas NV	10.66/95
				(USCR quotes same id. for both aircraft)	
7108 •	T-33A	**51-16989**		displ. in park, Jackson TN	72
			N989MS	D. N. Rounds, Manchester TN: reg. res.	23.6.86
				Michael J. Sohnly, Grand Forks ND	1.87/95
7153	T-33A	51-17414		(to l'Armee de l'Air as 117414)"338-HK"	
			F-GBET	OFEMA/Gyrafrance International, Frejorgues	.82
				(to R Thai AF as ......): del.	.82
7138 •	T-33A	**51-17445**		(to Belgian AF as FT15)	

			N1180C	Valiant Air Command, Titusville FL	23.9.81
				AG Central Aircraft Inc TX	83
				Stanley W. Cameron, Lubbock TX	7.83/84
				Allied Bank of Marble Falls, Marble Falls TX	12.86
				Courtesy Aircraft Inc, Rockford IL	1.87
			N410GH	Victor Haluska, Santa Monica CA	11.87/89
				Connie Kalitta Services, Lakeview OR	11.89
			N133CK	Kalitta Flying Services, Willow Run MI	3.92/95
7218 •	T-33A	**52-9164**		(to FA Peru as ....)	
			N61493	Hermes Technical International, Miami FL	11.92/95
7254 •	T-33A	**51-17463**		(to Belgian AF as FT16)	
			N533CB	Norman E. Hibbard, Oakland OR	6.90
				Connie Bowlin/Bowlin & Assoc., Griffin GA	92/94
				G & A Services Inc, Wilmington DE	2.5.94/95
				(flies as "USAF 35951")	
7362 •	T-33A	**51-17468**		(to Belgian AF as FT17)	
			N125AT	David E. Clayton, San Ramon CA/Stockton CA	7.90/95
7364 •	T-33A	**51-17470**		(to Italian AF as MM51-17470)	
				US reg. candidate	8.86
				I. N. (Junior) Burchinall/	
				Flying Tiger Air Museum, Brookston TX	94
7418 •	T-33A	**52-9333**		displ. in park, Antrium NH	73
				Bradley Air Museum, Windsor Locks CT	9.83/84
				New England Air Museum, Windsor Locks CT	.84/88
				Gerald N. Butterworth, West Kingstown RI	.88
			N8077X(2	Gerald N. Butterworth/Rhode Island Aircraft,	
				West Kingstown RI (rest. to fly)	7.89/90
7423	T-33A	52-9338	N942NA	NASA, Lyndon B. Johnson Space Center,	
				Houston TX	
				(ex NASA 942): stored MASDC	75
				rep. displ., Bridgeport CT as "29338"	
				(N942NA also rep. as 52-9335)	
7477	T-33A	51-17497		(to l'Armee de l'Air as 17497)"338-HS"	
			F-BKXM	OFEMA/Gyrafrance International, Frejorgues 3.82	
				(to R Thai AF as ......): del.	.82
7571 •	T-33A	52-9461	**N4698T**	University of Illinois, Urbana IL	66/92
7582	T-33A	51-17522		(to l'Armee de l'Air as 117522)"WZ"	
			F-GBEU	OFEMA/Gyrafrance International, Frejorgues	.82
				(to R Thai AF as ......): del.	.82
7584 •	T-33A	**51-17524**		(to Belgian AF as FT22)	
			N1180D	AG Central Aircraft Inc, TX	23.9.81
				Stanley W. Cameron, Lubbock TX	7.83/84
				Red Stevenson, Jenks OK	87/94
				Joseph V. O'Donnell, Portland ME	9.94/95
				(flies as "USAF 17524/TR-524")	
7594 •	T-33A	51-17534		(to Italian AF as MM51-17534)	
				C. H. Midkiff: US reg. candidate	8.86
				(quoted as "51-17624": above bel. correct)	
7689	T-33A	51-17544		(to l'Armee de l'Air as 17544)"10-KY,"314-WE"	
			F-GBEZ	OFEMA/Gyrafrance International, Frejorgues	2.83
				(to R Thai AF as .....): del.	.83
7691	T-33A	51-17546		(to R Norwegan AF as 3-KB)	
				(to l'Armee de l'Air as 17546)"10-KW"	
	F-.....			reg. for del. to Norway: del.	16.11.81
				R Norwegan AF Museum: displ. as "DP-P"	11.81/85
7716 •	T-33A	**52-9556**	**N9125Z**	reg. pending	72

c/n	Type	Serial	Reg.	History	Date
7807 •	T-33A	**52-9622**	**N86905**	Winona Area Technical School, Winona MN	5.73/95
7829 •	T-33A	**52-9644**	**N2220P**	Avtec Leasing & Sales: reg. candidate	12.1.90
				Donald C. Rounds, Manchester TN	7.90/92
				Leprino Aviation, Broomfield CO	11.93/95
8144	T-33A	52-9838		(to l'Armee de l'Air as 29838)"30-QZ","338-HK"	
			F-BJDY	OFEMA/Gyrafrance International, Frejorgues	5.80
				(to Republic of Singapore AF as ...)	13.5.80
				(del. via Bahrein 17.5.80)	
8149	T-33A	52-9843	N58417	Detroit Education Board, Detroit MI	66/76
8162	T-33A	52-9856	N49892	South Illinois University, Carbondale IL	.73/76
8173	T-33A	52-9867		(to l'Armee de l'Air as 29867)"338-HY"	
			F-BJDZ(1	OFEMA/Gyrafrance International, Frejorgues	5.80
				(rep. replaced by c/n 5798/F-BJDZ(2	
				for del. to RSAF 5.80)	
8229	T-33A	53-4890	N12270	Independent School District, Watertown SD	69/76
8245	T-33A	53-4906		(to FA Guatamala as .....)	
			TG-LAY	S. Perez, La Aurora, Guatamala	2.75
				C of A expired	7.8.75
8278 •	T-33A	53-4939	N1055Z	Janesville Vocational Technical School WI	77
				Blackhawk Technical School, Janesville WI	93
				offered for sale (with 53-5996)	2.93
			N152JS	reg. res.	2.95
8298	T-33A	53-4959		(to l'Armee de l'Air as 34959)	
			F-GBES	OFEMA/Gyrafrance International, Frejorgues	.82
				(to R Thai AF as ....): del.	.82
8306 •	T-33A	**53-4967**	**N47799**	Delgado Junior College, Lakefront Airport,	
				New Orleans LA	.73/88
				State of Louisiana, New Orleans LA: USCR	6.90/95
				Louisiana National Guard Military Museum,	
				Jackson Barracks, New Orleans LA: displ.	93/94
8336 •	T-33A	**53-4997**	**N73680**	SFO Community College, San Francisco CA	5.73/95
8349	T-33A	53-5010	N13006	reg. res.	.73
			N402S		
8459	T-33A	53-5120		(to l'Armee de l'Air as 35120)	
			F-GBEO	OFEMA/Gyrafrance International, Frejorgues	12.82
				(to R Thai AF as .....): del.	.82
8471	T-33A	53-5132		(to l'Armee de l'Air as 35132)"338-HC"	
			F-GBEN	OFEMA/Gyrafrance International, Frejorgues	12.82
				(to R Thai AF as .....): del.	.82
8486	T-33A	53-5147		(to l'Armee de l'Air as 35147)"338-HR"	
			F-BJNO	OFEMA/Gyrafrance International, Frejorgues	3.82
				(to R Thai AF as .....): del.	.82
8511	T-33A	53-5172		(to NASA as NASA 510)	
			N510NA	NASA, Langley Research Center, Hampton VA	78
8536	T-33A	53-5197		(to FA Guatemala as ....)	
			TG-LAX	S. Perez, La Aurora, Guatamala	2.75
				C of A expired	7.8.75
8554 •	T-33A	**53-5215**	**N8361**	Honolulu Community College, Honolulu HI	5.73/88
				Jack A. Myers, Half Moon Bay CA	11.88
				Coleman Warbird Museum, Coleman TX	90/95
				(stored dism., Dixie Air Parts, San Antonio TX 91/92)	
8577	RT-33A	53-5238		(to Italian AF as MM53-5238)"51-78"	
				for sale by auction, Treviso AB	25.9.86

				US reg. candidate	9.86
8586	T-33A	53-5247	N64351	St Louis University, Cahokia IL	76
8621	T-33A	53-5282		(to l'Armee de l'Air as 35282)"338-HM"	
			F-GBEQ	OFEMA/Gyrafrance International, Frejorgues	12.82
				(to R Thai AF as .....): del.	.82
8739 •	T-33A	**53-5400**		(to NASA as NASA 945)	
			N715NA	NASA, NAS Moffett Field CA	71/72
			N94481	Peralta Comm. College, Oakland Airport CA	11.73/95
8772 •	T-33A	**53-5433**		(to FA Peru as ....)	
			N5196X	Hermes Technical International, Miami FL	11.92/95
8926 •	T-33A	**53-5587**		(to Italian AF as MM53-5587)	
				for sale by auction, Capua AB	25.9.86
				US reg. candidate	9.86
				I. N. (Junior) Burchinall/	
				Flying Tiger Air Museum, Brookston TX	94
9015 •	T-33A TV-2 T-33B	**53-5676**		(to USN as Bu138073)	
			N7089D	USNAM, NAS Pensacola FL	8.93/95
9087	T-33A	53-5748		(to R Norwegian AF as .....)	
				(to l'Armee de l'Air as 35748)	
			F-BJXM	OFEMA/Gyrafrance International, Frejorgues 3.82	
				(to R Thai AF as ......): del.	.82
9134	T-33A	53-5794		(to R Norwegian AF as .....)	
				(to l'Armee de l'Air as 35794)	
			F-BJGY	OFEMA/Gyrafrance International, Frejorgues 3.82	
				(to R Thai AF as ......): del.	.82
9216	T-33A	53-5815	N4980	Delta Air Parts Co, Sun Valley CA	72/76
9251 •	T-33A	**53-5850**	N1453	San Diego Community College	
			N4605B	San Diego Community College,	
				San Diego-Montgomery Field CA	7.72/95
				(FAA quotes id. "9291")	
9266	T-33A	54-1577		(to l'Armee de l'Air as 41577)	
			F-BKVY	OFEMA/Gyrafrance International, Frejorgues	.82
				(to Republic of Singapore AF as 374): del.	.82
9424 •	T-33A	**53-5948**	**N62519**	Southwest Michigan College, Dowagiac MI	6.73/95
9461 •	T-33A	**53-5979**	**N4698T**	University of Illinois, Urbana IL	66/72
				Prairie Aviation Museum, Bloomington IL	94
9518 •	T-33A	**55-3021**	**N3497F**	Solano Community College, Suisun City CA	1.10.76/95
9522 •	T-33A	**55-3025**	**N512NA**	NASA	
				USMCM, MCAS Quantico VA	79
				USAFM, Minneapolis ANGB MN	88/94
9528 •	T-33A	**53-5996**	N1054Z	Janesville Vocational Technical School WI	77
				Blackhawk Technical School, Janesville WI	93
				offered for sale (with 53-4939)	2.93
			N142JS	reg. res.	2.95
9541	T-33A	53-6009		(to NASA as NASA 943)	
			N943NA	NASA, Houston TX	
				displ. Johnson City TN as "36009"	
9543	T-33A	53-6011		(to NASA as NASA 940)	
			N940NA	NASA, Houston TX	
				Davis Monthan AFB AZ: open storage	75
				sale rep., Davis Monthan AFB AZ: USCR	76/95
				noted stored Tulsa OK	4.82

9594 •	T-33A TV-2 T-33B	**55-3053**	 **N13007**	(to USN as Bu141538) New York City Education Board NY Sea-Air-Space Museum, New York NY (displ. on carrier USS Intrepid as "141538/538")	 66/72 91/92
9605 •	T-33A TV-2 T-33B	**55-3064**	 **N99472**	(to USN as Bu141549) Helena Vocational Tech School, Helena MT (open storage, unconv. "USN China Lake")	 76/95
9618	T-33A	55-3077		(to Italian AF as MM55-3077) US reg. candidate	 8.86
9658 •	T-33A	**53-6055**	N99095	School of the Ozarks, Point Lookout MO	1.77/95
9712 •	T-33A	**53-6091**	N11989 N8077X(1 N32GB	Lewis College, Lockport IL Gerald N. Butterworth/Rhode Island Aircraft, West Kingston RI Gerald N. Butterworth, West Kingston RI (rest., flies as "USAF 36091") Cloud Dancer Flying Club, Winter Haven FL	72/76 5.88 8.89/92 9.92/95
9779 •	T-33A	**55-4335**	N9979Q N400SP	Tech. College, Spokane WA : del. ex MASDC Spokane Community College, Spokane WA Steve L. Picatti, Boise ID ntu: Steve L. Picatti, Boise ID	10.12.76 84/91 4.91/95 5.91
9795 •	T-33A	**55-4351**	 N815NA	(to NASA as NASA 815) NASA, Edwards AFB CA Shasta Tehama Trinity, Redding CA Lewiston Community District, Lewiston CA	 69/72 76/94 11.94
9835	T-33A	55-4391	N1058	Sowela Technical Institute, Lake Charles LA	69/72
9843 •	T-33A	**55-4399**	**N87912**	Academy of Aeronautics, La Guardia NY (del. ex storage Davis Monthan AFB AZ 23.2.77) K & K Aircraft Inc, Bridgewater VA struck-off USCR	2.77/84 6.88 24.2.92
9923 •	T-33A	**56-1573**	N97477 N7477 **N5848F**	Honolulu Community College, Honolulu HI Jack A. Myers, Half Moon Bay CA Coleman Warbird Museum, Coleman TX Coleman Warbird Museum, Coleman TX (N5848F reg. as id. "56CWWM1573")	69/88 11.88 92/93 4.93/95
9924 •	T-33A	**56-1574**	**N8362**	Honolulu Community College, Honolulu HI Jack A. Myers, Half Moon Bay CA Coleman Warbird Museum, Coleman TX	73/88 11.88/92 95
1019 •	T-33A	**56-1669**	**N391P**	Purdue University, Lafayette IN sale reported, Vincennes IN	.73/76 3.81/92
1080	T-33A	56-1730	 N950NA N1449	(to NASA as NASA 950) NASA, Houston TX US Dept of Interior Geological Surveys, Water Resources Division Davis Monthan AFB AZ: open storage	 75
1097 •	T-33A	**56-1747**	**N43856**	Board of Education, Westbury NY	12.76/95
1099 •	T-33A	**56-1749**	N61749 **N155SF**	Bay Area Technical College, St Petersburg FL Aviation Consultants Inc, Tulsa OK Richard F. Bohannon, McAllen TX	 76/77 9.83/92
1102 •	T-33A TV-2 T-33B	**56-1752**	 **N40186**	(to USN as Bu143040) Lansing Community College, Lansing MI	 4.76/92
1145	T-33A	56-3661	N83615	Detroit High School, Detroit MI	.73
1150	T-33A	56-3666	 N941NA(2	(to NASA as NASA 941) NASA, Houston TX : to MASDC	 3.9.70

				Allied Aircraft, Tucson AZ : del. ex MASDC	2.8.78
1151 •	T-33A	**56-3667**	**N51SR**	Leroy Penhall/Fighter Imports Inc, Chino CA	74
				David C. Tallichet/MARC, Chino CA	7.74/95
				(FAA quote 57-0451, "1451" & "0451"; 51-17416 also quoted!)	
1155	T-33A	56-3671		(to NASA as NASA 937)	
			N937NA	NASA, Houston TX : retired to MASDC	20.11.70
				Allied Aircraft, Tucson AZ : del. ex MASDC	19.1.76
1173 •	T-33A	**56-3689**		(to NASA as NASA 939)	
			N939NA	NASA, Houston TX	.73/76
			N87678	Golden Triangle Votec School, Columbus MS	76/87
			N939NA	George W. Lancaster, Wilmington NC	11.87/95
				(flies as "USAF 63689")	
1282 •	T-33A	**57-0553**	**N57553**	South Illinois University, Carbondale IL	.73/94
				struck-off USCR	4.94
1294 •	T-33A	**57-0565**	**N22ES**	Western Michigan University MI reg. res.	2.85
				E. J. Saviano, Portage WI	4.85
				James E. Smith, Boulder CO/Fortine MT	4.87/95
1297 •	T-33A	**57-0568**	**N41839**	Victor Valley College, Victorville CA	76/88
				struck-off USCR	5.90
				USAFM, Edwards AFB CA	93/94
1298 •	T-33A	**57-0569**	**N64274**	George T. Baker Aviation School, Miami FL	1.74/90
				USNAM, NAS Pensacola FL	94
				Palm Beach Maritime Museum FL: loan	94
1302 •	T-33A	**57-0573**	**N99152**	Cincinnati Technical College, Cincinnati OH	.73/88
				sale rep., Chesterfield MO: USCR	89/95
1327 •	T-33A	**57-0598**	**N23745**	Area Vocational Tech. School, Tallahassee FL	8.72/92
1338 •	T-33A	**57-0609**	**N82852**	Sowela Technical Institute, Lake Charles LA	12.73/95
1412	T-33A	57-0683		(to l'Armee de l'Air as 70683)"338-HL"	
			F-GBEV	OFEMA/Gyrafrance International, Frejorgues	2.83
				(to R Thai AF as ......): del.	.83
1413	T-33A	57-0684		(to R Norwegan AF as DP-X)	
				(to l'Armee de l'Air as 70684)"30-QA"	
			F-BKVH	OFEMA/Gyrafrance International, Frejorgues	.82
				(to Republic of Singapore AF as 375): del.	.82
1480 •	T-33A	**57-0751**	N18853	ntu	.74
			N17076	Los Angeles School District, Mission Hills CA	6.74/92
1519 •	T-33A	**58-0470**	**N63313**	Area Vocational Tech. School, Tallahassee FL	10.73/92
				Florida Military Aviation Museum, St. Petersburg-Clearwater Airport	94
1520 •	T-33A	**58-0471**	**N94498**	Le Tourneau College, Longview TX	76/87
				Fred N. Ropkey, Longview TX	10.87/95
				(rest., ff.90 as "USAF 80471")	
1529 •	T-33A	**58-0480**	**N63311**	George T. Baker Aviation School, Miami FL	10.73/95
1540 •	T-33A	**58-0491**	**N94484**	Los Rios Community College, Sacramento CA	11.73/95
1541 •	T-33A	**58-0492**	**N24837**	Montcalm Community College, Sidney MT	76
				sale rep., Dowagiac MI	84/92
				struck-off USCR	21.7.93
1546	T-33A	58-0497	N87778	State Board for Education, Columbia SC	76
1558 •	T-33A	**58-0509**	**N57969**	Kirtland Community College, Roscommon MI	10.72/95

1588 •	T-33A	**58-0539**		Trident College, Charleston SC: ex MASDC	8.6.77/78
			N37998	Trident Technical College, Charleston SC	7.78/95
1591 •	T-33A	**58-0542**	**N10265**	Texas State Technical Institute, Waco TX	10.72/95
1595 •	T-33A	**58-0546**	**N93224**	Tarrant City Junior College, Fort Worth TX	.73/84
				Eagles Nest Of The Ozarks Inc, Springfield MO	4.86/95
1685	T-33A	58-0636	N83737	Warren High School, Gurnee IL	76
				sale rep., Chicago IL	11.80/95
1700 •	T-33A	**58-0651**	**N88769**	Southwest Tech. Institute, East Camden AR	3.73/95
1714 •	T-33A	**58-0665**		imported by Aero Technical Services Inc	5.88
			N658W	Jack A. Myers, Half Moon Bay CA	10.88
			N556RH	Randall K. Hames, Cliffside NC	4.91/95
1720 •	T-33A	**58-0671**		(to NASA as NASA 936)	
			N936NA	NASA, Houston TX: retired to MASDC by	75
				USAFM, Phoenix ANGB AZ	93/94
				(displ. as "USAF 58-0671")	
1746 •	T-33A	**58-0697**	**N49239**	Florence School District, Florence SC	76/84
				sale rep., Jacksonville FL	88
				Doan Helicopters Inc, New Smyrna Beach FL	7.91/92
				(rest. New Smyrna Beach, ff 9.91in USAF sc.)	
				offered for sale, Doan auction: TT 1650 hrs	30.10.92
1749 •	T-33A	**58-0700**	**N88812**	Florida Academy of Aerospace Technology,	
				St. Petersburg-Clearwater Airport FL	6.73/95
T33-15 •	CL-30	**RCAF21015**		RCAF BOC 19.5.53: SOC	16.5.62
	Silver Star			(to l'Armee de l'Air as 21015) "314-VF"	.62
	Mk. 3		F-WEQB	ferry to Dinard, ex storage Chateaudun AB	.85
			F-ZVLH (1	dep. Dinard, France on del. to Bolivia	12.7.85
				(to FA Boliviana as 621)	.85
T33-24 •	CL-30	**RCAF21024**		RCAF BOC 30.6.53: SOC	24.3.65
	Mk. 3		N157X	Aeronautical Specialties Inc, Long Beach CA	3.65/66
				Flight Test Research Inc, Long Beach CA	68/72
			N302FS	Flight Systems Inc, Mojave CA	5.77/89
				T-Bird Aviation, Mojave CA	3.90/95
T33-27	CL-30	RCAF21027		RCAF BOC 3.7.53: SOC	16.5.62
	Mk. 3			(to l'Armee de l'Air as 21027) "314-YP"	.62
			F-WEQA	ferry to Dinard, ex storage Chateaudun AB	.85
			F-ZVLC (1	dep. Dinard, France on del. to Bolivia	19.6.85
				(to FA Boliviana as 622)	
T33-42	CL-30	RCAF21042		RCAF BOC 30.7.53: SOC	16.5.62
	Mk. 3			(to l'Armee de l'Air as 21042) "314-VT"	.62
			F-WEQE	ferry to Dinard, ex storage Chateaudun AB	.85
			F-ZVLI (1	dep. Dinard, France on del. to Bolivia	19.6.85
				(to FA Boliviana as 623)	
T33-50	CL-30	RCAF21050		RCAF BOC 31.7.53: SOC	16.5.62
	Mk. 3			(to l'Armee de l'Air as 21050) "314-YQ"	.62
			F-WEQC	ferry to Dinard, ex storage Chateaudun AB	.85
			F-ZVLJ (1	dep. Dinard, France on del. to Bolivia	12.7.85
				(to FA Boliviana as 624)	.85
				wreck noted Santa Cruz AB, Bolivia	95
T33-81	CL-30	RCAF21081		RCAF BOC 3.9.53: SOC	16.5.62
	Mk. 3			(to l'Armee de l'Air as 21081) "314-YI"	.62
			F-WEQF	ferry to Dinard, ex storage Chateaudun AB	.85
			F-ZVLK (1	dep. Dinard, France on del. to Bolivia	12.7.85
				(to FA Boliviana as 625)	.85
T33-88	CL-30	RCAF21088		RCAF BOC 27.10.53: SOC	16.5.52
	Mk. 3			(to l'Armee de l'Air as 21088) "314-YL"	.62
			F-WEQQ	ferry to Dinard, ex storage Chateaudun AB	.85

			F-ZVLN (2	dep. Dinard, France on del. to Bolivia (to FA Boliviana as 626)	10.85
T33-98 •	CL-30 Mk. 3	**RCAF21098**	 **N99184**	RCAF BOC 22.10.53: SOC Flight Systems Inc, Mojave CA T-Bird Aviation, Mojave CA Fort Wayne Air Service, Fort Wayne IN Rick Brickert/Red Knight Airshows Inc, Fort Wayne IN : flies as "Red Knight"	10.11.70 2.77/88 3.89 6.89 7.90/95
T33-118•	CL-30 Mk. 3	**RCAF21118**	 **N99192**	RCAF BOC 2.12.53: SOC Flight Systems Inc, Mojave CA T-Bird Aviation, Mojave CA Blossom Company, Wilmington DE	10.11.70 2.77/88 3.89/92 4.95
T33-129•	CL-30 Mk. 3	**RCAF21129**	 N64776 **N84TB**	RCAF BOC 17.2.54: to inst. airframe A632 Creature Enterprises, Bridgehampton NY Thunderbird Aviation, Deer Valley AZ	30.7.59 77 9.77/95
T33-132	CL-30 Mk. 3	RCAF21132	 F-WEQK F-ZVLJ (2	RCAF BOC 7.12.53: SOC (to l'Armee de l'Air as 21132)"314-YV" ferry to Dinard, ex storage Chateaudun AB dep. Dinard, France on del. to Bolivia (to FA Boliviana as ....)	16.5.62 29.6.62 .85 10.85
T33-150	CL-30 Mk. 3 CT-133	RCAF21150	 C-GWHM	(later CAF 133150): BOC 30.3.54: SOC Arnie Carnegie, Edmonton ALTA (to FA Boliviana as FAB 615) crashed and dest., Punata, Bolivia	10.11.70 7.75 21.2.80
T33-152	CL-30 Mk. 3	RCAF21152	 F-WEQP F-ZVLC (3	RCAF BOC 5.1.54: SOC (to l'Armee de l'Air as 21152)"314-YN" ferry to Dinard, ex storage Chateaudun AB dep. Dinard, France on del. to Bolivia (to FA Boliviana as ....)	16.5.62 16.5.62 .85 11.85
T33-157•	CL-30 Mk. 3	**RCAF21157**	 N155X **N133AT**	RCAF BOC 12.1.54: SOC Omni Investment Group, Long Beach CA Jim Cullen, Broomfield CO Flight Systems Inc, Mojave CA Creature Enterprises, Bridgehampton NY Centurion Airways CA Aeronautical Test Vehicles,Newport Beach CA Aeronautical Test Vehicles,Newport Beach CA Advanced Aeronautical Enterprises Inc, Newport Beach CA Barron Thomas Aviation Inc, Dallas TX ISRMS, Land-o-Lakes FL	24.3.65 3.65/66 69 76 77 84 5.84 7.85 3.86 6.88/92 7.92/95
T33-159•	CL-30 Mk. 3	**RCAF21159**	 N96186 **N305FS**	(to RCN as 21159): BOC 9.2.54: SOC Flight Systems Inc, Mojave CA Flight Systems Inc, Mojave CA Tracor Flight Systems, Austin TX	10.11.70 9.76 9.77/91 12.91/95
T33-160•	CL-30 Mk. 3 Skyfox	**RCAF21160**	 N12414 **N221SF**	RCAF BOC 14.1.54: SOC Leroy Penhall/Fighter Imports Inc, Chino CA Murray McCormick Aerial Surveys Consolidated Leasing, Sacramento CA Skyfox Corp, Van Nuys CA Flight Test Research Inc, Englewood CO Flight Test Research Inc, Englewood CO (rebuilt as prototype Skyfox trainer, ff 23.8.83)	10.11.70 .73 75 77 1.83 8.83/95
T33-162	CL-30 Mk. 3 CT-133	RCAF21162	 CF-FIF	(later CAF as 133162): BOC 9.2.54: SOC Northwest Industries Ltd, Edmonton ALTA (to FA Boliviana as FAB 601): del. via Miami crashed, dest.	5.1.73 1.73 13.1.73 19.8.77
T33-182	CL-30 Mk. 3	RCAF21182		RCAF BOC 16.3.54: SOC (to l'Armee de l'Air as 21182)"314-UW"	16.5.62 12.6.62

			F-WEQO	ferry to Dinard, ex storage Chateaudun AB	.85
			F-ZVLK (2	dep. Dinard, France on del. to Bolivia	10.85
				(to FA Boliviana as ....)	
T33-185	CL-30 Mk. 3	RCAF21185		RCAF BOC 21.4.54: SOC	16.5.62
				(to l'Armee de l'Air as 21185) "314-YU"	29.5.62
			N4249S	Vince Clothier Corp, Phoenix AZ	5.81
				not del., struck-off USCR	1.85
T33-192•	CL-30 Mk. 3	**RCAF21192**		RCAF BOC 18.3.54: SOC	29.5.64
			N156X	Aeronautical Specialties Inc, Long Beach CA	3.65/66
				Flight Test Research Inc, Long Beach CA	68/72
				Flight Systems Inc, Mojave CA	73/77
			N304FS	Flight Systems Inc, Mojave CA	11.77/90
				Arthur W. McDonnell/McDonnell Enterprises Inc, Mojave CA	2.90
				T-33 Inc, Winter Park FL	8.90/95
				(flies as "USN Blue Angles/0")	
T33-195	CL-30 Mk. 3	RCAF21195		RCAF BOC 15.6.54: SOC	16.5.62
				(to l'Armee de l'Air as 21195)"314-YE"	16.5.62
			F-WEQR	ferry to Dinard, ex storage Chateaudun AB	.85
			F-ZVLM	dep. Dinard, France on del. to Bolivia	11.85
				(to FA Boliviana as ....)	
T33-200	CL-30 Mk. 3	RCAF21200		RCAF BOC 18.3.54: SOC	10.9.70
			N12420	Leroy Penhall/Fighter Imports Inc, Chino CA	.73
				Winchester Meteorology Division, New Haven CT	73/75
				(based Torino, Italy, del. via Prestwick 10.5.73)	
				dam. by hailstorm, Torino, Italy	22.6.73
				struck-off USCR : "sold for salvage"	7.10.75
				Ormond Haydon-Baillie, Duxford UK	.76
				del. to USA, via Prestwick	25.11.77
T33-211	CL-30 Mk. 3	RCAF21211		RCAF BOC 12.3.54: SOC	11.9.59
				(to l'Armee de l'Air as 21211)"314-YK"	9.59
			F-WEQL	ferry to Dinard, ex storage Chateaudun AB	.85
			F-ZVLI (2	del. via Glasgow to Bolivia	25.11.85
				(to FA Boliviana as 631)	
T33-221	CL-30 Mk. 3	RCAF21221		RCAF BOC 22.10.53: SOC	10.11.70
			N12424	Leroy Penhall/Fighter Imports Inc, Chino CA	72/74
T33-231•	CL-30 Mk. 3	**RCAF21231**		RCAF BOC 26.3.54: SOC	23.2.67
			N10018	E. Duke Vincent, Los Angeles CA	86
			N134AT	Aeronautical Test Vehicles,Newport Beach CA	1.87
			N333DV	Duke E. Vincent, Los Angeles CA	2.87/92
				Thomas J. Hickman, Amarillo TX	10.92/94
			N36TH	Thomas J. Hickman, Amarillo TX	11.94/95
T33-236•	CL-30 Mk. 3	**RCAF21236**		RCAF BOC 16.3.54: to RCN as 21236: SOC	10.1.70
			N99195	Flight Systems Inc, Mojave CA	2.77/89
				T-Bird Aviation, Mojave CA	3.89
				Neil J. McClain, Salt Lake City UT	3.90/95
T33-247	CL-30 Mk. 3	RCAF21247		RCAF BOC 24.3.54: SOC	16.5.62
				(to l'Armee de l'Air as 21247)"314-VO"	5.62
			F-WEQG	ferry to Dinard, ex storage Chateaudun AB	.85
			F-ZVLN (1	dep. Dinard, France on del. to Bolivia	26.8.85
				(to FA Boliviana as 632): crashed	2.92
T33-261•	CL-30 Mk. 3 CT-133	**RCAF21261**		(to RCN as 21261, later CAF 133261): BOC	31.3.54
				retired, stored Saskatoon CFB SASK: del.	7.12.66/72
				Ormond A. Haydon-Baillie: ex CAF disposals	26.5.72
			CF-IHB	Ormond A. Haydon-Baillie, Cold Lake ALTA	8.72/73
				(del. Canada to UK, arr. Southend 9.11.73)	
			G-OAHB	Ormond A. Haydon-Baillie, Duxford	9.5.74/80
				Brotway Ltd: dism. Duxford & Baginton	.80/82
			G-JETT	Clive Thompson/Anvil Aviation, Blackbushe	4.6.82
				(trucked to Coventry: ff Coventry 2.8.82)	
				Aces High Ltd, Duxford	83/85

				Patina Pty Ltd, Baginton	30.1.85
				(del. to USA, via Prestwick 14.7.85)	
			N33VC	Bruce Goessling/Combat Jet & Aerospace Museum, Chino CA	9.85
				Pacifica Investments Inc, Las Vegas NV	87
				Grob Aviation Inc, Wilmington DE	88
				(del. US to Switzerland, arr. Zurich 29.4.88)	
				John V. Crocker/Pegasus Aviation, Ione CA	7.90/95
				op: Old Flying Machine Co, Duxford	5.90/95
				(del. Switzerland-Duxford 1.5.90, flies as "USAF 54-21261")	
T33-265	CL-30 Mk. 3	RCAF21265		RCAF BOC 24.3.54: SOC	10.11.70
			N12418	Leroy Penhall/Fighter Imports Inc, Chino CA	.73/74
				Jack Ormes, Los Angeles CA	77
				Raymond F. Mabrey, Coon Rapids MI	3.82/94
				crashed dest., Selfridge ANGB MI (Mabrey k.)	11.6.94
T33-273	CL-30 Mk. 3	RCAF21273		RCAF BOC 26.5.54: SOC	10.11.70
			N12413	Leroy Penhall/Fighter Imports Inc, Chino CA	.73/74
				Richard Doebler, Milwaukee WI	77
				John R. Sandberg, Robstown TX	.82/88
				Rick Brickert & Dennis Sanders, Chino CA	.88/90
			N233RK	Frank C. Sanders, Chino CA	8.89/90
				Red Knight Air Shows, Chino CA	5.90
				crashed, dest., Roswell NM (Frank Sanders k.)	4.5.90
T33-288	CL-30 Mk. 3	RCAF21288		RCAF BOC 23.6.54: SOC	29.5.64
			N106D	Flight Test Research, Long Beach CA	3.65/68
				crashed near Mojave CA : pilot ejected	19.9.68
T33-295•	CL-30 Mk. 3	**RCAF21295**		RCAF BOC 6.5.54: SOC	10.11.70
			N12419	Leroy Penhall/Fighter Imports Inc, Chino CA	
			N4TM	Thomas McMullen, Fullerton CA	76
			N33EL	Ed P. Lunken, Cincinnati OH	10.81
			N72JR	Jim Robinson, Houston TX	7.85/86
				Jim Robinson/Combat Jets Flying Museum, Houston TX	12.86/92
				EAA Aviation Foundation, Oshkosh WI	5.92/95
T33-298•	CL-30 Mk. 3	**RCAF21298**		RCAF BOC 25.5.54: SOC	24.3.65
			CF-SSZ	rep. at Toronto-Malton ONT	65
			N109X	Aeronautical Specialties Inc, Long Beach CA	3.65/66
				Flight Test Research Inc, Long Beach CA	69/72
				Boeing Equipment Holding Co, Seattle WA	3.76/95
T33-306•	CL-30 Mk. 3	**RCAF21306**		RCAF BOC 7.6.54: SOC	10.11.70
			N99173	Flight Systems Inc, Mojave CA	2.77/78
			N306FS	Flight Systems Inc, Mojave CA	1.78/89
				T-Bird Aviation, Mojave CA	3.89/95
				(flies as "USAF 21306")	
T33-307	CL-30 Mk. 3	RCAF21307		RCAF BOC 31.5.54: SOC	16.5.62
				(to l'Armee de l'Air as 21307) "314-UT"	.62
			F-WEQN	ferry to Dinard, ex storage Chateaudun AB	.85
			F-ZVLD (3	dep. Dinard, France on del. to Bolivia	11.85
				(to FA Boliviana as ....)	
T33-325	CL-30 Mk. 3	RCAF21325		RCAF BOC	19.5.54/70
			CF-ADY	Lester Addie/Addie & Assoc. Ltd, Moncton NB	10.72
			N325DS	reg.	6.76
T33-329	CL-30 Mk. 3 CT-133	RCAF21329		(to RCN 21329, later CAF 133329)	
				BOC 27.5.54 : SOC	10.11.70
			N21120		
			N505DM		
			C-GWHO	Arnie Carnegie, Edmonton ALTA	7.75
				(to FA Boliviana as FAB-619)	.75
T33-341•	CL-30 Mk. 3	**RCAF21341**		(to RCN as 21341): BOC 17.6.54: SOC	10.11.70
			N12422	Leroy Penhall/Fighter Imports Inc, Chino CA	.73/74

				Kay J. Eckhardt, Salt Lake City UT	9.75/95
T33-342•	CL-30 Mk. 3	**RCAF21342**		RCAF BOC 27.6.54 : SOC	11.12.64
			N144M	Omni Investment Corp, Washington DC	12.64/66
				Flight Test Research Inc, Long Beach CA	69
				Paul B. MacCready, New Haven CT	72
				Flight Systems Inc, Mojave CA	76/77
			N303FS	Flight Systems Inc, Mojave CA	3.77/91
				Tracor Flight Systems, Austin TX	12.91/95
T33-369•	CL-30 Mk. 3	**RCAF21369**		RCAF BOC 30.8.54: SOC	10.11.70
			N12416	Leroy Penhall/Fighter Imports Inc, Chino CA	.73/74
				Ed Fisher, Kansas City KS	77
				Boeing Equipment Holding Co, Seattle WA	4.80/95
T33-375•	CL-30 Mk. 3	**RCAF21375**		RCAF BOC 9.7.54: SOC	10.11.70
		N33WR	N12430	Leroy Penhall/Fighter Imports Inc, Chino CA	.73/74
				Walter Rye, Cincinnati OH	76
				Harrah Corporation Unlimited, Portland OR	85
			N33HW	Harrah Corporation Unlimited, Portland OR	4.85/86
				Jet I Inc, Alexandria VA	88
				Robert de la Valle/ISRMS Inc, Land-o-Lakes FL	3.92/95
T33-379•	CL-30 Mk. 3	**RCAF21379**		RCAF BOC 16.7.54: SOC	18.5.65
			CF-SKH	National Research Council, Ottawa ONT	.65/70
			C-FSKH-X	NRC Flight Research Laboratory, Ottawa ONT	83/95
T33-400	CL-30 Mk. 3	RCAF21400		RCAF BOC 26.8.54: SOC	16.5.62
				(to l'Armee de l'Air as 21400) "314-TS"	.62
			F-WEQD	ferry to Dinard, ex storage Chateaudun AB	.85
			F-ZVLD	dep. Dinard, France on del. to Bolivia	19.6.85
				(to FA Boliviana as 634)	
T33-420	CL-30 Mk. 3	RCAF21420		RCAF BOC 16.9.54: SOC	11.9.59
				(to l'Armee de l'Air as 21420) "314-VK"	.59
			F-WEQI	ferry to Dinard, ex storage Chateaudun AB	.85
			F-ZVLC (2	dep. Dinard, France on del. to Bolivia	26.8.85
				(to FA Boliviana as 635)	
T33-439	CL-30 Mk. 3	RCAF21439		RCAF BOC 18.10.54: SOC	11.9.59
				(to l'Armee de l'Air as 21439) "314-VB"	.59
			N4249R	Vince Clothier Corp, Phoenix AZ	5.81
				not del., struck-off USCR	1.85
			F-WEQJ	ferry to Dinard, ex storage Chateaudun AB	.85
			F-ZVLD (2	del. via Glasgow to Bolivia	5.11.85
				(to FA Boliviana as 636)	
T33-440•	CL-30 Mk. 3	**RCAF21440**		BOC RCAF 19.10.54: SOC	10.11.70
			N12417	Leroy Penhall/Fighter Imports Inc, Chino CA	74
				Douglas Clark/Clark Aviation, Allandale FL	5.75/95
				(flies in "Thunderbirds" scheme)	
T33-456•	CL-30 Mk. 3	**RCAF21456**		(to RCN as 21456): BOC 5.1.55: SOC	24.3.65
			N158X	Mount Union Airport, Mount Union PA	3.65/66
				Playboy Missile Systems, Amarillo TX	69
				Playboy Missile Systems, Las Vegas NV	72
			N333MJ	Matt Jackson, Portland OR	2.82/84
				(flew in movie"The Right Stuff" as "11808")	
			N333JM	Jimmy McMillan, Breckenridge TX	.84
			N333MJ	Don H. Novas, Blackfoot ID	4.87/95
T33-464	CL-30 Mk. 3 CT-133	RCAF21464		(later CAF 133464): BOC 4.1.55: SOC	10.11.70
			N21464	reg.	.73
			C-GPEG	Arnie Carnegie, Edmonton ALTA	7.75
				(to FA Boliviana as FAB-618)	.75
T33-485	CL-30 Mk. 3	RCAF21485		RCAF BOC 27.4.55: SOC	16.5.62
				(to l'Armee de l'Air as 21485) "314-YR"	.62
			N4249R	Vince Clothier Corp, Phoenix AZ	5.81/85
				not del., struck-off USCR	1.85
			F-WEQM	ferry to Dinard, ex storage Chateaudun AB	.85

			F-ZVLH (2	del. via Glasgow to Bolivia	25.11.85
				(to FA Boliviana as 637)	
T33-488	CL-30	RCAF21488		(to RCN as 21488, later CAF 133488): BOC	16.12.54
	Mk. 3		C-GWHL	Arnie Carnegie, Edmonton ALTA	7.75
	CT-133			(to FA Boliviana as FAB-617)	.75
T33-489	CL-30	RCAF21489		RCAF BOC 19.5.55: SOC	16.5.62
	Mk. 3			(to l'Armee de l'Air as 21489) "314-UF"	.62
			N4249V	Vince Clothier Corp, Phoenix AZ	5.81/85
				not del., struck-off USCR	1.85
			F-WEQH	ferry to Dinard, ex storage Chateaudun AB	.85
			F-ZVLM	dep. Dinard, France on del. Bolivia	26.8.85
				(to FA Boliviana as ....)	
T33-535•	CL-30	**RCAF21535**		RCAF BOC 15.3.56: SOC	11.9.67
	Mk. 3			Northwest Aviation Heritage Museum ALTA	
			N35RV	Robert M. Vuksanovic, Dover NH	7.86/88
				Robert M. Vuksanovic, Caledonia WI	89/94
			N133RV	Robert M. Vuksanovic, Caledonia WI	12.94/95
T33-555•	CL-30	**RCAF21555**		RCAF BOC	6.9.56/70
	Mk. 3		N96178	Flight Systems Inc, Mojave CA	.76/77
			N301FS	Flight Systems Inc, Mojave CA	9.77/91
				Tracor Flight Systems, Austin TX	12.91/95
T33-556•	CL-30	**RCAF21556**		RCAF BOC	6.9.56/70
	Mk. 3		**N99179**	Flight Systems Inc, Mojave CA	2.77/89
				T-Bird Aviation, Mojave CA	3.89
				(open storage, faded RCAF sc., Mojave 80/90)	
				PLR Aircraft Leasing Co, Los Angeles CA	3.92/95
T33-557•	CL-30	**RCAF21557**		RCAF BOC	12.9.56/70
	Mk. 3		**N99175**	Flight Systems Inc, Mojave CA	2.77/89
				T-Bird Aviation, Mojave CA	3.89
				Neil J. McClain, Salt Lake City UT	3.90/95
				(flies as "RCAF 21557 Golden Hawks")	
T33-559•	CL-30	**RCAF21559**		RCAF BOC	12.56/70
	Mk. 3		N3370	Thunderbird Aviation, Deer Valley AZ	11.73/76
			N83TB	Thunderbird Aviation, Deer Valley AZ	.76/95
T33-566•	CL-30	**RCAF21566**		RCAF BOC	12.56/70
	Mk. 3		N99193	Flight Systems Inc, Mojave CA	2.77/85
			N307FS	Flight Systems Inc, Mojave CA	5.85/91
				Tracor Flight Systems, Austin TX	11.91/92
				Michael Dorn Inc, Los Angeles CA	2.94/95
T33-580	CL-30	RCAF21580		(later CAF 133580): BOC	17.5.57/70
	Mk. 3		C-GWHN	Arnie Carnegie, Edmonton ALTA	7.75
	CT-133			(to FA Boliviana as FAB-616)	.75
T33-582•	CL-30	**RCAF21582**		RCAF BOC	17.5.57/70
	Mk. 3		N99202	Flight Systems Inc, Mojave CA	2.77
			N92JB	John MacGuire/War Eagles Museum,	
				Santa Teresa NM	2.84/95
T33-590•	CL-30	RCAF21590		(to RCN as 21590): BOC 4.10.57: SOC	5.6.67
	Mk. 3		**CF-WIS**	National Research Council, Ottawa ONT	.67/70
			C-FWIS	National Research Council/	
				Flight Research Laboratory, Ottawa ONT	72/95
T33-640 •	CL-30	**RCAF21640**		(to RCN as 21640, CAF as 133640): BOC	6.1.59/70
	Mk. 3		CF-EHB	Ormond A. Haydon-Baillie, Toronto ONT	11.73
	CT-133			(flown Canada to UK : arr. Southend 30.11.73)	
			G-WGHB	Ormond A. Haydon-Baillie, Duxford	9.5.74/80
				Brotway Ltd: stored dism.	
				Clive Thompson/Anvil Aviation: stored dism.	6.82/83
				(stored dism. Duxford & Baginton .80/83,	
				moved by road to Southampton 3.8.85)	

-		CL-30 Mk. 3	RCAF21...	CP-1045	ferry reg. for flight Edmonton - FA Boliviana	
-		T-33A	-	N135AT	Advanced Aeronautical Enterprises Inc, Newport Beach CA	86
-	•	T-33A	-	**N330TR**	Raymond L. Keasler, Denton TX (FAA quote id. "A058")	7.90/95
-		T-33A	-		Vincent J. Menier OH: bankrupcy auction (id. "1904A" quoted)	3.85
-		T-33A	-		Vincent J. Menier OH: bankrupcy auction (id. "1988" quoted)	3.85
-	•	T-33A	-		(to Yugoslav AF as 051) stored unconv., Mojave CA	87/95
-	•	T-33A	-		(to Yugoslav AF as 054) stored unconv., Mojave CA	87/95

Serial	Type	History	Date
Nr110305 •	Me 262B-1a	10./NJG 11 "Red 8": captured Schleswig	5.45
/U1		(to RAF as AM 50, VH519)	
		del. to RAF Farnborough ex Schleswig	19.5.45
		dam. landing, RAF Ford (repaired)	6.7.45
		shipped to Capetown, South Africa: arr.	17.3.47
		SAAF Dunnottar AB: displ.	50/71
		S. African National Museum of Military History,	
		Saxonwold, Johannesburg	.70/94
		(static rest. Snake Valley AB .71/72)	
Nr110306	Me 262B-1a	10./NJG 11 "Red 6": captured Schleswig	5.45
	/U1	shipped ex France to USA on HMS Reaper	7.45
		(to USAAF as FE-610/T2-610)	.45/46
		Cornell University, Buffalo NY	c50
Nr110639 •	Me 262B-1a	III./EGJ2 "White 35": captured Lechfeld	.45
	/U1	shipped ex France to USA on HMS Reaper	7.45
		(to US Navy as Bu121448)	.45
		NAS Patuxent River MD: flight tests	.45
		NAS Willow Grove PA: displ. as "13"	12.46/93
		Herb Tischler/Texas Aircraft Factory,	
		Fort Worth-Meacham Field TX: loan	.93/95
		(pattern use for production of replica Me262s;	
		then static rest. to be returned to Willow Grove)	
Nr112372 •	Me 262A-1a	I./JG7 "Yellow 7": captured Fassberg	.45
		del. Farnborough ex Copenhagen	23.6.45
		(to RAF as AM 51, VK893)	.45
		RAF Cranwell: displ.	9.46/60
		(stored RAF Gaydon 60/73, RAF Finningley)	
		RAF Museum, RAF Cosford	77/85
		RAF Museum, RAF St Athan	12.85/89
		RAF Museum, RAF Cosford	.89/95
Nr500071 •	Me 262A-1b	III./JG7 "White 3"	
		forced landing Dubendorf AB, Switzerland	25.4.45
		(interned, stored Dubendorf AB 45/57)	
		Deutsches Museum, Munich: displ. as "3"	30.8.57/95
Nr500210 •	Me 262A-2a	II./KG51 "Black X"/"9K+XK"	
		captured Fassberg, Germany	7.5.45
		(to RAF as AM 81, VP554): flight trials	.45
		del. Farnborough ex Fassberg, via Manston	6.9.45
		shipped ex Liverpool to Melbourne, arr.	22.12.46
		RAAF Laverton VIC: stored	12.46/48
		Australian War Memorial: stored Sydney	2.48/55
		Australian War Memorial, Canberra ACT	.55/94
		RAAF Museum, RAAF Point Cook VIC: loan	71/88
		(stored AWM Mitchell Annexe, Canberra 92/94)	
Nr500491 •	Me 262A-1b	II./JG7 "Yellow 7": captured Lechfeld	.45
	/U3	shipped ex France to USA on HMS Reaper	7.45
		(to USAAF as FE-111)	.45
		Smithsonian Institute, stored Park Ridge IL	7.46
		NASM, Silver Hill MD	65/78
		NASM, Washington DC	80/94
- •	Me 262A-1a	"111": captured Lechfeld, Germany	.45
		shipped ex France to USA on HMS Reaper	7.45
		(to USN as Bu121442)	
		NAS Patuxent River MD: 10 hrs flight tests	.45/46
		NAS Philadelphia PA: SOC USN	31.1.47
		USAFM, Wright-Patterson AFB OH	.57/94
- •	Me 262A-1a	"White 25": captured Lechfeld	.45
	/U3	shipped ex France to USA on HMS Reaper	7.45
		(to USAAF as FE-4012/T2-4012)	.45/46
		Hughes Aircraft, Culver City CA: loan	.48
		Cal Aero Technical Institute, Glendale CA	c49/55

					The Air Museum, Claremont CA	c55/65
					The Air Museum, Ontario CA	65/70
					(rest. Ontario 69, displ. as "Luftwaffe/13")	
					Ed Maloney/Planes of Fame Museum, Chino	74/95
					(displ. as "Luftwaffe 111617/9")	
-	•	Me 262A			Earl Reinert/Victory Air Museum,	
					Mundelein IL	65/76
					Don Knapp, Abilene TX (rest. project)	87/90
4	•	Avia S.92	V-34		Narodni Technicke Muzeum , Prague	79
					Vojenske Muzeum, Kbely AB, Prague	84/94
					(displ. as "S92-4/V-34")	
51104	•	Avia CS.92	V-31		Vojenske Muzeum, Kbely AB, Czechoslovakia	73/86
					(displ. as "CS-92-5/V-35")	

MIKOYAN-GUREVICH MIG-15

2562	•	SBLim-2		(to Polish AF as 2562)	
				C. Panaitescu	
			N83GP	Vintage Wings Inc, Anchorage AK	4.3.93/95
3506	•	SBLim-2		(to Polish AF as 306)	
				Brunetto Flying Service, Coolidge AZ	3.94
				(shipped 3.94 ex storage Katovice AB, Poland)	
3804	•	SBLim-2		(to Polish AF as 3804)	
				Randal W. McFarlane, Brisbane QLD	.89
				(arr. by ship Melbourne VIC 7.89 : TT 155hrs	)
				Barry Batagol & Bruce Alexander/	
				Rivolta Investments, Melbourne VIC	.89
			VH-DIE	Barry Batagol, Melbourne VIC	18.1.91/92
				(ff Essendon 7.91, flies as Soviet AF "15")	
				Barry Hempel & Greg Schweikert,	
				Archerfield QLD : del.	14.3.92/95
27003	•	SBLim-2		(to Polish AF as .....)	
				Steve & Bruce Etchell	95
			N678	reg.	8.95
				(arr. dism. Santa Rosa CA .95 for rest.)	
81072	•	MiG-15bis		(to Chinese AF as 81072)	
			N7013L	Warren Sessler/China Technologies Inc	6.88/90
				(noted at Chino CA .88)	
				Planes of Fame/Fighter Jets Museum, Chino	93/94
				USNAM, MCAS El Toro CA: loan	93/94
				(displ. as "Chinese AF 81072")	
81676	•	MiG-15UTI		(to Chinese AF as 81676)	
			N7013N	Warren Sessler/China Technologies Inc	6.88
				(noted assembled at Chino CA .88)	
83277	•	MiG-15		(to Chinese AF as ....)	
				China Xinxing Corp	
			N2276H	Aero Trader Inc, Chino CA	15.5.94/95
10926	•	MiG-15		(to Polish AF as 126)	
				stored Sydney-Bankstown NSW	93/95
			VH-EKI	Reha R. Ekinci/Atlas Aviation, Sydney NSW	4.4.95
122071	•	F-2		(to Chinese Navy as 2071)	
				Keng's Firearms Specialty Inc: reg. candidate	25.2.93
			N996	Terence G. Klingele, Bellevue IL	3.93/95
122073	•	F-2		(to Chinese Navy as ....)	
				Unlimited Aircraft Ltd, Chino CA : arr. dism.	10.86
			N90601	Paul Entrekin, Pensacola FL	6.87
			N15PE	Paul Entrekin, Pensacola FL	9.87/95
				(ff Chino CA 29.7.87 as "Soviet AF 15")	
				USNAM, NAS Pensacola FL	13.11.93
137077	•	MiG-15		(to Chinese Navy as ....)	
				Unlimited Aircraft Ltd, Chino CA	3.87
137085	•	MiG-15		(to Chinese Navy as ....)	
				Champlin Fighter Museum, Mesa AZ	.86

			San Diego Aerospace Museum CA: loan	.86/93
			(displ. as "Chinese AF 70201")	
		N....	San Diego Aerospace Museum: reg. candidate	27.7.93
242266 •	SBLim-2		(to Polish AF as ....)	
		N41125	reg. res.	7.95
242271 •	SBLim-2		(to Polish AF as 2271)	
			Ian McGregor/LBA Systems, Retford UK	9.86
			(shipped Poland to Tees-side UK 10.86, then shipped to USA; assembled Reno NV)	
		N271JM	John MacGuire, Santa Teresa NM	3.87
			Al Reddick/Classics in American Aviation, Reno NV	6.87
			Howard Torman/Aviation Classics Ltd, Reno NV	8.89/92
			Evergreen Ventures Inc/ Evergreen Heritage Collection, Marana AZ	10.92/95
512032 •	SBLim-2		(to Polish AF as 2032)	
			Krzysztof Kulinski Classic Cars	
		N5557B	Brunetto Enterprises Inc, Dover DE	12.93/95
			(USCR quotes id. "1A512032")	
512036 •	SBLim-2		(to Polish AF as ....)	
			Arrow Crest Equities Pty Ltd, Perth WA	
		N115PW	Wilke & Associates Inc, Rocklin CA	12.6.92
			Cavanaugh Flight Museum, Dallas-Addison TX	6.93/95
		NX115PN	Cavanaugh Flight Museum, Dallas-Addison TX (flies as Polish "115")	95
522546 •	SBLim-2		(to Polish AF as ....)	
			Phoenix Warbirds, Phoenix AZ: adv. for sale	7.93
		N15UT	reg. res.	7.95
612782 •	SBLim-2		(to Polish AF as 2782)	
			Randal W. McFarlane, Brisbane QLD	.89
			(arr. by ship, Melbourne VIC 7.89 : TT 170)	
			Geoff Milne & John Rayner, Melbourne VIC	.89
			John Weymouth, Darwin NT	8.89
		VH-XIG	John Weymouth/Heli-Muster Pty Ltd,	10.90/95
			(ff Essendon 1.11.90, as "Soviet AF 15")	
			Fighter World, RAAF Williamtown NSW: displ.	94/95
622022 •	SBLim-2		(to Polish AF as 622)	
			Brunetto Flying Service, Coolidge AZ	3.94/95
			(shipped 3.94 ex storage Katovice AB, Poland: noted in outside storage, Coolidge AZ 10.95)	
622028 •	SBLim-2		(to Polish AF as 628)	
			Brunetto Flying Service, Coolidge AZ	3.94
			(shipped 3.94 ex storage Katovice AB, Poland)	
			Phoenix Warbirds, Phoenix AZ: reg. candidate	16.3.94
		N115MG	Paul Ottosi, Hidden Hills CA	25.8.94/95
622047 •	SBLim-2A		(to Polish AF as 6247)	
			Graham P. Hinkley, Shoreham: arr. dism.	8.7.92
		G-OMIG	Graham P. Hinkley, Shoreham	11.92/94
			(rest. Shoreham, ff 19.11.93)	
			Old Flying Machine Company, Duxford	11.94/95
			(flies as "Soviet AF 6247")	
622055 •	SBLim-2		(to Polish AF as 655)	
			Ian Kenny, Brisbane QLD	.90/92
			(stored Brisbane, pending rest.)	
712277 •	SBLim-2		(to Polish AF as 777)	
			Randal W. McFarlane, Brisbane QLD	.89
			(arr. by ship, Sydney NSW .89)	
		VH-LJP	ntu: Hockey Treloar, Sydney-Bankstown NSW	.90/94
			(stored dism. Bankstown, pending rest.)	
1A0017 •	Lim-2		(to Polish AF as 017)	
			imported to USA ex Poland	12.93
1A0358 •	SBLim-2		(to Polish AF as 358)	

			Richard G. Sugden, Jackson WY	95
			(arr. dism. Santa Rosa CA .95 for rest.)	
1A0626 •	SBLim-2		(to Polish AF as ....)	
			Phoenix Warbirds, Phoenix AZ: adv. for sale	7.93
1A01005•	SBLim-2		(to Polish AF as ....)	
			Phoenix Warbirds, Phoenix AZ: adv. for sale	7.93
1A02005•	SBLim-2		(to Polish AF as 205)	
		N687	Steven G. Penning, Windsor CA	31.1.94/95
1A03302•	SBLim-2		(to Polish AF as 3302)	
			imported into USA ex Poland	12.93
			K. Kulinski	
		N302LA	C. David Austin, Latrobe PA	1.6.94/95
1A03504•	SBLim-2		(to Polish AF as 304)	
			FTE Cenzin Co Ltd	
		N304SB	George Lazik, Van Nuys CA	21.7.93/95
			(shipped ex Poland .93, assembled Salt Lake City UT	
			flies as "Polish AF 304")	
1A03506•	SBLim-2		(to Polish AF as 306)	
			shipped to USA ex Katovice, Poland	3.94
		N15HQ	Josephs Four Inc, Fayetteville GA	15.6.94/95
1A05007•	SBLim-2		(to Polish AF as 007)	
			FTE Cenzin Co Ltd	
		N157GL	George Lazik, Van Nuys CA	21.7.93/95
			(shipped ex Poland .93, assembled Salt Lake City UT)	
1A06007•	MiG-15bis		(to Polish AF as 607)	
	SBLim-2A		Randal W. McFarlane, Brisbane QLD	.89
			(arr. by ship, Melbourne VIC 6.89 : TT 255)	
			F. W. (Bill) Pike, Sydney NSW	6.89
			Hockey Treloar, Sydney NSW	.89
		VH-BPG	Hockey Treloar, Sydney-Bankstown NSW	7.2.91/95
			(ff Bankstown 4.91, flies as "Polish AF 607")	
1A06015	SBLim-2		(to Polish AF as 015)	
			Randal W. McFarlane, Brisbane QLD	.89
			(arr. by ship Sydney NSW .89)	
			Gordon Glynn, Bankstown NSW	.89/92
		VH-LSN	Gordon Glynn, Sydney-Bankstown NSW	13.3.92/93
			(rest. Bankstown, ff 14.3.92 as "6015")	
			crashed, dest., near Canberra ACT	13.3.93
1A06021•	Lim-2		(to Polish AF as 6021)	
			Brunetto Flying Service, Coolidge AZ	3.94
			(shipped 3.94 ex storage Katovice AB, Poland)	
1A06026•	SBLim-2		(to Polish AF as 026)	
			Brunetto Flying Service, Coolidge AZ	3.94/95
			(shipped 3.94 ex storage Katovice AB, Poland:	
			noted in outside storage, Coolidge AZ 10.95)	
1A06036•	SBLim-2		(to Polish AF as 636)	
			Randal W. McFarlane, Brisbane QLD	.89
		VH-LKW	Hockey Treloar, Sydney-Bankstown NSW	.89/94
			(stored dism. Bankstown, pending rest.)	
1A06038•	Lim-1		(to Polish AF as 638)	
	SBLim-2		Ian McGregor/LBA Systems, Retford UK	9.86
			(shipped Poland to Tees-side UK 10.86, then	
			shipped to USA; assembled Reno NV)	
		N38BM	John MacGuire, Santa Teresa NM	23.1.87
			Al Reddick/Classics in American Aviation,	
			Reno NV	6.87
			Defense Test & Evaluation Agency,	
			Kirtland AFB NM	88/89
			struck-off USCR	10.89
			retired to AMARC, Davis-Monthan AFB AZ	.90/92
			Pima Air Museum, Tucson AZ	92/93
1A06040•	Lim-1		(to Polish AF as 640)	
	SBLim-2		Ian McGregor/LBA Systems, Retford UK	9.86
			(shipped Poland to Tees-side UK 10.86, then	
			shipped to USA; assembled Reno NV)	
		N40BM	John MacGuire/War Eagles Air Museum,	

			Santa Teresa NM	2.87/95
			(ass. Reno NV, flies as "Soviet AF 640")	
1A07010•	SBLim-2		(to Polish AF as 710)	
		N710DW	reg.	15.8.95
1A07031•	SBLim-2		(to Polish AF as 7031)	
			(noted stored Mierzecice AB, Poland 8.91)	
		N150MG	Fantasy Fighters, Santa Fe NM	26.7.93/95
1A07032•	SBLim-2		(to Polish AF as 7032)	
			Foreign Trade Enterprise Cenzen	
		N132DG	Donald A. Gianquitto, Melrose MA	26.7.94/95
1A07048•	SBLim-2		(to Polish AF as 748)	
		N78053	Mike Bauman, Olney IL	3.95
1A07050•	SBLim-2		(to Polish AF as 7050)	
			Barry Hempel, Brisbane QLD Australia	.93
			(shipped, arr. Brisbane-Archerfield 3.93)	
1A07056•	Lim-2		(to Polish AF as 7056)	
		N76584	Jacks Air Service, Greenville ME	4.11.93/95
1A08007•	SBLim-2		(to Polish AF as ....)	
			stored Sydney-Bankstown NSW	94/95
		VH-REH	Reha R. Ekinci/Atlas Aviation, Sydney NSW	4.4.95
			(id. assumed: "08007" quoted)	
1A08017•	SBLim-2		(to Polish AF as 8017)	
			Ian McGregor/LBA Systems, Retford UK	9.86
			(shipped Poland to Tees-side UK 10.86, then shipped to USA; assembled Reno NV)	
		N17KM	John MacGuire, Santa Teresa NM	2.87/90
			Al Reddick/Classics in American Aviation, Reno NV	6.87/90
			Howard Torman/Aviation Classics Limited, Reno NV	91
			Tacair Systems Inc, Reno NV	6.91/95
			(flies as "Soviet AF 17")	
1A09006•	SBLim-2		(to Polish AF as 906)	
			Randal W. McFarlane, Brisbane QLD	.89
			(arr. by ship, Melbourne VIC 7.89 : TT 100)	
			Greg Lovett, Essendon VIC	89/92
			(rest. Essendon, due to fly .92: stored)	
		VH-ADY	Greg Lovett, Melbourne VIC	23.6.92/95
1A09008•	SBLim-2		(to Polish AF as 908)	
			Graham P. Hinkley, Shoreham UK: arr.	12.10.92
			(stored Shoreham, pending rest. 92)	
1A09012•	SBLim-2		(to Polish AF as 012)	
			Lusso Service, Duiven Holland: arr.	8.10.91
			(stored Duiven: airworthy condition 10.91/92; shipped to USA, assembled Van Nuys CA 1.93)	
			J. W. Siglow	
		N9012	Robert L. Reid/Lusso Service, Mesa AZ	15.1.94/95
1A09015•	SBLim-2		(to Polish AF as 015)	
			Ian Kenny, Brisbane QLD	.90/92
			(stored Brisbane, pending rest.)	
1A10017•	SBLim-2		(to Polish AF as 017)	
			K. Kulinski	
		N15LC	C. David Austin, Latrobe PA: reg. candidate	1.6.94
			John K. Lloyd, Latrobe PA	1.6.94
			Raymond J. Weible, New Kensignton PA	5.95
1A12002•	SBLim-2		(to Polish AF as 202)	
			Randal W. McFarlane, Brisbane QLD	.89
			(arr. by ship, Melbourne VIC 7.89 : TT 265)	
			Reha R. Ekinci, Sydney NSW: arr. by road	7.7.89/90
			Kay Williamson, Sydney NSW	.90/92
			(rest. to fly, RAAF Richmond & Bankstown NSW)	
1A26012•	SBLim-2		(to Polish AF as 6012)	
			imported into USA ex Poland	12.93

C/n	Type	Reg	History	Date
			US reg. candidate	19.1.94
1A26016•	Mig 15		(to Polish AF as 216)	
			The Fighter Collection, Duxford UK : arr.	14.9.92/93
			(crated Duxford 3.93 for shipping to Australia)	
			Mike Kelly/Southair Aviation, Wanaka NZ	.93/94
		VH-NZM	Mike Kelly, Mosgiel NSW	12.93/95
			(civil conv. 93/95 at Sydney-Bankstown NSW,	
			as "Soviet 501)	
		ZK-MIG	reg. res: Southair Aviation, Wanaka NZ	.93/95
1B00822•	SBLim-2		(to Polish AF as 0822)	
			Ian McGregor/LBA Systems, Retford UK	9.86
			(shipped Poland to Tees-side UK 10.86, then	
			shipped to USA; assembled Reno NV)	
		N822JM	John MacGuire, Santa Teresa NM	1.87
			Al Reddick/Classics in American Aviation,	
			Reno NV (flew as "Soviet AF 822")	6.87
			Defense Test & Evaluation Agency,	
			Kirtland AFB NM	88/89
			retired to AMARC, Davis-Monthan AFB AZ	.90/92
			Pima Air Museum, Tucson AZ	92/93
			(rest., rolled-out 22.6.92 as "822")	
1B01013•	SBLim-2		(to Polish AF as 1013)	
			Ian McGregor/LBA Systems, Retford UK	9.86
			(shipped Poland to Tees-side UK 10.86, then	
			shipped to USA; assembled Reno NV)	
		N13KM	John MacGuire/War Eagles Air Museum,	
			Santa Teresa NM	2.87/95
		N106JB	War Eagles Air Museum, Santa Teresa NM	95
1B01016•	SBLim-2		(to Polish AF as 1016)	
			Ian McGregor/LBA Systems, Retford UK	9.86
			(shipped Poland to Tees-side UK 10.86, then	
			shipped to USA; assembled Reno NV)	
		N15YY	Donald R. Young, Santa Barbara CA	8.88/90
			Stephen J. Craig, Lawrence KS	10.93/95
1B01205•	SBLim-2		(to Polish AF as 1205)	
			Ian McGregor/LBA Systems, Retford UK	9.86
			(shipped Poland to Tees-side UK 10.86, then	
			shipped to USA; assembled Reno NV)	
		N205JM	John MacGuire, Santa Teresa NM	23.1.87
			Al Reddick/Classics in American Aviation,	
			Reno NV: lease	6.87
			Defense Test & Evaluation Agency,	
			Kirtland AFB NM	88/89
			struck-off USCR	10.89
			Davis-Monthan AFB AZ: open storage	.90/93
			Midland Air Museum, Coventry Airport UK	.93
			(planned to be shipped to UK for static displ.)	
1B01416•	SBLim-2		(to Polish AF as 1416)	
			Ian McGregor/LBA Systems, Retford UK	9.86
			(shipped Poland to Tees-side UK 10.86, then	
			shipped to USA; assembled Reno NV)	
		N416JM	John MacGuire/War Eagles Air Museum,	
			Santa Teresa NM	2.87/95
1B01420•	SBLim-2		(to Polish AF as 1420)	
			Ian McGregor/LBA Systems, Retford UK	8.86
			arr. dismantled, Retford	9.86
		G-BMZF	Aces High Ltd, North Weald : arr. dism.	22.12.86
			Fleet Air Arm Museum, RNAS Yeovilton	.87/95
			(repainted .93 as "North Korean AF 01420")	
1B01606•	SBLim-2		(to Polish AF as 1606)	
			Ian McGregor/LBA Systems, Retford UK	9.86
			(shipped Poland to Tees-side UK 10.86, then	
			shipped to USA; assembled Reno NV)	
		N606BM	John MacGuire/War Eagles Air Museum,	
			Santa Teresa NM	2.87/90
			Aviation Classics Ltd, Reno NV	4.94/95
1B01614•	SBLim-2		(to Polish AF as 1614)	
			Ian McGregor/LBA Systems, Retford UK	9.86
			(shipped Poland to Tees-side UK 10.86, then	
			shipped to USA; assembled Reno NV)	
		N614BM	John MacGuire/War Eagles Air Museum,	

			Santa Teresa NM	2.87/95
1B01621•	SBLim-2		(to Polish AF as 1621)	
			Ian McGregor/LBA Systems, Retford UK	9.86
			(shipped Poland to Tees-side UK 10.86, then shipped to USA; assembled Reno NV)	
		N621BM	John MacGuire/War Eagles Air Museum, Santa Teresa NM	2.87/95
1B01629•	SBLim-2		(to Polish AF as 1629)	
			Ian McGregor/LBA Systems, Retford UK	9.86
			(shipped Poland to Tees-side UK 10.86, then shipped to USA; assembled Reno NV)	
		N629BM	John MacGuire/War Eagles Air Museum, Santa Teresa NM	2.87/95
1B01979•	SBLim-2		(to Polish AF as ....)	
			Fighter Rebuilders Inc, Chino CA	88
			(noted under rebuild, Chino 8.88)	
- •	MiG-15UTI		(to Chinese AF as 83238)	
			stored as '3238', Phoenix-Deer Valley AZ	92
910-51 •	MiG-15		(to Chinese AF as 83277)	
			China Xinxing Corp Ltd	
		N87CN	Cinema Air, Carlsbad CA	14.6.91/95
- •	MiG-15		(to Chinese AF as 83177)	
			J. Curtiss Earl, Deer Valley AZ	.89/90
			Champlin Fighter Museum, Mesa AZ: loan	.90/92
			(noted open storage, Phoenix-Deer Valley AZ 5.92)	
- •	F-2		(to Chinese Navy as 0245)	
			Unlimited Aircraft Ltd, Chino CA	3.87
- •	F-2		(to Chinese Navy as 0411)	
			Unlimited Aircraft Ltd, Chino CA	3.87
- •	F-2		(to Chinese Navy as 1301)	
			Ed Maloney/Planes of Fame Museum, Chino CA	.88/90
			(arr. Chino dism. ex ship Long Beach CA .88)	
			Planes of Fame/Fighter Jets Museum, Chino	90/93
			(displ. as "Chinese 1301")	
- •	F-2		(to Chinese Navy as 1411)	
			Unlimited Aircraft Ltd, Chino CA	3.87/90
		N15MG	Combat Jets Flying Museum, Houston TX	10.87/92
			EAA Aviation Foundation, Oshkosh WI	5.92/95
			(flies as "Soviet AF 4115")	
- •	F-2		(to Chinese Navy as 1961)	
			Unlimited Aircraft Ltd, Chino CA	3.87
		N51MG	James E. Beasley, Philadelphia PA	3.89/95
- •	F-2		(to Chinese Navy as 2292)	
			Unlimited Aircraft Ltd, Chino CA	3.87
		N90589	First City Air Charter Ltd, Los Angeles CA	6.87/90
			(ff Chino 29.7.87; flies as "Soviet AF 1170")	
			James K. Wickersham, Danville CA: USCR	1.92/95
			Bill Reesman/Yak Attack Airshows Inc	5.92/94
			(flew as "Soviet AF 577")	
			badly dam., in-flight fire, Aurora CO	1.3.94

MIKOYAN-GUREVICH MIG-17

506 •	Lim-5		(to Polish AF as ....)	
			Phoenix Warbirds, Phoenix AZ: adv. for sale	7.93
0613 •	MiG-17		(to Chinese AF as ....)	
			China Ocean Helicopter Corp	
		N406DM	Consolidated Aviation Enterprises Inc, Burlington VT	1.88
			Dean Martin/Warplanes Inc, Burlington VT	90
			Doug C. Schultz, Francestown NH	6.91/95
			(flies in glossy black sc. "309")	

0704 •	MiG-17T		(to Chinese AF as ......)	
			China Ocean Helicopter Corp	
		N306DM	Consolidated Aviation Enterprises Inc, Burlington VT	1.88
			Dean Martin/Warplanes Inc, Burlington VT	90/91
			struck-off reg.	26.5.94
			(FAA quote id. as "0714", type as State Aircraft Factories MiG-17T)	
1321 •	MiG-17		(rep. to Polish AF as .....)	
		LN-MIG	Bjorn Bostad	17.2.92
1327 •	JJ-5		(to Chinese AF as ....)	
		N69PP	Poly Technologies Inc	13.2.90
			Peter Franks, Angel Fire NM	3.90/95
2507 •	F-4		(to Chinese AF as 2507)	
		N1VC	Morgan Merrill/Jet 1 Inc, Alexandria VA	88/90
			Stephen M. Rosenberg, Novato CA	92
			Terence G. Klingele, Belleville IL	12.94/95
			(USCR quotes id. as "2705")	
551604 •	MiG-17T		(to Chinese AF as ......)	
			China Ocean Helicopter Corp	
		N905DM	Consolidated Aviation Enterprises Inc, Burlington VT	1.88
			Dean Martin/Warplanes Inc, Burlington VT	10.89/95
1C0508 •	Lim-5		(to Polish AF as 508)	
		N1917M	Cavanaugh Flight Museum, Dallas-Addison TX	11.4.95
IC1020 •	Lim-5		Brunetto Flying Service, Coolidge AZ: shipped	.94
		N117MG	James B. Rossi, Ocala FL	5.95
1C1211 •	Lim-5		(to Polish AF as 1211)	
			Old Flying Macine Company, Duxford : arr.	9.95
1C1228 •	Lim-5		(to Polish AF as 1228)	
		N1817M	Cavanaugh Flight Museum, Dallas-Addison TX	11.4.95
1C1301 •	Lim-5		(to Polish AF as 1301)	
			Brunetto Flying Services, Coolidge AZ	3.94/95
1C1312 •	Lim-5		(to Polish AF as 1312)	
			(noted in outside storage, Mesa AZ 10.95)	
1C1319 •	Lim-5		(to Polish AF as 1319)	
			Brunetto Flying Services, Coolidge AZ	3.94/95
1C1321 •	Lim-5		(to Polish AF as 1321)	
			Krzysztof Kulinski Classic Cars	
		N69RB	Roy H. Bischoff, Fairview Heights IL	1.94
1C1413 •	Lim-5		(to Polish AF as 1413)	
			(noted in outside storage, Mesa AZ 10.95)	
1C1423 •	Lim-5		(to Polish AF as 1423)	
		N17QS	Ferrante Aviation, Vandergrift PA	11.93/95
1C1529 •	Lim-5		(to Polish AF as 1529)	
		N117BR	MiG Magic Inc, Tualatin OR	29.4.94/95
1C1605 •	Lim-5		(to Polish AF as 1605)	
			Brunetto Flying Services, Coolidge AZ	3.94/95
1C1611 •	Lim-5		(to Polish AF as 1611)	
			(noted in outside storage, Mesa AZ 10.95)	
1C1617 •	Lim-5P		(to Polish AF as 1617)	
			Planes of Fame Museum, Chino CA	.88/90
			Planes of Fame/Fighter Jets Museum, Chino	90/93
			(displ. as "Polish AF 1617")	
1C1703 •	Lim-5		(to Polish AF as 1703)	
			Brunetto Flying Services, Coolidge AZ	3.94/95

1C1705 •	Lim-5		(to Chinese AF as 1705)	
	Lim-6		Foreign Trade Enterprise Cenzin	
	Lim-6bis		Keng's Firearms Specialty Inc	
		N968	Terrence G. Klingele, Belleville IL: USCR	3.93/95
		N1705	Mario Feola, Gretna LA	12.5.94/95
1C1713 •	Lim-5		(to Polish AF as 1713)	
			Brunetto Flying Services, Coolidge AZ	3.94/95
1C1726 •	Lim-5		(to Polish AF as 1726)	
			(noted in outside storage, Mesa AZ 10.95)	
1F0102 •	Lim-5		(to Polish AF as 102)	
	Lim-6		Randal W. McFarlane, Brisbane QLD	.89
	Lim-6bis		Jack McDonald, Caboolture QLD	.90/94
			(rest. to fly, Caboolture QLD)	
1F0319 •	Lim-5		(to Polish AF as 319)	
			Brunetto Flying Services, Coolidge AZ	3.94/95
1F0325 •	Lim-5		(to Polish AF as 325)	
	Lim-6		MARC, Chino CA	90/94
	Lim-6bis		Quonset Air Museum, North Kingston RI: loan	7.92/94
1G1619 •	Lim-5		(to Polish AF as 619)	
			Ian Kenny, Brisbane QLD	.90/92
			(stored Brisbane, pending rest.)	
1J0434 •	Lim-5m		(to Polish AF as 434)	
	Lim-6		Randal W. McFarlane, Brisbane QLD	.89
	Lim-6bis		Hockey Treloar, Bankstown NSW	.90/93
		VH-ALG	Hockey Treloar, Sydney-Bankstown NSW	4.3.93/95
			(rest. Bankstown, due to fly .94)	
1J0438 •	Lim-5m		(to Polish AF as 438)	
	Lim-6bis		Joy-Co Ltd	
		N2153V	Wally Fisk/Amjet Aircraft Corp, St Paul MN	16.2.94
		N438MG	Amjet Aircraft Corp, St Paul MN	7.94/95
1J0505 •	Lim-5m		(to Polish AF as 505)	
	Lim-6bis	N2153K	Amjet Aircraft Corp, St Paul MN	15.2.94
		N505MG	Amjet Aircraft Corp, St Paul MN	22.6.94/95
1J0508 •	Lim-5		(to Polish AF as 508)	
			Brunetto Flying Services, Coolidge AZ	3.94/95
1J0511 •	Lim-5		(to Polish AF as 511)	
			Brunetto Flying Services, Coolidge AZ	3.94/95
1J0514 •	Lim-5		(to Polish AF as 514)	
			Brunetto Flying Services, Coolidge AZ	3.94/95
1J0522 •	Lim-5		(to Polish AF as 522)	
			Brunetto Flying Services, Coolidge AZ	3.94/95
1J0523 •	Lim-5		(to Polish AF as 523)	
			Brunetto Flying Services, Coolidge AZ	3.94/95
			(shipped 3.94 ex storage Katovice AB, Poland:	
			noted in outside storage, Coolidge AZ 10.95)	
1J0528 •	Lim-5m		(to Polish AF as 528)	
	Lim-6		Brunetto Flying Services, Coolidge AZ	3.94
			H. J. Quamme	
		N17HQ	Phoenix Warbirds Inc, Phoenix AZ	7.7.94
			Josephsfour Inc, Hartwell GA	7.94/95
1J0619 •	Lim-5m		(to Polish AF as 619)	
	Lim-6bis		FTE Cenzin Co Ltd	
		N619M	George Lazik, Van Nuys CA	21.7.93/95
			(shipped ex Poland .93, assembled at	
			Salt Lake City UT, flies as "Polish AF 619")	
1J0631 •	Lim-5m		(to Polish AF as 631)	
	Lim-6	**N73568**	Michael F. Bauman, Olney IL	3.95

151-38433 •	F-86A	**47-606**	N7793C	Reedley Joint Union High School, Reedley CA	66/69
			N57965	Ben W. Hall, Seattle WA	6.70/89
				(recov. derelict, ex scrapyard Fresno CA, trucked to Seattle 6.70: spares for rest. 48-0178)	
				Museum of Flight, Seattle WA	.89/93
				(stored Seattle-Paine Field WA: static rest.)	
151-43547 •	F-86A	**48-0178**		to vocational school, Fresno CA: inst. airframe	
				Glen Wackhold, Fresno CA: surplus store	68/70
			N68388	Ben W. Hall, Seattle WA	6.70/83
				(trucked Seattle 6.70 ex open storage Fresno; rest. Paine Field WA, ff 24.5.74)	
			N178	Ben W. Hall, Seattle WA	10.83/89
				Fort Wayne Air Service,	6.89/91
				Golden Apple Trust, UK	.90/91
			G-SABR	Op Golden Apple Operations Ltd, Stamford, UK	10.91/96
				ff 21.5.92 as "USAF 8178/FU-178")	
151-43611 •	F-86A	**48-0242**	**N196B**	noted, Chino CA	78/84
				Planes of Fame/Fighter Jets Museum, Chino CA	88/93
161-318•	F-86A	**49-1324**	**N57964**	Ben W. Hall, Seattle WA	78/95
170-75 •	F-86E	**50-0653**	N5637V	Hawaii Public College of Trade Instruction, Honolulu Airport HI	66/69
				USAFM, Hickam AFB Honolulu HI	79/93
172-120•	F-86E	**51-2837**		I. N. Burchinal/Flying Tiger Air Museum, Paris TX: displ.	75/94
			N190NB	I. N. Burchinal, Paris TX: reg. res.	10.85/94
				(USCR quotes id. "190")	
172-167•	F-86F	**51-2884**	**N57966**	Ben W. Hall, Seattle WA	78/92
				USAFM, Buckley ANGB CO	73/88
				(displ. as "USAF 112988")	
173-215•	F-86D F-86L	**51-6071**		Sergio Tomassoni, Buckeye AZ	
				(noted unconv., derelict at Buckeye AZ .78)	
			N3280U	Sergio Tomassoni, Buckeye AZ	82
				S & T Aerial Contractors, Buckeye AZ	16.8.82
			N86RJ	Robert A. Kemp, Reno NV	3.83/95
				Davis Monthan AFB Warrior Park AZ: listed	93
172-279	F-86E	51-12988	N86Z	Dave Zeuschel Racing Engines, Chino CA	3.8.82/87
				(recov. ex storage in CA orchard, rebuilt crashed & dest., Shafter CA (Zeuschel k.)	25.4.87
				(id. quoted as F-86F 51-2988 :this was F-86D)	
176-348•	F-86F	**51-13417**		(to Ejercito del Aire as C5-....): del. ex USAFE	.58
			N51RS	Mid Atlantic Air Museum, Middletown PA	11.87/96
187-84 •	F-86H	**52-2058**	**N205P**	Purdue University, Lafayette IN	66/69
				Civil Air Patrol, Lafayette IN	86
190-594•	F-86L	**52-4191**	**N2401H**	Hawaii Education Dept, Honolulu HI	66/69
				USAFM, Hickam AFB, Honolulu HI	73/93
191-304•	F-86F	**52-4608**		(test bed for Rocketdyne AR2-3 motor)	
			N57963	Robert D. Scott, San Martin CA	7.76/95
191-362•	F-86F	**52-4666**		(to FA Venezuela then FA Bolivia as 651)	85/94
				(recov. by Dixie Air Parts, San Antonio TX 3.94,	
			N860AG	reg.	7.95
191-385•	F-86F	**52-4689**		(to FA Venezuela then FA Bolivia as 658)	85/94
				(recov. by Dixie Air Parts, San Antonio TX 3.94,	
			N8630	reg. reserved	.95
191-427•	F-86F	**52-4731**		(to FA Venezuela then FA Bolivia as 656)	85/94
				(recov. by Dixie Air Parts, San Antonio TX 3.94, stored Dallas TX 95)	
			N86NA	reg. reserved	.95

Con. No.	Type	Serial	Reg.	History	Date
191-655•	F-86F	**52-4959**	**N105BH**	(to FA Argentina as ......)	
				World Wide Aircraft, Miami FL	9.90/92
				Airplane Exchange Co, Miami FL	6.92/95
191-658•	F-86F	**52-4962**		(to FA Argentina as C-111)	
			N7006G	Rick E. Sharpe/Warbirds Unlimited,	
				Rosharon TX	8.88
				(USCR quotes id. "SA111")	
191-682•	F-86F	**52-4986**		(to FA Argentina as .....)	
			N188RL	Coleman Warbird Museum, Coleman TX	6.3.90
				D K Precision Inc, Fort Lauderdale FL	6.90/92
				Michael E. Keenum, Palos Park IL	6.92/95
				op: Air Classics Air Museum, DuPage IL	94/95
191-708•	F-86F	**52-5012**		(to FA Argentina as ....)	
				Rick E. Sharpe/Warbirds Unlimited, Rosharon TX	
			N30CW	Western Wings Aircraft Sales, Oakland OR	11.89/90
				(flew as "Marines 25012/FU-012")	
			N4TF	Cinema Air, Carlsbad CA	4.90/95
				(flies as "USAF 25012")	
				(USCR quotes id. "SA119")	
191-809•	F-86F	**52-5113**		(rep. to FA Argentina as ......)	
				Coleman Warbird Museum, Coleman TX:	
				reg. candidate	6.2.92
191-812•	F-86F	**52-5116**		(to FA Argentina as C-119)	
			N7006J	Rick E. Sharpe/Warbirds Unlimited, Rosharon TX	8.88
				Bill Woods/Western Wings Aircraft Sales,	
				Oakland OR	5.89
			N3145T	Coleman Warbird Museum, Coleman TX	12.91/95
191-835•	F-86F	**52-5139**		(to FA Peruana as FAP.......)	
				recov. by Dave Zeuschel, Van Nuys CA	2.81
				(arr. dism. Chino CA 2.81, ff Chino 8.81)	
			N86F	Zeuschel Racing Engines, Reno NV	6.81
				John R. Sandberg, Robstown TX	.81/86
				Don Young/Exotics Leasing Corp, Santa Barbara CA	86/88
				Heritage Aircraft Sales,	
				Indianapolis IN	2.89/95
191-839•	F-86F	**52-5143**	**N25143**	William Simone, Fountain Valley CA	78
				Al Reddick & Les Crowder, Sunland CA	81
				Lesley L. Crowder, Sunland CA: USCR	8.81/95
				USMCAM, Quantico MCAS VA	94
				Kalamazoo Aviation History Museum MI: loan	94
201-484•	F-86D	**53-1040**	**N74062**	Aircraft Engine Enterprises Inc, Moore OK	66
				Tuxhorn Aviation, Phoenix AZ	69
				Aircraft Surplus Co, Tucson AZ	72/87
				AMCEP Inc, Tucson AZ	1.87/95
203-52 •	F-86H	**53-1250**		Rock Valley College, Rockford IL: del.	28.5.70/89
			N31250	Ed Buerckholtz/Spirit Fighters Inc,	
				Chesterfield MO	19.3.91/93
				Aeroplace Services Inc, Midlothion TX	5.94/95
244-83 •	FJ-4B Fury	**Bu143575**	N9255	Flight Systems Inc, Long Beach/Mojave CA	.71/77
			N400FS	Flight Systems Inc, Mojave CA	9.77/91
				(stored Mojave, last flew .82)	
				Larry Mockford/T-Bird Aviation, Mojave CA	.91/95
507 •	CL-13A Canadair Mk. 4	**RCAF19607**		(to RAF as XB733)	
				(to Italian AF as MM19607)	
			G-ATBF	Malcolm D. N. Fisher/Historic Aircraft	
				Preservation Society, Biggin Hill	24.3.66
				Reflectaire Ltd Museum, Blackpool, UK	69/72
				T. Bracewell, Much Hoole, Preston: stored	4.72/93
886 •	CL-13A Mk. 5 QF-86E	**RCAF23096**		Boeing Aircraft Co, Seattle WA	63/67
				(chase plane, loaned ex Canadian Govt.)	
			N8686F (1	Boeing Equipment Co, Seattle WA	22.9.67/74
				(del. to Seattle ex Moncton 21.12.67)	
				Targetair Ltd, Moncton NB	.74
			N74180 (2	Flight Systems Inc, Mojave CA: del.	26.7.74/80
				sale rep: USCR	86/95

985 •	CL-13A	**RCAF23195**		Maritime Aircraft Repair & Overhaul/	
	Mk. 5			Targetair Ltd, Moncton NB	
			N5591N	Flight Systems Inc, Mojave CA	5.2.80/86
				sale rep., Orlando FL	88/95
1016 •	CL-13A	**RCAF23226**		Maritime Aircraft Repair & Overhaul/	
	Mk. 5			Targetair Ltd, Moncton NB	
			N46883	Flight Systems Inc, Mojave CA	31.1.84
				Southern Cal. Aviation Inc, Corona Del Mar CA	86
				USAFM: struck-off USCR	12.86
				USAFM, England AFB LA	88/94
				(displ. as "F-86F USAF 24931")	
1021 •	CL-13A	**RCAF23231**		Maritime Aircraft Repair & Overhaul,	
	Mk. 5			Moncton NB	
			N231X	Bankers Leasing Inc, Washington DC	72
				Ronald Reynolds, Kansas City KS	78
				Flight Systems Inc, Mojave CA	.81/82
			N91FS	Tracor Flight Systems Inc, Mojave CA	6.82/95
1028 •	CL-13A	**RCAF23238**		Maritime Aircraft Repair & Overhaul/	
	Mk. 5			Targetair Ltd, Moncton NB	
				Flight Systems Inc, Mojave CA	21.11.84
				(noted dism. FSI compound, Mojave 10.84)	
			N86EB	Southern Cal. Aviation Inc, Corona Del Mar CA	1.85/86
				traded to USAFM: struck-off USCR	12.86
				USAFM, CA ANG, Point Mugu NAS CA	93
				(displ. as "USAF 49-1046")	
1031	CL-13A	RCAF23241		Maritime Aircraft Repair & Overhaul,	
	Mk. 5			Moncton NB	20.10.70
			N8544	Lockheed California Co, Palmdale CA	72
				(chase plane for L1011 programme)	
				crashed landing, Mojave CA	23.3.76
1049 •	CL-13A	**RCAF23259**		Maritime Aircraft Repair & Overhaul/	
	Mk. 5			Targetair Ltd, Moncton NB	
	QF-86E		**N98250**	Flight Systems Inc, Mojave CA	11.77/78
				US Army, Redstone Arsenal AL : USCR	86/95
1065	CL-13A	RCAF23275		Oshawa Chamber of Commerce, Oshawa ONT	22.6.70
	Mk. 5			(planned displ. in park)	69
			N275X	Richard L. Bingham/Spectrum Air Inc,	
				San Francisco CA	.71/72
				(civil conv., Toronto Island Airport ONT .71)	
				crashed on take-off, Sacramento CA	24.9.72
				(struck ice cream parlour, 22 killed, 28 hurt)	
1075 •	CL-13A	**RCAF23285**	CF-BKG	Maritime Aircraft Repair & Overhaul,	
	Mk. 5			Moncton NB	
			N8686D	Leroy Penhall/Fighter Imports Inc, Chino CA	73
				Flight Systems Inc, Mojave CA	77/78
			N87FS (1	Flight Systems Inc, Mojave CA	82
			N92FS	Tracor Flight Systems Inc, Mojave CA	6.82/95
1083 •	CL-13A	**RCAF23293**		Maritime Aircraft Repair & Overhaul/	
	Mk. 5			Targetair Ltd, Moncton NB	.70
			N4689H	Flight Systems Inc, Mojave CA: target tug	11.83/86
				Southern Cal. Aviation Inc, Corona del Mar CA	.86/88
				Morgan Merrill/Jet I Inc, Alexandria VA	4.89/90
				Fort Wayne Air Service,	
				Fort Wayne IN	2.91/92
				(rest. commenced Fort Wayne IN 4.91,	
				Cavanaugh Flight Museum,	
				Dallas-Addison TX	11.92/96
1104 •	CL-13A	**RCAF23314**	CF-BKH	Maritime Aircraft Repair & Overhaul,	
	Mk. 5			Moncton NB	
			N8687D	Leroy Penhall/Fighter Imports Inc, Chino CA	73
				Flight Systems Inc, Mojave CA	76
				Whittington Brothers/Air Sabre Inc,	
				West Palm Beach FL	.76/78
				MARC, Chino CA	80/86
				Combat Jets Flying Museum,	
				Houston TX	10.87/92
				EAA Aviation Foundation, Oshkosh WI	5.92/95
				(flies as USAF "12897/The Huff/FU-897")	
1113 •	CL-13A	**RCAF23323**		Maritime Aircraft Repair & Overhaul/	

	Mk. 5			Targetair Ltd, Moncton NB	
	QF-86E		**N98279**	Flight Systems Inc, Mojave CA	11.77/78
				(noted fire dump, Mojave CA 84)	
				US Army, Redstone Arsenal AL: USCR	86/95
1120 •	CL-13A	**RCAF23330**		Maritime Aircraft Repair & Overhaul/	
	Mk. 5			Targetair Ltd, Moncton NB	
			N86FN	Flight International Inc, Atlanta GA	11.84/85
				Flight International of Florida, Jacksonville FL	1.85/86
			N86JR	Combat Jets Flying Museum,	12.86/92
				Houston TX	
				EAA Aviation Foundation, Oshkosh WI	5.92/95
1128 •	CL-13A	**RCAF23338**		Maritime Aircraft Repair & Overhaul/	
	Mk. 5			Targetair Ltd, Moncton NB	
	QF-86E		N1N	Flight Systems Inc, Mojave CA	31.1.84/86
				USAFM, Chanute AFB IL	88
1134 •	CL-13A	**RCAF23344**		Maritime Aircraft Repair & Overhaul/	
	Mk. 5			Targetair Ltd, Moncton NB	
				Flight Systems Inc, Mojave CA	21.11.84
			N86EC	Southern Cal. Aviation Inc, Corona del Mar CA	1.85/86
				USAFM : struck-off USCR	12.86
				USAFM, Fairchild AFB WA	88/93
				(displ. as "USAF 91806")	
1153 •	CL-13A	**RCAF23363**	N74180(1	Maritime Aircraft Repair & Overhaul,	
	Mk. 5			Moncton NB	.69/74
	Mk. 6			(conv. to Mk. 6 for Pakistan AF project:	
				ff Mojave CA 30.1.72)	
			N8686F(2	Boeing Equipment Co, Seattle WA	.74/91
				Museum of Flight, Seattle-Boeing Field WA	12.91/96
1157 •	CL-13A	**RCAF23367**		Maritime Aircraft Repair & Overhaul/	
	Mk. 5			Targetair Ltd, Moncton NB	
	QF-86E		N8549	Lockheed California Co, Palmdale CA	75
			N92402	Flight Systems Inc, Mojave CA	9.76/77
			N86FS	Flight Systems Inc, Mojave CA	9.77/84
				(wfu Mojave 84, in service Mojave 93)	
				US Army, Redstone Arsenal AL: USCR	86/92
				Tracor Flight Systems, Mojave CA	12.91/95
				(noted in service, Mojave CA 12.93)	
1214	CL-13B	RCAF23424		RCAF BOC 14.1.55 SOC	13.8.65
	Mk. 6			(ex RCAF *Golden Hawks* Aerobatic Team)	
				Milt Harradance/Air Museum of Canada,	
				Calgary ALTA	9.8.65
			N186X	Flight Test Research Inc, Long Beach CA	8.65/68
				crashed Cantil CA : pilot ejected	19.6.68
1294 •	CL-13B	**RCAF23504**		Age of Flight Museum, Niagara Falls ONT	11.65/67
	Mk. 6			Brian Baird, Toronto ONT	69/77
				(stored Mesa AZ 69/74, stored dism. Chino 77)	
				Corwin Denney, Chino CA	.86
			N86CD	S. Bruce Goessling/Combat Jet & Aerospace	
				Museum, Chino CA	8.86/87
				Corporate Jets Inc, Scottsdale AZ	12.87
			N30CJ	Corporate Jets Inc, Scottsdale AZ	4.88/95
				(based Deccimomanuu AB, Sardinia .89,	
				Soesterberg AB, Netherlands .91:	
				mil. target-towing contracts)	
1390	CL-13B	RCAF23600	CF-JJB (2	Canadair Ltd	5.57
	Mk. 6			demonstrated Swiss AF, ret. RCAF Europe	5.57
1403	CL-13B	RCAF23613	CF-JJC	Canadair Ltd	25.4.57
	Mk. 6			demonstrated Swiss AF, ret. RCAF Europe	30.5.57
1418	CL-13B	RCAF23628	CF-JJB (1	Canadair Ltd	1.2.57
	Mk. 6			demonstrated Swiss AF, ret. RCAF Europe	1.3.57
1459 •	CL-13B	**RCAF23669**		(to SAAF as 350)	
	Mk. 6		**N3841V**	Flight Systems Inc, Mojave CA	3.83/95
1461 •	CL-13B	**RCAF23671**		(to SAAF as 352)	
	Mk. 6		**N38301**	Flight Systems Inc, Mojave CA	3.83/90
				(stored dism. unconv., Mojave 82/90)	
				Corporate Jets Inc, Scottsdale AZ	7.91/95

				(noted Scottsale AZ 3.93)	
1468 •	CL-13B Mk. 6	**RCAF23678**		(to SAAF as 359)	
			N3831B	Flight Systems Inc, Mojave CA	3.83/89
				M. D. Aire Co, Encino CA	5.91/95
1472 •	CL-13B Mk. 6	**RCAF23682**		(to SAAF as 363)	
			N3842H	Flight Systems Inc, Mojave CA	3.83/90
				(stored dism. unconv., Mojave 82/90)	
			N86CS	Gerald A. Smith, Paso Robles CA	6.91
			N3842H	Corporate Jets Inc, Scottsdale AZ	3.92/95
1474 •	CL-13B Mk. 6	**RCAF23684**		(to SAAF as 365)	
				Flight Systems Inc, Mojave CA	21.3.83
			N106JB	John MacGuire, Fort Hancock TX	4.83/95
				War Eagles Air Museum, Santa Teresa NM (flies as "SAAF 365")	90/95
1480	CL-13B Mk. 6	RCAF23690		(to SAAF as 371)	
			N3842J	Flight Systems Inc, Mojave CA	3.83/90
				(stored dism. unconv., Mojave CA 82/90)	
				T. J. Brown/National Airshows Inc, New Bern NC	8.91/93
				(flew in black sc. as *Sabre Dance*)	
				crashed, dest. airshow, El Toro MCAS CA	2.5.93
1482 •	CL-13B Mk. 6	**RCAF23692**		(to SAAF as 373)	
			N3844E	Flight Systems Inc, Mojave CA	3.83/90
				(stored dism. unconv., Mojave CA 82/90)	
				rep. sold to UK: struck off USCR	7.91
				Darryl G. Greenamyer, Ocala FL	92
				Amjet Aircraft Corp, St Paul MN	94
1487 •	CL-13B Mk. 6	**RCAF23697**		(to SAAF as 378)	
			N38453	Flight Systems Inc, Mojave CA	3.83/90
				(stored dism. unconv., Mojave CA 82/92)	
				Tracor Flight Systems, Austin TX	91/92
				Global Aerospace Inc, Newport Beach CA	9.92
				Albert C. Hansen, Mojave CA	6.10.94/95
				(rest. Mojave 93/94, flies as "USAF 1487/FU-487")	
1489 •	CL-13B Mk. 6	**RCAF23699**		(to SAAF as 380)	
			N3846J	Flight Systems Inc, Mojave CA	3.83/90
				(stored dism. unconv., Mojave CA 82/90)	
				Tracor Flight Systems, Austin TX	91/92
			N88FS	ntu: Tracor Flight Systems, Austin TX	9.91
			N3846J	Tracor Flight Systems, Austin TX	92
				Global Aerospace Inc, Newport Beach CA	9.92
				Jack M. Rosamond, Golden CO	4.93/94
			N86EX	Jack M. Rosamond, Golden CO	6.94/95
1490 •	CL-13B Mk. 6	**RCAF23700**		(to SAAF as 381)	
				SAAF Museum	
			N50CJ	Corporate Jets Inc, Scottsdale AZ	11.87/95
				(airfreighted dism. ex Johannesburg 8.1.88; conv.to military target tug at Corsica, based Soesterberg AB, Netherlands 91)	
1491 •	CL-13B Mk. 6	**RCAF23701**		(to SAAF as 382)	
			N3847H	Flight Systems Inc, Mojave CA	3.83
			N87FS (2	Tracor Flight Systems Inc, Mojave CA	4.84/95
1593	CL-13B Mk. 6			(to Luftwaffe as S6-1666; YA+043; BB+163; 01+02)	
			D-0113	Dornier, Oberpfaffenhofen WG	70/77
				Ormond Haydon-Baillie, Duxford UK	.77/79
				(stored dism., Wroughton UK .78/79)	
			N1039B	Flight Systems Inc, Mojave CA	4.79
			N81FS	Flight Systems Inc, Mojave CA	6.80/83
				struck-off USCR	8.83
1600 •	CL-13B Mk. 6			(to Luftwaffe as S6-1600; BB+170)	
			D-9538	Dornier, Oberpfaffenhofen: op. for Luftwaffe	70/77
				Ormond Haydon-Baillie, Duxford UK	.77/79
				(stored dism., Wroughton UK .78/79)	
			N1039C	Flight Systems Inc, Mojave CA	4.79/80
			N82FS	Flight Systems Inc, Mojave CA	5.80/93
			N186JC	Gerald A. & Connie L. Smith/ Smith & Sons Aircraft, Paso Robles CA	6.93/95
1666	CL-13B			(to Luftwaffe as S6-1666; BB+185)	

	Mk. 6		D-9540	Dornier, Oberpfaffenhofen: op. for Luftwaffe	70/77
				Ormond Haydon-Baillie, Duxford UK	.77/79
				(stored dism., Wroughton UK .78/79)	
			N1039D	Flight Systems Inc, Mojave CA	4.79
			N83FS	Flight Systems Inc, Mojave CA	
				crashed target towing, Tampa Bay FL	.83
				struck-off USCR	4.84
1675 •	CL-13B			(to Luftwaffe as S6-1675, later JD+103,	
	Mk. 6			BB+284, KE+104)	
				Messerschmitt-Bolkow-Blohm, Manching WG	70/77
				Ormond Haydon-Baillie, Duxford, UK	.77
				(stored dism., Wroughton UK .78/79)	
			N1039K	Flight Systems Inc, Mojave CA	4.79/81
			N80FS	Tracor Flight Systems Inc, Mojave CA	10.81/95
1710 •	CL-13B			(to Luftwaffe as S6-1710; JB+240)	
	Mk. 6		D-9541	Dornier, Oberpfaffenhofen: op. for Luftwaffe	70/77
				Ormond Haydon-Baillie, Duxford, UK	.77/79
				(stored dism., Wroughton UK .78/79)	
			N1039L	Flight Systems Inc, Mojave CA	4.79/81
			N89FS	Tracor Flight Systems Inc, Mojave CA	5.81/95
1711	CL-13B			(to Luftwaffe as S6-1711; JC+239; 01+08)	
	Mk. 6		D-FADE	H. C. Janus, Frankfurt	12.5.70
				crashed landing, Reichelsheim airfield	6.70
27-9 •	CA-27	**A94-909**		ff Fishermans Bend VIC	23.2.55
	Mk. 30			RAAF Wagga NSW : inst. airframe	86
				RAAF Richmond NSW: spares for A94-983	88
				Lang Kidby/Transcorp, Redcliffe QLD: dism.	.88/89
				Sanders Aviation, Chino CA	.89/95
				(rest. to fly, Chino CA)	
27-148 •	CA-27	**A94-914**		ff Fishermans Bend VIC 5.4.55: RAAF BOC	28.4.55
	Mk. 30			Les Arthur/Toowoomba Aero Museum QLD	84/86
				Gold Coast War Museum, Coolangatta QLD	.86/89
				sold at museum auction, incomplete	10.6.89
				Sanders Aviation, Chino CA	.89/95
				(rest. project)	
27-16 •	CA-27	**A94-916**		ff Fishermans Bend VIC 21.4.55: RAAF BOC	20.5.55
	Mk. 30			Sanders Aviation, Chino CA	.90
				Stallion 51, Kissimmee FL	.90/92
				Charles Osborne, Louisville KY	92/93
				(rest. Kissimmee & Louisville-Clark County)	
27-22 •	CA-27	**A94-922**		RAAF BOC 3.56: SOC	5.73
	Mk. 30			RAAF Amberley QLD: inst. airframe	80/90
				Geoff Moesker, Brisbane QLD	93/94
				(rest. to fly: A94-923 also held for static rest.)	
			VH-SRE	reg. res: stored dism. Camden NSW	95
27-45 •	CA-27	**A94-945**		ff Fishermans Bend VIC 9.3.56: RAAF BOC	10.56/73
	Mk. 32			(to Indonesian AF/TNI-AU as F-8604)	3.73
				Aero Trader, Chino CA	93
				(stored dism. Ocotillo Wells CA 93 "TS-8604/04")	
27-49 •	CA-27	**A94-949**		ff Fishermans Bend VIC 22.10.56: RAAF BOC	12.56/73
	Mk. 32			(to Indonesian AF/TNI-AU as F-8605)	3.73
				Aero Trader, Chino CA	93
				(stored dism. Ocotillo Wells CA 93 "F-8605/05")	
27-55 •	CA-27	**A94-955**		ff Fishermans Bend VIC 24.1.57: RAAF BOC	28.2.57/73
	Mk. 32			(to Indonesian AF/TNI-AU as F-8617)	11.73
				Aero Trader, Chino CA	93
				(stored dism. Ocotillo Wells CA 93 "F-8617/17")	
27-57 •	CA-27	**A94-957**		RAAF BOC 2.57: SOC	3.73
	Mk. 32			(to Indonesian AF/TNI-AU as F-8607)	3.73
				Aero Trader, Chino CA	93
				(stored dism. Ocotillo Wells CA 93 "F-8607/12")	
27-68 •	CA-27	**A94-968**		ff Fishermans Bend VIC 11.6.57: RAAF BOC	2.7.57/73
	Mk. 32			(to Indonesian AF/TNI-AU as F-8609)	3.73
				Aero Trader, Chino CA	93
				(stored dism. Ocotillo Wells CA 93 "F-8609/01")	

27-70 •	CA-27 Mk. 32	**A94-970**		ff Fishermans Bend VIC 24.5.57: RAAF BOC (to Indonesian AF/TNI-AU as inst. airframe) RAAF Wagga NSW : inst. airframe RAAF Richmond NSW : rest. to fly	4.7.57/73 3.73 87/88 .88/91
27-80 •	CA-27 Mk. 32	**A94-980**		ff Fishermans Bend VIC 26.9.57: RAAF BOC (to Indonesian AF/TNI-AU as F-8614) Aero Trader, Chino CA (stored dism. Ocotillo Wells CA 93 "TS-8614")	10.57/73 3.73 93
27-83 •	CA-27 Mk. 32	**A94-983**		ff Fishermans Bend VIC 12.11.57: RAAF BOC (to R Malaysian AF as FM1983) wfu Butterworth AB, Malaysia (rest. Butterworth, ff 7.7.78; to Australia by C-130; rebuilt RAAF Richmond NSW: ff 26.3.81) RAAF Museum, RAAF Point Cook VIC	11.57/71 11.71 .76/78 .81/92
			VH-PCM	RAAF Museum (flies as RAAF "A94-983")	2.5.88/95
27-94 •	CA-27 Mk. 32	**A94-354**		ff Fishermans Bend VIC 24.2.60: RAAF BOC (to R Malaysian AF as FM1354) Sanders Aviation, Chino CA Fighter Jets Museum, Chino CA: loan, displ. offered at auction, Santa Monica CA: not sold	2.3.60/69 10.69 .89/91 91/93 10.91
27-106 •	CA-27 Mk. 32	**A94-366**		ff Fishermans Bend VIC 28.3.61: RAAF BOC (to Indonesian AF/TNI-AU as F-8602) Aero Trader, Chino CA (stored dism. Ocotillo Wells CA 93 "F-8602/02")	9.5.61/73 3.73 93
27-109 •	CA-27 Mk. 32	**A94-369**		ff Fishermans Bend VIC 10.7.61: RAAF BOC (to R Malaysian AF as FM1369) Jeff Trappett, Morwell VIC (rest. to fly)	1.9.61/69 8.69 82/93
27-... •	CA-27 Mk. 32	**A94-**		(To R Malaysian AF as FM1909) (to Indonesian AF/TNI-AU as F-8619) Aero Trader, Chino CA (stored dism. Ocotillo Wells CA 93: "F-8619/19" with "FM1909" discernable)	 93
27-... •	CA-27 Mk. 32	**A94-**		(To R Malaysian AF as FM....) (to Indonesian AF/TNI-AU as F-8623) Aero Trader, Chino CA (stored dism. Ocotillo Wells CA 93 "F-8623/23")	 93
- •	F-86F	-	**N186SE**	Stuart Eberhardt, Danville CA (USCR quotes id. "001", type NA/Woods F-86)	11.94/95
- •	F-86E	-	**N6213F**	I. N. Burchinal Jr, Brookston TX (USCR quotes id. "2826")	8.2.93/95
- •	F-86D F-86L	-	**N9202Z**	Cal Northrop Tech. Institute, Inglewood CA (USCR quotes id. "2568") : struck-off USCR	63/87 10.87

North American F-100 Super Sabre

NORTH AMERICAN NAA F-100 SUPER SABRE

192-22 •	F-100A	**52-5777**	**N1453**	reg. res. USAFM, Hill AFB UT	.73 88/95
192-183•	F-100A	**53-1688**		displ. on pole in Arizona "31688/FW-688"	
			N100X	Flight Test Research Inc, Long Beach CA Flight Systems Inc, Mojave CA (static displ., FSI scheme, Mojave CA 77/81) USAFM, Edwards AFB CA (prev. incorrectly rep. as 54-2155)	.67/68 72/81 93
214-1 •	F-100C	**53-1709**	**N703NA**	NASA, Moffet Field CA San Jose State College Aero School, San Jose Municipal Airport CA	70/72 .72/86
217-352•	F-100C	**54-2091**		(to Turkish AF as 3-091)	
			N2011M	Tracor Flight Systems Inc, Mojave CA (del. Conya AB,Turkey to US,via Prestwick 9.8.89) (stored unconv., Mojave CA 90/94) Global Aerospace Inc, Newport Beach CA	7.89/92 5.92/94

				Albert C. Hansen, Mojave CA	9.94/95
224-155•	F-100D	**55-2888**		(to Turkish AF as 3-888)	
			N2011U	Tracor Flight Systems Inc, Mojave CA	7.89/92
				(del. Conya AB,Turkey to US,via Prestwick 9.8.89)	
				(stored unconv., Mojave CA 90)	
				Global Aerospace Inc, Newport Beach CA	2.93/95
225-120•	F-100D	**56-3022**	N8056S	Flight Systems Inc, Mojave CA	12.79/80
			N405FS	Flight Systems Inc, Mojave CA	2.80/86
				USAF/Tracor Flight Systems Inc, Mojave CA	86/95
243-102	F-100F	56-3826		(to RDAF as GT-826)	
			N32511	ntu:	
			N3252B	Flight Systems Inc, Mojave CA	10.82
				(del. Denmark to Filton UK 28.1.83)	
			N414FS	Tracor Flight Systems Inc, Hurn UK	26.3.83/95
				(mil. contracts, Greece & Europe)	
				crashed Scharhorn-Nigehorn, Germany	11.7.93
				struck-off USCR	3.95
243-118•	F-100F	**56-3842**		(to RDAF as GT-842)	
			N32511	Flight Systems Inc, Mojave CA	10.82
				(del. Denmark to Filton UK 27.1.83)	
			N417FS	Tracor Flight Systems Inc, Hurn UK	3.83/95
				(mil. contracts, Greece & Europe)	
243-120•	F-100F	**56-3844**		(to RDAF as GT-844)	
			N32511	ntu:	
			N3251X	Flight Systems Inc, Mojave CA	10.82
				(del. Denmark to Filton UK 27.1.83)	
			N415FS	Tracor Flight Systems Inc, Hurn UK	15.3.83/95
				(mil. contracts Greece & Europe 83/95,	
				del. Hurn-Keflavik to US 9.8.87, ret. Europe)	
243-175•	F-100F	**56-3899**	N8056Y	Flight Systems Inc, Mojave CA	10.79/80
			N404FS	Flight Systems Inc, Mojave CA	2.80/86
				USAF/Tracor Flight Systems Inc, Mojave CA	86/94
				struck-off USCR	21.7.94
243-192•	F-100F	**56-3916**		(to RDAF as GT-916)	
			N3251X	ntu:	
			N3251W	Flight Systems Inc, Mojave CA	10.82
				(del. Denmark to Filton UK 27.1.83)	
			N416FS	Tracor Flight Systems Inc, Hurn UK	3.83/95
				(mil. contracts, Greece & Europe)	
243-224•	F-100F	**56-3948**		(to Turkish AF as 3-948)	
			N2011V	Tracor Flight Systems Inc, Mojave CA	7.89/91
				(del. Conya AB,Turkey to US via Prestwick 9.8.89)	
				Global Aerospace Inc, Newport Beach CA	11.91/92
				(stored unconv., Mojave 90/92)	
				Thomas J. Hickman/Sierra Hotel Inc,	
				Dallas-Addison TX	8.92/95
				(rest. .93, flies as USAF "63948/FW-948")	
243-247•	F-100F	**56-3971**		(to RDAF as GT-971)	
			N3251U	Flight Systems Inc, Mojave CA	10.82
				(del. Denmark to Filton UK 27.1.83)	
			N419FS	Tracor Flight Systems Inc, Hurn UK	3.83/95
				(mil. contracts Greece & Europe,	
				del. Hurn-US 9.8.87, ret. to Europe)	
243-272•	F-100F	**56-3996**		(to RDAF as GT-996)	
			N3251S	Flight Systems Inc, Mojave CA	10.82
				(del. Denmark to Filton UK 28.1.83)	
			N418FS	Tracor Flight Systems Inc, Hurn UK	3.83/95
				crashed landing, Hurn	18.7.89
- •	F-100A	-	**N2206Z**	Robert A. Kemp, Sparks NV	11.89/95
				(USCR quotes id. "ATL-F100-A01")	